...uch stands side, ridden and

.....(74) P Bradley(5)

s) **SP TOTAL PERCENT** 66/1
(table ground), **Ptarmigan** 132

es BRED: Theakston Stud

(£528.90; CSF £133.91;

er to Ayr 4.05 today. 4th
30

r side here including the
ross from stall 17. He
p Hat, who ran much

ths covering the first
-with the first five all
ds' side, was sixth
the winner.

ce, quickening up
yards. He should
trip short of his

but edged left
hird over five
ly as he lost
t the sort to

und in her
e off her
cuses for
uited by

4.30
[OFF 4.30]

Faucets For Safe Showerin
Bathing & Handwashing Fi
Handicap (Class C)
For: 3-y-o and up Rated 0-90 1st £7,410 2nd £2,280 3rd £1,140

1 **PENNYS PRIDE (IRE)** (6) 6 8-4
b m by Pips Pride–Mursuma (Rarity) ....(56)
(Mrs M Reveley) held up in midfield, effort when not
and stumbled 2f out, led well inside final furlong, kept
£7,000–£500 each-way] [op 10/1 tchd 12/1, 14/1 in p

2 ½ **PULAU PINANG (IRE)** (12) 5 10-0 1 ....(80)
ch m by Dolphin Street (FR)–Inner ... headway
(G A Butler) midfield, headway ....
headed well inside ... long, ...(Gulf

...op) slowly into stride, headway wh
from 3f out to over 1f out, ran on fir
£4,500 ... 000(x2) ... each-v

...ux-Catch The Sun (Kalaglow) ....(70) R Winston

5 **LA YOLAM** (1) 3 9-12
(B Hanbury) prominent, outpaced over 2f ....(74) T E Durcan
furlong [bets of £7,000–£2 ... [tchd 7/1] 8/1
£1,400–£400(x2)

6 **...CIOUS AIR (USA)** ....(84)
(J R Weymes) close up ....(op 3/1 tchd 7/2 in places)
beaten

...up, headway over 1f out, kept on, nearest
[op 9/2] 4/1

Fuelled by Baileys Racing Range

Taking Your Horse To Water...

If you've ever had a dream of owning a racehorse but thought you'd never be able to afford it - think again.

We can make it reality for you.

Unlike other anonymous clubs and syndicates, Peter Harris Racing Stables' partnership scheme and easy payment terms has made it possible for racing enthusiasts to live their dream.

When you join a partnership, you join eleven like minded individuals in your chosen horse, each of you recognised as an owner. And as an owner you also get to name your thoroughbred, choose your racing colours and are welcome to visit your horse anytime you like.

To gain entry to this racing paradise you don't need to invest any capital - a simple monthly payment is all it takes (which you can even pay by credit card).

It covers all costs, horse purchase, training, farrier, jockey, vet and race entry fees, plus ALL other expenses. There are no hidden extras.

Water

THE JOY OF OWNERSHIP!
WITH

PETER HARRIS RACING STABLES

Call 01442 851328
or email enquiries@
peterharrisracing.co.uk

FOR YOUR FREE VIDEO TEL : 01442 851328

The power to perform, the stamina to succeed

Over fences

Photograph by Mark Johnston

Best Mate twice winner of The Cheltenham Gold Cup

Henrietta Knight: "We have all our horses on Blue Chip. We find Blue Chip Pro helps them to maintain condition, whilst Blue Chip Dynamic is wonderful for their joints. Both products are very palatable and easy to feed. We are delighted with the results."

On the all weather

Photograph by Steven Cargill

Brilliant Red winner of two Class C races

Jamie Poulton: "The introduction of Blue Chip Dynamic into Brilliant Red's diet has given him a completely new lease of life. He has won two class C races and he is without a doubt one of the best horses currently running on the all weather circuit."

Photograph courtesy of The Newmarket Journal

Indian Haven winner of Irish 2,000 Guineas at The Curragh

On the flat

Paul D'arcy: "Blue chip have helped us from the start, it has been a big big help. I can't over emphasise the difference Blue Chip Pro has made to our horses overall health and wellbeing. I also feed Blue Chip Dynamic across the board, not waiting until I've got a problem. It helps protect the 2 year old's joints and keeps the older horses enjoying their racing."

Blue Chip

THINK POSITIVE.
THINK IRISH-BRED.

DALAKHANI (IRE)

European Champion 3-year-old 2003......................**DALAKHANI (IRE)**
European Champion 3-year-old 2002......**ROCK OF GIBRALTAR (IRE)**
European Champion 3-year-old 2001........................**GALILEO (IRE)**
European Champion 3-year-old 2000..........................**SINNDAR (IRE)**

Contact ITM for information on racing and breeding in Ireland, including details of our Flight Reimbursement Scheme for overseas purchasers.

IRISH THOROUGHBRED MARKETING
www.itm.ie
The Curragh, Co. Kildare, Ireland.
Tel: +353-45-443 060. Fax: +353-45-443 061. E-Mail: info@itm.ie

A SUBSIDIARY OF
HORSE RACING
IRELAND

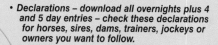

A unique sports story
A unique sports book

For the first time, the long-awaited
fully authorised biography of a
sporting legend.

Order your copy from Highdown,
RFM House, High Street, Compton,
Newbury, Berks RG20 6QQ
Tel: 01635 577610

111th
YEAR OF PUBLICATION

Raceform

HORSES

in Training 2004

ISBN 1 904317 51 0

INDEX TO GENERAL CONTENTS

Editor;   Simon Turner; Raceform Ltd, Compton, Newbury, Berkshire, RG20 6NL.
                            Fax: 01635 578101 E-mail: simon.turner@mgn.co.uk

Production Editor;   Alexia Smith; Eclipse Pedigrees, Weatherbys
                            Sanders Road, Wellingborough, NN8 4BX.

Orders;   Raceform Ltd., Compton, Newbury,
                            Berkshire, RG20 6NL. Tel: 01635 578080
                            Fax: 01635 578101 E-mail: rfsubscription@mgn.co.uk

Advertisements;   Alison Wheeler; Compton, Newbury,
                            Berkshire, RG20 6NL.
                            Tel: 01635 577610, Fax: 01635 578101

Printed by Woolnough Bookbinding Ltd., Irthlingborough, Northamptonshire, NN9 5SE.
Distributed to the Newstrade by MMC, Octagon House, White Hart Meadows, Ripley, Woking, Surrey, GU23 6HR. Tel: 01483 211222
Distributed in the booktrade by Orca Book Services, Stanley House, 3 Fleets Lane, Poole, Dorset BH15 3AJ. Tel: 01202 665432

© Raceform Ltd
Raceform Ltd is a wholly-owned subsidary of MGN Ltd
www.raceform.co.uk.

INDEX TO ADVERTISERS

2004

RACING FIXTURES

AND SALE DATES

(SUBJECT TO ALTERATION)

Flat fixtures are in **Black Type**; Jump in Light Type; Irish in *Italic*; French in ***Italic***; asterisk
(☆) indicates an evening meeting;
† indicates an All Weather meeting. Sale dates are at foot of fixtures

Foalings dates are shown for two-year-olds where these are provided,
and the purchase price (in guineas) as a yearling.

Please note that the price published for two-year-olds is the official
recorded purchase price, and not the price used by the British
Horseracing Board for race entry purposes.

JANUARY

Sun	Mon	Tues	Wed	Thur	Fri	Sat
				1 Catterick Cheltenham Exeter **Southwell†** *Fairyhouse* *Tramore*	**2** Ayr Folkestone **Wolverhampton†**	**3** **Lingfield†** Newcastle Sandown **Wolverhampton†** *Cork*
4 Plumpton **Southwell†** *Naas*	**5** **Southwell†** **Wolverhampton†**	**6** **Lingfield†** **Southwell†** Wetherby *Thurles*	**7** Hereford Musselburgh **Lingfield†** *Punchestown*	**8** **Southwell†** Wincanton **Wolverhampton†**	**9** Ludlow Towcester **Wolverhampton†**	**10** Ascot Haydock **Lingfield†** Uttoxeter Warwick *Navan*
11 *Leopardstown*	**12** Fontwell **Southwell†** **Wolverhampton†**	**13** Leicester Sedgefield **Southwell†**	**14** **Lingfield†** Newbury **Wolverhampton†**	**15** Catterick **Lingfield†** **Southwell†** *Down Royal*	**16** Huntingdon Kelso **Wolverhampton†**	**17** Kempton **Lingfield†** Wetherby Wincanton *Punchestown*
	Keeneland Sales	Keeneland Sales	Keeneland Sales	Keeneland Sales	Keeneland Sales	
18 *Cork* *Fairyhouse*	**19** Doncaster Plumpton **Wolverhampton†**	**20** Folkestone **Southwell†** Towcester	**21** Fakenham **Lingfield†** Newcastle	**22** Ludlow **Southwell†** Taunton *Gowran Park*	**23** Chepstow Musselburgh **Wolverhampton†**	**24** Catterick Cheltenham Haydock **Lingfield†** *Naas*
25 *Leopardstown*	**26** Fontwell Wetherby **Wolverhampton†**	**27** Leicester Sedgefield **Southwell†** *Tramore*	**28** Hexham Huntingdon **Lingfield†** *Navan*	**29** Plumpton **Southwell†** Warwick *Thurles*	**30** Doncaster Folkestone **Wolverhampton†**	**31** Ascot Ayr Doncaster Uttoxeter **Lingfield†** *Fairyhouse*
	Doncaster Sales	Doncaster Sales	Doncaster Sales			

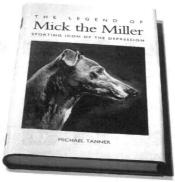

FEBRUARY

Sun	Mon	Tues	Wed	Thur	Fri	Sat
1 *Punchestown*	**2** Exeter Kempton **Wolverhampton†**	**3** **Lingfield†** **Southwell†** Taunton Tattersalls (IRE) Sales	**4** Leicester **Lingfield†** Newcastle Tattersalls (IRE) Sales	**5** Kelso **Southwell†** Towcester *Clonmel* Tattersalls Sales	**6** Catterick Hereford **Wolverhampton†** Tattersalls Sales	**7** Chepstow **Lingfield†** Sandown Wetherby *Naas*
8 Musselburgh **Southwell†** *Leopardstown*	**9** Fontwell **Southwell†** **Wolverhampton†** Goffs Sales	**10** Market Rasen Sedgefield **Southwell†** Goffs Sales	**11** Carlisle **Lingfield†** Ludlow Goffs Sales	**12** Huntingdon **Southwell†** Wincanton *Punchestown*	**13** Bangor Kempton **Wolverhampton†**	**14** Ayr Haydock **Lingfield†** Newbury **Wolverhampton†☆** *Gowran Park*
15 Hereford **Southwell†** *Navan*	**16** **Lingfield†** Plumpton **Wolverhampton†**	**17** Folkestone **Southwell†** **Wolverhampton†** Deauville Sales	**18** Leicester **Lingfield†** Musselburgh *Down Royal*	**19** Sandown **Southwell†** Taunton *Thurles*	**20** Fakenham Sandown **Wolverhampton†**	**21** Ascot **Lingfield†** Newcastle Wincanton *Fairyhouse*
22 Fontwell Towcester *Naas*	**23** Carlisle **Lingfield†** **Wolverhampton†** **Auteuil**	**24** **Lingfield†** Sedgefield **Southwell†** Fasig-Tipton Ascot Sales	**25** Doncaster **Lingfield†** Ludlow *Limerick*	**26** Huntingdon **Lingfield†** **Southwell†** *Limerick*	**27** Kempton Warwick **Wolverhampton†** **Saint-Cloud**	**28** Chepstow Haydock Kempton **Lingfield†** Warwick *Fairyhouse*
29 Musselburgh **Southwell†** *Clonmel* *Leopardstown* **Auteuil**						

MARCH

Sun	Mon	Tues	Wed	Thur	Fri	Sat
	1 Newcastle Plumpton **Wolverhampton†**	**2** Catterick Leicester **Lingfield†** *Maisons-Laffitte*	**3** Folkestone **Southwell†** Wetherby *Downpatrick*	**4** **Lingfield†** Ludlow Taunton *Thurles* **Saint-Cloud**	**5** Doncaster Newbury **Wolverhampton†** *Maisons-Laffitte*	**6** Doncaster Huntingdon Kelso Newbury *Navan* **Saint-Cloud**
7 Kempton Market Rasen *Naas* **Auteuil**	**8** Fontwell **Lingfield†** **Wolverhampton†**	**9** Exeter Hereford **Lingfield†**	**10** Bangor-on-Dee Catterick Chepstow	**11** Carlisle Towcester Wincanton *Clonmel* **Saint-Cloud**	**12** Ayr Leicester Sandown *Maisons-Laffitte*	**13** Ayr Newcastle Sandown **Wolverhampton†** *Wexford* **Saint-Cloud**
14 **Southwell†** Warwick *Cork* *Punchestown* **Auteuil**	**15** Plumpton Stratford Taunton	**16** Cheltenham Sedgefield **Southwell†** *Maisons-Laffitte*	**17** Cheltenham Huntingdon **Wolverhampton†** *Down Royal* *Limerick*	**18** Cheltenham Hexham **Southwell†** **Saint-Cloud**	**19** Fakenham **Lingfield†** Warwick *Maisons-Laffitte*	**20** Ascot **Lingfield†** Newcastle Uttoxeter *Tramore*
21 Carlisle Fontwell *Curragh* **Auteuil**	**22** Hereford Wetherby **Wolverhampton†**	**23** Exeter **Lingfield†** **Southwell†**	**24** Chepstow **Lingfield†** Towcester *Downpatrick* **Auteuil** Doncaster Sales	**25** Doncaster Ludlow Wincanton *Thurles* **Longchamp**	**26** Doncaster **Lingfield†** Newbury *Maisons-Laffitte*	**27** Bangor Doncaster Kempton Newbury **Wolverhampton†☆** *Navan* **Auteuil**
28 Kelsol Market Rasen *Leopardstown* *Limerick* **Saint-Cloud**	**29** **Lingfield†** Newcastle **Wolverhampton†** *Maisons-Laffitte*	**30** Folkestone Sedgefield **Southwell†** **Longchamp**	**31** Catterick **Lingfield†** Nottingham *Clonmel* **Saint-Cloud**			

APRIL

Sun	Mon	Tues	Wed	Thur	Fri	Sat
				1 Aintree **Leicester** Taunton *Longchamp*	**2** Aintree **Lingfield**† **Southwell**†† *Auteuil*	**3** Aintree Hereford **Lingfield**† Newcastle
4 Hexham Lingfield Wincanton *Curragh* *Tramore* **Longchamp**	**5** Kelso **Southwell** Windsor *Saint-Cloud*	**6** Exeter **Lingfield**† **Pontefract** *Maisons-Laffitte* Ascot Sale	**7** Folkestone Fontwell **Warwick** *Gowran Park* Doncaster Sales	**8** Bath Ludlow **Musselburgh** *Thurles* *Auteuil* Doncaster Sales	**9** *Saint-Cloud*	**10** Carlisle **Haydock** **Kempton** Newton Abbot *Cork* *Down Royal*
11 **Musselburgh** Plumpton Towcester *Cork* *Fairyhouse* **Longchamp** Fakenham	**12** Huntingdon **Kempton** Plumpton **Redcar** Sedgefield **Warwick** **Yarmouth** *Cork* *Fairyhouse* *Auteuil*	**13** Chepstow Exeter **Newmarket** *Fairyhouse* Tattersalls Keeneland Sales	**14** **Beverley** Cheltenham **Newmarket** *Saint-Cloud* Ascot Tattersalls Sales	**15** Cheltenham **Lingfield**†☆ **Newmarket** Ripon **Southwell**†† *Tipperary* **Longchamp** Tattersalls Sales	**16** Ayr **Newbury** **Southwell**††☆ Taunton☆ Thirsk *Maisons-Laffitte* Goffs France Sales	**17** Ayr Bangor **Newbury** **Nottingham**☆ Thirsk **Wolverahmpton**†☆ *Listowel* Goffs France Sales
18 Carlisle Stratford Wincanton *Leopardstown* *Listowel* *Auteuil*	**19** Hexham **Lingfield**† **Pontefract** **Windsor**☆ **Wolverhampton**†☆	**20** **Folkestone** Newcastle Southwell	**21** **Catterick** **Epsom** **Lingfield**†☆ Perth Worcester *Gowran Park* *Auteuil*	**22** **Beverley** Fontwell Perth **Salisbury**☆ **Wolverhampton**†☆ *Tipperary* **Longchamp**	**23** Chepstow☆ Perth **Sandown (Mixed)** **Warwick**☆ **Wolverhampton**†	**24** **Haydock**☆ **Leicester** Market Rasen Ripon **Sandown (Mixed)** **Wolverhampton**†☆ *Navan* *Auteuil*
25 **Brighton** Ludlow Wetherby *Curragh* *Sligo* **Longchamp**	**26** Hamilton **Newcastle**☆ Towcester **Windsor**☆ **Wolverhampton**†☆ *Chantilly*	**27** Bath **Lingfield**†☆ Newton Abbot **Southwell**††☆ *Punchestown*	**28** Ascot Cheltenham☆ Exeter Kelso ☆ **Pontefract** *Punchestown* *Saint-Cloud*	**29** Ayr☆ Hereford **Lingfield**†☆ **Redcar** **Southwell**†† *Punchestown* **Longchamp**	**30** Bangor☆ **Musselburgh** Nottingham Sedgefield☆ Worcester *Punchestown* *Chantilly*	

MAY

Sun	Mon	Tues	Wed	Thur	Fri	Sat
30	**31**					**1**
Fontwell **Newmarket** Uttoxeter *Limerick* **Auteuil**	Cartmel **Chepstow** Leicester Redcar Sandown *Ballinrobe*☆ **Saint-Cloud**					Haydock (mixed) Hexham☆ **Newmarket** Southwell☆ **Thirsk** Uttoxeter *Punchestown* **Saint-Cloud**
2	**3**	**4**	**5**	**6**	**7**	**8**
Hamilton **Newmarket** Salisbury *Gowran Park* *Navan* **Longchamp**	Doncaster Fontwell **Kempton** Newcastle **Warwick** *Curragh* *Down Royal* *Limerick* **Auteuil**	Bath **Brighton** Carlisle Catterick☆ *Exeter*☆ **Chantilly**	Chepstow **Chester** Fakenham☆ Kelso **Wolverhampton**†☆ *Naas*☆ **Saint-Cloud**	**Chester** Folkestone Ludlow☆ **Southwell**† Wetherby *Clonmel* **Longchamp**	**Chester** **Hamilton**☆ **Lingfield** Nottingham Wincanton☆ *Wexford*☆ **Chantilly**	**Beverley** Hexham **Lingfield** **Thirsk**☆ Warwick☆ Worcester *Kilbeggan*☆
9	**10**	**11**	**12**	**13**	**14**	**15**
Market Rasen Plumpton Uttoxeter *Killarney* *Leopardstown* **Auteuil**	**Kempton** Redcar Towcester☆ Windsor☆ **Wolverhampton**†☆ *Killarney*☆ **Maisons-Laffitte**	Hereford Newton Abbot☆ **Wolverhampton**†☆ **York** *Killarney* **Saint-Cloud**	**Brighton** Exeter Newcastle☆ Perth☆ **York** *Ballinrobe*☆ **Chantilly**	**Lingfield**†☆ Ludlow☆ Perth Salisbury **York** *Fairyhouse*☆ **Longchamp**	Aintree☆ **Hamilton**☆ Newbury Nottingham Yarmouth *Cork*☆ *Downpatrick*☆ **Auteuil**	Bangor **Newbury** Nottingham **Southwell**†☆ **Thirsk** Uttoxeter☆ *Downpatrick*
16	**17**	**18**	**19**	**20**	**21**	**22**
Fakenham **Ripon** Worcester *Gowran Park* *Navan* **Longchamp**	**Bath** Musselburgh☆ Newton Abbot **Windsor**☆ **Wolverhampton**† *Roscommon*☆ **Chantilly**	**Beverley** **Goodwood** Leicester☆ Redcar Towcester☆ **Auteuil**	Folkestone☆ **Goodwood** Kelso Sedgefield☆ **Southwell**† **Longchamp**	**Doncaster**☆ Goodwood Kelso☆ **Newcastle** Wetherby *Tipperary*☆	Ayr **Bath**☆ **Haydock** Newmarket Stratford☆ *Punchestown*☆	Ascot Catterick **Haydock** Kempton☆ **Newmarket** Stratford☆ *Curragh* **Maisons-Laffitte**
23	**24**	**25**	**26**	**27**	**28**	**29**
Brighton Hereford Southwell *Curragh* **Longchamp**	**Beverley** Carlisle Leicester **Thirsk**☆ **Windsor**☆ *Kilbeggan*☆ **Auteuil** Doncaster Baden-Baden Sales	Bangor☆ **Lingfield** Nottingham **Ripon** Sedgefield☆ Doncaster Sales	Cartmel Fontwell **Lingfield** **Goodwood**☆ **Ripon**☆ *Leopardstown*☆ **Maisons-Laffitte** Doncaster Sales	Ayr **Bath** Huntingdon☆ Newton Abbot Wetherby☆ *Fairyhouse*☆ **Longchamp** Doncaster Sales	**Brighton** Catterick **Pontefract**☆ Towcester☆ **Wolverhampton**† *Cork*☆ *Punchestown*☆ **Chantilly** Doncaster Sales	Cartmel☆ **Doncaster** Kempton **Lingfield**☆ **Musselburgh** *Limerick*☆ *Wexford*☆

JUNE

Sun	Mon	Tues	Wed	Thur	Fri	Sat
		1 Hexham☆ **Leicester** **Redcar** **Sandown** *Ballinrobe* ***Maisons-Laffitte*** Goffs Ascot Sales	**2** **Beverley**☆ **Kempton**☆ **Newcastle** **Nottingham** **Yarmouth** *Leopardstown* ***Longchamp*** Goffs Sales	**3** **Chepstow** **Hamilton** **Haydock** **Sandown**☆ *Uttoxeter* *Clonmel*☆ ***Saint-Cloud*** Goffs Sales	**4** **Catterick** **Epsom** **Goodwood**☆ **Haydock**☆ **Wolverhampton**† *Kilbeggan*☆ ***Auteuil***	**5** **Doncaster** **Epsom** **Haydock** **Newmarket**☆ *Perth*☆ *Worcester* *Tramore* ***Chantilly***
6 **Brighton** Perth **Stratford** *Gowran Park* *Tralee* ***Chantilly***	**7** **Folkestone** Newton Abbot **Pontefract**☆ **Windsor**☆ *Naas* *Tralee* ***Saint-Cloud***	**8** **Chester**☆ Huntingdon☆ **Redcar** **Salisbury** *Tralee* ***Auteuil***	**9** **Beverley** **Hamilton**☆ Hereford Market Rasen **Newbury**☆ *Leopardstown*☆	**10** **Brighton** **Newbury** **Southwell**† *Uttoxeter*☆ **Yarmouth** *Tipperary*☆ ***Longchamp***	**11** **Chepstow**☆ **Goodwood**☆ **Sandown** **Wolverhampton**† **York** *Navan*☆ *Wexford*☆	**12** **Bath** Hexham **Leicester**☆ **Lingfield**☆ **Sandown** **York** *Cork*☆
13 **Doncaster** **Salisbury** *Stratford* *Cork* *Roscommon*☆ ***Chantilly***	**14** **Brighton** **Carlisle** **Warwick**☆ **Windsor**☆ *Roscommon*☆ ***Saint-Cloud***	**15** **Royal Ascot** Hereford☆ **Newton Abbot**☆ Thirsk ***Auteuil***	**16** **Royal Ascot** **Hamilton** **Ripon**☆ **Southwell**† *Worcester*☆ *Naas*☆	**17** **Royal Ascot** **Ayr**☆ **Beverley**☆ **Ripon** **Southwell**† *Clonmel*☆ ***Longchamp***	**18** **Royal Ascot** **Ayr** **Goodwood**☆ **Newmarket**☆ **Redcar** *Down Royal*☆ *Limerick*☆ ***Maisons-Laffitte***	**19** **Royal Ascot** **Ayr** **Lingfield**☆ **Newmarket** **Redcar** **Warwick**☆ *Down Royal* ***Auteuil***
20 Hexham **Pontefract** **Warwick** *Gowran Park* *Navan*	**21** **Chepstow**☆ **Musselburgh** **Nottingham** **Windsor**☆ *Kilbeggan*☆ ***Chantilly***	**22** **Beverley** **Brighton** **Newbury**☆ Newton Abbot☆ ***Longchamp***	**23** **Bath**☆ **Carlisle** **Kempton**☆ **Salisbury** Worcester *Leopardstown*☆ ***Maisons-Laffitte***	**24** **Hamilton**☆ **Leicester**☆ **Newcastle** **Salisbury** **Thirsk** *Tipperary*☆ ***Chantilly*** Tattersalls (IRE) Sales	**25** **Folkestone** **Newmarket**☆ Market Rasen **Newcastle**☆ **Wolverhampton**†☆ *Curragh*☆ ***Auteuil*** Tattersalls (IRE) Sales	**26** **Chester** **Doncaster**☆ **Lingfield**☆ **Newcastle** **Newmarket** **Windsor** *Curragh* Goffs Sales
27 **Warwick** Uttoxeter **Windsor** *Curragh* ***Longchamp***	**28** **Musselburgh**☆ **Pontefract** **Windsor**☆ **Wolverhampton**† ***Chantilly***	**29** **Brighton** **Hamilton** Worcester *Sligo*☆ ***Auteuil***	**30** **Catterick** **Kempton**☆ **Lingfield** Perth **Yarmouth**☆ *Bellewstown*☆			

JULY

Sun	Mon	Tues	Wed	Thur	Fri	Sat
				1 Epsom☆ Haydock Newbury☆ Perth Yarmouth *Bellewstown*	**2** Beverley☆ Haydock Sandown Southwell Warwick *Bellewstown☆* *Limerick* Goffs France Sales	**3** Beverley Carlisle☆ Haydock Nottingham☆ Leicester Sandown *Leopardstown☆* *Limerick☆*
4 Brighton Market Rasen Redcar ***Saint-Cloud***	**5** Bath Musselburgh Ripon☆ Windsor☆ *Roscommon☆*	**6** Newmarket Pontefract Uttoxeter Wolverhampton†☆ *Roscommon☆* ***Deauville*** Tattersalls Sales	**7** Catterick Kempton☆ Lingfield Newmarket Worcester *Naas☆* Tattersalls Sales	**8** Doncaster☆ Epsom☆ Folkestone Newmarket Warwick *Tipperary☆* ***Deauville*** Tattersalls Sales	**9** Ascot Chepstow☆ Chester☆ Wolverhampton† York *Fairyhouse* *Wexford☆*	**10** Ascot Chester Hamilton☆ Nottingham Salisbury☆ York *Down Royal* ***Deauville***
11 Bath Haydock Stratford *Sligo* *Tipperary* ***Deauville***	**12** Ayr Newton Abbot Windsor☆ Wolverhampton†☆ *Killarney* ***Chantilly***	**13** Beverley Brighton *Killarney* ***Maisons-Laffitte*** Ascot Sales	**14** Catterick Kempton☆ Lingfield Uttoxeter Worcester☆ *Killarney☆* *Leopardstown☆* ***Maisons-Laffitte***	**15** Cartmel Doncaster☆ Epsom☆ Hamilton Leicester *Killarney*	**16** Carlisle Hamilton☆ Newbury Newmarket☆ Pontefract☆ Southwell *Kilbeggan☆* ***Maisons-Laffitte***	**17** Haydock☆ Lingfield☆ Market Rasen Newbury Newmarket Ripon☆ *Curragh* ***Maisons-Laffitte***
18 Newton Abbot Stratford *Ballinrobe* *Curragh*	**19** Ayr Beverley☆ Brighton Windsor☆ *Ballinrobe☆* Keeneland Sales	**20** Ayr Uttoxeter Keeneland Sales	**21** Catterick Leicester☆ Lingfield Sandown☆ Worcester *Naas☆* Fasig-Tipton Sales	**22** Bath Doncaster☆ Folkestone☆ Sandown Yarmouth *Limerick☆* Fasig-Tipton Sales	**23** Ascot Chepstow☆ Newmarket☆ Thirsk Wolverhampton† *Cork* *Fairyhouse*	**24** Ascot Lingfield☆ Newcastle Nottingham Salisbury☆ York *Leopardstown☆* *Wexford☆*
25 Ascot Newmarket Pontefract ***Maisons-Laffitte***	**26** Sedgefield Southwell† Windsor☆ Yarmouth☆ *Galway☆* ***Chantilly***	**27** Beverley Goodwood *Galway☆*	**28** Goodwood Kempton☆ Leicester☆ Musselburgh Newton Abbot *Galway*	**29** Carlisle Epsom☆ Goodwood Musselburgh☆ Stratford *Galway* ***Chantilly***	**30** Bangor Goodwood Newmarket☆ Nottingham☆ Thirsk *Galway☆*	**31** Doncaster Goodwood Hamilton☆ Lingfield☆ Newmarket Thirsk *Galway* ***Deauville***

AUGUST

Sun	Mon	Tues	Wed	Thur	Fri	Sat
1 **Chester** Market Rasen **Newbury** Galway *Wexford* ***Deauville***	**2** Carlisle☆ Newton Abbot **Ripon** **Windsor**☆ *Cork* *Naas*	**3** **Brighton** **Catterick** *Roscommon*☆ ***Deauville***	**4** **Brighton** Kempton☆ Newcastle Pontefract Yarmouth☆ *Sligo*☆	**5** Brighton☆ **Chepstow** Folkestone☆ **Haydock** **Yarmouth** *Sligo* *Tipperary*☆	**6** Haydock☆ **Lingfield** Newmarket☆ Sedgefield Worcester	**7** Ascot Ayr☆ Haydock Lingfield☆ **Newmarket** Redcar *Downpatrick* ***Deauville***
		Doncaster Sales	Doncaster Sales	Doncaster Sales		
8 **Leicester** **Redcar** Windsor *Cork* *Curragh* ***Deauville***	**9** Southwell **Thirsk**☆ **Windsor**☆ Wolverhampton† *Kilbeggan*☆	**10** **Bath** Newton Abbot ***Deauville***	**11** **Beverley** Hamilton☆ Salisbury **Sandown**☆ Yarmouth *Gowran Park*☆	**12** **Beverley** Chepstow☆ Haydock☆ Salisbury Sandown *Tramore*☆	**13** Catterick☆ **Folkestone** Newbury **Newcastle** Newmarket☆ *Tramore*☆	**14** Bangor Market Rasen☆ **Newbury** Newmarket Ripon **Goodwood**☆ *Tramore* ***Deauville***
		Fasig-Tipton Sales	Tattersalls (IRE) Fasig-Tipton Sales	Tattersalls (IRE) Fasig-Tipton Sales	Tattersalls (IRE) Sales	
15 **Bath** Pontefract Stratford *Curragh* *Tramore* ***Deauville***	**16** **Brighton** **Nottingham** Windsor☆ **Yarmouth**☆ *Roscommon*☆	**17** Hamilton York	**18** Carlisle Kempton☆ Nottingham☆ Worcester **York** *Sligo*☆	**19** Chepstow☆ **Chester** Fontwell☆ Wolverhampton† York *Tipperary*☆ ***Deauville***	**20** Ayr **Chester** Salisbury☆ Sandown Wolverhampton† *Kilbeggan*☆	**21** **Chester** Lingfield☆ Market Rasen Newton Abbot☆ **Ripon** Sandown *Curragh* ***Deauville***
						Deauville Sales
22 **Folkestone** Newton Abbot Southwell *Cork* *Fairyhouse* ***Deauville***	**23** **Hamilton** **Leicester** Windsor☆ Wolverhampton†☆ *Tralee*	**24** **Brighton** Perth☆ Worcester☆ **Yarmouth** *Tralee* ***Deauville***	**25** **Brighton** **Catterick** Perth *Tralee*	**26** Bangor **Lingfield** Musselburgh *Tralee*	**27** Bath☆ **Goodwood** Newcastle☆ Newmarket Thirsk ***Deauville***	**28** **Beverley** Cartmel **Goodwood** Newmarket Redcar☆ Windsor☆ *Ballinrobe*
Deauville Sales	Deauville Sales	Ascot Deauville Sales	Deauville Sales			
29 **Beverley** **Goodwood** Yarmouth *Ballinrobe* *Gowran Park* ***Deauville***	**30** Cartmel **Chepstow** **Epsom** Huntingdon **Newcastle** **Ripon** Warwick *Downpatrick*	**31** **Ripon** Sedgefield ***Deauville***				
	Fasig-Tipton Sales	Fasig-Tipton Sales				

SEPTEMBER

Sun	Mon	Tues	Wed	Thur	Fri	Sat
			1 **Lingfield** Newton Abbot **York** *Clonmel*	**2** **Carlisle** **Redcar** **Salisbury** *Limerick*	**3** **Chepstow** **Haydock** **Kempton** *Down Royal* **Auteuil**	**4** **Folkestone** **Haydock** **Kempton** **Stratford** **Thirsk** **Wolverhampton†** *Down Royal* Baden-Baden Sales
5 **Fontwell** **Worcester** **York** *Curragh* *Galway* **Longchamp**	**6** **Bath** **Newcastle** **Warwick** *Galway* **Chantilly**	**7** **Catterick** **Leicester** **Lingfield** *Galway* **Auteuil** Doncaster Sales	**8** **Doncaster** **Epsom** **Hereford** ***Chantilly*** Doncaster Sales	**9** **Chepstow** **Doncaster** **Epsom** **Longchamp** Doncaster Sales	**10** **Bangor** **Doncaster** **Sandown** *Kilbeggan* **Auteuil** Doncaster Sales	**11** **Carlisle** **Chester** **Doncaster** **Goodwood** **Musselburgh** *Leopardstown*
12 **Goodwood** **Hexham** **Stratford** **Longchamp**	**13** **Bath** **Musselburgh** **Redcar** *Roscommon* **Chantilly** Keeneland Sales	**14** **Salisbury** **Thirsk** **Yarmouth** Tattersalls (IRE) Keeneland Sales	**15** **Beverley** **Sandown** **Yarmouth** **Auteuil** Tattersalls (IRE) Keeneland Sales	**16** **Ayr** **Pontefract** **Yarmouth** *Tipperary* Tattersalls (IRE) Keeneland Sales	**17** **Ayr** **Newbury** **Nottingham** *Downpatrick* **Chantilly** Keeneland Sales	**18** **Ayr** **Catterick** **Lingfield** **Newbury** **Warwick** **Wolverhampton†☆** *Curragh* **Longchamp** Keeneland Sales
19 **Hamilton** Plumpton Uttoxeter *Curragh* *Listowel* Keeneland Sales	**20** **Chepstow** **Kempton** **Leicester** *Listowel* **Auteuil** Keeneland Sales	**21** **Beverley** Fontwell **Newmarket** *Listowel* **Maisons-Laffitte** Keeneland Sales	**22** **Goodwood** Perth Southwell *Listowel* **Chantilly** Keeneland Sales	**23** **Brighton** Perth **Pontefract** *Listowel* Keeneland Sales	**24** **Ascot** **Haydock** Worcester *Listowel* **Saint-Cloud** Keeneland Sales	**25** **Ascot** **Haydock** **Kempton** Market Rasen **Ripon** *Listowel* **Auteuil**
26 **Ascot** Huntingdon **Musselburgh** *Punchestown*	**27** **Bath** Hamilton Windsor	**28** Exeter **Nottingham** Sedgefield **Chantilly** Tattersalls Sales	**29** **Newcastle** **Nottingham** **Salisbury** **Maisons-Laffitte** Tattersalls Sales	**30** **Goodwood** Hereford **Newmarket** *Thurles* **Auteuil** Tattersalls Sales		

OCTOBER

Sun	Mon	Tues	Wed	Thur	Fri	Sat
31 **Lingfield†** Carlisle Huntingdon *Saint-Cloud*					**1** Hexham **Lingfield** Newmarket *Chantilly*	**2** **Brighton** Chepstow **Epsom** Newmarket Redcar Wolverhampton†☆ *Curragh* ***Longchamp*** Goffs France Sales
3 Kelso Market Rasen Uttoxeter *Tipperary* ***Longchamp***	**4** Plumpton **Pontefract** **Windsor** *Roscommon* Goffs Sales	**5** **Catterick** Huntingdon Stratford Tattersalls Goffs Sales	**6** Exeter **Lingfield†** Towcester *Downpatrick* ***Auteuil*** Tattersalls Goffs Sales	**7** Ludlow **Southwell†** Wincanton *Gowran Park* ***Saint-Cloud*** Tattersalls Goffs Sales	**8** **Ascot** Carlisle **York** *Gowran Park* ***Chantilly*** Tattersalls Goffs Sales	**9** **Ascot** Bangor Hexham **Warwick** **York** *Punchestown* ***Longchamp***
10 Bath Goodwood Newcastle *Curragh* *Limerick* ***Auteuil***	**11** Ayr Leicester Windsor **Maisons-Laffitte**	**12** Ayr Fontwell Leicester Ascot Sales	**13** **Lingfield†** Uttoxeter Wetherby *Navan* Tattersalls Sales	**14** Newmarket Taunton Worcester *Tramore* Tattersalls Sales	**15** Brighton Newmarket Redcar **Maisons-Laffitte** Tattersalls Sales	**16** Catterick Kelso **Newmarket** Stratford Yarmouth *Cork* ***Auteuil***
17 Hereford **Musselburgh** Market Rasen *Cork* *Naas* ***Longchamp***	**18** Plumpton **Pontefract** **Wolverhampton†** *Deauville* Doncaster Goffs Deauville Sales	**19** **Bath** Exeter **Southwell†** *Deauville* Goffs Deauville Doncaster Sales	**20** Chepstow Newcastle Nottingham *Navan* ***Deauville*** Goffs Doncaster Deauville Sales	**21** **Brighton** Haydock Ludlow ***Longchamp*** Baden-Baden Doncaster Sales	**22** Doncaster Fakenham Newbury **Saint-Cloud** Baden-Baden Doncaster Sales	**23** Carlisle **Doncaster** Kempton **Newbury** Wolverhampton† *Curragh* *Wexford* ***Auteuil*** Baden-Baden Sales
24 Aintree Towcester Wincanton *Galway* *Wexford* ***Longchamp***	**25** Leicester **Lingfield†** **Wolverhampton†** *Galway* *Leopardstown* **Maisons-Laffitte** Fasig-Tipton Tattersalls Sales	**26** Catterick Cheltenham Nottingham ***Saint-Cloud*** Tattersalls Fasig-Tipton Sales	**27** Cheltenham Sedgefield **Yarmouth** *Gowran Park* Tattersalls Sales	**28** **Lingfield†** Stratford Taunton ***Auteuil*** Tattersalls Sales	**29** Newmarket Uttoxeter Wetherby **Maisons-Laffitte**	**30** Ascot **Ayr** Chepstow Kelso **Newmarket** Wetherby **Wolverhampton†☆** *Naas*

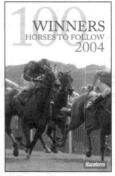

NOVEMBER

Sun	Mon	Tues	Wed	Thur	Fri	Sat
	1	**2**	**3**	**4**	**5**	**6**
	Plumpton **Redcar** Warwick *Auteuil*	**Catterick** Exeter Folkestone *Maisons-Laffitte*	Kempton **Musselburgh** Newton Abbot	Haydock **Nottingham** Towcester *Thurles*	Fontwell Hexham **Yarmouth** *Down Royal*	Ayr **Doncaster** Sandown Wincanton **Wolverhampton**†☆ *Down Royal* **Saint-Cloud**
	Tattersalls (IRE)	Tattersalls (IRE)	Tattersalls (IRE)	Tattersalls (IRE)	Tattersalls (IRE)	Tattersalls (IRE)
7	**8**	**9**	**10**	**11**	**12**	**13**
Ayr Market Rasen Southwell *Cork* *Navan* *Auteuil*	Carlisle **Southwell**† **Wolverhampton**†	Huntingdon Sedgefield **Southwell**† **Saint-Cloud**	**Lingfield**† Newbury *Fairyhouse* *Auteuil*	Lingfield Ludlow Taunton *Clonmel*	Cheltenham Newcastle **Wolverhampton**† *Maisons-Laffitte*	Cheltenham **Lingfield**† Uttoxeter Wetherby **Wolverhampton**† *Punchestown*
Fasig-Tipton Tattersalls (IRE) Sales	Tattersalls (IRE) Keeneland Sales	Ascot Tattersalls (IRE) Keeneland Sales	Tattersalls (IRE) Fasig-Tipton Keeneland Sales	Tattersalls (IRE) Fasig-Tipton Keeneland Sales	Fasig-Tipton Tattersalls (IRE) Keeneland Sales	Tattersalls (IRE) Keeneland Sales
14	**15**	**16**	**17**	**18**	**19**	**20**
Cheltenham Fontwell Haydock *Punchestown* *Auteuil*	Folkestone Leicester **Wolverhampton**†	**Lingfield**† Newton Abbot Towcester **Saint-Cloud**	Hexham Kempton **Southwell**† *Downpatrick* *Maisons-Laffitte*	Hereford Market Rasen Wincanton *Clonmel*	Ascot Exeter **Wolverhampton**†	Ascot Huntingdon **Lingfield**† Aintree **Wolverhampton**†☆ *Naas*
Tattersalls (IRE) Keeneland Sales	Doncaster Keeneland Sales	Doncaster Ascot Goffs Keeneland Sales	Doncaster Goffs (France) Keeneland Sales	Doncaster Goffs Keeneland Goffs France Sales	Goffs Doncaster Keeneland Sales	Goffs Sales
21	**22**	**23**	**24**	**25**	**26**	**27**
Aintree Fakenham Plumpton *Cork* *Navan* *Auteuil*	**Lingfield**† Ludlow **Southwell**† *Maisons-Laffitte*	Sedgefield **Southwell**† Warwick **Saint-Cloud**	Chepstow Lingfield Wetherby *Auteuil*	Carlisle Taunton Uttoxeter *Thurles*	Bangor Musselburgh **Wolverhampton**†	**Lingfield**† Newbury Newcastle Towcester **Wolverhampton**† *Fairyhouse* **Saint-Cloud**
Goffs Sales	Tattersalls Sales		Tattersalls Sales	Tattersalls Sales	Tattersalls Sales	Tattersalls Sales
28	**29**	**30**				
Doncster Leicester Newbury *Fairyhouse* *Auteuil*	Folkestone Newcastle **Wolverhampton**†	Hereford **Lingfield**† Newton Abbot **Saint-Cloud**				
	Tattersalls Sales	Tattersalls Sales				

DECEMBER

Sun	Mon	Tues	Wed	Thur	Fri	Sat
			1 Catterick Plumpton **Southwell†** Tattersalls Sales	**2** Leicester Market Rasen Wincanton *Thurles* Tattersalls Sales	**3** Exeter Sandown **Wolverhampton†** Tattersalls	**4** Chepstow Haydock **Lingfield†** Sandown Wetherby **Wolverhampton†☆** *Gowran Park* Deauville Sales
5 Kelso Warwick *Punchestown* Deauville Sales	**6** Ayr Newcastle **Wolverhampton†** Goffs Deauville Sales	**7** Fontwell Sedgefield **Southwell†** ***Deauville*** Goffs Sales	**8** Leicester **Lingfield†** Newbury *Clonmel* ***Deauville*** Goffs	**9** Huntingdon Ludlow Taunton Goffs Sales	**10** Cheltenham Doncaster **Wolverhampton†** Doncaster Goffs Sales	**11** Cheltenham Doncaster Lingfield **Southwell†** **Wolverhampton†☆** *Fairyhouse*
12 Musselburgh **Southwell†** *Cork* *Navan*	**13** Plumpton Towcester **Wolverhampton†** ***Deauville*** Tattersalls (IRE) Sales	**14** Folkestone **Southwell†** **Wolverhampton†** Tattersalls (IRE) Ascot Sales	**15** Bangor Hexham **Lingfield†** *Downpatrick*	**16** Catterick Exeter **Southwell†** *Gowran Park*	**17** Ascot Uttoxeter **Wolverhampton†**	**18** Ascot Haydock **Lingfield†** Newcastle Warwick *Navan*
19 *Thurles*	**20** Fakenham **Lingfield†** **Wolverhampton†**	**21** Fontwell **Lingfield†** **Southwell†** ***Deauville***	**22** **Lingfield†** Ludlow **Wolverhampton†**	**23**	**24**	**25**
26 Kempton Market Rasen Towcester Uttoxeter Wetherby Wincanton *Leopardstown* *Limerick*	**27** Ayr Huntingdon Kempton **Wolverhampton†** Wetherby *Down Royal* *Leopardstown* *Limerick* ***Deauville***	**28** Catterick Chepstow Leicester **Southwell†** *Leopardstown* *Limerick* ***Deauville***	**29** **Lingfield†** Musselburgh Newbury *Leopardstown* *Limerick*	**30** Haydock **Lingfield†** Taunton	**31** Sedgefield Warwick **Wolverhampton†** *Punchestown* *Tramore*	

INDEX TO TRAINERS
†denotes Permit to train under N.H. Rules only

Name	Team No.
BRADSTOCK, MR M. F.	057
BRAMALL, MRS S. A.	058
BRAVERY, MR G. C.	059
BRENNAN, MR OWEN	060
†BREWIS, MISS RHONA	061
BRIDGER, MR J. J.	062
†BRIDGES, MRS H. M.	063
BRIDGWATER, MR D. G.	064
BRIDGWATER, MR G. F.	065
BRISBOURNE, MR W. M.	066
BRITTAIN, MR C. E.	067
BRITTAIN, MR M. A.	068
†BROCKBANK, MR J. E.	069
†BROOKHOUSE, MR R. S.	070
BROOKSHAW, MR S. A.	071
BROTHERTON, MR R.	072
BROWN, MR G.	073
†BROWN, MR I. R.	074
†BROYD, MISS A. E.	075
†BRYANT, MISS M. P.	076
BUCKLER, MR R. H.	077
BUCKLEY, MR M. A.	078
BURCHELL, MR W. D.	079
BURGOYNE, MR P. V. J.	080
BURKE, MR K. R.	081
BURNS, MR JAMES G.	082
BURROUGH, MR S. C.	083
BUTLER, MR G. A.	084
BUTLER, MR P.	085
BYCROFT, MR N.	086

C

Name	Team No.
CALDWELL, MR T. H.	087
CALLAGHAN, MR N. A.	088
CAMACHO, MISS J. A.	089
CAMPION, MR A. M.	090
CANDLISH, MRS JENNIE	091
CANDY, MR HENRY D. N.	092
CARO, MR D. J.	093
CARROLL, MR A. W.	094

Name	Team No.
CARROLL, MR D.	095
†CARSON, MR R. M.	096
†CARTER, MR O. J.	097
CASE, MR B. I.	098
†CASTLE, MR J. M.	099
CECIL, MR H. R. A.	100
†CHADWICK, MR S. G.	101
CHAMINGS, MR P. R.	102
CHANCE, MR N. T.	103
CHANNON, MR M.	104
CHAPMAN, MR DAVID W.	105
CHAPMAN, MR M. C.	106
CHARLES-JONES, MR G. F. H.	107
CHARLTON, MR A.	108
CHARLTON, MR J. I. A.	109
CHARLTON, MR ROGER J.	110
CHUNG, MR G. C. H.	111
†CLARK, MR R. M.	112
CLAY, MR W.	113
CLEMENT, MR NICOLAS	114
CLINTON, MR P. L.	115
CLUTTERBUCK, MR K. F.	116
COAKLEY, MR D. J.	117
COLE, MR P. F. I.	118
COLLET, MR R.	119
COLLINGRIDGE, MR H. J.	120
†COLTHERD, MR W. S.	121
†CONNELL, LADY	122
COOMBE, MR M. J.	123
CORNWALL, MR J. R.	124
COTTRELL, MR L. G.	125
COWELL, MR R. M. H.	126
COX, MR C. G.	127
CRAGGS, MR R.	128
CRAIG, MISS I. E. L.	129
†CRESSWELL, MR J. K. S.	130
CROOK, MR A.	131
CUMANI, MR L. M.	132
CUNDELL, MR P. D.	133
CUNNINGHAM, MR M.	134
CUNNINGHAM, MR W. S.	135

A unique sports story
A unique sports book

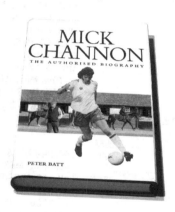

For the first time, the long-awaited fully authorised biography of a sporting legend.

Order your copy from Highdown, RFM House, High Street, Compton, Newbury, Berks RG20 6QO

HOLLINGSWORTH, MR A. F. 285
HOLLINSHEAD, MR R. 286
HORGAN, MR CON 287
HOURIGAN, MR M. 288
HOWE, MR H. S. 289
HOWLING, MR P. 290
†HUBBUCK, MR J. S. 291
HUGHES, MR D. T. 292

I

INCISA, DON E. 293
INGRAM, MR R. 294
IVORY, MR D. K. 295

J

JAMES, MR E. L. J. D. 296
JAMES, MR L. R. 297
JARVIS, MR A. P. 298
JARVIS, MR M. A. 299
JARVIS, MR W. 300
JEFFERSON, MR J. M. 301
JENKINS, MR J. R. W. 302
JENKS, MR W. P. 303
†JESSOP, MR A. E. M. 304
JOHNSON, MR B. R. 305
JOHNSON, MR J. H. 306
JOHNSON, MR ROBERT W. 307
JOHNSON, MRS S. M. 308
JOHNSON HOUGHTON, MR R. F. 309
JONES, MR A. E. 310
JONES, MR A. P. 311
†JONES, MR G. ELWYN 312
JONES, MRS M. A. 313
JONES, MR R. W. 314
JONES, MR T. M. 315

K

†KAVANAGH, MR H. M. 317
KEANE, MR D. P. 318
KEDDY, MR T. 319
KEIGHTLEY, MR S. L. 320
KELLY, MR G. P. 321
†KELSALL, MR P. 322
†KERR, MRS C. J. 323
KING, MRS A. L. M. 324
KING, MR ALAN 325
KING, MR J. S. 326
KING, MR N. B. 327
†KIRBY, MR F. 328
KIRK, MR S. A. 329
KITTOW, MR WILLIAM S. 330
KNIGHT, MISS H. C. 331
†KNIPE, MR R. F. 332

L

LAFFON-PARIAS, MR C. 333
LAMYMAN, MRS S. 334
LAVELLE, MISS E. C. 335
†LAY, MR B. L. 336
LE BROCQ, MRS J. L. 337
LEAHY, MR AUGUSTINE 338
LEAVY, MR B. D. 339
LEE, MR RICHARD 340
LEWIS, MR S. T. 341
LIDDERDALE, MR A. J. D. 342
LIDDIARD, MRS STEF 343
LITTMODEN, MR N. P. 344
LLEWELLYN, MR B. J. 345
†LLOYD, MR D. M. 346
†LLOYD, MR F. 347
LOCKWOOD, MR A. J. 348
LODER, MR D. R. 349
LUNGO, MR L. 350

Top Dog

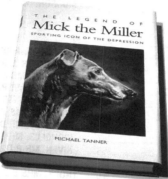

THE LEGEND OF MICK THE MILLER
Michael Tanner
£17.99 (+95p p&p)

Fairytale story of the legendary dog
who emerged from the backwoods of Ireland
to sweep all before him in the emerging sport
of greyhound racing of the 1930s

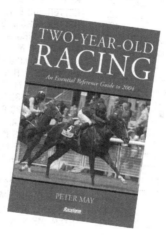

Name	Team No.
SHEEHAN, MR J. J.	494
SHEPPARD, MR M. I.	495
SHERWOOD, MR O. M. C.	496
SHERWOOD, MR S. E. H.	497
†SHIELS, MR R.	498
SHIRLEY-BEAVAN, MR S. H.	499
SIDDALL, MISS L. C.	500
SIMCOCK, MR D. M. L.	501
SLY, MRS P. M.	502
SMAGA, MR D.	503
SMART, MR B.	504
SMITH, MR A. D.	505
SMITH, MR G. J.	506
SMITH, MR JULIAN SIMON	507
SMITH, MR N. A.	508
SMITH, MRS NADINE	509
SMITH, MR R. J.	510
SMITH, MISS S.	511
SMITH, MRS S. J.	512
SOUTHCOMBE, MISS J. A.	513
SOWERSBY, MR M. E.	514
SPEARING, MR J. L.	515
†SPOTTISWOOD, MR P.	516
STACK, MR T.	517
STEWART, MR A. C.	518
†STIRK, MRS M. K.	519
†STODDART, MR D. R.	520
STOKELL, MISS ANN	521
†STOREY, MR F. S.	522
STOREY, MR W.	523
STOUTE, SIR M.	524
STRONGE, MR R. M.	525
STUBBS, MRS L.	526
SUPPLE, MR J. A.	527
SWAN, MR CHARLIE	528
SWINBANK, MR G. A.	529

Name	Team No.
TEAGUE, MR COLIN	532
†TETLEY, MRS P. A.	533
†THOMAS, MRS D.	534
†THOMAS, MR K. S.	535
THOMPSON, MR D. W.	536
THOMPSON, MR RONALD	537
†THOMSON, MRS B. K.	538
†THOMSON, MR R. W.	539
THORNTON, MR C. W.	540
THORPE, MRS A. M.	541
TINKLER, MR C.	542
TINNING, MR W. H.	543
TIZZARD, MR C. L.	544
TODHUNTER, MR D. M.	545
TOLLER, MR J. A. R.	546
TOMPKINS, MR M. H.	547
TOWNSLEY, MRS P. LAXTON	548
TREGONING, MR M. P.	549
†TUCKER, MR F. G.	550
TUER, MR E. W.	551
TURNELL, MR ANDREW	552
†TURNER, MR D. C.	553
TURNER, MR W. G. M.	554
†TUTTY, MRS K. J.	555
TWISTON-DAVIES, MR N. A.	556

U

Name	Team No.
UPSON, MR J. R.	557
USHER, MR M. D. I.	558

W

Name	Team No.
†WADE, MR J.	559
WADHAM, MRS L. A. M.	560
†WAGGOTT, MR N.	561
WAINWRIGHT, MR J. S.	562
†WALEY-COHEN, MR R. B.	563

Name	Team No.
WALLACE, MR MARK	567
WALTON, MRS K.	568
WARING, MRS BARBARA	569
†WARING, MR L.	570
WATSON, MR F.	571
†WATSON, LADY SUSAN	572
†WATT, MRS S. A.	573
WEBBER, MR P. R.	574
WEEDEN, MR M. J.	575
WEEDON, MR C. V.	576
WEGMANN, MR P.	577
WELD MR D. K.	578
†WELLICOME, MR D. R.	579
WELLINGS, MR MARK	580
WELLS, MR L.	581
WEYMES, MR J. R.	582
WHEELER, MR E. A.	583
WHILLANS, MR A. C.	584
WHITAKER, MR R. M.	585
†WHITEHEAD, MR A. J.	586
†WHITING, MR A. J.	587
WILESMITH, MR M. S.	588

Name	Team No.
†WILLCOCK, MS S. C.	589
WILLIAMS, MR D. L.	590
WILLIAMS, MR I. P.	591
WILLIAMS, MR N. S. L.	592
WILLIAMS, MR S. C.	593
WILLIAMS, MRS S. D.	594
WILLIAMS, MISS V. M.	595
WILLIAMSON, MRS L. V.	596
WILSON, MR A. J.	597
WILSON, MR C. R.	598
WILTON, MISS S. J.	599
WINGROVE, MR K. G.	600
WINKWORTH, MR P. L.	601
WINTLE, MR D. J.	602
WOOD, MR I. A.	612
WOODHOUSE, MR R. D. E.	603
†WORMALL, MISS J.	604
WRAGG, MR GEOFFREY	605

Y

Name	Team No.
†YOUNG, MR W. G.	606

PROPERTY OF HER MAJESTY

The Queen

Colours: Purple, gold braid, scarlet sleeves, black cap with gold fringe

Trained by **Sir M. Stoute,** Newmarket

1 **DESERT STAR,** 4yo b c Green Desert (USA)-Phantom Gold
2 **PROMOTION,** 4yo b c Sadler's Wells (USA)-Tempting Prospect

THREE-YEAR-OLDS

3 **BORDER CASTLE,** Grand Lodge (USA)-Tempting Prospect
4 **DARING AIM,** b f Daylami (IRE)-Phantom Gold
5 **DAY OF RECKONING,** b f Daylami (IRE)-Trying for Gold (USA)
6 **MACLEAN,** b c Machiavellian (USA)-Celtic Cross
7 **MAGNETIC POLE,** b c Machiavellian (USA)-Clear Attraction (USA)

TWO-YEAR-OLDS

8 **FLAG LIEUTENANT,** b c 26/2 Machiavellian (USA)-Fairy Godmother (Fairy King (USA))
9 **UNDERGRADUATE** (IRE), b c 19/4 Unfuwain (USA)-Starlet (Teenoso (USA))
10 **AVIEMORE,** b c 26/3 Selkirk (USA)-Film Script (Unfuwain (USA))
11 **BENEDICT,** b c 5/4 Benny The Dip (USA)-Abbey Strand (USA) (Shadeed (USA))

Trained by **Roger J. Charlton,** Marlborough

THREE-YEAR-OLDS

12 **ARTISTS LICENCE,** gr c Linamix (FR)-Once Upon a Time
13 **NAMESAKE,** ch f 6/3 Nashwan (USA)-Zenith

TWO-YEAR-OLDS

14 **NAVY LARK,** b c 10/2 Nashwan (USA)-Holly Blue (Bluebird (USA))
15 **SERVE TIME,** b c 22/3 Benny The Dip (USA)-Once Upon A Time (Teenoso (USA))
16 **VIRTUE,** b f 26/2 Vettori (IRE)-Zenith (Shirley Heights)
17 **LIFE'S A WHIRL,** b f 22/1 Machiavellian (USA)-Spinning Top (Alzao (USA))
18 **OUTSKIRTS,** b f 11/3 Selkirk (USA)-Beyond Doubt (Belmez (USA))
19 **FREE LIFT,** b f 8/4 Cadeaux Genereux-Step Aloft (Shirley Heights)
20 **OBVIOUS CHARM,** b f 16/5 Machiavellian (USA)-Clear Attraction (USA) (Lear Fan (USA))

Trained by **R. Hannon,** Marlborough

THREE-YEAR-OLD

21 **TURNSTILE,** gr c Linamix (FR)-Kissing Gate (USA)

TWO-YEAR-OLDS

22 **ISLAND AIR,** b g 5/2 Desert Style (IRE)-Island Story (Shirley Heights)
23 **MONEY MARKET,** b g 13/5 Machiavellian (USA)-Trying For Gold (Northern Baby (CAN))
24 **MARCHING SONG,** b c 23/2 Royal Applause-Marl (Lycius (USA))
25 **THE COIRES,** b c 18/3 Green Desert (USA)-Purple Heather (USA) (Rahy (USA))
26 **FORWARD MOVE** (IRE), b c 8/5 Dr Fong (USA)-Kissing Gate (USA) (Fan Qata (USA))

PROPERTY OF HER MAJESTY

The Queen

Trained by **N. J. Henderson**, Lambourn

30 FIRST LOVE, 8yo br g Bustino-First Romance
31 MOONSTREAM, 4yo b g Terimon-Lunnabelle
32 SEA CAPTAIN, 4yo b g Oscar (IRE)-Calabria
33 SHINING STRAND, 5yo ch g Karinga Bay-First Romance

Trained by **A. M. Balding**, Newbury

THREE-YEAR-OLD

34 ROYAL WARRANT, b c Royal Applause-Brand

TWO-YEAR-OLD

35 BANKNOTE, b c 6/4 Zafonic (USA)-Brand (Shareef Dancer (USA))

1
MR JONATHAN AKEHURST, Epsom
Postal: **South Hatch Stables, 44 Burgh Heath Road, Epsom, Surrey, KT17 4LX.**
Contact: **PHONE (01372) 745880 FAX (01372) 744231**

1 **ABRAXAS**, 6, b g Emperor Jones (USA)—Snipe Hall **Canisbay Bloodstock**
2 **AUDIENCE**, 4, b g Zilzal (USA)—Only Yours **Canisbay Bloodstock**
3 **CAPRICHO (IRE)**, 7, gr g Lake Coniston (IRE)—Star Spectacle **Canisbay Bloodstock**
4 **CHELSEA'S DIAMOND**, 4, b f Man Among Men (IRE)—Sharp Thistle **Chelsea Artisans Ltd**
5 **DEEPER IN DEBT**, 6, ch g Piccolo—Harold's Girl (FR) **Tipp-Ex Rapid Racing II**
6 **DUELLING BANJOS**, 5, ch g Most Welcome—Khadino **E & S Racing III**
7 **ESPERANCE (IRE)**, 4, ch g Bluebird (USA)—Dioscorea (IRE) **The Grass is Greener Partnership IV**
8 **FATHER ABRAHAM (IRE)**, 6, b g Idris (IRE)—Mothers Blessing **Mr A. D. Spence**
9 **FIREWORK**, 6, b g Primo Dominie—Prancing **The Grass is Greener Partnership III**
10 **GRIZEDALE (IRE)**, 5, ch g Lake Coniston (IRE)—Zabeta **Canisbay Bloodstock**
11 **HOLLYWOOD HENRY (IRE)**, 4, b g Bahhare (USA)—Takeshi (IRE) **Lonwin Partnership**
12 **KOMATI RIVER**, 5, b g Wesaam (USA)—Christening (IRE) **Miss Vivian Pratt**
13 **MARNIE**, 7, ch m First Trump—Miss Aboyne **The Grass is Greener Partnership**
14 **MARSAD (IRE)**, 10, ch g Fayruz—Broad Haven (IRE) **Canisbay Bloodstock**
15 **ROBIN SHARP**, 6, ch h First Trump—Mo Stopher **Canisbay Bloodstock**
16 **RYAN'S FUTURE (IRE)**, 4, b c Danetime (IRE)—Era **Mr Vimal Khosla**
17 **SPIRIT'S AWAKENING**, 5, b g Danzig Connection (USA)—Mo Stopher **Canisbay Bloodstock**
18 **STOLEN HOURS (USA)**, 4, b br c Silver Deputy (CAN)—Fasta (USA) **Mr A. D. Spence**
19 **TUNING FORK**, 4, b c Alzao (USA)—Tuning **Canisbay Bloodstock**
20 **UNLEADED**, 4, ch f Danzig Connection (USA)—Mo Stopher **Canisbay Bloodstock**
21 **WESTERN (IRE)**, 4, ch g Gone West (USA)—Madame Est Sortie (FR) **Mr H. R. Hunt**

THREE-YEAR-OLDS

22 **DR SYNN**, br c Danzero (AUS)—Our Shirley **Canisbay Bloodstock**
23 **GREATEST BY PHAR**, b g Pharly (FR)—Greatest Friend (IRE) **Mr Frank Sharratt**

2 MR N. W. ALEXANDER, Leslie
Postal: Kinneston, Leslie, Glenrothes, Fife, KY6 3JJ.
Contact: PHONE (01592) 840774 E-MAIL kinneston@aol.com

1 COPPER MOSS, 6, ch g Le Moss—Shiona Anne Mr Nicholas Alexander
2 FEARLESS FOURSOME, 5, b g Perpendicular—Harrietfield Alexander Family
3 FOUNTAIN BRIG, 8, b br g Royal Fountain—Lillies Brig Alexander Family
4 HAILSTORM (IRE), 11, ch g Glacial Storm (USA)—Sindys Gale Mr Jamie Alexander
5 HAYAAIN, 11, b g Shirley Heights—Littlefield Mr Jamie Alexander
6 JINFUL DU GRAND VAL (FR), 7, b g Useful (FR)—Marine (FR) Mr Jamie Alexander
7 LUCKY BRUSH (IRE), 10, b g Brush Aside (USA)—Luck Daughter Mr Jamie Alexander
8 MOON MIST, 6, gr m Accondy (IRE)—Lillies Brig Alexander Family
9 OLYMPIC STORM (IRE), 6, b g Glacial Storm (USA)—Philly Athletic Mr Jamie Alexander
10 WHISPERING MOOR, 5, br g Terimon—Larksmore Mrs Nicholas Alexander
11 WISE MAN (IRE), 9, ch g Mister Lord (USA)—Ballinlonig Star Mr Nicholas Alexander

Assistant Trainer: Mr Jamie Alexander

Amateur: Mr Jamie Alexander (11-0).

3 MR C. N. ALLEN, Newmarket
Postal: Byerley House, Warrington Street, Newmarket, Suffolk, CB8 8BA.
Contact: HOME (01638) 667870 YARD (01638) 561207 FAX (01638) 561603 MOBILE (07802) 692621 E-MAIL conrad@sportsdays.co.uk WEBSITE www.sports-days.com

1 ALICADABRA (IRE), 4, br c Ali-Royal (IRE)—Sea Magic (IRE) Alan Brazil Racing Club
2 BOOGIE MAGIC, 4, b f Wizard King—Dalby Dancer Alan Brazil Racing Club
3 4, B f Turtle Island (IRE)—Esh Sham (USA) Alan Brazil Racing Club
4 FLUKE BAY, 4, b f Air Express (IRE)—Mainmast Alan Brazil Racing Club
5 FRENCH GIGOLO, 4, ch g Pursuit of Love—French Mist Alan Brazil Racing Club
6 MISS TRINITY, 4, b f Catrail (USA)—Rosy Sunset (IRE) Alan Brazil Racing Club
7 MOROZOV (USA), 5, b h Sadler's Wells (USA)—High Hawk
8 MUSICAL GIFT, 4, ch c Cadeaux Genereux—Kazoo Mr T. P. Ramsden
9 PRINCE AARON (IRE), 4, b g Marju (IRE)—Spirito Libro (USA) Black Star Racing
10 ROYAL ATALZA (FR), 7, gr g Saint Preuil (FR)—Crystalza (FR) Mr T. P. Ramsden
11 WEECANDOO (IRE), 6, b m Turtle Island (IRE)—Romantic Air sportsdays.co.uk

THREE-YEAR-OLDS

12 CRIMSON KING (IRE), ch g Pivotal—Always Happy Alan Brazil Racing Club
13 EDIN BURGHER (FR), br g Hamas (IRE)—Jaljuli Alan Brazil Racing Club
14 JAKE THE SNAKE (IRE), ch c Intikhab (USA)—Tilbrook (IRE)
15 MOUNTCHARGE (IRE), b g Intikhab (USA)—Zorilla Alan Brazil Racing Club
16 Ch f Bien Bien (USA)—Starosta Alan Brazil Racing Club
17 SYLLABUS, b c Sillery (USA)—Corvalent Alan Brazil Racing Club
18 B g Botanic (USA)—Tenpenny Alan Brazil Racing Club

TWO-YEAR-OLDS

19 B f 12/2 Mind Games—Adorable Cherub (USA) (Halo (USA)) (15000) Alan Brazil Racing Club
20 Ch g 16/5 Erhaab (USA)—Corvalent (Busted) Alan Brazil Racing Club
21 B f 22/1 Dr Fong (USA)—Daisy May (In The Wings) (11000) Alan Brazil Racing Club
22 B g 13/3 Intikhab (USA)—Laraissa (Machiavellian (USA)) (11000) Alan Brazil Racing Club
23 B c 10/4 Spinning World (USA)—No Miss Kris (USA) (Capote (USA)) (17000) Alan Brazil Racing Club
24 B c 10/4 Green Desert (USA)—Rumpipumpy (Shirley Heights) (115000) Mr T. P. Ramsden
25 Ch c 27/4 Monashee Mountain—Schonbein (IRE) (Persian Heights) (8657) Alan Brazil Racing Club

4 MR R. H. ALNER, Blandford

Postal: **Locketts Farm, Droop, Blandford, Dorset, DT11 0EZ.**
Contact: **FAX/PHONE (01258) 817271 MOBILE (07767) 436375**
E-MAIL robertalner@btopenworld.com

1 **ALBERT HOUSE (IRE)**, 6, ch g Carroll House—Action Plan **Mr David O. Moon**
2 **AVAS DELIGHT (IRE)**, 6, b g Ajraas (USA)—Whothatis **Mr P. M. De Wilde**
3 **BARNARDS GREEN (IRE)**, 6, ch g Florida Son—Pearly Castle (IRE) **Mr T. H. Chadney**
4 **BOWLEAZE (IRE)**, 5, br g Right Win (IRE)—Mrs Cullen **Mr Martin Short**
5 **BUSH PARK (IRE)**, 9, b g Be My Native (USA)—By All Means **Mr H. Wellstead**
6 **COMMANCHE RUN (IRE)**, 8, b g Commanche Run—On A Dream **Mr David O. Moon**
7 **CRACKING DAWN (IRE)**, 9, b g Be My Native (USA)—Rare Coin **Mr Peter Bonner**
8 **DANSE SLAVE (FR)**, 5, b m Broadway Flyer (USA)—Snow Girl (FR) **S. W. D. Partnership**
9 **DELAWARE BAY**, 5, ch g Karinga Bay—Galacia (IRE) **Mr A. P. Hedditch**
10 **DILETIA**, 7, b m Dilum (USA)—Miss Laetitia (IRE) **Mr T. H. Chadney**
11 **DIONYSIAN (IRE)**, 5, ch g Be My Guest (USA)—Justitia **Paul Murphy & Frank Watson**
12 **DISTANT THUNDER (IRE)**, 6, b g Phardante (FR)—Park Breeze (IRE) **Old Moss Farm**
13 **EL HOMBRE DEL RÍO (IRE)**, 7, ch g Over The River (FR)—
          Hug In A Fog (IRE) **Perpetual Pub's Lazy Punters Black Book**
14 **EVEN MORE (IRE)**, 9, b g Husyan (USA)—Milan Moss **Mr G. Keirle**
15 **FOX IN THE BOX**, 7, b g Supreme Leader—Charlotte Gray **Mr Peter Bonner**
16 **GATEJUMPER (IRE)**, 6, b g Zaffaran (USA)—Nelly Don **Pell-mell Partners**
17 **GOTHAM (IRE)**, 7, gr g Gothland—Inchriver (IRE) **Pell-mell Partners**
18 **GUS DES BOIS (FR)**, 10, ch g Lampon (FR)—Fiacina (FR) **The CD Partnership**
19 **HERE COMES HENRY**, 9, ch g Dortino—Epryana **Mr A. D. & Mrs S. A. Old**
20 **HICKEY'S GIFT (IRE)**, 8, ch g Over The River (FR)—Chorabelle **Mr Alner**
21 **ISLANDS THORNS**, 5, b g Thowra (FR)—Holly Hatch **Mrs U. Wainwright**
22 **JOIZEL (FR)**, 7, b g Fill My Hopes (FR)—Anne de Boizel (FR) **Mr Paul Green**
23 **JONGLEUR COLLONGES (FR)**, 7, gr g Royal Charter (FR)—Soubrette Collonge (FR) **Mr Andrew Wiles**
24 **KADARA (FR)**, 5, b m Slip Anchor—Kadassa (IRE) **Mrs Norma Kelly**
25 **KEEPERS MEAD (IRE)**, 6, ch g Aahsaylad—Runaway Pilot **Mr J. C. Browne**
26 **KEWLAKE LANE**, 6, b m Afzal—Sheer Impulse **Mrs U. Wainwright**
27 **KINGSCLIFF (IRE)**, 7, b g Toulon—Pixies Glen **Mr A. J. Sendell**
28 **KOSMOS BLEU (FR)**, 6, ch g Franc Bleu Argent (USA)—Fee du Lac (FR) **Mr P. M. De Wilde**
29 **LE ROCHELAIS (FR)**, 5, ch g Goldneyev (USA)—Olympiade de Brion (FR) **Mr Martin Short**
30 **LORD CODE (IRE)**, 6, b g Arctic Lord—Tax Code **Mrs Norma Kelly**
31 **LORD HALFNOTHIN (IRE)**, 8, b g Mandalus—Midnight Seeker **Mr H. V. Perry**
32 **MANAWANUI (IRE)**, 6, b g Karinga Bay—Kiwi Velocity (NZ) **J. M. Dare, T. Hamlin, J. W. Snook**
33 **MILLCROFT SEASPRAY (IRE)**, 8, br g Good Thyne (USA)—Bucks Gift (IRE) **Mr John Carter**
34 **MOTCOMBE (IRE)**, 6, ch m Carroll House—Cooks Lawn **Lady Cobham**
35 **NO VISIBILITY (IRE)**, 9, b g Glacial Storm—Duhallow Lady (IRE) **Mr David O. Moon**
36 **ON LES AURA (IRE)**, 5, b g Germany—Another Thurn (IRE) **Mr David Constant**
37 **PECCADILLO (IRE)**, 10, b g Un Desperado (FR)—First Mistake **Mr Dwight Makins**
38 **PERFECT LIAISON**, 7, b g Alflora—Connie's Pet **Neil & Susie Dalgren**
39 **RIVER PARADISE (IRE)**, 8, ch g John French—Barbara Brook **Jobs Racing**
40 **ROMAN COURT (IRE)**, 6, b g Witness Box (USA)—Small Iron **Club Ten**
41 **RUGGED RIVER (IRE)**, 6, b g Over The River (FR)—Early Dalus (FR) **Miss H. J. Flower**
42 **SILVER INGOT (IRE)**, 5, gr g Gothland (FR)—
          Hotel Saltees (IRE) **J.Browne,Mrs C.Robertson,Mrs E.Woodhouse**
43 **SIR REMBRANDT (IRE)**, 8, b g Mandalus—Sue's A Lady **Mr A. Hordle**
44 **SPAGHETTI JUNCTION (IRE)**, 6, ch m Sir Harry Lewis (USA)—Up The Junction (IRE) **Mr Paul Murphy**
45 **SPRING GROVE (IRE)**, 9, b g Mandalus—Lucy Lorraine **Mr H. V. Perry**
46 **SWINCOMBE (IRE)**, 9, b g Good Thyne (USA)—Gladtogetit **Mr T. J. Whitley**
47 **THE LISTENER (IRE)**, 5, gr h Roselier (FR)—Park Breeze (IRE) **Old Moss Farm**
48 **TOMS GONE GREY (IRE)**, 5, gr g Gothland (FR)—Cpv Lady **Mr T. H. Chadney**
49 **TOULOUSE (IRE)**, 7, b g Toulon—Neasham **Pell-mell Partners**
50 **TWISTED LOGIC (IRE)**, 11, b g Tremblant—Logical View **Mr P. M. De Wilde**

5   MR E. J. ALSTON, Preston

Postal: **Edges Farm Stables, Chapel Lane, Longton, Preston, Lancashire, PR4 5NA.**
Contact: **PHONE (01772) 612120 FAX (01772) 619600 MOBILE (07879) 641660**
E-MAIL **eric1943@supanet.com**

1 **ALLIED VICTORY (USA)**, 4, b c Red Ransom (USA)—Coral Dance (FR) **Honest Traders**
2 **ASH LADDIE (IRE)**, 4, ch g Ashkalani (IRE)—Lady Ellen **Mrs Chris Harrington**
3 **ELLENS ACADEMY (IRE)**, 9, b g Royal Academy (USA)—Lady Ellen **Mr K. Lee and Mr I. Davies**
4 **FLYING EDGE (IRE)**, 4, b g Flying Spur (AUS)—Day Is Dawning (IRE) **The Eric Alston Partnership**
5 **GOODBYE MR BOND**, 4, b g Elmaamul (USA)—Fifth Emerald **Mr Peter J. Davies**
6 **INTRICATE WEB (IRE)**, 8, b g Warning—In Anticipation (IRE) **Mr Peter J. Davies**
7 **JOHNSTON'S DIAMOND (IRE)**, 6, b g Tagula (IRE)—Toshair Flyer **Mollington Golf Club Boys**
8 **MIDNIGHT PARKES**, 5, b g Polar Falcon (USA)—Summerhill Spruce **Mr Joseph Heler**
9 **NAKWA (IRE)**, 6, b g Namaqualand (USA)—Cajo (IRE) **Mr Alan Dick**
10 **PICCLED**, 6, b g Piccolo—Creme de Menthe (IRE) **The Pain And Heartache Partnership**
11 **PILGRIM PRINCESS (IRE)**, 6, b m Flying Spur (AUS)—Hasaid Lady (IRE) **Morris, Oliver, Pierce**
12 **RYMER'S RASCAL**, 12, b g Rymer—City Sound **Mr B. Chambers**
13 **TEDBURROW**, 12, b g Dowsing (USA)—Gwiffina **Mrs Irene Davies & Mr Peter J. Davies**
14 **TIME N TIME AGAIN**, 6, b g Timeless Times (USA)—Primum Tempus **Springs Equestrian Ltd**
15 **VELOCITYS IMAGE (IRE)**, 4, b f Tagula (IRE)—Pike Creek (USA) **The Eric Alston Partnership**

THREE-YEAR-OLDS

16 **JADAN (IRE)**, b g Imperial Ballet (IRE)—Sports Post Lady (IRE) **Mr Derrick Mossop**
17 **PICCOLO PRINCE**, ch g Piccolo—Aegean Flame **Burlington Partnership**

TWO-YEAR-OLDS

18 **LUCY PARKES**, ch f 16/2 Piccolo—Janette Parkes (Pursuit of Love) **Mr Joseph Heler**
19 **MONDELLO (IRE)**, b f 9/2 Tagula (IRE)—Teodora (IRE) (Fairy King (USA)) (8657) **Liam & Tony Ferguson**
20 **ROBURY**, b g 25/4 Robellino (USA)—Youdontsay (2000) **Whitehills Racing Syndicate**
21 **TIVISKI (IRE)**, b f 16/2 Desert Style (IRE)—Mummys Best (Bustino) (9000) **The Sel**

Other Owners: Mrs S. Y. Alston, Mr Barry Ashworth, Mr P. Baldwin, Mr M. F. H. Brown, Mr P. G. Buist, Mr John Ellison, Mr M. Fitzgerald, Mr B. Hawker, Mr A. Hopkins, Mr David Jones, Mr Michael Shaun Kelly, Mr D. Lightfoot, Mr G. Lowe, Mr H. E. Loxam, Mr J. Barrie Potter, Dr J. G. Randall, Mr J. C. Scott, Mr K. Smart, Mr J. F. Turley, Mr Barry Turner, Mrs S. A. C. Ward.

Assistant Trainer: Mrs Sue Alston

Jockeys (Flat): K Fallon (8-6, w.a.), W Supple (8-0, w.a.). **Amateur:** Miss Kim E Jones (9-12).

6   MR W. AMOS, Hawick

Postal: **Broadhaugh Farm, Newmill on Teviot, Hawick, Roxburghshire, TD9 0JX.**
Contact: **PHONE (01450) 850323 MOBILE (07810) 738149**

1 **CASTLE HATIM**, 6, b m Hatim (USA)—Castle Fountain **Mrs C. A. Warden**
2 4, B f Sayaarr (USA)—Estrela Vermelha **Mr J. E. Curry**
3 **EXTRA PROUD**, 10, ch g Dancing High—Spring Onion **Mr W. Amos**
4 **GRANNY ANNIE**, 5, b m Minster Son—Castle Fountain **Mr W. G. Macmillan**
5 5, Br m Cool Jazz—Our Dessa
6 **REIVERS MOON**, 5, b br m Midnight Legend—Here Comes Tibby **Mr J. W. McNeill**

7   MR M. APPLEBY, Claverdon

Postal: **The Chalet, Arden Park Stables, Manor Lane, Claverdon, Warwick, CV35 8NH.**
Contact: **HOME (01926) 842464 MOBILE (07884) 366421**

1 **CAPTAIN JAKE**, 9, b g Phardante (FR)—Cherry Crest **Clovers**
2 5, B m Glacial Storm (USA)—Dardulo Darlina **D.A.S.**

MR M. APPLEBY—continued

9 QUEST FOR ROME, 8, ch g Question of Pride—Unbeknown **Clovers**
10 4, B c Defacto (USA)—Wych Willow **Mr Ray Blackman**

Other Owners: Mr J. Hudson, Mr S. Parkes.

Assistant Trainer: Mr Lee Moulson

Jockey (Flat): S Righton (7-12). **Jockey (NH):** Sean Curran (10-0). **Conditional:** S Peltell (9-7).
Amateurs: Mr L Moulson (9-3), Miss Fiona Turner (8-7).

---

8 MR R. J. ARMSON, Melbourne
Postal: **Scotlands Farm, Burney Lane, Staunton-Harold, Melbourne, Derbyshire, DE73 1BH.**
Contact: **HOME (01332) 865383 OFFICE (01332) 865293 MOBILE (07811) 827678**

1 CALKE PARK, 7, gr g Neltino—Karena Park **Mr R. J. Armson**
2 EARL TOKEN, 8, b g Primitive Rising (USA)—Lady Token **Mr R. J. Armson**
3 EDGEMOOR PRINCESS, 6, b m Broadsword (USA)—Stubbin Moor **Mr R. J. Armson**
4 4, B g Teenoso (USA)—Karina's Carbon **Mr R. J. Armson**
5 4, Br f Alderbrook—One of Those Days **Mr R. J. Armson**
6 THE FENMAN, 6, b g Mazaad—Dalgorian (IRE) **Mr R. J. Armson**

Assistant Trainer: Mrs S Armson

Amateur: Mr R J Armson (10-7).

---

9 THE HON. MRS RICHARD ARTHUR, Hallington
Postal: **Bingfield, East Quarter, Hallington, Newcastle Upon Tyne, NE19 2LH.**
Contact: **PHONE (01434) 672219**

1 CAPYBARA (IRE), 6, b g Commanche Run—The Pledger **The Hon. Mrs Richard Arthur**
2 FEELING GRAND (IRE), 12, b g Naheez (USA)—Tourney's Girl **The Hon. Mrs Richard Arthur**

Amateur: Mr Freddy Arthur (9-7).

---

10 MR JEAN-RENE AUVRAY, Upper Lambourn
Postal: **Frenchman's Lodge Stables, Upper Lambourn, Hungerford, Berkshire, RG17 8QT.**
Contact: **PHONE/FAX (01488) 73740 MOBILE (07798) 645796**
E-MAIL jr.auvray@lambournracing.com WEBSITE www.lambournracing.com

1 BLESSED PLACE, 4, ch g Compton Place—Cathedra **Mr S. J. Edwards**
2 IRISHKAWA BELLEVUE (FR), 6, b br g Irish Prospector (FR)—Strakawa (FR) **The Magpie Partnership**
3 IT'S RUMOURED, 4, ch g Fleetwood (IRE)—Etourdie (USA) **The Simpsons Partnership**
4 L'ARTISTE BELLEVUE (FR), 5, b g Start Fast (FR)—Enus du Manoir (FR) **Mr Jean-Rene Auvray**
5 MOTHER SAYS, 8, b g Landyap (USA)—Miami Blues **Mrs Sian O'Gorman**
6 ONE FOR ME, 6, br m Tragic Role (USA)—Chantallee's Pride **Mr M. J. Lewin**
7 PURE FAST BELLEVUE (FR), 7, ch m Start Fast (FR)—Si Pure (FR) **Lambourn Racing**

THREE-YEAR-OLDS

8 BLAZE THE TRAIL, b f Classic Cliche (IRE)—Explorer **Newbury Racehorse Owners Group**
9 BOLD TRUMP, b g First Trump—Blue Nile **Mr M. J. Lewin**
10 TORTUETTE, b f Turtle Island (IRE)—Almossa **Mr Stuart McPhee**
11 TOUT LES SOUS, ch g Tout Ensemble—Suzie Sue (IRE) **Mrs R. J. Kettle**

TWO-YEAR-OLDS

11 MR N. G. AYLIFFE, Minehead
Postal: **Glebe Stables, Little Ham, Winsford, Minehead, Somerset, TA24 7JH.**
Contact: **PHONE (01643) 851265 MOBILE (07786) 918447**

1 **BLOSSOM WHISPERS,** 7, b m Ezzoud (IRE)—Springs Welcome **Mr D. T. Hooper**
2 **GRIFFIN'S LEGACY,** 5, b g Wace (USA)—Griffin's Girl **Mrs M. A. Barrett**
3 **KATHELLA (IRE),** 7, b m Fourstars Allstar (USA)—Niat Supreme (IRE) **Mr R. Allatt**
4 **RUBY GATE (IRE),** 9, b g Rashar (USA)—Vam Cas (IRE) **Mr D. T. Hooper**
5 **SPARKLING LASS,** 10, gr m Nicholas Bill—Sparkling Time (USA) **Mrs M. A. Barrett**
6 **WITHOUT PRETENSE (USA),** 6, b g St Jovite (USA)—Spark of Success (USA) **Mr Derek Jones**

Other Owners: Mr R. J. Wynn.

Jockey (NH): G Supple.

12 MR J. W. F. AYNSLEY, Morpeth
Postal: **Rye Hill Farm, Thropton, Morpeth, Northumberland, NE65 7NG.**
Contact: **PHONE (01669) 620271**

1 **BLACK ICE (IRE),** 13, b g Cataldi—Turbulent Lass **Mr J. W. F. Aynsley**
2 4, Ch g Duky—General Run **Mr J. W. F. Aynsley**

THREE-YEAR-OLDS
3 B f Endoli (USA)—Eve Pet

Assistant Trainer: J R Aynsley

Jockeys (NH): R Hodge, C McCormack, R McGrath. **Amateurs:** Mr J R Barlow, Mr J Walton.

13 MR A. BAILEY, Tarporley
Postal: **Sandybrow Stables, Little Budworth, Tarporley, Cheshire, CW6 9EG.**
Contact: **PHONE (01829) 760762 FAX (01829) 760370 MOBILE (07808) 734223**

1 **ABBALEVA,** 5, b m Shaddad (USA)—Bo' Babbity **Mr & Mrs Gannon, North Cheshire Trading**
2 **ALLEZ MOUSSON,** 6, b g Hernando (FR)—Rynechra **Dr K. Kaye**
3 **BELLA BEGUINE,** 5, b m Komaite (USA)—On The Record **Granite By Design Ltd**
4 **BODFARI ROSE,** 5, ch m Indian Ridge—Royale Rose (FR) **Mrs J. Bailey**
5 **CHARLIE'S GOLD,** 9, b g Shalford (IRE)—Ballet **Classic Gold**
6 **DOVEBRACE,** 11, b g Dowsing (USA)—Naufrage **Dovebrace Ltd Air-Conditioning-Projects**
7 **EMENCEE,** 7, b g Lucky Wednesday—Natfari **Morris Nicholson Cartwright Ltd**
8 **GOLDEN BOOT,** 5, ch g Unfuwain (USA)—Sports Delight **Mr Peter G. Freeman**
9 **HERNE BAY (IRE),** 4, b f Hernando (FR)—Charita—One For Jeannie **Mr T. R. Pearson**
10 **JEANNIE WIZ,** 4, b f Wizard King—One For Jeannie **Mrs J. Bailey**
11 **KATALI,** 7, ch m Clantime—Portvally **Mr John Edwards**
12 **KELBROOK,** 5, b g Unfuwain (USA)—Pidona **Mrs M. A. Clayton**
13 **KHUZDAR (IRE),** 5, ch g Definite Article—Moriyda (IRE) **Mr M. Channon**
14 **LADY MYTTON,** 4, ch f Lake Coniston (IRE)—The In-Laws (IRE) **Mr Gordon Mytton**
15 **LENNEL,** 6, b g Presidium—Ladykirk **Mr A. Bailey**
16 **MYTTON'S MAGIC,** 4, br g Danetime (IRE)—Maldinion **Mr A. Bailey**
17 **PATANDON GIRL (IRE),** 4, b f Night Shift (USA)—Petite Jameel (IRE) **Mr M. Channon**
18 **PRINCE OF THE WOOD (IRE),** 4, ch g Woodborough (USA)—Ard Dauphine (IRE) **The Four Of Us**
19 **QUEENS RHAPSODY,** 4, b br g Baryshnikov (AUS)—Digamist Girl (IRE) **Mr C. M. Martin**
20 **QUIBBLE,** 7, ch g Lammtarra (USA)—Bloudan (USA) **www.mark-kilner-racing.com (16)**
21 **SARN,** 5, b g Atraf—Covent Garden Girl **Mr S. A. Pritchard**
22 **THE FAIRY FLAG,** 6, ch m Inchinor—Good Reference (IRE) **Mrs V. Farrington**

THREE YEAR OLDS

MR A. BAILEY—continued
TWO-YEAR-OLDS

29 **BALLYCROY GIRL (IRE)**, ch f 2/4 Pennekamp (USA)—Hulm (IRE) (Mujtahid (USA)) (15000) **Mr R. Collins**
30 **HIGH ARCTIC**, b c 27/5 Pivotal—Ladykirk (Slip Anchor) (12000) **Mr & Mrs B. Howl**
31 **MICKLEDO**, b c 19/4 Perryston View—Ever So Lonely (Headin' Up) **Mr M. Turner**
32 **MYTTON'S DREAM**, b c 19/4 Diktat—Courtisane (Persepolis (FR)) (15000) **Mr Gordon Mytton**
33 **SAPPHIRE DREAM**, b f 8/3 Mind Games—Bombay Sapphire (Be My Chief (USA)) (7500) **Mr P. T. Tellwright**

Other Owners: Miss M. Archdeacon, Mr R. T. Collins, Mr R. J. Dawson, Mr M. L. Dean, Mr S. A. Ewart, Mr R. Farrington, Mrs C. L. Johnson, Mr David A. Jones, Mr Mark Kilner, Mrs S. A. Martin, Mrs B. May, Mr J. Meacham, North Cheshire Trading & Storage Ltd, Mr Gordon Richards, Mr John Williams.

Apprentice: Natalie Hassall. **Amateur:** Miss Victoria Cottrill.

---

14 MR K. C. BAILEY, Preston Capes
Postal: Grange Farm, Preston Capes, Daventry, Northamptonshire, NN11 3TQ.
Contact: PHONE (01327) 361733 FAX (01327) 361703
E-MAIL kim@kcbaileyracing.com WEBSITE www.kcbaileyracing.com

1 **AH YEAH (IRE)**, 7, b g Roselier (FR)—Serena Bay **The Dream Makers Partnership**
2 **BARCHAM AGAIN (IRE)**, 7, b g Aristocracy—Dante's Thatch (IRE) **Mr D. Allen**
3 **BAY KENNY**, 6, b g Karinga Bay—Erica Superba **Mr I. F. W. Buchan**
4 **BLANK CANVAS (IRE)**, 6, b g Presenting—Strong Cloth (IRE) **Mr D. Allen**
5 **CEDAR GREEN**, 10, br g Bustino—Explosiva (USA) **Mr J. Perriss**
6 **COUNTESS CAMILLA**, 7, br m Bob's Return (IRE)—Forest Pride (IRE) **The Fingers Crossed Partnership**
7 **EXTREMIST (USA)**, 5, b g Dynaformer (USA)—Strumming (IRE) **Be Lucky Partnership**
8 **FAMFONI (FR)**, 11, b g Pamponi (FR)—India Rosa (FR) **The Propelers Partnership**
9 **FIRST FLIGHT**, 8, br g Neltino—The Beginning **Major Basil Heaton**
10 **FRONT RANK (IRE)**, 4, b g Old Vic—Moppet's Last **The Shine On Partnership**
11 **FULGERE (IRE)**, 6, b g Sadler's Wells (USA)—Alignment (IRE) **Off The Bridle Partnership**
12 **GLENHAVEN BOY (IRE)**, 6, br g Satco (FR)—Dunabell Lady **Mr P. J. Vogt**
13 **GLENOGUE (IRE)**, 6, b m Hushang (IRE)—Glenamal **Big Hitters Racing Partnership**
14 **GOLDEN ROD**, 7, ch g Rainbows For Life (CAN)—Noble Form **Neil Rodway & Carol Cope**
15 **GRAYSLAKE (IRE)**, 8, b g King's Ride—Castlegrace (IRE) **Prof D.B.A. & Mrs H.E.Silk, D.J.Coldman**
16 **HARPOON HARRY (IRE)**, 7, ch g Alphabatim (USA)—Procastrian (IRE) **This Horse Is For Sale Partnership**
17 **HEARTOFMIDLOTHIAN (IRE)**, 5, ch g Anshan—Random Wind **Mr L. Haugh**
18 **JAYBEEDEE**, 8, b g Rudimentary (USA)—Meavy **Mrs C. A. T. Swire & Mr G. D. W. Swire**
19 **JENGA**, 7, ro m Minster Son—Maybe Daisy **Mr John Loudon**
20 **KELANTAN**, 7, b g Kris—Surf Bird **Have Fun Racing Partnership**
21 **KING OF GOTHLAND (IRE)**, 5, b br g Gothland (FR)—Rose Deer **The Norfolk Neighbours**
22 **LONGSHANKS**, 7, b g Broadsword (USA)—Brass Castle (IRE) **Mr D. A. Halsall**
23 **LORD OF THE REALM (IRE)**, 8, b g Mister Lord (USA)—Traditional Lady **Ladies of the Realm**
24 **LORD SEAMUS**, 9, b g Arctic Lord—Erica Superba **Mr I. F. W. Buchan**
25 **LORD SEAMUS**, 9, b g Arctic Lord—Citronelle (FR) **Mrs E. A. Kellar**
26 **LUCKY LUK (FR)**, 5, b g Lights Out (FR)—Lumiere du Feu (FR) **Mr G. P. D. Milne**
27 **LUSSINO (FR)**, 8, b g Esprit du Nord (USA)—Las-Cancellas **Mr D. Allen**
28 **METAL DETECTOR (IRE)**, 7, b g Treasure Hunter—Vulcan Belle **Graham and Alison Jelley**
29 **MORELUCK (IRE)**, 8, b g Roselier (FR)—Vulcan Belle **Mr W. J. Ives**
30 **MOUNT PRAGUE (IRE)**, 10, gr g Lord Americo—Celtic Duchess **This Horse Is For Sale Partnership**
31 **ONYOURHEADBEIT (IRE)**, 6, b g Glacial Storm (USA)—Family Birthday **Quicksilver Racing Partnership**
32 **PIRANDELLO (IRE)**, 6, ch g Shalford (IRE)—Scenic Villa **The Dream Makers Partnership**
33 **PREDESTINE (FR)**, 4, ch g Signe Divin (USA)—Smyrna (FR) **Mr Simon Cordingley**
34 **RAYGALE**, 7, b g Superpower—Little Missile **Mrs J. Way**
35 **RUN ATIM**, 6, ch g Hatim (USA)—Run Pet Run **Mr Peter Granger**
36 **SHERWOOD ROSE**, 8, gr m Mandalus—Cronlier **Mr Peter Granger**
37 **SIR BRASTIAS**, 5, b g Shaamit (IRE)—Premier Night **Mrs K. C. Bailey and Mrs F. Wills**
38 **SMITHLYN**, 7, b g Greensmith—Sunylyn **Mr J. Perriss**
38 **TERMINOLOGY**, 6, gr g Terimon—Rhyming Moppet **Mr J. Perriss**

MR K. C. BAILEY—continued

47 **WONDER WEASEL (IRE)**, 11, b g Lancastrian—The She Weasel **Mr D. A. Halsall**
48 **WOULD YOU BELIEVE**, 8, gr g Derrylin—Ramelton **Mr D. Allen**

Other Owners: Mrs S. E. Acland, Mr P. D. Ashdown, Mrs M. Barwell, Mr A. Baxter, Mr Alastair Beck, Mr A. J. Brettell, Mr A. D. Brown, Mr Ian Bullerwell, Mrs C. E. Cope, Mrs Christine Davies, Mr Huw Davies, Lt Col Mike Davies, Mrs Ginni Dessain, Mr J. M. Humphreys, Mr S. M. Jaggard, The Hon C. Leigh, Mrs Judith Milton, Mr Peter Mordaunt, Major G. H. W. Oakford, Mr F. H. M. Reid, Mr M. A. Sherwood, Lady St Clair-Ford, Mr Ashley Tabony, Mrs G. Wilson, Major R. G. Wilson.

Jockey (NH): J P McNamara (10-7). **Conditional:** D Flavin (10-0). **Amateur:** Mr J Newbold (10-0).

---

15 MRS L. P. BAKER, Maidstone
Postal: **1 Big Allington, Pilgrims Way, Hollingbourne, Maidstone, Kent, ME17 1RD.**
Contact: **PHONE (01622) 880655 MOBILE (07714) 264115**
E-MAIL lesley@bakerbloodstock.fsnet.co.uk

1 **CATFISH HUNTER**, 4, b g Safawan—Secret Account **Mrs L. P. Baker**

Assistant Trainer: M W Baker

---

16 MR A. M. BALDING, Kingsclere
Postal: **Park House Stables, Kingsclere, Newbury, Berkshire, RG20 5PY.**
Contact: **PHONE (01635) 298210 MOBILE (07774) 633791 E-MAIL admin@kingsclere.com**

1 **ANTICIPATING**, 4, b g Polish Precedent (USA)—d'Azy **Mr George Strawbridge**
2 **ARCTIC DESERT**, 4, b g Desert Prince (IRE)—Thamud (IRE) **Holistic Racing Ltd**
3 **BALLINGER EXPRESS**, 4, ch f Air Express (IRE)—Branston Ridge **Mrs Hazel Barber**
4 **BALLINGER RIDGE**, 5, b g Sabrehill (USA)—Branston Ridge **Mrs Hazel Barber**
5 **BOURGAINVILLE**, 6, b g Pivotal—Petonica (USA) **J. C. & J. R. & S. R. Hitchins**
6 **BRIAREUS**, 4, ch g Halling (USA)—Lower The Tone (IRE) **Miss E. J. Lambourne**
7 **COOL MONTY (IRE)**, 10, ch g Montelimar (USA)—Rose Ground **Mr Guy Luck**
8 **CROWN AGENT (IRE)**, 4, b g Mukaddamah (USA)—Supreme Crown (USA) **Miss A. V. Hill**
9 **DANCE PARTY (IRE)**, 4, b f Charnwood Forest (IRE)—Society Ball **Mrs John Davall**
10 **DESERT QUEST (IRE)**, 4, b c Rainbow Quest (USA)—Jumilla (USA) **Mrs B. Strudwick**
11 **DISKO BAY (IRE)**, 4, b f Charnwood Forest (IRE)—Mermaid Beach **Mr M. A. L. Evans**
12 **DISTANT PROSPECT (IRE)**, 7, b g Namaqualand (USA)—Ukraine's Affair (USA) **The Rae Smiths and Pauline Gale**
13 **DUBAIAN GIFT**, 5, b g Bahamian Bounty—Hot Lavender (CAN) **Dubai Thoroughbred Racing**
14 **EMERALD FIRE**, 5, b m Pivotal—Four-Legged Friend **Mr T. M. Mason**
15 **GOLDEN CHALICE (IRE)**, 5, ch g Selkirk (USA)—Special Oasis **Holistic Racing Ltd**
16 **GOLDEN DIXIE (USA)**, 5, ch g Dixieland Band (USA)—Beyrouth (USA) **Holistic Racing Ltd**
17 **GUNNER WELBURN**, 12, ch g Gunner B—Vedra (IRE) **W. A. Ritson/D. H. Hall**
18 **IRONY (IRE)**, 5, gr g Mujadil (USA)—Cidaris (IRE) **John Nicholls Ltd/Mobley Homes**
19 **LARA BAY**, 4, b f Polish Precedent (USA)—Way O'Gold (USA) **Winterbeck Manor Stud**
20 **LOCHRIDGE**, 5, ch m Indian Ridge—Lochsong **Mr J. C. Smith**
21 **MANICANI (IRE)**, 6, ch g Tagula (IRE)—Pluvia (USA) **Mr I. A. Balding**
22 **MOOR LANE**, 12, b g Primitive Rising (USA)—Navos **Mr R. P. B. Michaelson**
23 **OUR TEDDY (IRE)**, 4, ch g Grand Lodge (USA)—Lady Windley **The Beare Family**
24 **PALAWAN**, 8, br g Polar Falcon (USA)—Krameria **Mr M. A. L. Evans**
25 **PASSANDO**, 4, b f Kris—Iota **Mr I. A. Balding & Mrs B. Raymond**
26 **PASSING GLANCE**, 5, br h Polar Falcon (USA)—Spurned **Kingsclere Stud and Mr M. E. Wates**
27 **PENTECOST**, 5, ch g Tagula (IRE)—Boughtbyphone **J. C. J. R. & S. R. Hitchins**
28 **PHOENIX REACH (IRE)**, 4, b c Alhaarth (IRE)—Carroll's Canyon (IRE) **Winterbeck Manor Stud**
29 **QUEEN'S LODGE (IRE)**, 4, ch f Grand Lodge (USA)—Manilia (FR) **Mrs B. Strudwick**
30 **RENDOVA**, 5, ch g Darshaan—Mary Astor (FR) **J. C., J. R. & S. R. Hitchins**
31 **SPANISH GOLD**, 4, b f Vettori (IRE)—Spanish Heart **The Farleigh Court Racing Partnership**
32 **SPEED COP**, 4, ch f Cadeaux Genereux—Blue Siren **Mr J. C. Smith**

MR A. M. BALDING—continued
THREE-YEAR-OLDS

40 **ALBINUS**, gr c Selkirk (USA)—Alouette **Miss K. Rausing**
41 **ARCTIC QUEEN**, b f Linamix (FR)—Friend For Life **Mr D. J. Deer**
42 **AVERAMI**, b br f Averti (IRE)—Mara River **Kingsclere Stud**
43 **BORDER MUSIC**, b g Selkirk (USA)—Hot Thong (BRZ) **Miss K. Rausing**
44 **BRIEF ADVENTURE (USA)**, b f Diesis—Spurned (USA) **Kingsclere Stud**
45 **CHAMBRAY (IRE)**, b f Barathea (IRE)—Dream of Jenny **Mrs L. R. Lovell**
46 **CHASING THE DREAM (IRE)**, b f Desert Sun—Chipaya **Kennet Valley Thoroughbreds I**
47 **CONJUROR**, b c Efisio—Princess Athena **Kennet Valley Thoroughbreds IV**
48 **COUNT DRACULA**, b c Dracula (AUS)—Chipaya **Kennet Valley Thoroughbreds IV**
49 **DONASTRELA (IRE)**, b f Tagula (IRE)—David's Star **Guy Luck and Tom Cox**
50 **DORSET (USA)**, b f Deputy Commander (USA)—Draconienne (USA) **T. Farmer/I. A. Balding**
51 **DOWNING STREET (IRE)**, b c Sadler's Wells (USA)—Photographie (USA) **Mr M. Tabor**
52 **DUBAIAN MIST**, b f Docksider (USA)—Robellino Miss **Dubai Thoroughbred Racing**
53 **FLORIDA HEART**, ch f First Trump—Miami Dancer (USA) **Park House Partnership**
54 **GOLD RELIC (USA)**, b f Kingmambo (USA)—Gold Bust **Lord Lloyd Webber**
55 **GREY ADMIRAL (USA)**, gr c Cozzene (USA)—Remarkable Style **Mr D. H. Caslon**
56 **GROUND PATROL**, b g Ashkalani (IRE)—Good Grounds (USA) **Mr D. J. Deer**
57 **INDIANA BLUES**, ch f Indian Ridge—Blue Siren **Mr J. C. Smith**
58 **LADY ORIANDE**, b f Makbul—Lady Roxanne **Lord Huntingdon**
59 **LADY SOLEAS**, ch f Be My Guest (USA)—Farhana **Winterbeck Manor Stud**
60 **LOVEYOULONGTIME**, b f Compton Place—Sky Red **John Nicholls Ltd/Mobley Homes**
61 **MAKILA KING**, b g Wizard King—Roonah Quay (IRE) **The Pink Hat Racing Partnership**
62 **MR LAMBROS**, ch c Pivotal—Magical Veil **Winterbeck Manor Stud**
63 **PRINCE OF THEBES (IRE)**, b c Desert Prince (IRE)—Persian Walk (FR) **Dr E Harris/Miss M Green**
64 **PRINCESS ALINA (IRE)**, b f Sadler's Wells (USA)—Eilanden (IRE) **Columbus Costa Del Sol**
65 **RECOLLECTING**, b f Polish Precedent (USA)—Introducing **Mr George Strawbridge**
66 **RED BIRR (IRE)**, b g Bahhare (USA)—Cappella (USA) **John Nicholls (Banbury) Ltd**
67 **ROYAL WARRANT**, b c Royal Applause—Brand **The Queen**
68 **SAINT ETIENNE (IRE)**, b f Robellino (USA)—Stop Out **Robinski Bloodstock Limited**
69 **SOUND BLASTER (IRE)**, ch g Zafonic (USA)—Blasted Heath **Mr J. C. Smith**
70 **SPANISH ACE**, b c First Trump—Spanish Heart **The Farleigh Court Racing Partnership**
71 **STAR PUPIL**, ch c Selkirk (USA)—Lochangel **Mr J. C. Smith**
72 **TAG TEAM (IRE)**, ch c Tagula (IRE)—Okay Baby (IRE) **Magic Moments**
73 **TRENCH COAT (USA)**, ch c Gulch—Glamor Queen (USA) **Mr W. S. Farish**
74 **TRICK CYCLIST**, b c Mind Games—Sabonis (USA) **Park House Partnership**
75 **VARIETY CLUB**, b c Royal Applause—Starfida **The Variety Club Partnership**
76 **YOUR JUST LOVELY (IRE)**, b f Second Empire (IRE)—Nawaji (USA) **Coriolan Partnership**

TWO-YEAR-OLDS

77 **ALSU (IRE)**, b f 17/4 Fasliyev (USA)—Pourquoi Pas (IRE) (Nordico (USA)) (21644) **Columbus Costa Del Sol**
78 **ANGEL WING**, ch f 5/4 Barathea (IRE)—Lochangel (Night Shift (USA)) **Mr J. C. Smith**
79 **ANTONIO STRADIVARI (IRE)**, b c 18/3 Stravinsky (USA)—
Dearest (USA) (Riverman (USA)) (46381) **Columbus Costa Del Sol**
80 **ARRIVATO**, b f 13/2 Efisio—Beloved Visitor (USA) (Miswaki (USA)) **G. Tregaskes**
81 **BANKNOTE**, b c 6/4 Zafonic (USA)—Brand (Shareef Dancer (USA)) (Vision (USA)) (3000) **Winterbeck Manor Stud**
82 **BAY HAWK**, b c 30/1 Alhaarth (IRE)—Fleeting Vision (IRE) (Vision (USA)) **Winterbeck Manor Stud**
83 **CAPE GREKO**, gr c 22/4 Loup Sauvage (USA)—
Oneoftheditch (USA) (With Approval (CAN)) (35000) **Holistic Racing Ltd**
84 Ch c 30/4 Titus Livius (USA)—Crimada (IRE) (Mukaddamah (USA)) (13000)
85 Br c 30/1 Belong To Me (USA)—Cymbala (FR) (Assert) **Mr W. S. Farish**
86 B c 4/5 Montjeu (IRE)—Dance Clear (IRE) (Marju (IRE)) (150000) **Mr M. Tabor**
87 **DELLA SALUTE**, gr f 24/2 Dansili—Marie Dora (FR) (Kendor (USA)) **Lord Roborough**
88 **DUBAIAN QUEST**, b c 17/4 Victory Note (USA)—
Latch String (Thatch (USA)) (4500) **Dubai Thoroughbred Racing**
(6500) **Dubai Thoroughbred Racing**
89 **DUBAIAN SPIRIT**, b f 28/3 Revoque (IRE)—Silly Mid-On (Midyan (USA)) (36000) **Anthony & Valerie Hogarth**
90 Ch c 30/5 Cozzene (USA)—Fire And Shade (USA) (Shadeed (USA))

MR A. M. BALDING—continued

98 L'ESCAPADE (IRE), ch c 23/5 Grand Lodge (USA)—
Brief Escapade (IRE) (Brief Truce (USA)) (30000) **Ballygallon Stud**
99 LADY QUESNE (IRE), ch f 12/3 Alhaarth (IRE)—
Lady Moranbon (USA) (Trempolino (USA)) (16000) **Coriolan Partnership V**
100 Ch c 9/2 Dixieland Band (USA)—Lite Twilight (Twilight Agenda (USA)) (59524) **Blue Ribband**
101 Br f 6/2 Robellino (USA)—Loch Sabre (Sharpo) **Mr J. C. Smith**
102 B g 9/2 Compton Place—Loriner's Lass (Saddlers' Hall (IRE)) (6000) **G. Burbidge**
103 B f 8/3 Robellino (USA)—Mara River (Efisio) **Kingsclere Stud**
104 Ch c 15/3 Tagula (IRE)—Marimar (IRE) (Grand Lodge (USA)) (4946) **G. L. Weston**
105 Ch f 12/2 Valid Expectations—Melt My Heart (USA) (Peterhof (USA)) **Mr W. S. Farish**
106 Ch f 15/4 Kris—Natchez Trace (Commanche Run) (15000) **J. A. E. Hobby**
107 NORTHERN SECRET, b f 23/2 Sinndar (IRE)—
Northern Goddess (Night Shift (USA)) (20000) **N. Harris/J. Hobhouse**
108 OCEANCOOKIE (IRE), b f 10/2 Dashing Blade—
Sankaty Light (USA) (Summer Squall (USA)) (3600) **Miss Clare Balding**
109 Br f 27/4 Spinning World (USA)—Our Wildirish Rose (USA) (Irish Tower (USA)) **Mr W. S. Farish**
110 PITTSBURGH, ch c 17/3 Nashwan (USA)—Oatey (Master Willie) (24000)
111 Gr f 6/2 Silver Charm (USA)—Rare Opportunity (USA) (Danzig Connection (USA)) (29762) **Mr D. H. Caslon**
112 Br c 11/2 Diktat—Reason To Dance (Damister (USA)) (45000) **Tweenhills/Thurloe**
113 Br c 27/3 Indian Ridge—Rimba (Dayjur (USA)) **Mr George Strawbridge**
114 ROGUE, b f 5/2 Royal Applause—Mystique (Mystiko (USA)) **Winterbeck Manor Stud**
115 ROMAN ARMY (IRE), b c 22/5 Trans Island—
Contravene (IRE) (Contract Law (USA)) (11131) **Stamford Bridge Partnership**
116 B c 3/4 Makbul—Silken Dalliance (Rambo Dancer (CAN)) (CHF Partnership)
117 B f 9/3 Gone West (USA)—Silver Fling (USA) (The Minstrel (CAN)) **CHF Partnership**
118 SPEED OF SOUND, ch f 10/4 Zafonic (USA)—Blue Siren (Bluebird (USA)) **Mr George Strawbridge**
119 B f 12/4 Sinndar (IRE)—Speedybird (IRE) (Danehill (USA)) (60000) **Mr J. C. Smith**
120 B f 11/4 Sinndar (IRE)—Spurned (Robellino (USA)) **Mr George Strawbridge**
121 B c 27/4 Mujahid (USA)—Stolen Melody (Robellino (USA)) **Kingsclere Stud**
122 STORM CENTRE, ch c 15/2 Pivotal—Long View (Persian Bold) (18000)
123 STREET CRED, ch c 18/2 Bold Edge—Trump Street (First Trump) (18000) **Mrs Richard Plummer & Partners**
124 Ch c 16/5 Kingmambo (USA)—Style Setter (USA) (Manila (USA))
125 SUKUMA, ch f 27/3 Highest Honor (FR)—Selva (FR) (Darshaan) (12000) **Mr W. S. Farish**
126 TAPA, b f 14/1 Tagula (IRE)—Tweed Mill (Selkirk (USA)) (4800) **Mr M. A. L. Evans**
127 TUVALU (GER), ch c 8/4 Dashing Blade—Tepana (GER) (Polish Precedent (USA)) (12368) **D. H. Back**
128 YEOMAN LASS, b f 27/3 Bluebird (USA)—Alpine Time (IRE) (Tirol) (8500) **N. H. Harris**

Other Owners: Mr S. Alansari, Mr D. F. Allport, Mrs I. A. Balding, Mr R. P. Beare, Mrs V. I. Beare, Mr Peter Box, Mr J. A. Fergusson, Mr C. H. Fischer, Mr K. H. Fischer, Mrs Christine Foster, Mr Peter W. Haddock, Mr Duncan Heath, Lord Lane Of Horsell, Mr D. R. O. How, Mrs Anne Ireland, Mr G. R. Ireland, Ms L. La Plante, Mr R. A. Stuart Macdonald, Sir Nevil Macready, Mr F. Mani, Mr E. Mordukhovitch, Miss J. Philip-Jones, Mr A. F. Rae Smith, Mrs M. A. Rae Smith, Mr Michael C. Roberts, Mr N. J. F. Robinson, Mr Stephen L. Ross, Mrs Amanda Simmons, Mr R. A. Simmons, Mr A. M. Tolhurst, Mr Tim Walker, Mr M. E. Wates, Mrs E. M. Wechsler.

Assistant Trainer: I. A. Balding & S. Burgoyne

Jockey (Flat): M Dwyer. **Apprentices:** N Chalmers (7-13), L Keniry (8-2), R Killoran (8-3), A Parsons (7-3).
Amateur: Mr S Goswell (9-7).

---

17 **MR G. B. BALDING, Andover**
Postal: Kimpton Down Stables, Kimpton Farm, Andover, Hampshire, SP11 8PQ.
Contact: PHONE 1 (01264) 772278 PHONE 2 (01264) 771815 FAX (01264) 771221
E-MAIL serena@baldingtraining.fsnet.co.uk WEBSITE www.tobybalding.co.uk

1 ACCIPITER, 5, b g Polar Falcon (USA)—Accuracy **Miss B. Swire**
2 ANDROMACHE, 5, ch m Hector Protector (USA)—South Sea Bubble (IRE) **Mr J. T. Brown**
3 AUDIOSTREETDOTCOM, 7, ch g Risk Me (FR)—Ballagarrow Girl **Audiostreetdotcom Partnership**
4 BALLYADAM (IRE), 5, b c Risk Me (FR)—Ballagarrow Girl

MR G. B. BALDING—continued

12 **CHIEF CASHIER**, 9, b g Persian Bold—Kentfield **The Tachyarrhythmias**
13 **CRACKING WALKER (IRE)**, 8, ch g Rashar (USA)—Futile Walk **J.Harvey, H.Bogie, R.Spencer & T.Geake**
15 **DANCE DIRECTOR (IRE)**, 7, b g Sadler's Wells (USA)—Memories (USA) **Dr G. Madan Mohan**
16 **DESAILLY**, 10, ch g Teamster—G W Superstar **The Team**
17 **DICKIE DEADEYE**, 7, b g Distant Relative—Accuracy **Miss B. Swire**
18 **DILIZA**, 5, b m Dilum (USA)—Little White Lies **Redenham Racing Group**
19 **DREAM WITH ME (FR)**, 7, b g Johann Quatz (FR)—Midnight Ride (FR) **Dr G. Madan Mohan**
20 **DUKE OF MODENA**, 7, ch g Salse (USA)—Sharmalyne (FR) **Mr Leon Best**
21 **EAST HILL (IRE)**, 8, b g Satco (FR)—Ocean Jewel (USA) **Mr G. Richards**
22 **ENCHANTED OCEAN**, 5, b m Royal Academy (USA)—Ocean Jewel (USA) **Mrs J. Palmer & Mr S. Balding**
23 **FORMALISE**, 4, b g Forzando—Esilam **Mrs J. Palmer & Mr S. Balding**
24 **FULLY FLEDGED**, 4, b f Fraam—Alarming Motown **The P. K. Partnership**
25 **GLACIAL VALE (IRE)**, 5, b m Glacial Storm (USA)—Anna Valley **Miss B. Swire**
26 **GOLDEN BAY**, 5, ch m Karinga Bay—Goldenswift (IRE) **Goldie's Friends**
27 **GOLD RING**, 4, ch g Groom Dancer (USA)—Indubitable **Miss B. Swire**
28 **HARVIS (FR)**, 9, b g Djarvis (FR)—Tirana (FR) **Mr Peter Richardson**
29 **HISTORIC PLACE (USA)**, 4, b g Dynaformer (USA)—Captive Island **Miss Georgina Bishop**
30 5, B g Simply Great (FR)—Jupiter's Message **Argent Racing**
31 **JUSTINO**, 6, b g Bustino—Jupiter's Message **Mr G. B. Balding**
32 **KELTIC ROCK**, 5, ch g Bigstone (IRE)—Sibley **D J Erwin Bloodstock & Tony Geake**
33 **KILMORE QUAY (IRE)**, 9, ch g Over The River (FR)—Sustenance **Stan Miller,Max Aitken,Bill & John Craig**
34 **LATIMER'S PLACE**, 8, b g Teenoso (USA)—Pennethorne Place **Sir Christopher Wates**
35 4, Ch f Good Thyne (USA)—Leading The Act (IRE) **Mr Tony Geake**
36 **M'LORD**, 6, b g Mister Lord (USA)—Dishcloth **Dr G. Madan Mohan**
37 **MAD MICK MEESON**, 4, b g Whittingham (IRE)—Meeson Times **Messrs. Castle, Price & Harding**
38 **MARKER**, 4, ch g Pivotal—Palace Street (USA) **Miss B. Swire**
39 **OH TO BE**, 8, b g Weld—At Long Last **Lady G. Wates**
40 **ORION'S BELT**, 4, ch g Compton Place—Follow The Stars **Baldings (Training) Ltd**
41 **PARNASSIAN**, 4, ch g Sabrehill (USA)—Delphic Way **Miss B. Swire**
42 **PENNEYROSE BAY**, 5, ch m Karinga Bay—Pennethorne Place **Sir Christopher Wates**
43 **PINE MARTEN**, 5, b g Karinga Bay—Rakaposhi Queen **Mrs D. J. Hues**
44 **POLDEN CHIEF**, 4, br g Atraf—Maid of Mischief **Mrs P. Barnett**
45 **POMPEY CHIMES**, 4, b g Forzando—Silver Purse **Mr Clifford Warner**
46 **PRIZEMAN (USA)**, 6, b g Prized (USA)—Shuttle (USA) **The Prize Winners**
47 **RESTLESS WIND (IRE)**, 12, b g Celio Rufo—Trulos **The Kingfisher Partnership**
48 **SILVER LOUIE (IRE)**, 4, gr f Titus Livius (FR)—Shakamiyn **Mr & Mrs K. Finch**
49 **SPARTAN PLACE**, 4, b g Overbury (IRE)—Pennethorne Place **Sir Christopher Wates**
50 **THE PROOF**, 7, b g Rudimentary (USA)—Indubitable **Miss B. Swire**
51 **TURBO (IRE)**, 5, b g Piccolo—By Arrangement (IRE) **Mr Peter Richardson**
52 **UNCLE BERNON**, 5, ch g Pivotal—Magical Veil **Seabright Five**
53 **WEST PACES (IRE)**, 10, br g Lord Americo—Spanish Royale **Baldings (Training) Ltd**
   WIZARD OF EDGE, 4, b g Wizard King—Forever Shineing **Mr Peter Richardson**

THREE-YEAR-OLDS

54 **AMBER WAVES**, ch f Bahamian Bounty—Glamorous **Mr P. Balding & Mr P. Holmes**
55 **ANGEL MAID**, b f Forzando—Esilam **Mr S. Balding & Mrs J. Palmer**
56 Ch g Piccolo—Bob's Princess **Baldings (Training) Ltd**
57 **COUNT BORIS**, b g Groom Dancer (USA)—Bu Hagab (IRE) **The P.J. Partnership**
58 **CUGINA NICOLA**, b f Nicolotte—Cugina **Miss B. Swire**
59 **DULCIMER**, ch f Piccolo—Superspring **Miss Georgina Bishop**
60 **JOE LIEBERMAN**, b g Polish Precedent (USA)—Inchkeith **Dr J. M. Leigh**
61 **KING'S CAPRICE**, ch g Pursuit of Love—Palace Street (USA) **Miss B. Swire**
62 Br f Atraf—Maid of Mischief **Mrs P. Barnett**
63 **MISS TILLY**, b f Nicolotte—Little White Lies **Dr and Mrs John Merrington**
64 **MORGAN LEWIS (IRE)**, b g Orpen (USA)—Party Piece **Mrs G. Smith**
65 **NICK THE SILVER**, gr g Nicolotte—Brillante (FR) **Surgical Spirits**
66 **PERSIAN GENIE (IRE)**, br f Grand Lodge (USA)—Persia (IRE) **Mr Rex L. Mead**

MR G. B. BALDING—continued

TWO-YEAR-OLDS

72 **ARRIMAN**, ch c 21/3 Bien Bien (USA)—Spellbinder (IRE) (Magical Wonder (USA)) **The Dancing Partners**
73 **FINAL PROMISE**, b c 17/4 Lujain (USA)—Unerring (Unfuwain (USA)) (6000) **Sideways Racing**
74 **LA LUPA**, b f 22/2 Loup Savage (USA)—Cugina (Distant Relative) **Miss B. Swire**
75 **MISTER TOUBRIDGE**, ch c 18/5 Mister Baileys—So True (So Blessed) **Miss B. Swire**
76 **MOONSIDE**, gr f 11/4 Docksider (USA)—Moon Magic (Polish Precedent (USA)) (7000) **Mr Q. J. Jones**
77 **PALAIS POLAIRE**, ch f 29/4 Polar Falcon (USA)—Palace Street (USA) (Secreto (USA)) **Miss B. Swire**
78 B c 26/3 In The Wings—Persia (IRE) (Persian Bold) (20000) **Partnership**
79 **PEVERIL PARTY GIRL**, ch f 26/2 Classic Cliche (IRE)—Adradee (IRE) (Ajraas (USA)) **Mrs E. A. Haycock**
80 **PHILBY**, b c 16/5 Pursuit Of Love—Delphic Way (Warning) **Miss B. Swire**
81 **QUALITY STREET**, ch f 19/4 Fraam—Pusey Street Girl (Gildoran) (15000) **Rumble Racing**
82 **TILLY FLOSS**, ch f 27/4 Picolo—Lu Girl (IRE) (Mukaddamah (USA)) **Mr P. Richardson**
83 Ch f 15/3 Piccolo—Uplift (Bustino) (2000) **Mr D. Evans**

Other Owners: Mrs Sue Addington-Smith, Mrs Kathy Blackman, Dr W. Bogie, Mr K. F. Chittock, Mrs Margaret Geake, Mr Colston Herbert, Mrs Ellen Ann Hopkins, Mr M. C. Humby, Mr David N. King, Wing Comdr J. H. King, Mr P. Leopold, Mr S. Little, Sir Brian McGrath, Dr G. Middleton, Mr S. Singh, Mr Johnny Walker, Mrs Janet M. Walters, Mr John Walters, Mr R. C. Watts, Mrs S. Watts.

Assistant Trainer: Jonathan Geake

Jockeys (Flat): S Carson (8-0, w.a.), S Drowne (8-0, w.a.), R Mavlin (8-4, w.a.). **Jockeys (NH):** M Bradburne (10-0, w.a.), B Fenton (10-0, w.a.). **Apprentice:** R Thomas (7-7). **Conditional:** T Best (9-7), S Elliott (9-7). **Amateurs:** J.J. Best, Miss K Cuthbertson (9-7).

---

18 MR J. BALDING, Doncaster

Postal: **Mayflower Stables, Saracens Lane, Scrooby, Doncaster, South Yorkshire, DN10 6AS.**
Contact: **HOME (01302) 710096 MOBILE (07816) 612631**
E-MAIL j.balding@mayflowerstables.com

1 **ABSENT FRIENDS**, 7, b g Rock City—Green Supreme **Mrs Jo Hardy**
2 **BOWLEGS BILLY**, 4, gr g Raphane (USA)—Swallow Bay **Mr Billy Herring**
3 **CARK**, 6, b g Farfelu—Precious Girl **Mr J. E. Abbey**
4 **CLASSICAL SONG (IRE)**, 4, b f Fayruz—Dieci Anno (IRE) **The Classical Syndicate**
5 **CZAR WARS**, 9, b g Warrshan (USA)—Dutch Czarina **Men Behaving Badly**
6 **HENRY TUN**, 6, b g Chaddleworth (IRE)—B Grade **Mr J. Bladen**
7 **JUSTALORD**, 6, b g King's Signet (USA)—Just Lady **Mr T. H. Heckingbottom**
8 **LADY PROTECTOR**, 5, b m Sri Pekan (USA)—Scared **Simon Mapletoft Racing II**
9 **LAKE EYRE (IRE)**, 5, b m Bluebird (USA)—Pooh Wee **Mr J. C. Fretwell**
10 **LAKELANDS LADY (IRE)**, 4, ch f Woodborough (USA)—Beautyofthepeace (IRE) **Mr G. Griffiths**
11 **LARGS**, 4, ch f Sheikh Albadou—Madam Zando **Hollinbridge Racing**
12 **MATTY TUN**, 5, b g Lugana Beach—B Grade **Mrs O. Tunstall**
13 **PLAYFUL SPIRIT**, 5, b m Mind Games—Kalimat **Simon Mapletoft Racing II**
14 **PRECIOUS FREEDOM**, 4, b g Ashkalani (IRE)—Prayers'n Promises (USA) **Tykes And Terriers Racing Club**
15 **ROCKY REPPIN**, 4, b g Rock City—Tino Reppin **Sandown Park Stud**
16 **SCARY NIGHT (IRE)**, 4, b g Night Shift (USA)—Private Bucks (USA) **Mr Derrick Moss**
17 **SOBA JONES**, 7, b g Emperor Jones—Soba **Mr R. L. Crowe**
18 **STAR APPLAUSE**, 4, b f Royal Applause—Cominna **Mr Matt Leach**
19 **TEFI**, 6, ch g Efisio—Masuri Kabisa (USA) **Watchman Racing**
20 **TOM TUN**, 9, b g Bold Arrangement—B Grade **Mrs O. Tunstall**
21 **WINNING PLEASURE (IRE)**, 6, b g Ashkalani (IRE)—Karamana **Mr R. L. Crowe**

THREE-YEAR-OLDS

22 **BAYLAW STAR**, b c Case Law—Caisson **T C K Racing Partnership**
23 **COMPTON MICKY**, ch c Compton Place—Nunthorpe **Mr J. M. Lacey**
24 **FIRST ECLIPSE (IRE)**, b f Fayruz—Naked Poser (IRE) **UD Partners**

MR J. BALDING—continued
TWO-YEAR-OLDS

30 **AFTON**, ch f 1/4 Bien Bien (USA)—Madam Zando (Forzando) **Mrs G. A. R. Jones**
31 Ch f 25/2 Komaite (USA)—Areish (IRE) (Keen) **Mrs J. Everitt**
32 B f 17/4 Sure Blade (USA)—Delicious (Dominion) (5000) **Mr M. Leach**
33 **GIFTED LASS**, b f 11/3 Bold Edge—Meeson Times (Enchantment) (5000) **Mr M. Leach**
34 Ch f 22/3 Sure Blade (USA)—Magic Orb (Primo Dominie)
35 Ch f 6/3 Silver Patriarch—Muftuffenuf (Elmaamul) (USA) **Mrs J. Everitt**
36 B f 13/3 Namaqualand (USA)—Paris Mist (Paris House) (1400) **T. C. K. Partnership**
37 B c 5/4 Lugana Beach—Raisa Point (Raised Socially (USA)) **Mr J. Amass**
38 **SCARBOROUGH FLYER**, b c 14/4 Almaty (IRE)—Calamanco (Clantime) (14500) **Mrs Sheila Oakes**

Other Owners: Mr K. A. Bailey, Mrs C. M. Beresford, Mr D. C. Bichan, Mr C. Blaymire, Mr M. Carr, Ms L. Ellis, Mr M. V. Firth, Mrs J. Mapletoft, Mr Simon Mapletoft, Mr T. Mather, Mr Mike Nolan, Mr J. P. Severn, Mr A. L. Speight, Mr C. Wagstaff, Mrs E. Wagstaff, Mr P. Watson, Mr Richard Wright.

Assistant Trainer: Claire Edmunds

Jockey (Flat): Jason Edmunds (8-0).

---

19 **MR M. C. BANKS, Sandy**
Postal: **Manor Farm, Manor Farm Road,** Waresley, Sandy, Bedfordshire, SG19 3BX.
Contact: **PHONE (01767) 650563 MOBILE (07860) 627370 FAX** (01767) 652988

1 **KING CLAUDIUS (IRE)**, 8, b g King's Ride—Lepida **Mr M. C. Banks**
2 **LA FOLICHONNE (FR)**, 5, b m Useful (FR)—Allure Folle (FR) **Mrs M. C. Banks**
3 **LOCKSTOCKANDBARREL (IRE)**, 5, b g Needle Gun (IRE)—Quill Project (IRE) **Mrs M. C. Banks**
4 **POLY AMANSHAA (IRE)**, 12, b br g Nashamaa—Mombones **Mr M. C. Banks**
5 **STRONG DECISION (IRE)**, 7, br g Mandalus—Francois's Crumpet (IRE) **Mr M. C. Banks**

THREE-YEAR-OLDS

6 **MARSH ORCHID**, b g Lahib (USA)—Majalis **Mr M. C. Banks**

---

20 **MRS A. BARCLAY, Moreton-in-Marsh**
Postal: **Fotherop, Oddington,** Moreton-in-Marsh, Gloucestershire, GL56 0XF.

1 **GERRARD (IRE)**, 6, b g Jurado (USA)—Vienna Waltz (IRE) **Mrs Althea Barclay**
2 **ZIGGY'S WAY**, 9, b g Teenoso (USA)—Onaway **Mrs Althea Barclay**

---

21 **MR J. BARCLAY, Glenfarg**
Postal: **St Serf's, The Cobbles,** Kinnesswood, KY13 9HL.
Contact: **PHONE (01592) 840331 MOBILE (07712) 564568 E-MAIL** ccbarclay@btopenworld.com

1 **BLACKOUT (IRE)**, 9, b g Black Monday—Fine Bess **Mr Jim Barclay**
2 **SILVER PEARL**, 13, gr g Insan (USA)—Vanishing Trick **Miss L. Wood**
3 **WEE RIVER (IRE)**, 15, b g Over The River (FR)—Mahe Reef **Miss L. Wood**

Assistant Trainer: Miss Caroline Barclay

---

22 **MR D. W. BARKER, Richmond**
Postal: **Tancred Grange,** Scorton, Richmond, North Yorkshire, DL10 6AB.
MOBILE (07836) 260149

MR D. W. BARKER—continued

6 LE SAUVAGE (IRE), 9, b g Tirol—Cistus **Mr D. W. Barker**
7 SIERRA VISTA, 4, ch f Atraf—Park Vista **Mr D. Metcalfe & Mr D. W. Barker**
8 SUMMER SPECIAL, 4, b g Mind Games—Summerhill Special (IRE) **Alba Racing Syndicate**
9 TANCRED ARMS, 8, b m Clantime—Mischievous Miss **Mr D. W. Barker**
10 TANCRED MISS, 5, b m Presidium—Mischievous Miss **Mrs S. J. Barker**
11 TANCRED TIMES, 9, ch m Clantime—Mischievous Miss **Mr D. W. Barker & Mr R. Dobson**
12 WHINHILL HOUSE, 4, ch g Paris House—Darussalam **Mr J. J. Crosier**

THREE-YEAR-OLDS

13 FOX COVERT (IRE), b g Foxhound (USA)—Serious Contender (IRE) **Mr D. W. Barker**
14 MECCA'S MATE, gr f Paris House—Clancassie **Mr D. Metcalfe & Mr D. W. Barker**
15 MR WOLF, b c Wolfhound (USA)—Madam Millie **Mr P. Asquith**
16 RED MOUNTAIN, b c Unfuwain (USA)—Red Cascade (IRE) **Burns Farm Racing**
17 TANCRED IMP, b f Atraf—Tancred Mischief **Mr D. W. Barker**

TWO-YEAR-OLDS

18 B f 12/3 Danehill Dancer (IRE)—Appledorn (Doulab (USA)) (7420) **Ebor Racing**
19 B c 19/3 Mind Games—Champenoise (Forzando) (9000)
20 Ch f 23/1 Wolfhound (USA)—Darussalam (Tina's Pet) (7000)
21 B f 16/4 Orpen (USA)—Fairy Highlands (IRE) (Fairy King (USA)) (8039)
22 B f 2/4 Atraf—Summerhill Special (IRE) (Roi Danzig (USA)) (8039) **Mrs S. J. Barker**
23 B f 12/4 Atraf—Tancred Mischief (Northern State (USA)) **Mr D. W. Barker**

Other Owners: Mr Wayne Asquith, Mr K. Cameron, Mr A. Campbell, Mr D. G. Clayton, Mr S. Johnson, Mr I. McLeod.

Assistant Trainer: Pat Barker & Samantha Barker

---

23 **MISS S. BARKER, Foston**
Postal: **Foston Stud, Hay Lane, Foston, Derbyshire, DE65 5PJ.**
Contact: **PHONE (01283) 585036 MOBILE (07720) 854997**

1 PRINCE TARQUIN, 4, br g Overbury (IRE)—Civiki **Miss S. Barker**

Assistant Trainer: W A Corten

---

24 **SIR J. BARLOW, Nantwich**
Postal: **Ash House, Brindley, Nantwich, Cheshire, CW5 8HX.**
Contact: **OFFICE (01270) 524339 FAX (01270) 524047**

1 ASH BRANCH (IRE), 10, ch g Shardari—Etnas Princess **Sir John & Lady Barlow**
2 IVERAIN (FR), 8, b g Le Riverain (FR)—Ursala (FR) **Sir John & Lady Barlow**
3 LORD TIDDLYPUSH (IRE), 6, b g Lord Americo—Ag Rith Abhaile **Sir John & Lady Barlow**
4 ROWAN CASTLE, 8, ch g Broadsword (USA)—Brass Castle (IRE) **Sir John Barlow**
5 SILENT VOICE, 7, ch g Unfuwain (USA)—Symeterie (USA) **Sir John & Lady Barlow**

---

25 **MR M. A. BARNES, Brampton**
Postal: **Tarnside, Farlam, Brampton, Cumbria, CA8 1LA.**
Contact: **PHONE (01697) 746675**

1 ASHTON VALE, 5, ch g Ashkalani (IRE)—My Valentina **Mr M. Barnes**
2 CHARLIES BRIDE, 9, b br m Rich Charlie—Nordic Bride (IRE) **Pointerfarm Racing Partnership**
3 DABARPOUR (IRE), 8, b br g Alzao (USA)—Dabara (IRE) **Mr J. G. Graham**
4 IT'S A WIZARD, 4, b g Wizard King—Axed Again **Mr D. Maloney**
5 JOHN'S TREASURE (IRE), 4, b g Entrepreneur—Miscllah (IRE) **Mr A. Wm**

MR M. A. BARNES—continued

14 SKIDDAW ROSE (IRE), 8, gr m Terimon—Whimbrel **Mr John Wills**
15 SULLY SHUFFLES (IRE), 9, b g Broken Hearted—Green Legend (IRE) **Murphy's Law Partnership**
16 TEA'S MAID, 4, b f Wizard King—Come To Tea (IRE) **Mr G. White**
17 THE NEGOTIATOR, 10, ch g Nebos (GER)—Baie des Anges **Mr T. A. Barnes**

THREE-YEAR-OLDS

18 TORKIN WIND, ch g Chocolat de Meguro (USA)—Helm Wind **Mr M. Barnes**

TWO-YEAR-OLDS

19 INDIAN WIND, ch g 26/4 Chocolat De Meguro—Helm Wind (North Col) **Mr M. Barnes**

Other Owners: Mrs D. Chacewicz, Mr P. W. Chacewicz, Mr P. Clement, Mr W. Downs, Mr Steven Nightingale, Mr N. Ricioppo, Mr J. G. White, Mr T. Yates.

Jockeys (NH): Calvin McCormack (10-0), Paul Robson (w.a.). **Conditional:** D McGann.

---

26   **MR R. E. BARR, Middlesbrough**
Postal: Carr House Farm, Seamer, Stokesley, Middlesbrough, Cleveland, TS9 5LL.
Contact: PHONE (01642) 710687 (01642) 712737 MOBILE (07711) 895309

1 ALJOMAR, 5, b g College Chapel—Running For You (FR) **Mrs R. E. Barr**
2 AMARETTO EXPRESS (IRE), 5, b g Blues Traveller (IRE)—Cappuchino (IRE) **Mrs R. E. Barr**
3 COUNTESS ELTON (IRE), 4, ch f Mukaddamah (USA)—Be Prepared (IRE) **Mr P. Cartmell**
4 COURT MUSIC (IRE), 5, b br m Revoque—Lute And Lyre (IRE) **Mr G. Thornton**
5 FIRST BASE, 5, ch g First Trump—Rose Music **Mr Malcolm O'Hair**
6 FRIMLEY'S MATTERRY, 4, b c Bluegrass Prince (USA)—Lonely Street
7 IN GOOD FAITH, 12, b g Beveled (USA)—Dulcidene **Mr P. Cartmell**
8 MEHMAAS, 8, b g Distant Relative—Guest List **Middleham Park Racing XXIV**
9 NEXT FLIGHT (IRE), 5, b g Woodborough (USA)—Sans Ceriph (IRE) **Mrs R. E. Barr**
10 NOD YA HEAD, 8, ch m Minster Son—Little Mittens **Mr R. E. Barr**
11 PAY TIME, 5, b m Timeless Times (USA)—Payvashooz **Mrs C. Barr**
12 ROGERO, 5, b g Presidium—Richesse (FR) **Mr R. E. Barr**
13 STEPASTRAY, 7, gr g Alhijaz—Wandering Stranger **Mr D. Thomson**
14 STRENSALL, 7, b g Beveled (USA)—Payvashooz **Mr R. E. Barr**
15 TOEJAM, 11, ch g Move Off—Cheeky Pigeon **Mrs R. E. Barr**

THREE-YEAR-OLDS

16 GONE TO GROUND, ch g Foxhound (USA)—Charlie Girl **Mr P. Cartmell**

TWO-YEAR-OLDS

17 BLACK EYED PEA, gr f 5/5 Grey Desire—Cheeky Pigeon (Brave Invader (USA)) **C. Barr**

Other Owners: Mr S. P. French, Mr T. S. Palin.

Assistant Trainer: Mrs C Barr

   MR T. D. BARRON, Thirsk
Postal: Maunby House, Maunby, Thirsk, North Yorkshire, YO7 4HD.
Contact: PHONE (01845) 587435

1 BLAKESET, 9, ch g Midyan (USA)—Penset **Mr Nigel Shields**
2 BLONDE STREAK, 4, ch f Dumaani (USA)—Katiba (USA) **Mrs Liz Jones**   **Mr Nigel Shields**
3 EIGHT WOODS (IRE), 6, b g Woods of Windsor (USA)—Cd Super Targeting (IRE) **Mr Kevin Shaw**

MR T. D. BARRON—continued

13 **NEVEN,** 5, b g Casteddu—Rose Burton **Mr D. G. Pryde**
14 **OLD BAILEY (USA),** 4, gr g Lit de Justice (USA)—Olden Lek (USA) **Mr J. Baggott**
15 **OSCAR PEPPER (USA),** 7, b g Brunswick (USA)—Princess Baja (USA) **Mr Ian Armitage**
16 **PATRICIA PHILOMENA (IRE),** 6, br m Prince of Birds (USA)—Jeewan **Miss Pauline Laycock**
17 **PAWN IN LIFE (IRE),** 6, b g Midhish—Lady-Mumtaz **Mr Laurence O'Kane**
18 **PENWELL HILL (USA),** 5, b g Distant View (USA)—Avie's Jill (USA) **Mrs Liz Jones**
19 **POLAR KINGDOM,** 6, b g Pivotal—Scarlet Lake **Millie and Poppy Squire**
20 **QUEEN OF NIGHT,** 4, b f Piccolo—Cardinal Press **Mr Timothy Cox**
21 **ROYAL GRAND,** 4, ch c Prince Sabo—Hemline **Sporting Occasions Racing No 4**
22 **SPITFIRE BOB (USA),** 5, b g Mister Baileys—Gulf Cyclone (USA) **Mr Nigel Shields**
23 **TRANCE (IRE),** 4, ch g Bahhare (USA)—Lady of Dreams (IRE) **Mr Nigel Shields**
24 **WAHOO SAM (USA),** 4, ch g Sandpit (BRZ)—Good Reputation (USA) **Mr C. A. Washbourn**
25 **ZERO TOLERANCE (IRE),** 4, ch g Nashwan (USA)—Place de L'Opera **PV (The Hardliners)**

THREE-YEAR-OLDS

26 **ARE YOU THERE,** b f Presidium—Scoffera **Mr Ian Armitage**
27 **BALTIC WAVE,** b g Polish Precedent (USA)—Flourish **Mrs J. Hazell**
28 **COALAMI (USA),** b g Bianconi (USA)—Luppiano (USA) **Mr Laurence O'Kane**
29 **COUNTRYWIDE FLYER (IRE),** b g Revoque (IRE)—Unbidden Melody (USA) **Mr Nigel Shields**
30 **DISPOL KATIE,** ch f Komaite (USA)—Twilight Time **Mr W. B. Imison**
31 **EL PALMAR,** b g Case Law—Aybeegirl **Mr J. G. Brown**
32 **FIORE DI BOSCO (IRE),** b f Charnwood Forest (IRE)—Carabine (USA) **Miss Pauline Laycock**
33 **FIREBIRD RISING (USA),** b f Stravinsky (USA)—Capable (USA) **Mr C. A. Washbourn**
34 **FLIPANDO (IRE),** b g Sri Pekan (USA)—Magic Touch **Mrs J. Hazell**
35 **IMPERIAL ECHO (USA),** b g Labeeb—Regal Baby (USA) **Mr J. Stephenson**
36 **LUALUA,** ch g Presidium—Tawny **Mr Bernard Hathaway**
37 **MACPURSIE,** br f Botanic (USA)—Jeethgaya (USA) **Mr T. Calver**
38 **MISTRESS TWISTER,** b f Pivotal—Foreign Mistress **Mr Dave Scott**
39 **PALACE THEATRE (IRE),** b g Imperial Ballet (IRE)—Luminary **Mr Chris McHale**
40 **PARTNERS IN JAZZ,** gr c Jambalaya Jazz (USA)—
                                            Just About Enough (USA) **Sporting Occasions Racing No 2**
41 **QUINCANNON (USA),** b g Kayrawan (USA)—Sulalat **Mr George Houghton**
42 **SILVERHAY,** b g Inchinor—Moon Spin **D. C. Rutter P. J. Huntbach**
43 **SIR JASPER (IRE),** b g Sri Pekan (USA)—Ashover Amber **Mrs Liz Jones**
44 **THORNABY GREEN,** b c Whittingham (IRE)—Dona Filipa **Thornaby Racing Club**
45 **TITUS SALT (USA),** ch g Gentlemen (ARG)—Farewell Partner (USA) **Sporting Occasions Racing No 5**
46 **TYNE,** b c Komaite (USA)—High Typha **Mr Bernard Hathaway**

Other Owners: Mr K. J. Alderson, Mrs M. E. Armitage, Mr G. Bates, Mr E. Buck, Mrs D. Catlow, Mr Mel Catlow, Mr R. H. Coombe, Mr S. Knighton, Mr J. M. Lamont, Mrs J. R. Lamont, Mr R. Nolan.

Jockey (Flat): D Mernagh (7-10). **Apprentices:** Gemma Anderson (7-12), Laura Crawford (8-6), Phillip Makin (8-0).

---

28 **MR F. M. BARTON, Tarporley**
Postal: **Radley Wood Farm, Whitchurch Road, Spurstow, Tarporley, Cheshire, CW6 9TD.**
Contact: **PHONE (01829) 260453 MOBILE (07833) 960632**

1 **BEHARI (IRE),** 10, b g Kahyasi—Berhala (IRE) **Mr F. M. Barton**

Jockey (NH): Gary Lyons (w.a.). **Amateur:** Miss S Sharratt.

---

29 **MR P. BARY, Chantilly**
Postal: **5 Chemin des Aigles, 60500 Chantilly, France.**
Contact: **PHONE +33 (0) 3 44 57 14 03 FAX +33 (0) 3 44 67 20 15 E-MAIL p-bary@wanadoo.fr**

1 **BY FAR (FR),** 6, b h Machiavellian (USA)—Makri **Niarchos Family**
2 **CONDITION,** 4, ch f Deploy—Context **K. Abdullah**
3 **FOMALHAUT (USA),** 5, b h Spinning World (USA)—Coup de Folie (USA) **Niarchos Family**
4 **KALABAR,** 4, b c Kahyasi—Imbabala **K. Abdullah**
5 **SENSIBLE (FR),** 6, b h Sadler's Wells—Raisonnable **Niarchos Family**
6 **SIX PERFECTIONS (FR),** 4, b f Celtic Swing—Yogya (USA) **Niarchos Family**
7 **THREE MYSTERIES (IRE),** 4, gr f Linamix (FR)—Maid of Erin (USA) **Niarchos Family**
8 **WEIGHTLESS,** 4, ch c In The Wings—Orford Ness **K. Abdulla**

MR P. BARY—continued

9 **WELL DRESSED**, 4, b c Sadler's Wells (USA)—Bold Empress (USA) **K. Abdulla**
10 **WITHOUT CONNEXION (IRE)**, 5, b h Rainbow Quest (USA)—Flabbergasted (IRE) **Ecurie J. L. Bouchard**

THREE-YEAR-OLDS

11 **ABAKILA (IRE)**, b c Sadler's Wells (USA)—Angelica Tree (CAN) **Ecurie J. L. Bouchard**
12 **AMPHYCLES (FR)**, b f Machiavellian (USA)—Stella Berine (FR) **Mme P. de Moussac**
13 **ANGRY BARK (USA)**, ch f Woodman (USA)—Polemic (USA) **K. Abdulla**
14 **ANOTHER VALENTINE (FR)**, b f Bering—Bayourida (USA) **Peter Maher**
15 **ASTERIE**, b f Sadler's Wells (USA)—Raisonnable **Niarchos Family**
16 **ATLANDO (IRE)**, b c Hernando (FR)—Atlantic Blue (USA) **Sanremo '85 Srl**
17 **AWAKEN**, b f Zafonic (USA)—Dawna **K. Abdullah**
18 **BEKLA (FR)**, b c Machiavellian (USA)—Salvora (USA) **Niarchos Family**
19 **BLUE CANARI (FR)**, ch c Acatenango (GER)—Delicieuse Lady **Ecurie J. L. Bouchard**
20 **BLUE WING**, b c Bluebird (USA)—Warbler **K. Abdullah**
21 **BRIGHELLA**, b f Sadler's Wells (USA)—Massarossa **Baron E. de Rothschild**
22 **CASTLE RISING**, b c Indian Ridge—Orford Ness **K. Abdullah**
23 **COCONUT SHOW**, gr f Linamix (FR)—Vingt Et Une (FR) **Ecurie J. L. Bouchard**
24 **DENEBOLA (USA)**, b f Storm Cat (USA)—Coup de Genie (USA) **Niarchos Family**
25 **EARTHLING**, b c Rainbow Quest (USA)—Cruising Height **K. Abdullah**
26 **EARTHSEA (FR)**, ch f Machiavellian (USA)—Or Vision (USA) **Niarchos Family**
27 **ESPRIT LIBRE**, b f Daylami (IRE)—Biosphere **Grundy Bloodstock Ltd**
28 **FUTURE LEGEND**, ch c Lomitas—Proudy (IRE) **K. Abdullah**
29 **GREENBELT**, b c Desert Prince (IRE)—Emerald (USA) **K. Abdullah**
30 **HELIKE (USA)**, ch c Rahy (USA)—East of The Moon (USA) **Niarchos Family**
31 **HIGH FLASH (IRE)**, ch c Selkirk (USA)—Hint of Silver (USA) **Ecurie Stella Maris**
32 **KAYAK**, ch f Singspiel (IRE)—Kelang **Grundy Bloodstock Ltd**
33 **KYATIKYO**, ch c Machiavellian (USA)—Soul Dream (USA) **Niarchos Family**
34 **LEDI**, b c Night Shift (USA)—Napoli **Niarchos Family**
35 **LEILA (FR)**, ch f Lahint (USA)—Lespois **G. Sandor**
36 **LONE LOOK**, b f Danehill (USA)—Lone Spirit (IRE) **Skymarc Farm Inc.**
37 **LOVE OF THE GAME (IRE)**, b f Croco Rouge (IRE)—Lovealoch (IRE) **Grundy Bloodstock Ltd**
38 **MISCUT (IRE)**, b f Alzao (USA)—Miscast **Lady O'Reilly**
39 **MR SWEET (IRE)**, b c Irish River (FR)—Sweet Snow (USA) **Wattlefield Hall Stud**
40 **MUCH FASTER (IRE)**, b f Fasliyev (USA)—Interruption **Ecurie J. L. Bouchard**
41 **MUSEE (USA)**, gr f El Prado (IRE)—Foible (USA) **K. Abdullah**
42 **NEW SADLERS (IRE)**, b c Sadler's Wells (USA)—Dathiyna (IRE) **Ecurie Chalhoub**
43 **NOBLE REQUEST (FR)**, gr c Highest Honor (FR)—Restless Mixa (IRE) **Ecurie J. L. Bouchard**
44 **PAYPHONE**, b f Anabaa (USA)—Phone West (USA) **K. Abdullah**
45 **PERSISTENT MEMORY (USA)**, b f Red Ransom (USA)—Prevail (USA) **Skymarc Farm Inc.**
46 **PICK ME UP (IRE)**, b c Orpen (USA)—No Rehearsal (FR) **Ecurie J. L. Bouchard**
47 **REEL STYLE**, b f Rainbow Quest (USA)—Western Reel (USA) **K. Abdullah**
48 **SANDBOX (IRE)**, ch f Grand Lodge (USA)—Seralia **Lady O'Reilly**
49 **STAR ON STAGE**, b f Sadler's Wells (USA)—Field of Hope (IRE) **Grundy Bloodstock Ltd**
50 **SUMMER COOLER**, b c Danzig (USA)—City Dance (USA) **Ecurie J. L. Bouchard**
51 **TEXTILE**, b f Grand Lodge (USA)—Docklands (USA) **K. Abdullah**
52 **TOPIARY (IRE)**, b f Selkirk (USA)—Tossup (USA) **Skymarc Farm Inc.**
53 **VERSHWAN (FR)**, b c Nashwan (USA)—Verzasca (IRE) **Ecurie Stella Maris**

TWO-YEAR-OLDS

54 B c 16/4 Chester House (USA)—Ball Gown (USA) (Silver Hawk (USA)) (95238) **K. Abdullah**
55 **BEYOND THE DREAM (USA)**, b f 11/5 Fusaichi Pegasus—
East of The Moon (USA) (Private Account (USA)) **Niarchos Family**
56 B c 1/4 Kingmambo (USA)—Black Penny (USA) (Private Account (USA)) **Skymarc Farm Inc.**
57 **BLESSING**, b f 8/4 Dubai Millenium—Hydro Calido (Nureyev (USA)) **Lordship Stud**
58 B f 25/3 Machiavellian (USA)—Bolas (Unfuwain (USA)) **K. Abdullah**
59 B f 27/2 Dansili—Bold Empress (Diesis) **K. Abdullah**
60 **BRISBAN**, b c 17/3 Anabaa (USA)—Krajina (FR) (Holst (USA)) (25974) **Ecurie J. L. Bouchard**
61 **CADEAUX D'ETE (IRE)**, ch f 1/4 Cadeaux Genereux—
Summer Dance (FR) (Machiavellian (USA)) (48237) **Laghi SNC**
62 B c 16/2 Zafonic (USA)—Dawna (Polish Precedent (USA)) **K. Abdullah**
63 **DESERT CHILD**, b c 10/5 Green Desert (USA)—Bedside Story (Mtoto) (55000) **Grundy Bloodstock Ltd**
64 **DEVIL DANCER (FR)**, b c 17/4 Fasliyev (USA)—
Danse du Diable (IRE) (Sadler's Wells (USA)) (68027) **Ecurie J. L. Bouchard**
65 **DIVINE PROPORTIONS (USA)**, b f 1/1 Kingmambo (USA)—
Myth To Reality (FR) (Sadler's Wells (USA)) **Niarchos Family**

MR P. BARY—continued

66 B c 5/3 Grand Lodge (USA)—Docklands (USA) (Theatrical) **K. Abdullah**
67 **FAST ENOUGH (FR)**, b c 19/2 Anabaa (USA)—Odalisque (IRE) (Machiavellian (USA)) **Ecurie J. L. Bouchard**
68 **FAST TYCOON (IRE)**, b c 26/4 Fasliyev (USA)—
            Prickly Pearl (IRE) (Lahib (USA)) (117501) **Ecurie J. L. Bouchard**
69 B f 20/4 Inchinor—Fee des Mers (Alzao (USA)) **Baron E. de Rothschild**
70 **FOUNTAIN OF PEACE (USA)**, ch f 9/5 Kris S (USA)—
            Coup de Genie (USA) (Mr Prospector (USA)) **Niarchos Family**
71 B f 17/1 Stravinsky (USA)—Galanty Show (Danehill (USA)) **K. Abdullah**
72 **GLACE MAGIQUE (IRE)**, b f 31/3 King's Best (USA)—Ghostly (IRE) (Fairy King (USA)) **Skymarc Farm Inc.**
73 **GREAT LOOP (USA)**, b c 15/3 Seattle Slew (USA)—
            Turning Wheel (USA) (Seeking The Gold (USA)) **Niarchos Family**
74 Ch f 17/2 Alhaarth (IRE)—Imbabala (Zafonic (USA)) **K. Abdullah**
75 **INDOLENTE (IRE)**, b f 25/3 Diesis—
            Tycoon's Dolce (IRE) (Rainbows For Life (CAN)) (148423) **Ecurie J. L. Bouchard**
76 **KING'S FOLLY (FR)**, b f 18/5 King's Best (USA)—
            Latifolia (Dancing Brave (USA)) (61842) **Ecurie J. L. Bouchard**
77 B f 5/4 Anabaa (USA)—Libanoor (Highest Honor (FR)) **Ecurie Stella Maris**
78 **LONESOME ME (FR)**, b f 3/4 Zafonic (USA)—Lone Spirit (IRE) (El Gran Senor (USA)) **Skymarc Farm Inc**
79 B c 7/2 Sadler's Wells (USA)—Love Divine (Diesis) (170000) **Ecurie J. L. Bouchard**
80 B c 7/2 Sadler's Wells (USA)—Lungta (Storm Cat (USA)) **Niarchos Family**
81 **MACHINALE (USA)**, ch f 14/3 Kingmambo (USA)—Gold Bust (Nashwan (USA)) (216450) **Ecurie J. L. Bouchard**
82 **MARTINES (FR)**, gr f 19/2 Linamix (FR)—Fracci (Raise A Cup (USA)) **Grundy Bloodstock Ltd**
83 B c 30/4 Green Desert (USA)—Massarossa (Mr Prospector (USA)) **Skymarc Farm Inc.**
84 **MATERNELLE (FR)**, ro f 13/4 Machiavellian (USA)—
            Mare Aux Fees (Kenmare (FR)) (68027) **Ecurie J. L. Bouchard**
85 **MISDIRECT**, b f 25/2 Darshaan—Miscast (Kenmare (FR)) **Lady O'Reilly**
86 B f 1/1 Dream Well (FR)—Moon Is Up (Woodman (USA)) **Niarchos Family**
87 B f 21/3 Unfuwain (USA)—Mystery Tune (Commanche Run) **Baron E. de Rothschild**
88 **NAIYO**, b f 22/4 Diktat—Nokomis (Caerleon (USA)) **Scuderia Vittadini SRL**
89 **QUESTO**, b c 5/2 Zafonic (USA)—Quest of Fire (FR) (Rainbow Quest (USA)) (40197) **Ecurie Chalhoub**
90 B f 1/1 Dream Well (FR)—Rangoon Ruby (Sallust) **Niarchos Family**
91 **REINE D'AVRIL (FR)**, ch f 22/3 Le Triton—La Malombree (FR) (Sleeping Car (FR)) **P. Bary**
92 B f 31/1 Sadler's Wells (USA)—Remote Romance (USA) (Irish River (FR)) **Niarchos Family**
93 **RUGOSA**, b f 17/3 Highest Honor (FR)—Rose Noble (USA) (Vaguely Noble) **Plantation Stud**
94 **SAHARA SNOW**, gr f 1/5 Linamix (FR)—Sahara Sunrise (USA) (Houston (USA)) **Lady O'Reilly**
95 **SERANDINE (IRE)**, ch f 10/4 Hernando (FR)—Serafica (No Pass No Sale) **Lady O'Reilly**
96 B f 17/5 Anabaa (USA)—She's All Class (Rahy (USA)) **Laghi SNC**
97 B c 23/5 Machiavellian (USA)—Soul Dream (Alleged (USA)) **Niarchos Family**
98 **SPEAR POINT**, b c 21/3 Spectrum (IRE)—Seralia (Royal Academy (USA)) (68027) **Ecurie Chalhoub**
99 **SPRING PARTY (IRE)**, b f 15/3 Anabaa (USA)—Party Zane (Zafonic (USA)) **Ecurie J. L. Bouchard**
100 B c 24/3 Bahri (FR)—Stark Ballet (USA) (Nureyev (USA)) (78000) **K. Abdullah**
101 B c 11/4 Highest Honor (FR)—Summer Exhibition (Royal Academy (USA)) **K. Abdullah**
102 Ch f 26/1 Unfuwain (USA)—Tarocchi (USA) (Affirmed (USA)) **K. Abdullah**
103 **TIMIAS (USA)**, b c 9/4 Seeking The Gold—Dragonada (USA) (Nureyev (USA)) **Niarchos Family**
104 B f 4/5 Anabaa (USA)—Totality (Dancing Brave (USA)) **K. Abdullah**
105 B c 10/2 Linamix (FR)—Tuning (Rainbow Quest (USA)) **K. Abdullah**
106 **URBAN SUMMER (USA)**, b c 13/3 Red Ransom (USA)—
            Kamaina (USA) (Mr Prospector (USA)) **Niarchos Family**
107 **VEYRON (IRE)**, b c 22/4 Fasliyev (USA)—For Kicks (FR) (Top Ville) (98948) **Ecurie J. L. Bouchard**
108 B f 11/3 Verglas (IRE)—Vol Sauvage (FR) (Always Fair (USA)) (18552) **P. Bary**
109 B c 7/2 Cape Cross (IRE)—Wavy Paz (Bigstone (IRE)) **Ecurie Stella Maris**

Jockey (Flat): T Thulliez (9-4).

30	**MR R. BASTIMAN, Wetherby**

Postal: **Goosemoor Farm, Warfield Lane, Cowthorpe, Wetherby, West Yorkshire, LS22 5EU.**
Contact: **PHONE (01423) 359397**

1 **DESERT FURY**, 7, b g Warning—Number One Spot **Mr Robin Bastiman**
2 **MAROMITO (IRE)**, 7, b g Up And At 'em—Amtico **Mr Robin Bastiman**
3 **PEPPER ROAD**, 5, ch g Elmaamul (USA)—Floral Spark **Mr Peter Julian**
4 **SENNEN COVE**, 5, ch g Bering—Dame Laura (USA) **Border Rail & Plant Limited**
5 **SUNNYSIDE ROYALE (IRE)**, 5, b g Ali-Royal (IRE)—Kuwah (IRE) **S. Durkin, P. Earnshaw & J. Greenan**
6 **TUSCAN FLYER**, 6, b g Clantime—Excavator Lady **Mr John Endersby**

MR R. BASTIMAN—continued

7 **VALIANT ROMEO**, 4, b c Primo Dominie—Desert Lynx (IRE) **Mrs P. Bastiman**
8 **WERE NOT STOPPIN**, 9, b g Mystiko (USA)—Power Take Off **Mr I. B. Barker**

THREE-YEAR-OLDS

9 **DELTA LADY**, b f River Falls—Compton Lady (USA) **Coal Trade Partnership**
10 **FILLE GRIS**, gr f Double Trigger (IRE)—Cool Grey **Mr John Endersby**

TWO-YEAR-OLDS

11 B c 21/4 Compton Place—Jeewan (Touching Wood (USA)) (13000) **Mr Robin Bastiman**

Other Owners: Mr P. Harwood.

Jockey (Flat): H Bastiman (9-10). **Jockey (NH):** H Bastiman (9-10). **Amateur:** Miss Rebecca Bastiman (9-7).

---

31 MR B. P. J. BAUGH, Stoke on Trent
Postal: **Brooklands, Park Lane, Audley, Stoke on Trent, ST7 8HR.**
Contact: **STABLES (01782) 723144 HOME (01782) 723144 MOBILE (07771) 693666**

1 **BEAVER LODGE (IRE)**, 7, gr g Grand Lodge (USA)—Thistlewood **Mr J.H.Chrimes and Mr & Mrs G.W.Hannam**
2 **BOBERING**, 4, b g Bob's Return (IRE)—Ring The Rafters **Mr J.H.Chrimes and Mr & Mrs G.W.Hannam**
3 **COOL BART**, 4, ch g Cool Jazz—Margaretrose Anna **Mr J.H.Chrimes and Mr & Mrs G.W.Hannam**
4 **CROWN CITY (USA)**, 4, b f Coronado's Quest (USA)—Trisha Brown (USA) **Miss S. M. Potts**
5 **FOUR CANDLES**, 4, b f Perpendicular—Skyers Tryer **Mr J. H. Chrimes**
6 **JALOUHAR**, 4, b g Victory Note (USA)—Orient Way (IRE) **Miss S. M. Potts**
7 **MAYSBOYO**, 6, b g Makbul—Maysimp (IRE) **Mr J.H.Chrimes and Mr & Mrs G.W.Hannam**
8 **MEGAROLE**, 5, b g Tragic Role (USA)—Our Megan **Mr J.H.Chrimes and Mr & Mrs G.W.Hannam**
9 **MISTER BENJI**, 5, b g Catrail (USA)—Katy-Q (IRE) **Mr J.H.Chrimes and Mr & Mrs G.W.Hannam**
10 **MORRIS DANCING (USA)**, 5, b g Rahy (USA)—Summer Dance **Messrs Chrimes, Winn & Wilson**
11 **PETERS PAL**, 5, ch g Nalchik (USA)—Grey Runner **Mr J.H.Chrimes and Mr & Mrs G.W.Hannam**
12 **SMART SCOT**, 5, ch g Selkirk (USA)—Amazing Bay **Mr S. Day**
13 **THUMAMAH (IRE)**, 5, b m Charnwood Forest (IRE)—Anam **Mr J. H. Chrimes**
14 **XALOC BAY (IRE)**, 6, b g Charnwood Forest (IRE)—Royal Jade **Miss S. M. Potts**

THREE-YEAR-OLDS

15 **ALMANAC (IRE)**, b c Desert Style (IRE)—Share The Vision **Messrs Chrimes, Winn & Wilson**

Assistant Trainer: S Potts

---

32 MR C. C. BEALBY, Grantham
Postal: **North Lodge, Barrowby, Grantham, Lincolnshire, NG32 1DH.**
Contact: **OFFICE (01476) 564568 FAX (01476) 572391 MOBILE (07831) 538689**
E-MAIL trainer@northlodgeracing.co.uk

1 **ALL RIGHT FOR TIME**, 6, b m Sula Bula—Penny Falls **Mr G. H. Dook**
2 **ASHWELL (IRE)**, 5, gr g Anshan—Willshego **Mr C. J. Ireland**
3 **AVANTI TIGER (IRE)**, 5, b br g Supreme Leader—Reign of Terror (IRE) **Mr C. Martin**
4 6, Ch g Alflora (IRE)—Ballysax Lass **North Lodge Racing**
5 **CAYMAN WENT**, 5, b g Bering—Bonne Ile **Mr Irvin S. Naylor**
6 **CONTRACT KILLER**, 5, b g Contract Law (USA)—How Humble (IRE) **Auto Egg Partnership**
7 **COUNTBACK (FR)**, 5, b g Anabaa (USA)—Count Me Out (FR) **Blake Kennedy Partnership**
8 **DALUS PARK (IRE)**, 9, b g Mandalus—Pollerton Park **The Huntingdon Hopefuls**
9 **DI'S DILEMMA**, 6, b m Teenoso (USA)—Reve En Rose **Mr T. W. R. Bayley**
10 **EL HOMBRE**, 6, b g Afzal—Dunsilly Bell **Mr Michael Hill**
11 **ESKIMO PIE (IRE)**, 5, ch g Glacial Storm (USA)—Arctic Verb **Mr Irvin S. Naylor**
12 **FIRST OFFICER (USA)**, 7, b g Lear Fan (USA)—Trampoli (USA) **K. McGeorge & T. Radford**
13 **HICKERTHRIFTCASTLE**, 5, ch g Carlingford Castle—Sun Sprite **Mr Ady Boughen**
14 **HI PAL (IRE)**, 7, b g Phardante (FR)—Bright Princess (IRE) **Mr Ady Boughen**
15 **INDIAN LABURNUM (IRE)**, 7, b g Alphabatim (USA)—St Cristoph **Mrs Joan Martin**
16 **JEANIE'S LAST**, 5, b m Primitive Rising (USA)—Jean Jeanie **Mr Tony Evans**
17 **JOE MALONE (IRE)**, 5, b g Rashar (USA)—Bucktina **Foreneish Racing**
18 5, Ch g Roselier (FR)—Little Twig (IRE) **Farmers, Foresters & Financiers**
19 **LONGSTONE LOCH (IRE)**, 7, b g Executive Perk—Lyre-Na-Gcloc **Mr Ady Boughen**

MR C. C. BEALBY—continued

20 **MAGIC MISTRAL**, 6, b m Thowra (FR)—Festival of Magic (USA) **Maggie and Eric Hemming**
21 **NO ARGUMENT**, 5, b g Young Ern—As Sharp As **Mr Michael Hill**
22 **POINT OF ORIGIN (IRE)**, 7, b g Caerleon (USA)—Aptostar (USA) **Get Em Off**
23 **RAINBOWS WOOD**, 4, b g Rainbows For Life (CAN)—Little Twig (IRE) **North Lodge Racing**
24 **SAINT ALBERT**, 9, ch g Keen—Thimbalina **Mrs D. C. Samworth**
25 **THISTLECRAFT (IRE)**, 5, b g Warcraft (USA)—Thistletopper **The Wally Partnership**
26 **TRUE ALLIANCE (USA)**, 4, b g Brief Truce (USA)—Unforgetable Charm (IRE) **Mr Michael Hill**
27 **TRUSTING TOM**, 8, b g Teamster—Florista **Mr T. P. Radford**

Other Owners: Mr Michael G. H. Adcock, Mr Richard Adcock, Mr Paul Bagshaw, Mrs S. V. Bealby, Mr Robert Bingley, Mr Darren R. Blake, Mr Denis Cassidy, Mr Mark Chatterton, Mr Paul Clarkson, Mr A. Crowl, Dr D J Forecast, Mr C. J. Grindal, Mr M. J. Hazard, Mrs J. C. Holt, Mr Ken McGeorge, Mr W. McNeish, Mr Michael Ogburn, Mr W. N. Skelton, Mr N. D. Skinner, Mrs C. Stokes, Mrs S. J. Storer.

Assistant Trainer: Matthew Bond

Jockey (NH): N Fehily (10-0). **Conditional:** Flavin, D Flavin (10-0). **Amateur:** Mr Stuart Morris (9-10).

---

33 MR P. BEAUMONT, Brandsby

Postal: **Foulrice Farm, Brandsby, York, YO61 4SB.**
Contact: PHONE **(01347) 888208** FAX **(01347) 888208** MOBILE **(07801) 529783**
E-MAIL peterbeaumont@btconnect.com

1 **ALI OOP**, 7, b g Shareef Dancer (USA)—Happydrome **Mrs J. M. Plummer**
2 **ATLANTIC CROSSING (IRE)**, 7, b g Roselier (FR)—Ocean Mist (IRE) **Mr N. W. A. Bannister**
3 **BRANDSBY STRIPE**, 9, ch g Nomadic Way (USA)—I'm Fine **Brandsby Racing 2**
4 **CIONN MHALANNA (IRE)**, 6, b g Corrouge (USA)—Pennyland **Mr D. R. Brown & Miss E. E. Toland**
5 **COMPADRE**, 6, gr g Environment Friend—Cardinal Press **Mr J. Stephenson**
6 **DOUBLE DIPLOMACY**, 8, b g State Diplomacy (USA)—Malmo **Mrs E. Dixon**
7 **DRACAENA**, 7, b m State Diplomacy (USA)—Jay-Dee-Jay **Mr S. W. Knowles**
8 **FENCOTE GOLD**, 4, ch g Bob's Return (IRE)—Goldaw **Mrs H. M. Richardson**
9 **FENCOTE (IRE)**, 7, b g Norwich—Primrose Forest **Mrs H. M. Richardson**
10 **FLIGHT COMMAND**, 6, ch g Gunner B—Wing On **Mr N. W. A. Bannister**
11 **FOREVER WAYWOOD**, 5, ch g Rakaposhi King—I'm Fine **Wood Racing**
12 **FORONLYMO**, 5, b g Forzando—Polish Descent (IRE) **Commander David Wilmot-Smith**
13 **HEAD FOR THE HILLS**, 11, ch g Scottish Reel—Merry Cherry **Mr D. S. Bowring**
14 **HUNTERS TWEED**, 8, ch g Nashwan (USA)—Zorette (USA) **Mr Trevor Hemmings**
15 **HUSSARD COLLONGES (FR)**, 9, b g Video Rock (FR)—Ariane Collonges (FR) **Mr N. W. A. Bannister**
16 **HUTCH**, 6, b g Rock Hopper—Polly's Teahouse **Mr Robert Gibbons**
17 4, B g Rakaposhi King—I'm Fine **Peter Beaumont**
18 **IMPERTIO**, 10, b g Primitive Rising (USA)—Silly Beggar **Mrs S. Sunter**
19 **JODANTE (IRE)**, 7, ch g Phardante (FR)—Crashtown Lucy **Mr Trevor Hemmings**
20 **KEEN SKIMMER**, 4, b g Keen—The Firefly **Mrs A. P. Stead**
21 **KYLIE TIME (IRE)**, 7, ch g Good Thyne (USA)—Miss Kylogue (IRE) **Mr & Mrs Raymond Anderson Green**
22 **LORD RODNEY (IRE)**, 5, b g Hatim (USA)—Howcleuch **Estio Racing**
23 **MISS FENCOTE**, 8, b m Phardante (FR)—Jack's The Girl (IRE) **Mrs H. M. Richardson**
24 **MONTY'S QUEST (IRE)**, 9, b g Montelimar (USA)—A Bit of Luck (IRE) **Graham Frankland**
25 **MOORAMANA**, 5, ch g Alflora (IRE)—Petit Primitive **Mrs K. Ratcliffe**
26 **OCEAN DANCER**, 7, b g Primitive Rising (USA)—Bally Small **Mrs S. Sunter**
27 **PROFOWENS (IRE)**, 6, b g Welsh Term—Cutty Sark **Mr Trevor Hemmings**
28 4, B g Paris House—Renshaw Wood **Mrs J. M. Plummer**
29 **SHARPASTRIZAM (NZ)**, 9, b g Try To Stop Me—Atristazam (NZ) **Mr Trevor Hemmings**
30 **SHARP SINGLE (IRE)**, 8, b m Supreme Leader—Pollyville **Mr W. L. Smith**
31 **TA TA FOR NOW**, 7, b g Ezzoud (IRE)—Exit Laughing **Mrs V. M. Stewart**
32 **WINSOME GAIL (IRE)**, 7, b m Glacial Storm (USA)—Fruitcake (IRE) **Mrs L. Holloway**
33 **YOUNG CLAUDE**, 7, b g Le Moss—Deirdres Dream **Read O'Gorman Racing**
34 **YOUNG FALCON**, 4, ch f Young Ern—Northern Falcon **Mrs R. C. Hartley**

MR P. BEAUMONT—continued
THREE-YEAR-OLDS

35 B g Rakaposhi King—I'm Fine **Peter Beaumont**

Other Owners: Mr C. D. Butler, Mr Paul Clarkson, Mr B. Hayes, Mr C. Jackson, Mr Melvyn Johnson, Mr W. T. Kemp, Mr Les Lawson, Mr J. H. Marnell, Mr Charlie Parker, Mr J. Ratcliffe, Mrs A. H. Read, Mr J. G. Read, Mr Robert Turner, Mr J. A. J. Wood.

Assistant Trainer: Patrick Holmes

Jockey (NH): Russ Garrity (10-5). **Conditional:** James Clare.

---

34   **MR R. M. BECKETT, Lambourn**
Postal: Windsor House Stables, Crowle Road, Lambourn, Hungerford, Berkshire, RG17 8NR.
Contact: PHONE (01488) 71099 FAX (01488) 71099 MOBILE (07802) 219022
E-MAIL trainer@rbeckett.com

1 **BRASSIE**, 5, b g Celtic Swing—Gong **Mr A. D. G. Oldrey**
2 **DANEHILL STROLLER (IRE)**, 4, b g Danetime (IRE)—Tuft Hill **The Classic Strollers Partnership**
3 **LIGHT HEARTED LILY**, 5, b m Deploy—Darling Splodge **The Foxons Fillies Partnership**
4 **MOUNT BENGER**, 4, ch g Selkirk (USA)—Vice Vixen (CAN) **Young Guns Syndicate**
5 **STARRY MARY**, 6, b m Deploy—Darling Splodge **Mr A. Von Westenholz**

THREE-YEAR-OLDS

6 **ACCENDERE**, b g Machiavellian (USA)—Littlewick (IRE) **A.W.A. Partnership**
7 **CALOMERIA**, b f Groom Dancer (USA)—Calendula **Mr Christopher Spence**
8 **CATIE DASH**, ch f Daggers Drawn (USA)—Papita (IRE) **Absolute Solvents Ltd**
9 **DARK EMPRESS (IRE)**, br f Second Empire (IRE)—Good Reference (IRE) **Lady Marchwood**
10 Ch c Bien Bien (USA)—Dissolve **Absolute Solvents Ltd**
11 **DRY WIT (IRE)**, b f Desert Prince (IRE)—Nawasib (USA) **Mrs Richard Aykroyd**
12 **FFIZZAMO GO**, b g Forzando—Lady Lacey **Hamilton-Fairley Racing**
13 **HATCH A PLAN (IRE)**, b g Vettori (IRE)—Fast Chick **T.G.S. Sijpesteijn and Deal**
14 **HEAD OF STATE**, br g Primo Dominie—Lets Be Fair **Mr Pedro Rosas**
15 **JAILBIRD**, b f Nicolotte—Grace Browning **Mrs Robert Langton**
16 **MAN CRAZY (IRE)**, b f Foxhound—Schonbein (IRE) **Jock Strap Partners**
17 **MARIA BONITA (IRE)**, b f Octagonal (NZ)—Nightitude **Mr Pedro Rosas**
18 **MIX IT UP**, gr f Linamix (FR)—Hawayah (IRE) **Mr R. J. Cornelius**
19 **MOLINIA**, b f Nicolotte—Themeda **Larksborough Stud Limited**
20 **RONDELET (IRE)**, b g Bering—Triomphale (USA) **Mr Richard A Pegum & Mrs Richard Aykroyd**
21 **SOKOLE**, ch g Compton Place—Sally Green (IRE) **Larksborough Stud Limited**
22 **SOUTH FACE**, ch g Hector Protector (USA)—Crystal Cavern (USA) **Tweenhills Racing (Queenhill)**
23 **SOVIETTA (IRE)**, b f Soviet Star (USA)—La Riveraine (USA) **Mr J. H. Richmond-Watson**
24 **TELL THE TREES**, br f Tamure (IRE)—Bluebell Copse **Major R. P. Thorman**
25 **VAMP**, b f Dracula (AUS)—Circe **Mr A. D. G. Oldrey**

TWO-YEAR-OLDS

26 B f 13/3 Bold Edge—Ballet Rambert (Rambo Dancer (CAN)) (4000) **North Farm Stud**
27 **BIRD AWAY**, b f 2/2 Bien Bien (USA)—Grace Browning (Forzando) (1904) **Mrs Robert Langton**
28 **BIRD OVER**, b f 4/5 Bold Edge—High Bird (Polar Falcon (USA)) (857) **Mrs Robert Langton**
29 **CANELLE**, b f 6/4 Benny The Dip (USA)—Calendula (Be My Guest (USA)) **Mr Christopher Spence**
30 B c 15/4 Kayf Tara—Circe (Main Reef) **Mr A. D. G. Oldrey**
31 **COME ON JONNY (IRE)**, b c 2/5 Desert King (IRE)—Idle Fancy (Mujtahid (USA)) (20000) **Mr A. E. Frost**
32 **DANZILI BAY**, b c 30/1 Dansili—Lady Bankes (IRE) (Alzao (USA)) (38000) **The Mid-Landers**
33 B c 21/2 Rossini (USA)—Fastnet (Forzando) (17000) **Mr Pedro Rosas**
34 **GEISHA LADY (IRE)**, b f 15/4 Raise A Grand (IRE)—
         Mitsubishi Style (Try My Best (USA)) (3047) **Mrs R. Aykroyd and Mr R. S. G. Jones**
35 **HIGH DAWN (IRE)**, b c 20/3 Namid—Highbrook (USA) (Alphabatim) (15500) **Mr A. E. Frost**
36 **JENNA STANNIS**, ch f 28/3 Wolfhound (USA)—Darling Splodge (Elegant Air) **The Foxons Fillies Partnership**
37 **JOHNNY JUMPUP (IRE)**, ch c 18/2 Pivotal—Clarice Orsini (Common Grounds) (11000) **Mr & Mrs A. Briars**
38 B f 12/4 Imperial Ballet (IRE)—Joza (Marju (IRE)) **Zubieta Limited**
39 B f 19/3 Orpen (USA)—Lady Donna (Dominion) (30921) **Absolute Solvents Ltd**
40 **LITTLE WARNING**, b f 7/4 Piccolo—Iltimas (USA) (Dayjur (USA)) (8000) **Mr C. F. Colquhoun**
41 **MINNESINGER**, b f 15/4 Fraam—Rose Alto (Adonijah) (4019) **Mrs Richard Aykroyd**
42 **PURPLE DOOR**, b f 8/2 Daggers Drawn (USA)—
         Carreamia (Weldnaas (USA)) (4800) **The Don't Touch Partnership**
43 **RED RUDY**, ch c 22/3 Pivotal—Piroshka (Soviet Star (USA)) (14000) **Winding Wheel Partnership**

MR R. M. BECKETT—continued

44 **THREE ACES (IRE)**, ch f 28/4 Raise A Grand (IRE)—
Fallacy (Selkirk (USA)) (8500) **The Millennium Madness Partnership**
45 B f 10/2 Josr Algarhoud (IRE)—Unimpeachable (IRE) (Namaqualand (USA)) (10000) **Mr Jim Browne**
46 B f 20/2 Mind Games—Yanomami (USA) (Slew O' Gold (USA)) (16000) **Tweenhills Thurloe**

Other Owners: Mr A. Adams, Mrs K. Adams, Mrs Ralph Beckett, Mrs E. Benyon, Mrs Emma Benyon, Mr Alan Briars, Mrs C. M. Briars, Mr R. A. Coombes, Mr K. Craddock, Miss S. Davis, Mr P. A. Deal, Mr M. S. Edwards, Mr J. Foley, Mr A. E. Frost, Mrs A. Hamilton-Fairley, Mr Geoffrey Hamilton-Fairley, Mr G. J. Head, Mr J. Hornache, Mr R. S. G. Jones, Mrs J. Lovell, Mrs Catherine Lovell, Mr P. Mason, Mr M. Mitchell, Mr A. Owen, Mr Oliver Pawle, Mr R. A. Pegum, Mr Geoffrey Pooley, Mr E. Prosser, Mr D. Redvers, Mr Anthony Savin, Mr N. P. Savin, Mr G. Sijpesteijn, Mr N. Simmons, Mr J. Skeen, Hon Mrs H. Smyly, Mr J. Spence, Mr A. Spencer, Major Ian Thompson, Mrs M. Turney, Mr R. Whitehouse, Mr A. Williams, Mrs P. Williams.

Assistant Trainer: Miss Natasha Skidmore

---

35 MR KEVIN BELL, Wantage

Postal: **Antwick Stud, Letcombe Regis, Wantage, Oxon OX12 9LH.**
Contact: **OFFICE (01488) 638243 HOME 638820 MOBILE (07881) 814688**
E-MAIL grace.muir@virgin.net

1 **CITRUS MAGIC**, 7, b g Cosmonaut—Up All Night **Mines A Double Club**
2 **COLLEGE DELINQUENT (IRE)**, 5, br g College Chapel—St Cyr Aty (IRE) **Mr Martin Collins**
3 **CYRAZY**, 6, b m Cyrano de Bergerac—Hazy Kay (IRE) **Mr & Mrs David Sutton**
4 **DEFERLANT (FR)**, 7, ch g Bering—Sail Storm (USA) **Mrs G. McNeela**
5 **MAGGIE'S PET**, 7, b m Minshaanshu Amad (USA)—Run Fast For Gold **Mr Len Purdy**
6 **MISCHIEF**, 8, ch g Generous (IRE)—Knight's Baroness **Mrs A. Ellis**
7 **PRINCE SHAAMAAL**, 6, b g Shaamit (IRE)—Princess Alaska **The Upshire Racing Partnership**
8 **PRIORS DALE**, 4, b c Lahib (USA)—Mathaayl (USA) **Mrs L. Alexander**
9 **STATE OF BALANCE**, 6, ch m Mizoram (USA)—Equilibrium **North Farm Stud**
10 **WHAT A MONDAY**, 6, b g Beveled (USA)—Raise Memories **North Farm Partnership**

THREE-YEAR-OLDS

11 **MARKSGOLD (IRE)**, b c Goldmark (USA)—Lady of Shalott **Type 45 Partnership**
12 **MISTER RIGHT (IRE)**, ch g Barathea (IRE)—Broken Spirit (IRE) **Miss A. Jones**
13 **POWER TO BURN**, b g Superpower—Into The Fire **Red Hot Partnership**
14 **THE CLOWN**, b g Russian Revival (USA)—Fashion Bride (IRE) **North Farm Stud**
15 **TRIGGERS DOUBLE**, ch c Double Trigger (IRE)—Princess Alaska **No Fools Only Horses Partnership**

TWO-YEAR-OLDS

16 B f 13/3 Bold Edge—Ballet Rambert (Rambo Dancer (CAN)) (4000) **North Farm Stud**
17 **EDGE OF ITALY**, ch f 7/3 Bold Edge—
Brera (IRE) (Tate Gallery (USA)) **The Sing When You're Winning Partnership**
18 **GREENACRE LEGEND**, b c 11/4 Faustus—Alice Holt (Free State) (USA) **Fielden Racing Partnership**
19 **YOUNG BOLDRIC**, b g 12/3 Faustus (USA)—
Bold Byzantium (Bold Arrangement) **The Herewegoagain Partnership**

Other Owners: Mr K. Alexander, Mrs B. Benn, Mr A. Blackshaw, Miss C. Bullard, Ms L. Clark, Mr M. J. G. Clubb, Mr Paul Couchman, Mr Terence Couchman, Mr Timothy Couchman, Mr C. Footer, Mr M. Gregory, Mr A. Harding, Mrs B. Harding, Mr M. R. Haywood, Mr N. J. Hubbard, Mr T. Leach, Miss G. E. Muir, Mrs Alison Moir, Mrs A. Muir, Mr David J. Muir, Miss G. E. Muir, Mr S. Muir, Mr D. Naish, Mr P. Osborne, Mr B. Scarre, Mr M. Stretton, Mr A. Tansley, Miss N. Wiesenthal, Mrs C. Wilesmith.

Assistant Trainer: Miss Joanna Ellis

Jockey (Flat): D McCabe. **Jockeys (NH):** Sean Curran, Carl Llewellyn. **Amateur:** Miss Joanna Ellis (8-10).

---

36 MR M. L. W. BELL, Newmarket

Postal: **Fitzroy House, Newmarket, Suffolk, CB8 0JT.**
Contact: **PHONE (01638) 666567 FAX (01638) 668000 MOBILE (07802) 264514**
E-MAIL mlwbell.racing@virgin.net WEBSITE www.michaelbellracing.co.uk

1 **BARKING MAD (USA)**, 6, b g Dayjur (USA)—Avian Assembly (USA) **Mr Christopher Wright**
2 **BRAZILIAN TERRACE**, 4, ch f Zilzal (USA)—Elaine's Honor (USA) **Mrs G.Rowland Clark & M.L.W.Bell Racing**
3 **COODEN BEACH (IRE)**, 4, b f Peintre Celebre (USA)—Joyful (IRE) **Robert Brown & Partners**

MR M. L. W. BELL—continued

  4 **DUSKY WARBLER**, 5, b g Ezzoud (IRE)—Bronzewing **Sir Thomas Pilkington, Bt**
  5 **ONCE (FR)**, 4, gr g Hector Protector (USA)—Moon Magic **Lord Blyth**
  6 **OPERA KNIGHT**, 4, ch g In The Wings—Sans Escale (USA) **Mr Andrew Buxton, M.L.W. Bell Racing Ltd**
  7 **PRARIE WOLF**, 8, ch g Wolfhound (USA)—Bay Queen **Mr Bernard Warren**
  8 **PURE SPECULATION**, 4, b f Salse (USA)—Just Speculation (IRE) **Mr Christopher Wright**
  9 **SHABERNAK (IRE)**, 5, gr g Akarad (FR)—Salinova (FR) **Thurloe Thoroughbreds VII**
 10 **SONOMA (IRE)**, 4, ch f Dr Devious (IRE)—Mazarine Blue (USA) **Mrs P. D. Gray**
 11 **TOPKAMP**, 4, b f Pennekamp—Victoria Regia **Baron F. C. Oppenheim**
 12 **TRIPHENIA (IRE)**, 6, b g Ashkalani (IRE)—Atsuko (FR) **Mrs C. Parker**
 13 **VILAS**, 4, b c Inchinor—Arantxa **Mr R. A. Pegum**
 14 **ZILCH**, 6, ch g Zilzal (USA)—Bunty Boo **Mary Mayall, Linda Redmond, Julie Martin**

THREE-YEAR-OLDS

 15 **AMANKILA**, b f Revoque (IRE)—Steel Habit **Mr Luke Lillingston**
 16 **AUROVILLE**, b c Cadeaux Genereux—Silent Tribute (IRE) **Mr Richard I. Morris Jr**
 17 **BEACH PARTY (IRE)**, b f Danzero (AUS)—Shore Lark (USA) **Cheveley Park Stud**
 18 **BORDER SAINT**, b g Selkirk (USA)—Caramba **Stamford Bridge Partnership**
 19 **BURN**, ch f Selkirk (USA)—River Cara (USA) **Lord Hartington**
 20 **CUNNING PURSUIT**, b g Pursuit of Love—Mistilled (USA) **Mrs Maureen Buckley**
 21 **FARAWAY ECHO**, gr f Second Empire (IRE)—Salalah **Captain B. W. Bell**
 22 **GANYMEDE**, gr c Daylami (IRE)—Germane **Mr E. D. Kessly and Heatherwood Stud**
 23 **GENEROUS GESTURE (IRE)**, b f Fasliyev (USA)—Royal Bounty (IRE) **Mr & Mrs J. & P. Ransley**
 24 **GLEBE GARDEN**, b f Soviet Star (USA)—Trounce **Minster Stud & Mr Christopher Wright**
 25 **HIGH KICK**, gr c Sadler's Wells (USA)—High Tern **The Hon Peter Stanley and Partners**
 26 **LUCAYAN BELLE**, b f Cadeaux Genereux—Floppie (FR) **Lucayan Stud**
 27 **MAGIC STING**, ch c Magic Ring (IRE)—Ground Game **Mrs P. T. Fenwick**
 28 **NEEDLES AND PINS (IRE)**, b f Fasliyev (USA)—Fairy Contessa (IRE) **DGH Partnership**
 29 **NEVISIAN LAD**, b c Royal Applause—Corndavon (USA) **Sheikh Rashid Bin Mohammed**
 30 **OLIHIDER (USA)**, gr c Woodman (USA)—Ingot's Dance Away (USA) **Mrs D. J. Higgins**
 31 **ON CLOUD NINE**, ro f Cloudings (IRE)—Princess Moodyshoe **Mr & Mrs Frank Farrant**
 32 **OPALESCENT (IRE)**, b f Polish Precedent (USA)—Irish Light (USA) **Cheveley Park Stud**
 33 **PORTHCAWL**, b f Singspiel (IRE)—Dodo (IRE) **Usk Valley Stud**
 34 **PROMENADE**, b f Primo Dominie—Hamsah (IRE) **Cheveley Park Stud**
 35 **PURPLE RAIN (IRE)**, b f Celtic Swing—Calypso Grant (IRE) **Mr Christopher Wright**
 36 **RAVEL**, b c Fasliyev (USA)—Lili Cup (FR) **The Royal Ascot Racing Club**
 37 **RIVER OF BABYLON**, b f Marju (IRE)—Isle of Flame **The Hon Mrs J. M. Corbett & Mr C. Wright**
 38 **SHRINK**, b f Mind Games—Miss Mercy (IRE) **Mr Billy Maguire**
 39 **SILVER SASH (GER)**, gr f Mark of Esteem (IRE)—Salinova (FR) **Baron F. C. Oppenheim**
 40 **SOVIET THREAT (IRE)**, ch c Soviet Star (USA)—Veiled Threat (IRE) **Mr Billy Maguire & M.L.W.Bell Racing Ltd**
 41 **SPIN KING (IRE)**, b c Intikhab (USA)—Special Dissident **The Fitzrovians**
 42 **STYLISH SUNRISE (IRE)**, b c Desert Style (IRE)—Anita At Dawn (IRE) **Fitzroy Thoroughbreds**
 43 **TAMARILLO**, gr f Daylami (IRE)—Up And About **Sheikh Rashid Bin Mohammed**
 44 **TARDIS**, ch f Vettori (IRE)—Time Lapse **The Fitzrovians**
 45 **TEMPLE PLACE (IRE)**, b c Sadler's Wells (USA)—Puzzled Look (USA) **Mr M. B. Hawtin**
 46 **VENGEROV**, b c Piccolo—Shining Cloud **Mr R. A. Pegum**
 47 **VICARIO**, gr c Vettori (IRE)—Arantxa **Mr T. Redman, Mr P. Philips & Mr P. Coe**
 48 **WOODCRACKER**, ch g Docksider (USA)—Hen Harrier **Sir Thomas Pilkington, Bt**
 49 **WUNDERBRA (IRE)**, b f Second Empire (IRE)—Supportive (IRE) **Fitzroy Thoroughbreds**

TWO-YEAR-OLDS

 50 B f 3/2 Mister Baileys—Annapurna (IRE) (Brief Truce (USA)) (50000) **Usk Valley Stud**
 51 B f 26/4 Compton Place—
                    Banco Suivi (IRE) (Nashwan (USA)) (38000) **The Hon Mrs J. M. Corbett & Mr C. Wright**
 52 B f 5/4 Mujadil (USA)—Be Exciting (IRE) (Be My Guest (USA)) (4000) **Joy and Valentine Feerick**
 53 Ch f 10/2 King of Kings (IRE)—
                    Beyond The Realm (USA) (Stop The Music (USA)) (57000) **Mr C. Wright & The Hon Mrs J. M. Corbett**
 54 **BOLD DESIRE**, b f 21/4 Cadeaux Genereux—Polish Romance (IRE) (Danzig (USA)) **Cheveley Park Stud**
 55 **BRIGHT MOLL**, b f 11/3 Mind Games—Molly Brown (Rudimentary (USA)) (37000) **Mr Andrew Buxton**
 56 B c 20/2 Desert King (IRE)—Coyaima (GER) (Night Shift (USA)) (38000) **Thurloe Thoroughbreds**
 57 **DANCE AWAY**, ch f 11/2 Pivotal—Dance On (Caerleon (USA)) **Cheveley Park Stud**
 58 **ENTERTAIN**, b f 15/4 Royal Applause—Darshay (FR) (Darshaan) **Cheveley Park Stud**
 59 B c 1/5 Bachir (IRE)—Flourishing (IRE) (Trojan Fen) (14000)
 60 Br c 7/4 Dynaformer (USA)—
                    Forget About It (IRE) (Be My Guest (USA)) (107143) **Sheikh Rashid Bin Mohammed**

MR M. L. W. BELL—continued

61 **GLEN IDA**, ch c 17/3 Selkirk (USA)—
        Yanka (USA) (Blushing John (USA)) (62000) **Mr Andrew Buxton & Mr B J Warren**
62 **GOLDEN GATE (IRE)**, b c 21/4 Giant's Causeway—Bay Queen (Damister (USA)) **Mr B. J. Warren**
63 **HIGHER LOVE (IRE)**, b f 1/2 Sadler's Wells (USA)—Dollar Bird (IRE) (Kris) **DGH Partnership**
65 B f 21/3 Tipsy Creek (USA)—High Typha (Dowsing (USA)) (4500) **Mr Malcolm Caine**
66 **HOH INTREPID (IRE)**, b f 18/3 Namid—
        Bazaar Promise (Native Bazaar) (55658) **Mr David Allport & Mr Michael Lynch**
67 **HOH MY DARLING**, b f 28/4 Dansili—Now And Forever (IRE) (Kris) **Mr David Allport & Hoh Oilfield Services**
68 **KISSING LIGHTS (IRE)**, b f 10/3 Machiavellian (USA)—
        Nasaieb (Fairy King (USA)) (110000) **Mr M. B. Hawtin**
69 Ch c 24/2 Diesis—Lamsat Al Hob (Lion Cavern (USA)) **Sheikh Rashid Bin Mohammed**
70 **LANGSTON BOY**, b c 31/1 Namid—Blinding Mission (IRE) (Marju (IRE)) (50000) **Mr Derek Higgins OBE**
71 **LOUISE RAYNER**, b f 22/1 Vettori (IRE)—
        Showery (Rainbow Quest (USA)) (9500) **Richard Green (Fine Paintings)**
72 **MISS TRUANT**, b f 19/3 Zaha (CAN)—Miss Runaway (Runnett) (13000) **The Funny Hahas**
73 **MOTIVATOR**, b c 22/2 Montjeu (IRE)—Out West (USA) (Gone West (USA)) (75000) **The Royal Ascot Racing Club**
74 **MYSTERIOSA**, b f 23/3 Mujahid (USA)—Mrs Gray (Red Sunset) (64000) **The Waney Racing Group Inc.**
75 **OPALINE**, b c 27/4 Barathea (IRE)—Irish Light (USA) (Irish River (FR)) (18000) **Cheveley Park Stud**
76 **PATRONAGE**, b c 19/2 Royal Applause—
        Passionate Pursuit (Pursuit of Love) (160000) **Highclere Thoroughbred Racing**
77 **PEARL'S A SINGER (IRE)**, ch f 9/2 Spectrum (IRE)—
        Cultured Pearl (Lammtarra (USA)) (50000) **Mr Christopher Wright**
78 **PEPPERMINT TEA (IRE)**, b f 15/5 Intikhab (USA)—Karayb (IRE) (Last Tycoon) (23500) **DGH Partnership**
79 B c 4/4 Forzando—Philgwyn (Milford) (24000)
80 **RED SAM (IRE)**, ch c 15/3 Desert King (IRE)—Mustique Dream (Don't Forget Me) (26000) **Mr Terry Neill, MBE**
81 Ch f 22/2 Raise A Grand (IRE)—Repique (USA) (Sharpen Up) (20000) **Thurloe Thoroughbreds XIV**
82 **REVIVALIST**, b f 24/2 Benny The Dip (USA)—Brave Revival (Dancing Brave) (USA) **Cheveley Park Stud**
83 **ROYAL PARDON**, b f 11/2 Royal Applause—Miss Mercy (IRE) (Law Society (USA)) **Mr Billy Maguire**
84 B c 7/3 Sri Pekan (USA)—Sagrada (GER) (Primo Dominie) (28000) **Fitzroy Thoroughbreds**
85 **SILBER MOND**, gr c 15/2 Monsun (GER)—Salinova (FR) (Linamix (FR)) **Baron F. C. Oppenheim**
86 Ch f 22/4 King's Best (USA)—Sine Labe (USA) (Vaguely Noble) **Mr Luke Lillingston**
87 B f 7/4 Mark Of Esteem (IRE)—T G's Girl (Selkirk (USA)) (9523) **Mr Alan Parker**
88 **TINCTURE**, br f 5/5 Dr Fong (USA)—Miss d'Ouilly (FR) (Bikala) **Lady Carolyn Warren**
89 **USHINDI (IRE)**, b f 1/5 Montjeu (IRE)—Fern (Shirley Heights) (80395) **Mrs G. Rowland-Clark**
90 **WHATATODO**, b f 6/4 Compton Place—
        Emerald Dream (IRE) (Vision (USA)) (5500) **Mr M. Talbot-Ponsonby & Partners**
91 **WINDERMERE ISLAND**, b f 29/4 Cadeaux Genereux—Corndavon (Sheikh Albadou) **DGH Partnership**
92 **YOUNG THOMAS (IRE)**, ch c 29/4 Inchinor—Splicing (Sharpo) (10000) **North Sea Coasters**

Other Owners: Mr R. Baker, Mr Tony Bianchi, Mr J. R. Boughey, Mrs Tom Dyer, Mr Peter Fenwick OBE, Mr Michael Flynn, F. M. Conway Ltd, Mr M. Fotchman, Mr R. Frosell, Mr Ken Green, Mr D. G. Hardisty, Mr Frank Hendry, Mr Richard Holt, Mrs Anne Jenkins, Mr R. D. A. Kelly, Mr S. R. Leoni, Lostford Manor Stud, Mr & Mrs G. Lynch, Mr John Magnier, Mrs F. Mahony, Mr K. J. Mercer, Mrs S. Mercer, Mr & Mrs Richard Pilkington, Mr I. Purkiss, Mr Charles Rhodes, The Duke Of Roxburghe, Mr B. Sangster, Mr Michael Scotney, Mr Alasdair Simpson, Ms Janice Stinnes, Mr Andrew Tolhurst, Mr & Mrs Peter Waney, Mr Mark Watson, Mr R. Weatherby.

Assistant Trainer: Emma Wood

Jockeys (Flat): M Fenton, J Mackay. **Apprentice:** H Turner (7-12).

---

37 MR A. BERRY, Cockerham

Postal: **Moss Side Racing Stables, Crimbles Lane, Cockerham, Lancaster, LA2 0ES.**
Contact: **PHONE** (01524) 791179 **FAX** (01524) 791958 **MOBILE** (07880) 553515

1 **BEAUTEOUS (IRE)**, 5, ch g Tagula (IRE)—Beauty Appeal (USA) **Mr Paul J. Dixon**
2 **CARIBE (FR)**, 5, b h Octagonal (NZ)—Caring Society **Mr G. B. Bedford**
3 **CIRCUIT DANCER (IRE)**, 4, b g Mujadil (USA)—Trysinger (IRE) **Mr David Fish**
4 **CLASSIC LIN (FR)**, 4, gr f Linamix (FR)—Classic Storm **Mr David Fish**
5 **COUNTRYWIDE GIRL (IRE)**, 5, ch m Catrail (USA)—Polish Saga **Galaxy Moss Side Racing Clubs Limited**
6 **FRASCATI**, 4, b f Emarati (USA)—Fizzy Fiona **Lord Crawshaw**
7 **GDANSK (IRE)**, 7, b g Pips Pride—Merry Twinkle **Mr Alan Berry**
8 **INDIAN MUSIC**, 7, b g Indian Ridge—Dagny Juel (USA) **Mr Alan Berry**
9 **KIRKBY'S TREASURE**, 6, ro g Mind Games—Gem of Gold **Kirkby Lonsdale Racing**

MR A. BERRY—continued

10 **LION'S DOMANE**, 7, b g Lion Cavern (USA)—Vilany **Platinum Racing Club Limited**
11 **LONGMEADOWS BOY (IRE)**, 4, b g Victory Note (USA)—Kaori (IRE) **John Wilding**
12 **OBE ONE**, 4, b g Puissance—Plum Bold **Comtake Ltd**
13 **OTYLIA**, 4, ch f Wolfhound (USA)—Soba **Mr J. Nixon**
14 **PETER'S IMP (IRE)**, 9, b g Imp Society (USA)—Catherine Clare **Mr Ian Bolland**
15 **PHOENIX NIGHTS (IRE)**, 4, b g General Monash (USA)—Beauty Appeal (USA) **Mr Alan Berry**
16 **ROBWILLCALL**, 4, b f Timeless Times (USA)—Lavernock Lady **Mr William Burns**
17 **ROSSELLI (USA)**, 8, b g Puissance—Miss Rossi **Mr Alan Berry**
18 **SIMIANNA**, 5, b m Bluegrass Prince (IRE)—Lowrianna (IRE) **The Monkey Partnership**
19 **TALLY (IRE)**, 4, ch g Tagula (IRE)—Sally Chase **Mr Paul J. Dixon**
20 **TELEPATHIC (IRE)**, 4, b g Mind Games—Madrina **Pisani PLC**
21 **THE LEATHER WEDGE (IRE)**, 5, b h Hamas (USA)—Wallflower **Mr Alan Berry**
22 **TUSCAN DREAM**, 9, b g Clantime—Excavator Lady **Galaxy Moss Side Racing Clubs Limited**
23 **WALTZING WIZARD**, 5, b g Magic Ring (IRE)—Legendary Dancer **Mr Paul J. Dixon**

THREE-YEAR-OLDS

24 **AMBER FOX (IRE)**, b f Foxhound (USA)—Paradable (IRE) **Mr Derek Hilton**
25 **BETFRED**, b g Pursuit of Love—Shamaka **Mrs Mo Done**
26 **BRIAN POTTER**, b g Pursuit of Love—Elora Gorge (IRE) **Mr Alan Berry**
27 **CAMPBELLS LAD**, b g Mind Games—T O O Mamma's (IRE) **Campbells Kingdom**
28 **CHASE THE RAINBOW**, gr f Danzig Connection (USA)—Delta Tempo (IRE) **Mr Eric Nisbet**
29 **COMMANDO SCOTT (IRE)**, b g Danetime (IRE)—Faye **Mrs Ann Morris**
30 **DESIGNER CITY (IRE)**, b f Mujadil (USA)—Carnickian (IRE) **Mr K. G. Williams**
31 **GARNOCK BELLE (IRE)**, b f Marju (IRE)—Trojan Relation **Mr Robert Aird**
32 **GARNOCK VENTURE (IRE)**, b c Mujadil (USA)—Stay Sharpe (USA) **Mr Robert Aird**
33 **HILLSIDE GIRL (IRE)**, b f Tagula (IRE)—Kunucu (IRE) **Hillside Racing**
34 **LAVISH TIMES**, ch c Timeless Times (USA)—Lavernock Lady **Mr Paul J. Dixon**
35 Ch f Woodborough (USA)—Madrina
36 B g Sesaro (USA)—Megan's Dream (IRE)
37 **OBE BOLD (IRE)**, b f Orpen (USA)—Capable Kate (IRE) **Comtake Ltd**
38 **TROODOS JET**, b g Atraf—Costa Verde **Mr Anthony White**

TWO-YEAR-OLDS

39 B c 25/2 Dansili—Awtaar (USA) (Lyphard (USA)) (15000)
40 Ch c 28/4 Tipsy Creek (USA)—Beverley Monkey (IRE) (Fayruz) (5565)
41 **BLACK COMBE LADY (IRE)**, b f 22/4 Indian Danehill (IRE)—
                                   Floronda (CAN) (Vice Regent (CAN)) (5256) **Mr Stephen Lowthian**
42 Ch c 27/2 Tagula (IRE)—Changed Around (IRE) (Doulab (USA)) (8000)
43 B f 24/4 Slip Anchor—Charisse Dancer (Dancing Dissident (USA)) (800) **Mr & Mrs T. Bibby**
44 Ch c 18/3 Dancing Spree (USA)—Charlies Bride (IRE) (Rich Charlie) (4000)
45 **COUNTRYWIDE DREAM**, ch g 28/3 Definite Article—
                                   Grosvenor Miss (IRE) (Tirol) (9894) **Countrywide Racing**
46 Ch f 9/3 Tagula (IRE)—Danzig Craft (IRE) (Roi Danzig (USA)) (3091)
47 B f 24/4 Revoque—Delia (IRE) (Darshaan) (1236)
48 B f 24/1 Desert Sun—Goldfinch (Zilzal (USA)) (6493)
49 B f 18/4 Revoque—Gracious Gretclo (Common Grounds) (13000)
50 B c 3/4 Charnwood Forest (IRE)—Hanzala (FR) (Akarad (FR)) (15460) **Ansells Of Watford**
51 B c 7/2 Xaar—Heart (Cadeaux Genereux)
52 Br f 12/2 Hernando (FR)—Karen Blixen (Kris) (6183)
53 **KRISTIKHAB (IRE)**, ch c 21/2 Intikhab (USA)—Alajyal (IRE) (Kris) (12368) **Mr Jim Smith**
54 Br c 7/2 Timeless Times (USA)—Lavernock Lady (Don't Forget Me) (2200) **Mr Willie Burns**
55 B c 24/3 Kingsinger (IRE)—Lucky Dip (Tirol) (2500) **Mr Paul Dixon**
56 B f 4/3 Desert Style (IRE)—Madame Curie (Polish Precedent (USA)) (2473)
57 B f 4/3 Mujadil (USA)—Meursault (IRE) (Salt Dome (USA)) (15000)
58 **MICKEY BOGGITT**, b c 12/2 Mind Games—Valldemosa (Music Boy) (3000) **Mr Norman Jackson**
59 Br f 5/3 Namid—Misty Peak (IRE) (Sri Pekan (USA)) (6801)
60 Gr c 2/5 Tagula (IRE)—Mystic Belle (IRE) (Thatching) (11749) **Auldlyn Stud**
61 B f 2/4 Victory Note (USA)—Olivia's Pride (IRE) (Digamist (USA)) (3710)
62 B f 20/4 Monashee Mountain—Pam Story (Sallust) (3710)
63 B f 14/2 Mind Games—Pearls (Mon Tresor) (900)
64 B f 25/4 Tagula (IRE)—Radiance (IRE) (Thatching) (3000)
65 B f 5/4 Raise A Grand (IRE)—Red Riding Hood (FR) (Mummy's Pet) (741)
66 B f 16/4 Tagula (IRE)—Requena (Dom Racine (FR)) (4019)

MR A. BERRY—continued

67 THE TERMINATOR (IRE), b c 10/5 Night Shift (USA)—Surmise (USA) (Alleged (USA)) (8000) **Mr John Connor**
68 B f 21/4 Puissance—Via Dolorosa (Chaddleworth (IRE))

Other Owners: Mr Colin Barnfather, Mr Michael Burley, Mr C. Fallows, Mr N. T. Gormley, Mr Stuart Robinson, Mr G. M. Rooney, Mr J. Simpson.

Jockeys (Flat): John Carroll, Gary Carter, Francis Norton, Robert Winston. **Apprentices:** Paul Bradley, Donna Caldwell, Steven Donohoe, Christopher Ely, Mark Flynn, Patrick Mathers. **Amateurs:** Mr G Gibson, Mr A Young.

---

38 MR J. A. BERRY, Blackwater
Postal: **Ballyroe, Blackwater, Co. Wexford, Ireland.**
Contact: **PHONE +353 (0) 53 27205 MOBILE +353 (0) 8625 57537**

1 **BOOM ECONOMY (IRE),** 8, br g Black Monday—Miss Bula **E. Halley**
2 **COONOGUE (IRE),** 8, b g Jurado (USA)—Roriston Queen **P. Berry**
3 **CORSTON JIGTHYME (IRE),** 6, br g Good Thyne (USA)—Corston Dancer (IRE) **A. S. Lyburn**
4 **GALLOPING HOME (IRE),** 6, ch g Rashar (USA)—Gort Na Lynn (IRE) **N. O'Gorman**
5 **HOLY SAILOR (IRE),** 6, b g Rashar (USA)—Rostoonstown Lass (IRE) **A. Dunlop**
6 **IN TO THE SUNSET (IRE),** 6, b g Broken Hearted—Driftahead **J. A. Berry**
7 **LAURA CROFT (IRE),** 7, br m Mister Lord (USA)—Mizuna **M. Berry**
8 **LAUREL RIVER (IRE),** 9, b m Over The River (FR)—Laurelann **S. Neville**
9 **LORD OF THE FURZE (IRE),** 8, b g Lord Americo—Furry Gran **M. Devine**
10 **LOST IN THE SNOW,** 6, br g Artic Lord—Where Am I **J. P. Berry**
11 **MONARCH'S VIEW,** 6, b m King's Ride—Curraheen View **T. J. Whitley**
12 **NO TAILS TOLD,** 6, b m Glacial Storm—Askasilla **Ballyroe Syndicate**
13 **READY FOR TAKEOFF (IRE),** 7, br g Supreme Leader—Spread Your Wings (IRE) **J. P. Berry**
14 **READY TO LAND (IRE),** 6, ch g Phardante (FR)—Spread Your Wings (IRE) **J. P. Berry**
15 **RIVER GROVE (IRE),** 8, b m Over The River (FR)—Laurelann **Dr A. Cleary**
16 **RIVER TREASURE,** 7, b m Over The River (FR)—Erins Treasure **S. Corby**
17 **SNAPPER CREEK (IRE),** 8, b g Castle Keep—Vultang Lady **Manjana Syndicate**
18 **SUIL NA STOIRME (IRE),** 5, b g Glacial Storm (USA)—Shuil Athasach (IRE) **N. Foley**
19 **UNYOKE RIVER (IRE),** 8, b m Over The River (FR)—Paddy's Dancer **B. Murphy**
20 **UP FOR GRABS (IRE),** 6, b m Over The River (FR)—Bit of Fashion **M. Berry**

Assistant Trainer: Dan Doyle

Jockey (NH): C O Dwyer (10-0). **Conditional:** J Cullen. **Amateurs:** Mr J A Berry (10-7), Mr R M Moran (10-0), Mr J T Rath (10-7).

---

39 MR J. C. DE P BERRY, Newmarket
Postal: **Beverley House Stables, Exeter Road, Newmarket, Suffolk, CB8 8LR.**
Contact: **PHONE (01638) 660663**

1 **BIG BERTHA,** 6, ch m Dancing Spree (USA)—Bertrade **Miss Amanda Rawding**
2 **BRIEF GOODBYE,** 4, b g Slip Anchor—Queen of Silk (IRE) **Mr J. McCarthy**
3 **CRITICAL STAGE (IRE),** 5, b g King's Theatre (IRE)—Zandaka (FR) **The 1997 Partnership**
4 **DIAMOND MAXINE (IRE),** 4, b f Turtle Island (IRE)—Kawther **Diamond Racing Ltd**
5 **HARLOT,** 4, b f Bal Harbour—Queen of The Quorn **Mrs V. A. Ward**
6 **HENESEYS LEG,** 4, b f Sure Blade (USA)—Away's Halo (USA) **Mr Peter J. Skinner**
7 **JACK DAWSON (IRE),** 7, b g Persian Bold—Dream of Jenny **The Premier Cru**
8 **NORTHERN EXPOSURE,** 5, ch m Polar Falcon (USA)—Lucky Round **Mr L. Casey**
9 **ODABELLA (IRE),** 4, b f Selkirk (USA)—Circe's Isle **Mr John Berry**
10 **TAKE GOOD TIME (IRE),** 4, ch g Among Men (USA)—Bold Motion **Mr L. C. Wadey**
11 **TANAH MERA (AUS),** 4, ch f Nediym (IRE)—Wonder Road (AUS) **Mr & Mrs M. Tidmarsh**
12 **ZOLUBE (IRE),** 4, b f Titus Livius (FR)—Seattle Siren (USA) **Mrs Lorraine Thompson**

THREE-YEAR-OLDS

13 **A MONK SWIMMING (IRE),** br g Among Men (USA)—Sea Magic (IRE) **The 1997 Partnership**
14 **DESIREE (IRE),** b f Desert Story (IRE)—Elba (IRE) **Mr John Berry**
15 **DIAMOND GEORGE (IRE),** b g Sri Pekan (USA)—Golden Choice **Diamond Racing Ltd**
16 **EX MILL LADY,** br f Bishop of Cashel—Hickleton Lady (IRE) **Mrs Rosemary Moszkowicz**
17 **ROSEANNA,** b f Cyrano de Bergerac—Jade Pet **Miss Amanda Rawding**

MR J. C. DE P BERRY—continued
TWO-YEAR-OLDS

18 A FORTUNATE LIFE (IRE), b f 25/4 Desert Sun—Pirie (USA) (Green Dancer (USA)) (5565) **Mr John Berry**
19 ANTHONY'S FRIEND (IRE), ch f 22/4 Timeless Times (USA)—
Philmist (Hard Fought) (1800) **Mrs Lorraine Thompson**
20 BILKIE (IRE), ch c 14/4 Polish Precedent—Lesgor (USA) (Irish River (FR)) (12000) **Mr L. C. Wadey**
21 Gr f 2/4 Largesse—En Grisaille (Mystiko (USA)) (800) **Mrs Rosemary Moszkowicz**
22 LAST CHAPTER (IRE), b g 15/2 Desert Story (IRE)—Dutosky (Doulab (USA)) **Miss J. V. May**
23 MY OBSESSION (IRE), b g 29/4 Spectrum (IRE)—Little Love (Warrshan (USA)) (11749) **Mr John Berry**
24 NEAURUHOE (IRE), b f 16/5 Desert Sun—Snowcap (Snow Chief (USA)) (4019) **Mr John Berry**
25 PICOT DE SAY, b g 28/3 Largesse—Facsimile (Superlative) (800) **Mr H. R. Moszkowicz**
26 SERGEANT SMALL (IRE), b g 29/3 Dr Devious (IRE)—Yavarro (Raga Navarro (ITY)) (7420) **Mr John Berry**
27 B f 23/4 Cyrano De Bergerac—Tamara (Marju (IRE)) **Mr J. B. J. Richards**

Other Owners: Mr C. Benest, Mr W. F. Benter, Mr N. Blake, Mr K. Brown, Mr J. Dumas, Golden Vale Stud, Mr Gerry Grimstone, Mr A. Harbidge, Mr D. Huelin, Mr A. Le Brocq, Mr A. A. Lyons, Miss L. McCarthy, Mr D. Thompson, Mr P. Wright.

Jockeys (Flat): G Baker (8-9, w.a.), T E Durcan (8-3, w.a.), J Egan (8-0, w.a.), M Fenton (8-5, w.a.), Lisa Jones (7-9, w.a.). **Jockeys (NH):** J Culloty (10-0, w.a.), P Moloney (10-0, w.a.), T J Murphy (10-0, w.a.), V Slattery (10-0, w.a.). **Amateurs:** Miss F Pickard (8-0), Mr R Sims (12-0).

---

40   **MR N. BERRY, Earlswood**
Postal: **Green Acres Farm, Far Hill, Llanishen, Chepstow, Monmouthshire, NP16 6QZ.**
Contact: **OFFICE (01291) 641426/641689 HOME (01600) 860295 MOBILE (07802) 531316**

1 AINTNECESSARILYSO, 6, ch g So Factual (USA)—Ovideo **Box 40 Racing**
2 COOLFORE JADE (IRE), 4, ch f Mukaddamah (USA)—Cashel Princess (IRE) **Leeway Group Limited**
3 DEFINITELY SPECIAL (IRE), 6, b m Definite Article—Legit (IRE) **Leeway Group Limited**
4 EL PEDRO, 5, b g Piccolo—Standard Rose **Leeway Group Limited**
5 GOODWOOD PROMISE, 5, b g Primo Dominie—Noble Destiny **Leeway Group Limited**
6 INDIAN BAZAAR (IRE), 8, ch g Indian Ridge—Bazaar Promise **Leeway Group Limited**
7 OLITHEAGA, 9, ch g Safawan—Lyaaric **Box 40 Racing**
8 PANJANDRUM, 6, b g Polar Falcon (USA)—Rengaine (FR) **Leeway Group Limited**
9 THE GAIKWAR (IRE), 5, b h Indian Ridge—Broadmara (IRE) **Leeway Group Limited**

THREE-YEAR-OLDS

10 BACK AT DE FRONT (IRE), b f Cape Cross (IRE)—Bold Fashion (FR) **Leeway Group Limited**
11 RUMOUR MILL (IRE), b c Entrepreneur—Pursuit of Truth (USA) **Leeway Group Limited**
12 TAMARINA (IRE), ch f Foxhound (USA)—Tamasriya (IRE) **Leeway Group Limited**

Other Owners: Mrs A. Andijah, Mr B. Beale, A. A. Campbell, Ron Collins, W. H. Cooper, G. Eales, Mr R. M. D. Howells, M. Lawrance, E. Lloyd, Purple People Racing Partnership, Mr I. P. Radley, Mrs I. Shine, Mr J. Shine, The Square Milers.

Assistant Trainer: Mr R Harris

Jockeys (Flat): R Brisland (7-10), N Callan (8-3, w.a.), B Doyle (8-4, w.a.). **Apprentice:** M Savage (8-3). **Amateur:** Miss Emma Folkes (9-0).

---

41   **MR J. R. BEST, Maidstone**
Postal: **Scragged Oak Farm, Scragged Oak Road, Hucking, Maidstone, Kent, ME17 1QU.**
Contact: **PHONE (01622) 880276 FAX (01622) 880904 MOBILE (07889) 362154**
E-MAIL john.best@johnbestracing.com

1 A BEETOO (IRE), 4, b f Bahhare (USA)—Sonya's Pearl (IRE) **Mr C. Hales**
2 ALLY MAKBUL, 4, b f Makbul—Clarice Orsini **Mr Malcolm Ward**
3 AVALANCHE (FR), 7, gr g Highest Honor (FR)—Fairy Gold **The Downhill Partnership**
4 BURNT COPPER (IRE), 4, b g College Chapel—Try My Rosie **R.Blake, B.Blake, N.Webberley, R.Sackett**
5 CHARLIES DOUBLE, 5, b g Double Eclipse (IRE)—Pendil's Niece **The Highly Hopeful Club**
6 CRESSEX KATIE, 5, b m Komaite (USA)—Kakisa **Pennywise Racing Ltd**
7 EACHY PEACHY (IRE), 5, ch m Perugino (USA)—Miss Big John (IRE) **Mrs Megan Olley**
8 FOREVER MY LORD, 6, b g Be My Chief (USA)—In Love Again (IRE) **Mr Steve Cook**
9 GREEN ICENI, 5, br g Greensmith—Boadicea's Chariot **Mr Paul Hudson**
10 HIGH DIVA, 5, b m Piccolo—Gifted **Mr D. S. Nevison**

MR J. R. BEST—continued

11 HINCHLEY WOOD (IRE), 5, b g Fayruz—Audriano (IRE) **The Skomal Racing Partnership**
12 LEONOR DE SOTO, 4, b f Fraam—Wings Awarded **Mr Martin S. Thompson**
13 MASTER BREW, 6, b g Homo Sapien—Edithmead (IRE) **Mr G. J. Larby & Mr P. J. Smith**
14 MERCATO (FR), 6, b g Mansonnien (FR)—Royal Lie (FR) **Mr D. S. Nevison**
15 MINE BEHIND, 4, b c Sheikh Albadou—Arapi (IRE) **D. Gorton, M. Folan, R. Crampton**
16 PENNY VALENTINE, 4, ch f My Best Valentine—Precision Finish **Pennywise Racing Ltd**
17 RACING NIGHT (USA), 4, b g Lear Fan (USA)—Broom Dance (USA) **FF Racing Services Partnership XIV**
18 ROYALENTERTAINMENT (IRE), 6, b br m King's Ride—Spring Fiddler (IRE) **Mr D. S. Nevison**
19 ROYAL RACER (FR), 6, b g Danehill (USA)—Green Rosy (USA) **Mr & Mrs R. Dawbarn**
20 STEELY DAN, 5, b g Danzig Connection (USA)—No Comebacks **Mrs Louise Best**
21 STRATHCLYDE (IRE), 5, b g Petong—It's Academic **Pennywise Racing Ltd**
22 WHIPPASNAPPER, 4, b g Cayman Kai (IRE)—Give Us A Treat **Miss Vanessa Church**

THREE-YEAR-OLDS

23 KING OF DIAMONDS, b c Mtoto—Capricious Lass
24 KNIGHT ONTHE TILES (IRE), ch g Primo Dominie—Blissful Night **Green Acre Homes Ltd**
25 LITTLE EYE (IRE), b g Groom Dancer (USA)—Beaming **Mr & Mrs R. Dawbarn**
26 MISTER COMPLETELY (IRE), b g Princely Heir (FR)—Blue Goose **Eastwell Manor Racing Ltd**
27 OTAGO (IRE), b c Desert Sun—Martino **Mrs L. M. Askew**
28 SMOKIN JOE, b c Cigar—Beau Dada (IRE) **Pennywise Racing Ltd**
29 ST SAVARIN (FR), ch g Highest Honor (FR)—Sacara (GER) **Mr D. S. Nevison**
30 WILLHEGO, ch g Pivotal—Woodrising **G G Racing**

TWO-YEAR-OLDS

31 B c 2/3 Groom Dancer (USA)—Azula (Bluebird (USA)) (18000) **Mr D. S. Nevison**
32 B c 19/4 Forzando—Broom Isle (Damister (USA)) (16000) **Mr D. S. Nevison**
33 B g 25/3 Bahamian Bounty—Child Star (FR) (Bellypha) (6000) **Mr D. S. Nevison**
34 COMCATCHINI, ch c 1/3 Compton Place—
                        Baileys Firecat (Catrail (USA)) (21000) **The Weak At The Knees Partnership**
35 KINGSGATE BAY (IRE), b c 12/3 Desert Sun—Selkirk Flyer (Selkirk (USA)) (21000) **Mr John Mayne**
36 Ch c 18/2 Monashee Mountain—Lodema (IRE) (Lycius (USA)) (11749)
37 B c 11/4 Mark of Esteem (IRE)—No Comebacks (Last Tycoon) (9000)
38 Ch c 15/1 Forzando—Not So Generous (IRE) (Fayruz) (15000) **Mr D. S. Nevison**
39 B c 21/3 Mujahid (USA)—Stygian (USA) (Irish River (FR)) (20000) **Mr D. S. Nevison**

Other Owners: Mr G. K. Aldridge, Mrs Benita Blake, Mr R. Blake, Mrs A. C. Bowen, Mr S. A. Bowen, Mr Toby Brereton, Mr B. Cains, A. J. Cork, Mr R. B. Dawbarn, Mrs S. P. Dawbarn, Mr M. Folan, Mr Frank Gilmour, Mrs Deana Godmon, Mr. G. Godmon, Mr D. Gorton, Mr G. J. Larby, Mr Peter Nelson, Mr Steve Nelson, Mr Nick Newman, Mr N. Payne, Mr R. T. Sackett, Mr Peter J. Smith, Mr K. Sobey, Mrs N. Webberley.

Jockey (Flat): R Lake (7-13). **Conditional:** J Gray (9-7).

MR J. D. BETHELL, Middleham
Postal: **Clarendon House, Middleham, Leyburn, North Yorkshire, DL8 4NP.**
Contact: **PHONE (01969) 622962 FAX (01969) 622157**
E-MAIL james@jamesbethell.co.uk WEBSITES www.jamesbethell.co.uk www.clarendonracing.co.uk

1 CRATHORNE (IRE), 4, b g Alzao (USA)—Shirley Blue (IRE) **www.clarendonracing.com**
2 DERWENT (USA), 5, b g Distant View (USA)—Nothing Sweeter (USA) **Mr M. J. Dawson**
3 EBORACUM LADY (USA), 4, b f Lure (USA)—Konvincha (USA) **Mr M. J. Dawson**
4 KING HARSON, 5, b g Greensmith—Safari Park **Mr C. J. Burley**
5 LEIGHTON (IRE), 4, b g Desert Story—Lady Fern **www.clarendonracing.com**
6 MINE (IRE), 6, b m Primo Dominie—Ellebanna **Mr M. J. Dawson**
7 MITSUKI, 5, b m Puissance—Surrealist (ITY) **John E. Lund**
8 SCOTLAND THE BRAVE, 4, ch f Zilzal—Hunters of Brora (IRE) **Mr Robert Gibbons**
9 STRETTON (IRE), 6, br g Doyoun—Awayil (USA) **Mr M. J. Dawson**

THREE-YEAR-OLDS

10 DEANGATE (IRE), ch g Vettori (IRE)—Moonlight (IRE) **www.clarendonracing.co.uk**
11 FOSSGATE, ch g Halling (USA)—Peryllys **WWW.Clarendon Racing.Co.UK**
12 GRANSTON (IRE), gr g Revoque (IRE)—Gracious Gretclo **The Four Players Partnership**
13 HAVETOAVIT (USA), br g Theatrical—Summer Crush **John E. Lund**
14 LITTLE BOB, ch c Zilzal (USA)—Hunters of Brora (IRE) **Mr Robert Gibbons**

MR J. D. BETHELL—continued

15 MICKLEGATE, b f Dracula (AUS)—Primulette **WWW.Clarendon Racing.Co.UK**
16 SNOWED UNDER, gr g Most Welcome—Snowy Mantle **Mrs G. Fane**
17 TRUE MAGIC, b f Magic Ring (IRE)—True Precision **T. R. Lock**

TWO-YEAR-OLDS

18 ASKNINTH (IRE), b g 7/4 Marju (IRE)—Hayward (Indian Ridge) (15000) **Clarendon Thoroughbred Racing**
19 BOSCHETTE, b f 9/3 Dansili—Secret Dance (Sadler's Wells (USA)) (13000) **Mr C. J. Burley**
20 B g 7/4 Rossini (USA)—Cochiti (Kris) (8000)
21 B f 31/3 Tomba—Dark Kristal (IRE) (Gorytus (USA)) (5000) **J. Hamilton**
22 B f 20/2 Lujain (USA)—Dona Filipa (Precocious)
23 B g 29/4 Wolfhound (USA)—Dusty's Darling (Doyoun) (10000) **J. R. Whiteley**
24 FLAXBY, b g 30/4 Mister Baileys—Harryana (Efisio) (9000) **Clarendon Thoroughbred Racing**
25 INGLEBY CROSS, b f 2/2 Cape Cross (IRE)—
                        No Islands (Lomond (USA)) (12000) **Clarendon Thoroughbred Racing**
26 LOYALTY LODGE (IRE), ch c 7/4 Grandlodge (USA)—Gaily Grecian (IRE) (Ela-Mana-Mou) (42000) **John E. Lund**
27 Ch c 11/4 Pivotal—Scierpan (USA) (Sharpen Up) (42000) **John E. Lund**
28 STRAWBERRY DALE (IRE), b f 23/3 Bering—Manchaca (FR) (Highest Honor (FR)) (20000) **Mr M. J. Dawson**

Other Owners: Mrs James Bethell.

MR R. N. BEVIS, Malpas
Postal: **Welsh View, Back Lane, Threapwood, Malpas, Cheshire, SY14 7AT.**
Contact: **PHONE (01948) 770427 (0802) 446045**
E-MAIL richardnbevis@aol.com/welshviewstables@aol.com

1 BARABASCHI, 8, b g Elmaamul (USA)—Hills' Presidium **Mr Peter J. Doyle**
2 CONSTANT HUSBAND, 11, gr g Le Solaret (FR)—Miss Mirror **Mr Steve Corbett**
3 COPPER COIN (IRE), 10, b br g Mandalus—Two-Penny Rice **Miss N. C. Taylor**
4 COURT ORDEAL (IRE), 9, ch g Kris—In Review **Mr Steve Corbett**
5 ELEGANT CLUTTER (IRE), 6, b g Petorius—Mountain Hop (IRE) **Mr Kelvin Briggs**
6 HIGH JINKS, 9, b g High Estate—Waffling **Mr R. N. Bevis**
7 MAISIEBEL, 6, ch m Be My Native (USA)—High 'b' **Ewson Contractors**
8 REGGAE RHYTHM (IRE), 10, b g Be My Native (USA)—Invery Lady **Mr Peter J. Doyle**
9 5, b m Tragic Role (USA)—Waffling **E. Sharp**

THREE-YEAR-OLDS

10 B g Makbul—Miss Mirror **S. Corbett**

Assistant Trainer: R J Bevis

Amateur: Mr R N Bevis (10-5).

---

44 MRS P. F. BICKERTON, Market Drayton
Postal: **3 Pixley Cottages, Hinstock, Market Drayton, Shropshire, TF9 2TN.**
Contact: **PHONE (01952) 550384 MOBILE (07966) 441001**

1 BATH HOUSE BOY (IRE), 11, b g Don't Forget Me—Domiciliate **Mrs Pippa Bickerton**
2 NICE ONE TED (IRE), 8, b g Posen (USA)—Arburie **Mrs Pippa Bickerton**
3 PIXLEY, 4, ch g Saxon Farm—Lady Renton
4 SAXON MILL, 9, ch g Saxon Farm—Djellaba **Mrs Pippa Bickerton**

---

45 MR J. N. R. BILLINGE, Cupar
Postal: **Hilton Farm, Cupar, Fife, KY15 4QD.**
Contact: **PHONE (01334) 655180 MOBILES (07971) 831495/(07974) 753430**
E-MAIL billinge.hilton@virgin.net

1 ALBA ROSE, 5, gr m Overbury (IRE)—Belle Rose (IRE) **Mrs V. Gilmour**
2 DARNLEY, 7, b br g Henbit (USA)—Reeling **Sceptre House Golf Society**
3 DIAMOND DYNASTY, 7, b g Son Pardo—Reperage (USA) **Mr J. N. R. Billinge**
4 ESP HILL, 6, ch m Moscow Society (USA)—Heatheridge (IRE) **The Timbertops**
5 HURRICANE GEORGES, 8, b g Milieu—Miss Colonnette **Mrs S.E.Billinge & Mrs C.G.Braithwaite**
6 MOONZIE LAIRD (IRE), 6, b br g Good Thyne (USA)—Sweet Roselier (IRE) **Sceptre House Golf Society**

MR J. N. R. BILLINGE—continued

7 4, B f Thowra (FR)—Reeling **John Findlay,David Cupit,John Cupit**
8 **SAVANNAH MO (IRE)**, 9, ch m Husyan (USA)—Sweet Start **Mrs MM Wilson & Fife Foxhounds Racing**
9 **SEA LAUGHTER (IRE)**, 6, gr m Presenting—Bruna Rosa **Mrs R. Linzee Gordon & Mrs M. M. Wilson**
10 **SHAZAL**, 7, b m Afzal—Isolationist **Lordscairnie Racing**
11 **TEST OF FAITH**, 5, b g Weld—Gold Pigeon (IRE) **Hilton Racing Partnership**
12 **TULLIMOSS (IRE)**, 9, b m Husyan (USA)—Ballynattin Moss **Mrs S.E.Billinge & Mrs C.G.Braithwaite**

Other Owners: Mrs E. C. Bell, Mrs S. E. Billinge, Mrs C. G. Braithwaite, Mrs R. C. Carr, Mr A. J. Comette, Mr B. A. Cotton, Mr David Cupit, Mr John Cupit, Mr J. G. H. Fenton, Mr John Findlay, Mr C. F. Hallett, Mrs R. Linzee Gordon, Mr R. Scobbie, Mrs M. Wilson, Mrs M. V. Wolseley Brinton, Mrs S. M. Wood, Mr P. F. Wyborn, Mr J. C. Wythe.

Assistant Trainer: Mrs S E Billinge

Jockeys (NH): S Durack (10-0), G Lee (10-0), M H Naughton (10-0). **Apprentice:** C Eddery (10-0). **Amateur:** Mr O Nelmes (10-0).

---

46 ## MR K. BISHOP, Bridgwater
Postal: **Barford Park Stables, Spaxton, Bridgwater, Somerset, TA5 1AF.**
Contact: **PHONE/FAX (01278) 671437 MOBILE (07816) 837610**

1 **ASHLEY BROOK (IRE)**, 6, ch g Magical Wonder (USA)—Seamill (IRE) **Mrs E. K. Ellis**
2 **BARREN LANDS**, 9, b g Green Desert (USA)—Current Raiser **Mrs E. K. Ellis**
3 **BATHSHEBA**, 5, b m Overbury (IRE)—Winnow **Miss Marie Steele**
4 **DAMIER BAY**, 7, b g Karinga Bay—Mountain Mear **Mr K. Bishop**
5 **DODGER MCCARTNEY**, 6, ch g Karinga Bay—Redgrave Girl **Mr W. O. J. Davies**
6 **GRAVE DOUBTS**, 8, ch g Karinga Bay—Redgrave Girl **Bill Davies & Bernard Tottle**
7 **GUMLEY GALE**, 9, b g Greensmith—Clodaigh Gale **Portcullis Racing**
8 **JUST JASMINE**, 12, ch m Nicholas Bill—Linguistic **Mrs E. K. Ellis**
9 **KARING KENDA**, 5, ch m Karinga Bay—Song of Kenda
10 **KINGSMOOR**, 8, b g Regal Embers (IRE)—Cupids Bower **Mr R. D. Cox**
11 **LANGHAM LAKE**, 7, b g Endoli (USA)—Birbrook Girl **Mr R. H. Stevens**
12 **MONGER LANE**, 8, b m Karinga Bay—Grace Moore **Slabs And Lucan**
13 **MR MORRISSEY**, 7, ch g Karinga Bay—Barford Lass VII **Mr K. Bishop**
14 **QUABMATIC**, 11, b g Pragmatic—Good Skills **Eric's Friends Racing Partnership**
15 **REDGRAVE BAY**, 7, b m Karinga Bay—Redgrave Girl **Mr K. Bishop**
16 **REDGRAVE WOLF**, 11, ch m Little Wolf—Redgrave Rose **Mr K. Bishop**
17 **SACRIFICE**, 9, b g Arctic Lord—Kellyann **Mr Mike Cornish**
18 **SUREFAST**, 9, ch g Nearly A Hand—Meldon Lady **Mr Brian Derrick**

Other Owners: Mrs Freda Forster, Mr R. C. Hicks, Mr David John Jones, Mr C. J. Macey, Mr C. H. Roberts, Mr Victor Thorne, Mr B. H. E. Tottle, Mrs Pamela Westlake, Mr R. J. Whatley.

Assistant Trainer: Heather Bishop

Jockey (NH): R Greene (10-0).

---

47 ## MR A. G. BLACKMORE, Hertford
Postal: **'Chasers', Stockings Lane, Little Berkhamsted, Hertford, SG13 8LW.**
Contact: **PHONE (01707) 875060 MOBILE (07803) 711453**

1 **COOL ROXY**, 7, b g Environment Friend—Roxy River **Mr A. G. Blackmore**
2 **FLAMING CHEEK**, 6, b g Blushing Flame (USA)—Rueful Lady **Mr A. G. Blackmore**
3 **NAKED FLAME**, 5, b g Blushing Flame (USA)—Final Attraction **Mr A. G. Blackmore**

Assistant Trainer: Mrs P M Blackmore

Conditional: C Honour (9-11).

48   MR M. T. W. BLANSHARD, Upper Lambourn

Postal: Lethornes Stables, Upper Lambourn, Hungerford, Berkshire RG17 8QS.
Contact: PHONE (01488) 71091 FAX 73497 MOBILE (07785) 370093
E-MAIL blanshard.racing@virgin.net

1 **CUMBRIAN PRINCESS,** 7, gr m Mtoto—Cumbrian Melody **Mr David Sykes**
2 **DON'T TELL ROSEY,** 4, b g Barathea (IRE)—Patsy Western **Hertford Offset Ltd**
3 **KINGSCROSS,** 6, ch g King's Signet (USA)—Calamanco **Mrs D. Ellis**
4 **PATSY'S DOUBLE,** 6, b g Emarati (USA)—Jungle Rose **Mrs P. Buckley**
5 **PERFECT STORM,** 5, b h Vettori (IRE)—Gorgeous Dancer (IRE) **The Newchange Syndicate**
6 **SEWMORE CHARACTER,** 4, b c Hector Protector (USA)—Kyle Rhea **Aykroyd and Sons Ltd**
7 **SEWMUCH CHARACTER,** 5, b g Magic Ring (IRE)—Diplomatist **Aykroyd & Sons Ltd**
8 **SUN HILL,** 4, b g Robellino (USA)—Manhattan Sunset (USA) **Mr Stanley Hinton**
9 **THE TRADER (IRE),** 6, ch g Selkirk (USA)—Snowing **Mrs C. J. Ward**
10 **VICTORY VEE,** 4, b g Vettori (IRE)—Aldevonie **Mrs G. Milligan**
11 **VIN DU PAYS,** 4, b g Alzao (USA)—Royale Rose (FR) **J.Oliver,W.Garrett,C.J.Ward & Anne Page**

THREE-YEAR-OLDS

12 **DESERT BATTLE (IRE),** ch g Desert Sun—Papal **Mr & Mrs T. Parrott**
13 **DISCO DIVA,** ch f Spectrum (IRE)—Compact Disc (IRE) **Messrs Gale, Pople, Else, Budd & Epps**
14 **JUST ONE LOOK,** b f Barathea (IRE)—Western Sal **The Breeze In Partnership**
15 **MOLLY MOON (IRE),** gr f Primo Dominie—Snowing **Lady Bland**
16 **OUR LITTLE ROSIE,** b f Piccolo—Villella **Mrs R. G. Wellman**
17 **PELLA,** ch f Hector Protector (USA)—Norpella **Mrs S. Ward & Partners**
18 **ROYAL APPROACH,** b f Royal Applause—Passionelle **Mr J. M. Beever**
19 **SEW'N'SO CHARACTER (IRE),** b c Imperial Ballet (IRE)—Hope And Glory (USA) **Aykroyd and Sons Ltd**
20 **STYLISH DANCER,** b f Muhtarram (USA)—Iltimas (USA) **Mr W. Lloyd Hill**
21 **SUGARBABE,** b f Kirkwall—Lightning Legacy (USA) **Vino Veritas**
22 **THE JOBBER (IRE),** b g Foxhound (USA)—Clairification (USA) **A. R. B. Ward & Mrs C. J. Ward**
23 **ZULETA,** ch f Vettori (IRE)—Victoria **Mrs P. Clark**

TWO-YEAR-OLDS

24 **BOUNTIFUL,** gr f 14/1 Pivotal—Kinsaile (Robellino (USA)) **Lady Bland**
25 B c 22/4 Lujain (USA)—Carina Clare (Slip Anchor)
26 B f 18/4 Imperial Ballet (IRE)—London Rose (USA) (Machiavellian (USA)) (8039) **Mr Gordon Phillips**
27 B f 20/3 Mister Baileys—Lovely Heart (Midyan (USA)) **The First Timers**
28 **LOW FOLD FLYER,** ch c 7/5 Fraam—Maniere d'Amour (FR) (Baillamont (USA)) **Mr J. M. Beever**
29 **MULBERRY WINE,** b f 12/2 Benny The Dip (USA)—Top Berry (High Top) **Sir Christopher Bland**
30 **PAPSWOODMOSS,** ch f 21/4 Fleetwood (IRE)—Pab's Choice (Telsmoss) **Mr C. Papaioannou**
31 **PERFECT SCORE,** b c 20/2 Groom Dancer (USA)—Flawless (Warning) (21000) **Messrs Gale, Else & Oliver**
32 **PIPER LILY,** b f 3/2 Piccolo—Polly Golightly (Weldnaas (USA)) **Mr David Sykes**
33 B f 28/1 Tagula (IRE)—Queen of Silk (IRE) (Brief Truce (USA)) (5000) **Mrs R. Wellman**
34 B f 16/5 Danzero (AUS)—Shalverton (IRE) (Shalford (IRE)) (800)
35 **THE COMPOSER,** b c 16/3 Royal Applause—Superspring (Superlative) (26000) **Mrs C. J. Ward**
36 **THE FUND MANAGER,** b f 13/2 Zafonic (USA)—
                                                    Heuston Station (IRE) (Fairy King (USA)) (26000) **Mrs C. J. Ward**
37 B c 27/4 Efisio—Vilany (Never So Bold) **Mrs P. A. Clark**
38 **WEBSTER,** b g 4/3 Kingsinger—Worsted (Whittingham (IRE)) (5000) **Mrs D. Ellis**

Other Owners: Mr P Berg, Mr D. G. Chambers, Mr R. French, Mr Lloyd Hill, Mr D. Hughes, Mr T. Luard, Mr B. Maynard, Mr C. McKenna, Mr B. Mitchell, Mr R. Noel, Mrs M. A. Payne, Mr C. Philipson, Mr D. Poole, Mr R. A. Slater, Mr D. Sloan, Mrs S. Ward, Mr V. Ward, Mr J. B. Williams, Mrs T. L. Williams.

49   MR P. A. BLOCKLEY, Southwell

Postal: Barn One, Southwell Racecourse, Rolleston, Newark, Nottinghamshire, NG25 0TS.
Contact: PHONE (01636) 819082 MOBILE (07778) 318295

1 **AFRICAN SPUR (IRE),** 4, b g Flying Spur (AUS)—African Bloom **Mr David Wright**
2 **ALTITUDE DANCER (IRE),** 4, b g Sadler's Wells (USA)—Height of Passion **Mr J. D. Cotterill**
3 **BY ALL MEN (IRE),** 4, b g Among Men (USA)—Bellinzona **Mr J. P. Kok**
4 **COUP DE CHANCE (IRE),** 4, ch f Ashkalani (IRE)—Tout A Coup (IRE) **Mrs K. Cross**
5 **CROMABOO CAROUSAL,** 6, b m Missed Flight—Baladee **Mr John Wardle**
6 **DAUNTED (IRE),** 8, b g Priolo—Dauntess **Mrs Joanna Hughes**
7 **DELTA FORCE,** 5, b g High Kicker (USA)—Maedaley **Miss Emma Shally**
8 **EASTERN DAGGER,** 4, b g Kris—Shehana (USA) **Mr H. S. Gardiner**

MR P. A. BLOCKLEY—continued

9 **ESATTO**, 5, b g Puissance—Stoneydale **Brooklands Racing**
10 **GRASSLAND STAR (IRE)**, 7, b g Catrail (USA)—Dahar's Love (USA) **The Clever Cats**
11 **HIAWATHA (IRE)**, 5, b g Danehill (USA)—Hi Bettina **Mr Nigel Shields**
12 **HIDDEN DRAGON (USA)**, 5, b g Danzig (USA)—Summer Home (USA) **The Whitings**
13 **HIT'S ONLY MONEY (IRE)**, 4, br g Hamas (USA)—Toordillon (IRE) **Mr Clive Whiting**
14 **INTENSITY**, 8, b g Bigstone (IRE)—Brillante (FR) **Mr Bill Cahill**
15 **LAGGAN MINSTREL (IRE)**, 6, b g Mark of Esteem (IRE)—Next Episode (USA) **Propak Sheet Metal Limited**
16 **LUCAYAN MONARCH**, 6, ch g Cadeaux Genereux—Flight Soundly (IRE) **Mr A. C. Kirkham**
17 **LUXI RIVER (USA)**, 4, b g Diesis—Mariella (USA) **Mrs Joanna Hughes**
18 **MALOY (GER)**, 4, gr g Neshad (USA)—Monalind (GER) **Mr Carl Would**
19 **NOBLE PURSUIT**, 7, b g Pursuit of Love—Noble Peregrine **Miss F. V. Cove**
20 **OPTIMISTIC HARRY**, 5, b g Sir Harry Lewis (USA)—Miss Optimist **Bell House Racing Limited**
21 **OVIGO (GER)**, 5, b g Monsagem (USA)—Ouvea (GER) **The Dilum Partnership**
22 **RELLIM**, 5, b m Rudimentary (USA)—Tycoon Girl (IRE) **The Gumley Gropers**
23 **SHARED ACCOUNT (IRE)**, 10, b g Supreme Leader—Ribble Rabble **Mr Carl Would**
24 **SKIP OF COLOUR**, 4, b g Rainbow Quest (USA)—Minskip (USA) **Mr Trevor Sleath**
25 **SUPREME DREAMER (IRE)**, 5, br m Supreme Leader—Grangemills **Bell House Racing Limited**
26 **TEMPLE OF ARTEMIS**, 5, b h Spinning World (USA)—Casessa (USA) **Mr David Wright**
27 **THE BLOCK MONSTER (IRE)**, 5, b m Petorius—Balgren (IRE) **Mr J. Bowe**
28 **WAINWRIGHT (IRE)**, 4, b g Victory Note (USA)—Double Opus (IRE) **Miss Dionne Sarjantson**
29 **WEET WATCHERS**, 4, b g Polar Prince (IRE)—Weet Ees Girl (IRE) **Ed Weetman (Haulage & Storage) Ltd**

THREE-YEAR-OLDS

30 **ALIBONGO (CZE)**, ch g Dara Monarch—Alvilde **Czech Mates**
31 **AMAR (CZE)**, ch g Beccari (USA)—Autumn (FR) **Czech Mates**
32 **ARCTIC QUEEN**, br f Linamix (FR)—Thamud (IRE) **Winterbeck Manor Stud**
33 **BELLA BOY ZEE (IRE)**, b f Anita's Prince—Waikiki (USA) **Transbuild**
34 **BLUE EMPEROR (IRE)**, b g Groom Dancer (USA)—Bague Bleue (IRE) **Mikado Syndicate**
35 **BROOKLANDS LODGE (USA)**, ch f Grand Lodge (USA)—Princess Dixieland (USA) **Brooklands Racing**
36 **CELTIC DESERT (IRE)**, ch g Desert Story (IRE)—Quelle Celtique (FR) **Miss Victoria Hackett**
37 **CLANN A CHIEFTAIN**, ch g Atraf—Move Darling **The Dirty Dozen Partnership**
38 **COLLEGE TIME (IRE)**, b g Danetime (IRE)—Respectful (IRE) **Mr Clive Whiting**
39 **EMPEROR CAT (IRE)**, b g Desert Story (IRE)—Catfoot Lane **Mrs Joanna Hughes**
40 **FLYING RED (IRE)**, b f Entrepreneur—Mary Ellen Best (IRE) **Mr Trevor Sleath**
41 **JACOB (IRE)**, b g Victory Note (USA)—Persian Mistress (IRE) **Mr Joseph Smith**
42 **KEY PARTNERS (IRE)**, b g Key of Luck (USA)—Teacher Preacher (IRE) **Mr John Wardle**
43 **LIN IN GOLD (IRE)**, b g Second Empire (IRE)—Wasmette (IRE) **Mr J. P. Kok**
44 **LOLA'S DESTINY**, b f Mark of Esteem (IRE)—Kristiana **Holistic Racing Ltd**
45 **MISARO (GER)**, b g Acambaro (GER)—Misniniski **Mrs K. Cross**
46 **RED MONARCH (IRE)**, ch g Woodborough (USA)—Sans Ceriph (IRE) **Bigwigs Bloodstock III**
47 **SENOR SET (GER)**, b g Second Set (IRE)—Shine Share (IRE) **Mr Richard R. H. Whiting**
48 **SILVER EMPEROR (IRE)**, gr g Lil's Boy (USA)—Just Possible **Mr Richard R. H. Whiting**
49 **SMART BOY PRINCE (IRE)**, b g Princely Heir (IRE)—Miss Mulaz (FR) **Brooklands Racing**
50 **SMART STARPRINCESS (IRE)**, b f Soviet Star (USA)—Takeshi (IRE) **Brooklands Racing**
51 **SOUL PROVIDER (IRE)**, ch f Danehill Dancer (IRE)—Wing And A Prayer (IRE) **Brooklands Racing**
52 **SWORDS AT DAWN (IRE)**, ch f Daggers Drawn (USA)—Caraway **Mrs David Seed**
53 **TABARKA (IRE)**, b f Big Shuffle (USA)—Tirana (GER) **Dachel Stud**
54 **TANGO TANGO**, ch f Rudimentary (USA)—Lady Mabel **Grathby Estates Ltd**
55 **VENERDI TREDICI (IRE)**, b f Desert Style (IRE)—Stifen **Mrs K. Cross**
56 **WEET AN HAUL**, b g Danzero (AUS)—Island Ruler **Ed Weetman (Haulage & Storage) Ltd**
57 **WINGS OF MORNING (IRE)**, ch g Fumo di Londra (IRE)—Hay Knot **Ed Weetman (Haulage & Storage) Ltd**

TWO-YEAR-OLDS

58 B c 31/1 Lujain (USA)—Anatase (Danehill (USA)) (15460) **Bell House Racing Limited**
59 Ch c 16/2 Monashee Mountain—Curie Express (IRE) (Fayruz) (21644) **Mrs K. Cross**
60 Ch c 16/3 Mark Of Esteem (IRE)—Evrobi (IRE) (Grand Lodge (USA)) (18000) **Mr O. H. Kingsley**
61 B f 23/2 Night Shift (USA)—Lanelle (USA) (Trempolino (USA)) (40197) **Mrs K. Cross**
62 B c 16/2 Mujahid (USA)—Mabrookah (Deploy) (9000) **Mr G. Blott**
63 B c 13/4 Rossini (USA)—Sacred Heart (IRE) (Catrail (USA)) (15000) **Mrs Joanna Hughes**

MR P. A. BLOCKLEY—continued

64 WEET YER TERN (IRE), b c 3/4 Brave Act—
Maxime (IRE) (Mac's Imp (USA)) (21644) **Ed Weetman (Haulage & Storage) Ltd**
65 Ch c 8/4 Intikhab (USA)—Yellow Ribbon (IRE) (Hamas (IRE)) (18552) **Bell House Racing Limited**

Other Owners: Mrs D. E. Armitage, Mr M. H. Bates, Mr David John Boughton, Mr Peter G. Brown, Mr R. Buckland, Mr R. C. Cox, Mr Jim Goose, Mr K. G. Kibble, Mr O. H. Kingsley, Mr J. Laughton, Mr D. Linnett, Mr R. Linnett, Mr D. S. Lovatt, Mrs Rosalynd Norman, Mr D. Quelch, Mrs Eileen Raggett, Mr Michael Raggett, Mr R. Robinson, Mr Malcolm Stirland, Mr M. Sziler, Mr R. W. Thorne, Miss Aimie L. Whiting, Mrs J. Whiting, Miss Victoria J. Whiting.

Assistant Trainer: Joanna Hughes (07900) 680189

Jockeys (Flat): K Fallon (w.a.), Dean McKeown, G Parkin. **Apprentices:** Nolan, D Nolan (8-7), Derek Nolan (7-12), S Yourston (7-7). **Amateur:** Miss S. L. Renwick.

---

50 MR CHARLES B. BOOTH, Flaxton
Postal: **Gravel Pit Farm, Foston, Flaxton, York, YO60 7QD.**
Contact: **(01653) 618586**

1 BEZANT (IRE), 4, ch f Zamindar (USA)—Foresta Verde (USA) **Mr J. A. Porteous**
2 FIRST CLASS GIRL, 5, b m Charmer—Boulevard Girl **Mr C. B. B. Booth**
3 LITZINSKY, 6, b g Muhtarram (USA)—Boulevard Girl **Mr Paul Gascoigne**

THREE-YEAR-OLDS

4 LA FONTEYNE, b f Imperial Ballet (IRE)—Baliana **Mr J. A. Porteous**
5 ZABADOU, b g Abou Zouz (USA)—Strapped **Mr Paul Gascoigne**

TWO-YEAR-OLDS

6 BEAU LARGESSE, b g 8/3 Largesse—Just Visiting (Superlative) **Mrs R. Moszkowicz**
7 BELLE LARGESSE, b f 9/3 Largesse—Palmstead Belle (IRE) (Wolfhound (USA)) **Mrs R. Moszkowicz**
8 CREAM OF ESTEEM, b c 30/4 Mark of Esteem (IRE)—
Chantilly (FR) (Sanglamore (USA)) (9000) **Mr A. E. Graham**

---

51 MR M. R. BOSLEY, Wantage
Postal: **Kingston Lisle Farm Stables, Kingston Lisle, Wantage, Oxfordshire, OX12 9QH.**
Contact: **OFFICE/FAX (01367) 820115 MOBILE (07778) 938040**
E-MAIL martin@bosrace.fsnet.co.uk

1 ABSINTHER, 7, b g Presidium—Heavenly Queen **Mrs Jean M. O'Connor**
2 BIJOU DANCER, 4, ch g Bijou d'Inde—Dancing Diana **Mr A. J. Ilsley**
3 CLASSIC RUBY, 4, b f Classic Cliche (IRE)—Burmese Ruby **Mrs Jean M. O'Connor**
4 FAX TO SOOTY, 5, b g Factual (USA)—Saltina **Girls On Top Racing 2000**
5 MAKARIM (IRE), 8, ch g Generous (IRE)—Emmaline (USA) **Mrs Jean M. O'Connor**
6 MARAKASH (IRE), 5, b g Ashkalani (IRE)—Marilaya (IRE) **Mrs Jean M. O'Connor**
7 MIGHTY PIP (IRE), 8, b g Pips Pride—Hard To Stop **Mrs Jean M. O'Connor**
8 MONTAGNETTE, 10, ch m Gildoran—Deep Crevasse **Girls On Top Racing 2000**
9 QOBTAAN (USA), 5, b g Capote (USA)—Queen's Gallery (USA) **Inca Financial Services**
10 QUIET READING (USA), 7, b g Northern Flagship (USA)—Forlis Key (USA) **Mrs Jean M. O'Connor**
11 4, Br g Sadler's Way—Rocquelle
12 ROKY STAR (FR), 7, b g Start Fast (FR)—Rosydolie (FR) **N Turner, D Kelly, D Merricks, R Jones**
13 SILVER PROPHET (IRE), 5, gr g Idris (IRE)—Silver Heart **Mrs Jean M. O'Connor**
14 SIR ECHO (FR), 8, b g Saumarez—Echoes (FR) **Mr A. J. Ilsley**
15 SMART LORD, 13, br g Arctic Lord—Lady Catcher **The Blowingstone Partnership**

THREE-YEAR-OLDS

16 CHARIOT (IRE), ch c Titus Livius (FR)—Battle Queen **Mrs Jean M. O'Connor**

Other Owners: Mrs S. M. Brotherton, Mr G. H. Carson, Mrs N. C. Diment, Mrs Marinella Johnson, Mrs K. Whitaker.

Jockey (Flat): G Baker. **Jockey (NH):** S Curran. **Amateur:** Mrs Sarah Bosley (8-12).

52 MR P. BOWEN, Haverfordwest
Postal: Yet-Y-Rhug, Letterston, Haverfordwest, Pembrokeshire, SA62 5TB.
Contact: PHONE (01348) 840118 MOBILE (07811) 111234

1 BALLYCASSIDY (IRE), 8, br g Insan (USA)—Bitofabreeze (IRE) **Mr R. Owen**
2 BATTLE WARNING, 9, b g Warning—Royal Ballet (IRE) **Mr P. Bowen**
3 COOL CONNIE (IRE), 5, b m Commanche Run—Cool Thistle (IRE) **Green Plain Partnership**
4 CORK HARBOUR (FR), 8, ch g Grand Lodge (USA)—Irish Sea **Mr Marshall James**
5 COUNTESS KIRI, 6, b m Opera Ghost—Ballagh Countess **Mr David J. Evans**
6 COUNT TONY, 10, ch g Keen—Turtle Dove **Mr T. W. Raymond**
7 CRESSWELL QUAY, 11, ch g Bold Fox—Karatina (FR) **Mr Bruce McKay**
8 DRAGON KING, 3, b g Rakaposhi King—Dunsilly Bell **Mr R. Greenway**
9 HIGH DRAMA, 7, b br g In The Wings—Maestrale **Mr T. W. Raymond**
10 HIRVINE (FR), 6, ch g Snurge—Guadanella (FR) **Mr B. A. Crumbley**
11 IT'S DEFINITE (IRE), 5, b g Definite Article—Taoveret (IRE) **Mr R. Owen**
12 JOLLYOLLY, 5, gr g Environment Friend—Off The Air (IRE) **Mr Eamonn O'Malley**
13 KINNESCASH (IRE), 11, ch g Persian Heights—Gayla Orchestra **Mr D. R. James**
14 LITTLE DAPHNE, 6, b m Presenting—Glengarra Princess **Mr A. P. Davies**
15 MANHUNTER (IRE), 8, b g Mandalus—Pinata **Mr Sean Bryan**
16 MIAHEYYUN, 8, b g Bonny Scot (IRE)—Daunt Not **Mr B. Finneral**
17 MR ED (IRE), 6, ch g In The Wings—Center Moriches (IRE) **Mr Gwilym J. Morris**
18 PRINCE DE GALLES, 11, b g Prince des Coeurs (USA)—Royal Brush **Homebred Racing**
19 PRINCESS AIMEE, 4, b f Wizard King—Off The Air (IRE) **Mr Eamonn O'Malley**
20 QUIDDITCH, 4, b f Wizard King—Celtic Chimes **Homebred Racing**
21 REBELLE, 5, b br g Reprimand—Blushing Belle **Mr David John Robbins**
22 STEP QUICK (IRE), 10, ch g All Haste (USA)—Little Steps **Mr David A. Smith**
23 SWANSEA BAY, 8, b g Jurado (USA)—Slave's Bangle **Mr Peter Bowling**
24 TAKE THE STAND (IRE), 8, b g Witness Box (USA)—Denys Daughter (IRE) **The Courters**
25 TREASURED COIN, 6, b g Overbury (IRE)—Slip A Coin **Mr Eamonn O'Malley**
26 WOODSTOCK EXPRESS, 4, b g Alflora (IRE)—Young Tess **Mr Gwilym J. Morris**

Other Owners: Mr Colin Clarke, Mr Maurice Cole, Mr W. J. Evans, Mr P. Fullagar, Mr D. B. T. Hughes, Mr David James, Mr J. H. Mathias, Mr F. W. Ridge, Mr Chris Wall, Mrs Sarah Wall.

Assistant Trainer: K Bowen

Amateur: Mr G. Mark Barber (10-0).

53 MRS A. J. BOWLBY, Wantage
Postal: Gurnsmead Farm, Kingston Lisle, Wantage, Oxfordshire, OX12 9QT.
Contact: PHONE (01367) 820888 FAX (01367) 820880 MOBILE (07768) 277833
E-MAIL mandy@mandybowlby.com

1 ARICOVAIR (IRE), 4, ch g Desert Prince (IRE)—Linoise (FR) **The Reg Partnership**
2 FINNFOREST (IRE), 4, ch g Eagle Eyed (USA)—Stockrose **Finnforest (UK) Ltd**
3 HENRY ISLAND (IRE), 11, ch g Sharp Victor (USA)—Monterana **Mr J. A. Danahar**
4 LADY RACQUET (IRE), 5, b m Glacial Storm (USA)—Kindly Light (IRE) **The Norman Partnership**
5 LOOKSHARP LAD (IRE), 6, b g Simply Great (FR)—Merry Madness **Mr J. Shaw**
6 RIFFLES, 4, br f Alderbrook—Idiot's Lady

THREE-YEAR-OLDS

7 COTTON EASTER, b f Robellino (USA)—Pluck **The Reg Partnership**
8 CULTURED, b f Danzero (AUS)—Seek The Pearl **The Stay Positive Partnership**
9 DON ARGENTO, gr g Sri Pekan (USA)—Grey Galava **Stay Positive 2**
10 LYRICAL LADY, b f Merdon Melody—Gracious Imp (USA) **Mrs J. Harmsworth & Amanda Bowlby**
11 SCENIC FLIGHT, b f Distant View (USA)—Bird of Time (IRE) **Wits End Partnership**
12 SMOOTHLY DOES IT, b g Efisio—Exotic Forest **Michael Bowlby Racing**

Other Owners: Mr M. S. S. Bowlby, Mr S. J. Brown, Mr R. A. Cox, Ms C. E. Elphick, Mr H. A. Elphick, Mr David Erwin, Mr K. R. W. Hawkins, Mr Kelvin Jones, Mr R. D. Platt, Mr John D. Yates.

Assistant Trainer: Michael Bowlby

Jockey (Flat): E Ahern (w.a.).

54 MR S. R. BOWRING, Edwinstowe
Postal: **Fir Tree Farm, Edwinstowe, Mansfield, Nottinghamshire, NG21 9JG.**
Contact: **PHONE (01623) 822451**

1 **ACE-MA-VAHRA**, 6, b m Savahra Sound—Asmarina **Mr S. Burgan**
2 **ASWAN (IRE)**, 6, ch g Ashkalani (IRE)—Ghariba **APB Racing**
3 **BARZAK (IRE)**, 4, b c Barathea (IRE)—Zakuska **Clark Industrial Services Partnership**
4 **CARONTE (IRE)**, 4, b g Sesaro (USA)—Go Likecrazy **Mr D. H. Bowring**
5 **CEZZARO (IRE)**, 6, ch g Ashkalani (IRE)—Sept Roses (USA) **Mr D. H. Bowring**
6 **FAR NOTE (USA)**, 6, ch g Distant View (USA)—Descant (USA) **APB Racing**
7 **FIRST MAITE**, 11, b g Komaite (USA)—Marina Plata **Mr S. R. Bowring**
8 **KUSTOM KIT FOR HER**, 4, b f Overbury (IRE)—Antonias Melody **Charterhouse Holdings Plc**
9 **LITTLE DWARF**, 4, ch f Defacto (USA)—Mirror Four Sport **Clark Industrial Services Partnership**
10 **MIMAS GIRL**, 5, b m Samim (USA)—Cocked Hat Girl **Mr S. R. Bowring**
11 **OVERFIELDS**, 4, b g Overbury (IRE)—Honey Day **Mr S. R. Bowring**
12 **SEA YA MAITE**, 10, b g Komaite (USA)—Marina Plata **Mr S. R. Bowring**

THREE-YEAR-OLDS

13 **ACE MAITE**, b f Komaite (USA)—Asmarina **Ace Racing One**
14 **BREEZIT (USA)**, b f Stravinsky (USA)—Sharka **APB Racing**
15 **INMOM (IRE)**, b f Barathea (IRE)—Zakuska **Clark Industrial Services Partnership**
16 **KINGSMAITE**, b g Komaite (USA)—Antonias Melody **Mr S. R. Bowring**
17 **MARINAITE**, b f Komaite (USA)—Marina's Song **Mr S. R. Bowring**
18 **PEACE TREATY (IRE)**, b f Turtle Island (IRE)—Beautyofthepeace (IRE) **Mr G. E. Griffiths**
19 **REFLECTED LIFE**, b f Defacto (USA)—Mirror Four Sport **Clark Industrial Services Partnership**
20 **XPRES DIGITAL**, b c Komaite (USA)—Kustom Kit Xpres **Charterhouse Holdings Plc**

TWO-YEAR-OLDS

21 B f 15/4 Lugana Beach—Cocked Hat Girl (Ballacashtal (CAN)) **Mr S. R. Bowring**
22 B c 9/5 Presidium—Mirror Four Sport (Risk Me (FR)) **Mr S. R. Bowring**
23 **MISS TWIDDLES (IRE)**, b f 4/3 Desert King (IRE)—Zakuska (Zafonic (IRE)) **Clark Industrial Services Partnersip**

Other Owners: Ace Employment, Mr Paul Bacon, Mr D. D. Clark, Mr Jim Clark, Mrs Kathering Fogg, Mrs A, Potts, Mr Alan Potts.

Assistant Trainer: S Mitchell

Jockey (Flat): J Bramhill (7-10). **Amateur:** Mrs M Morris.

55 MRS S. C. BRADBURNE, Cupar
Postal: **Cunnoquhie Cottage, Letham, Cupar, Fife KY15 7RU**
Contact: **MOBILES (07769) 711064 (07768) 705722 PHONE (01337) 810325 FAX (01337) 810486**
E-MAIL susanbradburne@aol.com

1 **ALMIRE DU LIA (FR)**, 6, ch g Beyssac (FR)—Lita (FR) **Hardie, Cochrane, Paterson & Steel**
2 **ARCTIC LAGOON (IRE)**, 5, ch g Bering—Lake Pleasant (IRE) **Strath Pack Partnership**
3 **BODFARI SIGNET**, 8, ch g King's Signet (USA)—Darakah **Strath Pack Partnership**
4 **CAPRICCIO (IRE)**, 7, gr g Robellino (USA)—Yamamah **Lord Cochrane And Partners**
5 **CASE OF POTEEN (IRE)**, 8, b br m Witness Box (USA)—On The Hooch **Mrs P. Grant**
6 **CHERGAN (IRE)**, 11, b g Yashgan—Cherry Bright (IRE) **Copland, Hardie and Steel**
7 **KHARAK (FR)**, 5, gr g Danehill (USA)—Khariyda (FR) **Hardie, Robb, Copland & Steel**
8 **LANGE BLEU (FR)**, 5, ch g Beyssac (FR)—Dear Blue (FR)
9 **LION GUEST (IRE)**, 7, ch g Lion Cavern (USA)—Decrescendo (IRE) **Mr Cornelius Lysaght**
10 **MONSIEUR POIROT (IRE)**, 7, b g Lapierre—Mallia Miss (IRE) **The Hon Thomas Cochrane**
11 **NO PICNIC (IRE)**, 6, ch g Be My Native (USA)—Emmagreen **Broad and Cochrane**
12 **SPEED KRIS (FR)**, 5, b g Belmez—Pandia (USA) **Lord Cochrane And Partners**
13 **THE TINKER**, 9, b g Nomadic Way (USA)—Miss Tino **Mrs S. Irwin**

MRS S. C. BRADBURNE—continued

THREE-YEAR-OLDS

14 **NO HESITATION**, b g Terimon—Just A Minute

Other Owners: Mrs C. Broad, Lord Cochrane Of Cults, Mr Douglas Copland, Mr Timothy Hardie, Mrs C. M. Kennedy, Mr S. E. Kennedy, Mr G. Robb, Mr Guy Steel.

Assistant Trainer: J G Bradburne

Jockey (NH): Mark Bradburne (10-0).

---

56 MR J. M. BRADLEY, Chepstow
Postal: **Meads Farm, Sedbury Park, Chepstow, Gwent, NP16 7HN.**
Contact: PHONE (01291) 622486 FAX (01291) 626939 E-MAIL j.m.bradley@virgin.net

1 **BEYOND CALCULATION (USA)**, 10, ch g Geiger Counter (USA)—Placer Queen **Mr E. A. Hayward**
2 **BOANERGES (IRE)**, 7, br g Caerleon (USA)—Sea Siren **Mr E. A. Hayward**
3 **CHANTILLY GOLD (USA)**, 5, ch m Mutakddim (USA)—Bouffant (USA) **Three Card Syndicate**
4 **CORRIDOR CREEPER (FR)**, 7, ch g Polish Precedent (USA)—Sonia Rose (USA) **Mr G. & L. Johnson**
5 **CURRENCY**, 7, b g Sri Pekan (USA)—On Tiptoes **Mr Robert Bailey**
6 **EL GIZA (USA)**, 6, ch g Cozzene (USA)—Gazayil (USA) **Mr Raymond Tooth**
7 **ENJOY THE BUZZ**, 5, b h Prince of Birds (USA)—Abaklea (IRE) **Miss F. Fenley**
8 **FLYING FAISAL (USA)**, 6, b h Alydeed (CAN)—Peaceful Silence (USA) **Mr Clifton Hunt**
9 **FLY MORE**, 7, ch g Lycius (USA)—Double River (USA) **Mr E. A. Hayward**
10 **FULL SPATE**, 9, ch g Unfuwain (USA)—Double River (USA) **Mr E. A. Hayward**
11 **HIGH RIDGE**, 5, ch g Indian Ridge—Change For A Buck (USA) **James Leisure Ltd**
12 **JOHANNIAN**, 6, b h Hernando (FR)—Photo Call **Ms A. M. Williams**
13 **JUWWI**, 10, ch g Mujtahid (USA)—Nouvelle Star (AUS) **Mr J. M. Bradley**
14 **LONE PIPER**, 9, b g Warning—Shamisen **Mr J. M. Bradley**
15 **LORD CHAMBERLAIN**, 11, b g Be My Chief (USA)—Metaphysique (FR) **Mr W. C. Harries**
16 **MILLY'S LASS**, 6, b m Mind Games—Millie's Lady (IRE) **Ken Lock Racing Ltd**
17 **MISS LIBRATE**, 6, b m Librate—Hayley's Lass **Mr J. M. Bradley**
18 **ONE WAY TICKET**, 4, ch c Pursuit of Love—Prima Cominna **Saracen Racing**
19 **PAGEANT**, 7, br m Inchinor—Positive Attitude **Saracen Racing**
20 **PARKSIDE PURSUIT**, 6, b g Pursuit of Love—Ivory Bride **Velohorse.Com**
21 **PHECKLESS**, 5, ch g Be My Guest (USA)—Phlirty **Mr N. Houston**
22 **POOKA'S DAUGHTER (IRE)**, 4, b f Eagle Eyed (USA)—Gaelic's Fantasy (IRE) **Mr G. & L. Johnson**
23 **PRESENT 'N CORRECT**, 11, ch g Cadeaux Genereux—Emerald Eagle **Mr J. M. Bradley**
24 **QUEEN EXCALIBUR**, 5, ch m Sabrehill (USA)—Blue Room **Mr G. J. Hicks**
25 **ROXANNE MILL**, 6, b m Cyrano de Bergerac—It Must Be Millie **Dab Hand Racing**
26 **SABANA (IRE)**, 6, b g Sri Pekan (USA)—Atyaaf (USA) **Mr E. A. Hayward**
27 **SALVIATI (USA)**, 7, b g Lahib (USA)—Mother Courage **Mr J. M. Bradley**
28 **SEVEN NO TRUMPS**, 7, ch g Pips Pride—Classic Ring (IRE) **Mr E. A. Hayward**
29 **SHADY DEAL**, 8, b g No Big Deal—Taskalady **The Lovely Jubbly's**
30 **SWEET TALKING GIRL**, 4, b f Bin Ajwaad (IRE)—Arabellajill **Miss F. Fenley**
31 **TAPAU (IRE)**, 6, b m Nicolotte—Urtica (IRE) **Ms A. M. Williams**
32 **THE TATLING (IRE)**, 7, b br g Perugino (USA)—Aunty Eileen **Dab Hand Racing**
33 **THREAT**, 8, br g Zafonic (USA)—Prophecy (IRE) **Mrs J. K. Bradley**
34 **TOCCATA ARIA**, 6, b m Unfuwain (USA)—Distant Music **Mr Terry Warner**
35 **TOPPLING**, 6, b g Cadeaux Genereux—Topicality (USA) **Mr E. A. Hayward**
36 **TOUCH OF FAIRY (IRE)**, 8, b g Fairy King (USA)—Decadence **Mr M. Ioannou**
37 **VLASTA WEINER**, 4, b g Magic Ring (IRE)—Armaiti **Miss Diane Hill**

THREE-YEAR-OLDS

38 **FLEET ANCHOR**, b c Fleetwood (IRE)—Upping The Tempo **The Bourn Partners**

TWO-YEAR-OLDS

39 **A LITTLE TIPSY**, b c 18/3 Tipsy Creek (USA)—My Hearts Desire (Deploy) (500) **Mr G. J. Hicks**
40 **ANGELA'S GIRL**, gr f 7/4 Baryshnikov (AUS)—
                            Filly Bergere (IRE) (Sadler's Wells (USA)) (3000) **Mr K. C. Trotman**
41 **DOMINER (IRE)**, b c 16/3 Desert Prince (IRE)—Smart (IRE) (Last Tycoon) (10000) **Mr R. Miles**
42 **GAVIOLI (IRE)**, b c 12/3 Namid—Pamina (IRE) (Perugino (USA)) (16000) **Mr E. A. Hayward**
43 **HONORARY CITIZEN**, b c 31/3 Montjoy (USA)—Heart So Blue (Dilum (USA)) (500) **Mr G. J. Hicks**
44 **JUST BONNIE**, b c 1/4 Lujain (USA)—Fairy Flight (IRE) (Fairy King (USA))

MR J. M. BRADLEY—continued

45 **MRS WILLY NILLY,** ch f 16/5 Timeless Times (USA)—Laena (Roman Warrior) (1000) **Mr Derek Shinton**
46 **MS POLLY GARTER,** b f 9/2 Petong—Utopia (Primo Dominie) (2100) **Mr Derek Shinton**
47 **NINAH'S INTUITION,** b c 2/5 Piccolo—Gina of Hithermoor (Reprimand) (3000) **Mr Robert Bailey**
48 **RUBY'S DREAM,** b f 16/4 Tipsy Creek (USA)—Sure Flyer (Sure Blade (USA)) (1800) **Mr Gwilym Fry**
49 **ZIMBALI,** ch f 2/3 Lahib—Dawn (Owington) (1000) **Mr J. M. Bradley**

Other Owners: Mr S. M. Bucknall, Mrs B. V. Chennells, Mr I. R. Harris, Mr G. W. Holland, Mr R. Howley, Mr Martyn James, Mr Neil Jenkins, Mr G. Johnson, Mr L. Johnson, Mr D. Pearson, Mr Alan Pirie, Mrs V. M. Ralston, Mr Pete Smith, Mr Martyn Williams.

Assistant Trainer: Miss Hayley Davies

Jockey (Flat): P Fitzsimmons. **Jockey (NH):** R Johnson. **Apprentices:** C J Davies, Simon Jones. **Conditional:** C J Davies.

---

57 MR M. F. BRADSTOCK, Wantage
Postal: **The Old Manor Stables, Letcombe Bassett, Wantage, Oxfordshire, OX12 9LP.**
Contact: **PHONE (01235) 760780 FAX (01235) 760754 E-MAIL mark.bradstock@btinternet.com**

1 **AD ASTRA,** 5, b g Alhijaz—So It Goes **Mrs Mary E. Fitzpatrick**
2 **ALMARAVIDE (GER),** 8, ch g Orfano (GER)—Allerleirauh (GER) **Mr P. J. Constable**
3 **BAILEY'S BRO (IRE),** 7, br g Castle Keep—Boreen Bro **The Frankly Intolerable**
4 **BEAUCHAMP PRINCESS,** 6, b m Most Welcome—Beauchamp Buzz **The Shore Things**
5 5, B g Slip Anchor—Bobanlyn (IRE) **Mr J. Macleod**
6 **CHURLISH LAD (IRE),** 7, b g Commanche Run—Pennyala **The Frankly Intolerable**
7 **COSSACK DANCER (IRE),** 6, b g Moscow Society (USA)—Merry Lesa **The United Front Partnership**
8 5, B g Accordion—Cuilin Bui (IRE) **Mr P. J. Constable**
9 **GOOD BOOK (IRE),** 6, b g Good Thyne (USA)—Book of Rules (IRE) **The Silver Cloud Partnership**
10 **GO WHITE LIGHTNING (IRE),** 9, gr g Zaffaran (USA)—Rosy Posy (IRE) **Mr J. Macleod**
11 **IBIN ST JAMES,** 10, b g Salse (USA)—St James's Antigua (IRE) **Mr Dave Breakspear**
12 **IJIKA (FR),** 8, ch g Aelan Hapi (USA)—Belle des Airs (FR)
13 **INDESTRUCTIBLE (FR),** 5, b g Hero's Honor (USA)—Money Bag (FR) **The United Front Partnership**
14 **JAYED (IRE),** 6, b br g Marju (IRE)—Taqreem (IRE) **Miss J. C. Blackwell**
15 **KING HARALD (IRE),** 6, b g King's Ride—Cuilin Bui (IRE) **Piers Pottinger and P B-J Partnership**
16 **NEVER WONDER (IRE),** 9, b g John French—Mistress Anna **Ever The Optimists**
17 **NONANTAIS (FR),** 7, b g Nikos—Sanhia (FR) **The Frankly Intolerable**
18 **PRINCE MADOC (IRE),** 8, b br g King's Ride—Cuilin Bui (IRE)
19 **SAXON KINGDOM,** 5, b g Petoski—Saxon Magic **Miller Place Racing Club**
20 **SILVER GHOST,** 5, gr g Alderbrook—Belmore Cloud **The Silver Cloud Partnership**
21 **SOMETHING GOLD (FR),** 4, gr g Baby Turk—Exiled (USA) **Mr J. Macleod**
22 **TAMBO (IRE),** 9, b g Shardari—Carmen Lady **Mr Mark Tamburro**

Assistant Trainer: Sara Bradstock

Jockey (NH): M Bachelor (10-0). **Conditional:** J Bunsell (9-7).

---

58 MRS S. A. BRAMALL, Wexford
Postal: **Borleagh Manor, Inch, Gorey, Co. Wexford, Ireland.**
Contact: **PHONE +353 (0) 402 37811 FAX +353 (0) 402 37774 MOBILE +353 (0) 872 336030
E-MAIL suebramall@hotmail.com**

1 **ALACHANCE (FR),** 4, ch c Valanjou (FR)—Senzi (FR) **Mrs S. A. Bramall**
2 **FLORITCHEL (FR),** 7, b g Dark Stone (FR)—Aktia (FR) **Secret Four Syndicate**
3 **GREGORIO (FR),** 10, b br g Passing Sale (FR)—Apside (FR) **Miss Anna Bramall**
4 **HEEMANELA (IRE),** 9, b g Classic Secret (USA)—Ela Man Hee **Winning Post Racing Syndicate**
5 **HERITAGE,** 10, b h Danehill (USA)—Misty Halo **Mrs S. A. Bramall**
6 **HIBOU ROYAL (FR),** 9, b g Bad Conduct (USA)—Onde Royale (FR) **Mrs S. A. Bramall**
7 **HOLD THE RISK (FR),** 4, ch c Take Risks (FR)—Hold Her (FR) **Mrs S. A. Bramall**
8 **ICIBORG (FR),** 8, ch g Cyborg (FR)—Phedre II (FR) **Mrs S. A. Bramall**
9 **JAZZ DE FERBET (FR),** 7, b g Scooter Bleu (IRE)—Belle de Ferbet (FR) **Mrs S. A. Bramall**
10 4, B f Shernazar—Pennypot **Mrs S. A. Bramall**
11 **PIKACHU BLUE (IRE),** 8, ch g Boyne Valley—Mary Glen **Mrs S. A. Bramall**
12 **POINT FIX (FR),** 4, ch c General Holme (USA)—Night du Rheu (FR) **Mrs S. A. Bramall**

MRS S. A. BRAMALL—continued

13 **POT OF FAIRIES (IRE)**, 9, ch g Montelimar (USA)—Ladycastle **Mrs S. A. Bramall**
14 **SADR (NZ)**, 11, b g Cache of Gold (USA)—War Field (NZ) **Mrs S. A. Bramall**

THREE-YEAR-OLDS

15 B f Shernazar—Kittygale (IRE) **Mrs S. A. Bramall**

TWO-YEAR-OLDS

16 **BALLYMUN (FR)**, gr c 18/4 Sleepling Car (FR)—Ua Uka (FR) (Turgeon (FR)) (9276) **Mrs S. A. Bramall**
17 **JIM D'ANGE (FR)**, br c 13/5 Jimble (FR)—Poussiere d'Ange (FR) (Cadoudal (FR)) (3092) **Mrs S. A. Bramall**
18 Ch c 2/4 Shernazar—Kittygale (IRE) (Strong Gale) **Mrs S. A. Bramall**

Assistant Trainer: Miss Anna Bramall

Jockey (NH): John L Cullen (10-0).

---

59 **MR G. C. BRAVERY, Newmarket**
Postal: Revida Place, Hamilton Road, Newmarket, Suffolk, CB8 7JQ.
Contact: **STABLES/FAX** (01638) 668985 **HOME** (01638) 666231 **MOBILE** (07711) 112345
E-MAIL Braverygc@aol.com

1 **HUGWITY**, 12, ch g Cadeaux Genereux—Nuit d'Ete (USA) **Mrs F. E. Bravery**
2 **LADY LAUREATE**, 6, b m Sir Harry Lewis (USA)—Cyrillic **Blackfoot Bloodstock**
3 **STRIKING AMBITION**, 4, b br c Makbul—Lady Roxanne **Mr Peter Webb**

THREE-YEAR-OLDS

4 **EXPLICIT (IRE)**, ch c Definite Article—Queen Canute (IRE) **Byculla Thoroughbreds**
5 **GREY BOY (GER)**, gr c Medaaly—Grey Perri **Mrs Mary-Anne Parker**
6 **IN A FIT**, b f Intikhab (USA)—Millfit (USA)
7 **LA DANSEUSE**, b f Groom Dancer (USA)—Alik (FR) **Mr J. F. Dean**
8 **RICKY MARTAN**, ch c Foxhound (USA)—Cyrillic **Blackfoot Bloodstock**
9 **SEGUIDILLA (IRE)**, b f Mujadil (USA)—Alzeam (IRE) **The Marguerite Clifford Stable, LLC**
10 **SUSPICIOUS MINDS**, b f Anabaa (USA)—Paloma Bay (IRE) **Mr C. G. P. Wyatt**

TWO-YEAR-OLDS

11 Gr f 14/2 Aljabr (USA)—Cinderella Ball (USA) (Nureyev (USA)) (6500) **T. T. Partnership**
12 **MASTER MIKE**, b c 10/2 Lujain (USA)—Discretion (IRE) (Alzao (USA)) (18000) **Unicorn Free Spirit Partnership**
13 **MISS AMOUR**, b f 30/3 Pivotal—Georgia Stephens (USA) (The Minstrel (CAN)) (25973) **Mr Peter Webb**
14 B f 3/3 Night Shift (USA)—My Lucky Day (FR) (Darshaan) (21645) **Carrington & Partners**
15 B f 27/4 Mujadil (USA)—Neat Shilling (IRE) (Bob Back (USA)) (21000) **T. T. Partnership**
16 **NELLA FANTASIA (IRE)**, ch f 5/3 Giant's Causeway—
Paper Moon (IRE) (Lake Coniston (IRE)) (34013) **The Marguerite Clifford Stables, LLC**
17 **NEW JOURNEY (IRE)**, b c 22/2 Cape Cross (IRE)—Desert Skimmer (IRE) (Shadeed (USA)) **Mr Peter Webb**
18 **REACHING OUT (IRE)**, b c 3/2 Desert Prince (IRE)—Alwiyda (USA) (Trempolino (USA)) (32158) **Mr Peter Webb**
19 **STRIKING ENDEAVOUR**, b c 7/3 Makbul—Nineteenth of May (Homing) (16000) **Unicorn Free Spirit Partnership**

Other Owners: Mr Joss Collins, The Hon R. T. A. Goff, Mr Hugo Lascelles, Mr F. H. Lee, Sir Eric Parker, Penfold Bloodstock.

Apprentice: Kevin Jackson.

---

60 **MR OWEN BRENNAN, Worksop**
Postal: Sloswicks Farm, Broad Lane, Worksop, Nottinghamshire, S80 3NJ.
Contact: **PHONE** (01909) 473950

1 **ACOUSTIC (IRE)**, 10, br g Orchestra—Rambling Ivy **Lady Anne Bentinck**
2 **BONNYPRINCECHARLIE (IRE)**, 4, br g Elbio—Last Princess **Lady Anne Bentinck**
3 **COMMON GIRL (IRE)**, 6, gr m Roselier (FR)—Rumups Debut (IRE) **Mr J. W. Hardy**
4 **COPPEEN CROSS (IRE)**, 10, b g Phardante (FR)—Greek Opal **Mr O. Brennan**
5 **EXTRA CACHE (NZ)**, 11, br g Cache of Gold (USA)—Gizmo (NZ) **Lady Anne Bentinck**
6 **FIREAWAY**, 10, b g Infantry—Handymouse **Mrs Pat Brennan**
7 **GOLDHORN (IRE)**, 9, b g Little Bighorn—Stylish Gold (IRE) **Mr O. Brennan**
8 **MARYLAND (IRE)**, 7, b m Executive Perk—Raven Night (IRE) **Mr O. Brennan**

MR OWEN BRENNAN—continued

9 **MIGHTY MAN (IRE)**, 9, b g Mandalus—Mossy Mistress (IRE) **Lady Anne Bentinck**
10 **MISS CHINCHILLA**, 8, b m Perpendicular—Furry Baby **Mrs Pat Brennan**
11 **SWIFT SWALLOW**, 6, ch g Missed Flight—Alhargah **Mr Richard J. Marshall**
12 **TACOLINO (FR)**, 10, ch g Royal Charter (FR)—Tamilda (FR) **Mr John Sheridan**

---

61 **MISS RHONA BREWIS, Belford**
Postal: **Chester Hill, Belford, Northumberland, NE70 7EF.**
Contact: PHONE **(01668) 213239/281**

1 **CONCHITA**, 7, b m St Ninian—Carnetto **Mrs G. E. Brewis**
2 **CRACKADEE**, 5, b br g Alflora (IRE)—Carnetto **Miss Rhona Brewis**
3 **KEPPEL**, 4, b g Sir Harry Lewis (USA)—Kimberley Rose **Miss Rhona Brewis**
4 **PEPPERNICK**, 8, br g Alflora (IRE)—Nicolini **Mr R. Brewis**
5 **RED POKER**, 4, ch g Alflora (IRE)—Scarlet Ember **Mr R. Brewis**
6 **SCARLET MEMORY**, 5, b m Dancing High—Scarlet Ember **Mr R. Brewis**
7 **SUNNYCLIFF**, 11, b g Dancing High—Nicolini **Mr R. Brewis**
8 **TIMBERLEY**, 10, ch g Dancing High—Kimberley Rose **Miss Rhona Brewis**

---

62 **MR J. J. BRIDGER, Liphook**
Postal: **Upper Hatch Farm, Liphook, Hampshire, GU30 7EL.**
Contact: PHONE **(01428) 722528 FAX (01428) 722528 MOBILE (07785) 716614**
E-MAIL john@jbridger.fsbusiness.co.uk

1 **BORDER EDGE**, 6, b g Beveled (USA)—Seymour Ann **Allsorts**
2 **HARBOUR HOUSE**, 5, b g Distant Relative—Double Flutter **Mr Tommy Ware**
3 **JANES VALENTINE**, 4, b f My Best Valentine—Jane Herring **Mr Simon Taylor**
4 **LADY LIESEL**, 4, b f Bin Ajwaad (IRE)—Griddle Cake (IRE) **Mr Simon Taylor**
5 **LADYWELL BLAISE (IRE)**, 7, b m Turtle Island (IRE)—Duly Elected **Mr W. Wood**
6 **MYTHICAL CHARM**, 5, b m Charnwood Forest (IRE)—Triple Tricks (IRE) **Mr Tommy Ware**
7 **NEWCORR (IRE)**, 5, b g Magical Wonder (USA)—Avionne **Mr J. E. Gallagher**
8 **PIQUET**, 6, br m Mind Games—Petonellajill **Mr J. J. Bridger**
9 **TERRAQUIN (IRE)**, 4, b c Turtle Island (IRE)—Play The Queen (IRE) **Mr J. J. Bridger**
10 **TRIPTI (IRE)**, 4, b f Sesaro (USA)—Chatelsong (USA) **Mr W. Wood**
11 **ZINGING**, 5, b g Fraam—Hi Hoh (IRE) **Mr J. Jenner**

THREE-YEAR-OLDS

12 **CHARLIES PROFIT**, ch f Deploy—Care And Comfort **Mr Gayler William Chambers**
13 **COSTA DEL SOL (IRE)**, ch g General Monash (USA)—L'Harmonie (USA) **Life's a Beach**
14 **MUST BE SO**, b f So Factual (USA)—Ovideo **Mr Terry Thorn**

Other Owners: Miss Rachel Bridger, Mr P. J. Hague, Mrs J. E. Lunn, Mr Chris Marshall, Miss Jeanne Stamp, Mr Terry Thorn.

Assistant Trainer: Rachel Bridger

Amateur: Miss Donna Handley (9-7).

---

63 **MRS H. M. BRIDGES, Shaftesbury**
Postal: **Gears Mill, Shaftesbury, Dorset, SP7 0LT.**
Contact: PHONE **(01747) 852825**

1 **BALKIRK**, 7, ch g Selkirk (USA)—Balenare **Mrs H. M. Bridges**
2 **DARCEY MAE**, 6, b m Afzal—Belhelvie **Mrs H. M. Bridges**
3 **KATTEGAT**, 8, b g Slip Anchor—Kirsten **Mrs H. M. Bridges**
4 **SILVER SLEEVE (IRE)**, 12, b g Taufan (USA)—Sable Coated **Mrs H. M. Bridges**
5 **SOLO DANCER**, 6, ch m Sayaarr (USA)—Oiseval **Mrs H. M. Bridges**
6 **ST KILDA**, 7, b m Past Glories—Oiseval **Mrs H. M. Bridges**

Other Owners: Mrs R. C. Hayward.

Amateur: Miss Lucy Bridges (8-10).

64 MR D. G. BRIDGWATER, Winchcombe
Postal: **Slade Barn Farm, Pinnock, Winchcombe, Gloucestershire, GL54 5AX.**
Contact: **PHONE (01242) 609086/609233 FAX (01242) 609086 MOBILE (07831) 635817**

1 **AMUSEMENT**, 8, ch g Mystiko (USA)—Jolies Eaux **Daltagh Construction Ltd**
2 **BOSPHORUS**, 5, b g Polish Precedent (USA)—Ancara **Led Astray Again Partnership**
3 **CONSONANT (IRE)**, 7, ch g Barathea (USA)—Dinalina (FR) **The Rule Racing Syndicate**
4 **EGYPT POINT (IRE)**, 7, b g Jurado (USA)—Cherry Jubilee **Long Hill Partnership**
5 **ELLAMYTE**, 4, b f Elmaamul (USA)—Deanta In Eirinn **Mrs Mary Bridgwater**
6 **GILLESPIE (IRE)**, 5, b g Persian Bold—Share The Vision **The Rule Racing Syndicate**
7 **GOODTIMELADY (IRE)**, 10, br m Good Thyne (USA)—Peppardstownlady **Cheltenham Racing Ltd**
8 **HONOR ROUGE (IRE)**, 5, ch m Highest Honor (FR)—Ayers Rock (IRE) **Terry & Sarah Amos**
9 **ICEY RUN**, 4, b g Runnett—Polar Storm (IRE) **Miss V. Howard Evans**
10 **KEIMAR**, 5, b g Syrtos—Crimson Sol **Mrs Mary Bridgwater**
11 **KIEV (IRE)**, 4, b g Bahhare (USA)—Badrah (USA) **Terry & Sarah Amos**
12 **LASSER LIGHT (IRE)**, 4, b br g Inchinor—Light Ray **Miss S. Hill**
13 **MY CARAIDD**, 8, b m Rakaposhi King—Tochenka **Anita & Relton Minton**
14 **PUCKS WAY**, 5, b g Nomadic Way (USA)—Adventurous Lady **Miss E. E. Hill**
15 **RHETORIC (IRE)**, 5, b g Desert King (IRE)—Squaw Talk (USA) **Mr Alan A. Wright**
16 **RUN ON**, 6, b h Runnett—Polar Storm (IRE) **Miss V. Howard Evans**
17 **SLINKY MALINKY**, 6, b m Alderbrook—Winnie The Witch **The Cats Whiskers**
18 **SOCIETY PET**, 5, b m Runnett—Polar Storm (IRE) **Miss V. Howard Evans**
19 **THE BEDUTH NAVI**, 4, b c Forzando—Sweets (IRE) **Mr R. W. Neale**
20 **THE LADY WOULD (IRE)**, 5, ch m Woodborough (USA)—Kealbra Lady **Mr Alan A. Wright**
21 **TRUMPINGTON**, 5, ch m First Trump—Brockton Flame **Mr R. Paul Russell**
22 **YAKAREEM (IRE)**, 8, b g Rainbows For Life (CAN)—Brandywell **Mrs Mary Bridgwater**

Other Owners: Mrs S. P. Amos, Mr T. P. Amos, Mr C. L. Chatwin, Mr C. Cory, Mr Bill Joyce, Mr D. J. Mills, Mrs A. Minton, Mr W. R. Minton, Mr G. P. D. Walker.

65 MR G. F. BRIDGWATER, Claverdon
Postal: **The Rowans, 14 Shrewley Common, Shrewley, Warwickshire, CV35 7AP.**
Contact: **PHONE (01926) 840137 MOBILE (07769) 894400 E-MAIL bridgwater9@aol.com**

1 **EAGLE EYE BOY**, 10, b br g Roscoe Blake—Hayburnwyke **Mrs Gail Bridgwater**
2 **GEE BEE BOY**, 10, ch g Beveled (USA)—Blue And White **Woodnorton Hall - Evesham**
3 **ORO STREET (IRE)**, 8, b g Dolphin Street (FR)—Love Unlimited **Mrs Gail Bridgwater**
4 **PILIBERTO**, 4, br g Man of May—Briska (IRE) **Mr Les Muller**
5 **ROSSMAY (IRE)**, 7, b g Kasmayo—Ross Rag **Mrs Gail Bridgwater**
6 **VERIDIAN**, 11, b g Green Desert (USA)—Alik (FR) **Mr Les Muller**
7 **WINNIE FLIES AGAIN**, 8, b m Phardante (FR)—Winnie The Witch **Mrs Mary Bridgwater**

Other Owners: Mr J. O'Grady.

66 MR W. M. BRISBOURNE, Baschurch
Postal: **Ness Strange Stables, Great Ness, Shrewsbury, Shropshire, SY4 2LE.**
Contact: **PHONE (01743) 741536 OR 360 MOBILE (0780) 3019651**

1 **ADOBE**, 9, b g Green Desert (USA)—Shamshir **Mr P. R. Kirk**
2 **AL AWWAM**, 5, b g Machiavellian (USA)—Just A Mirage **Lynn Hammerton**
3 **ALI PASHA**, 5, b g Ali-Royal (IRE)—Edge of Darkness
4 **ALTHREY RULER (IRE)**, 11, b g Phardante (FR)—Keego's Aunt **Mr F. Lloyd**
5 **AMELIA (IRE)**, 6, b m General Monash (USA)—Rose Tint (IRE) **Mr Raymond McNeill**
6 6, Br m Saddlers' Hall (IRE)—Appealing **Mr K. Bennett**
7 **BACKWOODS**, 11, ch g In The Wings—Kates Cabin **Mr P. R. Kirk**
8 **BELLA PAVLINA**, 6, ch m Sure Blade (USA)—Pab's Choice **The Cartmel Syndicate**
9 **BEN HUR**, 5, b g Zafonic (USA)—Gayane **D. C. Rutter & H. Clewlow**
10 **BEVELLER**, 5, ch g Beveled (USA)—Klairover **Mr Nev Jones**
11 **BOB'S SHERIE**, 5, b m Bob's Return (IRE)—Sheraton Girl **Happy Times Ahead Partners**
12 **BRAVELY DOES IT (USA)**, 4, gr g Holy Bull—Vigors Destiny (USA) **Mr P. T. Williams**
13 **BUSCADOR (USA)**, 6, b g Crafty Prospector (USA)—Fairway Flag (USA) **Real Soda**
14 **CANTEMERLE (IRE)**, 4, b f Bluebird (USA)—Legally Delicious **Mr Ray Bailey**
15 **CAPER**, 4, b g Salse (USA)—Spinning Mouse **Mr & Mrs C. W. Wardle**
16 **CASHNEEM (IRE)**, 6, b g Case Law—Haanem **Law Abiding Citizens**

MR W. M. BRISBOURNE—continued

17 **CHAMPAIN SANDS (IRE)**, 5, b g Green Desert (USA)—Grecian Bride (IRE) **Mr G. W. Long**
18 **CHARLIE CHAPEL**, 5, b g College Chapel—Lightino **D. Shenton Syndicate**
19 **COLEHAM**, 6, b m Saddlers' Hall (IRE)—Katie Scarlett **Mr Barry Baggott**
20 **DARENEUR (IRE)**, 4, ch f Entrepreneur—Darayna (IRE) **Preece Haden Partners**
21 **DESERT ARC (IRE)**, 6, b g Spectrum (IRE)—Bint Albadou (IRE) **Mr Steve Roberts**
22 **DESERT QUILL (IRE)**, 4, ch f In The Wings—Aljood
23 **DINOFELIS**, 6, b g Rainbow Quest (USA)—Revonda (IRE) **Mr Mark Brisbourne**
24 **DISPOL VERITY**, 4, b f Averti (IRE)—Fawley Mist **Mr L. R. Owen**
25 **DOUBLE TURN**, 4, ch g Double Trigger (IRE)—Its My Turn **Mr G. Critchley**
26 **DUNN DEAL (IRE)**, 4, b g Revoque (IRE)—Buddy And Soda (IRE) **Mr Raymond McNeill**
27 **ELLOVAMUL**, 4, b f Elmaamul (USA)—Multi-Soft **Clayfields Racing**
28 **ELLWAY HEIGHTS**, 7, b g Shirley Heights—Amina **M.Gonzalez,A.Antonelli,D.Hopper,Preston**
29 **ESCALADE**, 7, b g Green Desert (USA)—Sans Escale (USA) **D. Slingsby**
30 **FORTUNA MEA**, 4, b f Mon Tresor—Veni Vici (IRE) **The Quorum**
31 **FRENCH RISK (IRE)**, 4, b g Entrepreneur—Troyes **Mrs Diane Tumman**
32 **GIUNCHIGLIO**, 5, ch g Millkom—Daffodil Fields **Mr J. Scott**
33 **GOLDBRICKER**, 4, b g Muhtarram (USA)—Sally Slade **Mr K. Bennett**
34 **GOLDEN COIN**, 8, ch g St Ninian—Legal Coin **Mr Bob Moseley**
35 **GOT TO BE CASH**, 5, ch m Lake Coniston (IRE)—Rasayel (USA) **Mrs B. Penton**
36 **GRADY**, 5, ch g Bluegrass Prince (IRE)—Lady Sabina **Mr W. M. Brisbourne**
37 **GREEN GINGER**, 8, ch g Ardkinglass—Bella Maggio **Mrs D. F. Garrett**
38 **HIRAYNA**, 5, b m Doyoun—Himaya (USA) **Preece Haden Partners**
39 **ICED DIAMOND (IRE)**, 5, b g Petardia—Prime Site (IRE) **Mr P. J. Williams**
40 **IFTIKHAR (USA)**, 5, b g Storm Cat (USA)—Muhbubh (USA) **Mr L. R. Owen**
41 **JIMJO**, 5, ch g Up And At 'em—Ushimado (IRE) **Mr A. Haydn**
42 **LADY RADMORE**, 5, b m Overbury (IRE)—Val's Jem **Mr J. R. Salter**
43 **LARK IN THE PARK (IRE)**, 4, ch f Grand Lodge—Jarrayan **Mia Racing**
44 **LAYASAR**, 4, br g Wizard King—Rasayel (USA) **Mrs B. Penton**
45 **LIEUDAY**, 5, b g Atraf—Figment **Mrs Sue Roberts**
46 **LIGHT THE DAWN (IRE)**, 4, ch f Indian Ridge—Flaming June (USA) **C. J. Partnership**
47 **LUXOR**, 7, ch g Grand Lodge (USA)—Escrime (USA) **Mia Racing**
48 **MAJOR ATTRACTION**, 9, gr g Major Jacko—Mr Friend Melody **Positive Partners**
49 **MERDIFF**, 5, b g Machiavellian (USA)—Balwa (USA) **Thats Racing Partnership**
50 **MERRYMAKER**, 4, b g Machiavellian (USA)—Wild Pavane **Black Toffee Partnership**
51 **MILK AND SULTANA**, 4, b f Millkom—Premier Princess **Mr D. M. Drury**
52 **MONSTER JAWBREAKER (IRE)**, 5, b g Zafonic (USA)—Salvora (USA) **J. T. S. (International) Ltd**
53 **MULTIPLOY**, 5, b m Deploy—Multi-Soft **D. Robson & A. Lynch**
54 **MURHILL'S PRIDE**, 6, b g Great Marquess—Penny's Wishing **Mr Mike Murray**
55 **OCTANE (USA)**, 8, b g Cryptoclearance (USA)—Something True (USA) **Mr K. Bennett**
56 **ONE A DACKIE**, 5, b m Lord Americo—Oriel Dream **Mr Jack Iddon**
57 **OPPORTUNE (GER)**, 8, b g Shirley Heights—On The Tiles **The Ox Hill Flyers**
58 **PAGE NOUVELLE (FR)**, 4, b f Spectrum (USA)—Page Bleue **Mr J. Sankey**
59 **PAVEMENT GATES**, 4, b f Bishop of Cashel—Very Bold **Mr M. Wynne-Jones**
60 **PENALTA**, 8, ch g Cosmonaut—Targuette **Mr John Smallman**
61 **PERUVIAN PRINCESS**, 5, gr m Missed Flight—Misty View **Ms Rosario Cornejo S. C.**
62 **POLLY PLUNKETT**, 4, b f Puissance—Expectation (IRE) **The C. J. Partnership**
63 **PURE MISCHIEF (IRE)**, 5, b g Alhaarth (IRE)—Bellissi (IRE) **The Cartmel Syndicate**
64 **RAINSTORM**, 9, b g Rainbow Quest (USA)—Katsina (USA) **C. M. & S. J. Owen**
65 **RANI TWO**, 5, b m Wolfhound (USA)—Donya **Mr B. L. Loader**
66 **RED SCORPION (USA)**, 5, ch g Nureyev (USA)—Pricket (USA) **Mrs E. M. Coquelin**
67 **REDSTAR ATTRACTION**, 6, ch g Nalchik (USA)—Star Gal **Magnate Racing**
68 **ROMAN MAZE**, 4, ch g Lycius (USA)—Maze Garden (USA) **The Jenko and Thomo Partnership**
69 **ROYAL INDULGENCE**, 4, b g Royal Applause—Silent Indulgence (USA) **Mr P. Evans**
70 **SAMUEL CHARLES**, 6, b g Green Desert (USA)—Hejraan (USA)
71 **SASPYS LAD**, 7, b g Faustus—Legendary Lady **Mr K. J. Oulton**
72 **SECRET'S OUT**, 8, b g Polish Precedent (USA)—Secret Obsession (USA) **Mr F. Lloyd**
73 **SMART JOHN**, 4, b g Bin Ajwaad (IRE)—Katy-Q (IRE) **Mr & Mrs D. J. Smart**
74 **SMIRFYS DANCE HALL (IRE)**, 4, b f Halling (USA)—Bigger Dances (USA) **Mrs Dian Plant**
75 **SMIRFYS SYSTEMS**, 5, b g Safawan—Saint Systems **Mrs Dian Plant**
76 4, B f Wizard King—State of Love **Mr Steve Parry**
77 **SUMMER SHADES**, 6, b m Green Desert (USA)—Sally Slade **Mr K. Bennett**
78 **TBM CAN**, 5, b g Rock City—Fire Sprite **Golden Furlong Racing**
79 **THE SPOOK**, 4, b g Bin Ajwaad (IRE)—Rose Mill
80 **TOKEWANNA**, 4, b f Danehill (USA)—High Atlas **Mr Steve Jennings**
81 **TRUSTED MOLE (IRE)**, 6, b g Eagled Eyed (USA)—Orient Air **Mr P. Evans**
82 **WHITE LEDGER (IRE)**, 5, ch g Ali-Royal (IRE)—Boranwood (IRE) **Mr A. Jones**

MR W. M. BRISBOURNE—continued

83 **YORK CLIFF**, 6, b g Marju (IRE)—Azm **Mr P. T. Williams**
84 **YOUNG IZZY**, 6, b m Superlative—Crab 'n Lobster (IRE)
85 **ZAHUNDA (IRE)**, 5, b m Spectrum (IRE)—Gift of Glory (FR) **The Nelson Pigs Might Fly Racing Club**
86 **ZOUCHE**, 4, b g Zamindar (USA)—Al Corniche (IRE) **Golden Furlong Racing**

THREE-YEAR-OLDS

87 **BEAVER DIVA**, b f Bishop of Cashel—Beaver Skin Hunter **Mr Stuart McPhee**
88 **BE MY ALIBI (IRE)**, ch f Daggers Drawn (USA)—Join The Party
89 **CALARA HILLS**, ch f Bluegrass Prince (IRE)—Atlantic Line **Mrs J. M. Russell**
90 **HARRIET (IRE)**, b f Grand Lodge (USA)—Accelerating (USA) **Mr J. Sankey**
91 **HI DARL**, ch f Wolfhound (USA)—Sugar Token **'We Believe In Miracles'**
92 **KUMARI (IRE)**, b f Desert Story (IRE)—Glow Tina (IRE) **Mr B. L. Loader**
93 **MILLY WATERS**, b f Danzero (AUS)—Chilly Waters **Mr J. Oldknow**
94 **MISKINA**, b f Mark of Esteem (IRE)—Najmat Alshemaal (IRE) **Black Toffee Partnership**
95 B f Danzero (AUS)—Petite Heritiere **Mr J. Oldknow**
96 **PRELUDE**, b f Danzero (AUS)—Dancing Debut **Mr Paul Burgoyne**
97 **ROYAL UPSTART**, b g Up And At 'em—Tycoon Tina **Mr Mark Brisbourne**
98 **SNOW CHANCE (IRE)**, ch f Compton Place—Snowscape **Mr K. Bennett**
99 **TURNER**, gr g El Prado (IRE)—Gaily Royal (IRE) **Mr M. Clare**

TWO-YEAR-OLDS

100 Ch f 20/2 Daggers Drawn (USA)—Amazona (IRE) (Tirol) (1500) **C. J. Partnership**
101 B f 7/5 Bettergeton—Flicker (Unfuwain (USA)) **Mr H. Clewlow**
102 Gr g 9/4 Cloudings (IRE)—Hill Farm Dancer (Gunner B) **Mr M. E. Hughes**
103 **IGNITION**, ch f 28/4 Rock City—Fire Sprite (Mummy's Game) (6200) **Mr M. F. Hyman**
104 **LADY SOLITAIRE**, b f 16/2 Mind Games—Natural Key (Safawan) (5000) **Mr John Smallman**
105 **MIRAGE PRINCE (IRE)**, ch g 20/4 Desert Prince (IRE)—
　　　　　　　　　　　　　Belle Bijou (Midyan (USA)) (10000) **Mr & Mrs D. J. Smart**
106 B g 30/3 Imperial Ballet (IRE)—No Tomorrow (IRE) (Night Shift (USA)) (2600)
107 B c 7/4 Fayruz—Opening Day (Day Is Done) (4000)
108 B f 21/4 Josr Algarhoud (IRE)—River of Fortune (IRE) (Lahib (USA)) (5000) **Lostford Manor Stud**
109 **SHARP N FROSTY**, bl g 12/3 Somayda (IRE)—Wily Miss (Teenoso (USA)) **Mr M. Wood**
110 **TAZZ**, b f 20/2 Priolo (USA)—Katy-Q (IRE) (Taufan (USA)) **Mr & Mrs D. J. Smart**
111 **ZENDARO**, b g 5/4 Danzero (USA)—Countess Maud (Mtoto) (6500) **Zen Partnership**

Other Owners: Mr M. Allsop, Mr T. D. Barson, Mr G. J. Baskott, Mr Christopher Chell, Mr P. Clare, Mr R. Edwards, Mr Colin Fitch, Mr James Hamer, Mr R. L. Hamer, Mr J. N. Harper, Mr Joseph Hogan, Mr M. E. Hughes, Mr J. W. Jenkins, Mr Arthur Lynch, Mrs Elaine Lynch, Mr D. Musgrave, Miss Sonia Nicholls, Mr A. Pitt, Mrs J. B. Pye, Miss B. E. Roberts, Mr David Robson, Mr J. Scott, Mr D. W. Sibson, Mr David N. Smith, Mr Dave Sutton, Mr J. F. Thomas, Mr A. Tickle, Mrs I. M. Tickle, Mr M. A. Tickle, Mr J. Tomlinson, Mr P. T. Williams, Mr Tony Wilson.

Assistant Trainer: Mrs Pam Brisbourne

Jockeys (Flat): G Baker (8-4), K Dalgleish (8-5), K Fallon (w.a.), S W Kelly (8-6), R Mullen (8-2). **Jockeys (NH):** A P McCoy (w.a.), R Thornton (10-0 w.a.). **Apprentices:** Paul Mulrennan (8-7), Ben Swarbrick (7-5). **Amateurs:** Mr Curtis Davies (8-10), Miss Diana Jones (9-3), Miss Katrina Rockey (9-7).

---

67   **MR C. E. BRITTAIN, Newmarket**
Postal: 'Carlburg', 49 Bury Road, Newmarket, Suffolk, CB8 7BY.
Contact: **OFFICE** (01638) 664347 **HOME** (01638) 663739 **FAX** (01638) 661744
MOBILE (07785) 302121 **E-MAIL** carlburgst@aol.com

1 **AMPOULE**, 5, b g Zamindar (USA)—Diamond Park (IRE) **Mr R. A. Pledger**
2 **BORREGO (IRE)**, 4, br c Green Desert (USA)—Pripet (USA) **Sheikh Marwan Al Maktoum**
3 **CAMP COMMANDER (IRE)**, 5, gr h Pennekamp (USA)—Khalatara (IRE) **A. J. Richards & S. A. Richards**
4 **CUDDLES (FR)**, 5, b m Anabaa (USA)—Palomelle (FR) **Mr A. J. Richards**
5 **DUTCH GOLD (USA)**, 4, ch c Lahib (USA)—Crimson Conquest (USA) **Sheikh Marwan Al Maktoum**
6 **INVADER**, 8, b h Danehill (USA)—Donya **Mr R. J. Swinbourne**
7 **LUNDY'S LANE (IRE)**, 4, b c Darshaan—Lunda (IRE) **Mr Saeed Manana**
8 **MEMBERSHIP (USA)**, 4, ch c Belong To Me (USA)—Shamisen **Mr Saeed Manana**
9 **MUHAREB (USA)**, 5, ch g Thunder Gulch (USA)—Queen of Spirit (USA) **Mr Saeed Manana**
10 **RAFFERTY (IRE)**, 5, ch g Lion Cavern (USA)—Badawi (USA) **Sheikh Marwan Al Maktoum**
11 **SANTANDO**, 4, b c Hernando (FR)—Santarem (USA) **Mr R. N. Khan**
12 **SHUSH**, 6, b g Shambo—Abuzz **Mrs C. E. Brittain**

MR C. E. BRITTAIN—continued

13 **TITIAN LASS**, 5, ch m Bijou d'Inde—Liebside Lass (IRE) **Mr Michael Clarke**
14 **WARRSAN (IRE)**, 6, b h Caerleon (USA)—Lucayan Princess **Mr Saeed Manana**

THREE-YEAR-OLDS

15 **ALBADI**, b c Green Desert (USA)—Lyrist **Mr Saeed Manana**
16 **AL SHUUA**, b f Lomitas—Sephala (USA) **Mr Saeed Manana**
17 **BAHIANO (IRE)**, ch c Barathea (IRE)—Trystero **Mr C. E. Brittain**
18 **BOXGROVE (FR)**, gr g Trempolino (USA)—Little Emily **Mr A. J. Richards**
19 **BUZZ BUZZ**, b f Mtoto—Abuzz **Mrs C. E. Brittain**
20 **CARLBURG (IRE)**, b g Barathea (IRE)—Ichnusa **Mr C. E. Brittain**
21 **CHERTSEY (IRE)**, ch f Medaaly—Cerisette (IRE) **Sheikh Marwan Al Maktoum**
22 **DAMI (USA)**, b f Dynaformer (USA)—Trampoli (USA) **Mr Saeed Manana**
23 **FLICKERING**, ch c Unfuwain (USA)—Warning Shadows (IRE) **Sheikh Marwan Al Maktoum**
24 **FORTHRIGHT**, b g Cadeaux Genereux—Forthwith **Wyck Hall Stud**
25 **FRAGRANT STAR**, gr f Soviet Star (USA)—Norfolk Lavender (CAN) **Mr C. E. Brittain**
26 **HE JAA (IRE)**, gr f Daylami (IRE)—Calpella **Mr Saeed Manana**
27 **MAZUNA (IRE)**, b f Cape Cross (IRE)—Keswa **Mr Saeed Manana**
28 **MENHOUBAH (USA)**, b f Dixieland Band (USA)—Private Seductress (USA) **Mr Saeed Manana**
29 **NASSIRA**, b f Singspiel (IRE)—Naskhi **Mr Saeed Manana**
30 **PAINTED MOON (USA)**, ch f Gone West (USA)—Crimson Conquest (USA) **Sheikh Marwan Al Maktoum**
31 **PARTY SPIN**, gr c Pivotal—Third Party **Mr Michael Clarke**
32 **PAYOLA (USA)**, b f Red Ransom (USA)—Bevel (USA) **Sheikh Marwan Al Maktoum**
33 **RIO DE JUMEIRAH**, b f Seeking The Gold (USA)—Tegwen (USA) **Abdullah Saeed BelHab**
34 **SHUHEB**, ch f Nashwan (USA)—Shimna **Mr Saeed Manana**
35 **SIERRA**, ch f Dr Fong (USA)—Warning Belle **Wyck Hall Stud**
36 **SYLVA ROYAL (IRE)**, gr f Royal Applause—Trim Star **Eddy Grimstead Ltd**
37 **TICERO**, ch c First Trump—Lucky Flinders **Mr J. S. Threadwell**

TWO-YEAR-OLDS

38 B f 16/2 King's Best (USA)—Allegheny River (USA) (Lear Fan (USA)) (40000) **Mr Saeed Manana**
39 B f 25/2 Daylami (IRE)—All Time Great (Night Shift (USA)) (27000) **Mr Saeed Manana**
40 B c 13/3 Singspiel (IRE)—Amber Fizz (USA) (Effervescing (USA)) **Mr Saeed Manana**
41 B c 23/1 Efisio—Arriving (Most Welcome) (25000) **Mr R. A. Pledger**
42 Ch f 22/4 Daylami (IRE)—Ascot Cyclone (USA) (Rahy (USA)) **Mr Mohammed Obaida**
43 B br c 13/2 Giant's Causeway—Aunt Pearl (USA) (Seattle Slew) **Mr Saeed Manana**
44 B c 15/5 Diktat—Badawi (USA) (Diesis) **Sheikh Marwan Al Maktoum**
45 **BAHAR SHUMAAL (IRE)**, b c 9/3 Dubai Millennium—High Spirited (Shirley Heights) **Mr Saeed Manana**
46 **CALIFORNIA GIRL**, ch f 9/3 Zafonic (USA)—Lady Georgia (Arazi) (USA)) **Mr A. J. Richards**
47 B f 27/4 Lemon Drop Kid (USA)—Celestial Bliss (USA) (Relaunch (USA)) **Mr Saif Ali**
48 Ch f 28/2 Dubai Millennium—Crimson Conquest (USA) (Diesis) **Sheikh Marwan Al Maktoum**
49 **DOCTOR'S CAVE**, b c 21/4 Night Shift (USA)—Periquitum (Dilum (USA)) (25000) **Mr A. J. Richards**
50 B f 9/2 Gone West (USA)—Fairy Garden (USA) (Lyphard (USA)) (32738) **Mr Saeed Manana**
51 B f 12/5 Kingmambo (USA)—Fairy Heights (IRE) (Fairy King (USA)) (53571) **Mr Saeed Manana**
52 B c 15/3 Distorted Humor (USA)—Fancy Ruler (USA) (Half A Year (USA)) **Winstar**
53 **FAVOURITA**, b f 4/3 Diktat—Forthwith (Midyan (USA)) **Wyck Hall Stud**
54 **GHASIBA (IRE)**, gr f 3/3 Daylami (IRE)—Night Owl (Night Shift (USA)) (54000) **Mr Saeed Manana**
55 Ch f 23/5 Machiavellian (USA)—Innocence (Unfuwain (USA)) (70000) **Mr Saif Ali**
56 Ch c 28/3 Entrepreneur—Kameez (IRE) (Arazi (USA)) **Mr Ali Saeed**
57 **KANDIDATE**, b c 15/4 Kabool—Valleyrose (IRE) (Royal Academy (USA)) (26000) **Mr A. J. Richards**
58 Ch c 23/4 Singspiel (IRE)—Love of Silver (USA) (Arctic Tern (USA)) **Mr Ali Saeed**
59 Ch c 18/2 Halling (USA)—Luana (Shaadi (USA)) (35000) **Mr Saeed Manana**
60 B f 30/1 Machiavellian (USA)—Lunda (IRE) (Soviet Star (USA)) (95000) **Mr Saeed Manana**
61 **MANSIYA**, ch f 8/5 Vettori (IRE)—Bay Shade (USA) (Sharpen Up) **Mr Saeed Manana**
62 B f 23/2 Lend A Hand—Mellow Jazz (Lycius (USA)) **Mr Saif Ali**
63 B f 5/4 Dansili—Mighty Flyer (IRE) (Mujtahid (USA)) (40000) **Mr Saeed Manana**
64 B f 18/4 Diktat—Military Tune (IRE) (Nashwan (USA)) (23000) **Mr Saeed Manana**
65 B f 12/3 Giant's Causeway—Mockery (Nashwan (USA)) (35000) **Mr Saeed Manana**
66 B f 28/2 Zafonic (USA)—Nefeli (First Trump) (40000) **Mr Saeed Manana**
67 **PARTY BOSS**, gr c 11/3 Silver Patriarch—Third Party (Terimon) (13000) **Mr Michael Clarke**
68 B c 3/6 King's Best (USA)—Place d'Honneur (FR) (Hero's Honor (USA)) (20000) **Mr Saif Ali**
69 B f 14/4 Fasliyev (USA)—Princess Amalie (USA) (Rahy (USA)) (12000) **Mr Saeed Manana**
70 **PUSSY CAT**, b f 10/3 Josr Algarhoud (IRE)—Swan Lake (FR) (Lyphard (USA)) **Mr A. J. Richards**
71 **RANSACKER**, b c 6/3 Bahamian Bounty—Hazy Heights (Shirley Heights) (25000) **Mr A. J. Richards**
72 B f 1/4 Silver Hawk (USA)—Ras Shaikh (USA) (Sheikh Albadou) **Mr Mohammed Obaida**
73 B f 3/2 Alhaarth (IRE)—Salul (Soviet Star (USA)) (14000) **Minister Enterprises**

MR C. E. BRITTAIN—continued

74 B c 12/2 Groom Dancer (USA)—Shady Point (IRE) (Unfuwain (USA)) **Sheikh Marwan Al Maktoum**
75 **SONNETTA,** b f 20/3 Indian Lodge (IRE)—Forum (Lion Cavern (USA)) **Wyck Hall Stud**
76 B f 24/4 Machiavellian (USA)—Sueboog (IRE) (Darshaan) **Mr Mohammed Obaida**
77 **SURREY WOODS (USA),** ch f 24/4 Rahy (USA)—Mediation (IRE) (Caerleon (USA)) (8929) **Mr Saif Ali**
78 **TONY JAMES (IRE),** b c 20/2 Xaar—Sunset Ridge (FR) (Green Tune (USA)) (13605) **Mr A. J. Richards**
79 **TOPIC,** br f 25/4 Vettori (IRE)—Dancing Spirit (IRE) (Ahonoora) (10000) **Wyck Hall Stud**
80 **TREBLE SEVEN (USA),** b br f 24/2 Fusaichi Pegasus—
Nemaa (The Minstrel (CAN)) (35714) **Mr Saeed Manana**
81 B c 15/3 Green Desert (USA)—Warning Shadows (IRE) (Cadeaux Genereux) **Sheikh Marwan Al Maktoum**
82 **YANKEY,** b c 6/3 Amfortas (IRE)—Key (Midyan (USA)) (3500) **Eddy Grimstead Ltd**
83 **YELLOW JERSEY,** b f 22/5 Mark Of Esteem (IRE)—La Bicyclette (FR) (Midyan (USA)) **Mr A. J. Richards**

68 MR M. A. BRITTAIN, Warthill
Postal: **Northgate Lodge, Warthill, York, YO19 5XR.**
Contact: **PHONE (01759) 371472 FAX (01759) 372915 E-MAIL email@melbrittain.co.uk**

1 **CONSENSUS (IRE),** 5, b m Common Grounds—Kilbride Lass (IRE) **Northgate Lodgers**
2 **DESIRES DESTINY,** 6, b m Grey Desire—Tanoda **Mr Mel Brittain**
3 **ETERNAL BLOOM,** 6, b m Reprimand—Forever Roses **Mr Mel Brittain**
4 **FELIDAE (USA),** 4, ch c Storm Cat (USA)—Colcon (USA) **Mr J. Jarvis**
5 **FIRST HARMONY,** 5, ch m First Trump—Enchanting Melody **Mr Mel Brittain**
6 **GLORY GIRL,** 4, ch f Factual (USA)—Glory Gold **Mr Mel Brittain**
7 **HOMERIC TROJAN,** 4, ch c Hector Protector (USA)—Housefull **Mr Barry Matthews**
8 **MEDALLA (FR),** 4, gr c Medaaly—Sharp Cracker (IRE)
9 **MELODIAN,** 9, b b Grey Desire—Mere Melody **Mr Mel Brittain**
10 **SANDORRA,** 6, b m Emperor Jones (USA)—Oribi **Mr Mel Brittain**
11 **SINDERBY,** 4, b f Factual (USA)—Tanoda **Mr Mel Brittain**
12 **STORMVILLE (IRE),** 7, b g Catrail (USA)—Haut Volee **Northgate Gold**
13 **TRINITY (IRE),** 8, b h College Chapel—Kaskazi **Miss Debi J. Woods**

TWO-YEAR-OLDS

14 B c 25/3 Grey Desire—Brief Star (IRE) (Brief Truce (USA))
15 B c 16/3 Grey Desire—Call Me Lucky (Magic Ring (IRE))
16 B f 13/2 Bahamian Bounty—Moly (Inchinor) (2000)
17 Ch f 20/3 Loup Sauvage (USA)—Rash (Pursuit of Love) (11000)
18 B f 30/1 Lujain (USA)—Talighta (USA) (Barathea (IRE)) (6200)
19 B c 12/4 Danzero (AUS)—Tarf (USA) (Diesis) (8000)

Other Owners: Mr J. Allan, Mrs I. Battla, Mr E. Bentham, Mrs S. C. Beswick, Mr Steven J. Box, Mrs C. M. Chambers, Mr K. T. Chambers, Mr L. Chambers, Mr P. Chambers, Mrs E. Charlesworth, Mr E. Clift, Miss J. F. Craze, Mr N. Dobbs, Mrs A. Foster, Mr M. Foster, Mr J. Gardner, Mr J. Gunn, Mr Richard Hardy, Mr A. Holmes, Miss S. King, Mr C. Knowles, Mr A. Pannett, Mr D. Parker, Mr C. Parks, Mrs L. Redhead, Mr B. Richards, Mr J. F. Richardson, Mrs S. Sim, Mr John Spencer, Mr M. J. Stannard, Mrs C. J. Taylor, Mr S. Taylor, Mr R. Upton, Mr Donald B. White, Mr N. Wilson, Mr John Winspear, Mr A. Wood.

Assistant Trainer: Neil Jordan (Head Lad)

Apprentice: Mark Lawson (7-13).

69 MR J. E. BROCKBANK, Carlisle
Postal: **Westward Park, Wigton, Cumbria, CA7 8AP.**
Contact: **PHONE (016973) 42391**

1 **BETABATIM (IRE),** 9, b g Alphabatim (USA)—Lucy Platter (FR) **Mr J. E. Brockbank**
2 **DISTRACTING,** 7, b m Royal Fountain—Icelandic Poppy **Mr J. E. Brockbank**
3 **ROYAL REFERENCE,** 8, br m Royal Fountain—Cross Reference **Mrs J. E. Brockbank**
4 **TRIVIAL (IRE),** 12, b m Rakaposhi King—Miss Rubbish **Mr T. Brockbank**

Assistant Trainer: Mrs C M Fitzgerald

Jockey (NH): Gino Carenza. **Amateurs:** Mr Luke Morgan, Mr Ranald Morgan.

70 MR R. S. BROOKHOUSE, Alcester
Postal: **Moor Hall Farm, Wixford, Alcester, Warwickshire, B49 6DL.**
Contact: **PHONE (01789) 778244**

1 **BLAZEAWAY (USA)**, 4, b br g Hansel (USA)—Alessia's Song (USA) **Mrs S. J. Brookhouse**
2 **HOPPERTREE**, 8, b g Rock Hopper—Snow Tree **Mr R. S. Brookhouse**
3 **LADY SANTANA (IRE)**, 7, b m Doyoun—Santana Lady (IRE) **Mrs S. J. Brookhouse**
4 **SHE'S THE LADY**, 4, b f Unfuwain (USA)—City of Angels **Mr R. S. Brookhouse**
5 **SOL CHANCE**, 5, ch g Jupiter Island—Super Sol **Mr R. S. Brookhouse**
6 **SOMEMANFORONEMAN (IRE)**, 10, b g Asir—Wintry Shower **Mr R. S. Brookhouse**
7 **THREE LIONS**, 7, ch g Jupiter Island—Super Sol **Mr R. S. Brookhouse**
8 **WIZARDTREE**, 5, ch g Presidium—Snow Tree **Mr R. S. Brookhouse**

Assistant Trainer: Liz Forletta

71 MR S. A. BROOKSHAW, Shrewsbury
Postal: **Preston Farm, Uffington, Shrewsbury, Shropshire, SY4 4TB.**
Contact: **PHONE (01743) 709227 FAX (01743) 709529 MOBILE (07973) 959986**
E-MAIL steve@brookshawracing.freeserve.co.uk

1 **BIT OF A GEM**, 8, b m Henbit (USA)—Krystle Saint **Mr D. J. Wheatley**
2 4, Ch f Classic Cliche (IRE)—Bowling Fort
3 **BUDE**, 5, gr g Environment Friend—Gay da Cheen (IRE) **Mr Laurie Briggs Jnr**
4 **CASHEL DANCER**, 5, b m Bishop of Cashel—Dancing Debut **Mr Ken Edwards**
5 **CASSIA HEIGHTS**, 9, b g Montelimar (USA)—Cloncoose (IRE) **Mr B. Ridge & Mr D. Hewitt**
6 **HOME MADE**, 6, b g Homo Sapien—Inch Maid **Mr S. A. Brookshaw**
7 **HOME TOR**, 7, b g Homo Sapien—Torus Queen **Miss H. Brookshaw**
8 **MAJOR BIT**, 8, b g Henbit (USA)—Cute Pam **Steven Brookshaw Racing Partnership I**
9 **MEENTAGH LOCH**, 7, ch g Never So Bold—Miss Pisces **Miss H. Brookshaw**
10 **PENNYAHEI**, 13, b m Malaspina—Pennyazena **Miss H. Brookshaw**
11 **POLLENSA BAY**, 5, b g Overbury (IRE)—Cloncoose (IRE) **Mr Ken Edwards**
12 **SILVER SAMUEL (NZ)**, 7, gr g Hula Town (NZ)—Offrande (NZ) **Redcroft Racing**
13 **SUSIE BURY**, 5, b m Overbury (IRE)—Susie's Money **The Highly Sociable Syndicate**
14 **TALBOT LAD**, 8, b g Weld—Greenacres Girl **Mr M. J. Talbot**
15 **THATCHERS LONGSHOT**, 7, ch g Gunner B—Formidable Lady **Mr S. A. Brookshaw**
16 **VALLEYMORE (IRE)**, 8, br g Jolly Jake (NZ)—Glamorous Brush (IRE) **T. G. K. Construction Ltd**
17 **WELSH WHISPER**, 5, b m Overbury (IRE)—Grugiar **Mr S. A. Brookshaw**

Other Owners: Mr Brian Davies, Mr D. I. Hewitt, Mrs S. A. Kenney, Mr R. Kent, Mr Arthur Phillips, Mrs Linda M. Powell, Mr B. Ridge, Mr Ian T. Smethurst.

Assistant Trainer: Heidi Brookshaw

72 MR R. BROTHERTON, Pershore
Postal: **Mill End Racing Stables, Netherton Road, Elmley Castle, Pershore, Worcestershire, WR10 3JF.**
Contact: **PHONE (01386) 710772 FAX (01386) 710772 MOBILE (07973) 877280**

1 **BAR OF SILVER (IRE)**, 4, ch g Bahhare (USA)—Shaping Up (USA) **Mr Roy Brotherton**
2 **BLAKESHALL QUEST**, 4, b f Piccolo—Corniche Quest (IRE) **Droitwich Jokers**
3 **BOJANGLES (IRE)**, 5, b g Danehill—Itching (IRE) **Mr Roy Brotherton**
4 **CLAPTRAP**, 4, b c Royal Applause—Stardyn **Miss Claire Stringer**
5 **INCA MOON**, 4, b f Sheikh Albadou—Incatinka **The Joiners Arms Racing Club Quarndon**
6 **KAMALA**, 5, b m Priolo (USA)—Fleeting Vision (IRE) **The Dirty Jumpers**
7 **KISS THE RAIN**, 4, b f Forzando—Devils Dirge **The Joiners Arms Racing Club Quarndon**
8 **MALMAND (USA)**, 5, ch g Distant View (USA)—Bidski (USA) **Carpe Diem Racing**
9 **NEUTRAL NIGHT (IRE)**, 4, b f Night Shift (USA)—Neutrality (IRE) **Mr Raymond N. R. Auld**
10 **RED DELIRIUM**, 8, b g Robellino (USA)—Made of Pearl (USA) **The Joiners Arms Racing Club Quarndon**
11 **SAVILE'S DELIGHT (IRE)**, 5, b g Cadeaux Genereux—Across The Ice (USA) **Mr Roy Brotherton**
12 **STAR LAD (IRE)**, 4, ch g Lake Coniston (IRE)—Simply Special (IRE) **Mr R. Austin & Mrs P. Austin**

MR R. BROTHERTON—continued
THREE-YEAR-OLDS

13 **UNINTENTIONAL**, b f Dr Devious (IRE)—Tamnia **Mr Raymond N. R. Auld**

Other Owners: Mrs P. Austin, Mr R. Austin, Mr A. Gandy, Mr Peter Guy, Mr J. R. Hall, Mr B. S. Harris, Mr R. S. Harris, Mr T. Martin, R. Smith, Mr M. J. Whitehall.

Jockey (Flat): I Mongan. **Jockey (NH):** W Marston. **Apprentice:** Luke Fletcher. **Amateur:** Mr Simon Walker.

---

73 | **MR G. BROWN, Hungerford**
Postal: Middle Pond, Ermin Street, Lambourn Woodlands, Hungerford, Berkshire, RG17 7BL.
Contact: PHONE (01488) 670071 FAX (01488) 670175 MOBILE (07785) 757090

1 **BLUE LEADER (IRE)**, 5, b g Cadeaux Genereux—Blue Duster (USA) **Mrs Amanda Killick**
2 **CAPTAIN HARDY (IRE)**, 5, b g Victory Note (USA)—Airey Fairy (IRE) **Mr A. King & Middle Pond Racing**
3 **GET THE POINT**, 10, b g Sadler's Wells (USA)—Tolmi **Berkshire Commercial Components Ltd**
4 **INIGO JONES (IRE)**, 8, b g Alzao (USA)—Kindjal **Mrs Amanda Killick**
5 **ISCA MAIDEN**, 10, b m Full Extent (USA)—Sharp N' Easy **Mrs C. A. Davies**
6 **MIDDLE POND**, 4, b g Relief Pitcher—Ketti **Berkshire Commercial Components Ltd**
7 **WATER KING (USA)**, 5, b g Irish River (FR)—Brookshield Baby (IRE) **Mrs Amanda Killick**

Conditional: James Peters. **Amateur:** James Davies.

---

74 | **MR I. R. BROWN, Bucknell**
Postal: The Royal George, Lingen, Bucknell, Shropshire, SY7 0DY.
Contact: PHONE (01544) 267322 FAX (01544) 267322
E-MAIL theroyalgeorge@lingen.fsbusiness.co.uk

1 **NOBLE PURSUIT (FR)**, 6, b g Pursuit of Love—Pipitina **Mr I. R. Brown**

Assistant Trainer: A. C. Brown

Amateur: Mr A Brown (9-7).

---

75 | **MISS A. E. BROYD, Crickhowell**
Postal: Penrhiw Farm, Llangenny, Crickhowell, Powys, NP8 1HD.
Contact: PHONE (01873) 812292 MOBILE (07885) 475492 E-MAIL alison.broyd@btopenworld.com

1 **MERITOCRACY (IRE)**, 6, b g Lahib (USA)—Merry Devil (IRE) **Miss Alison Broyd**

---

76 | **MISS M. P. BRYANT, Lewes**
Postal: Bevern Bridge Farm Cottage, South Chailey, Lewes, East Sussex, BN8 4QH.
Contact: PHONE (01273) 400638 MOBILE (07976) 217542

1 **BRYANTS ROONEY**, 8, ch g Prince Rooney (IRE)—Forever Blushing **Miss M. Bryant**
2 **FIRESIDE LEGEND (IRE)**, 5, b g College Chapel—Miss Sandman **Miss M. Bryant**
3 **FOREVER ROONEY**, 7, b g Prince Rooney (IRE)—Forever Blushing **Miss M. Bryant**
4 **NASONE (IRE)**, 13, b g Nearly A Nose (USA)—Skateaway **Miss M. Bryant**
5 **SPRINGER THE LAD**, 7, ch g Carlton (GER)—Also Kirsty **Miss M. Bryant**
6 **VICTORY SIGN (IRE)**, 4, b g Forzando—Mo Ceri **Miss M. Bryant**

---

77 | **MR R. H. BUCKLER, Bridport**
Postal: Melplash Court Farm, Melplash, Bridport, Dorset, DT6 3UH.
Contact: HOME (01308) 488318 FAX 488403 MOBILE (07785) 773957

1 **AIFUNG (IRE)**, 6, ch m Bigstone (IRE)—Palmyra (GER) **Mrs P. J. Buckler**
2 **ALFA SUNRISE**, 7, b g Alflora (IRE)—Gipsy Dawn **Mr Tony Fiorillo**
3 **ATALANTA SURPRISE (IRE)**, 7, ch g Phardante (FR)—Curragh Breeze **Mr Martyn Forrester**
4 **BASIL**, 11, br g Lighter—Thrupence **Mrs C. J. Dunn**
5 **BE MY OWN (IRE)**, 8, b g Lord Americo—No Slow **Mr R. H. Buckler**

MR R. H. BUCKLER—continued

6 **CLOUDY BLUES (IRE)**, 6, ro g Glacial Storm (USA)—Chataka Blues (IRE) **Mrs R. L. Haskins**
7 **FATHER D (IRE)**, 9, b g Mister Lord (USA)—Abraham Cross (IRE) **C. T. & A. Samways**
8 **GLACIAL EVENING (IRE)**, 8, b br g Glacial Storm (USA)—Cold Evening (IRE) **The Deadly Sins Partnership**
9 **HAIKAL**, 7, b g Owington—Magic Milly **The Crop Circle**
10 **HELIXIR DU THEIL (FR)**, 9, ch g Aelan Hapi (USA)—Manolette (FR) **The Manolettes**
11 **HERACLES**, 8, b g Unfuwain (USA)—La Masse **Mrs D. A. La Trobe**
12 **HE'S THE BOSS (IRE)**, 7, b g Supreme Leader—Attykee (IRE) **Mr M. J. Hallett**
13 **I HEAR THUNDER (IRE)**, 6, b g Montelimar (USA)—Carrigeen Gala **Mr Nick Elliott**
14 **JUST MUCKIN AROUND (IRE)**, 8, gr g Celio Rufo—Cousin Muck (IRE) **Twentyman**
15 **KEEPTHEDREAMALIVE**, 6, gr g Roselier (FR)—Nicklup **Mrs Mary Graves**
16 **KITIMAT**, 7, b g Then Again—Quago **The Eight Optimists**
17 **NATIVE CUNNING**, 6, b g Be My Native (USA)—Icy Miss **Mr Nick Elliott**
18 **PALOUSE (IRE)**, 8, gr g Toulon—Hop Picker (USA) **Woodland Flowers**
19 **PETEURESQUE (USA)**, 7, ch g Peteski (CAN)—Miss Ultimo (USA) **Woodland Flowers**
20 **PHAR CITY (IRE)**, 7, b g Phardante (FR)—Aunty Dawn (IRE) **Mrs T. Lewis**
21 **POYNTON HENRY (IRE)**, 8, b g Supreme Leader—Short Memories **The Desirables**
22 **REDBERRY HOLLY (IRE)**, 6, gr m Roselier (FR)—Solvia (IRE) **Mr R. H. Buckler**
23 **RIVER REINE (IRE)**, 5, br m Lahib (USA)—Talahari (IRE) **Mr L. G. Kimber**
24 **ROYAL FONTENAILLES (FR)**, 5, ch g Tel Quel (FR)—Sissi Fontenailles (FR) **The Ever Smiling Partnership**
25 **RUM POINTER (IRE)**, 8, b g Turtle Island (IRE)—Osmunda **Mr K. C. B. Mackenzie**
26 **TAKSINA**, 5, b m Wace (USA)—Quago **Mrs Timothy Lewis**
27 **UNSIGNED (USA)**, 6, b br g Cozzene (USA)—Striata (USA) **F. F. Racing Services Partnership II**
28 **WAREYTH (USA)**, 5, b br g Shuailaan (USA)—Bahr Alsalaam (USA) **Mr Chris Pugsley**
29 **WOZZECK**, 4, b g Groom Dancer (USA)—Opera Lover (IRE) **Mrs P. J. Buckler**

Other Owners: A. J. Cork, Mrs H. E. Shane, Mr K. Sobey, Mr M. A. Styles.

Assistant Trainer: Giles Scott (Head Lad)

Jockey (NH): B Hitchcott (10-0). **Conditional:** A Honeyball (9-11). **Amateur:** Mrs M Roberts (9-7).

 78

MR M. A. BUCKLEY, Stamford

Postal: **Potters Hill Stables, Morkery Lane, Castle Bytham, Stamford, Lincolnshire, NG33 4SP.**
Contact: **OFFICE (01780) 411158 FAX (01780) 410481 MOBILE (07808) 360488**

1 **ALDWYCH ARROW (IRE)**, 9, ch g Rainbows For Life (CAN)—Shygate **Mr M. A. Buckley**
2 **ARMAGNAC**, 6, b g Young Urn—Arianna Aldini **Mr C. C. Buckley**
3 **ASTON MARA**, 7, b g Bering—Coigach **Mrs D. J. Buckley**
4 **COME AWAY WITH ME (IRE)**, 4, b f Machiavellian (USA)—Vert Val (USA) **Mr C. C. Buckley**
5 **DISTANT COUSIN**, 7, b g Distant Relative—Tinaca (USA) **Mr C. C. Buckley**
6 **HAMPTON LUCY (IRE)**, 5, b m Anabaa (USA)—Riveryev (USA) **Mr C. C. Buckley**
7 **HIGH ESTEEM**, 8, b g Common Grounds—Whittle Woods Girl **Mrs N. W. Buckley & Mr G. N. Buckley**
8 **KITTYLEE**, 5, b m Bal Harbour—Courtesy Call **Fair Price Racing**
9 **LA TORTUGA**, 7, b g Turtle Island (IRE)—Ville Sainte (FR) **Mr Raymond Roberts**
10 **LAW MAKER**, 4, b g Case Law—Bo' Babbity **Mr Brian Cann**
11 **MABEL RILEY (IRE)**, 4, b f Revoque (IRE)—Mystic Dispute (IRE) **X8 Racing**
12 **PEYTO PRINCESS**, 6, b br m Bold Arrangement—Bo' Babbity **North Cheshire Trading & Storage Ltd**
13 **RETAIL THERAPY (IRE)**, 4, b f Bahhare (USA)—Elect (USA) **Mr C. C. Buckley**
14 **RIVER LARK (USA)**, 5, b m Miswaki (USA)—Gold Blossom (USA) **Mr M. A. Wright**
15 **ROAR WITH ME**, 6, gr m Arzanni—Courtesy Call **The Roaring Partnership**

THREE-YEAR-OLDS

16 **BARHOLM CHARLIE**, b g Atraf—Lady-H **The High Hopers**
17 **CONVINCE (USA)**, ch g Mt Livermore (USA)—Conical **Mr C. C. Buckley**
18 **LEZARA**, b f Aragon—Lezayre **Mr T. Marshall**
19 **TIZZY'S LAW**, b f Case Law—Bo' Babbity **North Cheshire Trading & Storage Ltd**

TWO-YEAR-OLDS

20 B f 6/5 Namaqualand (USA)—Bo' Babbity (Strong Gale) (2000) **North Cheshire Trading & Storage Ltd**
21 **CILLA'S SMILE**, b f 25/3 Lake Coniston (IRE)—Tinkerbird (Music Boy) **Mr J. Cleeve**
22 B f 10/3 Machiavellian (USA)—Speak Softly To Me (USA) (Ogygian (USA))
23 **XEIGHT EXPRESS (IRE)**, b f 7/3 Ashkalani (IRE)—Believing (Belmez (USA)) (5500) **X8 Racing**

Other Owners: Mr J. K. Ebbrell, Mr D. A. Leaton, Mr G. Lee, Mr D. J. Lockwood, Mrs C. M. Price, Mr N. M. Price.

79 MR W. D. BURCHELL, Ebbw Vale

Postal: Drysiog Farm, Briery Hill, Ebbw Vale, Gwent, NP23 6BU.
Contact: PHONE (01495) 302551 MOBILE (07980) 482860 FAX (01495) 352464
WEBSITE www.burchelldairuth@aol

1 **ADALPOUR (IRE)**, 6, b g Kahyasi—Adalya (IRE) **Lewis Racing**
2 **ALSYATI**, 6, ch g Salse (USA)—Rubbiyati **Mrs Linda Cognet**
3 **CHOCO ROCO**, 7, b g Faustus (USA)—Leilaway **The Cross Crusaders**
4 **FLAHIVE'S FIRST**, 10, ch g Interrex (CAN)—Striking Image (IRE) **Mr Don Gould**
5 **FORZACURITY**, 5, ch g Forzando—Nice Lady **Mr Don Gould**
6 **KING DAVID**, 5, b g Distant Relative—Fleur Rouge **Mr Brian Williams**
7 **LUNAR LORD**, 8, b g Elmaamul (USA)—Cache **Mr Brian Williams**
8 **MAGENTA RISING (IRE)**, 4, ch f College Chapel—Fashion Queen **Mr P. S. & Mrs N. G. Pritchard**
9 **NICK'S CHOICE**, 8, b g Sula Bula—Clare's Choice **Mr Don Gould**
10 **OUR DESTINY**, 6, b g Mujadil (USA)—Superspring **Three Acres Racing**
11 **PHARLY REEF**, 12, b g Pharly (FR)—Hay Reef **Mrs Ruth Burchell**
12 **STONEHENGE (IRE)**, 7, b g Caerleon (USA)—Sharata (IRE) **Three Acres Racing**
13 **TAFFRAIL**, 5, b g Slip Anchor—Tizona **Mr P. S. & Mrs N. G. Pritchard**
14 **WESLEY'S LAD (IRE)**, 10, b br g Classic Secret (USA)—Galouga (FR) **Mr Brian Williams**

Other Owners: Ms J. A. Evans, Mr A. Lewis, Mr B. T. Price, Mrs Maureen Price.

Assistant Trainer: Ruth Burchell

Jockey (Flat): R Price (8-6). **Jockey (NH):** A Scholes. **Amateurs:** Miss Emily Jones, Miss Eliza Tucker, Mr Nick Williams.

80 MR P. V. J. BURGOYNE, Marlborough

Postal: Fairmile Stables, Herridge, Collingbourne Ducis, Marlborough, Wiltshire, SN8 3EG.
Contact: PHONE (01264) 850088 FAX (01264) 850912 MOBILE (07796) 256060
E-MAIL andyhaines7@hotmail.com

1 **CADWALLADER (USA)**, 4, ch g Kingmambo (USA)—Light On Your Feet (USA) **Andrew Haynes Racing Ltd**
2 **COUNT ON US**, 4, ch g Danehill Dancer (IRE)—Capricious Lady (IRE) **Abacus Employment Services Ltd**
3 **KINGS TOPIC (USA)**, 4, ch g Kingmambo (USA)—Topicount (USA) **Topics Tarts**
4 **MAYERLING**, 7, b m Old Vic—Manon Lescaut **The Moonrakers**
5 **SENOR TORAN (USA)**, 4, b g Baratea (USA)—Applaud (USA) **Abacus Employment Services Ltd**

TWO-YEAR-OLDS

6 B c 18/4 Victory Note (USA)—Eurolink Virago (Charmer) (8000)
7 B c 27/4 Spectrum (IRE)—Fey Lady (IRE) (Fairy King (USA)) (5000)
8 **JUST COLIN (IRE)**, b c 3/3 Shinko Forest (IRE)—
Peaches And Cream (FR) (Rusticaro (FR)) **Dennis & Barbara Fuller**
9 **LITTLE MISS GRACIE**, gr f 22/4 Efisio—
Circled (USA) (Cozzene (USA)) (9000) **Abacus Employment Services Ltd**

Other Owners: Mr D. Barnes, Ms C. Berry, Mr J. R. Winward.

Assistant Trainer: Mr Andrew Haynes

81 MR K. R. BURKE, Leyburn

Postal: Spigot Lodge, Middleham, Leyburn, North Yorkshire, DL8 4TL.
Contact: PHONE (01969) 625088 FAX (01969) 625099 E-MAIL karl@karlburke.co.uk

1 **ACHILLES RAINBOW**, 5, ch g Deploy—Naughty Pistol (USA) **Mrs E. Burke**
2 **ARCTIC CHALLENGE (IRE)**, 10, b g Glacial Storm (USA)—Ruckinge Girl **Mr I. & Mrs A. Russell**
3 **BANUTAN (IRE)**, 4, b f Charnwood Forest (IRE)—Banariya (USA) **Kildare Racing Club**
4 **BLUE SKY THINKING (IRE)**, 5, b g Danehill Dancer (IRE)—Lauretta Blue (IRE) **Triple Trio Partnership**
5 **CASTLEBRIDGE**, 7, b g Batshoof—Super Sisters (AUS) **Mr P. Sweeting**
6 **CHISPA**, 4, b m Imperial Frontier (USA)—Digamist Girl (IRE) **Mrs Elaine M. Burke**
7 **COUNTYKAT (IRE)**, 4, b g Woodborough (USA)—Kitty Kildare (USA) **Mr I. Russell**
8 **DAINTREE AFFAIR (IRE)**, 4, b g Charnwood Forest (IRE)—Madam Loving **Mr P. Sweeting**
9 **ERRACHT**, 6, gr m Emarati (USA)—Port Na Blath **Mr P. Sweeting**
10 **FREE STYLE (GER)**, 4, ch f Most Welcome—Furiella **Mr P. Sweeting**

MR K. R. BURKE—continued

11 **HARRY POTTER (GER)**, 5, br g Platini (GER)—Heavenly Storm (USA) **Mrs E. Burke**
12 **INCHCOONAN**, 6, b m Emperor Jones (USA)—Miss Ivory Coast (USA) **Mr David McKenzie**
13 **JAGGED (IRE)**, 4, b g Sesaro (USA)—Latin Mass **The Jagged Partnership**
14 **MILLION PERCENT**, 5, b g Ashkalani (USA)—Royal Jade **Platinum Racing Club Limited**
15 **MR SPLIFFY (IRE)**, 5, b g Fayruz—Johns Conquerer (USA) **Mrs Elaine M. Burke**
16 **PARTY PLOY**, 6, b g Deploy—Party Treat (IRE) **Mr Ian A. McInnes**
17 **PLAYTIME BLUE**, 4, b g Komaite (USA)—Miss Calculate **Mr P. Sweeting**
18 **RADIANT BRIDE**, 4, ch f Groom Dancer (USA)—Radiancy (IRE) **Mrs E. Goodwin**
19 **REX ROMELIO**, 5, ch g Priolo (USA)—Romelia (USA) **Mr Draper**
20 **SOLLER BAY**, 7, b g Contract Law (USA)—Bichette **Mrs M. Bryce**
21 **STAGNITE**, 4, ch g Compton Place—Superspring **Mr P. Sweeting**
22 **SWIFT ALCHEMIST**, 4, b f Fleetwood (IRE)—Pure Gold **The Kennet Connection**
23 **TAKES TUTU (USA)**, 5, b g Afternoon Deelites (USA)—Lady Affirmed (USA) **Bigwigs Bloodstock**
24 **TINIAN**, 6, b g Mtoto—Housefull **Mrs E. Goodwin**
25 **VELVET RHYTHM**, 4, b f Forzando—Bold Gayle **Mr David McKenzie**
26 **WOODBURY**, 5, b m Woodborough (USA)—Jeewan **Mr P. Sweeting**

THREE-YEAR-OLDS

27 **A LITTLE BIT YARIE**, b g Paris House—Slipperose **Reds 4 Racing**
28 **BABY COME BACK**, b f Fayruz—Ide Say (IRE) **Mr C. Dower**
29 **BLUE POWER (IRE)**, b c Zieten (USA)—La Miserable (USA) **Mr F. Jeffers**
30 **CAPETOWN GIRL**, b f Danzero (AUS)—Cavernista **Danum Racing**
31 **DARING AFFAIR**, b f Bien Bien (USA)—Daring Destiny **Mr Nigel Shields**
32 **HIGH VOLTAGE**, ch g Wolfhound (USA)—Real Emotion (USA) **Mrs K. Halsall**
33 **IMPERIALISTIC (IRE)**, b f Imperial Ballet (IRE)—Shefoog **Bigwigs Bloodstock**
34 **MARCUS EILE (IRE)**, b c Daggers Drawn (USA)—Sherannda (USA) **Mr Denis Fehan**
35 **MILITARY TWO STEP (IRE)**, b g General Monash (USA)—Con Dancer **Mr M. Nelmes Crocker**
36 **PLATINUM PIRATE**, b g Merdon Melody—Woodland Steps **Platinum Racing Club Limited**
37 **QUIRKIE (IRE)**, b f Revoque (IRE)—Unheard Melody **Mr Scott Quirk**
38 **SAVERNAKE BRAVE (IRE)**, b c Charnwood Forest (IRE)—Jordinda (IRE) **Mr P. Sweeting**
39 **SCOTTISH EXILE (IRE)**, b f Ashkalani (IRE)—Royal Jade **Mrs Melba Bryce**
40 **SHANK ON FOURTEEN (IRE)**, b g Fayruz—Hever Rosina **Mr L. Westwood**
41 **SILVER RHYTHM**, ch f Silver Patriarch (IRE)—Party Treat (IRE) **Mr Ian A. McInnes**
42 B g Bien Bien (USA)—Tiama (IRE) **Mr F. Jeffers**
43 **WARES HOME (IRE)**, b c Indian Rocket—Pepilin **Mrs Y. Goodwin**
44 **YAMATO PINK**, ch c Bijou d'Inde—Time Or Never (FR) **Mr P. Sweeting**
45 **ZONNEBEKE**, b f Orpen (USA)—Canlubang **Mr John A. Duffy**

TWO-YEAR-OLDS

46 B f 25/2 Imperial Ballet (IRE)—Almasi (IRE) (Petorius) (800) **Mr J. Wilson Bloodstock**
47 Br f 20/3 Indian Lodge (IRE)—Arjan (IRE) (Paris House) **Mrs E. Burke**
48 B c 28/2 Orpen (USA)—Ballinlee (IRE) (Skyliner) (1000) **Mr M. Johnson**
49 B c 20/4 Fasliyev (USA)—Colchica (Machiavellian) (USA) (27000) **Mr C. Bryce**
50 B c 26/2 Rossini (USA)—Con Dancer (Shareef Dancer) (USA) (20000) **Mrs S. Jones**
51 B f 22/2 Robellino (USA)—Denial (Sadler's Wells (USA) (27000) **Mr M. Nelmes Crocker**
52 B f 24/4 Monashee Mountain—Forest Berries (IRE) (Thatching) (8657) **Mrs E. Burke**
53 Ch f 19/4 Raise A Grand (IRE)—Hever Rosina (Efisio) (8039) **Mrs E. Burke**
54 **HIGH MINDED**, b c 17/5 Mind Games—Pips Way (IRE) (Pips Pride) (21000) **Mr P. McCaughey**
55 Ch c 13/2 Bahamian Bounty—Indian Flag (Indian Ridge) **Mr P. Sweeting**
56 B c 30/4 General Monash (USA)—Jacobina (Magic Ring (IRE)) (2500) **Mr J. Wilson Bloodstock**
57 B c 17/3 Desert Style (IRE)—Mauras Pride (IRE) (Cadeaux Genereux) (1000) **Mr J. Wilson Bloodstock**
58 Br f 12/5 Environment Friend—Michelee (Merdon Melody)
59 Ch c 24/4 Daggers Drawn (USA)—Polaregina (FR) (Rex Magna (FR)) (10000) **Mr P. Sweeting**
60 Gr c 24/4 Paris House—Slipperose (Persepolis (FR)) (7000) **Mrs Sally Jones**
61 B f 9/3 Xaar—Topwinder (USA) (Topsider) (7500) **Mrs S. Jones**
62 Br f 6/4 Diktat—Waft (USA) (Topsider (USA)) (3000) **Mr J. Wilson Bloodstock**
63 B f 22/4 Komaite (USA)—Zamarra (Clantime) (6000) **Mrs E. Burke**
64 B c 2/4 Bold Fact (USA)—Zara's Birthday (IRE) (Waajib) (11500) **Mrs E. Burke**

Other Owners: J. C. Buchanan, Mr L. Clarke, Mr R. Dufficy, Mr R. W. Floyd, Mr Richard Hoiles, Mr F. O'Sullivan, Mrs A. Russell, Mr G. P. Townsend.

Assistant Trainer: Mrs E. Burke & Mrs H. Sweeting

Jockey (Flat): D Williams. **Apprentices:** R Keogh, A Reilly (8-0). **Amateurs:** Haley Clements (9-0), Mr Scott Dobson (9-0).

82 MR JAMES G. BURNS, Curragh

Postal: Landfall Paddocks, The Curragh, Co. Kildare, Ireland.
Contact: PHONE +353 (0) 45 441811 FAX +353 (0) 45 441213 MOBILE +353 (0) 86 8201212
E-MAIL landfall@eircom.net

1 **BELALZAO (IRE)**, 4, b f Alzao (USA)—Northumbrian Belle (IRE) **Paddy Doyle**
2 **BROGELLA (IRE)**, 4, b f Kings Theatre (IRE)—Metroella (IRE) **M. J. Manrahan**
3 **DANECARE (IRE)**, 4, b c Danetime (IRE)—Nordic Flavour (IRE) **Jim Carey**
4 **DOLPHIN BAY (IRE)**, 4, b c Dolphin Street (FR)—Stella Ann **Miss R Tonson-Rye**
5 **LEPIDUS (IRE)**, 7, br g Bob's Return (IRE)—Lepida **Miss Roseleen Tonson-Rye**
6 **MATADORA (IRE)**, 4, b f Kris—Sarah Stokes (IRE) **Mr Anthony Rogers**
7 **PEAK FARE (IRE)**, 4, b f Sri Pekan (USA)—City Imp (IRE) **William Fenlon**
8 **RED TITIAN (IRE)**, 4, ch f Titus Livius (FR)—Dauntess **Mrs Gemma Doyle**
9 **RIFFLE (FR)**, 4, b f Octagonal (NZ)—Delve (IRE) **Nigel Elwes**
10 **THEATRE STAR (USA)**, 4, b f Theatrical—Birmingham Express (USA) **James G. Burns**
11 **TURGESIUS (USA)**, 4, b c Ghazi (USA)—Makati (USA) **Owen Kiernan**

THREE-YEAR-OLDS

12 **ALEXANDER DUCHESS (IRE)**, b f Desert Prince (IRE)—Lionne **Mrs Noel O'Callaghan**
13 **ANNITAS DREAM (IRE)**, b f Desert Prince (IRE)—Divine Pursuit **Michael A. Ryan**
14 **ASHKADIMA (IRE)**, gr f Ashkalani (IRE)—Muqaddima (FR) **Ann Marie Hayes**
15 **ASTRILLE (IRE)**, b f Bahhare (USA)—Miss Dolly (IRE)
16 **CAPE FLATERY (IRE)**, b f Cape Cross (IRE)—Ayers Rock (IRE) **David O'Reilly**
17 **CHARMED FOREST (IRE)**, b f Shinko Forest (IRE)—Charmed Lady **Sean O'Keeffe**
18 **DESERT STREAM (IRE)**, ch c Desert Sun—Prime Site (IRE) **Owen McElroy**
19 **FIINA**, ch f Most Welcome—Finlandaise (FR) **Janet Chaplin**
20 **HASTY GIRL (IRE)**, b f Desert Sun—Fantasie (FR) **Tom Connolly**
21 **HEAVENS HELP (USA)**, b f Royal Academy (USA)—Heaven's Command **Lady O'Reilly**
22 **INSPECTORS CHOICE (IRE)**, ch f Spectrum (IRE)—Morcote (USA) **Ballylinch Stud**
23 **JINSKYS GIFT (IRE)**, gr f Cadeaux Genereaux—Majiinskaya (FR) **Ballylinch Stud**
24 **MRS ST GEORGE (IRE)**, b f Orpen—Tamarzana (IRE) **M. A. Kilduff**
25 **ROCHETTO (IRE)**, ch f Indian Rocket—Romangoddess (IRE) **Mrs J. A. Dene**
26 **ROSY DUDLEY (IRE)**, ch f Grand Lodge (USA)—Renzola **Mrs Eleanor Kent**
27 **SALLY (IRE)**, ch f Soviet Star (USA)—Shining Creek (CAN) **Miss Stephanie Von Schilcher**
28 **SOUTHERN BOUND (IRE)**, b f Fasliyev (USA)—Headrest **Mr G. T. Ryan**
29 **STRAYCAT STRUT (IRE)**, b c Fasliyev (USA)—Sister Golden Hair (USA) **Sean Burke**
30 **VADE RETRO (IRE)**, b f Desert Sun—Mevlana (IRE) **Edel Moloney**
31 **VICKY LANE**, b f Victory Note (USA)—City Imp (IRE) **Tim I. Naughton**
32 **VIKING STAR (IRE)**, ch c Indian Rocket—Nordic Flavour (IRE) **Jim Carey**

TWO-YEAR-OLDS

33 **BROSNA BELLE (IRE)**, b f 20/2 Imperial Ballet (IRE)—
  Northumbrian Belle (IRE) (Distinctly North (USA)) (24737) **M. A. Kilduff**
34 **CHAMPAGNE SPARKLE (IRE)**, b f 13/4 Sadler's Wells (USA)—Champagne Girl (Robellino (USA))
  John McEnery
35 **ETOILE D'INDE (IRE)**, ch f 25/2 Indian Rocket—Safe Home (Home Guard (USA)) (4328) **Jerry Hennessy**
36 **FOOL'S PENNY**, b f 18/4 Boundary (USA)—Abscond (Unbridled (USA)) (12000) **Max Ervine**
37 **GLINTING DESERT (IRE)**, b f 28/3 Desert Prince (IRE)—Dazzling Park (IRE) (Warning) **Mr Seamus Burns**
38 **GOLDEN DEW (IRE)**, b f 13/2 Montjeu (IRE)—Golden Cat (USA) (Storm Cat (USA)) **Mr G. W. Jennings**
39 Gr f 11/3 Orpen—Ikala (Lashkari) (9276) **James Carey**
40 B f 11/3 Raise A Grand (IRE)—Moto (Mtoto) (3710) **Jim Nicholson**
41 **LA PRIOLA (IRE)**, b f 29/3 Priola (USA)—Canadian Girl (IRE) (Rainbows For Life (CAN)) **Marco Valade**
42 B f 29/5 Rossini (USA)—Mafiosa (Miami Springs) (370) **Mrs T. P. Burns**
43 **ON TIME ARRIVAL (USA)**, ch f 29/1 Devil's Bag (USA)—
  St Agnes (USA) (St Jovite (USA)) (16079) **James G. Burns**
44 **PELICAN BAY (IRE)**, ch f 8/5 Night Shift (USA)—Capegulch (USA) (Gulch (USA)) (6183) **Mr G. W. Jennings**
45 B f 16/3 Revoque (IRE)—Preponderance (IRE) (Cyrano de Bergerac) (11131) **Colman O'Flynn**
46 B f 31/1 Diktat—Sadly Sober (IRE) (Roi Danzig (USA)) (24000) **Max Ervine**
47 B f 25/3 Elnadim (USA)—Style N' Elegance (USA) (Alysheba (USA)) (16079) **Mr G. W. Jennings**
48 B f 31/3 Tagula (IRE)—Summerhill (Habitat) (6183) **James G. Burns**
49 B f 31/1 Intikhab (USA)—Twin Logic (IRE) (Diesis) (13604) **Jack Hamilton**
50 Ch c 12/4 Night Shift (USA)—Virtue Rewarded (IRE) (Darshaan) (13604) **Colm Gavin**

MR JAMES G. BURNS—continued

51 B f 22/3 Majru (IRE)—Walting Matilda (Mujtahid (USA)) **Jim Nicholson**
52 **WHITESHADEOFPALE (IRE)**, gr f 5/4 Definate Article—Krayyalei (IRE) (Krayyan) (9276) **Lady O'Reilly**

Other Owners: Dermot Cantillon, Gerard Cullen, John McGuire, J. P. M. O'Connor Mrcvs, Michael Tolan.

Assistant Trainer: Martin Brew (Head Man) & Kenneth Egan (Head man)

Jockey (Flat): P A Carberry (8-11). **Amateur:** Mr J D Moore (w.a.).

---

83   **MR S. C. BURROUGH, Wellington**
Postal: **Gringles Farm, West Buckland, Wellington, Somerset, TA21 9LE.**
Contact: **PHONE/FAX (01823) 666837 MOBILE (07887) 958131**

1 ABILITY, 5, b g Alflora (IRE)—Beatle Song **Mrs Christine Priest**
2 ALGYMO, 4, b f Tamure (IRE)—Red Point **Mrs Maureen Emery**
3 BASSANO (USA), 10, b h Alwasmi (USA)—Marittima (USA) **Mrs Christine Priest**
4 BENNANABAA, 5, b g Anabaa (USA)—Arc Empress Jane (IRE) **Mr & Mrs Charles Hill**
5 BERENGARIO (IRE), 4, b g Mark of Esteem (IRE)—Ivrea **Mrs Deborah Potter**
6 BOLD CENTURY, 7, b g Casteddu—Bold Green (FR) **Hill, Kemp and Hill**
7 CHARLIES FUTURE, 6, b g Democratic (USA)—Faustelerie **Mr M. L. Lewis-Jones**
8 CHITA'S FLIGHT, 4, gr f Busy Flight—Chita's Cone **Mr Ivor Ham**
9 DEEP QUEST, 5, b g El Conquistador—Ten Deep **Five Deep Partnership**
10 IMTIHAN (IRE), 5, ch h Unfuwain (USA)—Azyaa **Mrs Christine Priest**
11 IN TUNE, 4, b c Distinctly North (USA)—Lingering **Mr Charles Hill**
12 KALUGA (IRE), 6, ch m Tagula (IRE)—Another Baileys **Mrs Christine Priest**
13 LADY MERCURY, 6, b m Rock Hopper—Bellezza **Allen and Bowler**
14 MENDIP MANOR, 6, b g Rakaposhi King—Broughton Manor **Mr Rob Croker**
15 MIDNIGHT SPIRIT, 4, b g Midnight Legend—West-Hatch-Spirit **Mr & Mrs Underhill**
16 MINSTER PARK, 5, b g Minster Son—Go Gipsy **The Three Diamonds Partnership**
17 MULAN PRINCESS (IRE), 4, b f Mukaddamah (USA)—Notley Park **Mr & Mrs Charles Hill and Mr Ray Moody**
18 MURTAKEZ, 4, b g Alhaarth (IRE)—Raaqiyya (USA) **Mr Martin Smith (Frome)**
19 NO SAM NO, 6, b m Reprimand—Samjamalifran **Mr G. Regan**
20 PAMELA ANSHAN, 7, b m Anshan—Have Form **Mrs Christine Priest**
21 SOMO (IRE), 6, b h Exit To Nowhere (USA)—Alathezal (USA) **Mrs Alison Batchelor**
22 STANS MAN CAN, 6, gr g Arzanni—Tais Toi **Mr Cliff Gaylard & Sara Ellis**
23 4, B f El Conquistador—Ten Deep **Mr Greg Knight**
24 TWOTENSFORAFIVE, 11, b g Arctic Lord—Sister of Gold **Mrs Christine Priest**
25 WIGMO PRINCESS, 5, ch m Factual (USA)—Queen of Shannon (IRE) **Mrs Christine Priest**

TWO-YEAR-OLDS

26 BRACKENORAH, b f 25/4 Double Trigger (IRE)—Little Preston (IRE) (Pennine Walk) (571) **Mr John Beer**
27 IAM FOREVERBLOWING, ch f 20/3 Dr Fong (USA)—Farhana (Fayruz) (23000) **Mrs Christine Priest**
28 MAKE IT HAPPEN NOW, b b r f 14/3 Octagonal (NZ)—
             Whittle Woods Girl (Emarati (USA)) (13000) **Mrs Christine Priest**
29 TROUBLESOME GERRI, b f 7/5 Thowra (FR)—Sid's Pretence (Southern Music) **Mr Les Browning**

Other Owners: Mr N. G. Allen, Mr P. O. Bowler, Miss J. Bown, Mr L. Cornell, Mrs S. L. Ellis, Mrs Sue Francis, Mr Cliff Gaylard, Mr G. W. Giddings, Mr C. K. Hill, Mr David Hill, Mrs Pamela Hill, Mr Stewart Kemp, Mrs Susan Kemp, Mrs C. A. Lewis-Jones, Mr R. Moody.

---

84   **MR G. A. BUTLER, Blewbury**
Postal: **Churn Stables, Churn Farm, Blewbury, Didcot, Oxfordshire, OX11 9HF.**
Contact: **PHONE (01235) 851997 FAX (01235) 851998 MOBILE (07973) 715122**
E-MAIL trainer@gerardbutler.co.uk WEBSITE www.gerardbutler.co.uk

1 ANNISHIRANI, 4, b f Shaamit (IRE)—Silent Miracle (IRE) **Mr John Vowles**
2 BALLY HALL (IRE), 4, b c Saddlers' Hall (IRE)—Sally Rose **Latona Leisure Limited**
3 BOSTON LODGE, 4, ch g Grand Lodge (USA)—Ffestiniog (IRE) **The International Carnival Partnership**
4 CAMELOT, 5, br g Machiavellian (USA)—Bombazine (IRE) **The International Carnival Partnership**
5 COMPTON BANKER (IRE), 7, br g Distinctly North (USA)—Mary Hinge **Mr Erik Penser**
6 COMPTON BOLTER (IRE), 7, b g Red Sunset—Milk And Honey **Mr Erik Penser**
7 COMPTON DRAKE, 5, b g Mark of Esteem (IRE)—Reprocolor **Mr Erik Penser**
8 COMPTON EAGLE, 4, b g Zafonic (USA)—Gayane **Mr Erik Penser**

MR G. A. BUTLER—continued

9 **COMPTON EARL**, 4, ch g Efisio—Bay Bay **Mr Erik Penser**
10 **COMPTON ECLAIRE (IRE)**, 4, ch f Lycius (USA)—Baylands Sunshine (IRE) **Mr Erik Penser**
11 **COMPTON ECLIPSE**, 4, ch g Singspiel (IRE)—Fatah Flare (USA) **Mr Erik Penser**
12 **JAGGER**, 4, gr c Linamix (FR)—Sweetness Herself **Mr C. McFadden**
13 **MAYSTOCK**, 4, ch f Magic Ring (IRE)—Stockline **Stock Hill Racing**
14 **NAYYIR**, 6, ch g Indian Ridge—Pearl Kite (USA) **Mr Abdulla Al Khalifa**
15 **PERFECT LOVE**, 4, b f Pursuit of Love—Free Spirit (IRE) **Mr & Mrs G. Middlebrook**
16 **SELF EVIDENT (USA)**, 4, b br c Known Fact (USA)—Palisade (USA) **Prince Faisal Bin Khaled Abdul Aziz**
17 **SENTINEL**, 5, ch g Hector Protector (USA)—Soolaimon (IRE) **Five Horses Ltd**
18 **SPINNAKER**, 4, b f Nashwan (USA)—Throw Away Line (USA) **Mr T. Holland-Martin**

THREE-YEAR-OLDS

19 **AFTER ALL (IRE)**, gr f Desert Story (IRE)—All Ashore **Mr Anthony Rogers**
20 **BEAUCHAMP STAR**, ch f Pharly (FR)—Beauchamp Cactus **Mr Erik Penser**
21 **BEAUCHAMP SUN**, b f Pharly (FR)—Beauchamp Jade **Mr Erik Penser**
22 **BEAUCHAMP SURPRISE**, ch f Pharly (FR)—Beauchamp Image **Mr Erik Penser**
23 **BEST FORCE**, b f Compton Place—Bestemor **Mr M. Berger**
24 **DALPE**, ch g Siphon (BRZ)—Double Stake (USA) **Mrs Sally Doyle**
25 **DEVIOUS AYERS (IRE)**, br g Dr Devious (IRE)—Yulara (IRE) **The Devious Partnership**
26 **DONNA VITA**, b f Vettori (IRE)—Soolaimon (IRE) **Five Horses Ltd**
27 **DVINSKY (USA)**, b c Stravinsky (USA)—Festive Season (USA) **Mr M. Tabor**
28 **FLAMBOYANT**, br f Danzero (AUS)—Fabulous **Cheveley Park Stud**
29 **HANDSOME CROSS (IRE)**, b c Cape Cross (IRE)—Snap Crackle Pop (IRE) **Cereal Partners**
30 B g Mtoto—Imperial Scholar (IRE)
31 **JACK SULLIVAN (USA)**, ch c Belong To Me (USA)—Provisions (USA) **The International Carnival Partnership**
32 **LAND OF NOD (IRE)**, b f Barathea (IRE)—Rafif (USA) **East Wind Racing Ltd**
33 **OLIVANDER**, b c Danzero (AUS)—Mystic Goddess (USA) **Cheveley Park Stud**
34 **PASS GO**, b g Kris—Celt Song (IRE) **Mr J. M. Brown**
35 **RINGSIDER (IRE)**, ch g Docksider (USA)—Red Comes Up (USA) **Mr S A O'Donoghue & Mr M V Deegan**
36 **RUWAYDA (IRE)**, b f Soviet Star (USA)—Profit Alert (IRE) **Mr Abdulla Al Khalifa**
37 **RYDAL (IRE)**, ch c Gilded Time (USA)—Tennis Partner (USA) **Mr & Mrs G. Middlebrook**
38 **SO DETERMINED (IRE)**, b g Soviet Star (USA)—Memory Green (USA) **Mr C. Reid**
39 **SOVIET SCEPTRE (IRE)**, ch c Soviet Star (USA)—Princess Sceptre **Cheveley Park Stud**
40 **STRIDENT (USA)**, ch c Deputy Commander (USA)—Regrets Only (USA) **Highclere Thoroughbred Racing XVI**
41 **TARFAH (USA)**, b f Kingmambo (USA)—Fickle **Mr Abdulla Al Khalifa**
42 **WARRAD (USA)**, b c Kingmambo (USA)—Shalimar Garden (IRE) **Mr Abdulla Al Khalifa**

TWO-YEAR-OLDS

43 B f 10/5 Indian Danehill (IRE)—African Dance (USA) (El Gran Senor (USA)) (19789)
44 B br c 9/2 Cape Town (USA)—Al Fahda (Be My Chief (USA)) (52000) **The International Carnival Partnership**
45 **ANGEL RAYS**, ch f 27/1 Unfuwain (USA)—Success Story (Sharrood (USA)) **Mr J. Raw**
46 B c 20/3 Barathea (IRE)—Aquarela (Shirley Heights) **Mr Abdulla Al Khalifa**
47 **BEAUCHAMP TESS**, b f 17/3 Pharly (FR)—Beauchamp Image (Midyan (USA)) **Mr Erik Penser**
48 **BEAUCHAMP TIGER**, b g 6/3 Pharly (FR)—Beauchamp Jade (Kalaglow) **Mr Erik Penser**
49 **BEAUCHAMP TRUMP**, b c 24/3 Pharly (FR)—Beauchamp Kate (Petoski) **Mr Erik Penser**
50 **BEAUCHAMP TURBO**, ch c 4/3 Pharly (FR)—Compton Astoria (Lion Cavern (USA)) **Mr Erik Penser**
51 **BEAUCHAMP TWIST**, b f 1/4 Pharly (FR)—Beauchamp Cactus (Niniski (USA)) **Mr Erik Penser**
52 **BEST GAME**, b c 29/3 Mister Baileys—Bestemor (Selkirk (USA)) **Mr M. Berger**
53 **BORN TO BE GOLD**, ch c 24/1 Bold Edge—
Birthday Venture (Soviet Star (USA)) **Julian Horn-Smith & Terry Barwick**
54 Ch c 15/3 Boundary (USA)—
Copper Play (USA) (Fast Play (USA)) (43289) **The International Carnival Partnership**
55 **CORKER**, ch c 15/2 Grand Lodge—Immortelle (Arazi (USA)) (88000) **Woodcote Stud Ltd**
56 **CYCLICAL**, b c 9/2 Pivotal—Entwine (Primo Dominie) **Cheveley Park Stud**
57 B br c 14/3 Cape Canaveral (USA)—Danryoss (IRE) (Danehill (USA)) (34013)
58 Ch c 26/4 Grand Lodge (USA)—Delirious Moment (IRE) (Kris) (70000) **Mr C. McFadden**
59 Ch c 29/4 Giant's Causeway—En Garde (USA) (Irish River (FR)) (58000)
60 **FIGARO'S QUEST (IRE)**, b c 15/3 Singspiel (IRE)—
Seren Quest (Rainbow Quest (USA)) **The Fairy Story Partnership**
61 **FORGERY (IRE)**, ch c 9/4 Dr Devious (IRE)—
Memory Green (USA) (Green Forest (USA)) (130000) **Highclere Thoroughbred Racing XXIII**
62 **GALLANTIAN (IRE)**, gr c 18/1 Turtle Island (IRE)—Galletina (IRE) (Persian Heights) **Mr Trevor Stewart**
63 Ch f 15/4 Entrepreneur—Guilty Secret (IRE) (Kris) **Mr Abdulla Al Khalifa**
64 B c 18/3 Dynaformer (USA)—Kentucky Lill (USA) (Raise A Native) (65000) **Prince Faisal Bin Khaled Abdul Aziz**
65 B f 19/2 American Chance (USA)—Kibitzing (USA) (Wild Again (USA)) **Mr & Mrs G. Middlebrook**

MR G. A. BUTLER—continued

66 **MASTER COBBLER (IRE)**, b c 20/4 Alhaarth (IRE)—
　　　　　Lady Joshua (IRE) (Royal Academy (USA)) (30920) **Mr A. D. Spence**
67 **MONTAGE (IRE)**, b c 5/4 Montjeu (IRE)—Ocean View (USA) (Gone West (USA)) (68000) **Mr A. D. Spence**
68 **NATALIE JANE (IRE)**, ch f 7/3 Giant's Causeway—Kirk (Selkirk (USA)) **Woodcote Stud Ltd**
69 **OPTIMUS (USA)**, ch c 6/5 Elnadim (USA)—
　　　　　Ajfan (USA) (Woodman (USA)) (32158) **Mr and Mrs Andrew P. Wyer**
70 B c 11/4 Spectrum (IRE)—Penang Pearl (FR) (Bering) **Mrs A. K. H. Ooi**
71 B c 5/3 Efisio—Pfalz (Pharly (FR)) (20000)
72 Ch c 2/5 Indian Ridge—
　　　　　Plume Bleu Pale (USA) (El Gran Senor (USA)) (52565) **Mr S. A. O'Donoghue & Mr M. V. Deegan**
73 **PRIME NUMBER (IRE)**, gr c 1/4 King's Best (USA)—
　　　　　Majinskaya (FR) (Marignan) (86580) **Mr A. D. Spence**
74 B br c 1/5 Green Desert (USA)—Romoosh (Formidable (USA)) **Mr Abdulla Al-Khalifa**
75 B c 29/4 Kingmambo (USA)—Salina Cookie (USA) (Seattle Dancer (USA)) **H.E.Sheikh Rashid Bin Mohammed**
76 **SEDGWICK**, b c 2/4 Nashwan (USA)—Imperial Bailiwick (Imperial Frontier (USA)) **Mr & Mrs G. Middlebrook**
77 B c 4/4 Inchinor—Suddenly (Puissance) (16079)
78 **SUMORA (IRE)**, b f 23/2 Danehill (USA)—Rain Flower (IRE) (Indian Ridge) (75000) **Mr R. E. Sangster**
79 **SUN SPRINKLES (USA)**, b f 20/2 A P Indy (USA)—
　　　　　England's Rose (USA) (Nureyev (USA)) **H.E.Sheikh Rashid Bin Mohammed**
80 **TAYLOR MAID**, b f 10/2 First Trump—Island Maid (Forzando) **Mr J. Vowles**
81 B c 2/4 Groom Dancer (USA)—Throw Away Line (USA) (Assert) (31000) **Mr T. Holland-Martin**
82 B c 14/2 Spectrum (IRE)—Valley Lights (IRE) (Dance of Life (USA)) (30000)
83 B c 23/1 Groom Dancer (USA)—Warning Star (Warning) (29000) **The International Carnival Partnership**

Other Owners: Mrs C. Bracher, Mrs Mary Collis, Mr M. V. Deegan, Mrs Ian Donaldson, Mr R. D. Donaldson, Mrs M. Fairbairn, Mr D. Gilbert, Mr N. A. Gill, The Hon H. Herbert, Highclere Thoroughbred Racing Ltd, Mr Brian Lown, Mr G. Middlebrook, Mrs L. Middlebrook, Mr S. A. O'Donoghue, Mr Rajan Russell.

Assistant Trainer: Tim Pitt

85	**MR P. BUTLER, Lewes**

Postal: Homewood Gate Racing Stables, Novington Lane, East Chiltington, Lewes, East Sussex, BN7 3AU.
Contact: PHONE (01273) 890124 MOBILE (07973) 873846 FAX (01273) 890124
E-MAIL homewoodgate@aol.com

1 **CELTIC TED**, 6, b g Celtic Swing—Careful Dancer **Mr Christopher W. Wilson**
2 **DEER DOLLY (IRE)**, 7, b m Welsh Term—Wild Deer **Mrs E. Lucey-Butler**
3 **FELLOW SHIP**, 4, b g Elmaamul (USA)—Genoa **Mr E. H. Whatmough**
4 **GEOGRAPHY (IRE)**, 4, ch g Definite Article—Classic Ring (IRE) **Homewoodgate Racing Club**
5 **L'ETANG BLEU (FR)**, 6, gr g Graveron (FR)—Strawberry Jam (FR) **Mrs E. Lucey-Butler**
6 **MISBEHAVIOUR**, 5, b g Tragic Role (USA)—Exotic Forest **Homewoodgate Racing Club**
7 **REGAL JONES (IRE)**, 4, b f Sovereign Water (FR)—Juleit Jones (IRE) **Mr John Plackett**
8 **RIVER AMORA (IRE)**, 9, b g Willie Joe (IRE)—That's Amora **Mrs P. A. Wood**
9 **ROMEO JONES**, 5, bl g Roselier (FR)—Juleit Jones (IRE) **Mrs Jean Plackett**
10 **SALIX BAY**, 8, b g Karinga Bay—Willow Gale **Mrs E. Lucey-Butler**

THREE-YEAR-OLDS

11 **EASILY AVERTED (IRE)**, b c Averti (IRE)—Altishaan **Mr Christopher W. Wilson**

Assistant Trainer: Mrs E Lucey-Butler

Conditional: R Butler-Lucey (9-0).

86	**MR N. BYCROFT, Malton**

Postal: Cotman Rise, Brandsby, York, YO61 4RN.
Contact: PHONE (01347) 888641 MOBILE (07802) 763227

1 **BRAVE KNIGHT**, 7, b g Presidium—Agnes Jane **Mr Piers Casimir-Mrowczynski**
2 **DARA MAC**, 5, b g Presidium—Nishara **Mr N. Bycroft**
3 **EFIDIUM**, 6, b g Presidium—Efipetite **Hambleton Racing Partnership**
4 **EFIMAC**, 4, b f Presidium—Efipetite **Mr N. Bycroft**
5 **LAIRD DARA MAC**, 4, b c Presidium—Nishara **Mr N. Bycroft**

MR N. BYCROFT—continued

6 **PETITE MAC**, 4, b f Timeless Times (USA)—Petite Elite **Mr N. Bycroft**
7 **SHOTLEY DANCER**, 5, ch m Danehill Dancer (IRE)—Hayhurst **Mr J. A. Swinburne**
8 **SPLODGER MAC (IRE)**, 5, b g Lahib (USA)—Little Love **Mr N. Bycroft**
9 **TEDSDALE MAC**, 5, ch g Presidium—Stilvella **Mr Barrie Abbott**

THREE-YEAR-OLDS

10 **AGGI MAC**, b f Defacto (USA)—Giffoine **Mr N. Bycroft**
11 **DIUM MAC**, b g Presidium—Efipetite **Mr N. Bycroft**
12 **PLUMPIE MAC (IRE)**, b f Key of Luck (USA)—Petrine (IRE) **Mr N. Bycroft**
13 **ROSIE MAC**, ch f First Trump—Carol Again **Mr B. F. Rayner**
14 **TOOTIN MAC**, b f Piccolo—Bangles **Mr N. Bycroft**

TWO-YEAR-OLDS

15 Ch c 28/3 Timeless Times (USA)—Petite Elite (Anfield) (500) **Mr N. Bycroft**
16 B f 26/1 Forzando—Umbrian Gold (IRE) (Perugino (USA)) (2000) **Mr N. Bycroft**
17 **WORLD AT MY FEET**, b f 16/3 Wolfhound (USA)—Rehaab (Mtoto) (1600) **Mr N. Bycroft**

Other Owners: Mrs H. Cavanagh, Mr R. C. Crawford, Mr J. H. Hemy, Mrs E. B. Hughes, Mr J. G. Lumsden, Mr Michael Marsh.

Assistant Trainer: J N Bycroft

Apprentice: Suzanne France (7-12).

---

87   MR T. H. CALDWELL, Warrington
Postal: **Burley Heyes Cottage, Arley Road, Appleton, Warrington, Cheshire, WA4 4RR.**
Contact: **PHONE (01565) 777275 FAX (01565) 777275 MOBILE (07879) 455767**

1 **ARLEY MIST**, 5, b m Environment Friend—Hilly-Down Lass **Mr R. K. Furness**
2 **CLEOPATRAS THERAPY (IRE)**, 7, b g Gone Fishin—Nec Precario **Mr T. H. Caldwell**
3 **GOLDEN SNOOPY (IRE)**, 7, ch g Insan (USA)—Lovely Snoopy (IRE) **Mr Stephen Tomkinson**
4 **LORD LUPIN (IRE)**, 8, b g Sadler's Wells (USA)—Penza **Mr T. H. Caldwell**
5 **MISS COSPECTOR**, 5, ch m Emperor Fountain—Gypsy Race (IRE) **Mr R. Cabrera-Vargas**
6 **NOT NOW GEORGE**, 5, b g Sovereign Water (FR)—Threads **Mrs S. J. Wall and Mr T. H. Caldwell**
7 **VOLUPTUOUS**, 4, b f Polish Precedent (USA)—Alzianah **Mr J. S. Camilleri**

THREE-YEAR-OLDS

8 **FAIRLY GLORIOUS**, b g Tina's Pet—Steamy Windows **Colin Mather & Stephen Tomkinson**

Other Owners: Mr C. W. Mather, Mrs S. J. Wall.

Assistant Trainer: Mrs P J Wharfe

Jockeys (Flat): John Carroll, Joe Fanning, A Nicholls, P Robinson. **Jockeys (NH):** A Dobbin, Rupert Wakley. **Amateurs:** Mr B W Wharfe (9-2), Mrs Pat Wharfe (9-7).

---

88   MR N. A. CALLAGHAN, Newmarket
Postal: **22 Hamilton Road, Newmarket, Suffolk, CB8 0NY.**
Contact: **HOME (01638) 664040 FAX (01638) 668446**

1 **COLONEL COTTON (IRE)**, 5, b g Royal Applause—Cutpurse Moll **Mr Jeremy Gompertz**
2 **DELEGATE**, 11, ch g Polish Precedent (USA)—Dangora (USA) **Mr N. A. Callaghan**
3 **ENCHANTED**, 5, b m Magic Ring (IRE)—Snugfit Annie **Norcroft Park Stud**
4 **FORT MCHENRY (IRE)**, 4, b g Danehill Dancer (IRE)—Griqualand **Mr M. Tabor**
5 **LILLI MARLANE**, 4, b f Sri Pekan (USA)—Fiveofive (IRE) **Mrs M. Foreman**
6 **MAGISTRETTI (USA)**, 4, b c Diesis—Ms Strike Zone (USA) **Mr M. Tabor**
7 **MAZEPA (IRE)**, 4, b c Indian Ridge—Please Believe Me **Paul & Jenny Green**
8 **ST PANCRAS (IRE)**, 4, b c Danehill Dancer (IRE)—Lauretta Blue (IRE) **Mr Michael Hill**
9 **TRESOR SECRET (FR)**, 4, b g Green Desert (USA)—Tresor (USA)

THREE-YEAR-OLDS

10 **ANUVASTEEL**, gr c Vettori (IRE)—Mrs Gray **Tipp-Ex Rapid Racing**
11 **BARBAJUAN (IRE)**, b c Danehill Dancer (IRE)—Courtier **Team Havana**

MR N. A. CALLAGHAN—continued

12 **BUCHANAN STREET (IRE)**, b c Barathea (IRE)—Please Believe Me **Paul & Jenny Green**
13 **CROCOLAT**, ch f Croco Rouge (IRE)—Lamanka Lass **Lord Clinton**
14 **FOOT FAULT (IRE)**, b f Danehill (USA)—Mockery **Mr John Livock**
15 **HAZYVIEW**, b c Cape Cross (IRE)—Euridice (IRE) **Mr T. Mohan**
16 Ch c Woodman (USA)—Leo Girl (USA) **Mr N. A. Callaghan**
17 **MOLCON (IRE)**, b g Danetime (IRE)—Wicken Wonder (IRE) **Mr Mark Venus**
18 **NOTABLE LADY (IRE)**, b f Victory Note (USA)—Griqualand **Mr N. A. Callaghan**
19 **NOTHING LOST**, b g Danzero (AUS)—South Sea Bubble (IRE) **Mr John Livock**
20 **ROAMING VAGABOND (IRE)**, ch c Spectrum (IRE)—Fiveofive (IRE) **Mrs M. Foreman**
21 **RUSSIAN RUBY (FR)**, b f Vettori (IRE)—Pink Sovietstaia (FR) **Mrs P. Reditt**
22 **SANBONAH (USA)**, b f King of Kings (IRE)—Oh Nellie (USA) **Mr M. Tabor**
23 **TARUSKIN (IRE)**, b g Danehill Dancer (IRE)—Jungle Jezebel **Mr M. Tabor**
24 **THREE SECRETS (IRE)**, b f Danehill (USA)—Castilian Queen **Norcroft Park Stud**
25 **TRANQUIL SKY**, b f Intikhab (USA)—Tranquillity **Mr G. H. Beeby & Lord Marchwood**

TWO-YEAR-OLDS

26 B c 19/3 Danehill Dancer (IRE)—Alpine Lady (IRE) (Tirol) (111317) **Mr M. Tabor**
27 Ch f 6/4 Giants Causeway (USA)—Amy Hunter (USA) (Jade Hunter (USA)) (180000) **Mr M. Tabor**
28 Ch c 19/3 Grand Lodge (USA)—Bathe In Light (USA) (Sunshine Forever (USA)) (160000) **Mr M. Tabor**
29 **BIBI HELEN**, b f 19/4 Robellino (USA)—Tarry Salse (Salse (USA)) **Miss V. H. Pearce**
30 **BLOOD MONEY**, b c 25/2 Dracula (AUS)—Guinea (Sillery (USA)) (15000) **Mr G. Hartigan**
31 **CARRAIG (IRE)**, b f 5/2 Orpen (USA)—Rose of Mooncoin (IRE) (Brief Truce (USA)) **Cunningham Racing**
32 Gr f 21/3 King Of Kings (IRE)—Check Bid (USA) (Grey Dawn II) **Mrs J. Doyle & Mrs P Shanahan**
33 B c 23/2 Monashee Mountain—Couriter (Saddlers' Hall (IRE)) **Team Havana**
34 B f 9/2 Benny The Dip (USA)—Cutpurse Moll (Green Desert (USA)) **Mr Jeremy Gompertz**
35 Ch c 6/5 Grand Lodge (USA)—Ghayah (IRE) (Night Shift (USA)) (70000) **John Livock Bloodstock Ltd**
36 **GOLDEN ASHA**, ch f 16/2 Danehill Dancer (IRE)—Snugfit Annie (Midyan (USA)) **Norcroft Park Stud**
37 **HEDINGHAM KNIGHT (IRE)**, b c 13/3 Fasliyev
                    Exclusive Davis (Our Native (USA)) (42000) **Mrs June Powell**
38 **JAY (IRE)**, ch f 31/3 Bluebird (USA)—Welsh Dawn (Zafonic (USA)) **Mr G. Hartigan**
39 B c 17/3 Danehill Dancer (IRE)—Lowtown (Camden Town) (35000)
40 B c 12/3 Dansili—Mashmoon (IRE) (Habitat)
41 B c 21/2 Fasliyev (USA)—Norcroft Joy (Rock Hopper) **Norcroft Park Stud**
42 B f 19/1 Fusaichi Pegasus—Oh Nellie (USA) (Tilt The Stars (CAN)) **Mr M. Tabor**
43 **PARSLEY'S RETURN**, b c 9/2 Danzero (AUS)—The Frog Queen (Bin Ajwaad (IRE)) (9000) **DTL Ltd**
44 **PENALTY KICK (IRE)**, b c 30/4 Montjeu (USA)
                    Dafrah (USA) (Danzig (USA)) (82000) **John Livock Bloodstock Ltd**
45 **REBEL REBEL (IRE)**, b c 25/3 Revoque (IRE)—French Quarter (Ile de Bourbon (USA)) **Six Star Racing**
46 B f 3/5 Danehill Dancer (IRE)—Shanoora (IRE) (Don't Forget Me) (24000)
47 B f 19/4 Vettori (IRE)—Spinning Mouse (Bustino) (10000) **Mr J. A. Bianchi**
48 Gr f 1/3 Luhuk (USA)—Starlight Dreams (USA) (Black Tie Affair) **Mrs J. Doyle & Mrs P. Shanahan**
49 B c 1/5 Kayasi—Sudden Spirit (FR) (Esperit du Nord (USA)) (26000) **Mr E. M. Kirtland**
50 B f 17/5 Royal Applause—Waypoint (Cadeaux Genereux) **Mrs P. Reditt**

Other Owners: Mr Clive Batt, Capt T Bulwer-Long, Family Amusements Ltd, Mr Raymond Farrington, Mr R. Hartley, Mr P. Milmo, Mr M. C. Moutray-Read, Mr A. Oldrey, Mr Andy J. Smith.

Amateur: Mr S Callaghan (10-0).

89   MISS J. A CAMACHO, Malton

Postal: Star Cottage, Welham Road, Norton, Malton, North Yorkshire, YO17 9DU.
Contact: PHONE (01653) 694901 MOBILE (07779) 318135
E-MAIL jacracing@starcottage.fsbusiness.co.uk

1 **FAVORISIO**, 7, br g Efisio—Dixie Favor **Elite Racing Club**
2 **LAGO D'ORO**, 4, b f Slip Anchor—Salala **Mrs S. Camacho**
3 **LAMPOS (USA)**, 4, b g Southern Halo (USA)—Gone Private (USA) **L. A. Bolingbroke**
4 **LAURO**, 4, b f Mukaddamah (USA)—Lapu-Lapu **Shangri-La Racing Club**
5 **ROYAL MELBOURNE (IRE)**, 4, ch g Among Men (USA)—Calachuchi **Jamie Spence**

THREE-YEAR-OLDS

6 **BABOUSHKA (IRE)**, b f Soviet Star (USA)—Kabayil **Elite Racing Club**
7 B g Charnwood Forest (IRE)—Calachuchi (IRE)

MISS J. A CAMACHO—continued

8 Ch g Polar Falcon—Kingdom Ruby (IRE)
9 NOD'S STAR, ch f Starborough—Barsham **G. B. Turnbull & B. Nordan**

TWO-YEAR-OLDS

10 B c 30/3 Pivotal—Dixie Favor (USA) (Dixieland Band (USA))
11 B f 7/3 Danzig Connection—Fairey Firefly (Hallgate) **Mrs S. Camacho**
12 B c 22/4 Tagula (IRE)—Nordan Raider (Domynsky) **Mrs S. Camacho & B. Nordan**
13 Ch f 18/4 Polar Falcon (USA)—Silky Heights (IRE) (Head For Heights) **Mrs S. Camacho**
14 B c 16/3 Xaar—Zalamalec (USA) (Septieme Ciel (USA)) (30000)

Other Owners: D. Fay, H. Gallagher, T. Hill, C. Howard, C. J. Murphy, Miss M. Noden, S. Postill, W. Riley, M. Wainwright.

Assistant Trainer: Mr S Brown

Jockeys (Flat): A Culhane (w.a.), R Winston (w.a.).

---

90 MR A. M. CAMPION, Malton
Postal: **Whitewell House Stables, Whitewall, Malton, North Yorkshire, YO17 9EH.**
Contact: **PHONE (01653) 692729 FAX (01653) 600066 MOBILE (07973) 178311
E-MAIL info@markcampion-racing.com WEBSITE www.markcampion-racing.com**

1 ARIZONA (IRE), 6, b g Sadler's Wells (USA)—Marie de Beaujeu (FR) **F. S. W. Partnership**
2 COMTE DE CHAMBORD, 8, gr g Baron Blakeney—Show Rose **Mr A. M. Campion**
3 COXWELL COSSACK, 11, ch g Gildoran—Stepout **F. S. W. Partnership**
4 GONE BONKERS (IRE), 9, b g Lord Americo—Lady Harrier **The Gone Bonkers Partnership**
5 MELOGRANO (IRE), 4, ch g Hector Protector (USA)—Just A Treat (IRE) **Faulkner West**

Other Owners: Mr N. A. Baxter, Mr R. N. Forman, Mr J. Keary, Mr C. C. Straw, Mr I. D. Woolfitt.

---

91 MRS JENNIE CANDLISH, Leek
Postal: **Basford Grange Racing Stables, Basford, Leek, Staffordshire, ST13 7ET.**
Contact: **PHONE (01538) 360324 FAX (01538) 361643 MOBILE (07976) 825134/(07977) 599596
E-MAIL candlishracing@aol.com**

1 BALLYBAY DEMENSE (IRE), 8, br g Bob Back (USA)—Coach Road **Mr N. M. Wynne**
2 BIG AL (IRE), 5, br g Lugana Beach—Indian Flower **Racing For You Limited**
3 BLACK BULLET (NZ), 11, br g Silver Pistol (AUS)—Monte d'Oro (NZ) **Mr Martin Jump**
4 BLAZING SADDLES (IRE), 5, b g Sadler's Wells (USA)—Dalawara (IRE) **Racing For You Limited**
5 COLUMBUS (IRE), 7, b g Sadler's Wells (USA)—Northern Script (USA) **Racing For You Limited**
6 COMMONWEALTH (IRE), 8, b g Common Grounds—Silver Slipper **Mr J. T. Summerfield**
7 DIAMOND RING, 5, b m Magic Ring (IRE)—Reticent Bride (IRE) **Crag Alliance**
8 DONEGAL SHORE (IRE), 5, b h Mujadil (USA)—Distant Shore (IRE) **Racing For You Limited**
9 FIELDING'S HAY (IRE), 8, b m Supreme Leader—Kates Fling (USA) **Greencard Golfers**
10 FIELDINGS SOCIETY (IRE), 5, ch g Moscow Society (USA)—Lone Trail (IRE) **Mr Martin Jump**
11 GOOD THYNE JOHNNY (IRE), 10, b g Good Thyne (USA)—Wiasma **New World Racing**
12 HARDI DE CHALAMONT (FR), 9, gr g Royal Charter (FR)—Naita II (FR) **Mr N. Heath**
13 HOPE DIAMOND (IRE), 6, ch g Bigstone (IRE)—Mujtahida (IRE) **Mr N. M. Wynne**
14 INCH' ALLAH (FR), 8, b g Royal Charter (FR)—Cadoudaline (FR) **Mr N. M. Wynne**
15 KENNY THE TRUTH (IRE), 5, b g Robellino (USA)—Just Blink (IRE) **S. A. Mace & A. P. Simmill**
16 MAJOR SHARK (FR), 6, b g Saint Preuil (FR)—Cindy Cad (FR) **Mr N. M. Wynne**
17 MILNER BE GOOD, 6, b m Weld—It Beat All **Greencard Golfers**
18 MILNER BE GREAT, 8, b g Weld—Bahama **Greencard Golfers**
19 NORMANDY SANDS (IRE), 6, b br g Namaqualand (USA)—Buzz Along **Mr N. M. Wynne**
20 OR AIBREAN, 4, b f Commanche Run—The Angel Leek **Mr R. D. Wild**
21 PRECIOUS LUCY (IRE), 5, gr m Kadrou (FR)—Teardrops Fall (FR) **Racing For You Limited**
22 PURE BRIEF (IRE), 7, b g Brief Truce (USA)—Epure **Mrs V. D. Gandola-Grey**
23 THAI LA, 4, gr ro c Rashik—Bonyalua Mill **Mr A. J. Cartlich**
24 TWO RIVERS (IRE), 5, b g Over The River (FR)—Clarin River (IRE) **Mr Martin Jump**
25 YOUPEEVEECEE (IRE), 8, b g Little Bighorn—Godlike **Greencard Golfers**

MRS JENNIE CANDLISH—continued
THREE-YEAR-OLDS

26 Ch g Rashik—Fabulous Molly **Racing For You Limited**

Other Owners: Mr Alan Baxter, Mr A. Bianchi, Mr A. J. Cartlich, Mr G. Corbett, Mr Reuben Fielding, Mr N. Heath, Mr C. M. Johnson, Mr M. Jump, Mr H. M. Massey, Mrs S. E. Massey, Mrs J. M. Phillips, Mr R. I. Phillips, Mr R. D. Wild.

Assistant Trainer: Mr James Robbie Candlish

Jockey (Flat): Neil Chalmers. **Conditional:** Richard Henry Hobson (10-0). **Amateurs:** Mr James Davies, Mr David Thomas Weekes (9-6).

---

92 MR HENRY D. N CANDY, Wantage
Postal: Kingston Warren, Wantage, Oxfordshire, OX12 9QF.
Contact: **PHONE (01367) 820276/514 FAX (01367) 820500 MOBILE (0836) 211264**

1 **AIRWAVE**, 4, b f Air Express (IRE)—Kangra Valley **Henry Candy & Partners**
2 **ARAGON'S BOY**, 4, ch g Aragon—Fancier Bit **Mr Paul W. H. Dixon**
3 **BISHOPRIC**, 4, b g Bishop of Cashel—Nisha **Girsonfield Ltd**
4 **BISHOPSTONE MAN**, 7, b g Piccolo—Auntie Gladys **Mr Henry Candy**
5 **CLARISSE**, 5, b m Salse (USA)—Celia Brady **Mrs David Blackburn**
6 **COALITION**, 5, b g Polish Precedent (USA)—Selection Board **Thurloe Thoroughbreds**
7 **GO POLAR**, 4, b f Polar Falcon (USA)—Twilight Patrol **The Chalfont Partnership**
8 **ISAZ**, 4, b c Elmaamul (USA)—Pretty Poppy **Mrs J. E. L. Wright**
9 **JAYER GILLES**, 4, br g Busy Flight—Jadidh **Mrs Susan Brimble**
10 **LITTLE ENGLANDER**, 4, b g Piccolo—Anna Karietta **The Earl Cadogan**
11 **NIVERNAIS**, 5, b g Forzando—Funny Wave **Mr M. Tricks**
12 **SPEED ON**, 11, b g Sharpo—Pretty Poppy **Mr Henry Candy**
13 **WIGGY SMITH**, 5, ch g Master Willie—Monsoon **Mrs G. M. Tricks**
14 **WILD OVATION**, 4, b c Royal Applause—Daring Ditty **Lady Whent & Friends**

THREE-YEAR-OLDS

15 **ADAPTABLE**, b f Groom Dancer (USA)—Adeptation (USA) **Major M. G. Wyatt**
16 **ALENUSHKA**, b f Soviet Star (USA)—National Portrait (USA) **Mrs F. Gordon & Partners**
17 **ANNA PANNA**, b f Piccolo—Miss Laetitia (IRE) **Mr T. H. Chadney**
18 **BONNETTS (IRE)**, ch f Night Shift (USA)—Brief Lullaby (IRE) **Major M. G. Wyatt**
19 **CALLED UP**, b g Easycall—Clued Up **Mrs M. F. Dale**
20 **CARINI**, b f Vettori (IRE)—Secret Waters **The Shotts Farm Partnership**
21 **CLASSICAL DANCER**, ch f Dr Fong (USA)—Gorgeous Dancer (IRE) **Mr J. Strange**
22 **COLLOQUIAL**, b g Classic Cliche (IRE)—Celia Brady **Mrs David Blackburn**
23 **ELA PAPAROUNA**, b f Vettori (IRE)—Pretty Poppy **Mrs J. E. L. Wright**
24 **FIREBIRD**, b f Soviet Star (USA)—Al Corniche (IRE) **Mr T. A. F. Frost**
25 **GOSLAR**, ch f In The Wings—Anna of Brunswick **Major M. G. Wyatt**
26 **GOWON**, b f Aragon—Fancier Bit **Mrs J. Rae-Smith**
27 **HERIOT**, b g Hamas (IRE)—Sure Victory (IRE) **Mr P. T. Walwyn**
28 **IRISH BLADE (IRE)**, b c Kris—Perle d'Irlande (FR) **Thurloe Thoroughbreds V**
29 **OSLA**, ch f Komaite (USA)—Orlaith **Mr Henry Candy**
30 **POLONIUS**, b g Great Dane (IRE)—Bridge Pool **Mr P. A. Deal & J. Dale**
31 **PONT ALLAIRE (IRE)**, b f Rahy (USA)—Leonila (USA) **Britton House Stud Ltd**
32 **RUM SHOT**, b c Efisio—Glass **Mr H. R. Mould**
33 **SOUNDWAVE**, br f Prince Sabo—Kangra Valley **Henry Candy & Partners**
34 **SPLIFF**, b c Royal Applause—Snipe Hall **Mr H. R. Mould**
35 **SYMPHONY PARKES**, b f Pivotal—My Melody Parkes **Mr J. Heler**
36 **TAKES TWO**, b f Atraf—Funny Wave **Mrs George Tricks**
37 **TOPPLE**, b f Master Willie—Top Cover **Mr W. M. Lidsey**
38 **UMIAK**, b f Unfuwain (USA)—Sampan **M. H. Dixon**
39 **WEIR'S ANNIE**, b f Puissance—Hyde Princess **Mr C. J. Burley**
40 **WILLOFCOURSE**, b g Aragon—Willyet **Mr Henry Candy**
41 **ZWADI (IRE)**, b f Docksider (USA)—Local Custom (IRE) **Mrs E. Roberts**

TWO-YEAR-OLDS

42 **ANNALS**, b f 19/2 Lujain (USA)—Anna of Brunswick (Rainbow Quest (USA)) **Major M. G. Wyatt**
43 **BLUE BOY**, b c 10/3 Mujahid (USA)—Something Blue (Petong) (60000) **Mr Paul W. H. Dixon**
44 **BOLD ACT (IRE)**, b c 8/4 Brave Act—Banco Solo (Distant Relative) (20000) **Mrs C. M. Poland**

MR HENRY D. N CANDY—continued

45 **BOW WAVE**, b c 18/2 Danzero (AUS)—Moxby (Efisio) (18000) **Henry Candy & Partners**
46 **CAESAR BEWARE (IRE)**, b g 8/2 Daggers Drawn (USA)—
Red Shareef (Marju (IRE)) (17000) **Mill House Partnership**
47 **ENTERTAINING**, b f 25/2 Halling (USA)—Quaver (USA) (The Minstrel (CAN)) **Girsonfield Ltd**
48 **IWUNDER (IRE)**, b f 25/3 King's Best (USA)—Sweetest Thing (IRE) (Prince Rupert (FR)) (70000) **Mr J. Ellis**
49 **JUBILEE DAWN**, b f 3/6 Mark Of Esteem (IRE)—Eveningperformance (Night Shift (USA))
50 **JUBILEE PARKES**, b f 26/4 Royal Applause—Lucky Parkes (Full Extent (USA)) **Mr Joseph Heler**
51 B c 9/4 Mujahid (USA)—Jungle Rose (Shirley Heights) (40000) **Caroline Wilson**
52 **MINNESOTA (USA)**, ch c 20/4 Silver Hawk (USA)—Coco (USA) (Storm Bird (CAN)) **Mr Philip Newton**
53 B c 3/2 Benny The Dip (USA)—Miss Laetitia (IRE) (Entitled)
54 B f 14/5 Kris—Pervenche (Latest Model) **Girsonfield Ltd**
55 B c 27/4 Anabaa (USA)—Riviere du Diable (USA) (Irish River (FR)) (45000) **Mr H. R. Mould**
56 Ch f 26/3 Mister Baileys—Royal Roulette (Risk Me (FR)) (8000)
57 **SEAMUS SHINDIG**, b g 26/4 Aragon—Sheesha (Shadeed (USA)) (2800) **Mr Henry Candy**
58 B c 8/3 Desert Sun—Snowspin (Carwhite) (18000)
59 **SUDDEN EDGE**, b c 6/5 Bold Edge—Surprise Surprise (Robellino (USA)) (6000) **Mrs J. E. L. Wright**
60 **THE ABBESS**, gr f 22/4 Bishop Of Cashel—Nisha (Nishapour (FR)) **Girsonfield Ltd**
61 B c 17/5 Bahri (USA)—Verbal Intrigue (USA) (Dahar (USA)) (19000)
62 **VIRGIN'S TEARS**, b f 23/4 Bishop Of Cashel—Lola Mora (Nearly A Hand) **Mr P. Burnard & Partners**
63 **WOODWOOL**, br f 9/2 Benny The Dip (USA)—Woodcrest (Niniski (USA)) **Major M. G. Wyatt**
64 **ZIGGY ZAGGY**, b f 19/3 Diktat—Gorgeous Dancer (IRE) (Nordico (USA))

Other Owners: Mr S. Broke, Mrs Henry Candy, Mrs J. Carter, Mrs Pam Carter, Mr P. Cowling, Mr W. Edmeades, Mr A. Ellis, Mr P. Fenwick, Mr T. Lakin, Mr T. Le Blanc-Smith, Caroline Macphail, Sir Arthur Norman, Mr T. Norman, Mrs N. R. Nutting, Mr A. Penfold, Penfold Bloodstock, Mr A. N. Solomons, Mr J. A. B. Stafford, Ian Stephenson, Major-Gen G. H. Watkins, Mr M. M. Wiltshire.

Jockey (Flat): Dane O'Neill (8-4). **Apprentices:** Chris Cavannagh (8-0), Charlotte Cox (7-10).

---

93 **MR D. J. CARO, Ledbury**
Postal: **Lilly Hall Stables, Little Marcle, Ledbury, Herefordshire, HR8 2LD.**
Contact: **PHONE** (01531) 631559 (01531) 632892 **FAX** (01531) 634049 **MOBILE** (07797) 721068
E-MAIL julie@lillyhall-demon.co.uk

1 **BOARDROOM DANCER (IRE)**, 7, b g Executive Perk—Dancing Course (IRE) **Mr D. J. Caro**
2 **CAPTAIN BRAVADO (IRE)**, 10, b g Torus—Miss Bavard **Mr J. A. S. Hardcastle**
3 **COOL SONG**, 8, ch g Michelozzo (USA)—Vi's Delight **Mr M. J. Weaver**
4 **DANTES VENTURE (IRE)**, 7, b g Phardante (FR)—Fast Adventure **Mrs J. F. Billington**
5 **GALAXY GIRL**, 9, b m Jupiter Island—Thats Our Girl **Mr D. J. Caro**
6 **GLACIAL RIVER (IRE)**, 11, ch g Glacial Storm (USA)—Lucky Trout **Mr D. J. Caro**
7 **HARBOUR POINT (IRE)**, 8, b g Glacial Storm (USA)—Forest Jane **Mr Eddie Moss**
8 **LORD RAPIER**, 11, b g Broadsword (USA)—Doddycross **Mr J. A. S. Hardcastle**
9 **MASTER JUBB**, 6, b g Petrizzo—Ziggy's Pearl (USA) **Ruggur Racing**
10 **PRESENTER (IRE)**, 4, ch g Cadeaux Genereux—Moviegoer **Mrs J. F. Billington**
11 **STEEL MILL (IRE)**, 9, gr g Roselier (FR)—Chatmando (IRE) **Mrs J. F. Billington**
12 **THE MURATTI**, 6, b g Afflora (IRE)—Grayrose Double **Mrs J. F. Billington**
13 **TOURNIQUET (IRE)**, 9, b g Torus—Treidlia **Mr D. J. Caro**

Other Owners: Mr M. D. Edwards, Mr Russell T. Gray, Mr P. D. H. Jubb, Mr A. A. Munce, Mr Guy Plante.

Jockeys (NH): Paul Maloney, T J Murphy. **Conditional:** James Davies, Mark Nicolls.

---

94 **MR A. W. CARROLL, Alcester**
Postal: **Moor Hall Stables, Wixford, Alcester, Warwickshire, B49 6DL.**
Contact: **HOME** (01386) 793459 **OFFICE** (01789) 772808 **MOBILE** (07770) 472431
E-MAIL awcarrollracing@aol.com **WEBSITE** www.awcarrollracing.com

1 **ADJIRAM (IRE)**, 8, b g Be My Guest (USA)—Adjriyna **Mr K. Marshall**
2 **AMBERSONG**, 6, ch g Hernando (FR)—Stygian (USA) **Pursuit Media**
3 **ANSWERED PROMISE (IRE)**, 5, ro g Highest Honor (FR)—Answered Prayer **Stampede Racing**
4 **BARON'S PHARAOH (IRE)**, 9, b g Phardante (FR)—Katomi **Mr R. H. Harris & Mr Barry Veasey**
5 **BARONS PHARJAN (IRE)**, 7, b g Phardante (FR)—Widden Pharly **Mr Barry Veasey**
6 **BOWD LANE JOE**, 5, gr g Mazaad—Race To The Rhythm **Mr R. H. Fox**
7 **BRAVE DANE (IRE)**, 6, b g Danehill (USA)—Nuriva (USA) **Mrs E. J. Righton**

MR A. W. CARROLL—continued

8 **BURUNDI (IRE)**, 10, b g Danehill (USA)—Sofala **Mr R. Owens**
9 **BUZ KIRI (USA)**, 6, b g Gulch (USA)—White Corners (USA) **Mr Serafino Agodino**
10 **CAPTAIN O'NEILL**, 10, b g Welsh Captain—The Last Tune **Mr D. Joyce**
11 **CERULEAN ROSE**, 5, ch m Bluegrass Prince (IRE)—Elegant Rose **Mr R. Willis**
12 **COMPTON AVIATOR**, 8, ch g First Trump—Rifada **Mr G. Nichol**
13 **DARK SOCIETY**, 6, b g Imp Society (USA)—No Candles Tonight **Group One Racing (1994) Ltd**
14 **ELA FIGURA**, 4, ch f The West (USA)—Chili Bouchier (USA) **Xunley Ltd**
15 **FLAPDOODLE**, 6, b m Superpower—My Concordia **Mr J. Halsey**
16 **FLASHANT**, 9, ch g Henbit (USA)—La Furze **Exors of Mr A. Bayman**
17 **FORTUNE POINT (IRE)**, 6, ch g Cadeaux Genereux—Mountains of Mist (IRE) **T. J. Racing Partners**
18 **HABIBTI SARA**, 4, ch f Bijou d'Inde—Cut Velvet (USA) **Mr Omar Samaha**
19 **HE WHO DARES (IRE)**, 6, b g Distinctly North (USA)—Sea Clover (IRE) **Mr Roger Clarke**
20 **HOPING**, 6, b m Kris—Shimmering (IRE) **Mrs D. Brown**
21 **KANZ WOOD (USA)**, 8, ch g Woodman (USA)—Kanz (USA) **Mr L. B. Thomas**
22 **KIND SIR**, 8, b g Generous (IRE)—Noble Conquest (USA) **Mr Layton T. Cheshire**
23 **LADY ARNICA**, 5, b m Ezzoud (IRE)—Brand **Mr Roger Clarke**
24 **MANDAHAR (IRE)**, 5, b g Bluebird (USA)—Madiriya **Langwood Racing**
25 **MIDSHIPMAN**, 5, b h Executive Man—Midler **Langwood Racing**
26 **MIGHTY GLEN (IRE)**, 6, gr g Roselier (FR)—Supreme Glen (IRE) **T. J. Plant & Lifting Services Ltd**
27 **MOVING EARTH (IRE)**, 11, b g Brush Aside (USA)—Park Breeze (IRE) **Pursuit Media**
28 **MR DIP**, 4, b g Reprimand—Scottish Lady
29 **MRS BOZ**, 4, b f Superpower—Bar None **Costelloe & Jadwat**
30 **MS TRUDE (IRE)**, 7, b m Montelimar (USA)—Pencil **Mr Gary J. Roberts**
31 **MY BIG SISTER**, 5, gr m Thethingaboutitis (USA)—My Concordia **Mr J. Halsey**
32 **NAUTICAL**, 6, gr g Lion Cavern (USA)—Russian Royal (USA) **Mr Gary J. Roberts**
33 **OUR CHELSEA BLUE (USA)**, 6, ch m Distant View (USA)—Eastern Connection (USA) **Mr Andy Taylor**
34 **RED BLAZER (NZ)**, 11, ch g Omnicorp (NZ)—Gay Reef **Mr K. Marshall**
35 **ROBBIE CAN CAN**, 5, b g Robellino (USA)—Can Can Lady **Mr K. F. Coleman**
36 **SHORT CHANGE (IRE)**, 5, b g Revoque (IRE)—Maafi Esm **Mr Dennis Deacon**
37 **SUPERCLEAN**, 4, ch f Environment Friend—Star Mover **Ms D. Holloway**
38 **TAYASH**, 4, b g Fleetwood (IRE)—Wassl's Sister **Mr A. W. Carroll**
39 **TIDAL**, 5, b m Bin Ajwaad (IRE)—So Saucy **Mrs B. Quinn**
40 **TUSCARORA (IRE)**, 5, b m Revoque (IRE)—Fresh Look (IRE) **Pursuit Media**
41 **UP THE GLEN (IRE)**, 10, b g Tale Quale—Etrenne **Pursuit Media**
42 **VIZULIZE**, 5, b m Robellino (USA)—Euridice (IRE) **Last Day Racing Partnership**
43 **YOUNGS FORTH**, 4, b f Most Welcome—Pegs **Mr M. Pattison**
44 **ZIET D'ALSACE (FR)**, 4, b f Zieten (USA)—Providenc Mill (FR) **Mr Dennis Deacon**

THREE-YEAR-OLDS

45 **BACKLASH**, b f Fraam—Mezza Luna **Mr L. B. Thomas**
46 **BARONS SPY (IRE)**, b g Danzero (AUS)—Princess Accord (USA) **Mr R. H. Harris**
47 **FILLIEMOU**, gr f Goldmark (USA)—St Louis Lady **Mrs P. Izamis**
48 **KING EGBERT (FR)**, b g Fasliyev (USA)—Exocet (USA) **Mr A. W. Carroll**
49 Ch f Forzando—Norska **R. Willis & S. Roberts**
50 **PEARNICKITY**, b f Bob's Return (IRE)—The Robe **Pearns Pharmacy**
51 **WAYWARD TALENT (IRE)**, ch c Yately Tavern (IRE)—Broadfield Lass (IRE) **Mr A. W. Carroll**

TWO-YEAR-OLDS

52 B f 27/3 Benny The Dip (USA)—Dance To The Top (Sadler's Wells (USA)) (4000) **Mr & Mrs R Wright**
53 **MISS COTSWOLD LADY**, b f 30/3 Averti (IRE)—Celtic Bay (USA) (Green Dancer (USA)) (5200) **Mr S. Bowkett**
54 Gr c 12/4 Titus Livius (FR)—Mystical Jumbo (Mystiko (USA)) (5000) **Mr Serafino godino**

Other Owners: Mr E. Buddle, Mr M. Costelloe, Mr K. Jadwat, Ms S. A. Kearney, Mr S. M. Kemp, Mr M. Lennon, Mr K. C. Payne, Mr A. D. Rogers, Mr M. Sheils.

Assistant Trainer: Emma Righton

MR D. CARROLL, Warthill
Postal: **Ashdene, Common Lane, Warthill, York, YO19 5XS.**
Contact: **OFFICE** (01759) 373083 **FAX** (01759) 373586 **HOME** (01904) 400674 **MOBILE** (07801) 553779 **E-MAIL** declan@dcarrollracing.com **WEBSITE** www.dcarrollracing.com

1 **BENBYAS**, 7, b g Rambo Dancer (CAN)—Light The Way **C. H. Stephenson & Partners**
2 **CLEVELAND WAY**, 4, b g Forzando—Fallal (IRE) **The Boot & Shoe Ackworth Partnership**

MR D. CARROLL—continued

3 MEZEREON, 4, b f Alzao (USA)—Blown-Over **Diamond Racing Ltd**
4 RUSH'N'RUN, 5, b g Kasakov—Runfawit Pet **Carrol Racing Ltd**
5 RUST EN VREDE, 5, b g Royal Applause—Souveniers **Mr A. Mann**
6 YORKIE, 5, b g Aragon—Light The Way **C. H. Stephenson & Partners**

THREE-YEAR-OLDS

7 ARGENT, b g Barathea (IRE)—Red Tiara (USA) **Mr M. Gleason**
8 DANEFONIQUE (IRE), b f Danetime (IRE)—Umlaut **E. Richmond & J. Hopkinson**
9 DIAMOND SHANNON (IRE), b f Petorius—Balgren (IRE) **Diamond Racing Ltd**
10 ELLIOT'S CHOICE (IRE), b c Foxhound (USA)—Indian City **J. Hopkinson and R. Peel**
11 Ch f Master Willie—Ginseng **Mrs G. Andrews**
12 INDENTEUR (IRE), b g Entrepreneur—Individual (USA) **Mr M. Gleason**
13 INDI ANO STAR (IRE), b g Indian Rocket—Audriano (IRE) **Mr A. S. Scott**
14 JOSHUA'S GOLD (IRE), b g Sesaro (USA)—Lady Of The Night (IRE) **K. H. Taylor Limited**
15 KEY OF GOLD (IRE), b g Key Of Luck (USA)—Damaslin **Viking Racing**
16 KINGS EMPIRE, b g Second Empire (IRE)—Dancing Feather **WRB 61 (The Claire King Syndicate)**
17 B f Petoski—Midnight Flotilla **Mrs G. Andrews**
18 SHE'S OUR LASS (IRE), b f Orpen (USA)—Sharadja (IRE) **We-Know Partnership**
19 SUGAR MAN, b g Defacto (USA)—Samana Cay **Mr Michael Ng**

TWO-YEAR-OLDS

20 COOL AS A MOOSE, b c 26/4 Groom Dancer (USA)—
                                  Purbeck (IRE) (Polish Precedent (USA)) (11000) **Mr M. Gleason**
21 B c 30/4 Key Of Luck (USA)—Green Belt (FR) (Tirol) (9894) **Wetherby Racing Bureau Ltd**
22 Ch f 19/4 Indian Lodge (IRE)—Indian City (Lahib (USA)) (4000) **Mr M. Barrett**
23 LOVE ATTACK (IRE), b f 18/3 Sri Pekan (USA)—Bradwell (IRE) (Taufan (USA)) (3215) **Diamond Racing Ltd**
24 MING VASE, b c 12/4 Vettori (IRE)—Minstrel's Dance (CAN) (Pleasant Colony (USA)) (8000) **Mr Michael Ng**
25 Gr c 16/3 Shinko Forest (IRE)—Natural Pearl (Petong) (14000) **Mr & Mrs I. H. Bendelow**
26 OLDSTEAD FLYER (IRE), b c 29/4 Foxhound (USA)—
                                  Princess Tycoon (IRE) (Lasy Tycoon) (1400) **Mr & Mrs I. H. Bendelow**
27 QUINOLENE (IRE), b f 30/3 Bachir (IRE)—Slayjay (IRE) (Mujtahid (USA)) (6000) **Mr M. Gleason**
28 YORKSHIRE LAD (IRE), b c 16/4 Second Empire (IRE)—
                                  Villaminta (IRE) (Grand Lodge (USA)) (6183) **Mr & Mrs I. H. Bendelow**

Other Owners: Mr Andrew Bates, Mr J. J. Devaney, Mr T. S. Ely, Mrs J. Gleason, Mr D. Hardy, Mr Lee Ibbotson, Mr Pete Murphy, Mr Stuat Scott, Sunpak Potatoes, Mr David Thompson.

Assistant Trainer: Paul Segwick

Apprentice: D Tudhope (8-2). **Amateur:** Miss D Allman (9-10).

MR R. M. CARSON, Lambourn
Postal: **58 Child Street, Lambourn, Hungerford, Berkshire, RG17 8NZ.**
Contact: **PHONE (01488) 72080 MOBILE (07751) 440182**

1 A RIGHT SET TWO, 12, ch g Island Set (USA)—Super Sol **Mr R. M. Carson**
2 HAIL THE KING (USA), 4, gr g Allied Forces (USA)—Hail Kris (USA) **Mrs P. Carson**

Assistant Trainer: Mrs P Carson

Jockey (NH): D Crosse (9-7, w.a.). **Conditional:** M Deady (9-7).

MR O. J. CARTER, Ottery St Mary
Postal: **Wild Green, Metcombe, Ottery St Mary, Devon, EX11 1RS.**
Contact: **(01404) 812607**

1 EARLY EDITION, 8, b g Primitive Rising (USA)—Ottery News **Mr O. J. Carter**
2 FIRST THOUGHT, 6, b m Primitive Rising (USA)—Precis **Mr O. J. Carter**
3 GONE MISSING, 5, b h Early Edition—Tom's Little Bet **Mr O. J. Carter**
4 5, Ch m Early Edition—Roodle Doodle **Mr O. J. Carter**
5 VAGUE IDEA, 11, gr g Tout Ensemble—Roodle Doodle **Mr O. J. Carter**

98 MR B. I. CASE, Banbury
Postal: **Edgcote House Stables, Edgcote, Chipping Warden, Banbury, Oxfordshire, OX17 1AG.**
Contact: PHONE (01295) 660909 FAX (01295) 660908 MOBILE (07808) 061223
E-MAIL info@bencaseracing.com WEBSITE www.bencaseracing.com561 2

1 **ALISA (IRE)**, 4, b f Slip Anchor—Ariadne (GER) **Fools and Horses**
2 **ANNABEE**, 7, gr m Norton Challenger—Annaway **P. P. Hall**
3 **BDELLIUM**, 6, b m Royal Vulcan—Kelly's Logic **Mr Neil Hutley**
4 **HALF INCH**, 4, b f Inchinor—Anhaar **Mrs M. Howlett**
5 **HARRY COLLINS**, 6, ch g Sir Harry Lewis (USA)—Run Fast For Gold **Mr B. I. Case**
6 **KENTISH WARRIER (IRE)**, 6, b g Warcraft (USA)—Garden County **Lady Jane Grosvenor**
7 **KINGS LINEN (IRE)**, 8, b g Persian Mews—Kings Princess **Mr Dudley C. Moore**
8 **LE JOYEUX (FR)**, 5, br g Video Rock (FR)—Agra (FR) **Mr Dudley C. Moore**
9 **MANOLITO (IRE)**, 10, b g Mandalus—Las-Cancellas **Mr & Mrs J. Hancock**
10 **SPECIAL CONSTABLE**, 6, b br g Derrylin—Lavenham's Last **Case Racing Partnership**
11 **THE VARLET**, 4, b g Groom Dancer (USA)—Valagalore **Mrs A. D. Bourne**

TWO-YEAR-OLDS

12 B g 5/5 Yaheeb (USA)—Lavenham's Last (Rymer) **Mr B. Case**

Other Owners: Mr & Mrs D. Baines, Mrs J. Broughton, Mr A. Case, Mrs S. Case, Mrs A. Charlton, Mrs Claire Clampitt, Mrs S. Cole, Lady Dalbiac, Dr T. A. Feddern, Lord Fellowes, Mr Paul Garratt, Mr R. Hagen, Mrs S. Harrison, Mrs M. Howlett, Mr & Mrs R. Hurley, Mr G. Nicholson, Mr & Mrs C. Nixey, Mr J. Nowell-Smith, Mrs K. Perrem, Mr & Mrs G. Rodenhurst, Mr Cliff Ward.

Conditional: C Honour (9-10).

99 MR J. M. CASTLE, Aylesbury
Postal: **Mottymead Farm, Long Crendon, Aylesbury, Buckinghamshire, HP18 9BE.**
Contact: PHONE (01844) 208107 FAX (01844) 201107 E-MAIL mottymead@hotmail.com

1 **MONTY BE QUICK**, 8, ch g Mon Tresor—Spartiquick **Mr J. M. Castle**

Assistant Trainer: Mrs S. J. Castle

100 MR H. R. A. CECIL, Newmarket
Postal: **Warren Place, Newmarket, Suffolk, CB8 8QQ.**
Contact: HOUSE (01638) 662387 OFFICE 662192 FAX 669005

1 **BAGAN (FR)**, 5, b br h Rainbow Quest (USA)—Maid of Erin (USA) **Niarchos Family**
2 **CALONNOG (IRE)**, 4, ch f Peintre Celebre (USA)—Meadow Spirit (USA) **Derek and Jean Clee**
3 **FINE PALETTE**, 4, ch c Peintre Celebre (USA)—Filly Mignonne (IRE) **Mrs Angela Scott**
4 **FORCE OF NATURE (USA)**, 4, b f Sadler's Wells (USA)—Yashmak (USA) **Mr K. Abdulla**
5 **HOME FLEET (USA)**, 4, ch c Gone West (USA)—All At Sea (USA) **Mr K. Abdulla**
6 **SAYADAW (FR)**, 4, b c Darshaan—Vingt Et Une (FR) **Niarchos Family**
7 **TIMBER ICE (USA)**, 4, b f Woodman (USA)—Salchow (USA) **Niarchos Family**
8 **YDING (IRE)**, 4, b f Danehill (USA)—Ship's Twine (IRE) **Derek and Jean Clee**

THREE-YEAR-OLDS

9 **AKIMBO (USA)**, b c Kingmambo (USA)—All At Sea (USA) **Mr K. Abdulla**
10 **ALMUNIA (IRE)**, b f Mujadil (USA)—Betelgeuse **Mr Felipe Hinojosa**
11 **APSARA**, br f Groom Dancer (USA)—Ayodhya (IRE) **Dr Catherine Wills**
12 **ARDERE (USA)**, ch f El Prado (IRE)—Flaming Torch **Mr K. Abdulla**
13 **ARTICULATION**, b c Machiavellian (USA)—Stiletta **Mr K. Abdulla**
14 **ASTUCE**, ch f Groom Dancer (USA)—Born Free **Mr L. Marinopoulos**
15 **CANZONETTA**, b f Zafonic (USA)—Light Step (USA) **Mr K. Abdulla**
16 **DAWN MIST (USA)**, b f Diesis—Summer Mist (USA) **Mr K. Abdulla**
17 **DENOUNCE**, b c Selkirk (USA)—Didicoy (USA) **Mr K. Abdulla**
18 **ENCOMPASS (FR)**, b f Sadler's Wells (USA)—Totality **Mr K. Abdulla**
19 **EYES ONLY (USA)**, b f Distant View (USA)—Yashmak (USA) **Mr K. Abdulla**
20 **FENDER**, b c Rainbow Quest (USA)—Rockfest (USA) **Mr K. Abdulla**
21 **FOCUS GROUP (USA)**, b c Kris S (USA)—Interim **Mr K. Abdulla**
22 **HONEYMOONING**, b f Groom Dancer (USA)—Ever Genial **Cliveden Stud**
23 **I HAD A SISTER (BEL)**, ch c Bid For Blue—Texas Cowgirl (IRE) **Mr P. Van Belle**
24 **INVASIAN (IRE)**, ch c Desert Prince (IRE)—Jarrayan **Dr K. Sanderson**

MR H. R. A. CECIL—continued

25 **ITHACA (USA)**, ch f Distant View (USA)—Reams of Verse (USA) **Mr K. Abdulla**
26 **KABIS BOOIE (IRE)**, ch c Night Shift (USA)—Perfect Welcome **www.KABIS.co.uk**
27 **LILLIANNA (IRE)**, ch f Barathea (IRE)—Machikane Akaiito (IRE) **Sykes Distribution Ltd**
28 **MISS MONICA (IRE)**, ch f Grand Lodge (USA)—Bea's Ruby (IRE) **Dr K. Sanderson**
29 **MODESTA (IRE)**, b f Sadler's Wells (USA)—Modena (USA) **Mr K. Abdulla**
30 **MOVIE QUEEN**, b f Danehill (USA)—Easy To Copy (USA) **Lordship Stud**
31 **MUSCIDA (USA)**, b f Woodman (USA)—Space Time (FR) **Mr J. Patel**
32 **NUNKI (USA)**, ch c Kingmambo (USA)—Aqua Galinte (USA) **Niarchos Family**
33 **PINCHING (IRE)**, ch f Inchinor—Input **Mr Raymond Tooth**
34 **PORTRAIT OF A LADY (IRE)**, ch f Peintre Celebre (USA)—Starlight Smile (USA) **Mr J. Shack**
35 **POSTERITAS (USA)**, b f Lear Fan (USA)—Imroz (USA) **Mr K. Abdulla**
36 **PRESENT ORIENTED (USA)**, ch c Southern Halo (USA)—Shy Beauty (CAN) **Mr Frederick J. Seitz**
37 **PRINCESS PERFECT (IRE)**, b f Danehill Dancer (USA)—Resiusa (ITY) **Sykes Distribution Ltd**
38 **RED DOT (USA)**, ch f Diesis—Rougeur (USA) **Mr K. Abdulla**
39 **ROMAN FORUM**, b c Selkirk (USA)—Flit (USA) **Mr K. Abdulla**
40 **SERRAMANNA**, ch f Grand Lodge (USA)—Spry **Plantation Stud**
41 **SINISTRA**, br f Dracula (AUS)—Sardegna **Plantation Stud**
42 **SPARKLE OF STONES (FR)**, b f Sadler's Wells (USA)—Gwydion (USA) **Niarchos Family**
43 **SPEEDINI (USA)**, ch c Jade Hunter (USA)—Joan L (USA) **Mr Frederick J. Seitz**

TWO-YEAR-OLDS

44 B c 4/2 Danehill (USA)—Arabesque (Zafonic (USA)) **Mr K. Abdulla**
45 **AWASH**, ch c 17/4 Coronado's Quest—All At Sea (USA) (Riverman (USA)) **Mr K. Abdulla**
46 B f 18/1 Zafonic (USA)—Clepsydra (Sadler's Wells (USA)) **Mr K. Abdulla**
47 Gr c 21/4 Giant's Causeway—Desert Bluebell (Kalaglow) (70000) **Tullamaine Castle Stud & Partners**
48 **DOOIE DANCER**, b c 28/2 Entrepreneur—Vayavaig (Damister (USA)) (36000) **www.KABIS.co.uk**
49 **ECCENTRICITY (USA)**, b f 20/4 Kingmambo (USA)—Shiva (JPN) (Hector Protector (USA)) **Niarchos Family**
50 **ESTRELLE (GER)**, ch f 17/3 Sternkoenig (IRE)—Enrica (Niniski (USA)) (13605) **Gerhard Schoningh**
51 B c 29/3 Selkirk (USA)—Flit (USA) (Lyphard (USA)) **Mr K. Abdulla**
52 **HACHITA**, ch f 18/1 Gone West (USA)—Choice Spirit (USA) (Danzig (USA)) **Mr K. Abdulla**
53 **HALLIARD**, b f 20/2 Halling (USA)—Felucca (Green Desert (USA)) **Mr K. Abdulla**
54 **HOMESTAY (USA)**, b c 17/1 Chester House (USA)—Jibe (USA) (Danzig (USA)) **Mr K. Abdulla**
55 **KABIS AMIGOS**, ch c 14/3 Nashwan (USA)—River Saint (USA) (Irish River (FR)) (22000) **www.KABIS.co.uk**
56 Ch c 31/1 Diesis—La Sky (IRE) (Law Society (USA)) **Lordship Stud**
57 **LA TRAVIATA (SWI)**, ch f 19/5 Grand Lodge (USA)—La Venta (USA) (Drone (USA)) (40000) **Mr J. Shack**
58 **LILAC MIST**, b f 4/5 Spectrum (IRE)—L'Ideale (USA) (Alysheba (USA)) (20000) **Mr J. Shack**
59 **LOVE ME TENDER**, b f 9/1 Green Desert (USA)—Easy To Love (USA) (Diesis) **Lordship Stud**
60 **LUMINESCENCE**, b f 10/3 Rainbow Quest (USA)—Licorne (Sadler's Wells (USA)) **Plantation Stud**
61 **MADAME MOGAMBO (USA)**, b f 23/2 Kingmambo (USA)—
                      Aqua Galinte (Kris S (USA)) (208333) **Sumaya Stables**
62 B f 8/2 Spectrum (IRE)—New Abbey (Sadler's Wells (USA)) **Mr K. Abdulla**
63 **PARISETTE**, b f 16/2 Dansili—Moulin Rouge (Shareef Dancer (USA)) **Mr & Mrs Homewood**
64 **POLITICAL INTRIGUE**, b c 12/2 Dansili—Quandary (Blushing Groom (FR)) **Mr K. Abdulla**
65 **RATHOR (IRE)**, b br c 13/5 Machiavellian (USA)—Raisonnable (Common Grounds) **Niarchos Family**
66 **SAVOIE**, ch f 1/4 Grand Lodge (USA)—Spry (Suave Dancer (USA)) **Plantation Stud**
67 **SCOTCH HOUSE**, ch f 2/3 Selkirk (USA)—Top Shop (Nashwan (USA)) **Cliveden Stud**
68 B c 29/1 Entrepreneur—Sierva (GER) (Darshaan) (20000) **Mr Michael Poland**
69 **STAGECRAFT (USA)**, b f 30/3 Diesis—Eternity (Suave Dancer (USA)) **Dr Catherine Wills**
70 **TEMPESTAD (IRE)**, b f 15/4 Giant's Causeway—Arutua (USA) (Riverman (USA)) (240000) **Sumaya Racing**
71 **THE COOIE (IRE)**, b c 14/2 Sadler's Wells (USA)—Propensity (Habitat) (35000) **www.KABIS.co.uk**
72 B c 13/3 Dr Fong (USA)—Verbose (USA) (Storm Bird (CAN)) **Mr K. Abdulla**
73 **VIBRATO (USA)**, b c 31/5 Stravinsky (USA)—
               She's Fine (USA) (Private Account (USA)) (68000) **Dreamfields Inc & Henry Cecil Co. Ltd**

Other Owners: Stephen Allott, Mr G. Barnard, Mr N. Gomersall.

Assistant Trainer: David Lanigan

Jockeys (Flat): T Quinn (8-4), W Ryan (8-2).

101 MR S. G. CHADWICK, Hayton
Postal: **Eskrigg, Hayton, Aspatria, Carlisle, Cumbria, CA7 2PD.**
Contact: **PHONE (016973) 21226**

1 **BOSS MORTON (IRE)**, 13, b g Tremblant—Sandy Kelly **Mr S. Chadwick**
2 **CHROMAZONE**, 7, gr m Roselier (FR)—Gold Bash **Mr S. Chadwick**
3 **FAWN PRINCE (IRE)**, 11, b g Electric—Regent Star **Mr S. Chadwick**
4 **HAYTON BOY**, 10, ch g Gypsy Castle—Young Christine (USA) **Mr S. Chadwick**
5 **JAMORIN DANCER**, 9, b g Charmer—Geryea (USA) **Mr S. Chadwick**
6 **MINSTER MEADOW**, 5, ch g Minster Son—Eddies Well **Mr S. Chadwick**
7 **MISS ARAGONT**, 5, b m Aragon—Uninvited **Mr S. Chadwick**

102 MR P. R. CHAMINGS, Basingstoke
Postal: **Inhurst Farm Stables, Baughurst, Tadley, Hampshire, RG26 5JS.**
Contact: **PHONE (01189) 814494 FAX (01189) 820454 MOBILE (07831) 360970**
E-MAIL chamingsracing@talk21.com

1 **BINANTI**, 4, b g Bin Ajwaad (IRE)—Princess Rosananti (IRE) **Mrs J. E. L. Wright**
2 **DANZIG STAR**, 4, b f Danzig Connection (USA)—Julie's Star (IRE) **Mr C. R. Black**
3 **DEPTFORD (IRE)**, 5, ch g Un Desperado (FR)—Katty London **Mr R. V. Shaw**
4 **GREY MISTRAL**, 6, gr m Terimon—Winnowing (IRE) **Mr R. V. Shaw**
5 **HAVE SOME FUN**, 4, ch g Bering—Hilaris **Mrs Ann Jenkins**
6 **HAWK**, 6, b g A P Jet (USA)—Miss Enjoleur (USA) **Twenty Twenty Research**
7 **KING'S BALLET (USA)**, 6, b g Imperial Ballet (IRE)—Multimara **Patrick Chamings Sprint Club**
8 **KINGS MISTRAL (IRE)**, 11, b g Strong Gale—Mrs Simpson **Mr R. V. Shaw**
9 **LEISURELY WAY**, 5, b m Kris—Arietta's Way (IRE) **Mrs Alexandra J. Chandris**
10 **LIFTED WAY**, 5, b h In The Wings—Stack Rock **Mrs Alexandra J. Chandris**
11 **LYRICAL WAY**, 5, b g Vettori (IRE)—Fortunate **Mrs Alexandra J. Chandris**
12 **MARK YOUR WAY**, 4, b g Spectrum (IRE)—Titania's Way **Mrs Alexandra J. Chandris**
13 **MY VALENTINE**, 5, gr g Samim (USA)—Sea Farer Lake **Mr Dave Holland**
14 **PORT ST CHARLES (IRE)**, 7, b br g Night Shift (USA)—Safe Haven **Twenty Twenty Research**
15 **ROMERO**, 8, b g Robellino (USA)—Casamurrae **Fraser Miller Racing**
16 **RUSSIAN APPLAUSE**, 4, b g Royal Applause—Zeffirella **Inhurst Farm Stables Partnership**
17 **SECOND OF MAY**, 4, ch f Lion Cavern (USA)—Giant Nipper **Mrs Alexandra J. Chandris**
18 **SHARPINCH**, 6, b g Beveled (USA)—Giant Nipper **Mrs Ann Jenkins**
19 **THE LEADER**, 11, b g Ardross—Leading Line **Inhurst Farm Stables Partnership**
20 **USK VALLEY (IRE)**, 9, b g Tenby—Penultimate (USA) **Inhurst Farm Stables Partnership**
21 **WOODLAND BLAZE (IRE)**, 5, b g Woodborough (USA)—Alpine Sunset **Patrick Chamings Sprint Club**

THREE-YEAR-OLDS

22 **ALABOUNTY**, ch f Bahamian Bounty—Alasib **Mrs J. E. L. Wright**
23 **ENCORA BAY**, b f Primo Dominie—Brave Revival **Mr P. R. Chamings**
24 **GLIDING BY**, ch f Halling (USA)—Waft (USA) **Mrs Ann Jenkins**
25 **NEPHETRITI WAY (IRE)**, b f Docksider—Velvet Appeal (IRE) **Mrs Alexandra J. Chandris**
26 **NIOBE'S WAY**, b f Singspiel (IRE)—Arietta's Way (IRE) **Mrs Alexandra J. Chandris**
27 **NOTHING MATTERS**, b f Foxhound (USA)—Dawn Alarm **Mr C. R. Black**
28 **STELLA MARAIS (IRE)**, b f Second Empire (IRE)—Karakapa (FR) **Mr John C. Murphy**
29 **TAKE A BOW**, b c Royal Applause—Giant Nipper **Mrs J. E. L. Wright**

TWO-YEAR-OLDS

30 Ch f 19/4 Guy Butters (GR)—Alika's Dance (USA) (Green Dancer (USA)) (11428) **Mrs Alexandra J. Chandris**
31 **BOB BAILEYS**, b g 13/3 Mister Baileys—Bob's Princess (Bob's Return (IRE)) (4000) **Mrs J. E. L. Wright**
32 B c 10/3 Denebola Way (GR)—Dada (GR) (Ice Reef) (8571) **Mrs Alexandra J. Chandris**
33 Ch c 21/2 Unfuwain (USA)—Dancing Mirage (GR) (Machiavellian (USA)) (40000) **Mrs Ann Jenkins**
34 Ch c 26/3 Dr Fong (USA)—Fleet Key (Afleet (CAN)) (3000)
35 Br c 17/2 Tony Galvin (GR)—Fortunate Way (GR) (Wadood (USA)) (14285) **Mrs Alexandra J. Chandris**
36 B c 15/3 King's Best (USA)—Koumiss (Unfuwain (USA)) (80000) **Mrs Alexandra J. Chandris**
37 B f 8/2 Fascinating Way (GR)—Light Wind (GR) (Lai Lai (GR)) (7142) **Mrs Alexandra J. Chandris**
38 B f 7/5 Cadeaux Genereux—May Light (Midyan (USA)) (32000) **Mrs Alexandra J. Chandris**
39 B f 13/2 Wadood (USA)—Northern Moon (Ile de Bourbon (USA)) (11428) **Mrs Alexandra J. Chandris**

Other Owners: Mrs J. R. Foster, Mr F. T. Lee, Mr B. G. Slade, Mr K. W. Tyrrell.

Amateur: Mr D Alers-Hankey (10-0).

103 MR N. T. CHANCE, Upper Lambourn

Postal: **Berkeley House Stables, Upper Lambourn, Hungerford, Berkshire, RG17 8QP.**
Contact: **OFFICE** (01488) 73436 **MOBILE** (07785) 300168 **FAX** (01488) 72296
E-MAIL noel.chance@virgin.net

1 **BEAU GESTE (IRE)**, 6, b g Beau Sher—Celia's Pet (IRE) **Mrs M. Chance**
2 **BEFORE THE MAST (IRE)**, 7, br g Broken Hearted—Kings Reserve **Mr A. D. Weller**
3 **BEYOND THE PALE (IRE)**, 6, gr g Be My Native (USA)—Cyrano Imperial (IRE) **Mr A. D. Weller**
4 **CAPTAIN KHINEL (IRE)**, 6, b g Persian Mews—Tearaway Lady (IRE) **The Cardinal Syndicate**
5 **CIGARILLO (IRE)**, 6, br g Vestris Abu—Rose-Anore **Mr C. C. Shand Kydd**
6 **CORPORATE PLAYER (IRE)**, 6, b g Zaffaran (USA)—Khazna **Mr A. D. Weller**
7 **CROOKSTOWN CASTLE (IRE)**, 6, gr g Castle Keep—Moorstown Rose (IRE) **Mrs M. C. Sweeney**
8 **DANS PRIDE (IRE)**, 6, b g Presenting—Mindyourown (IRE) **Mr Brian Jacobs**
9 **DIRECT FLIGHT (IRE)**, 6, ch g Dry Dock—Midnight Mistress **Top Flight Racing**
10 **FLAME CREEK (IRE)**, 8, b g Shardari—Sheila's Pet (IRE) **Martin Wesson Partners**
11 **FREE RETURN (IRE)**, 9, ch g Magical Wonder (USA)—Free Reserve (USA) **Mrs Jill Cox**
12 **GAELIC FLIGHT (IRE)**, 6, b br g Norwich—Ash Dame (IRE) **Top Flight Racing 3**
13 **GOLD AGAIN (IRE)**, 6, b g Old Vic—Thomastown Girl **Dan Jim Partnership**
14 **INTYMCGINTY (IRE)**, 7, b g Port Lucaya—Mother Tongue **Let's Get Ready To Rumble Partnership**
15 **IRISH FLIGHT (IRE)**, 7, ch g Duky—Arewehavingfunyet **Court Jesters Partnership 2**
16 **KATY JONES (IRE)**, 4, b f Alderbrook—Just Jodi (IRE) **Mrs R. Greener**
17 **LA LUNA (IRE)**, 7, b m Gothland (FR)—Diane's Glen **Mrs S. Rowley-Williams**
18 **LISSARA (IRE)**, 6, b g Glacial Storm (USA)—Bonnies Glory **Mrs Rose Boyd**
19 **LORD OF BEAUTY (FR)**, 4, ch g Medaaly—Arctic Beauty (USA) **Warren, Upton & Chenkin & Townson**
20 **MAKE IT A DOUBLE (IRE)**, 6, ch g Zaffaran (USA)—La Danse **Mrs M. Chance**
21 **MARCHING PREMIER (IRE)**, 5, ch g Zaffaran (USA)—The Marching Lady (IRE) **Premier Chance Racing**
22 **MEGAPAC (IRE)**, 6, b g Supreme Leader—Mistress Gale (IRE) **Mr Brian Jacobs**
23 **MIO CARO (FR)**, 4, ch g Bering—Composition (USA) **Mr Mike Browne**
24 **MURPHY'S CARDINAL (IRE)**, 8, b g Shernazar—Lady Swinford **Mr T. Conway & Mrs Conway**
25 **MYSTERIOUS LORD (IRE)**, 5, br g Mister Lord (USA)—Brogue Melody (IRE) **The Sporting Divots**
26 **NEW MISCHIEF (IRE)**, 6, b g Accordion—Alone Party (IRE) **R. W. and J. R. Fidler**
27 5, b g Alflora (IRE)—Northwood Star **Mr T. Hayes**
28 **NO TURNING BACK (IRE)**, 5, b g Shernazar—Offaly Rose (IRE) **Mr Ian Murray**
29 **PASSENGER OMAR (IRE)**, 6, b g Safety Catch (USA)—Princess Douglas **Mrs V. Griffiths**
30 **PERFECT MATCH (IRE)**, 6, b br g Un Desperado (FR)—Imperial Blue (IRE) **Mr A. D. Weller**
31 **PLATINUM POINT (IRE)**, 5, b g Norwich—Blackhill Lass (IRE) **Mr David Gallacher**
32 **PRAIRIE LORD (IRE)**, 4, b g Lord of Appeal—Johara (USA) **Mrs S. Rowley-Williams**
33 **PRIDE OF FINEWOOD (IRE)**, 6, ch g Old Vic—Macamore Rose **Finewood Joinery Products**
34 **PRINCESSE SONIA (FR)**, 4, ch f Ashkalani (IRE)—Chirrup (FR) **Mrs N. Kelly**
35 **READY TO RUMBLE (IRE)**, 9, ch g Phardante (FR)—My Only Hope **Let's Get Ready To Rumble Partnership**
36 **RED RUFFLES (IRE)**, 5, b g Anshan—Rosie Ruffles (IRE) **T. F. C. Partnership**
37 **RIVER CITY (IRE)**, 7, b g Norwich—Shuil Na Lee (IRE) **Mrs S. Rowley-Williams & Partners**
38 **SANDS OF THYNE (IRE)**, 6, ch g Good Thyne (USA)—Yesterdays Gorby (IRE) **Mr A. D. Weller**
39 **SEA FERRY (IRE)**, 8, b g Ilium—Nicholas Ferry **Mr A. D. Weller**
40 4, B f Supreme Leader—Shannon Spray **Mrs N. Kelly**
41 **SLEEPING ROUGH (IRE)**, 7, b g Un Desperado—Zuhal **Mr A. D. Weller**
42 5, Ch g Witness Box (USA)—Some Gossip **Simpson & Castledine**
43 **SOUTHWESTERN (IRE)**, 5, br g Roselier (FR)—Catchthegoose **Mrs M. Sweeney**
44 **SOVIET SOCIETY (IRE)**, 6, b g Moscow Society (USA)—Catchmenot (IRE) **Mrs Rose Boyd**
45 **STILL SPEEDY (IRE)**, 8, b g Toulon—Gorge **Simpson, Still & Castledine**
46 **THE JOLLY BEGGAR (IRE)**, 6, gr g Jolly Jake (NZ)—Silk Empress **Shearwater Bray Syndicate**
47 **TRUST ME (IRE)**, 5, gr g Roselier (FR)—Lady Owenette (IRE) **Mrs M. Chance & Mr T. Warner**

THREE-YEAR-OLDS

48 **MISS JULIE JAY (IRE)**, b f Bahhare (USA)—Gentle Papoose **Mr Brian Jacobs**

Other Owners: Mr George Creighton, Mr K. H. Foster, Mr A. K. Gregory, Mr S. R. Harman, Mr J. P. Kelly, Mrs J. McKay, Mr Danny O'Sullivan, Mr A. J. Viall.

Assistant Trainer: Ian Yeates

Jockeys (Flat): J F McDonald (w.a.), J D Smith (w.a.). **Jockeys (NH):** T Doyle (w.a.), S Durack (w.a.), M Fitzgerald (w.a.). **Conditional:** Michael Deady (9-7), William Kennedy (9-7). **Amateurs:** Mr R F Coonan (10-0), Mr Neil Harris (10-7).

104 **MR M. CHANNON, West Ilsley**
Postal: West Ilsley Stables, West Ilsley, Newbury, Berkshire, RG20 7AE.
Contact: PHONE (01635) 281166 FAX (01635) 281177 E-MAIL mick@mick-channon.com

1 ALMIZAN (IRE), 4, b c Darshaan—Bint Albaadiya (USA) Sheikh Ahmed Al Maktoum
2 ARRY DASH, 4, b g Fraam—Miletrian Cares (IRE) Mike & Denise Dawes
3 B A HIGHFLYER, 4, b g Compton Place—Primulette The Highlife Racing Club
4 CHAMPION LION (IRE), 5, b g Sadler's Wells (USA)—Honey Bun Mr P. Trant
5 CHECKIT (IRE), 4, br c Mukaddamah (USA)—Collected (IRE) Mr Tim Corby
6 CLARADOTNET, 4, b f Sri Pekan (USA)—Lypharitissima (FR) Greenfield Stud
7 DIGITAL, 7, ch g Safawan—Heavenly Goddess Mr W. G. R. Wightman
8 FLOTTA, 5, ch g Elmaamul (USA)—Heavenly Goddess Mr W. G. R. Wightman
9 FRUIT OF GLORY, 5, b m Glory of Dancer—Fresh Fruit Daily Buy And Sell Partnership
10 GAZING (USA), 4, b f Gulch (USA)—Hidden Dreams Sheikh Mohammed
11 IMPERIAL DANCER, 6, b h Primo Dominie—Gorgeous Dancer (IRE) Mr Peter Taplin
12 IN THE PINK (IRE), 4, gr f Indian Ridge—Norfolk Lavender (CAN) Mrs D. J. Buckley
13 JAY GEE'S CHOICE, 4, b g Barathea (IRE)—Llia Mr John Guest
14 JOINT STATEMENT, 5, b g Barathea (IRE)—Gena Ivor Ridgeway Downs Racing
15 KEW THE MUSIC, 4, b g Botanic (USA)—Harmonia Miss Bridget Coyle
16 LONDONNETDOTCOM (IRE), 4, ch f Night Shift (USA)—Hopeful Sign Derek and Jean Clee
17 MALAPROPISM, 4, ch g Compton Place—Mrs Malaprop Mr Michael A. Foy
18 MASTER ROBBIE, 5, b g Piccolo—Victoria's Secret (IRE) Mr Alec Tuckerman
19 MILLENNIUM FORCE, 6, b g Bin Ajwaad (IRE)—Jumairah Sun (IRE) Mr A. Merza
20 MISTERNANDO, 4, b c Hernando (FR)—Mistinguett (IRE) Mr John Duggan
21 NAAHY, 4, ch c Bahamian Bounty—Daffodil Fields Kuwait Racing Syndicate 2001
22 NAJEEBON (FR), 5, ch h Cadeaux Genereux—Jumairah Sun (IRE) Mr A. Merza
23 NIGHT WOLF, 4, gr g Indian Ridge—Nicer (IRE)
24 PATANDON GIRL (IRE), 4, b f Night Shift (USA)—Petite Jameel (IRE) Mr R. Gurney
25 PIC UP STICKS, 5, gr g Piccolo—Between The Sticks A. Ball & W. Harrison-Allan
26 POLAR FORCE, 4, ch g Polar Falcon (USA)—Irish Light (USA) Ridgeway Downs Racing
27 ROYAL MILLENNIUM (IRE), 6, b g Royal Academy (USA)—Galatrix Jackie & George Smith
28 SATTELIGHT, 4, b f Fraam—Ajig Dancer Timberhill Racing Partnership
29 TOWER OF LONDON, 4, ch g Hector Protector (USA)—Special Guest Mr Jean-Claude Chalmet
30 WOOD FERN (UAE), 4, b c Green Desert (USA)—Woodsia Mr M. Channon

THREE-YEAR-OLDS

31 AMEYRAH (IRE), b f In The Wings—Alfaaselah (GER) Mr A. Merza
32 ARFINNIT (IRE), b g College Chapel—Tidal Reach (USA) Mr Tim Corby
33 BAAWRAH, ch c Cadeaux Genereux—Kronengold (USA) Sheikh Ahmed Al Maktoum
34 BLACK OVAL, b f Royal Applause—Corniche Quest (IRE) Glass Associates
35 CALDY DANCER (IRE), ch f Soviet Star (USA)—Smile Awhile (USA) Mr Mohammed Rashid
36 CATALINI, ch c Seeking The Gold (USA)—Calando (USA) Sheikh Mohammed
37 CATHERINE HOWARD, b f Kingmambo (USA)—Darling Flame (USA) Sheikh Mohammed
38 CHARLIE TANGO (IRE), b g Desert Prince (IRE)—Precedence (IRE) Mr Patrick Trant
39 COMPTON'S ELEVEN, gr g Compton Place—Princess Tara PCM Racing
40 Ch c Titus Livius (FR)—Dancing Sunset (IRE) Mrs Theresa Burns
41 DERNIER DANSE, b f Fasliyev (USA)—Dernier Cri Mrs John Moore
42 EBN NAAS (IRE), b g Dayjur (USA)—Katakana (USA) Sheikh Ahmed Al Maktoum
43 ERTE, ch g Vettori (IRE)—Cragreen Mr Peter Taplin
44 FIDDLES MUSIC, b f Fraam—Fiddles Delight W. R. Channon
45 FIRE FINCH, ch f Halling (USA)—Fly For Fame Mrs John Moore
46 FIRST DAWN, ch f Dr Fong (USA)—Delight of Dawn Diane & John Dewhurst
47 FUN AND GAMES (IRE), ch f Rahy (USA)—Sharpwitted Sheikh Mohammed
48 GATWICK (IRE), b c Ali-Royal (IRE)—Airport Mr W. H. Ponsonby
49 HANA DEE, b f Cadeaux Genereux—Jumairah Sun (IRE) Mr Aziz Merza
50 HATHLEN (IRE), b c Singspiel (IRE)—Kameez (USA) Sheikh Ahmed Al Maktoum
51 ILWADOD, b c Cadeaux Genereux—Wedoudah (IRE) Sheikh Ahmed Al Maktoum
52 JAZZ SCENE (IRE), b c Danehill Dancer (USA)—Dixie Jazz Mr R. E. Sangster
53 JUMEIRAH SCARER, b g Tagula (IRE)—Mountain Harvest (FR)
54 LEG SPINNER (IRE), b g Intikhab (USA)—Road Harbour (USA) Mr Peter Savill
55 LE TISS (IRE), b c Croco Rouge (IRE)—Manarah Mr P. Trant
56 B f City Honours (USA)—Little Sega (FR)
57 LYRICAL GIRL (USA), b f Orpen (USA)—Lyric Theatre (USA) C. S. G. Limited
58 MAHMOOM, ch c Dr Fong (USA)—Rohita (IRE) Sheikh Ahmed Al Maktoum
59 MAJESTIC DESERT, b f Fraam—Calcutta Queen Mr Jaber Abdullah
60 MAJOR SMILE, ch g Wolfhound (USA)—Session Mr John Sillett

MR M. CHANNON—continued

61 **MAKFOOL (FR)**, b c Spectrum (IRE)—Abeyr **Sheikh Ahmed Al Maktoum**
62 **MAMBINA (USA)**, ch f Kingmambo (USA)—Sonata **Mr R. A. Scarborough & Mr M. Jojkitty**
63 **MARIAH (IRE)**, b f Danzig (USA)—Race The Wild Wind (USA) **Mr R. A. Scarborough**
64 **MILLBAG (IRE)**, b br c Cape Cross (IRE)—Play With Fire (FR) **Sheikh Ahmed Al Maktoum**
65 **MISSATTITUDE**, gr f Silver Patriarch (IRE)—Phil's Folly **Phil Jen Racing**
66 **MOKABRA (IRE)**, b c Cape Cross (IRE)—Pacific Grove **Sheikh Ahmed Al Maktoum**
67 **MOMMKIN**, b f Royal Academy (USA)—Walimu (IRE) **Sheikh Ahmed Al Maktoum**
68 **NAADDEY**, b c Seeking The Gold (USA)—Bahr **Sheikh Ahmed Al Maktoum**
69 **NAZZWAH**, ch f Rahy (USA)—Baaderah (IRE) **Sheikh Ahmed Al Maktoum**
70 **NEGWA (IRE)**, b f Bering—Ballet **Kuwait Racing Syndicate 2001**
71 **NIGHTS CROSS (IRE)**, b c Cape Cross (IRE)—Cathy Garcia (IRE) **Ridgeway Downs Racing**
72 **NORTH SEA (IRE)**, b f Selkirk (USA)—Sea Spray (IRE) **Mr Jaber Abdullah**
73 **NOUVEAU RICHE (IRE)**, ch f Entrepreneur—Dime Bag **Mr Nicholas Cooper**
74 **QUICKSTYX**, b f Night Shift (USA)—Red Bouquet **Mr John Breslin**
75 **RIMSKY (IRE)**, gr g Silver Patriarch (IRE)—Mistinguett (IRE) **Mr John Duggan**
76 **ROMEO'S DAY**, ch g Pursuit of Love—Daarat Alayaam (IRE) **Heart Of The South Racing**
77 **ROYAL LOGIC**, b f Royal Applause—Lucie Edward **The Long And The Short**
78 **RUGGTAH**, gr f Daylami (IRE)—Raneen Alwatar **Sheikh Ahmed Al Maktoum**
79 **SAINTLY PLACE**, ch g Compton Place—Always On A Sunday **W. Harrison-Allan, D. Bellamy, M. Wilson**
80 **SAKHYA (IRE)**, b f Barathea (IRE)—Um Lardaff **Mr Ziad A. Galadari**
81 **SAN LORENZO (UAE)**, ch f Machiavellian (USA)—Sanchez **Sheikh Mohammed**
82 **SENESCHAL**, b c Polar Falcon (USA)—Broughton Singer (IRE) **Mr Peter Taplin**
83 **SHAABAN (IRE)**, b c Woodman (USA)—Ashbilya (USA) **Sheikh Ahmed Al Maktoum**
84 **SIGNORA PANETTIERA (FR)**, ch f Lord of Men—Karaferya (USA) **The Mystery Partnership**
85 **SILCA'S GIFT**, b f Cadeaux Genereux—Odette **Aldridge Racing Limited**
86 **THEMESOFGREEN**, ch g Botanic (USA)—Harmonia **Miss Bridget Coyle**
87 **THE STICK**, b f Singspiel (IRE)—Fatah Flare **Mr M. Channon**
88 **TIZ MOLLY (IRE)**, ch f Definite Article—Almadaniyah **Mr John M. Richards**
89 **TOP SEED (IRE)**, b c Cadeaux Genereux—Midnight Heights **Mr John Livock**
90 **TRULY WONDERFUL (IRE)**, ch f Highest Honor (FR)—Ahliyat (USA) **Mr M. A. Foy**
91 **VICTORY LAP (GER)**, ch f Grand Lodge (USA)—Vicenca (USA) **Mr Jaber Abdullah**
92 **WAAEDAH (IRE)**, ch f Halling (USA)—Agama (USA) **Sheikh Ahmed Al Maktoum**
93 **WOU OODD**, ch f Barathea (IRE)—Abyaan (IRE) **Sheikh Ahmed Al Maktoum**

TWO-YEAR-OLDS

94 B f 17/1 Fraam—Ajig Dancer (Niniski (USA)) **Timberhill Racing Partnership**
95 B br c 25/3 Cape Cross (IRE)—Alexander Confranc (IRE) (Magical Wonder (USA)) (130000) **Mr John Guest**
96 **AL GARHOUD BRIDGE**, b c 3/2 Josr Algarhoud (IRE)—Pluck (Never So Bold) (24737) **Mr Jaber Abdullah**
97 **ARABIAN DANCER**, b f 12/2 Dansili—Hymne (Saumarez) (3000) **Mr Jaber Abdullah**
98 **BAG OF GOLD**, b c 15/3 Anabaa (USA)—Hiddnah (USA) (Affirmed (USA)) **Mr Jaber Abdullah**
99 **BALL BOY**, b c 19/1 Xaar—Tanz (IRE) (Sadler's Wells (USA)) (49474) **John Livock Bloodstock**
100 Ch f 20/4 Vettori (IRE)—Between The Sticks (Pharly (FR)) (7500) **Mr Shaun Cunningham**
101 **BIBURY FLYER**, br f 13/2 Zafonic (USA)—
      Affair of State (IRE) (Tate Gallery (USA)) (35000) **Ridgeway Downs Racing**
102 **BOBBIE LOVE**, ch c 9/4 Fraam—Enlisted (IRE) (Sadler's Wells (USA)) (30000) **Mr Graeme Love**
103 **BOLD CHEVRAK**, b c 10/2 Bold Edge—Curlew Calling (IRE) (Pennine Walk) (22262) **Mr Tim Corby**
104 **BRIANNSTA (IRE)**, b c 19/4 Bluebird (USA)—Nacote (IRE) (Mtoto) (10000) **Mr B. Brooks**
105 B f 25/1 Barathea (IRE)—Brigadiers Bird (IRE) (Mujadil (USA)) **Barry Walters Catering**
106 B f 3/5 Lujain (USA)—Chief Ornament (USA) (Chief's Crown (USA)) **Sheikh Ahmed Al Maktoum**
107 **CORNICHE DANCER**, b f 1/1 Marju (IRE)—Sellette (IRE) (Selkirk (USA)) (22000) **Mrs A. M. Jones**
108 B f 17/1 Cadeaux Genereux—Cream Tease (Pursuit of Love) (40000) **Kuwait Racing Syndicate**
109 **CROSS TIME (USA)**, b br c 18/3 Cape Cross (IRE)—
      Reine Maid (USA) (Mr Prospector (USA)) (46381) **Mr Jaber Abdullah**
110 **DAHTEER (IRE)**, b c 10/2 Bachir (USA)—Reematna (Sabrehill (USA)) **Sheikh Ahmed Al Maktoum**
111 **DANCE FLOWER (IRE)**, b f 11/2 Cape Cross (IRE)—
      Ninth Wonder (USA) (Forty Niner (USA)) (58000) **Mr Jaber Abdullah**
112 **DESERT MOVE (IRE)**, b f 30/4 Desert King—
      Campestral (USA) (Alleged (USA)) (30920) **Mr Jaber Abdullah**
113 **DIAMOND DAN (IRE)**, b c 11/5 Foxhound (USA)—Kawther (Tap On Wood) (6801) **Diamond Racing Ltd**
114 **DIKTATIT**, b f 31/1 Diktat—Mystique Smile (Music Boy) (23000) **Mr Tim Corby**
115 **DOCTOR BAILEY**, b c 22/5 Mister Baileys—Frustration (Salse (USA)) (32000) **Mr Jaber Abdullah**
116 B f 1/5 Fraam—Fading (Pharly (FR)) **Mr Peter Taplin**
117 **FEDERATION (IRE)**, b c 6/3 Desert Prince (IRE)—Fajjoura (IRE) (Fairy King (USA)) (30000) **Sheikh Mohammed**
118 Ch f 20/4 Bahamian Bounty—Flying Wind (Forzando) **Heart of The South Racing**

MR M. CHANNON—continued

119 **FORCE IN THE WINGS (IRE)**, b f 26/4 In The Wings—
Cathy Garcia (IRE) (Be My Guest (USA)) (64934) **Mr Jaber Abdullah**

120 B c 13/5 Dansili—Gayane (Nureyev (USA)) (9000)

121 **GIMASHA**, b f 23/3 Cadeaux Genereux—First Waltz (FR) (Green Dancer (USA)) **Ziad A. Galadari**

122 **GOLD MAJESTY**, b f 27/4 Josr Algarhoud (IRE)—Calcutta Queen (Night Shift (USA)) (35868) **Mr Jaber Abdullah**

123 **GOLD QUEEN**, b f 12/2 Grand Lodge (USA)—
Silver Colours (USA) (Silver Hawk (USA)) (120000) **Mr Jaber Abdullah**

124 **HALLHOO (IRE)**, gr c 3/3 Indian Ridge—
Nuit Chaud (USA) (Woodman (USA)) (210000) **Sheikh Ahmed Al Maktoum**

125 **HAPPY BANKER (IRE)**, gr c 4/2 With Approval (CAN)—
Tropical Paradise (USA) (Manila (USA)) (48000) **Mr Jaber Abdullah**

126 **HENRIK**, b c 21/3 Primo Dominie—Clincher Club (Polish Patriot (USA)) (100000) **Mr John Breslin**

127 **JOINT ASPIRATION**, ch f 2/5 Pivotal—Welcome Home (Most Welcome) (36000) **Ridgeway Downs Racing**

128 B c 18/4 Cadeaux Genereux—Jumairah Sun (IRE) (Scenic) (105000) **Sheikh Mohammed**

129 **KALMINI (USA)**, b f 25/4 Rahy (USA)—Kilma (USA) (Silver Hawk (USA)) **Sheikh Ahmed Al Maktoum**

130 **KAPAJE**, b f 17/4 Lake Coniston (IRE)—Reina (Homeboy) (3000) **Diamond Racing Ltd**

131 B c 31/1 Royal Applause—Keen Melody (USA) (Sharpen Up)

132 B f 14/3 Zafonic (USA)—Kerry Ring (Sadler's Wells (USA)) **Sheikh Mohammed**

133 **KING MARRAKECH (IRE)**, b c 14/1 King's Best (USA)—
Tenue d'Amour (FR) (Pursuit of Love) (68027) **Mr Jaber Abdullah**

134 **KING ZAFEEN (IRE)**, b c 15/2 Lend A Hand—
Groom Dancing (Groom Dancer (USA)) (50000) **Mr Jaber Abdullah**

135 **LA CUENTA (IRE)**, b f 11/5 Barathea (IRE)—Orlena (Gone West (USA)) (23500) **Mr Tim Corby**

136 B c 25/4 Rossini (USA)—Livry (USA) (Lyphard (USA)) (40000) **Mr Jaber Abdullah**

137 B c 27/4 Lujain (USA)—Lovely Millie (IRE) (Bluebird (USA)) **Mohammed Al Nabouda**

138 **LOVE THIRTY**, b f 3/3 Mister Baileys—Polished Up (Polish Precedent (USA)) (120000) **John Livock Bloodstock**

139 B c 9/3 Zafonic (USA)—Lypharitissima (FR) (Lightning (FR)) **Greenfield Stud**

140 **MAGIC TREE (UAE)**, ch f 25/1 Timber Country (USA)—Moyesii (USA) (Diesis) **Sheikh Mohammed**

141 **MAHMJRA**, b c 24/2 Josr Algarhoud (IRE)—
Jamrat Samya (IRE) (Sadler's Wells (USA)) **Sheikh Ahmed Al Maktoum**

142 **MAJESTIC RANIA (IRE)**, ch f 21/2 Giant's Causeway—Crystal Ring (IRE) (Kris) (130000) **Mr Jaber Abdullah**

143 **MAJEST SAKEENA (IRE)**, b f 3/3 King's Best (USA)—
Shy Danceuse (FR) (Groom Dancer (USA)) (136054) **Jaber Abdullah**

144 **MAKEPEACE (IRE)**, b c 9/4 Xaar—Marillette (USA) (Diesis) **Sheikh Mohammed**

145 **MARHABA MILLION (IRE)**, gr c 21/4 Linamix (FR)—Modelliste (Machiavellian (USA)) **Mr Jaber Abdullah**

146 **MARHABA YA ZAIN**, b f 29/1 Anabaa (USA)—Legende d'Or (FR) (Diesis) **Mr Jaber Abdullah**

147 B c 3/4 Spectrum (IRE)—Mary Magdalene (Night Shift (USA)) (21644)

148 **MASTER JOSEPH**, b c 12/4 Mister Baileys—Petit Peu (IRE) (Kings Lake (USA)) (18000) **Alec Tuckerman**

149 B f 3/2 Rahy (USA)—Millstream (USA) (Dayjur (USA)) **Sheikh Ahmed Al Maktoum**

150 **MIN ASL WAFI (IRE)**, b f 26/3 Octagonal (NZ)—Shy Lady (FR) (Kaldoun (FR)) **Mr Jaber Abdullah**

151 B f 17/4 Alhaarth (IRE)—Miss Willow Bend (USA) (Willow Hour (USA)) (32000) **Sheikh Mohammed**

152 **MOONMAIDEN**, ch f 13/2 Selkirk (USA)—Top Table (Shirley Heights) **Derek & Jean Clee**

153 **MOZAFIN**, b c 12/3 Zafonic (USA)—Bedara (Barathea (IRE)) (58000) **Mr Jaber Abdullah**

154 **MUJAZAF**, b c 25/4 Grand Lodge (USA)—Decision Maid (USA) (Diesis) (150000) **Mr Jaber Abdullah**

155 B f 25/3 Xaar—My Lass (Elmaamul (USA)) **Mr John Guest**

156 B f 4/4 Fraam—Natalie Jay (Ballacashtal (CAN))

157 **NOORAIN**, ch f 5/4 Kabool—Abeyr (Unfuwain (USA)) **Sheikh Ahmed Al Maktoum**

158 B f 10/3 Xaar—Once In My Life (IRE) (Lomond (USA)) **Sheikh Mohammed**

159 B f 22/3 Desert Style (IRE)—Option (IRE) (Red Ransom (USA)) (8000)

160 B f 22/1 Emarati (USA)—Perfect Partner (Be My Chief (USA)) **Mrs Jean Keegan**

161 Br c 14/2 Pivotal—Persian Air (Persian Bold) (130000) **Sheikh Mohammed**

162 B c 29/1 Timber Country (USA)—Poised (Rahy (USA)) **Sheikh Mohammed**

163 B f 4/3 Machiavellian (USA)—Polisonne (Polish Precedent (USA)) **Sheikh Mohammed**

164 **PRESS EXPRESS**, ch c 11/3 Entrepreneur—Nawaji (USA) (Trempolino (USA)) **Mr Tareq Al Mazeedi**

165 **PROPRIOCEPTION (IRE)**, ch f 14/5 Danehill Dancer (IRE)—
Pepper And Salt (Double Schwartz) (12368) **Ridgeway Downs Racing**

166 **QUEEN'S DANCER**, b f 17/4 Groom Dancer (USA)—Special Beat (Bustino) **Carmel Wardley**

167 **QUEEN AL ANDALOUS (IRE)**, ch f 2/2 King's Best (USA)—
Speremm (IRE) (Sadler's Wells (USA)) (30000) **Mr Jaber Abdullah**

168 B f 2/2 Lujain (USA)—Rain And Shine (FR) (Rainbow Quest (USA)) **Mr Aziz Merza**

169 **RAIN STOPS PLAY (IRE)**, b c 20/3 Desert Prince (IRE)—
Pinta (IRE) (Ahonoora) (68026) **John Livock Bloodstock**

170 B c 9/2 Josr Algarhoud (IRE)—Raneen Alwatar (Sadler's Wells (USA)) **Sheikh Ahmed Al Maktoum**

171 B f 31/1 Machiavellian (USA)—Risque Lady (Kenmare (FR)) (100000) **Sheikh Mohammed**

172 B f 13/4 Inchinor—Robin (Slip Anchor) (30920)

173 **ROCAMADOUR**, b c 10/2 Celtic Swing—Watch Me (IRE) (Green Desert (USA)) **Mr Salem Suhail**

MR M. CHANNON—continued

174 **ROSALINDA,** b f 30/4 Green Desert (USA)—Nijoodh (Selkirk (USA)) **Mr Jaber Abdullah**
175 Gr c 10/2 Machiavellian (USA)—Rowassi (Green Desert (USA)) **Sheikh Ahmed Al Maktoum**
176 **ROYAL FATIMA (IRE),** b f 25/2 Fasliyev (USA)—
Royal Bounty (IRE) (Generous (IRE)) (74211) **Newsells Park Stud**
177 **ROYAL JET,** b c 3/5 Royal Applause—Red Bouquet (Reference Point) (58000) **Mr Jaber Abdullah**
178 Ch c 1/3 Sinndar (IRE)—Sacristy (Godswalk (USA)) (18552)
179 **SADIE THOMPSON (IRE),** b f 2/2 King's Best (USA)—
Femme Fatale (Fairy King (USA)) (130000) **Sheikh Mohammed**
180 **SEA HUNTER,** b c 10/2 Lend A Hand—Ocean Grove (IRE) (Fairy King (USA)) (110000) **Sheikh Mohammed**
181 B f 28/3 Lujain (USA)—Search Party (Rainbow Quest (USA)) (6183)
182 B f 11/2 Kingmambo (USA)—Shimaal (Sadler's Wells (USA)) **Sheikh Mohammed**
183 **SHIVAREE,** ch f 13/4 Rahy (USA)—Shmoose (IRE) (Caerleon (USA)) **Sheikh Mohammed**
184 **SHUJUNE AL HAWAA (USA),** ch f 16/2 Grand Lodge (USA)—
Bank On Her (USA) (Rahy (USA)) (35000) **Mr Jaber Abdullah**
185 **SIGNORINA ROSSA,** b f 24/2 Royal Applause—Song of Skye (Warning) **C. Fenaroli & F. T. Adams**
186 B f 13/5 Josr Algarhoud (IRE)—Silankka (Slip Anchor) (4200)
187 **SMOOTH JAZZ,** b c 27/2 Zafonic (USA)—Halska (Unfuwain (USA)) (105132) **Mr P. D. Savill**
188 **STAN'S GIRL,** b f 14/3 Fraam—Gigetta (USA) (Brief Truce (USA)) (14500) **The Stan James Winners**
189 **STANBURY (USA),** ch c 7/1 Zamindar (USA)—Staffin (Salse (USA)) (130000) **Sheikh Mohammed**
190 B f 19/3 Fraam—Stride Home (Absalom) **Mr Peter Taplin**
191 **SUNSET STRIP,** b c 9/4 Josr Algarhoud (IRE)—Shady Street (Shadeed (USA)) **Sheikh Mohammed**
192 B br f 19/4 Timber Country (USA)—Tanami (Green Desert (USA)) **Sheikh Mohammed**
193 **TETRA SING (IRE),** b f 31/3 Sinndar (IRE)—Tetralogy (USA) (Mt Livermore (USA)) (40197) **Newsells Park Stud**
194 B f 15/3 Bianconi (USA)—Tip Tap Toe (USA) (Pleasant Tap (USA)) (1236)
195 **TOSS THE CABER (IRE),** ch c 10/4 Dr Devious (USA)—Celtic Fling (Lion Cavern (USA)) **Mr P. D. Savill**
196 **TOUFAN EXPRESS,** ch c 19/3 Fraam—Clan Scotia (Clantime) (5200) **Mr Jaber Abdullah**
197 **TOURNEDOS (IRE),** b c 9/3 Rossini (USA)—Don't Care (IRE) (Nordico (USA)) (18552) **Ridgeway Downs Racing**
198 **UMNIYA (IRE),** b f 22/3 Bluebird (USA)—Sparky's Song (Electric) (40000) **Kuwait Racing Syndicate**
199 **VICTORY HYMN (IRE),** b f 28/4 Victory Note (USA)—
Nordic Union (IRE) (Nordico (USA)) (7420) **Henry Ponsonby**
200 **WASALAT (USA),** b f 27/1 Bahri (USA)—Saabga (USA) (Woodman (USA)) **Sheikh Ahmed Al Maktoum**
201 B f 26/3 Emarati (USA)—Wrong Bride (Reprimand) **Mrs Jean Keegan**
202 **YAJBILL (IRE),** b c 23/2 Royal Applause—Tee Cee (Lion Cavern (USA)) (140000) **Sheikh Ahmed Al Maktoum**
203 **ZAHARAT ALUWITH,** ch f 7/4 Primo Dominie—
Sandicliffe (USA) (Imp Society (USA)) (30000) **Mr Jaber Abdullah**

Other Owners: Mr F. T. Adams, Anthony Andrews, Martin Bishop, G. Blackwell, Mr Nigel Bunter, Mrs J. M. Channon, Mr Derek D. Clee, Mrs Jean P. Clee, Mrs C. A. Fenaroli, Mrs Belinda Harvey, Richard Hill, Mr N. J. Hitchins, Kevin Hudson, Mr R. Jewers, Mrs Jean Keegan, Mr Terry Leigh, Ms K. Lowe, Mike Channon Bloodstock Ltd, Richard Newsholme, Sir Arthur Norman, Dr R. P. Norwich, Mr Robin Olley, Mr John Penny, Carole Roper, Mr G. A. E. Smith, Mrs G. A. E. Smith, Phil Stevenson, Surrey Laminators Ltd, Team Havana, Village Racing, Whitwell Racing, Mr J. A. Williams.

Assistant Trainer: Paul Deegan

Jockeys (Flat): Chris Catlin (7-10), A Culhane (8-4), T E Durcan (8-3). **Apprentices:** Dean Corby (8-1), Sam Hitchcott (8-1), Tom O'Brien (7-12), Brian O'Neill (8-1). **Amateur:** Miss Tania Dzieciolowska.

---

105 MR DAVID W. CHAPMAN, York
Postal: Mowbray House Farm, Stillington, York, YO61 1LT.
Contact: **PHONE (01347) 821683 CAR PHONE (07966) 513866 FAX (01347) 821683**

1 **CATERHAM COMMON,** 5, b g Common Grounds—Pennine Pink (IRE) **Mr David W. Chapman**
2 **CHANTEUSE,** 4, b f Rudimentary (USA)—Enchanting Melody **Mr Michael Hill**
3 **DIAMOND RACKET,** 4, b g Cyrano de Bergerac—Reina **Mr David W. Chapman**
4 **DRURY LANE (IRE),** 4, b br c Royal Applause—Ghost Tree (IRE) **Mr Michael Hill**
5 **HEADLAND (USA),** 6, b br g Distant View (USA)—Fijar Echo (USA) **Mr Harold D White**
6 **IPLEDGEALLEGIANCE (USA),** 8, b g Alleged (USA)—Yafill (USA) **Mr J. M. Chapman**
7 **LEMARATE (USA),** 7, b g Gulch (USA)—Sayyedati **Mr David W. Chapman**
8 **LEVELLED,** 10, b g Beveled (USA)—Baino Charm (USA) **Mr David W. Chapman**
9 **MARABAR,** 6, b m Sri Pekan (USA)—Erbaya (IRE) **Miss N. F. Thesiger**
10 **MISS OCEAN MONARCH,** 4, ch f Blue Ocean (USA)—Faraway Grey **Mr David W. Chapman**
11 **MISTER RUSHBY,** 6, b g Hamas (IRE)—Final Rush **Mr David W. Chapman**
12 **ON THE TRAIL,** 7, ch g Catrail (USA)—From The Rooftops (IRE) **Mr J. M. Chapman**
13 **PADDYWACK (IRE),** 7, b g Bigstone—Millie's Return (IRE) **Mr T. S. Redman**
14 **PEARTREE HOUSE (IRE),** 10, b g Simply Majestic (USA)—Fashion Front **Mr J. M. Chapman**

MR DAVID W. CHAPMAN—continued

15 QUITO (IRE), 7, b r Machiavellian (USA)—Qirmazi (USA) **Mr Michael Hill**
16 REDOUBTABLE (USA), 13, b h Grey Dawn II—Seattle Rockette (USA) **Mr David W. Chapman**
17 SHARP HAT, 10, b g Shavian—Madam Trilby **Miss N. F. Thesiger**
18 SOAKED, 11, b g Dowsing (USA)—Water Well **Mr David W. Chapman**
19 SUPREME SALUTATION, 8, ch g Most Welcome—Cardinal Press **Mr David W. Chapman**
20 TANAFFUS, 4, ch g Cadeaux Genereux—El Rabab (USA) **Mr Michael Hill**
21 TORRENT, 9, ch g Prince Sabo—Maiden Pool **Mr David W. Chapman**
22 VALAZAR (USA), 5, b g Nicholas (USA)—Valor's Minion (USA) **Give Your Head a Shake Syndicate**
23 ZARIN (IRE), 6, b g Inzar (USA)—Non Dimenticar Me (IRE) **Mr J. M. Chapman**

THREE-YEAR-OLDS

24 DANDY JIM, b c Dashing Blade—Madam Trilby **Miss N. F. Thesiger**

Other Owners: Mr Derrick Armstrong, Mr J. B. Salkeld, Mr P. A. Salkeld.

Assistant Trainer: Mrs M Chapman

Jockey (Flat): A Culhane. **Amateur:** Mr Richard Clark (11-2).

---

106 **MR M. C. CHAPMAN, Market Rasen**
Postal: **Woodlands Racing Stables, Woodlands Lane, Willingham Road, Market Rasen, Lincolnshire, LN8 3RE.**
Contact: **PHONE (01673) 843663 FAX (01673) 843663 MOBILE (07971) 940087**

1 AGUILA LOCO (IRE), 5, ch g Eagle Eyed (USA)—Go Likecrazy **Mr K. D. Blanch**
2 AMANDA'S LAD (IRE), 4, b g Danetime (IRE)—Art Duo **Mr Eric Knowles**
3 ASHTAROUTE (USA), 4, b f Holy Bull (USA)—Beating The Buzz (IRE) **Twinacre Nurseries Ltd**
4 BLUNHAM, 4, b g Danzig Connection (USA)—Relatively Sharp **Twinacre Nurseries Ltd**
5 BRILLIANTRIO, 6, ch m Selkirk (USA)—Loucoum (FR) **Mr R. B. Baldwin**
6 CROMWELL (IRE), 9, b g Last Tycoon—Catherine Parr (USA) **Sir Stanley Clarke**
7 DALRIATH, 5, b m Fraam—Alsiba **Mr M. B. Gielty**
8 EI EI, 9, b g North Briton—Branitska **Mrs S. M. Richards**
9 GRANDMA LILY (IRE), 6, b m Bigstone (IRE)—Mrs Fisher (IRE) **David Fravigar,Alan Mann,David Marshall**
10 HAZEL MERE, 4, b f Gildoran—After Time
11 HOME BY SOCKS (IRE), 5, ch m Desert King (IRE)—Propitious (IRE) **Mrs S. M. Richards**
12 ILOVETURTLE (IRE), 4, b g Turtle Island (IRE)—Gan Ainm (IRE) **Coverscope Ductwork & Reedkleen Supplies**
13 KNOWN MANEUVER (USA), 6, b g Known Fact (USA)—
                        Northern Maneuver (USA) **David Fravigar,Alan Mann,David Marshall**
14 METICULOUS, 6, gr g Eagle Eyed (USA)—Careful (IRE) **Mr Eric Knowles**
15 NICIARA (IRE), 7, b g Soviet Lad (USA)—Verusa (IRE) **Mr A. Mann**
16 WIN ALOT, 6, b g Aragon—Having Fun **Coverscope Ductwork & Reedkleen Supplies**

THREE-YEAR-OLDS

17 COTTINGHAM (IRE), b c Perugino (USA)—Stately Princess **Twinacre Nurseries Ltd**
18 FAYRZ PLEASE (IRE), ch g Fayruz—Castlelue (IRE) **Coverscope Ductwork & Reedkleen Supplies**
19 SIEGFRIEDS NIGHT (IRE), ch g Night Shift (USA)—Shelbiana (USA) **Mr K. D. Blanch**

Jockey (NH): Lee Vickers (9-11). **Apprentice:** Andrew Webb (7-5).

---

107 **MR G. F. H. CHARLES-JONES, Okehampton**
Postal: **Millaton Farm, Bridestowe, Okehampton, Devon, EX20 4QG.**
Contact: **PHONE (01837) 861100 CAR (07836) 275292**

1 ANGIE'S DOUBLE, 4, ch f Double Trigger (IRE)—Arch Angel (IRE) **Mr P. H. Wafford**
2 BRACKEN FIRE, 10, b m Jupiter Island—Dragon Fire **Mr R. A. Hughes**
3 GAINFUL, 5, ch m Elmaamul (USA)—Regain **Miss Helen Wynne**
4 KAY BEE VENTURE, 5, ch m Karinga Bay—Take The Veil **Okebrooke Racing**
5 WHIPPERS DELIGHT (IRE), 16, ch g King Persian—Crashing Juno **Mrs Jessica Charles-Jones**

MR G. F. H. CHARLES-JONES—continued
THREE-YEAR-OLDS
6 KATZ PYJAMAS (IRE), b f Fasliyev (USA)—Allepolina (USA) **Miss Helen Wynne**

Other Owners: Mr C. J. Field, Mr D. G. West.

Assistant Trainer: Jessica Charles-Jones

Jockey (Flat): Joanna Badger (7-10, w.a.). **Apprentice:** Charlotte Cox (7-12, w.a.). **Conditional:** C Honour. **Amateurs:** Mr A Charles-Jones (10-0), Mr James White (9-7, w.a.).

---

108 MR A. CHARLTON, Marlborough
Postal: **c/o East Woodhay House, Newbury, Berkshire, RG20 0NF.**
Contact: **PHONE (01264) 852789 MOBILE (07968) 463044**
E-MAIL clbracing@lineone.net WEBSITE www.clbracing.com

1 BIRTH OF THE BLUES, 8, ch g Efisio—Great Steps **Miss Juliet E. Reed**
2 INVITATION, 6, b g Bin Ajwaad (IRE)—On Request (IRE) **Woodhaven Racing Syndicate**
3 MAGIC STONE, 4, br g Magic Ring (IRE)—Ridgewood Ruby (IRE) **The Ruby Partnership**
4 SARIBA, 5, b m Persian Bold—En Vacances (IRE) **Mrs Sarah J. Diamandis**
5 SEMPRE SORRISO, 4, b f Fleetwood (IRE)—Ever Genial **Mr P. J. Haycock**
6 TORTUGA DREAM (IRE), 5, b g Turtle Island (IRE)—Tycoon's Catch (IRE) **Mr P. J. Haycock**
7 WELLINGTON HALL (GER), 6, b g Halling (USA)—Wells Whisper (FR) **Allan Darke & Tom Matthews**

THREE-YEAR-OLDS
8 CICATRICE, ch c Wolfhound (USA)—Capricious Lady (IRE) **Miss Juliet E. Reed**
9 FRAAMTASTIC LASS, ch f Fraam—Audrey Grace **The Snowy Syndicate**
10 LUCHI, ch f Mark of Esteem (IRE)—Penmayne **Mr A. Charlton**
11 MR STROWGER, b c Dancing Spree (USA)—Matoaka **Mr A. Charlton**
12 PICAFILLY, b f Piccolo—My Preference **Robert F Oliver Pauline S Oliver**
13 RED CONTACT (USA), b c Sahm (USA)—Basma (USA) **Mr A. Charlton**
14 SUDDEN IMPULSE, b f Silver Patriarch (IRE)—Sanshang (FR) **Mr J. M. Sancaster**

Other Owners: Mr P. G. Haran, Mrs J. P. Haycock, Mr Anthony Kelly, Mr C. Leafe, Mr R. E. Scott, Mr D. Tye.

Assistant Trainer: Mr Carl Leafe

Jockeys (Flat): D O'Neill, R Smith. **Apprentice:** D Bashton.

---

109 MR J. I. A. CHARLTON, Stocksfield
Postal: **Mickley Grange, Stocksfield, Northumberland, NE43 7TB.**
Contact: **PHONE (01661) 843247 MOBILE (07850) 007415**

1 BYWELL BEAU (IRE), 5, b g Lord Americo—Early Dalus (IRE) **Mr W. F. Trueman**
2 CAPTAIN MURPHY (IRE), 6, b g Executive Perk—Laura Daisy **Mr M. H. Walton**
3 DECENT ROSE (IRE), 6, ch m Roselier (FR)—Decent Banker **Sydney Ramsey & Partners**
4 HOT AIR (IRE), 6, b g Air Display (USA)—Lyraisa **Mr J. I. A. Charlton**
5 LUNAR MAXWELL, 9, b g Dancing High—Pauper Moon **Mr J. W. Robson**
6 MILLERBURN (IRE), 5, b g Ajraas (USA)—Granalice **The Tyne and Rede Partnership**
7 NO KIDDING, 10, b g Teenoso (USA)—Vaigly Fine **Miss J. Palmer**
8 PEGGY SIOUX (IRE), 7, b m Little Bighorn—Gayable **Mr John Hogg**
9 SEA KNIGHT (IRE), 7, b g Beau Sher—Meaney **Mr J. I. A. Charlton**
10 SNOWY (IRE), 6, gr g Pierre—Snowy Gunner **Mr & Mrs Raymond Anderson Green**
11 TOBESURE (IRE), 10, b g Asir—Princess Citrus (IRE) **Mr Richard Nixon**

Other Owners: Ms J. M. Findlay, Mrs Anita Green, Mr Syd Ramsey, Ms J. Rutherford, Mr J. T. Stobbs, Mr J. W. Walton, Mr M. J. Walton.

Assistant Trainer: George A Charlton

Conditional: B Gibson (w.a.).

110   MR ROGER J. CHARLTON, Beckhampton

Postal: **Beckhampton House, Marlborough, Wilts, SN8 1QR.**
Contact: **OFFICE** (01672) 539533 **FAX** (01672) 539456 **HOME** (01672) 539330
E-MAIL r.charlton@virgin.net

1 **AVONBRIDGE,** 4, b c Averti (IRE)—Alessia **Mr D. J. Deer**
2 **BORDER SUBJECT,** 7, b g Selkirk (USA)—Topicality (USA) **Mr & Mrs P. Orton & Beckhampton Stables**
3 **DEPORTIVO,** 4, b c Night Shift (USA)—Valencia **Mr K. Abdulla**
4 **DOMIRATI,** 4, b g Emarati (USA)—Julia Domna **Exors of Mr D. Shirley**
5 **DOROTHY'S FRIEND,** 4, b g Grand Lodge (USA)—Isle of Flame **Mr M. Myers & Beckhampton Stables**
6 **MIDAS WAY,** 4, ch g Halling (USA)—Arietta's Way (IRE) **Mrs Alexandra J. Chandris**
7 **PATAVELLIAN (IRE),** 6, b g Machiavellian (USA)—Alessia **Mr D. J. Deer**
8 **PRESUMPTIVE (IRE),** 4, b c Danehill (USA)—Demure **Ecurie Pharos**
9 **SEEL OF APPROVAL,** 5, b g Polar Falcon (USA)—Petit Point (IRE) **Mrs A. E. Morgan**
10 **SKI JUMP (USA),** 4, gr g El Prado (IRE)—Skiable (IRE) **Mr K. Abdulla**
11 **TRADE FAIR,** 4, b c Zafonic (USA)—Danefair **Mr K. Abdulla**

THREE-YEAR-OLDS

12 **ALDERNEY RACE (USA),** ch c Seeking The Gold (USA)—Oyster Catcher (IRE) **Britton House Stud Ltd**
13 **APRON (IRE),** b f Grand Lodge (USA)—Sultana **Lady Rothschild**
14 **ARTISTS LICENCE,** gr g Linamix (FR)—Once Upon A Time **The Queen**
15 **AVESSIA,** b f Averti (IRE)—Alessia **Mr D. J. Deer**
16 **BAKHTYAR,** gr g Daylami (IRE)—Gentlesse **Tarville Int Limited & C. Coleridge-Cole**
17 **BALAVISTA (USA),** br c Distant View (USA)—Balabina (USA) **Mr K. Abdulla**
18 **BIG HURRY (USA),** b f Red Ransom (USA)—Call Me Fleet (USA) **Ecurie Pharos**
19 **BLUE MONDAY,** b c Darshaan—Lunda (IRE) **Mountgrange Stud**
20 **CHANGARI (USA),** b f Gulch—Danzari **Mr K. Abdulla**
21 **CIRCE'S MELODY (IRE),** b f Entrepreneur—Circe's Isle **Mr A. E. Oppenheimer**
22 **COLOUR WHEEL,** ch c Spectrum (IRE)—Risanda **Mr K. Abdulla**
23 **DEUXIEME (IRE),** b f Second Empire (IRE)—Kardelle **Beckhampton Stables Ltd**
24 **EXTRA COVER (IRE),** b g Danehill Dancer (IRE)—Ballycurrane (IRE) **John Livock Bloodstock Ltd**
25 **GLIDE,** ch g In The Wings—Ash Glade **Mr K. Abdulla**
26 **HATCH,** ch c Cadeaux Genereux—Footlight Fantasy (USA) **Mr B. E. Nielsen**
27 **INVITING (USA),** b f Exploit (USA)—Raging Apalachee (USA) **Mrs John Magnier & Mr M. Tabor**
28 **JOSEPHUS (IRE),** ch c King of Kings (IRE)—Khulasah (USA) **Mountgrange Stud**
29 **KALI,** gr f Linamix (FR)—Alkarida (FR) **Miss M. Gordon Watson**
30 **KIND (IRE),** b f Danehill (USA)—Rainbow Lake **Mr K. Abdulla**
31 **LA CORUNA,** b f Deploy—Valencia **Mr K. Abdulla**
32 **MATCHPLAY,** ch f Nashwan (USA)—Alligram (USA) **Ecurie Pharos**
33 **MEGAN'S BAY,** b f Muhtarram (USA)—Beacon **Mrs M. E. Slade**
34 **MESSE DE MINUIT (IRE),** ch c Grand Lodge (USA)—Scrimshaw **Mountgrange Stud**
35 **MOTORWAY (IRE),** b c Night Shift (USA)—Tadkiyra (IRE) **Mountgrange Stud**
36 **MY HOPE (IRE),** b f Danehill (USA)—Lady Elgar (IRE) **Mr Albert Yemm**
37 **NAMESAKE,** ch f Nashwan (USA)—Zenith **The Queen**
38 **NIGHTSPOT,** ch g Night Shift (USA)—Rash Gift **Mr D. J. Deer**
39 **NUTS FOR YOU (IRE),** b f Sri Pekan (USA)—Moon Festival **Mountgrange Stud**
40 **PANZER (GER),** b g Vettori (IRE)—Prompt **Lady Rothschild**
41 **PARC AUX BOULES,** gr c Royal Applause—Aristocratique **Mountgrange Stud**
42 **PATRIMONY,** ch f Cadeaux Genereux—Repeat Warning **Ecurie Pharos**
43 **RAREFIED (IRE),** b c Danehill (USA)—Tenuous **Mr K. Abdulla**
44 **SAILMAKER (IRE),** ch g Peintre Celebre (USA)—Princess Amalie (USA) **Mr Michael Pescod**
45 **SAINT PETER,** ch g Mark of Esteem (IRE)—Inseparable **Mr S. M. De Zoete**
46 **SKETCH (IRE),** b f Perugino (USA)—Skew **Lady Rothschild**
47 **SONG OF VALA,** ch g Peintre Celebre (USA)—Yanka (USA) **Mr A. Parker**
48 **SWAYTHE (USA),** b f Swain (IRE)—Caithness (USA) **Mr K. Abdulla**
49 **TENTATIVE (USA),** ch f Distant View (USA)—Danzante (USA) **Mr K. Abdulla**
50 **THREE VALLEYS (USA),** ch c Diesis—Skiable (IRE) **Mr K. Abdulla**
51 **TUMBAGA (USA),** b c Seeking The Gold (USA)—Didina **Mr K. Abdulla**
52 **VERASI,** b g Kahyasi—Fair Verona (USA) **Mr D. J. Deer**
53 **VERKHOTINA,** b f Barathea (IRE)—Alusha **Mr A. E. Oppenheimer**
54 **WAKE UP HENRY,** ch g Nashwan (USA)—River Saint (USA) **Lucayan Stud**
55 **WATER TAXI,** ch c Zafonic (USA)—Trellis Bay **Mr K. Abdulla**
56 **WELL KNOWN,** b f Sadler's Wells (USA)—Danefair **Mr K. Abdulla**
57 **WORCESTER LODGE,** ch g Grand Lodge (USA)—Borgia **Lady Rothschild**

MR ROGER J. CHARLTON—continued

59 **ZALDA**, ch f Zilzal (USA)—Gold Luck (USA) **Mr D. J. Deer**
60 **ZATHONIA**, b f Zafonic (USA)—Danthonia (USA) **Mr K. Abdulla**

TWO-YEAR-OLDS

61 **AQUILONIA**, b f 24/2 Giant's Causeway—Leonila (IRE) (Caerleon (USA)) (80000) **Britton House Stud**
62 B f 12/1 Dansili—Blue Gentian (USA) (Known Fact (USA)) **Mr K. Abdulla**
63 **BRAG (IRE)**, b f 26/3 Mujadil (USA)—Boast (Most Welcome) **Lady Rothschild**
64 Ch f 16/2 Cadeaux Genereaux—Canis Star (Wolfhound (USA)) **Mr A. E. Oppenheimer**
65 B c 20/5 Sadler's Wells (USA)—Cattermole (USA) (Roberto (USA)) **Mr K. Abdulla**
66 **DIFFERENT STORY (USA)**, b f 31/3 Stravinsky—Yamuna (USA) (Forty Niner (USA)) **Mr K. Abdulla**
67 B c 18/4 Pursuit of Love—Discomatic (USA) (Roberto (USA)) **Mr K. Abdulla**
68 **DRIVE ME WILD (IRE)**, b c 23/4 Indian Ridge—Wild Bluebell (IRE) (Bluebird (USA)) (74211) **Mountgrange Stud**
69 B c 7/3 Montjeu (IRE)—Elaine's Honor (USA) (Chief's Crown (USA)) (50000) **Thurloe Thoroughbreds**
70 **FOR A DANCER (IRE)**, b c Unfuwain (USA)—
                                           Another Dancer (FR) (Groom Dancer (USA)) (200000) **Mountgrange Stud**
71 **FREE LIFT**, ch f 8/4 Cadeaux Genereux—Step Aloft (Shirley Heights) **The Queen**
72 **GERMANICUS**, b c 3/2 Desert King (IRE)—Simacota (GER) (Acatenango (GER)) (70000) **Mr Michael Pescod**
73 B c 27/2 Zafonic (USA)—Greenvera (USA) (Riverman (USA)) (65476) **Mr B. E. Nielsen**
74 **HEIDI'S DASH (IRE)**, b f 16/3 Green Desert (USA)—
                                           Child Prodigy (IRE) (Ballad Rock) (140000) **Mr Albert Yemm**
75 **INCHIBAR**, ch c 5/2 Inchinor—Chocolate Fog (USA) (Mt Livermore (USA)) (40197) **Mrs M. E. Slade**
76 Ch c 14/4 Halling (USA)—Ivorine (USA) (Blushing Groom (FR)) **Mr K. Abdulla**
77 **JALISSA**, b f 13/5 Mister Baileys—Juliet Domna (Dominion) **Exors of Mr D. Shirley**
78 **JAZZ COMPOSER (USA)**, ch c 15/3 Dixieland Band (USA)—
                                           Tussle (USA) (Kris S (USA)) (80357) **Mr B. E. Nielsen**
79 B f 25/5 Kahyasi—Kerali (High Line) **Mr K. Abdulla**
80 Ch f 6/2 Giant's Causeway—La Belle Otero (USA) (Nureyev (USA)) **The Marston Partnership**
81 **LIFE'S A WHIRL**, b f 22/1 Machiavellian (USA)—Spinning Top (Alzao (USA)) **The Queen**
82 B c 14/4 Darshaan—Mannakea (USA) (Fairy King (USA)) (250000) **Mr B. E. Nielsen**
83 **MEIKLE BARFIL**, b c 25/3 Compton Place—Oare Sparrow (Night Shift (USA)) **Mr H. Keswick**
84 **NAVY LARK**, ch c 10/2 Nashwan (USA)—Holly Blue (Bluebird (USA)) **The Queen**
85 **OBVIOUS CHARM**, b f 16/5 Machiavellian (USA)—Clear Attraction (USA) (Lear Fan (USA)) **The Queen**
86 **OUTSKIRTS**, ch f 11/3 Selkirk (USA)—Beyond Doubt (Belmez (USA)) **The Queen**
87 **PAINT POT**, ch f 7/2 Spectrum (IRE)—Knell (IRE) (Unfuwain (USA)) **Lady Rothschild**
88 **PEEP SHOW**, b f 15/2 In the Wings—Arderelle (FR) (Pharly (FR)) **Lady Rothschild**
89 **PIKE BISHOP (IRE)**, br c 23/3 Namid—Pink Cashmere (IRE) (Polar Falcon (USA)) (62000) **Mr Michael Pescod**
90 **PIPER'S ASH (USA)**, b f 13/4 Royal Academy—Merida (Warning) **Mr K. Abdulla**
91 **PISHOGUE (USA)**, b c 19/2 El Prado—Deep Magic (Gone West (USA)) **Mr K. Abdulla**
92 B f 8/4 Desert Prince (IRE)—Rainbow Lake (Rainbow Quest (USA)) **Mr K. Abdulla**
93 **RING OF FIRE (IRE)**, b c 24/1 Royal Applause—
                                           Emerald Cut (Rainbow Quest (USA)) (300000) **Mountgrange Stud**
94 **ROMAN VILLA (USA)**, b c 14/3 Chester House (USA)—Danzante (USA) (Danzig (USA)) **Mr K. Abdulla**
95 **LASSO** Ch f 19/2 Indian Ridge—Rosse (Kris) **Mr A. E. Oppenheimer**
96 **RUSTLER**, b c 22/4 Green Desert (USA)—Borgia (Machiavellian (USA)) **Lady Rothschild**
97 **KATAMANDA (IRE)** B c 21/3 Danehill (USA)—Scruple (IRE) (Catrail (USA)) (140000) **Mountgrange Stud**
98 **SEA WALL**, b c 10/3 Giant's Causeway—Spout (Salse (USA)) **Lady Rothschild**
99 **SERVE TIME**, ch c 22/3 Benny The Dip (USA)—Once Upon A Time (Teenoso (USA)) **The Queen**
100 **STAR WOOD (IRE)**, b f 8/4 Montjeu (IRE)—Woodwin (IRE) (Woodman (USA)) **Lady Vestey**
101 **STRAWBERRY LEAF**, ch f 3/2 Unfuwain (USA)—Satin Bell (Midyan (USA)) **Mr N. Jones**
102 Ch c 16/5 Grand Lodge (USA)—Tenuous (Generous (IRE)) **Mr K. Abdulla**
103 **VIRTUE**, ch f 26/2 Vettori (IRE)—Zenith (Shirley Heights) **The Queen**
104 **RHYTHMIC DANCE (IRE)** B c 31/3 Fasliyev (USA)—
                                           Whispered Melody (Primo Dominie) (34013) **Thurloe Thoroughbreds**

Assistant Trainer: Tom Grantham

---

111 **MR G. C. H. CHUNG, Newmarket**
Postal: **Linden Lodge Stables, Rowley Drive, Newmarket, Suffolk, CB8 0NH.**
Contact: PHONE (01638) 664348/(01638) 663833 FAX (01638) 660338 MOBILE (07802) 204281
E-MAIL greg.chung@lineone.net

1 **EVERLAND (IRE)**, 5, b g Namaqualand (USA)—Ukraine's Affair (USA) **Mr H. C. Chung**
2 **IVOR MEADOWS**, 4, b g Mtoto—Heresheis **Mr A. J. Thompson**
3 **LUCEFER (IRE)**, 6, b g Lycius (USA)—Maharani (USA) **Mr I. J. Pattle**

MR G. C. H. CHUNG—continued

4 **MANDARIN SPIRIT (IRE)**, 4, b g Primo Dominie—Lithe Spirit (IRE) **Mr Peter Tsim**
5 **ORIENTAL MOON (IRE)**, 5, ch m Spectrum (IRE)—La Grande Cascade (USA) **Mr G. C. H. Chung**
6 **SALFORD ROCKET**, 4, b g Slip Anchor—Mysterious Maid (USA) **The Ace Partnership**
7 **SHATIN HERO**, 4, ch c Lion Cavern (USA)—Moogie **Mr Peter Tsim**
8 **SHATIN SPECIAL**, 4, ch f Titus Livius (FR)—Lawn Order **Mr Peter Tsim**
9 **VAL DE MAAL (IRE)**, 4, ch g Eagle Eyed (USA)—Miss Bojangles **Mr A. W. Ansell**

THREE-YEAR-OLDS

10 **COMPASSION (IRE)**, b f Alhaarth (IRE)—Titania **Mr Peter Tsim**
11 **EVENING FRAGRANCE**, gr g Bluegrass Prince (IRE)—Evening Falls **Mr G. C. H. Chung**
12 **GLOBAL ACHIEVER**, b c Key of Luck (USA)—Inflation **Dr Johnny Hon**
13 B c General Monash (USA)—Spoilt Again **The Maybe This Time Partnership**

TWO-YEAR-OLDS

14 B c 31/5 Killer Instinct—Anetta (Aragon) (9000) **Mr Peter Tsim**
15 B c 27/4 Chester House (USA)—Celibataire (FR) (Saumarez) (60000)

Other Owners: Mrs Coralie A. Chong, Mrs S. Chung, Mr B. L. Stephens, Mr K. E. Woollacott.

Jockeys (Flat): Royston French, Jamie Mackay, Seb Sanders. **Apprentice:** Dean P Williams (7-5).
Amateur: Mr T Thomas (8-7).

---

112 **MR R. M. CLARK, Linlithgow**
Postal: Bonnytoun Farm, Linlithgow, West Lothian, EH49 7LP.
Contact: **PHONE (01506) 842075 FAX (01506) 846745 MOBILE (07715) 121387**

1 **HICKLETON CLUB**, 5, b g Aragon—Honest Opinion

---

113 **MR W. CLAY, Stoke-on-Trent**
Postal: Saverley House Farm, Saverley Green, Fulford, Stoke-On-Trent, Staffordshire, ST11 9QX.
Contact: **PHONE (01782) 392131**

1 **BETTERGETGONE**, 5, b m Bettergeton—Impromptu Melody (IRE) **Mr Trevor Farrow & Mr Brian Holt**
2 **BINT ST JAMES**, 9, b m Shareef Dancer (USA)—St James's Antigua (IRE) **Mrs J Dutton, Mr T Farrow**
3 **ESCORT**, 8, b g Most Welcome—Benazir
4 **IMPERO**, 6, b g Emperor Jones (USA)—Fight Right (FR) **Mr B. Donkin**

Amateur: Guy Lewis (9-11).

---

114 **MR NICOLAS CLEMENT, Chantilly**
Postal: **37, Avenue de Joinville, 60500 Chantilly, France.**
Contact: **PHONE +33 (0) 44 57 59 60 FAX +33 (0) 44 57 70 84 E-MAIL clementoffice@wanadoo.fr**

1 **ALFIERI (IRE)**, 4, ch c Ashkalani (IRE)—Alinea (USA)
2 **AM BROSE**, 5, ch h Nureyev (USA)—Madame Premier (USA)
3 **JOBEUR (FR)**, 4, b c Sicyos (USA)—Top Nue (FR)
4 **KAP VERDE**, 4, ch c Bering—Karapucha (IRE)
5 **LYNDAAR**, 4, b c Barathea (IRE)—Lobmille
6 **MAILLE BLU (FR)**, 4, b c Epervier Bleu—Bric Mamaille (FR)
7 **PANFILO**, 9, b h Thatching—Reveuse du Soir
8 **SABLE FIN (FR)**, 4, b c Marchand de Sable (USA)—Lady Petronille (FR)
9 **SAVARINO**, 4, b br c Anabaa (USA)—Princesse Bilbao (FR)
10 **STELLARETTE (IRE)**, 4, ch f Lycius (USA)—To The Skies (USA)
11 **WITTICISM**, 4, b f Barathea (IRE)—Applecross

THREE-YEAR-OLDS

12 **ARRONDIE (FR)**, b f Inchinor—Arvika (FR)
13 **BLANDU (IRE)**, b c Green Desert (USA)—Princesse Bilbao (FR)
14 **CARMENGA**, b f Tiger Hill (IRE)—Confines (IRE)
15 **CATCH THE MOON (IRE)**, ch f Peintre Celebre (USA)—Sensitivity (USA)
16 **CHINASABRE (FR)**, ch f Sabrehill (USA)—Shenzehn (FR)

MR NICOLAS CLEMENT—continued

17 **CIVIL RIGHTS (USA)**, b c Seeking The Gold—Coretta (IRE)
18 **CLOON (USA)**, b f Lure (USA)—Axe Creek (USA)
19 **DOLMA (FR)**, b f Marchand de Sable (USA)—Young Manila (USA)
20 Ch f Gone West (USA)—Escrow Agent (USA)
21 **FESTIVITE (IRE)**, b f Fasliyev (USA)—Quatre Saisons (FR)
22 **JARDIN ROYAL (IRE)**, b f Royal Academy (USA)—Justine Au Jardin (USA)
23 **KILLOE (USA)**, b f Kris S (USA)—Seewillo (USA)
24 **KING OF SAHARA (IRE)**, b c Desert King (USA)—Debbie's Law (IRE)
25 **LA RENO (IRE)**, b c Brief Truce (USA)—La Venta (USA)
26 **LATERALLE (IRE)**, b f Unfuwain (USA)—La Splendide (FR)
27 **LITHIA (IRE)**, ch f Barathea (IRE)—Lisheba (USA)
28 **LUCKY SHARK (FR)**, b f Midyan (USA)—Landed (USA)
29 **MISE EN PLACE**, b f Dr Fong (USA)—Oleana (USA)
30 **NABRICO (IRE)**, b c Stravinsky (USA)—Danse du Diable (IRE)
31 **OSLO LADY (IRE)**, b f Barathea (IRE)—Tres de Cem (NOR)
32 **TREMTARTAR (FR)**, ch f Trempolino (USA)—Tartaruga (USA)
33 **TULIPE TRIP (USA)**, b f Royal Acedmy (USA)—Tulipe Noire (USA)
34 **WAITING FOR FAME (IRE)**, b f In The Wings—Debbie's Next (USA)

TWO-YEAR-OLDS

35 B f 3/5 Kingmambo (USA)—Anklet (USA) (Wild Again (USA)) (125000)
36 Ch c 1/3 Lure (USA)—Axe Creek (USA) (Gulch (USA))
37 **BOA ESTRELA (IRE)**, b f 24/2 Intikhab (USA)—Charita (IRE) (Lycius (USA)) (65000)
38 **CONGLEVE (IRE)**, ch c 22/2 Ashkalani (IRE)—Freedom Flame (Darshaan) (43290)
39 **DOMAN (IRE)**, ch c 27/4 Stravinsky (USA)—Aube d'Irlande (IRE) (Selkirk (USA)) (105132)
40 B f 22/2 Almutawakel—Echoes (FR) (Niniski (USA)) (92763)
41 **FITELL (IRE)**, b c 23/2 Xaar—Slippering (Shining Steel) (41434)
42 B f 11/3 Halling (USA)—Flawlessly (FR) (Rainbow Quest (USA)) (46382)
43 B f 14/2 Septieme Ciel (USA)—Green Song (FR) (Green Tune (USA)) (50711)
44 **HELTER SKELTER (IRE)**, b f 28/4 Priolo (USA)—Heavenly Music (USA) (Seattle Song (USA))
45 **HORSE UPSTAIRS (IRE)**, b c 20/2 Danehill (USA)—Sensitivity (USA) (Blushing John (USA))
46 B f 7/4 Lomitas—Lacatena (GER) (Acatenango (GER)) (49474)
47 B f 5/5 Mr Greeley (USA)—Madeleine's Blush (USA) (Rahy (USA)) (5952)
48 **MARINE BLEUE (IRE)**, b f 14/3 Desert Prince (IRE)—Mirina (FR) (Pursuit of Love)
49 Gr c 10/5 Linamix (FR)—Pawnee Dancer (IRE) (Dancing Brave) (49474)
50 **PRIERE**, b f 23/2 Machiavellian (USA)—Play Around (IRE) (Niniski (USA))
51 Ch f 29/3 Cadeaux Genereaux—Red Rabbit (Suave Dancer (USA)) (25000)
52 Ch f 17/3 Giant's Causeway—Red Roses Story (FR) (Pink (FR)) (64935)
53 B f 27/3 Intikhab (USA)—Ribot's Guest (IRE) (Be My Guest (USA)) (98948)
54 B f 20/2 Xaar—Special Dancer (Shareef Dancer (USA)) (18552)
55 **STAR DE L'AIR (FR)**, b c 20/3 Starborough—Armee de L'Air (Elegant Air) (53803)
56 **SWEET VENTURE (FR)**, b c 9/5 Verglas (IRE)—Bitter Sweet (FR) (Esprit du Nord (USA)) (9894)
57 B f 19/2 Diktat—Tricorne (Green Desert (USA)) (38342)
58 **USAGE DE MONDE**, gr f 26/2 Highest Honor (FR)—Caslon (FR) (Deep Roots) (30921)
59 Ch c 6/2 Giant's Causeway—Vanishing Prairie (USA) (Alysheba (USA))
60 **VRACCA**, ch f 27/3 Vettori (FR)—Crystal Cavern (USA) (Be My Guest (USA)) (58000)

---

115 MR P. L. CLINTON, Doveridge
Postal: **Lordlea Farm, Marston Lane, Doveridge, Ashbourne, Derbyshire, DE6 5JS.**
Contact: **PHONE (01889) 566356 MOBILE (07815) 142642 E-MAIL clintonracing@supanet.com**

1 **LET'S PARTY (IRE)**, 4, b f Victory Note (USA)—Mashoura **The Buckers**
2 **PARADISE GARDEN (USA)**, 7, b g Septieme Ciel (USA)—Water Course (USA) **Mr P. L. Clinton**
3 **RUNNING DE CERISY (FR)**, 10, ch g Lightning (FR)—Niloq (FR) **The Buckers**
4 **ZAMYATINA (IRE)**, 5, br m Danehill Dancer (IRE)—Miss Pickpocket (IRE) **In The Clear Racing**

THREE-YEAR-OLDS

5 **IMPERIAL ROYALE (IRE)**, ch g Ali-Royal (IRE)—God Speed Her **The Buckers**

Other Owners: Mr G. Worrall.

Assistant Trainer: G Worrall

Amateur: Mr P Collington.

116 **MR K. F. CLUTTERBUCK, Newmarket**
Postal: **Pond House Stables, Church Lane, Exning, Newmarket, Suffolk, CB8 7HF.**
Contact: **PHONE (01638) 577043 MOBILE (0973) 317848**

1 BALLA D'AIRE (IRE), 9, b br g Balla Cove—Silius **Mr K. F. Clutterbuck**
2 BONNY BUSONA, 4, b f Abou Zouz (USA)—La Busona (IRE) **Mr K. F. Clutterbuck**
3 LORD ROCHESTER, 8, b g Distant Relative—Kentfield **Mr K. F. Clutterbuck**
4 MELTONIAN, 7, ch g Past Glories—Meltonby **Mr K. F. Clutterbuck**
5 MISTER GRAHAM, 9, b g Rock Hopper—Celestial Air **Mr K. F. Clutterbuck**

Assistant Trainer: Nick Hyde

117 **MR D. J. COAKLEY, West Ilsley**
Postal: **Keeper's Stables, West Ilsley, Newbury, Berkshire, RG20 7AH.**
Contact: **PHONE (01635) 281622 MOBILE (07768) 658056**
E-MAIL denis@coakley99.freeserve.co.uk

1 TAKRIR (IRE), 7, b g Bahri (USA)—Ice House **Mr David F. Wilson**

THREE-YEAR-OLDS

2 I WISH I KNEW, br g Petong—Hoh Dancer **Mr James Kerr**
3 KESHYA, b f Mtoto—Liberatrice (FR) **Finders Keepers Partnership**
4 MOCCA (IRE), b f Sri Pekan (USA)—Ewan (IRE) **Mocca Partnership**
5 B f Orpen (USA)—Mystery Night (FR) **Exors of the Late J. J. Henderson**
6 SOLOR, b c Spectrum (IRE)—Bayadere (USA) **Bolam Hurley Ross**
7 SWEET PICKLE, b f Piccolo—Sweet Wilhelmina **Mr Chris van Hoorn**
8 TROMP, ch c Zilzal (USA)—Sulitelma (USA) **Mr Chris van Hoorn**

TWO-YEAR-OLDS

9 B br c 7/4 Zamindar (USA)—Fantastic Bloom (VEN) (Imperial Ballet (IRE)) (11500)
10 PRINCE VETTORI, b c 8/2 Vettori (IRE)—Bombalarina (IRE) (Barathea (IRE)) (20000) **Hurley, Pattinson**
11 RIDDER, b c 5/1 Dr Fong (USA)—Frond (Alzao (USA)) (20000) **Mr Chris van Hoorn**
12 SIRCE (IRE), b g 19/4 Josr Algarhoud (IRE)—Trading Aces (Be My Chief (USA)) (3500) **Mrs D. Topley**
13 B f 12/2 Dr Fong (USA)—Tranquillity (Night Shift (USA)) (4000) **Count Calypso Racing**

Other Owners: Mr R. J. Bolam, Mr P. M. Emery, Mr Richard J. Evans, Lady Huntingdon, Mr L. M. A. Hurley, Countess Of Lonsdale, Mr Tony Pattinson, Mr I. R. Thomas, Mr I. Topley, Mr Reg Whitehead.

118 **MR P. F. I. COLE, Whatcombe**
Postal: **Whatcombe, Wantage, Oxfordshire, OX12 9NW.**
Contact: **PHONE (01488) 638433 FAX (01488) 638609 E-MAIL pfi.cole@virgin.net**

1 ARCHDUKE FERDINAND (FR), 6, ch g Dernier Empereur (USA)—
Lady Norcliffe (USA) **The Hon Mrs J.M.Corbett & Mr C.Wright**
2 BARMAN (USA), 5, ch g Atticus (USA)—Blue Tip (FR) **Sir George Meyrick**
3 CAMBERLEY (IRE), 7, b g Sri Pekan (USA)—Nsx **H.R.H. Sultan Ahmad Shah**
4 CAPITANO CORELLI (IRE), 5, b ro h Sadler's Wells (USA)—Ahead **Mr Alessandro Gaucci**
5 CERTAIN JUSTICE (USA), 6, gr g Lit de Justice (USA)—Pure Misk **The Blenheim Partnership**
6 COOL TEMPER, 8, b g Magic Ring (USA)—Ovideo **Mr M. J. G. Clubb**
7 CORNELIUS, 7, b g Barathea (IRE)—Rainbow Mountain **Sir George Meyrick**
8 CORTON (IRE), 5, gr g Definite Article—Limpopo **Mrs Belinda Harvey**
9 CRAFTY CALLING (USA), 4, b c Crafty Prospector (USA)—Glorious Calling (USA) **Mr Craig B. Singer**
10 HARCOURT (USA), 4, b c Cozzene (USA)—Ballinamallard **Sir George Meyrick**
11 KOOL (IRE), 5, b g Danehill Dancer (USA)—New Rochelle (IRE) **Richard Green (Fine Paintings)**
12 MR DINOS (IRE), 5, b h Desert King (IRE)—Spear Dance **Mr C. Shiacolas**
13 OFFICER'S PINK, 4, ch f Grand Lodge (USA)—Arethusa **Mr Frank Stella**
14 SALAGAMA (IRE), 4, br f Alzao (USA)—Waffle On **Mrs Sheila Mitchell**
15 SIENA STAR (IRE), 6, b g Brief Truce (USA)—Gooseberry Pie **N. Frankham & B. Gover**
16 SOVEREIGN DREAMER (USA), 4, b c Kingmambo (USA)—Spend A Dream (USA) **Mr Ben Arbib**
17 SQUIRTLE TURTLE, 4, ch g Peintre Celebre (USA)—Hatten Gardens **Mrs P. F. I. Cole**
18 SWING WING, 5, b g In The Wings—Swift Spring (FR) **Sir Martyn Arbib**
19 TOTAL TURTLE (IRE), 5, b g Turtle Island (IRE)—Chagrin d'Amour (IRE) **W. J. Smith and M. D. Dudley**
20 ZIETORY, 4, b f Zieten (USA)—Fairy Story (IRE) **The Fairy Story Partnership**

MR P. F. I. COLE—continued
THREE-YEAR-OLDS

21 **AFRICAN DREAM,** b g Mark of Esteem (IRE)—Fleet Hill (IRE) **P. F. I. Cole Ltd**
22 **AKRITAS,** b c Polish Precedent (USA)—Dazzling Heights **Mr C. Shiacolas**
23 **BEEJAY,** b f Piccolo—Letluce **Mr A. H. Robinson**
24 **BLUE TOMATO,** b c Orpen (USA)—Ocean Grove (IRE) **Mrs Stephanie Smith**
25 **BUKIT FRASER (IRE),** b c Sri Pekan (USA)—London Pride (USA) **H.R.H. Sultan Ahmad Shah**
26 **CERTAIN FACT (USA),** b c Sir Cat (USA)—Pure Misk **The Blenheim Partnership**
27 **DR THONG,** ch c Dr Fong (USA)—Always On My Mind **Mr Frank Stella**
28 **EISTEDDFOD,** ch g Cadeaux Genereux—Ffestiniog (IRE) **Elite Racing Club**
29 **EMBASSY SWEETS (USA),** b f Affirmed (USA)—Leaveemlaughing (USA) **Mr Frank Stella**
30 **FINE SILVER (IRE),** gr c Intikhab (USA)—Petula **SIV Corporation**
31 **FRANGIPANI (IRE),** b f Sri Pekan (USA)—Sharkashka (IRE) **P. F. I. Cole Ltd**
32 **GIRL WARRIOR (USA),** ch f Elusive Quality (USA)—Qhazeenah **Mr Anthony Speelman**
33 **GOOD VIBRATIONS,** b f Bijou d'Inde—Showcase **Mr Christopher Wright**
34 **HAPPY CRUSADER (IRE),** b c Cape Cross (IRE)—Les Hurlants (IRE) **Team Havana**
35 **HORNER (USA),** b c Rahy (USA)—Dynashore (CAN) **Sir George Meyrick**
36 **IMPARTIAL,** b c Polish Precedent (USA)—Always Friendly **Mr Anthony Speelman**
37 **KEEPERS KNIGHT (IRE),** b c Sri Pekan (USA)—Keepers Dawn (IRE) **P. F. I. Cole Ltd**
38 **KING OF SCOTS,** ch g Halling (USA)—Ink Pot (USA) **P. F. I. Cole Ltd**
39 **MARKSGOLD (IRE),** b g Goldmark (USA)—Lady of Shalott **Type 45 Partnership**
40 **MISS PROCURER (IRE),** b f Entrepreneur—Kariyh (USA) **Mrs Christopher Hanbury**
41 **MR TAMBOURINE MAN (IRE),** b c Rainbow Quest (USA)—
                          Girl From Ipanema **The Hon Mrs J.M.Corbett & Mr C.Wright**
42 **PETER PAUL RUBENS (USA),** ch c Belong To Me (USA)—Skybox (USA) **Richard Green (Fine Paintings)**
43 **POWERFUL PARRISH (USA),** b f Quiet American (USA)—Parish Business (USA) **Mr G. J. Beck**
44 **PUTRA SAS (IRE),** b c Sri Pekan (USA)—Puteri Wentworth **H.R.H. Sultan Ahmad Shah**
45 **SARISTAR,** b f Starborough—Sari **Mr R. A. Instone**
46 **SCIENCE ACADEMY (USA),** ch f Silver Hawk (USA)—Dance Design (IRE) **Sir Martyn Arbib**
47 **SECRETARY GENERAL (IRE),** b c Fasliyev (USA)—Katie McLain (USA) **The Blenheim Partnership**
48 **SHANNKARA'S QUEST (USA),** b br c Coronado's Quest (USA)—Shannkara (IRE) **Mr Craig B. Singer**
49 **SOUND OF FLEET (USA),** ch c Cozzene (USA)—Tempo (USA) **Meyrick, Smith, Landis & Cole**
50 **STARMIX,** br c Linamix (FR)—Danlu (USA) **Sir Martyn Arbib**
51 **SUPAMACH (IRE),** b f Machiavellian (USA)—Supamova (USA) **Sir Martyn Arbib**
52 **THE BUTTERFLY BOY,** ch c Inchinor—Crime of Passion **Mr & Mrs C Wright & Hon Mrs J M Corbett**
53 **THOMAS LAWRENCE (USA),** ch c Horse Chestnut (SAF)—Olatha (USA) **Richard Green (Fine Paintings)**
54 **VENEZIANA,** ch f Vettori (IRE)—Fairy Story (IRE) **The Fairy Story Partnership**
55 **WESTERN ROOTS,** ch g Dr Fong (USA)—Chrysalis **Mr David Murrell**

TWO-YEAR-OLDS

56 **ANDRONIKOS,** ch c 27/3 Dr Fong (USA)—Arctic Air (Polar Falcon (USA)) (57000) **Mr C. Shiacolas**
57 **LEAGUE OF NATIONS (IRE)** B c 22/1 Indian Danehill (IRE)—
                          Athens Belle (IRE) (Groom Dancer (USA)) (25973) **The Blandford Partnership**
58 **RUSSIAN GENERAL (IRE)** B c 11/2 Soviet Star (USA)—Azra (IRE) (Danehill (USA)) (34013) **The Blandford Partnership**
59 **BRECON BEACON,** b c 3/3 Spectrum (IRE)—Ffestiniog (IRE) (Efisio) **Elite Racing Club**
60 **COURAGEOUSLY,** b c 27/1 Aljabr (USA)—Eishin Eleuthera (IRE) (Sadler's Wells) (14000) **Mr R. A. Instone**
61 **CREATIVE CHARACTER,** b br c 7/5 Theatrical—Shannkara (IRE) (Akarad (FR)) **Mr Craig B. Singer**
62 B c 10/2 Dansili—Crime Ofthecentury (Pharly (FR)) (31000) **Mr Christopher Wright**
63 **DEPUTY OF WOOD (USA),** b br f 24/2 Deputy Minister (CAN)—
                          Wood of Binn (Woodman (USA)) (130952) **Mr Craig B. Singer**
64 **DUNMAGLASS (USA),** ch c 5/3 Cat Thief (USA)—Indian Fashion (USA) (General Holme (USA)) **Mr Faisal Salman**
65 **ENCHANCED RIGHT (IRE),** b c 10/3 Sadler's Wells (USA)—
                          Whitesville (IRE) (Top Ville) (25000) **W. J. Smith and M. D. Dudley**
66 **FINNEGANS RAINBOW,** ch c 9/5 Spectrum (IRE)—Fairy Story (IRE) (Persian Bold) **The Fairy Story Partnership**
67 **FRENCH GOLD,** b f 7/3 Bien Bien (USA)—Shalad'or (Golden Heights) (5238) **G. J. & Mrs M. Palmer**
68 **HALCYON EXPRESS (IRE)** B c 13/4 Mujadil (USA)—
                          Hakkaniyah (Machiavellian (USA)) (17000) **The Blandford Partnership**
69 B f 19/2 Cadeaux Genereux—
                          Iberian Dancer (CAN) (El Gran Senor (USA)) (9000) **Bernard Gover Bloodstock Trading Ltd**
70 **IGOR PROTTI,** b c 27/3 Opening Verse (USA)—La Busona (IRE) (Broken Hearted) **Mr V. de Siero**
71 Ch c 29/1 Cadeaux Genereux—Katrina (IRE) (Ela-Mana-Mou) (200000) **H.R.H. Sultan Ahmad Shah**
72 **LEGALLY FAST (USA),** b c 29/4 Deputy Minister (CAN)—
                          Earthly Angel (Crafty Prospector (USA)) **Mr Craig B. Singer**
73 **LUIS MELENDEZ (USA),** ch c 8/3 Horse Chestnut (SAF)—
                          Egoli (USA) (Seeking The Gold (USA)) **Richard Green (Fine Paintings)**

MR P. F. I. COLE—continued

74 B c 13/3 Danehill (USA)—Music And Dance (USA) (Northern Dancer) (61842) **Mr M. Tabor**
75 **NANTON (USA)**, gr ro c 18/3 Spinning World (USA)—
Grab The Green (USA) (Cozzene (USA)) **Sir George Meyrick**
76 B c 12/2 Spectrum (IRE)—Oh Hebe (IRE) (Night Shift (USA)) (55000)
77 B c 8/2 Groom Dancer (USA)—Pekan's Pride (Sri Pekan (USA)) **H.R.H. Sultan Ahmad Shah**
78 B br c 26/2 Southern Halo (USA)—Perfect Arc (USA) (Brown Arc (USA)) **Mr Frank Stella**
79 Gr f 21/4 Danehill Dancer (IRE)—Persian Mistress (IRE) (Persian Bold) (20000) **Mr Andy J. Smith**
80 B br c 31/3 Silver Hawk (USA)—
Petite Triomphe (USA) (Wild Again (USA)) (101190) **H.R.H. Sultan Ahmad Shah**
81 **PLANET TOMATO (IRE)**, b c 14/2 Soviet Star (USA)—
Via Splendida (IRE) (Project Manager) (58000) **Mrs Stephanie Smith**
82 B f 19/1 Sri Pekan (USA)—Puteri Wentworth (Sadler's Wells (USA)) **H.R.H. Sultan Ahmad Shah**
83 **RAKATA (USA)**, b f 15/4 Quiet American (USA)—Haleakala (IRE) (Kris) (53571) **Mr A. H. Robinson**
84 B br c 21/5 Mt Livermore (USA)—Shiitake (USA) (Green Dancer (USA)) (56548) **Mr C. Shiacolas**
85 **SONGTHRUSH (USA)**, gr f 2/3 Unbridled's Song (USA)—
Virgin Michael (USA) (Green Dancer (USA)) **The Hon Mrs J.M.Corbett & Mr C.Wright**
86 **SPEIGHTSTOWN**, gr c 23/1 Grand Lodge (USA)—Farfala (FR) (Linamix (FR)) **Sir Martyn Arbib**
87 **STRATEGIC QUEST (USA)**, b f 28/4 Rainbow Quest (USA)—Danlu (USA) (Danzig (USA)) **Sir Martyn Arbib**
88 **SWELL LAD**, b c 1/2 Sadler's Wells (USA)—Lydara (USA) (Alydar (USA)) (80000) **Sir Martyn Arbib**
89 **SWINDON (USA)**, b f 18/3 Kingmambo (USA)—Dance Design (IRE) (Sadler's Wells (USA)) **Sir Martyn Arbib**
90 **THE DUKE OF DIXIE (USA)**, b c 20/3 Dixieland Band (USA)—
Money Madam (USA) (A P Indy (USA)) **Mr G. J. Beck**
91 **THUNDER CALLING (USA)**, b f 9/5 Thunder Gulch (USA)—
Glorious Calling (USA) (Nijinsky (CAN)) **Mr Craig B. Singer**
92 B c 20/2 Xaar—Via Camp (Kris) (27000) **The Blandford Partnership**

Other Owners: Mr T. M. Bird, The Hon Mrs J. M. Corbett, Mr M. D. Dudley, Sir Mervyn Dunnington-Jefferson, Mr R. A. Esau, Mr G. N. Frankham, Mr Robert Frosell, Gilridge Bloodstock Ltd, Mr E. R. Goodwin, Mr M. R. Haywood, Mr Tony Hill, Kirtlington Stud Ltd, Mrs Kenneth Landis, Mr Charles Meyrick, Miss Daisy Meyrick, Mr G. W. Meyrick, Mr M. C. Moutray-Read, Miss M. Noden, Mr G. Palmer, Mrs M. Palmer, Mrs Francesca Schwarzenbach, Miss C. S. Scott-Balls, Mr William J. Smith, Mrs Janice Stinnes, David M. Thomas, Mr Das H. T. Wijeratne.

Assistant Trainer: Oliver Cole, Liam Kelly

Amateurs: Mrs H Clubb, Mr O. Cole.

---

119 **MR R. COLLET, Chantilly**
Postal: **32, Avenue Marie Amelie, 60500 Chantilly, France.**
Contact: **OFFICE 03 44 57 06 72 HOME 57 59 27 FAX 57 32 25 MOBILE (0608) 789709**
E-MAIL collet-robert@wanadoo.fr

1 **ALCACA (IRE)**, 6, b h Alzao (USA)—Cap Camarat (CAN) **Mr Vallin**
2 **ALLODIAL LAND (USA)**, 5, b h Woodman (USA)—Min Elreeh (USA) **Mr Vallin**
3 **ANODE**, 5, ch m Lion Cavern (USA)—Amor's Princess (USA) **Mr Vallin**
4 **ASO ROCK (IRE)**, 6, b g King's Theatre (IRE)—Zelda (IRE) **Mr Shen**
5 **AVENUE MONTAIGNE (FR)**, 5, b m Take Risks (FR)—Valley Road (FR) **Mr Shen**
6 **BALLINASLOE (FR)**, 8, b h Rose Laurel—Killekenny (FR) **Mr Collet**
7 **BLEU D'ECOSSE (FR)**, 4, b c Saumarez—Great Care (USA) **Mr Hayoz**
8 **CHOCKING**, 4, b c Halling (USA)—Mrs Croesus (USA) **Mr Vallin**
9 **COMEDIE DIVINE (FR)**, 5, ch m Lesotho (USA)—Tosca de Bellouet (FR) **Mr Collet**
10 **DESERT SAND (FR)**, 4, ch c Simon du Desert (FR)—Goutte d'Eau **Mr Collet**
11 **DESERT THREAT (IRE)**, 4, b f Desert Prince (IRE)—Veiled Threat (IRE) **Mr Strauss**
12 **DIABLE MIX**, 5, gr h Linamix (FR)—Diamonaka (FR) **Mr Vallin**
13 **DOM FONTENAIL (FR)**, 5, b g Tel Quel (FR)—Ninon Fontenail (FR) **Mr Vallin**
14 **ESPOIR DU BOCAGE (FR)**, 9, b h Epervier Bleu—Skay (FR) **Mr Lorain**
15 **GARGALHADA FINAL**, 7, b h Sabrehill (USA)—Secret Waters (USA) **Mr Vallin**
16 **HEINSTEIN (IRE)**, 4, b c Night Shift (USA)—Crumpetsfortea (IRE) **M. Vidal**
17 **IRIK STAR (IRE)**, 4, b c Highest Honor (FR)—Silver Peak (FR) **Mr Larsson**
18 **JAMESON DU BERLAIS (FR)**, 5, b g Royal Charter (FR)—Anais du Berlais (FR) **Mr Hayoz**
19 **JIVAGO (IRE)**, 5, b h Hernando (FR)—Swalina (USA) **Mr Strauss**
20 **KING'S SHOW**, 5, b h King's Theatre (IRE)—Shamaya (IRE) **Mr Shen**
21 **KING'S DRAMA (IRE)**, 4, b c King's Theatre (IRE)—Last Drama (IRE) **Mr Tanaka**
22 **KNOCK DOWN (IRE)**, 5, b m Oscar (IRE)—Bottle of Knock (IRE) **Mr Lorain**
23 **LAST ROMAN (IRE)**, 7, b g Salse (USA)—Athene (IRE) **Mr Collet**
24 **MARCHAND DE DAMES (FR)**, 5, b h Marchand de Sable—Madame Nathalie (FR) **Ecurie O Fabien**

MR R. COLLET—continued

25 **MEDIEVALE (FR)**, 4, b f Lost World (IRE)—Haiya (FR) **Mr Shen**
26 **MESANGE ROYALE (FR)**, 4, b f Garde Royale—Beautywal (FR) **Mr Vallin**
27 **MIKOS (FR)**, 4, b c Sicyos—Sex Pistol **Mr Esposito**
28 **MILORD DES BORDES (FR)**, 4, ch c Cyborg (FR)—Miss Recitation (FR) **Mr Collet**
29 **MOCHAM GLEN (FR)**, 7, b br h Midyan (USA)—Marsoumeh (USA) **Mr Andreani**
30 **ON LINE (FR)**, 4, ch c Green Tune (USA)—Odwalla **Mr Le Blan**
31 **PORTO SEGOURO (FR)**, 4, b c Octagonal (NZ)—Alanya (FR) **Mr Vallin**
32 **PSYCHEE DU BERLAIS (FR)**, 4, gr f Saint Preuil (FR)—Rosacotte (FR) **Mr Hayoz**
33 **SKYROCK (USA)**, 5, b h Sky Classic (CAN)—Landholder (USA) **Mr Shen**
34 **SONG OF WAR (IRE)**, 5, b g Lost World (IRE)—Seconde Bleue **Mr Sarti**
35 **SPHINX DU BERLAIS (FR)**, 5, b h Nikos—La Taiga (FR) **Ecurie Cour Mola**
36 **SUPREME TALENT**, 5, b br m Desert King (IRE)—Gold Script (FR) **Mr Shen**
37 **TI FOR TOO**, 8, b h Exit To Nowhere—Mysterious Plans **P. Vidal**
38 **TIGER GROOM**, 7, b h Arazi (USA)—Rifada **Mr Collet**
39 **TYCOON'S HILL (IRE)**, 5, b h Danehill (USA)—Tycoon's Drama (IRE) **Mr Strauss**
40 **ZANYBOY (FR)**, 4, bl c Night Shift (USA)—Party Zane **Mr Maeder**

THREE-YEAR-OLDS

41 **ANGE GARDIEN (IRE)**, b c King's Theatre (IRE)—Settler **Mr Strauss**
42 **DEZIRING (IRE)**, b c Desert Prince (IRE)—Zelding (IRE) **Mr Strauss**
43 **DORA (FR)**, ch f Trempolino (USA)—Springtime Melody (USA) **Mr Collet**
44 **DREAM MACHINE (IRE)**, b c Machiavellian (USA)—Truly A Dream (IRE) **Mr Strauss**
45 **FEU FOLLET (FR)**, b c Night Shift (USA)—Dinalina (FR) **Mr Strauss**
46 **GOLDENPHEE (FR)**, b f Gold Away (USA)—Onphee (FR) **Mr Collet**
47 **LANDERNEAU (IRE)**, b f Desert Prince (IRE)—Pont-Aven **Mr Strauss**
48 **LE BOSS (FR)**, b c Ski Chief (USA)—Angel Victory (IRE) **Mr Zaccour**
49 **LE BYZANTIN (USA)**, gr c Dynaformer (USA)—Venize (IRE) **Mr Strauss**
50 **MY SWEETY (FR)**, gr f Simon du Desert (FR)—Zenne (FR) **Mr Collet**
51 **NEW BERE (FR)**, gr c Verglas (IRE)—Shadeed Vallee (USA) **Mr Collet**
52 **NITE TRIPPA (FR)**, b c Exit To Nowhere (USA)—Nativelee (FR) **Mr Collet**
53 **SABRE BLEU (FR)**, b c Sabrehill (USA)—Beauty Bell (FR) **M. Vidal**
54 **SAGA (FR)**, b f Noble Premier—Sokala (FR) **Mr Vallin**
55 **SARA MOON (IRE)**, b f Barathea (IRE)—Diner de Lune (IRE) **Mr Strauss**
56 **SIDNEY HARBOUR (FR)**, b c Octagonal (NZ)—Suadif (FR) **M. Vidal**
57 **SIMON LE MAGICIEN (FR)**, gr c Simon du Desert (FR)—Crimson Shadows **M. Vidal**
58 **SIN EL FIL (IRE)**, b c Night Shift (USA)—Soeur Ti (FR) **Mr Ecurie Chalhoub**
59 **SPECTATEUR (FR)**, ch c Entrepreneur—Spectacular Joke (USA) **Mr De Moussac**
60 **TONIGHT (FR)**, b c Linnos (JPN)—Toomixa (FR) **Mr Vallin**
61 **TURK AND CAICOS (USA)**, b f Keos (USA)—Turkoticoturko (USA) **Mr Zaccour**
62 **VELIANA (FR)**, b f Vettori (IRE)—Shavya **Mr Vallin**
63 **VIE PRIVEE (FR)**, ch f Highest Honor (FR)—Missy Dancer **M. Vidal**
64 **VILLA MINERVA (FR)**, ch c Raintrap—Rome (FR) **Mr Collet**
65 **WHIPPER (FR)**, b c Miesque's Son (USA)—Myth To Reality (FR) **Mr Strauss**

TWO-YEAR-OLDS

66 B c 24/2 Aljabr (USA)—Al Saqiya (USA) (Woodman (USA)) (43290) **M. Vidal**
67 **HIT THE SKY (IRE)**, b f 3/3 Cozzene (USA)—Cerulean Sky (IRE) (Darshaan) **Mr Strauss**
68 **INTHEMOODFORLOVE (IRE)**, b f 4/5 Anabaa (USA)—Trust In Love (FR) (Exit To Nowhere (USA)) **Mr Strauss**
69 **JUST FOR HONOR (FR)**, gr f 4/3 Highest Honor (FR)—Laquifan (USA) (Lear Fan (USA)) (12368) **Mr Trichter**
70 **LA CROISETTE (FR)**, b f 23/2 Starborough—Charming Quest (USA) (Quest For Fame) **Mr Collet**
71 **NEW LARGUE (USA)**, b f 10/4 Distant View (USA)—New Story (USA) (Dynaformer (USA)) **Mr Strauss**
72 **NIPPING (FR)**, b f 18/2 Night Shift (USA)—Zelda (FR) (Caerleon (USA)) **Mr Strauss**
73 **RADUGA**, ch f 11/4 Sinndar (IRE)—Volcania (FR) (Neustrien (USA)) (47619) **Mr Larsson**
74 **RUE DE LAPPE (FR)**, bl c 1/4 Highest Honor (FR)—Kadouville (FR) (Kaldoun (FR)) (25974) **Mr Segura**
75 B f 25/2 Soviet Star (USA)—Settler (Darshaan) **Mr Strauss**
76 **SINGAPORE SUN (FR)**, b c 28/3 Goldmark—
All For Hope (USA) (Sensitive Prince (USA)) **Haras De La Sas**
77 B f 2/3 Tagula (IRE)—The Good Life (IRE) (Rainbow Quest (USA)) **Mr Strauss**
78 **TOO NICE (FR)**, gr c 12/5 Kaldounevees (FR)—Toomixa (FR) (Linamix (FR)) (45145) **Mr Vallin**
79 **VALTORI (FR)**, b c 16/3 Vettori (IRE)—Vaidaia (Sadler's Wells (USA)) (11750) **Mr Collet**

120 MR H. J. COLLINGRIDGE, Newmarket

Postal: **Harraton Court Stables, Chapel Street, Exning, Newmarket, Suffolk, CB8 7HA.**
Contact: **PHONE/FAX (01638) 577258 MOBILE (07748) 614912**
E-MAIL hugh@headquartersracing.co.uk WEBSITE www.headquarterspartnership.co.uk

1 **ARRAN**, 4, ch c Selkirk (USA)—Humble Pie **Los Quatros Bandidos**
2 **BADRINATH (IRE)**, 10, b g Imperial Frontier (USA)—Badedra **Mr D. T. Thom**
3 **BRIERY MEC**, 9, b g Ron's Victory (USA)—Briery Fille **Mr N. H. Gardner**
4 **CARGO**, 5, b g Emarati (USA)—Portvasco **The Headquarters Partnership**
5 **CAROLINA MORNING (IRE)**, 4, gr f Entrepreneur—Caroline Lady (JPN) **Four-Tune Racing**
6 **CONCERT HOUSE (IRE)**, 4, b f Entrepreneur—Classic Heights **The Headquarters Partnership Ltd**
7 **GUARDIAN SPIRIT**, 5, b m Hector Protector (USA)—
   Amongst The Stars (USA) **The Headquarters Partnership Ltd**
8 **HARMONIC (USA)**, 7, b m Shadeed (USA)—Running Melody **Mr Alan Macalister**
9 **LADY OF GDANSK (IRE)**, 5, ch m Danehill Dancer (IRE)—Rebecca's Girl (IRE) **Mr K. W. & Mrs L. A. Styles**
10 **LEOBALLERO**, 4, ch g Lion Cavern (USA)—Ball Gown **C. V. Lines and M. Mason**
11 **LE RUBAN BLEU (IRE)**, 5, ch g Bluebird (USA)—Minervitta **Mr K. W. & Mrs L. A. Styles**
12 **MUST BE MAGIC**, 7, b g Magic Ring (IRE)—Sequin Lady **The Headquarters Partnership Ltd**
13 **NO CHANCE TO DANCE (IRE)**, 4, b c Revoque—Song of The Glens **The Headquarters Partnership Ltd**
14 **PERSIAN PEARL**, 5, b m Hurricane Sky (AUS)—Persian Fountain (IRE) **The Kendow Partnership**
15 **SEMPER PARATUS (USA)**, 5, b g Foxhound (USA)—Bletcha Lass (AUS) **The Tin Man Partnership**
16 **SEYED (IRE)**, 4, b g Desert Prince (IRE)—Royal Bounty (IRE) **Mr V. Smith**
17 **STORMONT (IRE)**, 4, gr c Marju (IRE)—Legal Steps (IRE) **Mr K. W. & Mrs L. A. Styles**
18 **TOLEDO SUN**, 4, b g Zamindar (USA)—Shafir (USA) **Monkey a Month Racing**
19 **TROFANA FALCON**, 4, b g Polar Falcon (USA)—Silk St James **Greenhills Partnership**

THREE-YEAR-OLDS

20 **ASK THE CLERK (IRE)**, b g Turtle Island (IRE)—Some Fun **Mr R. J. Baines**
21 **EVOQUE**, b f Revoque (IRE)—Chimere (FR) **Mr G. B. Amy**
22 **HELLO IT'S ME**, b g Deploy—Evening Charm (IRE) **Mrs P. A. L. Butler**
23 **MASTER THEO (USA)**, b c Southern Halo (USA)—Lilian Bayliss (IRE) **Mr K. W. & Mrs L. A. Styles**
24 **SILVER TRACES (USA)**, br c Silver Hawk (USA)—Traces of Gold (USA) **Mr Alan Macalister**
25 **SINGLET**, ch c Singspiel (IRE)—Ball Gown **C. V. Lines and M. Mason**
26 **SUMMERISE**, b f Atraf—Summerhill Special (IRE) **Mrs Henrietta Charlet**
27 **VELOCITAS**, b g Magic Ring (IRE)—Folly Finnesse **The Headquarters Partnership Ltd**

Jockey (Flat): J Quinn. **Jockeys (NH):** S Curran, P Hide. **Amateur:** Miss Alison Hutchinson (9-5).

121 MR W. S. COLTHERD, Selkirk

Postal: **Clarilawmuir Farm, Selkirk, TD7 4QA.**
Contact: **PHONE (01750) 21251 MOBILE (0780) 1398199**

1 **CORBIE LYNN**, 7, ch m Jumbo Hirt (USA)—Kilkenny Gorge **Mr S. Coltherd**
2 **MAID TO TALK**, 10, b m Arctic Lord—Chatty Lass **Mr S. Coltherd**
3 **MIDLEM MELODY**, 8, b m Syrtos—Singing Hills **Mr S. Coltherd**
4 **POONY HAW**, 5, b m Minster Son—Miss Brook **Mr S. Coltherd**

THREE-YEAR-OLDS

5 B f Cayman Kai (IRE)—Miss Brook **Mr S. Coltherd**

Jockeys (NH): B Harding, G Lee.

122 LADY CONNELL, Brackley

Postal: **Steane Park, Brackley, Northamptonshire, NN13 6DP.**
Contact: **PHONE (01280) 705899**

1 **BARON STEANE (IRE)**, 5, b g Lord Americo—Lottosprite (IRE) **Mrs Lisa Gregory**
2 **CABIN BOY**, 9, ch g Royal Vulcan—Maytide **Sir Michael Connell**
3 **COURT ADJOURN**, 7, b g North Col—Tapalong **Sir Michael Connell**
4 **COURT ALERT**, 9, b g Petoski—Banbury Cake **Mr J. E. Connell**
5 **DREAM ON BABY**, 5, b m Broadsword—Sarah Dream (IRE) **Sir Michael Connell**
6 **EXCEPTIONNEL (FR)**, 5, b g Subotica (FR)—The Exception (FR) **Lady Connell**
7 **HILLTOP HARRY (IRE)**, 7, b g Commanche Run—Whats In A Name (IRE) **Sir Michael Connell**
8 **MAESTRO PLEASE (IRE)**, 5, b g Old Vic—Greek Melody (IRE) **Mr S. J. Connell**

LADY CONNELL—continued
9 **PRIVATE PETE**, 11, ch g Gunner B—Vedra (IRE) **Sir Michael Connell**
10 **WILL STEANE**, 5, ch g Master Willie—Deep Pier **Mr Simon Connell**
11 **YER FATHER'S YACHT (IRE)**, 4, b g Desert Story (IRE)—Alchiea **Sir Michael Connell**

123 MR M. J. COOMBE, Weymouth
Postal: **Sea Barn Farm, Fleet, Weymouth, Dorset, DT3 4ED.**
Contact: **PHONE (01305) 782218/761745 FAX (01305) 775396 E-MAIL wib@seabarn.fsnet.co.uk**

1 **OSCAR BILL (IRE)**, 5, b g Oscar (IRE)—Forecast Rain (IRE) **Mr Chris Pugsley**

Other Owners: Bagwell Farm Touring Park, M. J. C. Builders Ltd, West Fleet Holiday Farm.

Assistant Trainer: Mrs M Roberts

Amateur: Mrs M Roberts (9-7).

124 MR J. R. CORNWALL, Melton Mowbray
Postal: **April Cottage, Pasture Lane, Hose, Melton Mowbray, Leicestershire, LE14 4LB.**
Contact: **PHONE (01664) 444453 MOBILE (07939) 557091**

1 **BARTON BOG (IRE)**, 10, gr g Roselier (FR)—Al's Niece **Mr J. R. Cornwall**
2 **BUZYBAKSON (IRE)**, 7, b br g Bob Back (USA)—Middle Verde (USA) **Mr J. R. Cornwall**
3 **KADOUKO (FR)**, 11, b g Cadoudal (FR)—Perle Bleue (FR) **Mr J. R. Cornwall**
4 **PEACEMAKER (IRE)**, 12, br g Strong Gale—Gamonda **Mr J. R. Cornwall**
5 **POLISH PILOT (IRE)**, 9, b g Polish Patriot (USA)—Va Toujours **Mr J. R. Cornwall**
6 **RUNAWAY BISHOP (USA)**, 9, b br g Lear Fan (USA)—Valid Linda (USA) **Mr J. R. Cornwall**
7 **STAND EASY (IRE)**, 11, b g Buckskin (FR)—Geeaway **Mr J. R. Cornwall**
8 **STRONG MAGIC (IRE)**, 12, br g Strong Gale—Baybush **Mr J. R. Cornwall**
9 **THE MAJOR (NZ)**, 11, ch g Try To Stop Me—Equation (NZ) **Mr J. R. Cornwall**

Conditional: R Hobson (10-0).

125 MR L. G. COTTRELL, Cullompton
Postal: **Sprinters, Dulford, Cullompton, Devon, EX15 2DX.**
Contact: **PHONE (01884) 266320**

1 **CHEVRONNE**, 4, b g Compton Place—Maria Isabella (FR) **Dulford Strollers**
2 **DESERT VALENTINE**, 9, b g Midyan (USA)—Mo Ceri **Mrs Lucy Halloran**
3 **GO GO GIRL**, 4, ch f Pivotal—Addicted To Love **Mr H. C. Seymour**
4 **HAWRIDGE PRINCE**, 4, b g Polar Falcon (USA)—Zahwa **Mr Eric Gadsden**
5 **JUST A GLIMMER**, 4, b f Bishop of Cashel—Rockin' Rosie **Manor Farm Packers Ltd**
6 **PRINCESS MAGDALENA**, 4, ch f Pennekamp (USA)—Reason To Dance **Mr Eric Gadsden**

THREE-YEAR-OLDS
7 **RUB OF THE GREEN**, b g Groom Dancer (USA)—Green Light (FR) **Manor Farm Packers Ltd**
8 **TARTIRUGA (IRE)**, b g Turtle Island (IRE)—Palio Flyer **Fourever Hopeful**

TWO-YEAR-OLDS
9 **AGILETE**, b c 8/5 Piccolo—Ingerence (FR) (Akarad (FR)) (22000) **J.Bosworth, H.Seymour, A.Walsh & T.Walsh**
10 **ANGEL SPRINTS**, b f 25/2 Piccolo—Runs In The Family (Distant Relative) (16000) **Mrs L. Halloran**
11 **INCHCAPE ROCK**, ch f 17/3 Inchinor—
Washm (USA) (Diesis) (18000) **J.Boswell,Baroness S.Maltzahn,A&T Walsh**
12 Ch c 17/4 Polish Precedent (USA—
Looks Sensational (USA) (Majestic Light (USA)) (32000) **Mr E. J. S. Gadsden**
13 **TAKE THE PLUNGE**, b f 19/4 Benny The Dip (USA)—Pearly River (Elegant Air) **P. A. & M. J. Reditt**

Other Owners: Mr Gerry Albertini, Mr John Boswell, Mr D. J. Cole, Mr M. J. Collins, Mr R. C. Dollar, Mr P. J. Gorman, Mrs Jenny Hopkins, Mrs Ruth Perry.

Assistant Trainer: Mrs P M Cottrell & Mr L Jefford

Jockeys (Flat): A Daly, A Dettori (w.a.), J Egan, M Fenton, I Mongan, J Quinn. **Amateur:** Mr L Jefford (10-0).

126 MR R. M. H. COWELL, Newmarket
Postal: **Bottisham Heath Stud, Six Mile Bottom, Newmarket, Suffolk, CB8 0TT.**
Contact: **PHONE (01638) 570330 FAX (01638) 570246 MOBILE (07785) 512463**

1. **CAPTAIN DARLING (IRE)**, 4, b g Pennekamp (USA)—Gale Warning (IRE) **Mr A. Dunmore**
2. **EMMERVALE**, 5, b m Emarati (USA)—Raintree Venture **Miss Diana Birkbeck**
3. **ESTIMATION**, 4, b f Mark of Esteem (IRE)—Mohican Girl **Bottisham Heath Stud**
4. **FOREVER PHOENIX**, 4, b f Shareef Dancer (USA)—With Care **Mr J. M. Greetham**
5. **GAELIC PROBE (IRE)**, 10, b g Roi Danzig (USA)—Scottish Gaelic (USA) **Mr A. Dunmore**
6. **HUSKY (POL)**, 6, b g Special Power—Hallo Bambina (POL) **Mrs J. M. Penney**
7. **INCHING**, 4, b f Inchinor—Tshusick **Mr Allen Rix**
8. **JONNY EBENEEZER**, 5, b g Hurricane Sky (AUS)—Leap of Faith (IRE) **Mrs J. M. Penney**
9. **MAJLIS (IRE)**, 7, b g Caerleon (USA)—Ploy **Mr Terry Warner**
10. **ROSES OF SPRING**, 6, gr m Shareef Dancer (USA)—Couleur de Rose **Bottisham Heath Stud**
11. **SOMERTON (POL)**, 6, b g Saphir (GER)—Sobota (POL) **Mrs S. Nelson, A. Stennett & T. Warner**
12. **TARKWA**, 5, gr m Doyoun—Shining Fire **Mr J. B. Robinson**

THREE-YEAR-OLDS

13. **CHADWELL LAD**, b g Vettori (IRE)—Elle Reef **Hackberry Bloodstock**
14. **MARY CARLETON**, ch f Halling (USA)—Anne Bonny **Bottisham Heath Stud**
15. **SPARKLING CLEAR**, b f Efisio—Shoot Clear **Bottisham Heath Stud**
16. **TREGENNA**, b f Forzando—Nineteenth of May **Mr & Mrs D. A. Gamble**
17. **TSARBUCK**, b c Perugino (USA)—Form At Last **Mr S. P. Shore**
18. **TUAREG (IRE)**, b c Ashkalani (IRE)—Shining Fire **Mr J. B. Robinson**

TWO-YEAR-OLDS

19. **BREGAGLIA**, ch f 24/3 Zaha (CAN)—Strath Kitten (Scottish Reel) **Miss C. Sharp**
20. **CANADIAN DANEHILL (IRE)**, b c 13/4 Indian Danehill (IRE)—
San Jovita (CAN) (St Jovite (USA)) **Blue Metropolis**
21. **ETERNALLY**, ch c 22/4 Timeless Times (USA)—
Nice Spice (IRE) (Common Grounds) (4500) **Bottisham Heath Stud**
22. **HIAMOVI (IRE)**, b c 24/2 Monashee Mountain—Dunfern (Wolver Hollow) **Blue Metropolis**
23. **IMPERATRICE**, b f 20/2 Emperor Jones (USA)—Fine Honor (FR) (Highest Honor (FR)) **Mr J. Vowles**
24. **ROWANBERRY**, b f 30/4 Bishop of Cashel—Raintree Venture (Good Times (ITY)) **Miss Diana Birkbeck**
25. **VERY CLEAR**, b f 30/4 Loup Sauvage (USA)—Shoot Clear (Bay Express) **Bottisham Heath Stud**

Other Owners: Sin Wear.

127 MR C. G. COX, Hungerford
Postal: **Beechdown Farm, Sheepdrove Road, Lambourn, Hungerford, Berkshire, RG17 7UN.**
Contact: **OFFICE (01488) 73072 FAX (01488) 73500 MOBILE (07740) 630521**
E-MAIL info@clivecox.co.uk

1. **HEY PRESTO**, 4, b g Piccolo—Upping The Tempo **The Beechdown Flyers**
2. **IONIAN SPRING (IRE)**, 9, b g Ela-Mana-Mou—Well Head (IRE) **Elite Racing Club**
3. **LAGO D'ORTA (IRE)**, 4, ch c Bahhare (USA)—Maelalong (IRE) **Mr Dennis Shaw**
4. **MOLLY'S SECRET**, 6, b m Minshaanshu Amad (USA)—Secret Miss **The Two M'S Partnership**
5. **NEW SEEKER**, 4, b c Green Desert (USA)—Ahbab (IRE) **Elite Racing Club**
6. **NOBLE BARON**, 8, gr g Karinga Bay—Grey Baroness **Mr T. Y. Bissett**
7. **PACIANO (IRE)**, 4, b g Perugino (USA)—Saucy Maid (IRE) **The Beech Nuts**
8. **PENRIC**, 4, b g Marju (IRE)—Nafhaat (USA) **Mr P. G. Horrocks**
9. **SILCHESTER DREAM**, 6, ch m Karinga Bay—Raghill Hannah **The Silchester Racing Club**

THREE-YEAR-OLDS

10. **ABACO SUNSET**, ch f Bahamian Bounty—Thicket **The Desert Island Partnership**
11. **AUTUMN FLYER (IRE)**, ch g Salse (USA)—Autumn Fall (USA) **Mr Dennis Shaw**
12. **DAGOLA (IRE)**, b g Daggers Drawn (USA)—Diabola (USA) **The Originals**
13. **DAYDREAM DANCER**, gr f Daylami (IRE)—Dancing Wolf (IRE) **The Grey Lady Partnership**
14. **OUT AFTER DARK**, b c Cadeaux Genereux—Midnight Shift (IRE) **The Night Owls**
15. **PERFECT HINDSIGHT (IRE)**, b g Spectrum (IRE)—Vinicky (USA) **Stephen Barrow, Amity Finance, B.A.S.I.C**
16. **REHEARSAL**, b c Singspiel (IRE)—Daralaka (IRE) **Elite Racing Club**
17. **THYOLO (IRE)**, ch c Bering—Topline (GER) **Mr Mike Watts and Mr Steve Woodhams**

MR C. G. COX—continued

TWO-YEAR-OLDS

18 COUNT KRISTO, br c 22/2 Dr Fong (USA)—
                                  Aryadne (Rainbow Quest (USA)) (86580) **Mr and Mrs P. Hargreaves**
19 DANCING ROSE (IRE), b f 21/4 Danehill Dancer (IRE)—Shinkoh Rose (FR) (Warning) (32000) **Partnership**
20 FORMIDABLE WILL (FR), b c 26/3 Efisio—Shewillifshewants (IRE) (Alzao (USA)) (32000) **Partnership**
21 HOLD THE FLAG (IRE), b c 26/4 Lend A Hand—Hever Golf Mover (Efisio) (5000) **J. Francome and Partners**
22 INHERENT (IRE), ch f 23/3 In The Wings—Serpentara (Kris) (30000) **Elite Racing Club**
23 LOOK AT THE STARS (IRE), b c 21/4 Bachir (IRE)—
                                  Pizzazz (Unfuwain (USA)) (18552) **S. Barrow, A. Parsons & P. Stevenson**
24 B c 9/4 Dansili—Magic Slipper (Habitat) (35000) **Partnership**
25 Ch f 17/1 Ashkalani (IRE)—Marabela (IRE) (Shernazar) **Mr Charles Cruden**
26 SAMBARINA (IRE), b f 26/2 Victory Note (USA)—Brazilia (Forzando) (28447) **Partnership**
27 SECRET MOMENT, b c 4/5 Polar Prince (IRE)—Inchtina (Inchinor) **Mrs C. Stevenson**
28 SOUTHERN SHORE (IRE), ch c 20/3 Erhaab (USA)—Intisab (Green Desert (USA)) (50000) **Mr Dennis Shaw**
29 SPIELBOUND, b f 5/3 Singspiel (IRE)—Fragrant Belle (USA) (Al Nasr (FR)) (45000) **Elite Racing Club**
30 SURWAKI (USA), b c 5/4 Miswaki (USA)—Quinella (Generous (IRE)) (55658) **Mr Dennis Shaw**

Other Owners: Mr John H. Cook, Mrs T. L. Cox, Mr Tony Hill, Mr T. G. Leslie, Mr B. D. Makepeace, Mrs P. Makepeace, Mr Michael Mulhern, Miss M. Noden.

Jockey (Flat): P Robinson (w.a.). **Apprentice:** Ashleigh Horton (7-12).

---

128 **MR R. CRAGGS, Sedgefield**
Postal: **East Close Farm, Sedgefield, Stockton-On-Tees, Cleveland, TS21 3HW.**
Contact: **PHONE (01740) 620239 FAX (01740) 623476**

1 GALLEY LAW, 4, ch g Most Welcome—Miss Blitz **Mr Ray Craggs**
2 IF BY CHANCE, 6, ch g Risk Me (FR)—Out of Harmony **Mr Ray Craggs**
3 MISS FLEURIE, 4, b f Alzao (USA)—Miss Sancerre **Mr Ray Craggs**
4 WATERPARK, 6, b m Namaqualand (USA)—Willisa **Mr Ray Craggs**

THREE-YEAR-OLDS

5 B f Cayman Kai (IRE)—Distinctly Laura (IRE) **Mr Ray Craggs**
6 HIGH SWAINSTON, ch g The West (USA)—Reamzafonic **Mr Ray Craggs**

Assistant Trainer: Miss J N Craggs

Amateur: Miss Nicola Craggs (9-0).

---

129 **MISS I. E. L. CRAIG, Collingbourne Ducis**
Postal: **Highlands House, Herridge, Collingbourne Ducis, Marlborough, Wiltshire SN8 3EG.**
Contact: **PHONE (01264) 850646 FAX (01264) 850015 E-MAIL ielcraig@hotmail.com**

1 BELALCAZAR, 5, b g El Conquistador—Ruby Celebration **Mr & Mrs P. R. Ensor**
2 ELLWAY PROSPECT, 4, ch f Pivotal—Littlemisstrouble (USA) **Mr C. H. Bothway**
3 4, B f Busy Flight—Flaming Rose (IRE) **Mrs M. L. Luck**
4 IRISHMAN (IRE), 10, b g Bob Back (USA)—Future Tense (USA) **Miss I. E. L. Craig**
5 SHERZABAD (IRE), 7, b br g Doyoun—Sheriya (USA) **Mr G. J. Luck & Mrs R. De Rougemont**
6 VERTEDANZ (IRE), 4, b f Sesaro (USA)—Blade of Grass **Mrs D. C. Samworth**
7 WHETHER THE STORM (IRE), 8, b g Glacial Storm (USA)—Minimum Choice (IRE) **Miss I. E. L. Craig**
8 WOTAN (FR), 5, ch g Beaudelaire (USA)—Woglinde (USA) **Mrs M. L. Luck**

Other Owners: Mr R. Cave, Miss. A Jones, The Countess Of Lonsdale, Miss S. Samworth, Mr A. Shaw.

Assistant Trainer: James Luck

Jockey (NH): J Culloty (w.a.).

130 MR J. K. S. CRESSWELL, Oakamoor
Postal: Stoneydale Farm, Oakamoor, Stoke-On-Trent, Staffordshire, ST10 3AH.
Contact: HOME (01538) 702362 OFFICE (01782) 324606 FAX (01782) 324410

1 BROTHER TED, 7, b g Henbit (USA)—Will Be Wanton **Mr J. K. S. Cresswell**
2 EARLS ROCK, 6, b g Gunner B—Will Be Wanton **Mr J. K. S. Cresswell**
3 GOOD FRIEND, 5, b m Environment Friend—Gunner Be Good **Mr J. K. S. Cresswell**
4 HEATHY GORE, 5, ch m Environment Friend—Hazel Hill **Mr J. K. S. Cresswell**

Assistant Trainer: Mrs E M Cresswell

131 MR A. CROOK, Leyburn
Postal: Lilac Cottage, Harmby, Leyburn, North Yorkshire, DL8 5PD.
Contact: PHONE/FAX (01969) 640303 MOBILE (07764) 158899
E-MAIL andycrookracing@fsmail.net

1 BEHAN, 5, ch g Rainbows For Life (CAN)—With Finesse **Mr Keith Nicholson**
2 BORDER BANDIT (IRE), 5, b g Shahanndeh—Mwanamio **W. Graham & J. Gordon**
3 GLADYS AYLWARD, 4, b f Polar Falcon (USA)—Versami (USA) **Leeds Plywood and Doors Ltd**
4 HAREWOOD END, 6, b g Bin Ajwaad (IRE)—Tasseled (USA) **John Sinclair (Haulage) Ltd**
5 HERE COMES STEVE, 7, b g Primitive Rising (USA)—Keldholme **The Here Comes Steve Partnership**
6 JOE DI CAPO (IRE), 9, b g Phardante (FR)—Supreme Glen (IRE) **Mr Joe Buzzeo**
7 LADIES FROM LEEDS, 5, b m Primitive Rising (USA)—Keldholme **Mr Stef Stefanou**
8 LUCKY CATCH (IRE), 6, b g Safety Catch (USA)—Lucky Monday **Lucky Catch Partnership**
9 PORNIC (FR), 10, b g Shining Steel—Marie de Geneve (FR) **John Sinclair (Haulage) Ltd**
10 ROMAN STAR, 9, b g Teenoso (USA)—Mulloch Brae **Mr Richard Berry**
11 RYALUX (IRE), 11, b g Riverhead (USA)—Kings de Lema (IRE) **Mr William Lomas**
12 SAJOMI RONA (IRE), 7, ch g Riberetto—Mauma Lady (IRE) **Jay Dee Bloodstock Limited**
13 SPAINKRIS, 5, b g Kris—Pennycairn **Mr M. Wainright**
14 THESAURUS, 5, gr g Most Welcome—Red Embers **Mr Keith Nicholson**
15 TOM JELLY, 6, b g Elmaamul (USA)—Primitive Gift **Mr M. Wainright**
16 TROOPER, 10, b g Rock Hopper—Silica (USA) **Mr R. M. Bakes**

THREE-YEAR-OLDS

17 SHEAPYS LASS, b f Perugino (USA)—Nilu (IRE) **Sheapy's Lass Partnership**

Other Owners: Mr James Byrne, Mr J. W. Coates, Mrs Anna Dent, Mr J. D. Gordon, Mr W. Graham, Mr G. Heap, Mrs S. Hollingsworth.

Jockeys (NH): F Keniry, G Lee, R McGrath, A Ross. **Conditional:** Andrew Brimble.

132 MR L. M. CUMANI, Newmarket
Postal: Bedford House Stables, Bury Road, Newmarket, Suffolk, CB8 7BX.
Contact: PHONE (01638) 665432 FAX (01638) 667160 E-MAIL luca.cumani@virgin.net

1 ALKAASED (USA), 4, b c Kingmambo (USA)—Chesa Plana **Mr M. R. Charlton**
2 ETTRICK WATER, 5, ch g Selkirk (USA)—Sadly Sober (IRE) **Mrs E. H. Vestey**
3 FEEL GOOD FACTOR, 4, b g Singspiel (IRE)—Colorspin (FR) **Lancen Farm Partnership**
4 FERNERY, 4, b f Danehill (IRE)—Fern **Fittocks Stud Ltd**
5 JUBILEE TIME, 4, b c Mark of Esteem (IRE)—Bella Colora **Lancen Farm Partnership**
6 KING'S COUNTY (IRE), 6, b g Fairy King (USA)—Kardelle **Mr Gary Coull**
7 KUSTER, 8, b g Indian Ridge—Ustka **Mrs Luca Cumani**
8 LEBENSTANZ, 4, b br f Singspiel (IRE)—Reamur **Aston House Stud**
9 LITERATIM, 4, b c Polish Precedent (USA)—Annie Albright (USA) **Aston House Stud**
10 LOVES TRAVELLING (IRE), 4, b g Blues Traveller (IRE)—Fast Love (IRE) **Mr G. Robotti**
11 MAXILLA (IRE), 4, b br f Lahib (USA)—Lacinia **Mr L. Marinopoulos**
12 MEPHISTO (IRE), 5, b g Machiavellian (USA)—Cunning **Mrs Angie Silver**
13 MILLAFONIC, 4, b c Zafonic (USA)—Milligram **Lancen Farm Partnership**
14 PONGEE, 4, b f Barathea (IRE)—Puce **Fittocks Stud Ltd**
15 SALSELON, 5, b h Salse (USA)—Heady **Scuderia Briantea**
16 SARIN, 6, b g Deploy—Secretilla (USA) **Oakview Racing**
17 SPURADICH (IRE), 4, b c Barathea (IRE)—Svanzega (USA) **Scuderia Rencati Srl**
18 STARRY LODGE (IRE), 4, b c Grand Lodge (USA)—Stara **Mr R. C. Thompson**
19 STEALING BEAUTY (IRE), 4, b f Sadler's Wells (USA)—Imitation **Mr G. Callanan**

MR L. M. CUMANI—continued

20 **SUNSTRACH (IRE)**, 6, b h Polar Falcon (USA)—Lorne Lady **Scuderia Rencati**
21 **TITINIUS (IRE)**, 4, ch c Titus Livius (FR)—Maiyria (IRE) **Mr L. Marinopoulos**
22 **TRUENO (IRE)**, 5, b g Desert King (IRE)—Stitching (IRE) **Mrs Liz Jones**

THREE-YEAR-OLDS

23 **AESCULUS (USA)**, b f Horse Chestnut (SAF)—Crafty Buzz (USA) **Lord Hartington**
24 **ALGHAAZY (IRE)**, b c Mark of Esteem (IRE)—Kentmere (FR) **Sheikh Mohammed Obaid Al Maktoum**
25 **ALJAFLIYAH**, ch f Halling (USA)—Arruhan (IRE) **Sheikh Mohammed Obaid Al Maktoum**
26 **ANTIGIOTTO (IRE)**, ch g Desert Story (IRE)—Rofool (IRE) **Equibreed S.R.L.**
27 **CAVALGATA (IRE)**, ch f Desert Story (IRE)—Winter Pageant **Aston House Stud**
28 **COPPICE (IRE)**, ch c Rainbow Quest (USA)—Woodwin (IRE) **Lord Vestey**
29 **FORGED (IRE)**, b c Peintre Celebre (USA)—Imitation **Mr G. Callanan**
30 **GHANTOOT**, ch c Inchinor—Shall We Run **Sheikh Mohammed Obaid Al Maktoum**
31 **HELM (IRE)**, b c Alhaarth (IRE)—Pipers Pool (IRE) **Highclere Racing**
32 **IDEALISTIC (IRE)**, b f Unfuwain (USA)—L'Ideale (USA) **Fittocks Stud Ltd**
33 **IMOGENE**, br f Inchinor—Esperis (IRE) **Mr L. Marinopoulos**
34 **INDUSTRIAL STAR (IRE)**, ch c Singspiel (IRE)—Faribole (IRE) **Mr Albert S. N. Hu**
35 **KISS AGAIN**, b f Halling (USA)—Kissogram **Helena Springfield Ltd**
36 **LOST SOLDIER THREE (IRE)**, b g Barathea (IRE)—Donya **Sheikh Mohammed Obaid Al Maktoum**
37 **MANDATUM**, b g Mtoto—Reamur **Aston House Stud**
38 **MA YAHAB**, ch c Dr Fong (USA)—Bay Shade (USA) **Sheikh Mohammed Obaid Al Maktoum**
39 **NEWNHAM (IRE)**, ch c Theatrical—Brief Escapade (IRE) **Mrs Belinda Strudwick**
40 **NEW YORK CITY (IRE)**, b c Alzao (USA)—Eurolinka (IRE) **Eurolink Group Plc**
41 **OCREOLA (USA)**, b f Arch (USA)—Flippers (USA) **H. Lascelles**
42 **PLAY BOUZOUKI**, b f Halling (USA)—Balalaika **Helena Springfield Ltd**
43 **PRENUP (IRE)**, ch f Diesis—Mutual Consent (IRE) **Fittocks Stud**
44 **PUKKA (IRE)**, b c Sadler's Wells (USA)—Puce **Fittocks Stud**
45 **REDI (ITY)**, b c Danehill Dancer (IRE)—Rossella **Equibreed S.R.L.**
46 **SAHARA STORM (IRE)**, b f Desert Prince (IRE)—Deluge **Easton Park Stud**
47 **SBARBAA**, ch c Pivotal—The In-Laws (IRE) **Scuderia Rencati Srl**
48 **SCRIPTORIUM**, b c Singspiel (IRE)—Annie Albright (USA) **Aston House Stud**
49 **SELEBELA**, ch f Grand Lodge (USA)—Risarshana (FR) **Scuderia Rencati Srl**
50 **SHABI HANG**, b f Singspiel (IRE)—Hejraan (USA) **Sheikh Mohammed Obaid Al Maktoum**
51 **SILK SUIVANTE (IRE)**, b f Danehill (USA)—White Satin (IRE) **The Leigh Family**
52 **SILVERINE (USA)**, br f Silver Deputy (CAN)—Special Broad (USA) **Mr & Mrs James Wigan**
53 **SOLO SOLE (ITY)**, b c Grand Lodge (USA)—Storm Flash **Equibreed S.R.L.**
54 **SUMMER SERENADE**, b f Sadler's Wells (USA)—Summer Sonnet **Sheikh Mohammed**
55 **SWAHILI DANCER (USA)**, b c Swain (IRE)—Bella Ballerina **Lancen Farm Partnership**
56 **TAPIOKA CITY (USA)**, b f Danehill (USA)—Taroob (USA) **Sheikh Mohammed**
57 **TEAM PLAYER**, b c Mark of Esteem (IRE)—Colorspin (FR) **Lancen Farm Partnership**
58 **TUSSAH**, gr f Daylami (IRE)—Bombazine (USA) **The Leigh Family**
59 **ZEITGEIST (IRE)**, b c Singspiel (IRE)—Diamond Quest **Mr L. Marinopoulos**
60 **ZURI (IRE)**, b f Kris S (USA)—Amizette (USA) **The Leigh Family**

TWO-YEAR-OLDS

61 **ALLIED CAUSE**, ch f 2/2 Giant's Causeway—Alligram (USA) (Alysheba (USA)) **Helena Springfield Ltd**
62 **BOSSI (IRE)**, b f 12/3 Sadler's Wells (USA)—Brocatelle (Green Desert (USA)) **Kilboy Estates**
63 **CAMPLI (IRE)**, b c 13/5 Zafonic (USA)—Sept A Neuf (Be My Guest (USA)) (30921) **Equibreed Srl**
64 B g 21/2 Arch (USA)—Crafty Buzz (USA) (Crafty Prospector (USA)) **Marquess of Hartington**
65 B f 30/4 Sadler's Wells (USA)—Dangerous Diva (IRE) (Royal Academy (USA)) **Bob Lanigan**
66 B f 4/2 In The Wings—Dark Veil (Gulch (USA)) **Aston House Stud**
67 **DASH TO THE TOP**, b f 20/2 Montjeu (IRE)—Millennium Dash (Nashwan (USA)) **Helena Springfield Ltd**
68 **DONYA ONE**, b f 25/2 Cadeaux Genereux—
               Fadhah (Mukaddamah (USA)) **Sheikh Mohammed Obaid Al Maktoum**
69 **EDAS**, b c 13/4 Celtic Swing—Eden (Polish Precedent (USA)) **Mr L. Marinopoulos**
70 **FAMCAPII (IRE)**, b c 24/2 Montjeu (IRE)—Scostes (Cadeaux Genereux) **Scuderia Rencati Srl**
71 **FATUR**, b c 21/2 Singspiel (IRE)—Du du (IRE) (Law Society (USA)) **Scuderia Rencati Srl**
72 **FLAMAND (USA)**, ch f 23/3 Miswaki (USA)—
               Sister Sorrow (USA) (Holy Bull (USA)) (27828) **Lady Carolyn Warren**
73 **GOLBAND**, b f 28/1 Cadeaux Genereux—
               Hatheetham (IRE) (Machiavellian (USA)) **Sheikh Mohammed Obaid Al Maktoum**
74 **JAZRAWY**, b c 2/2 Dansili—
               Dalila di Mare (IRE) (Bob Back (USA)) (85000) **Sheikh Mohammed Obaid Al Maktoum**
75 B f 15/5 Montjeu (IRE)—Kama Tashoof (Mtoto) (25000) **Equibreed Srl**
76 B c 4/4 Diesis—Lilian Bayliss (IRE) (Sadler's Wells (USA)) (61842) **Allevamento La Nuova Searra Srl**

MR L. M. CUMANI—continued

77 **MASSARO PAPE (IRE)**, b c 30/4 Intikhab (USA)—Megeve (IRE) (Ahonoora) (18552) **Equibreed Srl**
78 **METRICAL**, b f 5/2 Inchinor—Salligram (Salse (USA)) **Fittocks Stud**
79 **MISS HANKS (IRE)**, b f 2/4 Fasliyev (USA)—Akamantis (Kris) (68027) **Allevamento La Muova Searra Srl**
80 Ch f 30/3 Atticus (USA)—My Shafy (Rousillon (USA)) **Mr Christopher Wright**
81 **NASRAWY**, b c 1/5 Grand Lodge (USA)—
                By Charter (Shirley Heights) (100000) **Sheikh Mohammed Obaid Al Maktoum**
82 Ch f 15/3 Alhaarth (IRE)—Northjet (Q)
83 **OAKEN**, b c 3/3 Efisio—Exotic Forest (Dominion) (25000) **Mr L. Marinopoulos**
84 **PAMIR (IRE)**, b c 20/4 Namid—Mijouter (IRE) (Coquelin (USA)) (50000) **Mrs E. H. Vestey**
85 Ch f 15/3 Alhaarth (IRE)—Pennysylvania (USA) (Northjet) **Scuderia Rencati Srl**
86 **PRIDE OF NATION (IRE)**, b c 9/4 Danehill Dancer (IRE)—Anita Via (IRE) (Anita's Prince) (40197) **Equibreed Srl**
87 **QUIZZICAL QUESTION (IRE)**, ch f 11/4 Bob Back (USA)—
                Quality of Life (Auction Ring (USA)) (43289) **Allevamento Ghalloblu**
88 B f 1/5 Singspiel—Real Time (Polish Precedent (USA)) **Aston House Stud**
89 **RETURN OF THE KING**, b c 3/5 Nashwan (USA)—Someone Special (Habitat) **Lancen Farm Partnership**
90 **SHABAWY (IRE)**, b c 1/3 Indian Danehill (IRE)—
                Winsome Girl (Music Boy) (85000) **Sheikh Mohammed Obaid Al Maktoum**
91 **SHARED DREAMS**, b f 29/4 Seeking The Gold—Coretta (IRE) (Caerleon (USA)) **The Leigh Family**
92 B c 25/2 Sinndar (IRE)—Shy Minstrel (USA) (The Minstrel (CAN)) (82000) **Lord Delaware**
93 B f 20/1 Namid—Sidelined (IRE) (In The Wings) (32000) **Allevamento Gialloblu**
94 **SOHGOL (IRE)**, ch f 7/2 Singspiel (IRE)—
                Arruhan (IRE) (Mujtahid (USA)) **Sheikh Mohammed Obaid Al Maktoum**
95 Ch c 10/1 Pivotal—Spanish Craft (IRE) (Jareer (USA)) (50000) **Scuderia Rencati Srl**
96 **SWAINS BRIDGE (USA)**, b c Swain (USA)—Saraa Ree (USA) (Caro) **Mr Christopher Wright**
97 **TERENZIUM (IRE)**, b c 27/3 Cape Cross (IRE)—Tatanka (ITY) (Luge) (68027) **Scudetia Rencati Srl**
98 B c 1/5 Halling (USA)—Titanias Way (Fairy King (USA)) **Scuderia Rencati Srl**
99 **VALIOS (IRE)**, b c 30/3 Royal Applause—
                Swing And Brave (IRE) (Arctic Tern (USA)) (48000) **Mr L. Marinopoulos**
100 **ZALIMAR (IRE)**, b f 3/4 Montjeu (IRE)—Zanella (IRE) (Nordico (USA)) **Mr Ben Goldsmith**
101 **ZAS**, b c 7/5 Dansili—Esperis (IRE) (Warning) **Mr L. Marinopoulos**
102 **ZEEBA (IRE)**, b f 15/1 Barathea (IRE)—Donya (Mill Reef (USA)) **Sheikh Mohammed Obaid Al Maktoum**

Other Owners: Sir Eric Parker, Duke Of Roxburghe, Mr Paul G. S. Silver, Mr R. J. Stevenson, Mr E. H. Vestey, Miss Helena
Weinfeld, Mr M. Weinfeld.

Assistant Trainer: Guillermo Arizkorreta

Apprentice: N Mackay (7-3). **Amateur:** Miss F Cumani (10-7).

133	**MR P. D. CUNDELL, Compton**
	Postal: Roden House, Wallingford Road, Compton, Newbury, Berkshire, RG20 6QR.
	Contact: PHONE (01635) 578267 FAX (01635) 578267

1 **ESSAY BABY (FR)**, 4, b f Saumarez—Easter Baby **Mr J. S. B. Anderson**
2 **LADY MCNAIR**, 4, b f Sheikh Albadou—Bonita Bee **Mr Ian M. Brown**
3 **MAN THE GATE**, 5, b g Elmaamul (USA)—Girl At The Gate **Mr John G. Morley**
4 **MASTER MCNAIR (IRE)**, 6, br g Glacial Storm (USA)—Pollyville **Mr Ian M. Brown**
5 **NAWOW**, 4, b g Blushing Flame (USA)—Fair Test **Mr Ian M. Brown**
6 **SENNA (IRE)**, 4, b g Petardia—Saborinie **Mr John Davies (Stonehill)**
7 **TARANAKI**, 6, b h Delta Dancer—Miss Ticklepenny **Mr Eric Evers**
8 **THREE DAYS REIGN**, 10, br g Camden Town—Little Treat **Entre-Nous**

THREE-YEAR-OLDS

9 **ANDALUZA**, b f Mujadil (USA)—Hierarchy **Mr Pedro Rosas**
10 **EL MAGNIFICO**, b g Forzando—Princess Poquito **Mr Pedro Rosas**
11 **IFFY**, b g Orpen (USA)—Hopesay **Mr Nigel Johnson-Hill**
12 **SEVILLANO**, b g Nicolotte—Nashville Blues (IRE) **Mr Pedro Rosas**

MR P. D. CUNDELL—continued
TWO-YEAR-OLDS

13 **KINTBURY CROSS,** b g 25/4 Kylian (USA)—Cebwob (Rock City) **Miss H. C. Fraser**
14 **LOITOKITOK,** b g 12/3 Piccolo—Bonita Bee (King of Spain) **Mr Ian M. Brown**

Other Owners: Mrs S. M. Booker, Mr N. Dickin, Mr W. M. Dobson, Mr M. R. Kent.

Amateur: Miss Cheryl Nosworthy (9-0).

---

134 **MR M. CUNNINGHAM, Navan**
Postal: **Gormanstown Stables, Kildalkey, Navan, Co.Meath, Ireland.**
Contact: **PHONE +353 (0) 46 94 31672 FAX +353 (0) 46 94 31467**

1 **AON SUIL AMHAIN (IRE),** 6, b m Supreme Leader—Glen Dieu **Mrs P. Campbell**
2 **BAMPA (IRE),** 5, b h Welsh Term—Bold Lillian (IRE) **Mr Herb M. Stanley**
3 **BATTENBURG (IRE),** 7, b g Good Thyne (USA)—Luminous Run **John R. Donohoe**
4 **BAYLETTA (IRE),** 5, b m Woodborough (USA)—Excruciating (CAN) **Michael J. Wiley**
5 **BEANCOUNTER (IRE),** 7, b g Satco (FR)—Madame Venard **O. F. Syndicate**
6 **COCCINELLE (IRE),** 6, b m Great Marquess—Nuit d'Ete (USA) **Brendan Kelly**
7 **CRAIGTOWN BOY,** 5, b g Oscar (IRE)—Yarra Glen **Mr John McKeague**
8 **CRAOBH RUA,** 7, b g Lord Americo—Addies Lass **Mrs Megan McManus**
9 **GLENBAR (IRE),** 8, b m Leading Counsel (USA)—Glen Dieu **J. O'Flanagan**
10 5, B m Arctic Lord—Glen Dieu **Mrs Michael Cunningham**
11 **GREAT CHAOS (IRE),** 5, b h Great Commotion (USA)—Hassosi (IRE) **Banagher Glen Syndicate**
12 **HARD TO HANDLE (IRE),** 4, b g Dr Massini (IRE)—Lady Callianire (USA) **Mr Herb M. Stanley**
13 **HOOKEDONAFEELING (IRE),** 6, ch m Shernazar—Fireblends (IRE) **Mrs Paul Shanahan & Mr Peter Magnier**
14 **INISHDUBH (IRE),** 4, b g Turtle Island (IRE)—Bold Lillian (IRE) **Banagher Glen Syndicate**
15 **JUST A SPIN,** 7, b g Homo Sapien—Hilly-Down Lass **Herb M. Stanley**
16 **LEADAMURRAYDANCE (IRE),** 8, b m Supreme Leader—Dancingcinderella **Mrs Michael Cunningham**
17 **LEGAL EXPRESS (IRE),** 6, b br g Phardante (FR)—She's Pretty **Mrs Marie T. Regan**
18 **MAPLE LEAF (IRE),** 7, b br g Phardante (FR)—Lady Sirat **Herb M. Stanley**
19 **NANCYS BRIDGE (IRE),** 5, b br m Old Vic—St Christoph **Canal Racing Syndicate**
20 **NORTHSIDER (IRE),** 6, b g King's Ride—Atlantic Hope **F. Connon**
21 **PENNY FARTHING,** 6, br m Mind Games—Souveniers **Mayoco Syndicate**
22 **PROPERTY PARTNERS (IRE),** 7, b g Roselier (FR)—Ballymac Lady **Mr F. B. Heaslip**
23 **RIVER QUOILE,** 8, b g Terimon—Carrikins **Mrs Megan MacManus**
24 **SUPREME BEING (IRE),** 7, b g Supreme Leader—Parsonetta **Mrs B. Lynch**
25 **SYBIL HEAD,** 5, b m Beneficial—Lovely Stranger **Mr John McKeague**
26 **TARA'S GIFT (IRE),** 6, b m Midhish—Bold Lillian (IRE) **Miss Tara Cunningham**

THREE-YEAR-OLDS

27 **HE WAS IT,** b c Turtle Island (IRE)—Holly's Gold (IRE) **Mrs B. Lynch**
28 **INDIAN'S LANDING (IRE),** b c Barathea (IRE)—
We've Just Begun (USA) **Herb M. Stanley & Mrs Michael Cunningham**
29 B c Orpen (USA)—Sherabi (IRE) **Herb M. Stanley**

TWO-YEAR-OLDS

30 B f 13/4 Orpen (USA)—Bold Lillian (IRE) (Bold Arrangement) **Mrs Michael Cunningham**
31 B f 9/6 Leading Counsel (USA)—Glen Dieu (Furry Glen) **Mrs Michael Cunningham**
32 Ch f 11/4 Orpen (USA)—Holly's Gold (IRE) (Mac's Imp (USA)) (1855) **Mrs Brian Lynch**
33 B c 29/6 Leading Counsel (USA)—Noeleen's Delight (IRE) (Le Bavard (FR)) **Mrs Michael Cunningham**
34 B c 26/4 Orpen (USA)—We've Just Begun (USA) (Huguenot (USA)) **Mrs Brian Lynch**

Assistant Trainer: Tara Cunningham

---

135 **MR W. S. CUNNINGHAM, Yarm**
Postal: **Embleton Farm, Garbutts Lane, Hutton Rudby, Yarm, Cleveland, TS15 0DN.**
Contact: **PHONE (01642) 701290 MOBILE (07885) 158703**

1 **AMALFI COAST,** 5, b g Emperor Jones (USA)—Legend's Daughter (USA) **Ann and David Bell**
2 **ANACAPRI,** 4, b f Barathea (IRE)—Dancerette **Ann and David Bell**
3 **ARIZONA DESERT (IRE),** 4, b g Desert Story (IRE)—Happy Tidings **Ann and David Bell**
4 **BOLD AMUSEMENT,** 14, ch g Never So Bold—Hysterical **Ann and David Bell**

MR W. S. CUNNINGHAM—continued

   5 **FIZZY POP**, 5, b m Robellino (USA)—Maria Isabella (FR) **Ann and David Bell**
   6 **PLAYFUL DANE (IRE)**, 7, b g Dolphin Street (FR)—Omicida (IRE) **Ann and David Bell**

Other Owners: Mrs Ann Bell, Mr David Bell.

Assistant Trainer: Vicky Cunningham

---

136   **MR K. CUNNINGHAM-BROWN, Stockbridge**
Postal: **Danebury Place, Stockbridge, Hampshire, SO20 6JX.**
Contact: **PHONE (01264) 781061 FAX (01264) 781061 MOBILE (07802) 500059**
E-MAIL kcb@unicheq.com WEBSITE kcb@unicheq.co.uk

   1 **BEN EWAR**, 10, b g Old Vic—Sunset Reef **Mr A. J. Richards**
   2 **BOLD EFFORT (FR)**, 12, b g Bold Arrangement—Malham Tarn **Mr A. J. Richards**
   3 **BUGLE CALL**, 4, b g Zamindar (USA)—Petillante **Mr A. J. Richards**
   4 **COMANCHE WOMAN**, 4, b f Distinctly North (USA)—Possibility **Danebury Racing Stables Limited**
   5 **FIREWORKS (FR)**, 4, gr g Kendor (FR)—Little Emily **Mr A. J. Richards**
   6 **MANGUS (IRE)**, 10, b g Mac's Imp (USA)—Holly Bird **Danebury Racing Stables Limited**
   7 **MORNING SUN**, 4, b f Starborough—Malham Tarn **Mr A. J. Richards**
   8 **REPETOIRE (FR)**, 4, ch f Zafonic (USA)—Lady Kate (USA) **Mr A. J. Richards**
   9 **SUNSET BLUES (FR)**, 4, ch g Green Tune (USA)—Sunset Reef **Mr A. J. Richards**

Assistant Trainer: Ricky Todd

Jockeys (Flat): C Catlin, D O'Neil. **Jockey (NH):** B Fenton.

---

137   **MR B. J. CURLEY, Newmarket**
Postal: **104 Centre Drive, Newmarket, Suffolk, CB8 8AP.**
Contact: **PHONE (01638) 668755**

   1 **AQUA PURA (GER)**, 5, b h Acatenango (GER)—Actraphane **Mrs B. J. Curley**
   2 **CRISTOFORO (IRE)**, 7, b g Perugino (USA)—Red Barons Lady (IRE) **Mr P. Byrne**
   3 **FAIRY WIND (GER)**, 7, b h Dashing Blade—Fairy Bluebird **Mrs B. J. Curley**
   4 **IN SPIRIT (IRE)**, 6, b g Distinctly North (USA)—June Goddess **Mr D. Donovan**
   5 **KALOU (GER)**, 6, br g Law Society (USA)—Kompetenz (IRE) **Mr P. Byrne**
   6 **LILLEBROR (GER)**, 6, b h Top Waltz (FR)—Lady Soliciti (GER) **Mrs B. J. Curley**
   7 **MANHATTAN VIEW (IRE)**, 5, b g Kadeed (IRE)—Haunted For Sure (IRE) **Mr D. Donovan**
   8 **MUSKATSTURM (GER)**, 5, b g Lecroix (GER)—Myrthe (GER) **Mrs B. J. Curley**
   9 **SHAHM (IRE)**, 5, b g Marju (IRE)—Istibshar **Mrs B. J. Curley**
  10 **THE THIRD CURATE (IRE)**, 9, b g Fairy King (USA)—Lassalia **Mr P. Byrne**

Assistant Trainer: Desmond Donovan

Jockeys (Flat): S W Kelly, J P Spencer (8-2). **Jockey (NH):** Brian Murphy. **Apprentice:** P J Scallan. **Conditional:** Brian Murphy. **Amateur:** Mr Paul Maloney.

---

138   **MR T. A. K. CUTHBERT, Carlisle**
Postal: **26 Eden Grange, Little Corby, Carlisle, Cumbria, CA4 8QW.**
Contact: **PHONE (01228) 560822 STABLES (01228) 561328 FAX (01228) 560822**
MOBILE (07747) 843344

   1 **EXALTED (IRE)**, 11, b g High Estate—Heavensward (USA) **Mr Roy Thorburn & Mrs Elva Maxwell**
   2 **GIVUSACUDDLE**, 11, ch m Little Wolf—Royal Marie **Mr T. A. K. Cuthbert**
   3 **HEBENUS**, 5, b g Hamas (IRE)—Stinging Nettle **Mrs Joyce Cuthbert**
   4 **NOTHING DAUNTED**, 7, ch g Selkirk (USA)—Khubza **Mr W. Hurst**
   5 **SIREN SONG (IRE)**, 13, b g Warning—Nazwa **Mrs Joyce Cuthbert**
   6 **WAFIR (IRE)**, 12, b g Scenic—Taniokey **Mr T. A. K. Cuthbert**

THREE-YEAR-OLDS

   7 **BISHOPS BOUNCE**, b c Bishop of Cashel—Heights of Love **Mr W. Hurst**

Amateur: Miss Helen Cuthbert (9-0).

139 MR HARVEY J. CYZER, Newmarket
Postal: **The Trainer's House, Sefton Lodge, 8 Bury Road, market, Suffolk, CB8 7BT.**
Contact: **PHONE (01638) 668669 MOBILE (07780) 675676 E-MAIL hc@hcyzer.com**

1 **SILENT STORM**, 4, ch c Zafonic (USA)—Nanda

THREE-YEAR-OLDS

2 **BAG 'O' NAILS (IRE)**, b c Desert Prince (IRE)—Dulcinea
3 **CASTLETON**, b c Cape Cross (IRE)—Craigmill
4 Gr ro c Unbridled's Song (USA)—Diamond Dream (FR)
5 **FAIR OPTIONS**, gr c Marju (IRE)—Silver Singing (USA)
6 **FLEETING IMAGE**, ch c Piccolo—Daylight Dreams
7 **KOOL KARMA**, ch c Rainbow Quest (USA)—Kundalini (USA)
8 **LADY TAVERNER**, b f Marju (IRE)—Prompting
9 **ON EVERY STREET**, b c Singspiel (IRE)—Nekhbet
10 **SEA OF GOLD**, b f Docksider (USA)—Shadow Bird
11 **SHOW NO FEAR**, b c Groom Dancer (USA)—La Piaf (FR)
12 **TRAYTONIC**, b c Botanic (USA)—Lady Parker (IRE)
13 **VICAT COLE**, ch c Hector Protector (USA)—Dancing Spirit (IRE)

TWO-YEAR-OLDS

14 **ADMINISTRATOR**, ch c 30/1 Unfuwain (USA)—Squaw Talk (USA) (Gulch (USA)) (16000)
15 **HEATHCOTE**, b c 22/2 Unfuwain (USA)—Chere Amie (USA) (Mr Prospector (USA)) (9500)

Other Owners: Algarve Partnership, Ms L. Binns, Mr H. Burgess, Mrs C. A. Cyzer, Mr Colin Darey, Mr R. Dutton, Mr Bill Gredley, Mrs L. Jarvis, Mr I. Lawson, Maktown At Maktown, Mr W. Paterson, Mr Barry Root, The Sefton Lodge Partnership, Mrs Sheen.

140 MR L. A. DACE, Findon
Postal: **Burchett Stables, Muntham Farm, Northend, Findon, West Sussex, BN14 0RQ.**
Contact: **OFFICE (01403) 780889 MOBILE (07949) 401085**

1 **BROOMERS HILL (IRE)**, 4, b g Sadler's Wells (USA)—Bella Vitessa (IRE) **The Tuesday Syndicate**
2 **FAILTE (IRE)**, 6, b g Most Welcome—Esh Sham (USA) **Mr J. J. Smith**
3 **FLECTHEFAWNA (IRE)**, 8, b g Glacial Storm (USA)—Lady Sperrin **Churchfields Partnership**
4 **FOXTROTROMEOYANKEE**, 4, b g Tragic Role (USA)—Hope Chest **Mr Bryan Fry**
5 **GREYTON (IRE)**, 11, gr g Zaffaran (USA)—Rosy Posy (IRE) **Mr Brendan Laverty**
6 **HAVE-NO-DOUBT (IRE)**, 10, b g Glacial Storm (USA)—Lady Kas **Mr D. Newman**
7 **ITALIAN COUNSEL (IRE)**, 7, b g Leading Counsel (USA)—Mullaghroe **Mr B. V. Ward & Mr C. Feeney**
8 **ITCHINTOGO (IRE)**, 6, b g Namaqualand (USA)—Lamp of Phoebus (USA) **Miss S. L. O'Neill**
9 **ITSABOY**, 4, b g Wizard King—French Project (IRE) **Mr Luke Dace**
10 **KELTIC HERITAGE (IRE)**, 10, gr g Roselier (FR)—Peek-A-Step (IRE) **Mr Danny O'Sullivan**
11 **QUEL FONTENAILLES (FR)**, 6, b g Tel Quel (FR)—Sissi Fontenailles (FR) **The Tuesday Syndicate**
12 **SCENIC LADY (IRE)**, 8, b m Scenic—Tu Tu Maori (IRE) **Mrs Yvonne Davess**
13 **TRUSTING PADDY (IRE)**, 7, b g Synefos (USA)—Homefield Girl (IRE) **Mr D. Newman**
14 **WEE DANNY (IRE)**, 7, b g Mandalus—Bonne Bouche
15 **YOU DA MAN (IRE)**, 7, b g Alzao (USA)—Fabled Lifestyle **Mr Luke Dace**

Other Owners: Mrs Marion Christmas, Mr C. Feeney, Mr A. B. Ford, Mr M. K. Titchner, Mr B. V. Ward, Mr Michael H. Watt.

Amateur: Miss Louise Brewer (8-10).

141 MRS H. DALTON, Shifnal
Postal: **Norton House, Norton, Shifnal, Shropshire, TF11 9ED.**
Contact: **PHONE (01952) 730322 FAX (01952) 730722 MOBILE (07785) 972131**
E-MAIL heatherdalton@shropshire.fslife.co.uk

1 **ACQUIRED (IRE)**, 6, b br m Presenting—The Scarlet Dragon **Michael Scott & Martin Timlin**
2 **ACTIVE ACCOUNT (USA)**, 7, b br g Unaccounted For (USA)—Ameritop (USA) **Mrs Heather Dalton**
3 **ANDALEER (IRE)**, 9, b m Phardante (FR)—Dunleer Duchess **Mr M. Richards and Mr G. Stone**
4 **ANGELENA BALLERINA**, 6, gr m Roselier (FR)—True Clown **Mr & Mrs Peter Orton**
5 **ANKLES BACK (IRE)**, 7, b g Seclude (USA)—Pedalo **Mr Ray Bailey**
6 **ANOTHER BALLY**, 8, gr g Neltino—Michele My Belle **F. Sheridan**
7 **AVADI (IRE)**, 6, b g Un Desperado (FR)—Flamewood **Mrs Julie Martin**

MRS H. DALTON—continued

8 **BEARAWAY (IRE)**, 7, b g Fourstars Allstar (USA)—Cruiseaway **Paternosters Racing**
9 **BEFORE DARK (IRE)**, 6, b g Phardante (FR)—Menebeans (IRE) **Mr C. B. Compton**
10 **BE MY FRIEND (IRE)**, 8, ch g Be My Native (USA)—Miss Lamb **Mr J. Hales**
11 5, b m Alderbrook—Bridepark Rose (IRE) **Mr Tom Segrue**
12 **CARLUCCIOS QUEST**, 6, gr g Terimon—Jindabyne **Mrs C. S. Wilson**
13 **CASSIA GREEN**, 10, gr g Scallywag—Casa's Star **Mrs J. Greenway**
14 5, Gr g Roselier (FR)—Charming Mo (IRE) **Mr Malcolm B. Jones**
15 **ELLA FALLS (IRE)**, 9, b m Dancing Dissident (USA)—Over Swing (FR) **Mr Ray Bailey**
16 **FIRST TRUTH**, 7, b g Rudimentary (USA)—Pursuit of Truth (USA) **Mr Ray Bailey**
17 **FROSTY RUN (IRE)**, 6, b g Commanche Run—Here To-Day **Mr C. B. Compton**
18 **JAKE'S CASTLE**, 5, b g Shambo—Brass Castle (IRE) **Mr H. Shirley**
19 **JUST KATE**, 5, b m Bob's Return (IRE)—M I Babe **Mr C. B. Brookes**
20 **LEARN THE LINGO**, 8, b g Teenoso (USA)—Charlotte Gray **Mr David M. Hughes**
21 **L'ORAGE LADY (IRE)**, 6, ch m Glacial Storm (USA)—Commanche Glen (IRE) **Simpson, Shirley and Dalton**
22 **LORD OF THE HILL (IRE)**, 9, b g Dromod Hill—Telegram Mear **Mr Tom Segrue**
23 **MAGIC MUSIC (IRE)**, 5, b m Magic Ring (IRE)—Chiming Melody **Mr Ray Bailey**
24 **MCQUEEN (IRE)**, 4, ch g Barathea (IRE)—Bibliotheque (USA) **Mr R. Edwards and Mr W. J. Swinnerton**
25 **MOUNT COOK (FR)**, 4, b g Gold And Steel (FR)—Debandade (FR) **Miss L. Hales**
26 **MY ACE**, 6, b m Definite Article—Miss Springtime **Hop Pole Racing & Mr R. Burrows**
27 **NEW BIRD (GER)**, 9, b g Bluebird (USA)—Nouvelle Amour (GER) **Mr David M. Hughes**
28 **NEWS MAKER (IRE)**, 8, b g Good Thyne (USA)—Announcement **Mrs Caroline Shaw**
29 **NOVEL IDEA (IRE)**, 6, ch g Phardante (FR)—Novelist **Mrs Caroline Shaw**
30 **PREMIUM FIRST (IRE)**, 5, ch g Naheez (USA)—Regular Rose (IRE) **Hill Fuels Limited**
31 **PROPER POSH**, 6, b m Rakaposhi King—Rim of Pearl **Mr W. D. Hockenhull**
32 **QUALITY FIRST**, 11, b g Un Desperado (FR)—Vipsania **Mr A. N. Dalton**
33 **SIENNA SUNSET (IRE)**, 5, ch m Spectrum (IRE)—Wasabi (IRE) **Mr Ray Bailey**
34 **SIR BOB (IRE)**, 12, br g Aristocracy—Wilden **Mrs Lucia Farmer**
35 **TERRE DE JAVA (FR)**, 6, b g Cadoudal (FR)—Terre d'Argent (FR) **Miss L. Hales**

Other Owners: Mr M. Ball, Mr R. L. Burrows, Mr J. N. Dalton, Mr Richard Edwards, Mr P. J. Grealis, Mr David Jenks, C. O. Lynch, Mr David R. Martin, Mr T. O'Connor, Mr Peter Orton, Mrs Susan Orton, Mr M. Richards, Mr M. J. Scott, Mr M. Shirley, Mr Richard Simpson, Mr G. Stone, Mr J. Swinnerton, Mr Martin Timlin.

Assistant Trainer: Miss Serena Easy & Robert Fletcher

Jockeys (Flat): John Egan (w.a.), Ian Mongan (w.a.), Seb Sanders (w.a.). **Jockey (NH):** Richard Johnson (w.a.). **Conditional:** T Greenway. **Amateurs:** Mr Richard Burton (11-0), Mr Richard Spate.

---

142 MR P. T. DALTON, Burton-on-Trent
Postal: **Dovecote Cottage, Bretby Park, Bretby, Burton-On-Trent, Staffordshire, DE15 0RB.**
Contact: **HOME (01283) 221922 OFFICE 221922 FAX 229657 MOBILE (07774) 240753**
E-MAIL daltonpauldalton@aol.co.uk

1 **ALIAS (IRE)**, 6, br g Allegoric (USA)—Snowdrifter **Mr C. Corbin**
2 **ANGUILLA**, 9, b g Rudimentary (USA)—More Wise **Mrs Lucia Farmer**
3 **BLAZING HILLS**, 8, ch g Shaab—Cottage Blaze **Mrs Julie Martin**
4 **BOBBI ROSE RED**, 7, ch m Bob Back (USA)—Lady Rosanna **Mrs Julie Martin**
5 **BROOK FORTE**, 5, b m Alderbrook—Lucia Forte **Mrs Lucia Farmer**
6 **CRISIS (IRE)**, 8, b g Second Set (IRE)—Special Offer (IRE) **Mrs R. S. Perkins**
7 **DONIE DOOLEY (IRE)**, 6, ch g Be My Native (USA)—Bridgeofallen (IRE) **Mrs Julie Martin**
8 **HIDDEN DEPTH**, 5, b g Classic Cliche (IRE)—Rochestown Lass **Miss Charlotte A. I. Perkins**
9 **PRIMA CASA**, 4, ch f First Trump—Welcome Home **Mrs Joanne Woods**

Other Owners: Mr David R. Martin, Mr R. A. H. Perkins.

Assistant Trainer: Susan Dalton

---

143 MR H. D. J. DALY, Ludlow
Postal: **Downton Hall Stables, Ludlow, Shropshire, SY8 3DX.**
Contact: **OFFICE (01584) 873688 FAX 873525 MOBILES (07710) 973042 (07720) 074544**
E-MAIL hdjdaly@aol.com

1 **ALDERBURN**, 5, b g Alderbrook—Threewaygirl **Mrs D. P. G. Flory**
2 **ALGARVE**, 7, b g Alflora (IRE)—Garvenish **Mr Trevor Hemmings**

MR H. D. J. DALY—continued

3 **BILLYVODDAN (IRE)**, 5, b g Accordion—Derryclare **Mr Trevor Hemmings**
4 **BONUS BRIDGE (IRE)**, 9, b g Executive Perk—Corivia **Lady Knutsford**
5 **BROWN FLYER**, 7, gr g Baron Blakeney—Brown Veil **Mrs A. G. Lawe**
6 **BURDENS BOY**, 8, br g Alflora (IRE)—Dalbeattie **Furrows Ltd**
7 **BURDENS GIRL**, 7, ch m Alflora (IRE)—Dalbeattie **Furrows Ltd**
8 **CAPTAIN RAWLINGS**, 5, ch g Lancastrian—Coombesbury Lane **Mr N. F. Williams**
9 **CLEVER THYNE (IRE)**, 7, b g Good Thyne (USA)—Clever Milly **Mrs Geoffrey Churton**
10 **CONQUER (IRE)**, 9, b g Phardante (FR)—Tullow Performance **Mr M. Ward-Thomas**
11 **COURSING RUN (IRE)**, 8, ch g Glacial Storm (USA)—Let The Hare Run (IRE) **The Hon Mrs A. E. Heber-Percy**
12 **FAR TO FALL (IRE)**, 6, br g Phardante (FR)—Fall About **Vicky Jeyes Helen Plumbly Jane Trafford**
13 **FERIMON**, 5, br g Terimon—Rhyming Moppet **Strachan Myddleton Gabb Stoddart Lawson**
14 **FIERY PEACE**, 7, ch g Tina's Pet—Burning Mirage **Mr R. M. Kirkland**
15 **GREEN TANGO**, 5, br g Greensmith—Furry Dance (USA) **Mrs Strachan,Gabb,Lady Barlow & Harford**
16 **HAND INN HAND**, 8, b g Alflora (IRE)—Deep Line **Patrick Burling Developments Ltd**
17 **HAUT CERCY (FR)**, 9, b g Roi de Rome (USA)—Mamoussia (FR) **The Wiggin Partnership**
18 **IN ACCORD**, 5, ch g Accordion—Henry's True Love **Mr T. F. F. Nixon**
19 **IRONSIDE (IRE)**, 5, b g Mister Lord (USA)—The Helmet (IRE) **Mrs A. Reid Scott & Mrs G. Leigh**
20 **ISLAND FORTRESS**, 5, ch m Infantry—Misty Fort **Mr J. B. Sumner**
21 **JAKARI (FR)**, 7, b g Apeldoorn—Tartifume II (FR) **The Earl Cadogan**
22 **JIVAROS (FR)**, 7, br g Video Rock (FR)—Rives (FR) **Mrs G. Leigh**
23 **JUDAIC WAYS**, 10, b g Rudimentary (USA)—Judeah **Mr D. Sandells & Mr T. Broderick**
24 **KADOUN (FR)**, 5, gr g Sleeping Car (FR)—Dea de Chaumont (FR) **Million in Mind Partnership**
25 **KING BEE (IRE)**, 7, b g Supreme Leader—Honey Come Back **Mr Trevor Hemmings**
26 **LADY DYNAMITE**, 4, b f Glacial Storm (USA)—Lady Elle (IRE) **Mr C. G. Johnson**
27 **LANCASTRIAN JET (IRE)**, 13, b g Lancastrian—Kilmurray Jet **The Hon Mrs A. E. Heber-Percy**
28 **LANNKARAN (IRE)**, 11, b g Shardari—Lankarana **The Hon Simon Sainsbury**
29 **LONG WALK (IRE)**, 7, br g King's Ride—Seanaphobal Lady **The Earl Cadogan**
30 **LORD MOOSE (IRE)**, 10, b g Mister Lord (USA)—Moose (IRE) **The Hon Simon Sainsbury**
31 **LOUGH DANTE (IRE)**, 6, b g Phardante (FR)—Shannon Lough (IRE) **Mr Michael Lowe**
32 **MACONNOR (IRE)**, 7, b g Religiously (USA)—Door Belle **Mr Daniel O'Connor**
33 **MAKE HASTE SLOWLY**, 7, b g Terimon—Henry's True Love **Mr T. F. F. Nixon**
34 **MARTHA'S KINSMAN (IRE)**, 5, b g Petoski—Martha's Daughter **Mr M. Ward-Thomas**
35 **MISSILE (FR)**, 4, b g Gunboat Diplomacy (FR)—Elysea (FR) **The Behrajan Partnership**
36 **OPERA HALL**, 4, b f Saddlers' Hall (IRE)—Opera Hat (IRE) **Ladywood Farm**
37 **PALARSHAN (FR)**, 6, b br g Darshaan—Palavera (FR) **Mrs A. L. Wood**
38 **PARLOUR GAME**, 8, br m Petoski—Henry's True Love **Mr G. A. Greaves**
39 **POLYANTHUS JONES**, 5, b m Sovereign Water (FR)—Cindie Girl **Patrick Burling Developments Ltd**
40 **RAKALACKEY**, 6, br g Rakaposhi King—Celtic Slave **Mr B. G. Hellyer**
41 **RUSSIAN STEPPES (IRE)**, 6, gr g Moscow Society (USA)—Pryana **Mrs John Nesbitt**
42 **SAAFEND ROCKET (IRE)**, 6, b g Distinctly North (USA)—Simple Annie **Ludlow Racing Partnership**
43 **STAR ANGLER (IRE)**, 6, b g Supreme Leader—So Pink (IRE) **Lady Knutsford**
44 **STARTING AGAIN**, 10, b g Petoski—Lynemore **Mr & Mrs M. P. Wiggin**
45 **SUPREME HOPE (USA)**, 5, b g Supreme Leader—Flaming Hope (IRE) **Mrs Geoffrey Churton**
46 **THISISYOURLIFE (IRE)**, 8, b g Lord Americo—Your Life **The Earl Cadogan**
47 **TRAVELLERS HEIR (IRE)**, 6, ch g Montelimar (USA)—
                                    Allaracket (IRE) **Mrs Strachan, Griffith, Lewis & Graham**
48 **TRINKET (IRE)**, 6, br g Definite Article—Alamiya (IRE) **Mrs Strachan, Mrs Gabb & Jim Morris**
49 **TROODOS VALLEY (IRE)**, 5, b g Executive Perk—Valleymay (IRE) **Mr D. Sandells**
50 **WATERBERG (IRE)**, 9, b g Sadler's Wells (USA)—Pretoria **Mr R. M. Kirkland**

Other Owners: Lady Susan Barlow, Mr A. R. Bromley, Mr Roy Burden, Mr John Coward, Mr J. H. Day, Mr Graham Goode, Mr H. Harford, Mr R. L. C. Hartley, Mrs A. Hellyer, Mrs Tanya Hill, Mr A. C. Mack, Mr Simon Marsh, Mr D. Minton, Mr David Nicholson, Mr Michael Opperman, Mr & Mrs M. Saunders, Mr Denys Simmons, Mrs A. Timpson, Major P. G. Verdin, Mr J. R. Weatherby, Mr M. D. Wiggin, Mr R. Wiggin.

Assistant Trainer: Tom Gretton

Jockeys (NH): M Bradburne, R Johnson (w.a.). **Conditional:** J P Byrne. **Amateur:** Mr M Barber.

144 MR V. R. A. DARTNALL, Barnstaple

Postal: **Higher Shutscombe Farm, Charles, Brayford, Barnstaple, Devon, EX32 7PU.**
Contact: **PHONE (01598) 710280 FAX (01598) 710708 MOBILE (07974) 374272**
E-MAIL victor-dartnall@dartnall-racing.freeserve.co.uk

1 **BETTER THYNE (IRE)**, 8, ch g Good Thyne (USA)—Cailin Cainnteach **Mr R. F. Woodward**
2 **DUSIT DOWN (IRE)**, 5, b g Anshan—Windy Road **Mr Nick Viney**
3 **HAWADETH**, 9, ch g Machiavellian (USA)—Ghzaalh (USA) **Mr Nick Viney**
4 **HERE'S JOHNNY (IRE)**, 5, ch g Presenting—Treble Base (IRE) **The Big Boys Toys Partnership**
5 **HIRED GUN (IRE)**, 5, b g Needle Gun (IRE)—Monahullen Rose (IRE)
6 **KARANJA**, 5, b g Karinga Bay—Proverbial Rose **Mr D. G. Staddon**
7 **LORD SAM (IRE)**, 8, b br g Supreme Leader—Russian Gale (IRE) **Plain Peeps**
8 **MOUNT CLERIGO (IRE)**, 6, b g Supreme Leader—Fair Ava (IRE) **Mr Stewart Andrew**
9 **PHILOMENA**, 5, b m Bedford (USA)—Mandalay Miss **Dorset Racing**
10 **POLLIGANA**, 8, b g Lugana Beach—Pollibrig **Mr W. Westacott**
11 **ROCKLEY BEACH (IRE)**, 5, b g Tidaro (USA)—Green Fairy **Double P Partnership**
12 **ROSARIAN (IRE)**, 7, b g Fourstars Allstar (USA)—Only A Rose **Mr A. Hordle**
13 **RUSSIAN LORD (IRE)**, 5, br g Topanoora—Russian Gale (IRE)
14 **SILKWOOD TOP (IRE)**, 5, b g Norwich—Brave Mum **Mr O. C. R. Wynne & Mrs S. J. Wynne**
15 **STROMA GALE (IRE)**, 4, b g Old Vic—Christines Gale (IRE) **Lisa & James Mackenzie**
16 **VINGIS PARK (IRE)**, 6, b g Old Vic—Lady Glenbank **Mr Nick Viney**
17 **WEST HILL GAIL (IRE)**, 5, b m Roselier (FR)—V'Soske Gale (IRE) **Mr D. G. Staddon**
18 **YOUNG DANCER (IRE)**, 6, b g Eurobus—Misquested **Mr D. G. Staddon**

Other Owners: Mr G. A. Dove, Mr Bill Hinge, Mr Bob Leatherdale, Mr C. Painter, Mr S. M. Perry, Miss A. Woolley.

Assistant Trainer: G A Dartnall

Jockey (NH): J Culloty (w.a.).

145 MISS L. V. DAVIS, Stafford

Postal: **The Stables, Hillcrest, Bradley Lane, Levedale, Stafford, ST18 9AH.**
Contact: **PHONE (07940) 923452 MOBILE (07986) 394187**

1 **BLUE HAWK (IRE)**, 7, ch g Prince of Birds (USA)—Classic Queen (IRE) **Miss Louise Davis**
2 **BOBBY BLAKENEY**, 9, gr g Blakeney—Coming Out **Miss Louise Davis**
3 **FARMER JOSH**, 10, b g Dancing High—Millie Duffer **Miss Louise Davis**
4 **KALISKO (FR)**, 14, b g Cadoudal (FR)—Mista (FR) **Miss Louise Davis**

146 MISS Z. C. DAVISON, East Grinstead

Postal: **Shovelstrode Racing Stables, Shovelstrode Lane, Ashurstwood, East Grinstead, West Sussex, RH19 3YN.**
Contact: **PHONE (01342) 323153 MOBILE (07813) 321709**

1 **ABRACADABJAR**, 6, b g Royal Abjar (USA)—Celt Song (IRE) **Mrs J. Irvine**
2 **ANNODYCE**, 6, b m Faustus (USA)—Coleford (USA) **Auld Firm Partnership**
3 **BACK IN THE GAME**, 8, ch g Phountzi (USA)—Chasmarella **Mrs J. Irvine**
4 **BARON ALLFOURS**, 12, gr g Baron Blakeney—Georgian Quickstep **The Secret Circle**
5 **DISTANT ROMANCE**, 7, br m Phardante (FR)—Rhine Aria **Mr A. A. Goldson**
6 **GREAT OAKS**, 10, b g Sylvan Express—Springdale Hall (USA) **The Secret Circle**
7 8, Ch m Karinga Bay—G W Superstar **Mrs J. Irvine**
8 **HI LILY**, 8, b m Jupiter Island—By Line **Mr Richard Antony Jones**
9 **LOCK INN**, 5, b g Dolphin Street (FR)—Highest Bid (FR) **Mr Paul Leavy & Mrs Susan Emmett-Leavy**
10 5, B g Phountzi (USA)—Miss Ark Royal **The Secret Circle**
11 4, B c Perpendicular—Miss Bordeaux (IRE)
12 **OCKLEY FLYER**, 5, b g Sir Harry Lewis (USA)—Bewails (IRE) **Mr Alan Walder**
13 **ROMAN RAMPAGE**, 5, b g Perpendicular—Roman Moor **Mr Barry Ward**
14 **SHIRLEY OAKS (IRE)**, 6, b m Sri Pekan (USA)—Duly Elected **Auld Firm Partnership**
15 **SPIDER BOY**, 7, b g Jupiter Island—Great Dilemma **Mr Derek Ash**
16 **WELLFRANKO (IRE)**, 9, b g Camden Town—Electana **The Secret Circle**
17 **ZAFFRE (IRE)**, 5, gr m Mtoto—Zeferina (IRE) **Rags To Riches**

MISS Z. C. DAVISON—continued

THREE-YEAR-OLDS

18 **CLEARING SKY (IRE)**, gr f Exploit (USA)—Litchfield Hills (USA) **Clearing Sky Partnership**
19 **SAUCY PICKLE**, b f Makbul—Bewails (IRE) **Mr Alan Walder**

TWO-YEAR-OLDS

20 B f 4/3 Makbul—Bewails (IRE) (Caerleon (USA)) **The Secret Circle**
21 B f 5/3 Second Empire (IRE)—Cairde Nua (IRE) (Mukaddamah (USA)) (3091) **Mrs J. Irvine**
22 B f 17/4 Inzar (USA)—Saniwood (IRE) (Law Society (USA)) (2349) **Mrs J. Irvine**
23 B f 12/3 Charnwood Forest—Sea Glen (IRE) (Glenstal) (1545) **Mrs J. Irvine**
24 B f 23/3 Indian Lodge (IRE)—Spire (Shirley Heights) (4328) **Secret Circle**
25 B f 11/5 Wizard King—Three Star Rated (IRE) (Pips Bride) (1236) **Secret Circle**

Other Owners: Mrs N. D. A. Blatch, Miss L. J. Johnson, Mr L. Jones, Mr M. Mathews, Mr D. McPherson, Mr G. Morley, Mr K. W. Touhey, Mr Antony Waters.

Assistant Trainer: A Irvine

Amateur: Miss Gemelle Davison.

---

147 **MR W. DE BEST-TURNER, Calne**
Postal: **North Farm Stables, West Overton, Marlborough, Wiltshire, SN8 1QE.**
Contact: HOME **(07977) 910779** FAX **(01249) 811955** E-MAIL william@debestracing.fsnet.co.uk

1 **ARANA**, 9, b m Noble Patriarch—Pod's Daughter (IRE) **The Spanish Connection**
2 **BELTANE**, 6, b g Magic Ring (IRE)—Sally's Trust (IRE) **Mrs Gillian Swanton**
3 **QUARTER TO**, 5, gr m Chocolat de Meguro (USA)—Miss Lakeland **The Spanish Connection**
4 **TIME FLYER**, 4, b c My Best Valentine—Sally's Trust (IRE) **Mrs Gillian Swanton**

THREE-YEAR-OLDS

5 **BEAU JAZZ**, br c Merdon Melody—Ichor **Mr W. de Best-Turner**
6 **ONYX**, b c Bijou d'Inde—Prime Surprise **Mr W. de Best-Turner**
7 **STEPPENWOLF**, gr c Cesaro (USA)—Lozzie **Mr W. de Best-Turner**
8 **ZARNEETA**, b f Tragic Role (USA)—Compton Amber **Mr W. de Best-Turner**

Other Owners: Mr K. De Best, Mrs J. De Best-Betist.

Assistant Trainer: Gillian Swanton

Amateur: Mrs I De Best (8-10).

---

148 **MR B. DE HAAN, Lambourn**
Postal: **Fair View, Long Hedge, Lambourn, Newbury, Berkshire, RG17 8NA.**
Contact: PHONE **(01488) 72163** FAX **(01488) 71306** MOBILE **(07831) 104574**
E-MAIL Ben@bdehaan.fsnet.co.uk

1 **AGITANDO (IRE)**, 8, b g Tenby—Crown Rose **The Inspirations Partnership**
2 **BLUE CANYON (IRE)**, 6, b g Phardante (FR)—Miss Gosling **Willsford Racing Incorporated**
3 **BOLD MOMENTO**, 5, b g Never So Bold—Native of Huppel (IRE) **Mr William A. Tyrer**
4 **CHARLIE BUBBLES (IRE)**, 7, b g Un Desperado (FR)—Bounty (IRE) **Flora Charlie Limited**
5 **INDIAN SCOUT (IRE)**, 9, b g Phardante (FR)—Kemchee **Indian Scout Partnership**
6 5, B m Supreme Leader—Kemchee
7 **LORD DUNDANIEL (IRE)**, 7, b br g Arctic Lord—Killoskehan Queen **Willsford Racing Incorporated**
8 **MASTER REX**, 9, ch g Interrex (CAN)—Whose Lady (USA) **Miss Louise Challis**
9 **NEOPHYTE (IRE)**, 5, gr g Broken Hearted—Dunmahon Lady **The Neophyte Four**
10 **NEW ERA (IRE)**, 10, b g Distinctly North (USA)—Vaguely Deesse (USA) **Sidtenga Syndicate**
11 **OVERLORD (IRE)**, 7, b g Lord Americo—Straddler's Hill (IRE) **The Longhedge Partnership**
12 **REEL DANCER**, 7, b g Minshaanshu Amad (USA)—Sister Rosarii (USA) **The Play 4 Partnership**
13 **REGENTS WALK (IRE)**, 6, b g Phardante (FR)—Raw Courage (IRE) **Mrs D. Vaughan**
14 **SCARAMOUCHE**, 4, b g Busy Flight—Laura Lye (IRE)
15 **SERRAFINA**, 4, ch f Bluegrass Prince (IRE)—Josifina **Miss Louise Challis & Mr John Simms**
16 **THE GREY BUTLER (IRE)**, 7, gr g Roselier (FR)—Georgic **Mrs D. Vaughan**
17 **WONTCOSTALOTBUT**, 10, b m Nicholas Bill—Brave Maiden **Wontcostalot Partnership**

MR B. DE HAAN—continued

THREE-YEAR-OLDS

18 **AVERLLINE**, b f Averti (IRE)—Spring Sunrise **Mrs D. Vaughan**
19 **BAYOU PRINCESS**, ch f Bluegrass Prince (IRE)—Josifina
20 Br f Danehill Dancer (IRE)—Blue Sioux

TWO-YEAR-OLDS

21 **LITTLE LAURITA**, b f 29/3 Overbury (IRE)—Laura Lye (IRE) (Carlingford Castle)

Other Owners: Mr O. Austin, Mr J. R. Blackmore, Mr D. M. Cafferty, Mr A. A. Clifford, Mr R. L. Clifford, Mr C. W. Foreman, Mr Duncan Heath, Mr T. G. Horley, Mr B. R. Jervis, Mr David Klein, Mr C. D. Lyall, Mr P. T. Mott, Mr J. D. Murtagh, Mr Campbell Ross, Mr R. Stevens, Mrs F. Walwyn.

Jockey (Flat): D Kinsella. **Jockeys (NH):** L Cummins, R Flavin. **Conditional:** R Cosgrave (9-7).

149
MR A. J. DEAKIN, Cannock
Postal: **7 Hornbeam Crescent, Hazel Slade, Cannock, Staffordshire, WS12 5SU.**
Contact: **PHONE (01543) 424262 MOBILE (07880) 666986**
E-MAIL tonydeakin@hornbeamracing.freeserve.co.uk

1 **LATE HARVEST (NZ)**, 12, b g Tarrago (ITY)—Pamira (AUS) **Mr A. J. Deakin**
2 **SADLER'S SECRET (IRE)**, 9, b g Sadler's Wells (USA)—Athyka (USA) **Mr A. J. Deakin**

TWO-YEAR-OLDS

3 B f 1/4 Overbury (IRE)—Gladys Emmanual (Idiot's Delight) **Mr A. J. Deakin**

150
MR W. W. DENNIS, Bude
Postal: **Thorne Farm, Bude, Cornwall, EX23 0LU.**
Contact: **PHONE (01288) 352849 FAX (01288) 352849**

1 **STARS'N'STRIPES (IRE)**, 6, b g Lord Americo—Drumdeels Star (IRE) **Mr W. W. Dennis**
2 **STRATCO (IRE)**, 10, b br g Satco (FR)—No Slow **Mr W. W. Dennis**

Jockey (NH): D R Dennis (10-0). **Amateur:** Mr T Dennis (10-5).

151
MR A. R. DICKEN, Dunbar
Postal: **The Stables House, Woodlands Racing Stables, Belton, East Lothian, EH42 1RG.**
Contact: **PHONE (01368) 865850 MOBILE (07768) 383237**

1 **CHARTER ROYAL (FR)**, 9, gr g Royal Charter (FR)—Tadjmine (FR) **Got To Be In It To Win It Partnership**
2 **CLOWNFISH**, 10, b g Silly Prices—Sea Sand **Got To Be In It To Win It Partnership**
3 **COUSTOU (IRE)**, 4, b g In Command (IRE)—Carranza (IRE) **Mr & Mrs Raymond Anderson Green**
4 **ENTERTAINER (IRE)**, 8, b g Be My Guest (USA)—Green Wings **Mr Ron Affleck**
5 **JEROM DE VINDECY (FR)**, 7, ch g Roi de Rome (USA)—Preves du Forez (FR) **Mr Ron Affleck**
6 **MELSTAIR**, 9, b g Terimon—Kevins Lady **Mr A. R. Dicken**
7 **OCTOBER MAGIC**, 5, b m Hatim (USA)—Wand of Youth **Jim & Wendy Beaumont**
8 **WILD ABOUT HARRY**, 7, ch g Romany Rye—Shylyn **Mr Ron Affleck**

Assistant Trainer: Mrs J A Dicken

Conditional: T Siddle (w.a.).

152
MR R. DICKIN, Stratford-on-Avon
Postal: **Alscot Racing Stables, Alscot Park, Atherstone On Stour, Stratford-Upon-Avon, Warwickshire, CV37 8BL.**
Contact: **PHONE (01789) 450052 FAX 450053 MOBILE (07979) 518593 (07979) 518594**
E-MAIL claire.dickin@tesco.net r.dickin@virgin.net

1 **ARCTIC SPIRIT**, 9, b g Arctic Lord—Dickies Girl **The Lordy Racing Partnership**
2 **BILL BROWN**, 6, b g North Briton—Dickies Girl **The Lordy Racing Partnership**
3 **BOBOSH**, 8, b g Devil's Jump—Jane Craig **Mr Haydn Gott**

MR R. DICKIN—continued

4 **BONFIRE NIGHT (IRE)**, 8, b m Air Display (USA)—Smokey Path (IRE) **Mrs A. L. Merry**
5 **BREEMA DONNA**, 6, b m Sir Harry Lewis (USA)—Donna Del Lago **Mr M. MacCarthy**
6 **CAPTAINS TABLE**, 11, b g Welsh Captain—Wensum Girl **Mr Les Pike**
7 **CASH 'N' CREDIT**, 6, b m Homo Sapien—Not Enough **The Cash 'N' Creditors**
8 **CEDAR**, 7, gr g Absalom—Setai's Palace **Mr D. J. Jackson**
9 **CHANNAHRLIE (IRE)**, 10, gr g Celio Rufo—Derravarragh Lady (IRE) **Mr J. C. Clemmow**
10 **ELLABURY**, 5, b m Overbury (IRE)—Kayella **Mrs J.Cumiskey, Mr M.Doocey, Mr T.Joyce**
11 **ERINS LASS (IRE)**, 7, b m Erins Isle—Amative **Stratford Members Club**
12 **GOLDEN TAMESIS**, 7, b g Golden Heights—Escribana **Tamesis & Partners**
13 **GUZZLE**, 4, b f Puget (USA)—Convamore Queen (IRE) **Mr Ian Beale**
14 **HANBRIN ROSE**, 7, gr m Lancastrian—Rymolbreese **John Hanley John Brindley**
15 **JACARADO (IRE)**, 6, b g Jurado (USA)—Lady Mearba (IRE) **R. G. & R. A. Whitehead**
16 **JACDOR (IRE)**, 10, b g Be My Native (USA)—Bellalma **Jackie Matthews & Doreen Evans**
17 **JACK OF SPADES (IRE)**, 8, b g Mister Lord (USA)—Dooney's Daughter **Mr E. R. Clifford Beech**
18 **JACOPO (FR)**, 7, b g Grand Tresor (FR)—Qolombine (FR) **Fairfield Flyers**
19 **KADITO**, 8, b g Petoski—Kadastr (FR) **Mr A. P. & Mrs C. P. Paton**
20 **KARIBLUE**, 6, ch m Imp Society (USA)—Kadastra (FR) **Mr A. P. Paton**
21 4, Ch f Thethingaboutitis (USA)—Katie's Jewel **Mr Andrew Bull**
22 **KELTIC BLUE (IRE)**, 5, b g Blues Traveller (IRE)—White Caps **The Alscot Blue Group**
23 **LITTLE TERN (IRE)**, 5, b m Terimon—Miss Fern **Mr R. T. S. Matthews**
24 **LOGGER RHYTHM (USA)**, 4, b g Woodman (USA)—Formidable Dancer (USA) **The Six Fellers**
25 **LUCKY DO (IRE)**, 7, b g Camden Town—Lane Baloo **Mr D. A. N. Ross**
26 **MAYBESEVEN**, 10, gr g Baron Blakeney—Ninth of May **The Diamond Seven Partnership**
27 **MISTER KINGSTON**, 13, ch g Kinglet—Flaxen Tina **Mrs C. M. Dickin**
28 **NEWICK PARK**, 9, gr g Chilibang—Quilpee Mai **Newick Park Partnership**
29 **NOT TO BE MISSED**, 6, gr m Missed Flight—Petinata **Only Horses and Fools**
30 **PARSON JACK**, 7, b g Bedford—Scobitora **Mr R. T. S. Matthews**
31 **PRAIRIE MINSTREL (USA)**, 10, b g Regal Intention (CAN)—Prairie Sky (USA) **E. R. C. Beech & B. Wilkinson**
32 **RAZZAMATAZZ**, 6, b g Alhijaz—Salvezza (IRE) **Mr & Mrs J. Cooper**
33 **REGAL TERM (IRE)**, 6, b g Welsh Term—Regal Hostess **R. G. & R. A. Whitehead**
34 **ROMANY DREAM**, 6, b m Nomadic Way (USA)—Half Asleep **The Snoozy Partnership**
35 **SAILING THROUGH**, 4, b g Bahhare (USA)—Hopesay **Mr Paul Armour**
36 **SISSINGHURST STORM (IRE)**, 6, b br m Good Thyne (USA)—Mrs Hill **Mr Brian Clifford**
37 **TOP GALE (IRE)**, 5, b m Topanoora—Amy's Gale (IRE) **Mr Graham Moses**
38 **TRICKY THYNE (IRE)**, 5, b g Good Thyne (USA)—Cuban Vacation **J. T. W. Racing**
39 4, B br g Luso—Tudor Doe (IRE) **Mr Charles Eden**
40 **VICOMTE THOMAS (FR)**, 4, b g Highest Honor (FR)—Vigorine (FR) **J. T - W Racing**
41 **WANNA SHOUT**, 6, b m Missed Flight—Lulu **E. R. C. Beech & B. Wilkinson**
42 **WATERMOUSE**, 4, b g Alhaarth (IRE)—Heavenly Waters **Mrs C. M. Dickin**
43 **WHISTLING SONG**, 9, ch m True Song—Sancal **Mrs C. M. Dickin**
44 **WRENS ISLAND (IRE)**, 10, br g Yashgan—Tipiton **Wholebuild Ltd**

THREE-YEAR-OLDS

45 **GULFOSS**, b f Gunner B—Ballintava **Mr David A. N. Ross**
46 **MISTER TRICKSTER (IRE)**, b c Woodborough (USA)—Tinos Island (IRE) **The Tricksters**

TWO-YEAR-OLDS

47 B f 28/3 Bahhare (USA)—Westside Flyer (Risk Me (FR)) (2000) **Mr C. J. Dickin**

Other Owners: Mrs Susan Brown, Mr C. N. Butters, Ms Joanne Clark, Mr M. J. Dent, Mr C. J. Dickin, Mr Kevin Doocey, Mr P. A. J. Doyle, Mr W. P. Evans, Mr E. D. Fraser, Mr N. W. Imlah, Mrs Alison Jelley, Mr T. G. Jones, Wing Comdr J. H. King, Mrs J. M. Mann, Mr D. C. Marten, Mr Peter Matthews, Mr W. L. Miles, Mr A. Nicholls, Mr G. N. Potts, Mr Nick Scotland, Mr John N. Simpson, Mr Alan Varey, Mr Brian Wilson.

Assistant Trainer: Claire Dickin

Jockeys (NH): David Dennis (w.a.), B Hitchcott (9-7). **Conditional:** John Pritchard (9-0).

153 **MR MICHAEL W. DICKINSON, Maryland**
Postal: Tapeta Farm, 100 Piney Creek Lane, North East Maryland 21901, U.S.A.
Contact: PHONE 410 287 4567 FAX 410 287 8410 E-MAIL mwd@dol.net

1 **A HUEVO (USA)**, 8, b g Cool Joe (USA)—Verabald (USA) **Mark Hopkins**
2 **BOWMAN MILL (USA)**, 6, ch h Kris S (USA)—Aletta Maria (USA) **Dr John Chandler**

MR MICHAEL W. DICKINSON—continued

3 **CHAN CHAN (USA)**, 5, b g Spinning World (USA)—Candy Charm (USA) **Gallop, LLC**
4 **GREEN GROOM (USA)**, 5, ch h Green Tune (USA)—Mizanaze (USA) **Mikael Magnusson**
5 **KANDULA (USA)**, 4, ch c Benny The Dip (USA)—Move (USA) **Winchell Thoroughbreds, LLC**
6 **KOSADE (USA)**, 4, b f Cozzene (USA)—Daad (USA) **H. E. Faisal Alhegelan**
7 **PRICELESS QUALITY (USA)**, 4, ch f Elusive Quality (USA)—Catumbella (USA) **Cherokee River Ranch**
8 **SARIE MARAIS (USA)**, 4, ch f Unbridled (USA)—Aletta Maria (USA) **Dr John Chandler**
9 **SILVER SINGER (USA)**, 4, b f Silver Deputy (USA)—Singing Heart (USA) **VHW Stables**
10 **SOTO (USA)**, 4, ch c Dehere (USA)—Subtle Fragrance (USA) **Gallop, LLC**
11 **YOUGHAL BAY (USA)**, 5, b g Mecke (USA)—Mighty Intimate (USA) **Anstu Stables**

THREE-YEAR-OLDS

12 **DYNAMIA (USA)**, b f Dynaformer (USA)—Easter Symphony (USA) **Dr John Chandler**
13 **MASTER WILLIAM (CAN)**, ch c King of Kings (IRE)—Numberonedance (USA) **Kenneth Ramsey**
14 **PADDINGTON (USA)**, ch c Saint Ballado (USA)—Painted Portrait (USA) **Gallop, LLC**
15 **POLISH FLOWER (USA)**, b f Danzig (USA)—Flower Canyon (USA) **Gary Knapp**
16 **POLISH TRICK (USA)**, b c Clever Trick (USA)—Sunk (USA) **Favourites Racing Ltd**
17 **TAPIT (USA)**, gr c Pulpit (USA)—Tap Your Heels (USA) **Winchell Thoroughbreds, LLC**
18 **WESTERN RANSOM (USA)**, b f Red Ransom (USA)—Western Mind (USA) **Dr John Chandler**

TWO-YEAR-OLDS

19 B f 19/2 Woodman (USA)—Antequera (USA) (Green Dancer (USA)) **Jack Ruzicho**
20 B c 21/4 Deputy Minister (USA)—Chip (USA) (Norquestor (USA)) **William Rickman, Sr**
21 Ch f 23/5 Spinning World (USA)—Country Casual (USA) (Royal Roberto (USA)) **Roy Gottlieb**
22 **HOME FROM OZ (USA)**, ch f 13/4 Pulpit (USA)—
⠀⠀⠀⠀⠀⠀⠀⠀⠀⠀⠀Tap Your Heels (USA) (Norquestor (USA)) (2976) **David Shashura**
23 **SPIRIT OF SHERWOOD (USA)**, ch c 11/5 Deputy Commander—
⠀⠀⠀⠀⠀⠀⠀⠀⠀⠀⠀Don Cat (USA) (Forest Wildcat (USA)) (26786) **William Rickman, Sr**

---

154 MR A. DICKMAN, Sandhutton
Postal: Breckenbrough House (2nd Yard), Sandhutton, Thirsk, North Yorkshire, YO7 4EL.
Contact: PHONE (01904) 488549 HOUSE (01845) 587432 MOBILE (07977) 694777

1 **DUSTY WUGG (IRE)**, 5, b m General Monash (USA)—Welsh Berry (USA) **Mr George Houghton**
2 **INTER VISION (USA)**, 4, b c Cryptoclearance (USA)—Fateful (USA) **The Milan Partnership**
3 **THE OLD SOLDIER**, 6, b g Magic Ring (IRE)—Grecian Belle **The Maroon Stud**
4 **WUB CUB**, 4, b f Averti (IRE)—Ray of Hope **Mr Allan Dickman**

THREE-YEAR-OLDS

5 **FROM THE NORTH (IRE)**, ch f Foxhound (USA)—Best Swinger (IRE) **Mrs B. M. Bennett**

TWO-YEAR-OLDS

6 **KOOL OVATION**, b c 19/4 Royal Applause—Carrie Kool (Prince Sabo) (3000) **The Marooned Crew**
7 **OUTRAGEOUS FLIRT (IRE)**, b f 4/2 Indian Lodge (IRE)—Sofia Aurora (USA) (Chief Honcho (USA)) (8657)
8 **PROPELLOR (IRE)**, ch c 27/3 Pivotal—Clunie (Inchinor) (19000) **The Marooned Crew**

Other Owners: Mr Andrew Dickman, Mr L. L. Dickman, Mr R. Dimmock, Mr Gerald Geraghty.

Assistant Trainer: B Bennett

Jockeys (Flat): P Hanagan (7-12), R Winston (8-4). **Jockey (NH):** S Stronge (10-4). **Apprentice:** A Beech (8-4).

---

155 MR J. E. DIXON, Carlisle
Postal: Moorend, Thursby, Carlisle, Cumbria, CA5 6QP.
Contact: PHONE (01228) 711019

1 **HIRT LODGE**, 13, ch g Jumbo Hirt (USA)—Holly Lodge **Mrs S. F. Dixon**
2 **JUMBO'S DREAM**, 13, b g Jumbo Hirt (USA)—Joyful Star **Mrs E. M. Dixon**
3 **JUMBO STAR**, 14, ch g Jumbo Hirt (USA)—Joyful Star **Mrs E. M. Dixon**
4 **SWEET MILLY**, 9, b m Milieu—Another Joyful **Mrs S. F. Dixon**

156 MR JOHN P. DODDS, Alnwick
Postal: **South Hazelrigg, Chatton, Alnwick, Northumberland, NE66 5RZ.**
Contact: **HOUSE (01668) 215216 MOBILE (07710) 346076 FAX (01668) 215216**
E-MAIL jpd@hazelrigg.fsnet.co.uk

1 **DANCING DILL**, 9, b m Dancing High—Some Shiela
2 **DINGO DANCER**, 11, b g Dancing High—Some Shiela
3 5, B br m Presenting—Establish (IRE)
4 **MILLIESOME**, 6, b m Milieu—Some Shiela
5 **RACING LORD (IRE)**, 7, b g Lord Americo—Miss Kertina (IRE)

Assistant Trainer: C. E. Brownless

Jockeys (NH): Mark Bradburne (9-7), Calvin McCormack (10-0), Robert Thornton (10-0).

157 MR M. J. K. DODS, Darlington
Postal: **Denton Hall Farm, Piercebridge, Darlington, Co. Durham, DL2 3TY.**
Contact: **PHONE (01325) 374270 FAX (01325) 374020 MOBILE (07860) 411590/(0777) 3290830**

1 **AAHGOWANGOWAN (IRE)**, 5, b m Tagula (IRE)—Cabcharge Princess (IRE) **Mr D. Vic Roper**
2 **AL AZHAR**, 10, b g Alzao (USA)—Upend **Mr G. Spencer**
3 **BALAKIREF**, 5, b g Royal Applause—Pluck **Septimus Racing Group**
4 **BETTY'S PRIDE**, 5, b m Lion Cavern (USA)—Final Verdict (IRE) **Betty's Brigade**
5 **BUNDY**, 8, b g Ezzoud (IRE)—Sanctuary Cove **Mr A. J. Henderson**
6 **COMMITMENT LECTURE**, 4, b f Komaite (USA)—Hurtleberry (IRE) **Mrs B. Riddell**
7 **FLYING TACKLE**, 6, ch g First Trump—Frighten The Life **Mr Neil Harrison**
8 **HULA BALLEN**, 4, ch f Weldnaasn (USA)—Ballon **Mrs P. Knox & Mrs J. Hutchinson**
9 **JEDEYDD**, 7, b g Shareef Dancer (USA)—Bilad (USA) **Mrs K. S. Pratt and Partners**
10 **JOHN O'GROATS (IRE)**, 6, b g Distinctly North (USA)—Bannons Dream (IRE) **Mr J. A. Wynn-Williams**
11 **LUNAR DRAM**, 6, ch g Cosmonaut—Moonshine Malt **Mr Les Waugh**
12 **MICKLEDOR**, 4, ch f Lake Coniston (IRE)—Shamasiya (FR) **Mr D. B. Stanley**
13 **MR BOUNTIFUL (IRE)**, 6, b g Mukaddamah (USA)—Nawadder **Denton Hall Racing Ltd**
14 **PETANA**, 4, gr f Petong—Duxyana (IRE) **The 4 Aces**
15 **POLISH CORRIDOR**, 5, b g Danzig Connection (USA)—Possibility **Mr Russ Mould**
16 **ROTUMA (IRE)**, 5, b g Tagula (IRE)—Cross Question (USA) **Denton Hall Racing Ltd**
17 **SMITH N ALLAN OILS**, 5, b g Bahamian Bounty—Grand Splendour **Smith & Allan Racing**
18 **STORYTELLER (IRE)**, 10, b g Thatching—Please Believe Me **Mrs Karen S. Pratt**
19 **THORALBY**, 5, b g Son Pardo—Polish Lady (IRE) **Harris Racing Partnership**
20 **ZHITOMIR**, 6, ch g Lion Cavern (USA)—Treasure Trove (USA) **Mr M. J. K. Dods**

THREE-YEAR-OLDS
21 **AGUILERA**, ch f Wolfhound (USA)—Mockingbird **Mr Doug Graham**
22 **ANICAFLASH**, b f Cayman Kai (IRE)—Sharp Top **Mrs B. Riddell**
23 **DEFANA**, b g Defacto (USA)—Thalya **Denton Hall Racing Ltd**
24 **DIVINE SPIRIT**, b g Foxhound (USA)—Vocation (IRE) **Mr A. Mallen**
25 **HOLLY WALK**, ch f Dr Fong (USA)—Holly Blue **Mrs B. Riddell**
26 **QUEEN'S ECHO**, b f Wizard King—Sunday News'n'echo (USA) **Mr D. C. Batey**
27 **SIR BOBBY**, b g Kylian (USA)—Ishona **Mrs Patsy Monk**
28 **SON OF THUNDER (IRE)**, ch g Dr Fong (USA)—Sakura Queen (IRE) **Mr Russ Mould**
29 **SPRING BREEZE**, ch g Dr Fong (USA)—Trading Aces **Mrs C. E. Dods**

TWO-YEAR-OLDS
30 B g 21/4 Orpen (USA)—Bright Prospect (USA) (Miswaki (USA)) (37000) **Partnership**
31 B f 14/2 King of Kings (IRE)—Dixieline City (USA) (Dixieland Band (USA)) (13000) **Mrs Karen S. Pratt**
32 B c 23/4 Fayruz—Lyrical Vision (IRE)—Vision (USA)) (22000) **A. Wynn Williams & Ptns**
33 B g 17/2 Zahah (CAN)—Misty Moon (Polar Falcon (USA)) (13000) **Mr G. Spencer**
34 B g 25/2 Rossini (USA)—Picnic Basket (Pharly (FR)) (7420) **A. Monk & D. Kirsopp**
35 B g 23/3 Josr Algarhoud (USA)—Primulette (Mummy's Pet) (16000) **G. Spencer**
36 **ROYAL FLYNN**, b c 26/3 Royal Applause—Shamriyna (IRE) (Darshaan) (26000) **A. Wynn Williams**
37 Ch c 3/5 Shinko Forest (IRE)—Sea Modena (IRE) (Mac's Imp) (4019) **V. Spinks**
38 B f 24/2 Almutawakel—Society Fair ((FR) (Always Fair) (USA)) **Mr M. J. K. Dods**

MR M. J. K. DODS—continued

39 B f 2/4 Piccolo—Sunshine Coast (Posse (USA)) (13000) **Mr D. Hughes & Partners**
40 Br f 12/3 Pennekamp (USA)—Tripe Zee (USA) (Zilzal (USA)) **Dwayne Woods & John Jackson**

Other Owners: Mr J. W. Andrews, Mr Craig Banister, Mrs Stella Barclay, Mr J. N. Blackburn, Mr S. A. Breakwell, Mr P. J. Carr, Mr Paul Clarkson, Mr H. R. Harris, Mrs J. M. Harris, Mr B. G. Hurst, Mrs R. Olivier, Mr D. J. Stokell, Mr Roger Stokell, Mr Foster Watson.

Assistant Trainer: C Dods

---

158 MR B. N. DORAN, Broadway
Postal: Peasebrook Racing, Peasebrook Farm, Cheltenham RoaBroadway, Worcestershire, WR12 7LX.
Contact: **HOME (01386) 858980 MOBILE (07711) 570869 E-MAIL** doranracer@ad.com

1 BOULTON, 4, b c Syrtos—Penny Dip **R. P. & M. Berrow**
2 DON FAYRUZ (IRE), 12, b g Fayruz—Gobolino
3 JULANDI, 5, ch m Southern Music—Dull'un **Mr B. N. Doran**
4 PRAYERFUL, 5, b m Syrtos—Pure Formality **Mr P. N. Exton**
5 SILVER MISTRESS, 5, gr m Syrtos—Galava (CAN) **Mr B. N. Doran**
6 STAR WONDER, 4, b f Syrtos—Galava (CAN) **R. P. & M. Berrow**
7 TOP OF THE STACK, 6, b g Syrtos—Just Hannah **Mr B. N. Doran**
8 TRICKEY NICK, 5, b g Nomadic Way (USA)—Nicky's Choice **Mr Dave Nicholls**

THREE-YEAR-OLDS

9 B gr g Syrtos—Galava (CAN) **R. P. & M. Berrow**

TWO-YEAR-OLDS

10 Ro f 26/3 Kris—Galava (CAN) (Graustark) (14000) **R. P. & M. Berrow**
11 SUPERIOR DREAM, b c 22/5 Superpower—Calofornia Dreamin (Slip Anchor) **Mr D. Bunn**

Other Owners: Mr Roy Cresswell, Mr J. Danahar, Mrs Jo Mitchel, Mr Roger Mitchel, Mr J. Smart.

Jockey (Flat): Dale Gibson (7-11). **Jockeys (NH):** Vince Slattery (10-0), Frank Windsor-Clive (9-7).

---

159 MR FRANCOIS DOUMEN, Bouce
Postal: Le Gue, 61570 Bouce, France.
Contact: **HOME** +33 (0) 2 33 26 91 46 **OFFICE** +33 (0) 2 33 67 11 59 **FAX** +33 (0) 2 33 67 82 37
MOBILE +33 (0) 6 07 42 33 58 **E-MAIL** doumenecouves@wanadoo.fr

1 ARBOR VITAE (FR), 6, b h Double Bed (FR)—Gloire de Rose
2 BARACOUDA (FR), 9, b g Alesso (USA)—Peche Aubar (FR)
3 BEST BELOVED (FR), 7, b h Double Bed (FR)—Gloire de Rose
4 BLUE CANYON (FR), 6, b g Bering—Nini Princess (IRE)
5 CASH IS KING (FR), 8, b h Second Set (IRE)—Flash of Dream (IRE)
6 CLETY (FR), 8, b h Sillery (USA)—La Bucaille (FR)
7 COUREUSE (FR), 4, b f Jeune Homme (USA)—Rigoureuse (USA)
8 DOUBLE TONIC (FR), 5, b h Double Bed (FR)—Jimka (FR)
9 FILS A PAPA (FR), 5, b g Double Bed (FR)—Syvanie (FR)
10 FIRST GOLD (FR), 11, b g Shafoun (FR)—Nuit d'Or II (FR)
11 FLEET OF FOOT, 4, b f Zamindar (USA)—Harefoot
12 FOUDRE FOLLE (FR), 4, ch f Dr Devious (USA)—L'Annee Folle (FR)
13 GLUCOSE (FR), 7, b g Double Bed (FR)—Sclos (FR)
14 INNOX (FR), 8, b g Lute Antique (FR)—Savane III (FR)
15 JEUX OLYMPIQUES (FR), 7, b g Scooter Bleu (IRE)—Banassa (FR)
16 KELAMI (FR), 6, b g Lute Antique (FR)—Voltige de Nievre (FR)
17 KENTUCKY GOLD (FR), 4, b f Hector Protector (USA)—Too Advanced (USA)
18 KOKIN (FR), 6, b g Video Rock (FR)—Tulipp d'Avril (FR)
19 KRACH (FR), 6, b g Lute Antique (FR)—Voilette (FR)
20 LADYKISH (FR), 5, b m Comte du Bourg (FR)—Turkish Lady (FR)
21 L'AMI (FR), 5, ch g Lute Antique (FR)—Voltige de Nievre (FR)
22 L'AS DE PIC (FR), 5, b h Ragmar (FR)—Victoria V (FR)
23 LAST DANCE (GER), 5, ch g Monsun (GER)—Lilian (GER)
24 LE CHATELIER (FR), 5, b h Kadalko (FR)—Tulipp d'Avril (FR)

MR FRANCOIS DOUMEN—continued

25 **LINGO (FR)**, 5, ch h Ragmar (FR)—Queenly (FR)
26 **LOUSTIQ (FR)**, 5, b h Lute Antique (FR)—Edie (FR)
27 **LUPIN (FR)**, 5, b g Luchiroverte (IRE)—Amarante II (FR)
28 **MA'AM (FR)**, 4, b f Garde Royale—French Kiss IV (FR)
29 **MAITRE (FR)**, 4, ch g Ragmar (FR)—Ebene d'Avril (FR)
30 **MARELLE (FR)**, 4, b f Video Rock (FR)—Voilette (FR)
31 **MARKI (FR)**, 4, b g Video Rock (FR)—Payse (FR)
32 **MAROCAIN (FR)**, 4, b g Kadalko (FR)—Breda II (FR)
33 **MATELOT (FR)**, 4, b g Epervier Bleu—Gloria IV (FR)
34 **MAYEUL (FR)**, 4, ch g Luchiroverte (IRE)—Elbe (FR)
35 **MI AMIGO (FR)**, 4, gr g Dom Alco (FR)—Voltige de Nievre (FR)
36 **MIG (FR)**, 4, ch g Ragmar (FR)—Edie (FR)
37 **MILLENIUM ROYAL (FR)**, 4, b c Mansonnien (FR)—Pink Cahmapagne (FR)
38 **MISS PRISM (USA)**, 4, b f Theatrical—Ensorcelles Moi (USA)
39 **MONZON (FR)**, 4, b g Kadalko (FR)—Queenly (FR)
40 **MOULIN RICHE (FR)**, 4, b g Video Rock (FR)—Gintonique (FR)
41 **OUED (FR)**, 4, gr c Double Bed (FR)—Tibriza
42 **PACY'S RIDGE (IRE)**, 4, b f Indian Ridge—Pacy (USA)
43 **PRATO (GER)**, 4, ch g Kornado—Prairie Lila (GER)
44 **ROYAL BABY (FR)**, 12, b g Garde Royale—Babylonie (FR)
45 **ROYALE POUR MOI (FR)**, 4, b f Cadoudal (FR)—Girl Vamp (FR)
46 **ROYAL PARADISE (FR)**, 4, b g Cadoudal (FR)—Crystalza (FR)
47 **SAMANDO (FR)**, 4, ch f Hernando—Samshu (FR)
48 **STATYRA (FR)**, 4, ch f Double Bed (FR)—Syvanie (FR)
49 **SUNRISE BED (FR)**, 4, b f Double Bed (FR)—Belle Chaumiere
50 **TARQUE (IRE)**, 4, b g Revoque (IRE)—Tarquinia (IRE)
51 **TERENEZ (FR)**, 4, b c Desert King (IRE)—Dibenoise (FR)
52 **VIC TOTO (FR)**, 7, b h Kaid Pous (FR)—Koberta (FR)

THREE-YEAR-OLDS

53 **ANABAA REPUBLIC (FR)**, b f Anabaa (USA)—Gigawatt (FR)
54 **DANAW (FR)**, b c Lomitas—Damanka (IRE)
55 **DANCEROY (FR)**, b c Deploy—Dancereine (FR)
56 **DOUBLE CRÈME (FR)**, ch g Double Bed (FR)—Chester County
57 **DOUBLE SHINE (IRE)**, ch f Double Bed (FR)—Jimshine (FR)
58 **FRED ASTOR (FR)**, b g Baryshnikov (AUS)—Mary Astor (FR)
59 **GOLD MARK (FR)**, ch f Mark of Esteem (IRE)—Gold Script (FR)
60 **LA CIGUE (FR)**, b f Revoque (IRE)—River Tweed
61 **MARIE MADELAINE (FR)**, ch f Lord of Men—The Trollop (FR)
62 **MIEUX MIEUX (IRE)**, b f Mark of Esteem (IRE)—L'Annee Folle (FR)
63 **MILRANE (FR)**, b c Rajpoute (FR)—Bulgaria (FR)
64 **MISS BEHAVIOUR (FR)**, b f Dolpour—Guard's Gala
65 **MOKUM (FR)**, b c Octagonal (NZ)—Back On Top (FR)
66 **NARUKHA RAJPUT (FR)**, b f Rajpoute—French Kiss IV (FR)
67 **NEVEZE (FR)**, b g Rajpoute—Uzelle V (FR)
68 **NOCTANBULE (FR)**, b g Subotica (FR)—Calvi IV (FR)
69 **NOUVEAU MAIRE (FR)**, b g Ragmar—Countess Fellow (FR)
70 **OUT OF WOODS (USA)**, b f Woodman (USA)—Save Me The Waltz (IRE)
71 **STAG PARTY (FR)**, ch c Exit To Nowhere (USA)—Marital Bliss (FR)
72 **STAR SAPHIRE (FR)**, b f Piccolo—Sonic Sapphire
73 **SUNRISE SPIRIT (FR)**, b g Double Bed (FR)—Belle Chaumiere
74 **TEESDALE (FR)**, b f Mark of Esteem (IRE)—Malham Tarn
75 **TIGNASSE (FR)**, b f Double Bed (FR)—Off Guard (FR)
76 **WHAT A PICTURE (FR)**, ch f Peintre Celebre (USA)—Style For Life (IRE)

TWO-YEAR-OLDS

77 **CARDOUN JIM (FR)**, b g 14/2 Cardoun (FR)—Jolie Jim (FR) (Double Bed (FR))
78 **DESERT JIM (FR)**, ch c 1/5 Desert King (IRE)—Jimshine (FR) (Shining Steel)
79 **EL BADIL (FR)**, b c 25/2 Double Bed (FR)—Syvanie (FR) (Sicyos (USA))
80 **FUJAIRAH (SWI)**, b f 8/2 Sri Pekan (USA)—Fresh Look (IRE) (Alzao (USA))
81 **GIGOLINO (FR)**, ch c 18/3 Trempolino (USA)—Gigawatt (FR) (Double Bed (FR))
82 **IRUNARRI (FR)**, gr f 12/4 Kendor (FR)—Aristi (FR) (Synefos (USA)) (34013)
83 **JIMIST (FR)**, ch f 15/5 River Mist (USA)—La Chenottaie (FR) (R B Chesne) (2473)
84 **KASBAH BLISS (FR)**, b c 26/2 Kahyasi—Marital Bliss (FR) (Double Bed (FR))
85 **MEDAILLE (FR)**, gr f 23/3 Medaaly—Super Rose (FR) (Darshaan)

MR FRANCOIS DOUMEN—continued

86 **ORMELLO (FR)**, b c 23/5 Cyborg (FR)—Galante V (FR) (Vorias (USA))
87 **OSANA (FR)**, b c 4/5 Video Rock (FR)—Voilette (FR) (Brezzo (FR))
88 **OUISTITI (FR)**, ch c 6/6 Ragmar (FR)—Elbe (FR) (Royal Charter (FR))
89 **SPECTROFOLLE (FR)**, b f 15/3 Spectrum (IRE)—L'Annee Folle (FR) (Double Bed (FR))
90 **SPRING A LEEK (FR)**, ch f 21/4 Saratoga Springs—Back On Top (FR) (Double Bed (FR))
91 **STEED (FR)**, b c 11/2 Double Bed (FR)—River Tweed (Selkirk (USA))
92 **SUNRISE HAVELI (FR)**, ch f 4/4 Rajpoute (FR)—Belle Chaumiere (Gildoran (IRE))
93 Ch c 17/4 Vettori (IRE)—Zakota (IRE) (Polish Precedent (USA)) (16697)

Other Owners: Mrs Charles-Antoine Armand, Mr Fritz Von Ballmoos, Mr Marcel Benavides, Mr Michel Bessis, Mr Claude Botton, Mr Louis De Bourgoing, Mr Richard Britten-Long, Mr Marc De Chambure, Mr Michael Charlton, Mrs Jessica Cobham, Mr Melwyn Davies, F. F. Racing Limited, Mr Fraguier, Mr Dirk Grauert, Haras D'Ecouves, Haras De Saint Pair Du Mont, Mrs Marie-Joelle Levesque, Mr J. A. McCarthy, Mr J. P. McManus, Marquise De Moratalla, Mr Robert Ng, Sir Peter O'Sullevan, Mrs Denela Platt, Mr Henri De Pracomtal, Mr Eric Puerari, Mr A. J. Richards, Mr Jean-Claude Seroul, Mr Michael Somerset-Leeke, Mr Emmanuel Tassin, Mr Hubert Tassin, Uplifting Bloodstock Ltd, Mr Joerg Vasicek, Mr Hans Peter Vogt, Mr Hans Wirth.

Jockey (Flat): Thierry Thulliez. **Jockey (NH):** Thierry Doumen. **Amateurs:** Mr Robert Danloux, Mr Herve Naggar.

---

160 MR S. L. DOW, Epsom

Postal: **Clear Height Stables, Derby Stables Road, Epsom, Surrey, KT18 5LB.**
Contact: **PHONE (01372) 721490 FAX (01372) 748099 MOBILE (07860) 800109**
E-MAIL (S. Dow) clear.height1.com@virgin.net (Office) clear.height.com@virgin.net

1 **ABUELOS**, 5, b g Sabrehill (USA)—Miss Oasis **Mr J. Noonan**
2 **DANAKIL**, 9, b g Warning—Danilova (USA) **The Danakilists**
3 **GALLERY GOD (IRE)**, 8, ch g In The Wings—El Fabulous (FR) **John Robinson and Derek Stubbs**
4 **GOLDEN DUAL**, 4, b g Danehill (USA)—Golden Digger (USA) **Mr J-P. Lim**
5 **GOODWOOD PRINCE**, 4, b g Emperor Jones (USA)—Scarlet Lake **The Churston Family**
6 **HEKTIKOS**, 4, ch g Hector Protector (USA)—Green Danube (USA) **Mr M. G. Mackenzie**
7 **ICANNSHIRT (IRE)**, 4, b g Night Shift (USA)—Cannikin (IRE) **Mr R. E. Anderson**
8 **ISLAND STAR (IRE)**, 4, b g Turtle Island (IRE)—Orthorising **Mr T. G. Parker**
9 **MADAME MARIE (IRE)**, 4, b f Desert King (IRE)—Les Trois Lamas (IRE) **Mrs M. E. O'Shea**
10 **ORIGINAL SIN (IRE)**, 4, b g Bluebird (USA)—Majakerta (IRE) **Clear Height Racing**
11 **QUANTUM LEAP**, 7, b g Efisio—Prejudice **Mrs M. E. O'Shea**
12 **SOCIAL CONTRACT**, 7, b g Emarati (USA)—Just Buy Baileys **Lesley & Terry Shepherd**
13 **SOLDERSHINE**, 7, b g Weld—Dishcloth **Mr P. McCarthy**
14 **TURTLE VALLEY (IRE)**, 8, b g Turtle Island (IRE)—Primrose Valley **Cazanove Clear Height Racing**

THREE-YEAR-OLDS

15 **ALIANNA (FR)**, b f Anabaa (USA)—Ambassadrice (FR) **T. G. Parker & G. Brain**
16 **ALMOST WELCOME**, b c First Trump—Choral Sundown **Michael Baker, Tom Parker & Partners**
17 **BETTALATEHANNEVER (IRE)**, ch g Titus Livius (FR)—Shambodia (IRE) **Mr J. R. May**
18 **HEAD BOY**, ch g Forzando—Don't Jump (IRE) **R. E. Anderson & Mrs. L. Jenkins**
19 **NIGHT STORM**, b f Night Shift (USA)—Monte Calvo **Anderson, Connolly, Jenkins and Thornton**
20 **PHAT PEOPLES BEACH**, b f Pharly—Eclectic **Mr T. G. Parker**
21 **REDBANK (IRE)**, b g Night Shift (USA)—Bush Rose **Mrs M. E. O'Shea**
22 **WHITGIFT ROCK**, b c Piccolo—Fly South **Whitgift Racing**

TWO-YEAR-OLDS

23 **AMAYA SILVA**, b f 16/2 Silver Patriarch (IRE)—Queen of Tides (IRE) (Soviet Star (USA)) **Mr T. G. Parker**
24 Ch c 27/3 Mark of Esteem (IRE)—Aurora Bay (IRE) (Night Shift (USA)) (12000) **Mr P. Wheatley**
25 **COOMBE CENTENARY**, b f 6/4 Robellino (USA)—
                              Shining Dancer (Rainbow Quest (USA)) (5800) **Coombe Wood Racing Syndicate**
26 **TAIPAN TOMMY (IRE)**, ch c 11/2 Shinko Forest (IRE)—
                              Adieu Cherie (IRE) (Bustino) (26000) **John Robinson and Derek Stubbs**

Other Owners: Mr Michael Baker, Dr C. A. Barnett, Mr G. Brain, Mrs L. S. Buttery, Mr D. G. Churston, Mr J. M. Connolly, Mr R. Gurney, Mrs L. Jenkins, Mr J. O'Connell, Mr Chris Page, Mr. John Robinson, Mr Nigel S. Scandrett, Mrs Lesley Shepherd, Mr T. Shepherd, Dr Derek Stubbs, Mr W. Thornton, Mr D. M. White.

Apprentice: Joe Corfill Brown (8-6). **Conditional:** Luke Smith (9-7). **Amateur:** Daniel Hutchison (9-7).

161 MR C. J. DOWN, Cullompton
Postal: **Upton Farm, Cullompton, Devon, EX15 1RA.**
Contact: **PHONE/FAX (01884) 33097**

1 **ALAKDAR (CAN)**, 10, ch g Green Dancer (USA)—Population **Ms L. Stark**
2 **ANIMAL MAGIC**, 4, b f Shareef Dancer (USA)—Blessed Lass (HOL) **Mrs A. Baker**
3 **ANOTHER COPPER**, 8, ch g Bandmaster (USA)—Letitica **Mrs Taplin & Mr T. Whitten**
4 **ANOTHER DIAMOND (IRE)**, 6, b m First Trump—Rockin' Rosie **Mr A. Baker & Mr G. Waterman**
5 **ARDWELSHIN (FR)**, 6, b g Ajdayt (USA)—Reem Dubai (IRE) **Mr Ken Field**
6 **BEAU SUPREME (IRE)**, 7, b g Supreme Leader—Miss Sabreur **Mrs R. Vicary**
7 **CAN'T BE SCRABBLE**, 11, b g Gargoor—Scribble Along **Mr J. Selby**
8 **CAVALLINO**, 4, b g Double Trigger (IRE)—Young Kermit **Mr & Mrs A. Loze**
9 **CHARALAMBOUS (USA)**, 7, b g Hermitage (USA)—Hula Lei (USA) **Mrs A. Baker & Mr G. Waterman**
10 **CRAFTY MISS (IRE)**, 5, b m Warcraft (USA)—Mrs Rumpole (IRE) **Mr M. Rusden**
11 **DEALER DEL**, 10, b g Deltic (USA)—No Deal **Mrs G. Leeves**
12 **ELHEBA (IRE)**, 5, b g Elbio—Fireheba (ITY) **Three To One**
13 **ELVERLENA**, 8, b m Miner's Lamp—Elver Season **mrs S. Corck & Mrs F. Down**
14 **FINAL DEAL (IRE)**, 5, b g Rashar (USA)—Cute Boro (IRE) **Mr P. Holland**
15 **FLURRY**, 5, gr m Terimon—Queens Favourite **Mr J. Selby**
16 **FOOLING AROUND**, 6, ch m Jester—Scribble Along **Mr J. Selby**
17 **HERE COMES HARRY**, 8, ch g Sunley Builds—Coole Dolly Day **Miss Claire Howarth**
18 **HOW IS THE LORD (IRE)**, 8, b g Lord Americo—Joaney How **Mr G. Waterman**
19 **I MOVE EARTH**, 7, b m Bandmaster (USA)—Lady of Milton **Mr F. Champion**
20 **JACKS JEWEL (IRE)**, 7, b g Welsh Term—September Daydream (IRE) **Mr Ken Field**
21 **JOYFUL PRINCESS**, 4, b f Gildoran—Joyful Pabs **Mr Mike Rowe**
22 **KARINGA COIN**, 6, ch g Karinga Bay—Coinridge **Mr Edward Darke**
23 **LADY ALDERBROOK (IRE)**, 4, b f Alderbrook—Madame President (IRE) **Mr B. Greening**
24 **LADY LEWIS**, 8, b m Sir Harry Lewis—Gaygo Lady **Mr B. Greening**
25 **LAGO DI LEVICO**, 7, ch g Pelder (IRE)—Langton Herring **Mr J. Radford & Mr M. Lavis**
26 **LE MILLIARDAIRE (FR)**, 5, b g General Holme (USA)—Vanila Fudge **Mr G. Waterman**
27 **LIKE A BREEZE**, 5, bl m Bob Back (USA)—Whatagale **Mr G. Rowe**
28 **LINUS**, 6, b g Bin Ajwaad (IRE)—Land Line **Mr G. Doel**
29 **LIZZY'S FIRST**, 12, b g Town And Country—Lizzy Longstocking **Mr S. Goss**
30 **MILLCROFT REDROCK**, 5, ch g High Roller (IRE)—Dark Row (IRE) **Mr J. Carter**
31 **MILLCROFT SEASCAPE**, 5, b g Good Thyne (USA)—Dante's Ville **Mr J. Carter**
32 **MILLCROFT SEASPRAY (IRE)**, 8, br g Good Thyne (USA)—Bucks Gift **Mr J. Carter**
33 **MISS LEWIS**, 6, b m Sir Harry Lewis (USA)—Teelyna **May & Edwards**
34 **PROBUS LADY**, 6, ch m Good Times (ITY)—Decoyanne **Mr M. Beard**
35 **PROBUS LORD**, 9, b g Rough Stones—Decoyanne **Mr M. Beard**
36 4, B f Luso—Real Town (IRE) **Mr M. Swift**
37 **RIDEAWAY ROSE (IRE)**, 8, b m King's Ride—Miss Rockaway **Mr G. Waterman**
38 **SILENTTOUCHOFTIME (IRE)**, 6, b m Hymns On High—Ballinaboy Queen (IRE) **Mr J. Selby**
39 **STILL RUNS DEEP**, 5, b m Karinga Bay—Millers Action **Mr M. Langdell**
40 **STURM UND DRANG**, 10, ch g Selkirk (USA)—Historiette **Mr B. Reeder**
41 **TEAM CAPTAIN**, 10, ch g Teamster—Silly Sausage **Mr P. Hickman**
42 **THELONIUS**, 9, ch g Statoblest—Little Sega (FR) **Mr M. Morris**
43 **VALDERRAMA**, 4, ch g Lahib (USA)—Silky Heights (IRE) **Mr G. Waterman**

Jockeys (NH): James Davies (9-7), Roddy Green (10-0), Richard Hobson (10-2), Jo Tizzard (10-0).

162 MISS J. S. DOYLE, East Garston
Postal: **Flemington, Upper Lambourn, Hungerford, Berkshire, RG17 8QH.**
Contact: **HOUSE (01488) 72222 YARD (01488) 72223 MOBILE (07831) 880678**

1 **CHINA JACK (IRE)**, 6, b g West China—Camp Bay (IRE) **Mrs Rhona Alexander**
2 **GENERALS LASTSTAND (IRE)**, 6, b g Little Bighorn—Our Dorcet **Mrs Rhona Alexander**
3 **GIVERAND**, 5, b m Royal Applause—Petersford Girl (IRE) **Miss Jacqueline S. Doyle**
4 **HERES HARRY**, 4, b c Most Welcome—Nahla **The Safe Six**
5 **SOMAYDA (IRE)**, 9, b g Last Tycoon—Flame of Tara **The Somayda Partnership**
6 **ZANAY**, 8, b g Forzando—Nineteenth of May **Mr Tom Ford**

THREE-YEAR-OLDS

7 B f Bluegrass Prince (IRE)—Midnight Romance

MISS J. S. DOYLE—continued
TWO-YEAR-OLDS

8 B f 27/2 Grand Lodge (USA)—Beaming (Mtoto) (2000) **Miss Jacqueline S. Doyle**
9 Ch f 15/2 Tagula (IRE)—Rose of Shuaib (IRE) (Caerleon (USA)) (3000) **Miss Jacqueline S. Doyle**

Other Owners: Mr R. J. Fitch, Mr P. J. Howlett, Mr A. W. Regan, Mr Ken Washbourne.

Apprentice: James Doyle (7-7). **Amateur:** Miss Sophie Doyle (8-0).

---

163 **MR C. DREW, Rampton**
Postal: **Fox End Stables, 83 King Street, Rampton, Cambridgeshire, CB4 8QD.**
Contact: **PHONE/FAX (01954) 250772**

1 DUNMIDOE, 4, b f Case Law—Rion River (IRE) **Mr C. Drew**
2 MADAME ROUX, 6, b m Rudimentary (USA)—Foreign Mistress **Miss P. Drew**
3 REPUBLICAN LADY, 12, b m Battle Hymn—Sweet Helen **Mr C. Drew**
4 SIMON'S SEAT (USA), 5, ch g Woodman (USA)—Spire (USA) **Mrs E. Reid Mrs R. Chambers Mr A. Plumb**
5 SUGAR SNAP, 4, b f Sesaro (USA)—Cuddle Bunny (IRE) **Mr C. Drew**
6 TWICE BRIGHT, 8, br g Precocious—Sweet Helen

THREE-YEAR-OLDS

7 PATRICIA RAY, b f Young Ern—Lombard Ships

Assistant Trainer: Miss Polly Drew

Amateur: Miss P Drew (8-7).

---

164 **MR C. J. DREWE, Didcot**
Postal: **Lower Cross Farm, Blewbury Road, East Hagbourne, Didcot, Oxfordshire, OX11 9ND.**
Contact: **PHONE (01235) 813124 MOBILE (07787) 503709**

1 BRIGHT TIMES AHEAD, 6, ch m Rainbows For Life (CAN)—Just A Second **W. P. Long**
2 GINSKI, 8, b g Petoski—Upham Lass **Mr C. J. Drewe**
3 TAKE A RAIN CHECK (IRE), 7, b m Rainbows For Life (CAN)—Just A Second **The Coskett Partnership**
4 TIME TO PARLEZ, 13, b g Amboise—Image of War **Mrs J. Strange**

Other Owners: Mr Peter Benson, Mrs Jane Drewe, Mrs J. M. Johnstone, Mr P. J. Minns.

Jockeys (NH): B Hitchcott, R Thornton.

---

165 **MRS A. DUFFIELD, Leyburn**
Postal: **Sun Hill Racing Stables, Sun Hill Farm, Constable Burton, Leyburn, North Yorkshire, DL8 5RL.**
Contact: **PHONE (01677) 450303 MOBILE (07802) 496332 FAX (01677) 450993**
E-MAIL ann.duffield1@virgin.net

1 ALLEGEDLY RED, 5, ch m Sabrehill (USA)—Tendency **Mrs L. J. Tounsend & S. & G. Scaffolding**
2 BRILLYANT DANCER, 6, b m Environment Friend—Brillyant Glen (IRE) **Clarks New Town**
3 CHARMING ADMIRAL (IRE), 11, ch m Shareef Dancer (USA)—Lilac Charm **The Old Spice Girls**
4 FREINDLYPERSUASION, 4, b c Shambo—Sea Sky **Mr Billy Maguire**
5 GIVE HIM CREDIT (USA), 4, b g Quiet American (USA)—Meniatarra (USA) **Mrs L. J. Tounsend**
6 MIDGES PRIDE, 4, b g Puissance—It's All Academic (IRE) **Friends Of The Late Neil Midgley**
7 NOBLE HOUSE, 7, ch g Gildoran—Trust To Luck **Mr R. Renny**
8 RIFLEMAN (IRE), 4, ch g Starborough—En Garde (USA) **Mr S. Adamson**
9 YOUNG TOT (IRE), 6, b g Torus—Lady-K (IRE) **North Briton Racing**

THREE-YEAR-OLDS

10 BLUE NUN, b f Bishop of Cashel—Matisse **Turf 2000 Limited**
11 CONSTABLE BURTON, b g Foxhound (USA)—Actress **Turf 2000 Limited**
12 NAMED AT DINNER, ch c Halling (USA)—Salanka (IRE) **Mr T. Palin & Mr C. Wilcock**
13 PRAIRIE SUN (GER), b f Law Society (USA)—Prairie Flame (IRE) **Miss Helen Wynne**
14 SEALILY (IRE), gr f Docksider (USA)—Hariyana (IRE) **Miss Betty Duxbury**

MRS A. DUFFIELD—continued

TWO-YEAR-OLDS

15 B c 14/3 Bahhare (USA)—Baileys First (IRE) (Alzao (USA)) (11131)
16 B c 21/3 Dr Fong (USA)—Chatterberry (Aragon) (12000) **Boursly Racing Syndicate**
17 DANEHILL FAIRY (IRE), b f 28/3 Danehill Dancer—
                                Turntable (IRE) (Dolphin Street (FR)) (3400) **Miss B. Duxbury**
18 B c 2/5 Most Welcome—Marjorie's Orchid (Petong) (1000)
19 B br c 9/3 Orpen (USA)—Naivement (IRE) (Doyoun) (5000)
20 PRINCE NAMID, b c 28/3 Namid—Fen Princess (IRE) (Trojan Fen) **Mr Stuart Adamson**
21 Ch f 17/3 Titus Livius (FR)—Scotia Rose (Tap On Wood) (7111) **Miss Helen Wynne**
22 Ch f 14/2 Most Welcome—Sweet Dreams (Selkirk (USA)) (1545)
23 UNLIMITED, b c 1/4 Bold Edge—Cabcharge Blue (Midyan (USA)) (7000) **Mrs L. J. Townsend & Mr R. Renny**

Assistant Trainer: George Duffield

Jockey (Flat): George Duffield (w.a.).

---

166 | MR B. W. DUKE, Lambourn
Postal: **Coppington Stables, Greenways, Lambourn, Berkshire, RG17 7LG.**
Contact: **PHONE (01488) 71888 MOBILE (07967) 252182**

1 BEN LOMAND, 4, ch g Inchinor—Benjarong **Mr P. J. Moriarty**
2 BLACKCHURCH MIST (IRE), 7, b m Erins Isle—Diandra **Brendan W. Duke Racing**
3 CASTAIGNE (FR), 5, ch m Pivotal—Storm Warning **Susan Livesey, Ian Griffiths**
4 COCTAIL LADY (IRE), 4, ch f Piccolo—Last Ambition (IRE) **Oak Green Racing Partnership**
5 COPPINGTON FLYER (IRE), 4, ch f Eagle Eyed (USA)—Miss Flite (IRE) **Brendan W. Duke Racing**
6 GRAND OPINION (IRE), 5, b g Grand Plaisir (IRE)—Cousin Rose **The G. S. M. Group**
7 OSCARS VISION (IRE), 4, ch f Oscar Schindler (IRE)—Eyelet (IRE) **Brendan W. Duke Racing**
8 SEBISTINA (IRE), 4, b f Entrepreneur—Jovine (USA) **Ms Fiona Bolger**
9 SKELLIGS ROCK (IRE), 4, b c Key of Luck (USA)—Drew (IRE) **Mr P. J. Moriarty**

THREE-YEAR-OLDS

10 BAILAORA (IRE), b br c Shinko Forest (IRE)—Tart (FR) **Exors of the Late Mr R. M. J. Kingston**
11 JANGO MALFOY (IRE), ch c Russian Revival (USA)—Sialia (IRE) **Mr Joe Duke**
12 KURINGAI, b c Royal Applause—Talighta (USA) **Miss A. C. Telling**
13 TARANAI (IRE), ch f Russian Revival (USA)—Miss Flite (IRE) **The Southern Lights**
14 ZOLUSHKA (IRE), ch f Russian Revival (USA)—Persian Myth **Exors of the Late Mr R. M. J. Kingston**

Other Owners: Mr Steve Greenhough, Mr Ian Griffiths, Mr G. A. Hancox, Ms Susan Livesey, Mr M. I. Morris, Mr P. L. Murray, Mr Michael O'Connor.

Assistant Trainer: A C Telling

Amateur: Mr A Price (9-7).

---

167 | MR N. A. DUNGER, Pulborough
Postal: **Generation House, Coombelands Stables, Pulborough, West Sussex, RH20 1BP.**
Contact: **PHONE (01798) 872194 MOBILE (07790) 631962 & (07748) 380493**

1 THE TEUCHTER, 5, b g First Trump—Barefoot Landing (USA) **Mr N. A. Dunger**

Assistant Trainer: Mrs D Dunger

Amateur: Mr T. J Malone (9-7).

---

168 | MR E. A. L. DUNLOP, Newmarket
Postal: **Gainsborough Stables, Hamilton Road, Newmarket, Suffolk, CB8 0TE.**
Contact: **PHONE (01638) 661998 FAX (01638) 667394**
E-MAIL edunlop@gainsborough-stables.co.uk WEBSITE www.edunlop.com

1 ANANI (USA), 4, ch c Miswaki (USA)—Mystery Rays (USA) **Mr Mohammed Jaber**
2 BLYTHE KNIGHT (IRE), 4, ch c Selkirk (USA)—Blushing Barada (USA) **Maktoum Al Maktoum**

MR E. A. L. DUNLOP—continued

3 **COURT MASTERPIECE,** 4, b c Polish Precedent (USA)—Easy Option (IRE) **Maktoum Al Maktoum**
4 **DESERT ROYALTY (IRE),** 4, b f Alhaarth (IRE)—Buraida **Mrs Janice Quy**
5 **HIP HOP HARRY,** 4, b c First Trump—Rechanit (IRE) **Lucayan Stud**
6 **ROCKET FORCE (USA),** 4, ch c Spinning World (USA)—Pat Us (USA) **Mr Saeed Suhail**
7 **SWIFT TANGO (IRE),** 4, b g Desert Prince (IRE)—Ballet Society (FR) **Mr Khalifa Sultan**
8 **UROWELLS (IRE),** 4, b g Sadler's Wells (USA)—Highest Accolade **Mr Ahmed BuHaleeba**
9 **WONDROUS JOY,** 4, ch f Machiavellian (USA)—Girl From Ipanema **Winning Post Limited**

THREE-YEAR-OLDS

10 **ABLAJ (IRE),** ch c Horse Chestnut (SAF)—Passe Passe (USA) **Mr Abdulla BuHaleeba**
11 **ABSOLUTELYTHEBEST (IRE),** b c Anabaa (USA)—Recherchee **Mr Saeed Suhail**
12 **ADEEBA (IRE),** b f Alhaarth (IRE)—Nedaarah **Mr Ahmed BuHaleeba**
13 **APEX,** ch c Efisio—Royal Loft **Mr P. Milmo**
14 **ARTISTICIMPRESSION (IRE),** b c Rainbow Quest (USA)—Entice (FR) **Maktoum Al Maktoum**
15 **AT YOUR REQUEST,** gr c Bering—Requesting **Maktoum Al Maktoum**
16 **AYAAM (IRE),** b f Danehill (USA)—Dangerous Diva (IRE) **Mr Ahmed BuHaleeba**
17 **BUBBLING FUN,** b f Marju (IRE)—Blushing Barada (USA) **Maktoum Al Maktoum**
18 **BUNYAH (IRE),** ch f Distant View (USA)—Miss Mistletoes (IRE) **Mr Hamdan Al Maktoum**
19 **CHARLIE BEAR,** ch c Bahamian Bounty—Abi **Old Road Securities Plc**
20 **DERAASAAT,** ch f Nashwan (USA)—Nafhaat (USA) **Mr Hamdan Al Maktoum**
21 **DOCTORATE,** b c Dr Fong (USA)—Aunt Tate **Mr P. G. Goulandris**
22 **ESTIHLAL,** b f Green Desert (USA)—Ta Rib (USA) **Mr Hamdan Al Maktoum**
23 **FINDERS KEEPERS,** b g Selkirk (USA)—La Nuit Rose (FR) **Maktoum Al Maktoum**
24 **GENTLEMAN'S DEAL (IRE),** b c Danehill (USA)—Sleepytime (IRE) **Mr Khalifa Sultan**
25 **GO BETWEEN,** b f Daggers Drawn (USA)—Pizzicato **Mr Ahmed BuHaleeba**
26 **GOLDEN EMPIRE (USA),** br c Red Ransom (USA)—Golden Gorse (USA) **Mr Ahmed BuHaleeba**
27 **GOLDEN GRACE,** b c Green Desert (USA)—Chief Bee **Mr Saeed Suhail**
28 **INNOCENT REBEL (USA),** ch c Swain (IRE)—Cadeaux d'Amie (USA) **Maktoum Al Maktoum**
29 **JOHNNY ROOK (IRE),** ch c Woodman (USA)—Tani (USA) **Mr Abdulla BuHaleeba**
30 **KABREET,** b c Night Shift (USA)—Red Rabbit **Jumeirah Racing**
31 **LATE OPPOSITION,** b c Unfuwain (USA)—Hawa (USA) **Mr Saeed Maktoum Al Maktoum**
32 **MAMBO MOOD (USA),** gr f Kingmambo (USA)—Gray Mood (USA) **Hesmonds Stud**
33 **MATRIMONY,** b c Groom Dancer (USA)—Zonda **Mohammed Al Nabouda**
34 **MITH HILL,** b c Daylami (USA)—Delirious Moment (IRE) **Mr Mohammed Jaber**
35 **MOMENTS I TREASURE (USA),** ch f Mt Livermore (USA)—Munnaya (USA) **Maktoum Al Maktoum**
36 **MOONSHAFT (USA),** br c Capote (USA)—Moonshine Girl (USA) **Mr Saeed Maktoum Al Maktoum**
37 **MR INDEPENDENT (IRE),** b c Cadeaux Genereux—Iris May **John Brown & Megan Dennis**
38 **MUMBO JUMBO,** gr f Daylami (IRE)—Mythical Magic **Maktoum Al Maktoum**
39 **MUSIC MIX (IRE),** gr c Linamix (FR)—Baldemara (FR) **Mr Khalifa Sultan**
40 **MUTAFANEN,** gr c Linamix (FR)—Doomna (IRE) **Mr Hamdan Al Maktoum**
41 **MUTAKAAREB,** b g Inchinor—Rock Face **Mr Hamdan Al Maktoum**
42 **MUTASSEM (FR),** b c Fasliyev (USA)—Fee Eria (FR) **Mr Hamdan Al Maktoum**
43 **NEDWA,** b f In The Wings—Bint Kaldoun (IRE) **Mr Mohammed Jaber**
44 **NIGHT TIDE,** b f Rainbow Quest (USA)—Dream Bay (USA) **Maktoum Al Maktoum**
45 **NO DILEMMA (USA),** ch g Rahy (USA)—Cascassi (USA) **Maktoum Al Maktoum**
46 **OBAY,** ch c Kingmambo (USA)—Parade Queen (USA) **Mr Abdulla BuHaleeba**
47 **ONE OF DISTINCTION,** b f Nashwan (USA)—Air of Distinction (IRE) **Normandie Stud Ltd**
48 **OUIJA BOARD,** b f Cape Cross (IRE)—Selection Board **The Earl of Derby**
49 **POST AND RAIL (USA),** b c Silver Hawk (USA)—Past The Post (USA) **Hesmonds Stud**
50 **RAHEED (IRE),** b g Daggers Drawn (USA)—In Due Course (USA) **Mr Khalid BuHaleeba**
51 **SAINTLY SCHOLAR (USA),** b f Danzig (USA)—Tres Facile (USA) **Mr Khalid BuHaleeba**
52 **SECRET PLACE,** ch g Compton Place—Secret Circle **Mr Khalifa Sultan**
53 **SEED AL MAHA (USA),** b f Seeking The Gold (USA)—Fairy Queen (IRE) **Mr Mohammed Jaber**
54 **SEPARATED (USA),** b f Unbridled (USA)—Lemhi Go (USA) **Cheveley Park Stud**
55 **SKY GALAXY (USA),** ch f Sky Classic (CAN)—Fly To The Moon (USA) **Mr Saeed Maktoum Al Maktoum**
56 **SOMEONE'S ANGEL (USA),** gr f Runaway Groom (CAN)—Yazeanhaa (USA) **Maktoum Al Maktoum**
57 **SPRINGTIME ROMANCE (USA),** br f Kris S (USA)—Khamsin (USA) **Maktoum Al Maktoum**
58 **SUNNY LADY (FR),** ch f Nashwan (USA)—Like The Sun (USA) **Maktoum Al Maktoum**
59 **SUNSET MIRAGE (USA),** br f Swain (IRE)—Yafill (USA) **Maktoum Al Maktoum**
60 **SWEET REPOSE (USA),** b f Gulch (USA)—Bint Baladee **Maktoum Al Maktoum**
61 **TABADUL (IRE),** b c Cadeaux Genereux—Amaniy (USA) **Mr Hamdan Al Maktoum**
62 **THARA'A (IRE),** b f Desert Prince (IRE)—Tycoon's Drama (IRE) **Mr Mohammed BuHaleeba**

TWO-YEAR-OLDS

63 B c 14/4 Tagula (IRE)—Acidanthera (Alzao (USA)) (18552) **Partnership 2**

MR E. A. L. DUNLOP—continued

64 **AKRAAN,** ch f 29/3 Erhaab (USA)—Nafhaat (USA) (Roberto (USA)) **Mr Hamdan Al Maktoum**
65 **ARNO RIVER,** ch c 7/3 Halling (USA)—Moonlights Saunter (USA) (Woodman (USA)) **Maktoum Al Maktoum**
66 **BADAT,** b c 9/5 King's Best (USA)—Hawriyah (USA) (Dayjur (USA)) **Mr Hamdan Al Maktoum**
67 B c 29/4 Green Desert (USA)—Barbarella (Bering) **Mr Khalifa Sultan**
68 **BINT IL SULTAN (IRE),** b f 2/2 Xaar—Knight's Place (IRE) (Hamas (IRE)) (115000) **Mr Mohammed Jaber**
69 **BRIDEGROOM,** b c 17/3 Groom Dancer (USA)—La Piaf (FR) (Fabulous Dancer (USA)) **Cheveley Park Stud**
70 **CALL ME MAX,** b c 3/3 Vettori (IRE)—
    Always Vigilant (Lear Fan (USA)) (20000) **Ors, Woods, Weatherby, Davies & Stone**
71 **CARPET RIDE,** ch c 21/2 Unfuwain (USA)—Fragrant Oasis (USA) (Rahy (USA)) **Maktoum Al Maktoum**
72 **COME WHAT AUGUSTUS,** b c 17/2 Mujahid (USA)—
    Sky Red (Night Shift (USA)) (30000) **Storm Again Syndicate**
73 B c 22/2 Miswaki (USA)—Dancing Action (USA) (Danzatore (CAN)) (36000) **Mr Abdulla BuHaleeba**
74 **DESERT CLASSIC,** b f 28/2 Green Desert (USA)—High Standard (Kris) **Maktoum Al Maktoum**
75 B f 30/3 Bahri (USA)—Dixie Eyes Blazing (USA) (Gone West (USA)) (75000) **Mr Ahmed BuHaleeba**
76 B f 25/5 Nashwan (USA)—Doomna (IRE) (Machiavellian (USA)) **Mr Hamdan Al Maktoum**
77 **DUROOB,** b c 17/1 Bahhare (USA)—Amaniy (USA) (Dayjur (USA)) **Mr Hamdan Al Maktoum**
78 **EAHTA,** b f 8/3 Octagonal (NZ)—Malabarista (FR) (Assert) (5500) **Mr Patrick Milmo**
79 **EPIPHANY,** br f 1/5 Zafonic (USA)—Galette (Caerleon (USA)) **Cliveden Stud**
80 **FORT AUGUSTUS (USA),** b c 8/5 Quiet American (USA)—Fife (IRE) (Lomond (USA)) **Maktoum Al Maktoum**
81 **GARHOUD,** b c 25/4 Grand Lodge (USA)—Puce (Darshaan) (95000) **Mr Mohammed Jaber**
82 **GHURRA (USA),** b f 31/3 War Chant (USA)—Futuh (USA) (Diesis) **Mr Hamdan Al Maktoum**
83 **GOLD CONVENTION,** ch c 30/3 Cadeaux Genereux—Bialy (USA) (Alydar (USA)) **Maktoum Al Maktoum**
84 Ch c 31/3 Ashkalani (IRE)—Golden Way (IRE) (Cadeaux Genereux) **Mr Ahmed BuHaleeba**
85 **GRANITE ROCK (IRE),** b c 25/4 Imperial Ballet (IRE)—
    Billie Bailey (USA) (Mister Baileys) (22262) **The Granite Partnership**
86 **INNOCENT SPLENDOUR,** b f 26/2 Mtoto—
    Maureena (IRE) (Grand Lodge (USA)) (18000) **The Granite Partnership**
87 **INSHAAD (IRE),** b f 3/2 Alhaarth (IRE)—Jedwa (IRE) (Lead On Time (USA)) (85000) **Mr Hamdan Al Maktoum**
88 B c 6/3 Orpen (USA)—Joyfullness (USA) (Dixieland Band (USA)) (8000) **The Serendipity Partnership**
89 Ch c 17/3 Grand Lodge (USA)—Kardelle (Kalaglow) (110000) **Mr Ahmed BuHaleeba**
90 B f 10/2 Inchinor—Lady Abigail (IRE) (Royal Academy (USA)) (8039) **The Serendipity Partnership**
91 **LAKE NIPIGON,** b f 14/3 Selkirk (USA)—Hawait Al Barr (Green Desert (USA)) **Maktoum Al Maktoum**
92 **LALAPANZI (USA),** ch f 17/4 Diesis—Yazeanhaa (Zilzal (USA)) **Maktoum Al Maktoum**
93 **LATE RUSH (USA),** b f 31/3 Broad Brush (USA)—Cumulate (USA) (Gone West (USA)) **Maktoum Al Maktoum**
94 **MOSTANAD,** b c 12/2 Alhaarth (IRE)—Jeed (IRE) (Mujtahid (USA)) **Mr Hamdan Al Maktoum**
95 B f 2/3 Dr Fong (USA)—Odette (Pursuit of Love) (125000) **Mr Abdulla BuHaleeba**
96 **PACIFIC STAR (IRE),** b c 14/4 Tagula (IRE)—Acidanthera (Alzao (USA)) (18552) **The Jaspar Partnership**
97 B f 2/3 Indian Danehill (IRE)—Peig Sayers (IRE) (Royal Academy (USA)) (5000) **Mr Edward Dunlop**
98 **POLISH EAGLE,** b c 14/1 Polish Precedent—Tinashaan (IRE) (Darshaan) (60000) **Hesmonds Stud**
99 **QAWAAFIL (USA),** b f 13/2 Intidab (USA)—Indihash (USA) (Gulch (USA)) **Mr Hamdan Al Maktoum**
100 **RAPID ROMANCE (USA),** b f 15/5 Theatrical—Fast Nellie (USA) (Ack Ack (USA)) **Maktoum Al Maktoum**
101 **RED RACKETEER (USA),** b c 1/5 Red Ransom (USA)—
    Furajet (USA) (The Minstrel (CAN)) **Maktoum Al Maktoum**
102 **ROAD RAGE (IRE),** b f 18/1 Giant's Causeway—Endorsement (Warning) **Cliveden Stud**
103 **ROAD TO HEAVEN (USA),** ch c 7/3 Southern Halo (USA)—
    Glory Way (USA) (Woodman (USA)) (65476) **Hesmonds Stud**
104 **SEYAADI,** b c 20/1 Intikhab (USA)—Sioux Chef (Be My Chief) (55000) **Mr Hamdan Al Maktoum**
105 **SHARABY (IRE),** b f 26/3 Cadeaux Genereux—Shawanni (Shareef Dancer (USA)) **Maktoum Al Maktoum**
106 **SHINE A LIGHT (USA),** ch f 27/2 Diesis—Moonshine Girl (USA) (Shadeed (USA)) **Saeed Maktoum Al Maktoum**
107 **SILVER BARK,** b f 26/1 Royal Applause—Agent du Bois (USA) (Silver Hawk (USA)) **Hesmonds Stud**
108 **SPRING CHARM (IRE),** ch f 4/3 Inchinor—Arabis (Arazi (USA)) **Cliveden Stud**
109 **TARABUT,** b f 19/2 Green Desert (USA)—Nbadhaat (USA) (Mr Prospector (USA)) **Mr Hamdan Al Maktoum**
110 **TARANTULA (USA),** ch f 11/2 Namid—Esquiline (USA) (Gone West (USA)) (11131) **The Jaspar Partnership**
111 B c 1/5 Green Desert (USA)—Ta Rib (USA) (Mr Prospector (USA)) **Mr Hamdan Al Maktoum**
112 **TESARY,** b f 9/4 Danehill (USA)—Baldemara (FR) (Sanglamore (USA)) **Mr Khalifa Sultan**
113 **TOP FORM (IRE),** b f 27/3 Almutawakel—
    Top of The Form (IRE) (Masterclass (USA)) (40000) **Ors, Woods, Weatherby, Davies & Stone**
114 **TRIPLE TWO,** ch f 2/2 Pivotal—Tara's Girl (Fayruz) (12000) **Cheveley Park Stud**
115 **ZAHEYAH,** gr f 16/2 Dansili—Arinaga (Warning) (55000) **Mr Mohammed Jaber**

Other Owners: Lady Burrell, Mr G. Campbell, Mr R. Channing, Mr J. Davies, Sir Alex Ferguson, Mr D. Gold, Mr C. Gordon-Watson, Miss L. Hatch, Mr C. Kilroy, Mr K. Mercer, Mr M. Mitchell, Mr P. Morgan, Mr M. Newcombe, Mr S. Purdew, Mr G. Ramsay, Mr D. Roberts, Mrs L. Spencer, Lord Spens, Mr A. Stone, Mr J. Strauss, Mr A. Stroud, Mr J. Weatherby, Mr J. Wills, Mr D. Woods, Mr W. Wyatt.

Assistant Trainer: William Knight

169 **MR J. L. DUNLOP, Arundel**
Postal: **Castle Stables, Arundel, West Sussex, BN18 9AB.**
Contact: PHONE (01903) 882194 FAX (01903) 884173
E-MAIL jldunlop@enta.net WEBSITE www.jldunlop.co.uk

1 **AJEEL (IRE)**, 5, b g Green Desert (USA)—Samheh (USA) **Mr Hamdan Al Maktoum**
2 **ALBANOV (IRE)**, 4, b c Sadler's Wells (USA)—Love For Ever (IRE) **Mr Michael H. Watt**
3 **ALMUTASADER**, 4, b c Sadler's Wells (USA)—Dreamawhile **Mr Hamdan Al Maktoum**
4 **BENEVENTA**, 4, b f Most Welcome—Dara Dee **Mr R. N. Khan**
5 **BIG BAD BOB (IRE)**, 4, br c Bob Back (USA)—Fantasy Girl (IRE) **Windflower Overseas Holdings Inc**
6 **CARA FANTASY (IRE)**, 4, b f Sadler's Wells (USA)—Gay Fantasy **Windflower Overseas Holdings Inc**
7 **CHANCELLOR (IRE)**, 6, ch h Halling (USA)—Isticanna (USA) **Mr M. J. Al-Qatami**
8 **DANDOUN**, 6, b h Halling (USA)—Moneefa **H.R.H. Prince A. A. Faisal**
9 **EMTEE**, 4, b g Hector Protector (USA)—Moneefa **Mr J. L. Dunlop**
10 **EXCELSIUS (IRE)**, 4, ch c Dr Devious (IRE)—Folgore (USA) **Mr Vito Schirone**
11 **HARLESTONE GREY**, 6, gr g Shaamit (USA)—Harlestone Lake **Mr J. L. Dunlop**
12 **HEIR TO BE**, 5, b g Elmaamul (USA)—Princess Genista **I. H. Stewart-Brown**
13 **IMPERSONATOR**, 4, b g Zafonic (USA)—Conspiracy **Earl Cadogan**
14 **LARGO (IRE)**, 4, ch f Selkirk (USA)—Lady of The Lake **Capt. J. MacDonald-Buchanan**
15 **MAGHANIM**, 4, b c Nashwan (USA)—Azdihaar (USA) **Mr Hamdan Al Maktoum**
16 **MILLENARY**, 7, b h Rainbow Quest (USA)—Ballerina (IRE) **Mr L. Neil Jones**
17 **MUQBIL (USA)**, 4, ch c Swain (IRE)—Istiqlal (USA) **Mr Hamdan Al Maktoum**
18 **NOFA'S MAGIC (IRE)**, 4, b f Rainbow Quest (USA)—Garah **H.R.H. Prince A. A. Faisal**
19 **PERSIAN LIGHTNING (IRE)**, 5, b g Sri Pekan (USA)—Persian Fantasy **Windflower Overseas Holdings Inc**
20 **PHOTOFIT**, 4, b g Polish Precedent (USA)—Photogenic **Nicholas Cooper**
21 **PRINCE TUM TUM (USA)**, 4, br c Capote (USA)—La Grande Epoque (USA) **Mr Robin F. Scully**
22 **STOOP TO CONQUER**, 4, b g Polar Falcon (USA)—Princess Genista **I. H. Stewart-Brown**
23 **TERESA**, 4, b f Darshaan—Morina (USA) **Sir Eric Parker**

THREE-YEAR-OLDS

24 **ALALOOF**, b f Swain (IRE)—Alattrah (USA) **Mr Hamdan Al Maktoum**
25 **AL BEEDAA (USA)**, ch f Swain (IRE)—Histoire (FR) **Mr Hamdan Al Maktoum**
26 **ALSHAWAMEQ (IRE)**, b g Green Desert (USA)—Azdihaar (USA) **Mr Hamdan Al Maktoum**
27 **ALYOUSUFEYA (IRE)**, ch f Kingmambo (USA)—Musicale (USA) **Mr Hamdan Al Maktoum**
28 **ARTIST RIFLE (IRE)**, b c Orpen (USA)—Rosy Scintilla (IRE) **Mr J. L. Dunlop**
29 **ASHWAAQ (USA)**, b f Gone West (USA)—Wasnah (USA) **Mr Hamdan Al Maktoum**
30 **BAFFLE**, b f Selkirk (USA)—Elude **Plantation Stud**
31 **CAMROSE**, ch c Selkirk (USA)—Tularosa **Mr Nicholas Cooper**
32 **CHANTERELLE (IRE)**, ch f Indian Ridge—Chantereine (USA) **Mr Nicholas Cooper**
33 **CHAPELCO**, b c Robellino (USA)—Lady Kris (IRE) **J. L. Dunlop**
34 **CORPS DE BALLET (IRE)**, b f Fasliyev (USA)—Dwell (USA) **Mrs P. G. M. Jamison**
35 **COVENTINA (IRE)**, gr f Daylami (IRE)—Lady of The Lake **Capt. J. MacDonald-Buchanan**
36 **FLYING ADORED**, b f Polar Falcon (USA)—Shining High **Mrs M. Burrell**
37 **FOREVER FANTASY (IRE)**, b g Daylami (IRE)—Gay Fantasy **Windflower Overseas Holdings Inc**
38 **GOODWOOD FINESSE (IRE)**, b f Revoque (IRE)—
                          Key To Paris (ARG) **Goodwood Racehorse Owners Group (Nine)**
39 **GRETNA**, ch f Groom Dancer (USA)—Llia **Capt. J. MacDonald-Buchanan**
40 **GROWLER**, ch g Foxhound (USA)—Femme Femme (USA) **Mr P. D. Player**
41 **HASAYIS**, b f Danehill (USA)—Intiza (USA) **Mr Hamdan Al Maktoum**
42 **HATHRAH (IRE)**, gr f Linamix (FR)—Zivania (IRE) **Mr Hamdan Al Maktoum**
43 **HEZAAM (IRE)**, b c Red Ransom (USA)—Ashraakat (USA) **Mr Hamdan Al Maktoum**
44 **IQTE SAAB (USA)**, b c Bahri (USA)—Shuhrah (USA) **Mr Hamdan Al Maktoum**
45 **JEDBURGH**, b c Selkirk (USA)—Conspiracy **The Earl Cadogan**
46 **KARAMEA (SWI)**, gr f Rainbow Quest (USA)—Karapucha (IRE) **Mrs S. Egloff**
47 **KODIAC**, b c Danehill (USA)—Rafha **Prince A. A. Faisal**
48 **KRISTAL'S DREAM (IRE)**, b f Night Shift (USA)—Kristal's Paradise (IRE) **Windflower Overseas Holdings Inc**
49 **LAWAAHEB (IRE)**, b c Alhaarth (IRE)—Ajayib (USA) **Mr Hamdan Al Maktoum**
50 **LET THE LION ROAR**, b c Sadler's Wells (USA)—Ballerina (IRE) **Mr L. Neil Jones**
51 **LITTLE LONDON**, b g Bahhare (USA)—North Kildare (USA) **Eurolink Group P.L.C.**
52 **LITTLESTAR (IRE)**, b c Robellino (USA)—Green Charter **Mr Benny Andersson**
53 **LOLA LOLA (IRE)**, b f Piccolo—French Gift **Raymond Tooth**
54 **LUCKY AGAIN (IRE)**, br g Be My Guest (USA)—Persian Fantasia **Windflower Overseas Holdings Inc**
55 **MAALOOF**, b c A P Indy (USA)—Alabaq (USA) **Mr Hamdan Al Maktoum**
56 **MADAEH (USA)**, b f Swain (IRE)—Tamgeed (USA) **Mr Hamdan Al Maktoum**
57 **MAID TO TREASURE (IRE)**, b f Rainbow Quest (IRE)—Maid For The Hills **Mrs Philippa Cooper**
58 **MANGO MISCHIEF (IRE)**, ch f Desert King (IRE)—Eurolink Mischief **The Antoniades Family**

MR J. L. DUNLOP—continued

59 **MAYAGUANA**, b f Bahamian Bounty—Madurai **Mr J. L. Dunlop**
60 **MOTU (IRE)**, b g Desert Style (IRE)—Pink Cashmere (IRE) **Mrs M. E. Slade**
61 **MUHAYMIN (USA)**, ch c A P Indy (USA)—Shadayid (USA) **Mr Hamdan Al Maktoum**
62 **MUKAFEH (USA)**, b c Danzig (USA)—Bint Salsabil (USA) **Mr Hamdan Al Maktoum**
63 **MUSTAKHLAS (USA)**, ch c Diesis—Katiba (USA) **Mr Hamdan Al Maktoum**
64 **MUTAHAYYA (IRE)**, b c Peintre Celebre (USA)—Winsa (USA) **Mr Hamdan Al Maktoum**
65 **NATALIYA**, b f Green Desert (USA)—Ninotchka (USA) **Miss K. Rausing**
66 **PENNY STALL**, b f Silver Patriarch (IRE)—Madiyla **Bloomsbury Stud**
67 **PERSIAN DAGGER (IRE)**, b c Daylami (IRE)—Persian Fantasy **Windflower Overseas Holdings Inc**
68 **POULE DE LUXE (IRE)**, b f Cadeaux Genereux—Likely Story (IRE) **D. K. Thorpe/ Susan Abbott Racing**
69 **PROTECTING HEIGHTS (IRE)**, br g Hector Protector (USA)—
Height of Fantasy (IRE) **Windflower Overseas Holdings Inc**
70 **PURR**, b g Pursuit of Love—Catawba **Plantation Stud**
71 **RACE THE ACE**, b g First Trump—Princess Genista **Mr I. H. Stewart-Brown**
72 **RAVE REVIEWS (IRE)**, b g Sadler's Wells (USA)—Pieds de Plume (FR) **H.R.H. Prince A. A. Faisal**
73 **ROSSALL POINT**, b g Fleetwood (IRE)—Loch Clair (IRE) **J. L. Dunlop**
74 **RUMBLING BRIDGE**, ch g Air Express (IRE)—Rushing River (USA) **Earl Cadogan**
75 **SANTA CATERINA (IRE)**, b f Daylami (IRE)—Samara (IRE) **Nigel & Carolyn Elwes**
76 **SNOW GOOSE**, b f Polar Falcon (USA)—Bronzewing **Sir Thomas Pilkington**
77 **SPOTLIGHT**, ch f Dr Fong (USA)—Dust Dancer **Hesmonds Stud Ltd**
78 **SWAGGER STICK (USA)**, gr c Cozzene (USA)—Regal State (USA) **Mr Robin F. Scully**
79 **THAJJA (IRE)**, b c Daylami (IRE)—Jawlaat (USA) **Mr Hamdan Al Maktoum**
80 **TIZI OUZOU (IRE)**, ch f Desert Prince (IRE)—Tresor (USA) **Mr E. Puerari**
81 **TRULLITTI (IRE)**, b f Bahri (USA)—Penza **Mrs S. Rogers**
82 **ZAQRAH (USA)**, b f Silver Hawk (USA)—Istiqlal (USA) **Mr Hamdan Al Maktoum**

TWO-YEAR-OLDS

83 **AHDAAF (USA)**, b f 23/2 Bahri (USA)—Ashraakat (USA) (Danzig (USA)) **Mr Hamdan Al Maktoum**
84 **ALPINE GOLD (IRE)**, b f 3/5 Montjeu (IRE)—Ski For Gold (Shirley Heights) **Windflower Overseas Holdings Inc**
85 B c 11/3 Second Empire (IRE)—Ar Hyd Y Knos (Alzao (USA)) (5000) **Harry Dunlop Racing Partnership**
86 **ASAATEEL (IRE)**, br c 11/4 Unfuwain (USA)—Alabaq (USA) (Riverman (USA)) **Mr Hamdan Al Maktoum**
87 Ch c 11/5 In The Wings—Azyaa (Kris) (21000) **Eurostrait Ltd**
88 **BADDAM**, b c 26/3 Mujahid (USA)—Aude La Belle (FR) (Ela-Mana-Mou) (15000) **Mr N. Martin**
89 **BEFORE TIME**, ch c 24/2 Giant's Causeway—Original Spin (IRE) (Machiavellian (USA)) (75000) **Mr R. Barnett**
90 **BERTROSE**, ch c 2/3 Machiavellian (USA)—Tularosa (In The Wings) **Mr Nicholas Cooper**
91 **BOBSPIN (IRE)**, gr b 23/1 Namid—Bobbydazzle (Rock Hopper) (65000) **Hesmonds Stud Ltd**
92 Ch c 24/4 Selkirk (USA)—Breadcrumb (Final Straw) (15000)
93 **CASSYDORA**, b f 28/2 Darshaan—Claxon (Caerleon (USA)) **Hesmonds Stud Ltd**
94 B c 30/1 Nashwan (USA)—Conspiracy (Rudimentary (USA)) (60000) **Earl Cadogan**
95 **COUP D'ETAT**, b c 27/3 Diktat—Megdale (FR) (Waajib) **Susan Abbott Racing**
96 **DANCINGINTHECLOUDS (IRE)**, b f 9/4 Rainbow Quest (USA)—
Ballerina (IRE) (Dancing Brave (USA)) **Mr L. Neil Jones**
97 **DAWN'S LAST SHOT (IRE)**, b c 11/3 Son Of Sharp Shot—
Dawn Star (High Line) **Windflower Overseas Holdings Inc**
98 B c 15/3 Lear Fan (USA)—Dippers (Polish Numbers (USA)) **Mr O. Murphy**
99 **DISH DASH (IRE)**, b c 22/3 Desert Style (IRE)—Entracte (Henbit (USA)) (30920) **Mr P. L. Wroughton**
100 **DOWNLAND (USA)**, gr f 2/4 El Prado (IRE)—Quelle Affaire (USA) (Riverman (USA)) **Mr R. F. Scully**
101 **EBTIKAAR (IRE)**, b c 1/5 Darshaan—Jawlaat (USA) (Dayjur (USA)) **Mr Hamdan Al Maktoum**
102 Ch c 18/5 Almutawakel—Eschasse (USA) (Zilzal (USA)) (15000)
103 **FALSAFI**, b c 5/2 Royal Applause—Hoh Dancer (Indian Ridge) (240000) **Mr Hamdan Al Maktoum**
104 **FANTASIA'S FOREST (IRE)**, b f 17/3 Shinko Forest (IRE)—
Persian Fantasia (Alzao (USA)) **Windflower Overseas Holdings Inc**
105 **FANTASTIC LUCK (IRE)**, b c 20/4 Josr Algarhoud (IRE)—
Fantastic Fantasy (Lahib (USA)) **Windflower Overseas Holdings Inc**
106 **FARDI (IRE)**, b c 26/4 Green Desert (USA)—Shuruk (Cadeaux Genereux) **Mr Hamdan Al Maktoum**
107 **FLAG POINT (IRE)**, b c 4/4 Indian Danehill (IRE)—
Bianca Cappello (IRE) (Glenstal (USA)) (18000) **Mrs S. Boscawen**
108 **GASSAEAD (USA)**, ch f 22/5 Aljabr (USA)—Histoire (FR) (Riverman (USA)) **Mr Hamdan Al Maktoum**
109 **GIFTED MUSICIAN (IRE)**, b c 7/3 Sadler's Wells (USA)—Photogenic (Midyan (USA)) **Mr Nicholas Cooper**
110 **GINGIEFLY**, b c 9/2 Sinndar (IRE)—Native Ring (FR) (Bering) (15000) **Mr N. Martin**
111 **GOLDEN FURY (IRE)**, b c 18/2 Cadeaux Genereux—Galaxie Dust (USA) (Blushing Groom (USA)) **Hesmonds Stud Ltd**
112 **GOODWOOD SPIRIT**, b c 6/3 Fraam—
Rechanit (IRE) (Local Suitor (USA)) (28000) **Goodwood Racehorse Owners Group (Ten)**
113 **HADDAAF (USA)**, b c 15/3 Kingmambo—Bint Salsabil (USA) (Nashwan (USA)) **Mr Hamdam Al Maktoum**
114 Ch g 3/5 Erhaab (USA)—Harlestone Lake (Riboboy (USA)) **Mr J. L. Dunlop**

MR J. L. DUNLOP—continued

115 **HEAT OF THE NIGHT,** b f 12/5 Lear Fan (USA)—Hot Thong (BRZ) (Jarraar (USA)) **Miss K. Rausing**
116 **ISSA,** b f 21/4 Pursuit of Love—Catawba (Mill Reef (USA)) **Plantation Stud**
117 **KARLU (GER),** ch c 1/2 Big Shuffle (USA)—Krim (GER) (Lagunas) (32000) **Pat Eddery Racing**
118 **KINDA (FR),** bl f 20/4 Desert King (IRE)—Moneefa (Darshaan) **H.R.H. Prince A. A. Faisal**
119 **KONG (IRE),** b c 19/2 Sadler's Wells (USA)—Hill of Snow (Reference Point) **Mr L. Neil Jones**
120 Ch f 3/4 Grand Lodge (USA)—Koniya (USA) (Doyoun) **Mrs P. G. M. Jamison**
121 **LADEENA (IRE),** b f 20/2 Dubai Millennium—Aqaarid (USA) (Nashwan (USA)) **Mr Hamdan Al Maktoum**
122 B f 4/2 Zafonic (USA)—Llyn Gwynant (Persian Bold) **Capt. J. MacDonald-Buchanan**
123 B f 14/3 Danzero (AUS)—Madurai (Chilibang) **Mr J. L. Dunlop**
124 **MAKAASED (IRE),** br c 10/4 Erhaab (USA)—
　　　　Khawater (USA) (Silver Hawk (USA)) (50000) **Mr Hamdan Al Maktoum**
125 B f 6/3 Mtoto—Missed Again (High Top) **Capt. J. MacDonald-Buchanan**
126 **MODRAJ,** b f 27/4 Machiavellian (USA)—Saleela (USA) (Nureyev (USA)) **Mr Hamdan Al Maktoum**
127 **MOKARABA,** ch f 18/2 Unfuwain (USA)—Muhaba (USA) (Mr Prospector (USA)) **Mr Hamdan Al Maktoum**
128 **MOTARASSED,** b c 1/4 Green Desert (USA)—
　　　　Sayedati Eljamilah (USA) (Mr Prospector (USA)) **Mr Hamdan Al Maktoum**
129 **MPENZI,** b f 12/1 Groom Dancer (USA)—Muschana (Deploy) **Nigel & Carolyn Elwes**
130 **MUNSEF,** b c 18/3 Zafonic (USA)—Mazaya (IRE) (Sadler's Wells (USA)) **Mr Hamdan Al Maktoum**
131 **MURAABET,** b c 5/3 Dubai Millennium—Mahasin (USA) (Danzig (USA)) **Mr Hamdan Al Maktoum**
132 **MUSEEB (USA),** b c 8/5 Danzig (USA)—Elle Seule (USA) (Exclusive Native (USA)) **Mr Hamdan Al Maktoum**
133 **MUTAMAASEK (USA),** b c 19/3 Swain (IRE)—Tamgeed (USA) (Woodman (USA)) **Mr Hamdan Al Maktoum**
134 **NAZAAHA (USA),** gr f 5/2 Elnadim (USA)—Taatof (IRE) (Lahib (USA)) **Mr Hamdan Al Maktoum**
135 **PEEPTOE (IRE),** ch f 25/3 Machiavellian (USA)—Alfaguara (USA) (Red Ransom (USA)) (92763) **Mr G. Clark**
136 **PILLARS OF WISDOM,** ch c 26/4 Desert Prince (IRE)—
　　　　Eurolink Mischief (Be My Chief (USA)) **The Antoniades Family**
137 **QUEEN OF ICENI,** b f 14/4 Erhaab (USA)—Princess Genista (Ile de Bourbon (USA)) **Mr I. H. Stewart-Brown**
138 **SABBIOSA (IRE),** b f 7/3 Desert Prince (IRE)—Alla Marcia (USA) (Marju (IRE)) (22000) **Susan Abbott Racing**
139 **SANAD (USA),** ch c 30/4 Kingmambo—
　　　　Caerless (IRE) (Caerleon (USA)) (100000) **Mr Hamdan Al Maktoum**
140 **SCARLET INVADER (IRE),** b c 1/2 Indian Ridge—Scarlet Plume (Warning) (27000) **Mr P. L. Wroughton**
141 **SCENT,** b f 13/5 Groom Dancer (USA)—Sweet Pea (Persian Bold) **Mr N. M. H. Jones**
142 B g 8/4 Mtoto—Shibui (Shirley Heights) (13000) **Mr J. L. Dunlop**
143 **SILVER SONG,** gr c 20/2 Silver Patriarch—
　　　　Singing The Blues (Bonny Scot (IRE)) **Emmanuel & Neighbour Partnership**
144 **SOLOZAIDA (IRE),** ch f 18/2 Singspiel (IRE)—Messila Rose (Darshaan) (28000) **Lady Mary Manton**
145 **SPANISH RIDGE (IRE),** b c 18/3 Indian Ridge—Spanish Lady (IRE) (Bering) **Windflower Overseas Holdings Inc**
146 **TEEBA (USA),** ch f 27/4 Seeking The Gold—Shadayid (USA) (Shadeed (USA)) **Mr Hamdan Al Maktoum**
147 **THAKAFAAT (IRE),** b f 11/2 Unfuwain (USA)—Frappe (IRE) (Inchinor) (160000) **Mr Hamdan Al Maktoum**
148 **TOHAMA,** b f 31/1 In The Wings—Tanouma (USA) (Miswaki (USA)) **H.R.H. Prince A. A. Faisal**
149 **TOMBOLA (FR),** b c 12/4 Trempolino (USA)—Green Charter (Green Desert (USA)) **Mr B. Andersson**
150 **UNFURLED (IRE),** ch c 5/4 Unfuwain (USA)—Peony (Lion Cavern (USA)) (85000) **Mrs M. Slade**
151 **USTAD (IRE),** b c 28/2 Giant's Causeway—Winsa (USA) (Riverman (USA)) **Mr Hamdan Al Maktoum**
152 **VELVET HEIGHTS (IRE),** b c 21/3 Barathea (IRE)—
　　　　Height of Fantasy (IRE) (Shirley Heights) **Windflower Overseas Holdings Inc**
153 B c 5/4 Mister Baileys—War Shanty (Warrshan (USA)) (10000) **Harry Dunlop Racing Partnership**
154 **WUJOUD,** b c 9/3 Alzao (USA)—Rahayeb (USA) (Kris) **Mr Hamdan Al Maktoum**
155 **YANTRA,** ch f 19/3 Indian Ridge—Divine Quest (Kris) **Plantation Stud**

Other Owners: Mrs D. Abbott, Mrs Afaf Alessa, Sheikh Ahmad Yousuf Al Sabah, Mr Hamad A. Alsumait, Mr W. Armitage, Mr A. Bahbahani, Mr James Barber, Mr D. Bingley, Miss J. Bradford, Mr I. D. Cameron, Mr W. P. Churchward, Lord & Lady Clarendon, Mr N. Clark, Mrs H. Croker-Poole, Mr J. Darby, Mrs L. Darling, Mrs A. Finn, Mr J. Flower, Mr G. Galazka, Mrs L. Godbere-Dooley, Lord Nicholas Gordon-Lennox, Mr N. Graham, Mr A. Grazebrook, Mr J. Hughes, Mr G. Landau, Sir Nevil Macready, Mr M. J. Meacock, Mr K. Al-Mudaf, Mr Tareq Al-Mazeedi, Mr F. Packard, Sir P Payne-Gallwey, Mr E. Perry, Sir Michael Pickard, Capt A. Pratt, Mr L. Reed, Mr T. Ricketts, G. Roddick, Miss D. Shirley, The Hon Sir David Sieff, Mr M. Stevenson, Mr A. J. Struthers, Mr M. Sugden, Mr D. Thorpe, Mr P Townsend, Mr E. S. Tudor-Evans, Mr I. De Wesselow, Mr T. Wilson.

Assistant Trainer: Robert Allcock & Harry Dunlop

170 MRS C. A. DUNNETT, Norwich

Postal: **College Farm, Hingham, Norwich, Norfolk, NR9 4PP.**
Contact: **PHONE (01953) 850596 FAX (01953) 851364 MOBILE (07775) 793523**
E-MAIL **christine.dunnett@lineone.net**

1 BREEZY BUY, 5, gr g Terimon—Wordy's Wind **Mr L. Wordingham**
2 GONE'N'DUNNETT (IRE), 5, b g Petardia—Skerries Bell **College Farm Thoroughbreds**
3 KENNINGTON, 4, ch g Compton Place—Mim **Mr Andy Middleton**
4 MR MALARKEY (IRE), 4, b g Pivotal—Girl Next Door **Mr T. S. Child & Partners**
5 SEAN'S MEMORY (USA), 4, b g Theatrical—Memories (IRE) **Mrs Christine Dunnett**
6 TATA NAKA, 4, ch f Nashwan (USA)—Overcast (IRE) **Mr Andy Middleton**
7 WARDEN WARREN, 6, b g Petong—Silver Spell **Annwell Inn Syndicate**
8 WONDER BROOK, 4, b f Alderbrook—Wordy's Wonder **Mr L. Wordingham**

THREE-YEAR-OLDS

9 ABSOLUTELY FAB (IRE), ch f Entrepreneur—Hamama (USA) **The Star Seekers**
10 CAPTAIN FEARLESS, ch g Defacto (USA)—Madam Poppy **The Daydreamers**
11 B g Spectrum (IRE)—College Night (IRE) **Mrs Christine Dunnett**
12 DUNNETT AGAIN (IRE), b g Petardia—Pat Said No (IRE) **Mrs Christine Dunnett**
13 HE'S A ROCKET (IRE), b g Indian Rocket—Dellua (IRE) **Mrs Christine Dunnett**
14 PARDON MOI, ch f First Trump—Mystical Song **Mr Andy Middleton**
15 SHIFTY NIGHT (IRE), b f Night Shift (USA)—Bean Island (USA) **Mr G. Price**

TWO-YEAR-OLDS

16 Ch g 16/3 Pivotal—Red Typhoon (Belfort (FR)) (4500)
17 B g 27/4 Indian Rocket—Soviet Girl (IRE) (Soviet Star (USA)) (4100)
18 B g 15/3 Vettori (IRE)—Starfida (Soviet Star (USA)) (1500)
19 Ch f 25/5 Bahamian Bounty—Try Vickers (USA) (Fuzzbuster (USA)) (1800)

Other Owners: Mr R. A. Botham, Mr G. Bromley, Mr M. L. Clements, Mr B. Day, Mr O. Nugent, Mr S. Stringer, Mr T. Watts.

171 MR C. A. DWYER, Newmarket

Postal: **Cedar Lodge Racing Stables, Hamilton Road, Newmarket, Suffolk, CB8 0NQ.**
Contact: **OFFICE & FAX (01638) 667857 MOBILE (07831) 579844 HOME (01638) 668869**
E-MAIL **Getadwyer@aol.com**

1 GENTLE RESPONSE, 4, b f Puissance—Sweet Whisper **Mr G. Hale**
2 MADHAHIR (IRE), 4, b c Barathea (IRE)—Gharam (USA) **Mr M M Foulger, Mr I Dodd, Mr G Darrall**
3 RASID (USA), 6, b g Bahri—Makadir (USA) **Mr David L. Bowkett**
4 RIPPLE EFFECT, 4, ch f Elmaamul (USA)—Sharp Chief **Miss Lilo Blum**
5 TRUSTED INSTINCT (IRE), 4, b c Polish Precedent (USA)—Trust In Luck (IRE) **Cedar Lodge 2000 Syndicate**
6 WILLHEWIZ, 4, b c Wizard King—Leave It To Lib **Mrs C. Goode**

THREE-YEAR-OLDS

7 GLENDALE, ch g Opening Verse (USA)—Kayartis **Mrs J. A. Cornwell**
8 TOP PLACE, b f Compton Place—Double Top **Mr M. M. Foulger & Mrs S. Dwyer**
9 WHO'S WINNING (IRE), ch g Docksider (USA)—Quintellina **Casino Racing Partnership**

TWO-YEAR-OLDS

10 B g 30/4 Loup Sauvage (USA)—Blessed Event (Kings Lake (USA)) (14000) **The Vintage Group**
11 B c 1/3 Trans Island—Flimmering (Dancing Brave (USA)) (14841) **Blake & Wait Ltd**
12 B f 30/4 Tipsy Creek (USA)—Habibi (Alhijaz) (5000) **Mrs Shelley Dwyer**
13 B f 27/4 Cape Cross (IRE)—Lady At War (Warning) (6801) **S B Components (International) Ltd**
14 Ch c 26/3 Wolfhound (USA)—Niggle (Night Shift (USA)) (4600) **Mr Arashan Ali**
15 B f 14/2 Royal Applause—Thicket (Wolfhound (USA)) (12000) **Mr P. & Mrs A. Venner**

Assistant Trainer: Shelley Dwyer

Jockey (Flat): N Callan (w.a.).

172 MR S. A. EARLE, Marlborough

Postal: **Fox Twitchen, East Kennett, Marlborough, Wiltshire, SN8 4EY.**
Contact: **PHONE (01672) 861157 FAX (01672) 861157 MOBILE (07850) 350116**
E-MAIL simon@simonearleracing.com WEBSITE www.simonearleracing.com

1 **CAP CLASSIQUE**, 5, b g Classic Cliche (IRE)—Champenoise **Lovely Bubbly Racing**
2 **CLOUDY SKY (IRE)**, 8, b g Sadler's Wells (USA)—Dancing Shadow
3 **IMPULSIVO**, 4, ch g Millkom—Joytime **Mrs E. W. Pegna**
4 **KAVI (IRE)**, 4, ch g Perugino (USA)—Premier Leap (IRE) **Mr E. Wilmott**
5 **LOVE MAIL**, 6, b m Pursuit of Love—Wizardry **Mr A. Galvin**
6 **LOYOLA**, 4, ch f New Reputation—Stay With Me **Miss R. Wakeford**
7 **MISS WIZADORA**, 9, ch m Gildoran—Lizzie The Twig **Miss Jenny Grant**
8 **NORTHERN VALENTINE**, 6, b g Alflora (IRE)—Northern Jinks
9 **SAUCY NIGHT**, 8, ch g Anshan—Kiss In The Dark **Mr E. Wilmott**
10 **SILENT DREAM**, 6, b g Alflora (IRE)—Silent Surrender
11 **STAROSKI**, 7, b m Petoski—Olnistar (FR) **Mr E. Wilmott**
12 **TIME BOMB**, 7, b m Great Commotion (USA)—Play For Time

Other Owners: Dr M. J. O'Brien, Mr R. Rosenberg.

Jockey (NH): S Earle (11-0).

173 MR M. W. EASTERBY, Sheriff Hutton

Postal: **New House Farm, Sheriff Hutton, York, North Yorkshire, YO60 6TN.**
Contact: **PHONE (01347) 878368 FAX (01347) 878204 MOBILE (07831) 347481**

1 **ACOMB**, 4, b g Shaamit (IRE)—Aurora Bay (IRE) **Mr Giles W. Pritchard-Gordon**
2 **ACTUAL**, 4, b g Factual (USA)—Tugra (FR) **Mrs P. A. H. Hartley**
3 **ARAWAN (IRE)**, 4, b g Entrepreneur—Asmara (USA) **William Johnstone Racing**
4 **BELISARIO (IRE)**, 8, b g Distinctly North (USA)—Bold Kate **Mr Paul G. Jacobs**
5 **BLESSINGINDISGUISE**, 11, b g Kala Shikari—Blowing Bubbles **Mr A. G. Black**
6 **BLUE BUSTER**, 4, b g Young Buster (IRE)—Lazybird Blue (IRE) **Mr John Connor**
7 **BLUE SPINNAKER (IRE)**, 5, b g Bluebird (USA)—Suedoise **G. Sparkes G. Hart S Curtis & T Dewhirst**
8 **BROADWAY SCORE (USA)**, 6, b g Theatrical—Brocaro (USA) **Mr David Scott**
9 **BROWNINGS EXPRESS**, 5, b g Elmaamul (USA)—Chushan Venture **LPS Racing**
10 **BUTTRESS**, 5, b h Zamindar (USA)—Furnish **Lord Daresbury**
11 **CAT'S WHISKERS**, 5, b g Catrail (USA)—Haut Volee **The Four Legged Friends**
12 **CAULKLEYS BANK**, 4, b g Slip Anchor—Mayroni **Mr S. Hull**
13 **CHAPTER HOUSE (USA)**, 5, b g Pulpit (USA)—Lilian Bayliss (IRE) **Lord Daresbury**
14 **CHARLIES MEMORY**, 5, b g Blushing Flame (USA)—Hat Hill **Mr J. W. P. Curtis**
15 **COTTAM GRANGE**, 4, b c River Falls—Karminski **Mr Peter Easterby**
16 **DAYENOO (FR)**, 4, b g Subotica (FR)—La Cenomane (FR) **Mr G. H. Sparkes**
17 **DENBY (IRE)**, 4, b g Sri Pekan (USA)—Latch Key Lady **Mr David Scott**
18 **DIX BAY**, 5, b g Teenoso (USA)—Cooks Lawn **Lord Daresbury**
19 **DOUBLE DEAL**, 5, ch m Keen—Close The Deal **R. S. Cockerill (Farms) Ltd**
20 **ELVINGTON BOY**, 7, ch g Emarati (USA)—Catherines Well **Mr K. Hodgson & Mrs J. Hodgson**
21 **EMPEROR'S WELL**, 5, ch g First Trump—Catherines Well **Mr K. Hodgson & Mrs J. Hodgson**
22 **GALA SUNDAY (USA)**, 4, b g Lear Fan (USA)—Sunday Bazaar (USA) **Mr F. Murphy**
23 **GARY'S PIMPERNEL**, 5, b g Shaddad (USA)—Pennine Star (IRE) **Lord Daresbury**
24 **GASTORNIS**, 6, ch g Primitive Rising (USA)—Meggies Dene **Lord Daresbury**
25 **GOHH**, 8, ch g Alflora (IRE)—Lavenham's Last **Mrs P. A. H. Hartley**
26 **GRAFT**, 5, b g Entrepreneur—Mariakova (USA) **Mrs Jean Turpin**
27 **GROUND BREAKER**, 4, b g Emperor Jones (USA)—Startino **The Woodford Group**
28 **HILLS OF GOLD**, 5, b g Danehill (USA)—Valley of Gold (FR) **Mr G. Hart, Mr D. Scott & Mr G. Sparkes**
29 **KINGS SQUARE**, 4, b g Bal Harbour—Prime Property (IRE) **Mr A. G. Black & Mr J. E. H. Quickfall**
30 **LOUGH BOW (IRE)**, 6, b g Nicolotte—Gale Force Seven **Mrs Anne Jarvis**
31 **LUMINOUS**, 4, b f Double Eclipse (IRE)—Kilcoy (USA) **Mr G. Reed**
32 **MARSH RUN**, 5, b m Presenting—Madam Margeaux (IRE) **Mrs M. E. Curtis**
33 **MELDRUM MEG**, 4, b g Bal Harbour—Strathrusdale **Brig Racing Club**
34 **MIDDLETHORPE**, 7, b g Noble Patriarch—Prime Property (IRE) **Mr J. H. Quickfall & Mr A. G. Black**
35 **MINSTER GLORY**, 13, b g Minster Son—Rapid Glory **Mrs P. A. H. Hartley**
36 **MOONLIT HARBOUR**, 5, b g Bal Harbour—Nuit de Lune (IRE) **Mr Steve Hull**
37 **MOUNT HILLABY (IRE)**, 4, b f Mujadil (USA)—Tetradonna (IRE) **Mr D F Spence & Mr J Southway**
38 **NEW WISH (IRE)**, 4, b g Ali-Royal (IRE)—False Spring (IRE) **Mrs Angela K. Geraghty**
39 **NIGHT MAIL**, 4, b g Shaamit (IRE)—Penlanfeigan **Night Mail Partnership**
40 **NOW AND AGAIN**, 5, b g Shaamit (IRE)—Sweet Allegiance **Mrs M. E. Curtis**

MR M. W. EASTERBY—continued

41 **NOWELL HOUSE**, 8, ch g Polar Falcon (USA)—Langtry Lady **Mr John Walsh**
42 **ONE FIVE EIGHT**, 5, b g Alflora (IRE)—Dark Nightingale **Mr J. W. P. Curtis**
43 **PARKNASILLA**, 4, b g Marju (IRE)—Top Berry **Lady Bland**
44 **PRESTON BROOK**, 7, b g Perpendicular—Tommys Dream **Lord Daresbury**
45 **PRINCES THEATRE**, 6, b g Prince Sabo—Frisson **Mr M. W. Easterby**
46 **REAL SHADY**, 7, b g Bob's Return (IRE)—Madam Margeaux (IRE) **Lord Daresbury**
47 **RING OF ROSES**, 5, b m Efisio—True Ring **Mr G. Reed**
48 **ROSEDALE GARDENS**, 4, b g Fleetwood (IRE)—Freddie's Recall **David & Stephen Dudley**
49 **SCOLT HEAD**, 5, b g Bal Harbour—Curlew Calling (IRE) **Lord Daresbury**
50 4, B c Amfortas (IRE)—So Saucy **Lord Daresbury**
51 **SPORTING GESTURE**, 7, ch g Safawan—Polly Packer **Mr Steve Hull**
52 **SPORTSMAN (IRE)**, 5, b g Sri Pekan (USA)—Ardent Range (IRE) **Mr G. H. Sparkes**
53 **STRONG HAND**, 4, b f First Trump—Better Still (IRE) **Mrs Jean Turpin**
54 **SUPER NOMAD**, 9, b g Nomadic Way (USA)—Super Sue **Brian Hutchinson & David & Steven Dudley**
55 **SUPER SAMMY**, 8, br m Mesleh—Super Sue **Whitestonecliffe Racing Partnership**
56 **THE HIGHERHO**, 4, ch g Forzando—Own Free Will **Lord Daresbury**
57 **THE NOMAD**, 8, b g Nomadic Way (USA)—Bubbling **Mr S. Brewer,Mr D. Sugars & Mr B. Parker**
58 **TICKTON FLYER**, 6, b g Sovereign Water (FR)—Contradictory **Mr T. D. Rose & Mr J. S. Dale**
59 **TOP DIRHAM**, 6, ch g Night Shift (USA)—Miller's Melody **Mr Steve Hull**
60 **TROUBLE MOUNTAIN (USA)**, 7, br g Mt Livermore (USA)—Trouble Free (USA) **Mrs Jean Turpin**
61 **TSCHIERTSCHEN**, 4, ch g Master Willie—Smocking **Lord Daresbury**
62 **WE'LL MEET AGAIN**, 4, ch g Bin Ajwaad (IRE)—Tantalizing Song (CAN) **Mr Guy Reed**
63 **WESTCOURT DREAM**, 4, ch f Bal Harbour—Katie's Kitty **Mr K. Hodgson & Mrs J. Hodgson**
64 **WHATDO YOU WANT (IRE)**, 4, b f Spectrum (IRE)—Soviet Pretender (USA) **Mr G. Reed**
65 **WILLIAM'S WELL**, 4, ch g Superpower—Catherines Well **Mr K. Hodgson & Mrs J. Hodgson**

THREE-YEAR-OLDS

66 **BANK GAMES**, b c Mind Games—Piggy Bank **Graham Sparkes & Stephen Curtis**
67 **BARTON FLOWER**, br f Danzero (AUS)—Iota **Sir Stanley Clarke**
68 **EGO TRIP**, b c Deploy—Boulevard Rouge (USA) **Mr K. Hodgson & Mrs J. Hodgson**
69 **INDIAN RUM**, b g Spectrum (IRE)—Apache Squaw **Mary, Lady Manton & Mr Guy Reed**
70 **LORD ARTHUR**, b g Mind Games—Flower O'Cannie (IRE) **Mr C. F. Spence & Mrs E. Rhind**
71 **MIDNIGHT PRINCE**, b c Dracula (AUS)—Phylian **Mr K. Hodgson & Mrs J. Hodgson**
72 **MILL END TEASER**, b f Mind Games—Mill End Quest **Mr W. T. Allgood**
73 **MRS SPENCE**, b f Mind Games—Maid O'Cannie **Mr J. Wade**
74 **NAFFERTON HEIGHTS (IRE)**, b c Peintre Celebre (USA)—Gold Mist **Mr T. C. Dewhirst & Mr S. J. Curtis**
75 **NASSTAR**, b g Bal Harbour—Prime Property (IRE) **Mr A. G. Black**
76 **ORION EXPRESS**, b c Bahhare (USA)—Kaprisky (IRE) **L P S Racing**
77 **PARIS DREAMER**, b f Paris House—Stoproveritate **Mr Silvano Scanu**
78 **POACHER'S PARADISE**, ch g Inchinor—Transylvania **Mr E. A. Brook**
79 **REVERSIONARY**, b c Poyle George—Harold's Girl (FR) **Mr A. G. Black & Mr A. M. Hedley**
80 **ROYAL DISTANT (USA)**, ch f Distant View (IRE)—Encorenous (USA) **Mr R. Moore**
81 **SKY COVE**, b g Spectrum (IRE)—Aurora Bay (IRE) **Mary, Lady Manton**
82 **THE WARLEY WARRIOR**, b g Primo Dominie—Brief Glimpse (IRE) **A. Greenwood, G. Allan & S. Windle**
83 **UHURU PEAK**, ch c Bal Harbour—Catherines Well **Mr K. Hodgson & Mrs J. Hodgson**

TWO-YEAR-OLDS

84 **ANELYN'S GIFT**, ch f 1/2 Namid—Northern Bird (Interrex (CAN)) (15000) **The Woodford Group**
85 B c 22/4 Josr Algarhoud (IRE)—Boulevard Rouge (USA) (Red Ransom (USA)) **Mr & Mrs K. Hodgson**
86 Ch f 10/5 Paris House—Catherines Well (Junius (USA)) **Mr & Mrs K. Hodgson**
87 B f 16/2 Diktat—Dalu (IRE) (Dancing Brave (USA)) (21000) **Mr S. Hull**
88 **DARN BOLD**, ch f 3/5 Bold Edge—Thimbalina (Salmon Leap (USA)) (800) **Mr John E. Garrett**
89 **EMMAS VENTURE**, b f 6/3 Paris House—Emma Amour (Emarati (USA)) **Mr K. Wreglesworth**
90 Gr c 12/3 Zafonic (IRE)—Estarova (FR) (Saint Estephe (FR)) (37105) **Mr S. Hull**
91 **FLOWER POT MAN**, b c 6/2 Zaffaran (USA)—Calabria (Neltino) **Mary, Lady Manton**
92 **FOLD WALK**, ch f 27/4 Paris House—Georgia (Missed Flight) **Mr A. G. Black**
93 **FOLLY MOUNT**, b c 9/5 Anabaa (USA)—Height of Folly (Shirley Heights) (26000) **Mrs L. J. Turpin**
94 B f 14/3 Lujain (USA)—Haut Volee (Top Ville) **David & Stephen Dudley**
95 **HIGH PETERGATE (IRE)**, b f 21/3 Mujadil (USA)—Anamara (IRE) (Fairy King (USA)) (24737) **Mr S. Hull**
96 **JOSHAR**, b f 10/4 Paris House—Penny Hasset (Lochnager) **Mr F. Murphy & Mr G. Sparkes**
97 **LADY DAN (IRE)**, b f 9/2 Danzero (AUS)—Dubai Lady (Kris) (7500) **Mary, Lady Manton**
98 **LORD JOHN**, b c 1/5 Piccolo—Mahbob Dancer (FR) (Groom Dancer (USA)) (900) **Mr J. Wade**
99 B c 22/2 Mind Games—Love Letters (Pursuit of Love) (7000) **Mr G. Pritchard-Gordon**
100 **MILL END CHATEAU**, ch c 18/5 Paris House—Mill End Quest (King's Signet (USA)) **Mr W. T. Allgood**
101 **PEE JAY'S DREAM**, ch c 22/4 Vettori (IRE)—Langtry Lady (Pas de Seul) **Mr P. Bown**

MR M. W. EASTERBY—continued

102 **SELKIRK STORM (IRE)**, b c 12/2 Trans Island—Force Divine (FR) (L'Emigrant (USA)) (16000) **Morecool Racing**
103 **SNOOKERED AGAIN**, b c 8/3 Lujain (USA)—Highest Bid (FR) (Highest Honor (FR)) **Mr R. Edmonds**
104 **WOODFORD WONDER (IRE)**, b f 17/3 Xaar—Unscathed (Warning) (3200) **The Woodford Group**
105 **WORD PERFECT**, b f 27/4 Diktat—Better Still (IRE) (Glenstal (USA)) **Mrs L. J. Turpin**
106 **ZAGREUS (GER)**, gr c 7/4 Fasliyev (USA)—Zephyrine (IRE) (Highest Honor (FR)) (30000) **Mr T. Dewhirst**

Other Owners: Mr A. Bairstow, Mr P. E. Bayley, Mr S. H. J. Brewer, Mr Steve Crowley, Ms Anne Dawson, Mr P. Hampshire, Mr P. A. H. Hartley, Mr I. R. Hatton, Mr Andrew M. Hedley, Mr P. Holloway, Mr Brian Hutchinson, Mr Robert Parker, Mr D. H. S. Sugars, Mr L. C. Welburn, Mrs E. J. Wright.

Assistant Trainer: R O'Ryan

Jockeys (Flat): Dave Gibson, T Lucas (8-5). **Jockey (NH):** R McGrath. **Apprentice:** Paul Mulrennan. **Conditional:** G Carenza. **Amateur:** Mr Thomas E Greenall.

---

174 MR T. D. EASTERBY, Malton
Postal: **Habton Grange, Great Habton, Malton, North Yorkshire, YO17 6TY.**
Contact: **PHONE (01653) 668566 FAX (01653) 668621**

1 **ARTIE**, b g Whittingham (IRE)—Calamanco **Mr A. Arton**
2 **BARTON HILL**, 7, b g Nicholas Bill—Home From The Hill (IRE) **Sir Stanley Clarke**
3 **BOLLIN EDWARD**, 5, b g Timeless Times (USA)—Bollin Harriet **Sir Neil Westbrook**
4 **BOLLIN JANET**, 4, b f Sheikh Albadou—Bollin Emily **Lady Westbrook**
5 **BOLLIN JEANNIE**, 4, b f Royal Applause—Bollin Joanne **Lady Westbrook**
6 **BOURGEOIS**, 7, ch g Sanglamore (USA)—Bourbon Girl **Mr C. H. Stevens**
7 **CERTA CITO**, 4, b f Mind Games—Bollin Dorothy **K C Partnership II**
8 **COUNTY CLASSIC**, 5, b m Noble Patriarch—Cumbrian Rhapsody **Mr T. J. Benson**
9 **DAZZLING BAY**, 4, b g Mind Games—Adorable Cherub (USA) **GHMW Racing**
10 **DOE NAL RUA (IRE)**, 7, b g Mister Lord (USA)—Phardante Girl (IRE) **The G-Guck Group**
11 **EDMO HEIGHTS**, 8, ch g Keen—Bodham **Edmolift UK Ltd**
12 **EDMO YEWKAY (IRE)**, 4, b br g Sri Pekan (USA)—Mannequin (IRE) **Edmolift UK Ltd**
13 **FAYR JAG (IRE)**, 5, b g Fayruz—Lominda (IRE) **Mr Jonathan Gill**
14 **FLIGHTY FELLOW (IRE)**, 4, ch g Flying Spur (AUS)—Al Theraab (USA) **Mr T. H. Bennett**
15 **GOLDEN NUN**, 4, b f Bishop of Cashel—Amber Mill **Mr T. G. & Mrs M. E. Holdcroft**
16 **GO TECH**, 4, b g Gothenberg (IRE)—Bollin Sophie **Ryedale Partners No 4**
17 **JEEPSTAR**, 4, b g Muhtarram (USA)—Jungle Rose **Miss E. Jeeps and Partners**
18 **JUST ONE SMILE (IRE)**, 4, b f Desert Prince (IRE)—Smile Awhile (USA) **Mr Jim Blair**
19 **KENTUCKY BLUE (IRE)**, 4, b g Revoque (IRE)—Delta Town (USA) **Mr C. H. Stevens**
20 **KING'S BOUNTY**, 8, b g Le Moss—Fit For A King **Mr C. H. Stevens**
21 **KING'S PROTECTOR**, 4, b c Hector Protector (USA)—Doliouchka **Mr Joe Buzzeo**
22 **LITTLE DOCKER (IRE)**, 7, b g Vettori (IRE)—Fair Maid of Kent (USA) **Mr C. H. Stevens**
23 **LOOPY LINDA (IRE)**, 6, b g Simply Great (FR)—Albane **Mr Ron George**
24 B f Saddlers' Hall (IRE)—Loshian (IRE)
25 **MINIVET**, 9, b g Midyan (USA)—Bronzewing **Oakhill Wood Stud**
26 **MONARCH'S PURSUIT**, 10, b g Pursuit of Love—Last March **Mrs Jean P. Connew**
27 **MOON**, 5, br m Simply Great (FR)—New Broom (IRE) **Mr D. F. Sills**
28 **MOST DEFINITELY (IRE)**, 4, b g Definite Article—Unbidden Melody (USA) **Mr B. Batey**
29 **MR ALBERT (IRE)**, 5, ch g Flemensfirth (USA)—Parkroe Lady (IRE) **Mrs Jean P. Connew**
30 **RAGAMUFFIN**, 6, ch g Prince Sabo—Valldemosa **Mrs Jennifer E. Pallister**
31 **RAPHAEL**, 5, b m Perugino (USA)—Danny's Miracle **Mrs K. Arton**
32 **ROMAN MISTRESS (IRE)**, 4, ch f Titus Livius (FR)—Repique (USA) **Mr W. H. Ponsonby**
33 **SCOTTON GREEN**, 13, ch g Ardross—Grange Hill Girl **The I.B. & B.D.F. Partnership**
34 **SILVER COIN (IRE)**, 4, gr g Night Shift (USA)—Eurythmic **Mr C. H. Stevens**
35 **SILVER KNIGHT**, 6, gr g Simply Great (FR)—Hysteria **Mr C. H. Stevens**
36 **SOMNUS**, 4, b g Pivotal—Midnight's Reward **Legard Sidebottom & Sykes**
37 **STONE COLD**, 7, ch g Inchinor—Vaula **Six Diamonds Partnership**
38 **TEDSTALE (USA)**, 6, ch g Irish River (FR)—Carefree Kate (USA) **Mr M. J. Dawson**
39 **THEWHIRLINGDERVISH (IRE)**, 6, ch g Definite Article—Nomadic Dancer (IRE) **Major I. C. Straker**
40 **TOM FRUIT**, 7, b g Supreme Leader—Forever Mine (IRE) **David & Steven Dudley**
41 **TOUGH LOVE**, 5, ch g Pursuit of Love—Food of Love **The Gordon Partnership**
42 **TRIBAL DISPUTE**, 7, b g Primitive Rising (USA)—Coral Princess **Mrs Jennifer E. Pallister**
43 **TURGEONEV (FR)**, 9, gr g Turgeon (USA)—County Kerry **Mr D. F. Sills**
44 **UP TEMPO (IRE)**, 6, b g Flying Spur (AUS)—Musical Essence **Mr T. H. Bennett**
45 **WITCH'S BREW**, 7, b m Simply Great (FR)—New Broom (IRE) **Mrs Bridget Tranmer**
46 **YOUNG MR GRACE (IRE)**, 4, b c Danetime (IRE)—Maid of Mourne **Mr Norman Jackson**

MR T. D. EASTERBY—continued

THREE-YEAR-OLDS

47 ATHOLLBROSE (USA), b g Mister Baileys—Knightly Cut Up (USA) **Mrs P. D. Croft**
48 BALLYOAN BAY, b f Mind Games—Adorable Cherub (USA) **Mr W. H. Ponsonby**
49 BAY SOLITAIRE, b g Charnwood Forest (IRE)—Golden Wings (USA) **Mr D. A. West**
50 BOLLIN ANNABEL, b f King's Theatre (IRE)—Bollin Magdalene **Lady Westbrook**
51 BOLLIN ARCHIE, b c First Trump—Bollin Joanne **Sir Neil Westbrook**
52 BOLSHEVIK (IRE), b g Fasliyev (USA)—Cheviot Amble (IRE) **Sue Tindall and Hazel Lowrey**
53 CHARNOCK BATES ONE (IRE), b f Desert Sun—Fleetwood Fancy **Charnock Bates**
54 CLASSIC EVENT (IRE), ch c Croco Rouge (IRE)—Delta Town (USA) **Mr C. H. Stevens**
55 COULD SHE BE MAGIC (IRE), b f Titus Livius (FR)—Ponteilla (FR) **Mr Malcolm Caine**
56 CUMBRIAN COURAGE (IRE), b g Orpen (USA)—Bold Timing **Cumbrian Industrials Ltd**
57 DANESMEAD (IRE), b c Danehill Dancer (IRE)—Indian Honey **Susie Dicker, Hazel Lowrey & Sue Tindall**
58 DISTANT TIMES, b c Orpen (USA)—Simply Times (USA) **Times of Wigan**
59 EAGLE FEATHERS, b f Indian Ridge—Flying Squaw **Burton Agnes Stud**
60 EBORACUM (IRE), b f Alzao (USA)—Fire of London **Mr T. H. Bennett**
61 EXTREMELY RARE (IRE), b f Mark of Esteem (IRE)—Colourflash (IRE) **Mr T. H. Bennett**
62 FLASH RAM, ch g Mind Games—Just A Gem **Mr Lee Connolly**
63 GAIETY GIRL (USA), b f Swain (IRE)—Knoosh (USA) **Mr Peter C. Bourke**
64 GASPARINI (IRE), ch c Docksider (USA)—Tarjou **Mrs C. A. Hodgetts**
65 JAIPUR GAIT, b f Thowra (FR)—Dawn Gait **Mrs Ian Wills**
66 JEROME, b c Nicolotte—Mim **Mrs Janis MacPherson**
67 KENTUCKY EXPRESS, b c Air Express—Hotel California (IRE) **Mr C. H. Stevens**
68 KILLERBY NICKO, ch g Pivotal—Bit of A Tart **Mr A. Arton**
69 LOUISIADE (IRE), b g Tagula (IRE)—Titchwell Lass **Mr & Mrs W. J. Williams**
70 MIND ALERT, b g Mind Games—Bombay Sapphire **Mr T. H. Bennett**
71 MISS ELOISE, b f Efisio—Zaima (IRE) **Slatch Farm Stud**
72 MORE SLEEPERS (USA), ch c Miswaki (USA)—Brandywine Belle (USA) **The Insomniacs**
73 MRS MOH (IRE), b f Orpen (USA)—My Gray (FR) **Salifix**
74 PAY ATTENTION, b f Revoque (IRE)—Catch Me **Ryedale Partners No 6**
75 PLAUSABELLE, b f Royal Applause—Sipsi Fach **C. H. Newton Jnr Ltd**
76 PRINCESS KIOTTO, b f Desert King (IRE)—Ferghana Ma **Mr Roy Matthews**
77 RIGONZA, ch g Vettori (IRE)—Desert Nomad **Mrs Janis MacPherson**
78 ROMAN THE PARK (IRE), b f Titus Livius (FR)—Missfortuna **Middleham Park Racing II**
79 SIR GALAHAD, ch g Hector Protector (USA)—Sharpening **Mrs Jennifer E. Pallister**
80 THEATRE BELLE, b f King's Theatre (IRE)—Cumbrian Rhapsody **Divison Bell Partnership**
81 THE RIP, ch c Definite Article—Polgwynne **Major I. C. Straker**
82 TIMES REVIEW (USA), b c Crafty Prospector (USA)—Previewed (USA) **Times of Wigan**
83 WEDOWANNAGIVEUTHAT (IRE), b f Desert Prince (IRE)—Mimansa (USA) **Fastest Finger Partnership**
84 WING COLLAR, b f In The Wings—Riyoom (USA) **Mr and Mrs J. D. Cotton**

TWO-YEAR-OLDS

85 BOLLIN MICHAEL, b c Celtic Swing—Bollin Zola (Alzao (USA)) **Sir Neil Westbrook**
86 GOLDEN SQUAW, ch f 26/1 Grand Lodge (USA)—Wig Wam (IRE) (Indian Ridge) (3500) **Mrs Jean P. Connew**
87 IRISH PIPER, b c 26/3 Piccolo—Freddie's Recall (Warrshan (USA)) (15000) **Mr Maurice P. Lindsay**
88 B c 30/1 Brave Act—Lulu Island (Zafonic (USA)) (13000) **Mrs Janis MacPherson**
89 MARK YOUR CARD, ch f 20/4 Mark Of Esteem (IRE)—
　　　　　　　　　　　　　　　　Charolles (Ajdal (USA)) (10000) **Mr T. G. & Mrs M. E. Holdcroft**
90 MIMI MOUSE, br f 17/3 Diktat—Shifty Mouse (Night Shift (USA)) (14000) **Mrs Jean P. Connew**
91 B c 5/2 Mind Games—Salacious (Sallust) (36000) **Mrs Janis MacPherson**
92 SWEET MARGUERITE, b f 21/2 Diktat—Margarets Gift (Beveled (USA)) **Margarets Partnership**
93 WONDERFUL MIND, b c 12/2 Mind Games—
　　　　　　　　　　　Signs And Wonders (Danehill (USA)) (25000) **Mr T. G. & Mrs M. E. Holdcroft**

Other Owners: Mr Edward Birkbeck, Mr S. D. Brearley, Mr S. I. Charnock-Bates, Mrs B. Cotton, Mr J. D. Cotton, Mr David Currie, Mrs Susie Dicker, Mr Roger Dowsett, Mr David Dudley, Mr Steven Dudley, Mrs M. H. Easterby, Mr J. Ennis, Sir Alex Ferguson, Lady Legard, Mrs Hazel Lowrey, Mr D. J. P. McWilliams, Mr A. Meale, Peter Molony, Mr J. S. Sexton, Mr Richard T. Vickers, Mr T. S. Palin, Mr A. H. Raby, Mr N. A. Ryall, Mr J. H. Sexton, Mr R. Sidebottom, Mr Duncan Smith, Mrs Ivan Straker, Mr David G. Sutbeland, Sir Tatton Sykes, Mr R. Taylor (York), Mrs Sue Tindall, Mr Andrew Voss, Mr G. H. M. Walker, Mr A. Williams, Mr D. J. P. Williams, Mrs M. Williams, Mr W. J. Williams.

Jockey (NH): R Garritty.

175 MR B. J. ECKLEY, Brecon
Postal: **Closcedi Farm, Llanspyddid, Brecon, Powys, LD3 8NS.**
Contact: **PHONE (01874) 622422**

1 4, B g Lord Americo—Alice Smith **Mr Brian Eckley**
2 4, B g Luso—Jaunty June **Mr Brian Eckley**
3 **MISS RIDEAMIGHT**, 5, b m Overbury (IRE)—Nicolynn **Mr Brian Eckley**
4 **SMITH'S TRIBE**, 6, gr g Homo Sapien—Alice Smith **Mr Brian Eckley**
5 **WITNESS TIME (IRE)**, 8, b g Witness Box (USA)—Lisnacoilla **Mr Brian Eckley**

176 MR D. EDDY, Newcastle Upon Tyne
Postal: **The Byerley Stud, Ingoe, Newcastle Upon Tyne, Tyne and Wear, NE20 0SZ.**
Contact: **PHONE (01661) 886356 FAX (01661) 886484**

1 **A FEW BOB BACK (IRE)**, 8, b g Bob Back (USA)—Kottna (USA) **Mr Brian Chicken**
2 **DUNASKIN (IRE)**, 4, b g Bahhare (USA)—Mirwara (IRE) **Mrs I. Battla**
3 **ELA AGORI MOU (IRE)**, 7, ch g Ela-Mana-Mou—La Courant (USA) **Mr Brian Chicken**
4 **FAIR SHAKE (IRE)**, 4, b g Sheikh Albadou—Shamrock Fair **Mr I. R. Clements**
5 **FLOWING RIVER (IRE)**, 6, ch g Over The River (FR)—Minature Miss **Mrs H. Scotto**
6 **KRISTENSEN**, 5, ch g Kris S (USA)—Papaha (IRE) **Equiname Ltd**
7 **LEWS A LADY**, 6, ch m Sir Harry Lewis (USA)—Pretty Gayle **Miss Gwen Gibson**
8 **RIVER MIST (IRE)**, 5, ch m Over The River (FR)—Minature Miss **Mrs H. Scotto**
9 **SAHEM (IRE)**, 7, b g Sadler's Wells (USA)—Sumava (IRE) **Mr Robert Gray**

THREE-YEAR-OLDS

10 **ACE COMING**, b g First Trump—Tarry **Mr I. R. Clements**

Other Owners: Mr Kevin Elliott.

Assistant Trainer: Karen McLintock

177 MR G. F. EDWARDS, Minehead
Postal: **Summering, Wheddon Cross, Minehead, Somerset, TA24 7AT.**
Contact: **PHONE (01643) 831549 MOBILE (07970) 059297 E-MAIL dazjock001@hotmail.com**

1 **BERMUDA (IRE)**, 5, b g Sadler's Wells (USA)—Sequel (IRE) **Mr G. F. Edwards**
2 **CEDAR RANGERS (USA)**, 6, b g Anabaa (USA)—Chelsea (USA) **Mr G. F. Edwards**
3 **HOPE VALUE**, 9, b g Rock City—Folle Idee (USA) **Mr G. F. Edwards**
4 **TUSCAN TEMPO**, 5, ch g Perugino (USA)—Fact of Time **Mr G. F. Edwards**

Amateur: Mr D Edwards (10-0).

178 MR C. R. EGERTON, Chaddleworth
Postal: **Heads Farm Stables, Chaddleworth, Newbury, Berkshire, RG20 7EU.**
Contact: **OFFICE (01488) 638771 FAX (01488) 638832 HOME (01488) 638454 MOBILE (07795) 220630 E-MAIL charles.egerton@virgin.net WEBSITE www.charlesegerton.com**

1 **AURAZURE (IRE)**, 6, gr h Roselier (FR)—Siul Currach **Mrs Sandra A. Roe**
2 **BENJAMIN BUCKRAM (IRE)**, 5, br g Topanoora—Red Bit (IRE) **Mr Mark Haynes**
3 **BISON KING (IRE)**, 7, b g King's Ride—Valantonia (IRE) **Mrs Evelyn Hankinson**
4 **DRAGON HUNTER (IRE)**, 9, b g Welsh Term—Sahob **Douglas, Davis, Urquhart**
5 **DRUIDS CONFEDERACY (IRE)**, 6, ch m Great Marquess—Winsome Blends (IRE) **Bush Syndicate**
6 **GRAPHIC APPROACH (IRE)**, 6, b g King's Ride—Sharp Approach **Mr Peter Orton**
7 **IT'S JUST HARRY**, 7, b g Tragic Role (USA)—Nipotina **Mr James Blackshaw**
8 **LITTLE ENAM (IRE)**, 8, gr g Un Desperado (FR)—Black Pheasant (IRE) **Mr R. K. Carvill**
9 **MICKEY CROKE**, 7, b g Alflora (IRE)—Praise The Lord **Lady Lloyd Webber**
10 **RUBBERDUBBER**, 4, b g Teenoso (USA)—True Clown **Mr & Mrs Peter Orton**
11 **RUSTIC CHARM (IRE)**, 4, b f Charnwood Forest (IRE)—Kabayil **Elite Racing Club**
12 **SMALL SHOTS**, 7, br g Roselier (FR)—My Adventure (IRE) **Mr B. G. Pomford**
13 **STAGE BY STAGE (USA)**, 5, ch g In The Wings—Lady Thynn (FR) **Mrs Evelyn Hankinson**
14 **TYPHOON TILLY**, 7, b g Hernando (FR)—Meavy **Mrs Evelyn Hankinson**
15 **VALANCE (IRE)**, 4, br g Bahhare (USA)—Glowlamp (IRE) **M. Haynes, A. & J. Allison, J. Weatherby**
16 **WINDING RIVER (IRE)**, 7, b g Montelimar (USA)—Bellora (IRE) **Elite Racing Club**

MR C. R. EGERTON—continued
THREE-YEAR-OLDS

17 **AIRGUSTA (IRE)**, b c Danehill Dancer (IRE)—Ministerial Model (IRE) **Team Havana**
18 **EDGEHILL (IRE)**, b c Ali-Royal (IRE)—Elfin Queen (IRE) **Mrs Evelyn Hankinson**
19 **GROUND COMMAND (USA)**, b g Kingmambo (USA)—Cymbala (USA) **W. Farish Jnr / G. Bolton**
20 **POINT CALIMERE (IRE)**, b g Fasliyev (USA)—Mountain Ash **R. E. Sangster & C. R. Egerton**
21 **PRE EMINANCE (IRE)**, b c Peintre Celebre (USA)—Sorb Apple (IRE) **Mr R. E. Sangster**
22 **RUSSIAN SYMPHONY (USA)**, ch c Stravinsky (USA)—Backwoods Teacher (USA) **Mrs Evelyn Hankinson**
23 **VINANDO**, ch c Hernando (FR)—Sirena (GER) **Mrs Evelyn Hankinson**
24 **WARBRECK**, ch c Selkirk (USA)—Wigging **Mrs Evelyn Hankinson**

Other Owners: The Hon William Astor, Mr R. F. Bailey, Mr J. P. Cavanagh, Mr A. Drummond, Mr Tony Gray, Mr M. G. Grimsey, Mr Tony Hil, Mr Alex Miller, Mr M. C. Moutray-Read, Miss M. Noden, Mr B. V. Sangster, D. Thomas, Mr Steve Thompson.

Assistant Trainer: Dennis Benneyworth & David Plunkett (Head lad)

Jockey (NH): J A McCarthy (10-0, w.a.).

---

179 **MR E. A. ELLIOTT, Rushyford**
Postal: **Planting House, Windlestone Park, Rushyford, Ferryhill, Co. Durham, DL17 0LZ.**
Contact: **PHONE (01388) 720383 FAX (01388) 722355**

1 **DREAM ON WILLIE (IRE)**, 7, b g Synefos (USA)—Mrs Mahon's Toy (IRE) **Mr Eric A. Elliott**
2 **GIRL BAND (IRE)**, 6, b m Bluebird (USA)—Bandit Girl **Mrs Anne E. Elliott**
3 **PLACE ABOVE (IRE)**, 8, b g Alphabatim (USA)—Lucky Pit **Mr Eric A. Elliott**
4 **SHAKWAA**, 5, ch m Lion Cavern (USA)—Shadha **Mrs Anne E. Elliott**

---

180 **MR BRIAN ELLISON, Malton**
Postal: **Spring Cottage Stables, Langton Road, Norton, Malton, North Yorkshire, YO17 9PY.**
Contact: **HOME (01653) 690005 OFFICE (01653) 690004 MOBILE (07785) 747426**
E-MAIL ellisonracing@aol.com

1 **ARTISTIC STYLE**, 4, b c Anabaa (USA)—Fine Detail (IRE) **Mr & Mrs D. A. Gamble**
2 **AUTUMN FANTASY (USA)**, 5, b h Lear Fan (USA)—Autumn Glory (USA) **Mr Ashley Carr**
3 **BARNEYS SON (IRE)**, 6, b g Wakashan—The Real Gael (IRE) **AKV Cladding Fabrications Ltd**
4 **BATSWING**, 9, b g Batshoof—Magic Milly **Mr Ashley Carr**
5 **BERGAMO**, 8, b g Robellino (USA)—Pretty Thing **Rasen Goes Racing**
6 **CD FLYER (IRE)**, 7, ch g Grand Lodge (USA)—Pretext **Mr Keith Middleton**
7 **COLEMANSTOWN**, 4, b g Charnwood Forest (IRE)—Arme Fatale (IRE) **Mr Brian Ellison**
8 **CONQUERING LOVE (IRE)**, 6, b g Pursuit of Love—Susquehanna Days (USA) **Mr Keith Middleton**
9 **COURT OF APPEAL**, 7, ch g Bering—Hiawatha's Song (USA) **Spring Cottage Syndicate No 2**
10 **CRUNCHY (IRE)**, 6, ch g Common Grounds—Credit Crunch (IRE) **The Half Moon Club**
11 **EVEREST (IRE)**, 7, ch g Indian Ridge—Reine d'Beaute **Mr I. S. Sandhu and Partners**
12 **FATEHALKHAIR (IRE)**, 12, ch g Kris—Midway Lady (USA) **Mr R. Wagner**
13 **GOLD NATIVE (IRE)**, 6, br g Be My Native (USA)—Goldiyana (FR) **Mr K. M. Everitt**
14 **GREAT AS GOLD (IRE)**, 5, b g Goldmark (USA)—Great Land (USA) **Mr Keith Middleton**
15 **HOPE SOUND (IRE)**, 4, b g Turtle Island—Lucky Pick **Mr R. Wagner**
16 **JIMMY BYRNE (IRE)**, 4, ch g Red Sunset—Persian Sally (IRE) **Mr Keith Middleton**
17 **LORD CONYERS (IRE)**, 5, b m Inzar (USA)—Primelta **The Lord Conyers Racing Partnership**
18 **MISTER ARJAY (USA)**, 4, b c Mister Baileys—Crystal Stepper (USA) **Mr Keith Middleton**
19 **MISTER MAL (IRE)**, 8, b g Scenic—Fashion Parade **Mrs Andrea M. Mallinson**
20 **MR FORTYWINKS (IRE)**, 10, ch g Fools Holme (USA)—Dream On **Miss Nuala Cassidy**
21 **OPEN HANDED (IRE)**, 4, b g Cadeaux Genereux—Peralta (IRE) **Mrs Andrea M. Mallinson**
22 **PERESTROIKA (IRE)**, 6, ch g Ashkalani (IRE)—Licentious **Mr Keith Middleton**
23 **PETONGSKI**, 6, b g Petong—Madam Petoski **Mr Keith Middleton**
24 **PROUD WESTERN (USA)**, 6, b br g Gone West—Proud Lou (USA)
25 **RONNIE FROM DONNY (IRE)**, 4, b g Eagle Eyed (USA)—New Rochelle (IRE) **Mr Keith Middleton**
26 **SCRAMBLE (USA)**, 6, ch g Gulch—Syzygy (ARG) **Mr Keith Middleton**
27 **SEA MARK**, 8, ro g Warning—Mettlesome **AKV Cladding Fabrications Ltd**
28 **SHALBEBLUE (IRE)**, 7, b g Shalford (IRE)—Alberjas (IRE) **Four Clubs**
29 **SHAYADI (IRE)**, 7, b g Kahyasi—Shayrdia (IRE) **Mr Ashley Carr**
30 **SIR NORTHERNDANCER (IRE)**, 5, b h Danehill Dancer (USA)—Lady At War **Mr Keith Middleton**
31 **TORRID KENTAVR (USA)**, 7, b g Trempolino—Torrid Tango (USA) **Mr Graeme Redpath**
32 **TRANSIT**, 5, b h Lion Cavern (USA)—Black Fighter (USA) **Mr Graeme Redpath**

MR BRIAN ELLISON—continued

33 **TURTLE DANCER (IRE)**, 6, b g Turtle Island (IRE)—Love Me Please (IRE) **Mr Ashley Young**
34 **UNTIDY DAUGHTER**, 5, b m Sabrehill (USA)—Branitska **Alderclad Roofing,S.Rutter,G.Hamilton**
35 **WOODLAND SPIRIT**, 5, b g Charnwood Forest (IRE)—Fantastic Charm (USA) **Mr Keith Middleton**
36 **ZIBELINE (IRE)**, 7, b g Cadeaux Genereux—Zia (USA) **Mr Ashley Carr**

THREE-YEAR-OLDS

37 **BETHANYS BOY (IRE)**, ch g Docksider (USA)—Daymoon (USA) **Mr Graeme Redpath**
38 **DARING GAMES**, b f Mind Games—Daira
39 **FOURSWAINBY (IRE)**, b g Foxhound (USA)—Arena **Mr Keith Middleton**
40 Ch c Pharly (FR)—Gay Sarah

Other Owners: Miss C. L. C. Adams, Alderclad Roofing Ltd, Mr L. A. Bolingbroke, Mr Paul Clarkson, Mr D. R. Cope, Mrs R. Cope, Mr M. J. Dyas, Ms L. Ellis, Mrs Alison Gamble, Mr D. A. Gamble, Mr L. A. Hambrook, Mr Geoffrey Hamilton, Mr R. D. Hannigan, Mr Michael Howitt, Mr C. Jenkins, Mr Stuart King, Mr John J. Maguire, Mr A. Marucci, Mr John Allan Milburn, Mr G. J. Price, Mr Henry Rix, Mr S. V. Rutter, Mr I. S. Sandhu, Mr Simon Smith, Mr W. P. Smith, Mr L. Straszewski, Mr J. K. Thompson, Dr M. G. Williams.

Assistant Trainer: L Ellison

Jockey (Flat): P Hannagan (w.a.). **Jockey (NH):** V Keane. **Apprentice:** T Hamilton. **Amateurs:** Miss L Ellison, Mr C Lidster.

---

181 MR D. R. C. ELSWORTH, Whitsbury
Postal: Whitsbury Manor Racing Stables, Whitsbury, Fordingbridge, Hampshire, SP6 3QB.
Contact: OFFICE (01725) 518889 (HOME) 518274 FAX 518747 MOBILE (07771) 804828
E-MAIL david.elsworth@virgin.net

1 **BARRY ISLAND**, 5, b g Turtle Island (IRE)—Pine Ridge **Mr Matthew Green**
2 **FINISHED ARTICLE (IRE)**, 7, b g Indian Ridge—Summer Fashion **The Caledonian Racing Society**
3 **FIRST BALLOT**, 8, br g Perugino (USA)—Election Special
4 **FLAMENCO BRIDE**, 4, b f Hernando (FR)—Premier Night **The Churston Family**
5 **FOODBROKER FOUNDER**, 4, ch g Groom Dancer (USA)—Nemea (USA) **Food Brokers Ltd**
6 **GAELIC LORD (IRE)**, 9, b g Mister Lord (USA)—Mum's Eyes **Mr Godfrey Wilson**
7 **INDIAN CREEK**, 6, br h Indian Ridge—Blue Water (USA) **Exors of the Late S. Cohn**
8 **ISLAND SOUND**, 7, b g Turtle Island (IRE)—Ballet **Mrs Michael Meredith**
9 **KATHOLOGY (IRE)**, 7, b g College Chapel—Wicken Wonder (IRE) **McDowell Racing**
10 **MISS POPPETS**, 4, ch f Polar Falcon (USA)—Alifandango (IRE) **Food Brokers Ltd**
11 **NORSE DANCER (IRE)**, 4, b c Halling (USA)—River Patrol **Mr J. C. Smith**
12 **PAWN BROKER**, 4, ch g Selkirk (USA)—Dime Bag **Mr Raymond Tooth**
13 **PETROSA (IRE)**, 4, ch f Grand Lodge (USA)—Top Brex (FR) **Mr M. Tabor**
14 **SAINT ALEBE**, 5, b g Bishop of Cashel—Soba Up **The Howarting's Partnership**
15 **SAN HERNANDO**, 4, b g Hernando (FR)—Sandrella (IRE) **The National Stud Owner-Breeders' Club**
16 **SPANISH DON**, 6, b g Zafonic (USA)—Spanish Wells (IRE) **Mr Richard J. Cohen**
17 **WAVERTREE BOY (IRE)**, 4, ch g Hector Protector (USA)—Lust **Wavertree Racing Club (2002)**

THREE-YEAR-OLDS

18 **ALFRIDINI**, ch c Selkirk (USA)—Vivre En Paix **Mr A. Heaney**
19 **APPOLONIOUS**, b c Case Law—Supreme Thought **Mr Derek Simester**
20 **BETTY STOGS (IRE)**, b f Perugino (USA)—Marabela (IRE)
21 **CALEDONIAN (IRE)**, b c Soviet Star (USA)—Supercal **The Caledonian Racing Society**
22 **CONSTANTIUS**, b g Halling (USA)—Premier Night **The Churston Family**
23 **ELZEES**, b c Magic Ring (IRE)—White Flash **Mr D. R. C. Elsworth**
24 **FARNBOROUGH (USA)**, b c Lear Fan (USA)—Gretel
25 **FOXILLA (IRE)**, ch f Foxhound (USA)—Lilissa **Mr J. Wotherspoon**
26 **MICHABO (IRE)**, b g Robellino (USA)—Mole Creek **Mrs Michael Meredith**
27 **MISTRESS POLLY**, b f Polish Precedent—Misbelief **W.V. & Mrs E.S. Robins**
28 **MOSCOW TIMES**, b c Soviet Star (USA)—Bargouzine **Mr M. Tabor**
29 **NEVER CRIED WOLF**, b g Wolfhound (USA)—Bold Difference **The Abbey Lyddite Partnership**
30 **RIVER GYPSY**, b c In The Wings—River Erne (USA) **Mr J. C. Smith**
31 **SALFORD CITY (IRE)**, b c Desert Sun—Summer Fashion **Mr M. Tabor**
32 **SKIDMARK**, b c Pennekamp (USA)—Flourishing (IRE) **Mr Raymond Tooth**
33 B f Emperor Jones—Soba Up **The Oh So Soba Partnership**
34 **STAGE RIGHT**, b c In The Wings—Spot Prize (USA) **Mr J. C. Smith**
35 **TIPSY LADY**, b f Intikhab (USA)—Creme de Menthe (IRE) **W.V. & Mrs E.S. Robins**

MR D. R. C. ELSWORTH—continued

36 **TOPKAT (IRE)**, b g Simply Great (FR)—Kitty's Sister **Mr R. Standring**
37 **WHITSBURY CROSS**, b c Cape Cross (IRE)—Vallauris **McDowell Racing**

TWO-YEAR-OLDS

38 **ART LEGEND**, b c 1/3 Indian Ridge—
        Solo Performance (IRE) (Sadler's Wells (USA)) (13604) **Mr Matthew Green**
39 **CANARY ISLAND (IRE)**, b c 18/5 Polar Falcon (USA)—Yellow Trumpet (Petong) (18552) **Mrs A. J. K. Dunn**
40 **CAPE COLUMBINE**, b f 31/1 Diktat—Cape Merino (Clantime) (33000) **Mr D. R. C. Elsworth**
41 Ch f 11/1 Halling (USA)—Careyes (IRE) (Sadler's Wells (USA)) (48000) **Mr Matthew Green**
42 **DARLING DEANIE (IRE)**, ch f 10/5 Sinndar (IRE)—
        Blushing Melody (IRE) (Never So Bold) (41000) **Mrs D. M. Solomon**
43 B c 23/4 Zafonic (USA)—Dodo (IRE) (Alzao (USA)) (14000) **W.V. & Mrs E.S. Robins**
44 **DOUBLE SPECTRE (IRE)**, b c 23/2 Spectrum (IRE)—Phantom Ring (Magic Ring (IRE)) **Mr J. C. Smith**
45 **GARIBALDI (GER)**, ch c 17/4 Acatenango (GER)—
        Guanhumara (Caerleon (25000) **The Bramfield Racing Syndicate**
46 B br f 22/3 Gulch (USA)—Harda Arda (USA) (Nureyev (USA)) **Mr J. C. Smith**
47 Ch c 10/3 Zafonic (USA)—Highland Rhapsody (IRE) (Kris) (45000) **Mr A. J. Thompson**
48 **JUBILEE DREAM**, b c 27/3 Bluebird (USA)—Last Dream (IRE) (Alzao (USA)) **W.V. & Mrs E.S. Robins**
49 Ch c 28/2 Spectrum (IRE)—Juno Madonna (IRE) (Sadler's Wells (USA)) (13000)
50 **MISSIE BAILEYS**, ch f 6/4 Mister Baileys—Jilly Woo (Environment Friend) **Mrs J. Wotherspoon**
51 Ch c 15/5 Indian Lodge (IRE)—Miss Rossi (Artaius (USA)) (20000) **Mr J. David Abell**
52 Ch c 17/2 Entrepreneur—
        Mountain Dancer (IRE) (Rainbow Quest (USA)) (18000) **The Caledonian Racing Society**
53 **OBERON's PRIZE**, b c 15/4 King's Theatre (IRE)—Taj Victory (Final Straw) **Sir Gordon Brunton**
54 **OCEAN GIFT**, b c 23/2 Cadeaux Genereux—Sea Drift (FR) (Warning) **Mr J. C. Smith**
55 **SELMA**, ch f 15/4 Selkirk (USA)—Mish Mish (Groom Dancer (USA)) **Miss K. Rausing**
56 **SHIRE (IRE)**, b c 10/2 Trans Island—Trebles (IRE) (Kenmare (FR)) (13000)
57 **SOMETHING EXCITING**, ch f 7/3 Halling (USA)—Faraway Waters (Pharly (FR)) (20000) **Setsquare Recruitment**
58 B f 15/5 Desert Sun—Summer Fashion (Moorestyle) **Dr D. B. Davis**
59 **THE GEEZER**, ch c 4/3 Halling (USA)—Polygueza (FR) (Be My Guest (USA)) (21000) **Mr J. C. Smith**
60 **TOP GEAR**, b c 12/3 Robellino (USA)—Bundle (Cadeaux Genereux) (30000) **Mrs P. J. Sheen**
61 **TUCKER**, b c 9/4 Inchinor—Tender Moment (IRE) (Caerleon (USA)) **Mr Ray Richards**
62 B f 29/4 Lujain (USA)—Vallauris (Faustus (USA)) (14000)
63 **WAVERTREE ONE OFF**, b g 9/4 Diktat—Miss Clarinet (Pharly (FR)) (4638) **Wavertree Racing Club Syndicate C**
64 **WINDSTRIKE**, b f 9/3 Diktat—South Wind (Tina's Pet) **Mr J. C. Smith**

Other Owners: Mr David Blacklocks, Mrs Jean Brown, Mrs L. S. Buttery, Mr Keith Childs, Mr D. G. Churston, Mr Paul Clifton, Ms Anne Dawson, Ms A. J. Fairbrass, Mr Alastair Hodge, Mr Gordon Li, Mrs J. R. Metcalfe, Mr P. A. Metcalfe, Mrs Shirley Robins, Mr W. V. Robins, Mr D. D. Sutherland.

Assistant Trainer: Mrs Jean Brown

Amateur: Mr Owen Nelmes (9-7).

---

182   **MR I. EMMERSON, Chester-Le-Street**
Postal: Holmside Park, Holmside, Edmondsley, Co. Durham, DH7 6EY.
Contact: PHONE (01913) 710507 MOBILE (07813) 408814

1 **AIR OF ESTEEM**, 8, b g Forzando—Shadow Bird **Durham Thoroughbred Racing**
2 **BEST LEAD**, 5, b g Distant Relative—Bestemor **Mr Ian Emmerson**
3 **DISPOL PETO**, 4, gr g Petong—Plie **Durham Thoroughbred Racing**
4 **FAYRWAY RHYTHM (IRE)**, 7, b g Fayruz—The Way She Moves **Ms Josie Swinburn**
5 **GLENVIEWS POLLY (IRE)**, 4, b f Poliglote—Fun Board (FR) **Mr Ian Emmerson**
6 **TAP**, 7, b g Emarati (USA)—Pubby **Trade Direct Bathrooms & Furniture**
7 **TWO STEPS TO GO (USA)**, 5, b g Rhythm (USA)—Lyonushka (CAN) **Mr Ian Emmerson**

THREE-YEAR-OLDS

8 **DUGGAN'S DILEMMA (IRE)**, b g Lake Coniston (IRE)—Miss Ironwood **Mr Ian Emmerson**
9 **KATIE'S BATH TIME**, b f Lugana Beach—Eucharis **Mr Ian Emmerson**
10 **KATIE'S EMPIRE (IRE)**, gr g Second Empire (IRE)—Zest (USA) **Mr Ian Emmerson**
11 **KATIE'S ROLE**, b f Tragic Role (USA)—Mirkan Honey **Mr Ian Emmerson**
12 **TURF PRINCESS**, b f Wizard King—Turf Moor (IRE)

MR I. EMMERSON—continued
TWO-YEAR-OLDS

  13 KATIE'S BISCUIT, b f 28/4 Cayman Kai (IRE)—Peppers (IRE) (Bluebird (USA))

Jockey (Flat): A Nicholls (w.a.). **Jockey (NH):** M Bradburne (w.a.). **Apprentice:** D Fentiman. **Conditional:** N Hannity.

---

183 **MR A. M. ENNIS, Dorking**
Postal: Henfold House Stables, Henfold Lane, Beare Green, Dorking, Surrey, RH5 4RW.
Contact: HOME/OFFICE/FAX (01306) 631529 MOBILE (07970) 424017
E-MAIL albert@henfoldstables.co.uk WEBSITE www.henfoldstables.co.uk

  1 BEARE NECESSITIES (IRE), 5, ch g Presenting—Lady Laburnum **Mr A. T. A. Wates**
  2 FRESH RUN (FR), 5, b g Kadalko (FR)—Tatifly (FR) **Mr A. T. A. Wates**
  3 GENERAL TANTRUM (IRE), 7, b g Ilium—Barna Havna **Mr J. G. M. Wates**
  4 HOUSE WARMER (IRE), 5, ch g Carroll House—Under The Duvet (IRE) **Mr A. T. A. Wates**
  5 IBIS ROCHELAIS (FR), 8, b g Passing Sale (FR)—Ta Rochelaise (FR) **Mr A. T. A. Wates**
  6 MOSSAR (FR), 4, b g Passing Sale (FR)—Beatty's (FR) **Mr A. T. A. Wates**
  7 PORT DU SALUT (FR), 4, br g Garde Royale—Landevennec (FR) **Mr A. T. A. Wates**
  8 RODDY THE VET (IRE), 6, ch g Be My Native (USA)—Caronia **Lady Wates**
  9 THERE GOES WALLY, 5, b g Lyphento (USA)—Dutch Majesty **Mrs Frances Smith**
 10 WALCOT LAD (IRE), 8, b g Jurado (USA)—Butty Miss **Boddington, Burke, Camis**

Other Owners: Mr Richard Boddington, Mr J. A. Burke, Mr Fred Camis, Mr Leonard Fuller.

---

184 **MR G. P. ENRIGHT, Lewes**
Postal: The Oaks, Old Lewes Racecourse, Lewes, East Sussex, BN7 1UR.
Contact: PHONE (01273) 479183 FAX (01273) 479183

  1 CARLY BAY, 6, b m Carlton (GER)—Polly Minor **Mr A. O. Ashford**
  2 DICKINSONS BAY, 6, b m Arrasas (USA)—Lb's Girl **Mr Joseph Taylor**
  3 DUTCH STAR, 5, b m Alflora (IRE)—Double Dutch **McManus/Fuller**
  4 GRAN CLICQUOT, 9, gr m Gran Alba (USA)—Tina's Beauty **Mrs M. Enright**
  5 HIGH POINT (IRE), 6, b g Ela-Mana-Mou—Top Lady (IRE) **The Aedean Partnership**
  6 HOMEBRED BUDDY, 5, ch g Environment Friend—Royal Brush **Homebred Racing**
  7 PEPPERSHOT, 4, b g Vettori (IRE)—No Chili **Mr R. Gurney**
  8 ROME (IRE), 5, br g Singspiel (IRE)—Ela Romara **G. R. Macdonald, K. Fitchie, M. Enright**
  9 WELSH ASSEMBLY, 8, ch g Presidium—Celtic Chimes **Mr G. P. Enright**

THREE-YEAR-OLDS

 10 CORTON DENHAM, ch c Wolfhound (USA)—Wigit **Mr Anthony A. Etheridge**
 11 LAKAAM, b f Danzero (AUS)—Langtry Lady **Whitesmith Farm Stud**

Other Owners: Mrs Madeleine E. Etheridge, Ms K. Fitchie, Mr Leonard Fuller, Mr G. Macdonald, Ms A. McManus, Mrs
Michelle Stevenson, Mr Russell Stevenson, Mr Chris Wall, Mrs Sarah Wall.

Assistant Trainer: Mrs M Enright

Jockey (NH): R Thornton (10-0). **Amateurs:** Mrs M Enright (8-7), Mr J Pemberton (9-7).

---

185 **MR J. M. P. EUSTACE, Newmarket**
Postal: Park Lodge Stables, Park Lane, Newmarket, Suffolk, CB8 8AX.
Contact: PHONE (01638) 664277 FAX (01638) 664156 MOBILE (07802) 243764
E-MAIL james@parklodgestables.demon.co.uk WEBSITE www.jameseustace.com

  1 BLUE PATRICK, 4, gr g Wizard King—Great Intent **Blue Peter Racing 2**
  2 BRIOSO (IRE), 4, b g Victory Note (USA)—Presently **Mr Peter Hillman**
  3 DUNOWEN (IRE), 9, b g Be My Native (USA)—Lulu Buck **Mrs T. S. Matthews**
  4 FINAL DIVIDEND (IRE), 8, b g Second Set (IRE)—Prime Interest (IRE) **Mr Charles Curtis**
  5 LANDING STRIP (IRE), 4, b g Dolphin Street (FR)—Funny Cut (IRE) **Mr G. Carstairs**
  6 LAST APPOINTMENT (USA), 4, b c Elusive Quality (USA)—Motion In Limine (USA) **Mr Michael Scott**
  7 LIGHT BRIGADE, 5, b g Kris—Mafatin (IRE) **Mr Charles Curtis**
  8 MALAK AL MOULOUK (USA), 4, ch g King of Kings (IRE)—Honor To Her (USA) **Mr Felix Kwan**

MR J. M. P. EUSTACE—continued

9 **OVERRIDE (IRE)**, 4, b c Peintre Celebre (USA)—Catalonda **Mr Paul Kan**
10 **WELCOME STRANGER**, 4, b g Most Welcome—Just Julia **Mr H. R. Moszkowicz**

THREE-YEAR-OLDS

11 **ANATOLIAN QUEEN (USA)**, b f Woodman (USA)—Imia (USA) **Mr Y. Gelgin**
12 **ANDURIL**, ch c Kris—Attribute **Stephen Hodge & Peter Hillman**
13 **ASHFIELD**, ch f Zilzal (USA)—Ninaki (USA) **Major M. G. Wyatt**
14 **CHIGORIN**, b g Pivotal—Belle Vue **Mr D. A. Rosenbaum**
15 **CONSIDINE (USA)**, b c Romanov (IRE)—Libeccio (NZ) **Mr Elias Haloute**
16 **EMPRESS EUGENIE (FR)**, b f Second Empire (IRE)—High Finish **Blue Peter Racing 4**
17 **FOUR KINGS**, b c Forzando—High Cut **Mr J. C. Smith**
18 **LOCATOR (IRE)**, b c Mujadil (USA)—Lifeboat (IRE) **Mr George Darling**
19 **ORCADIAN**, b g Kirkwall—Rosy Outlook (USA) **Mr J. C. Smith**
20 **TEXAS PENNY**, b f Pennekamp (USA)—Poker Chip **Mr J. C. Smith**

TWO-YEAR-OLDS

21 **ARIODANTE**, b g 20/1 Groom Dancer (USA)—Maestrale (Top Ville) (9000)
22 **CETSHWAYO**, ch c 27/2 Pursuit of Love—Induna (Grand Lodge (USA)) (3500) **Mr I. P. Blance**
23 **DRALION**, ch c 10/3 Dr Fong (USA)—Rosy Outlook (USA) (Trempolino (USA)) **Mr J. C. Smith**
24 **ELMS SCHOOLBOY**, ch c 27/4 Komaite (USA)—Elms Schoolgirl (Emarati (USA)) **Mr J. D. Moore**
25 **HIGH CARD**, b c 18/4 So Factual (USA)—High Cut (Dashing Blade) **Mr J. C. Smith**
26 **HIGHLAND CASCADE**, ch f 24/2 Tipsy Creek (USA)—
            Highland Hannah (IRE) (Persian Heights) (3500) **Mr J. M. Ratcliffe**
27 **INNPURSUIT**, b c 16/2 Inchinor—Quest For The Best (Rainbow Quest (USA)) (16000) **Mr G. Carstairs**
28 **KILLA QUEEN**, b f 18/3 Killer Instinct—
            Prime Surprise (Primo Dominie) (500) **Friends of the Turf Racing Limited**
29 **MARNE (IRE)**, b c 14/3 Mtoto—Perfect Poppy (Shareef Dancer (USA)) (2500) **Mrs I. P. Blance**
30 **MISTER AZIZ (IRE)**, b c 10/4 Mister Baileys—
            Aziz Presenting (IRE) (Charnwood Forest (IRE)) (8700) **Park Lane Racing**
31 **MOONSTRUCK**, ch c 4/4 Fraam—Easter Moon (FR) (Easter Sun) (19000)
32 **RAFFISH**, ch g 20/2 Atraf—Valadon (High Line) (10000) **Blue Peter Racing 5**
33 **ROMANTIC GIFT**, b c 12/2 Cadeaux Genereux—Last Romance (IRE) (Last Tycoon) **Mr J. C. Smith**
34 **ROYAL WISH**, b f 1/3 Royal Applause—Be My Wish (Be My Chief (USA)) **Mr J. C. Smith**
35 **RUBY WINE**, b f 17/4 Kayf Tara—Cribella (USA) (Robellino (USA)) **Mrs R. M. Wilson**
36 **TRANSACTION (IRE)**, ch c 13/3 Trans Island—Meranie Girl (IRE) (Mujadil (USA)) (19000) **Mr George Darling**
37 **WESTER LODGE (IRE)**, ch c 24/2 Fraam—
            Reamzafonic (Grand Lodge (USA)) (25000) **Mr and Mrs R. H. Brewer**

Other Owners: Mr Stephen Appelbee, Mr R. H. Brewer, Mrs R. H. Brewer, Mrs James Eustace, Mr James R. B. George, Mr Stephen Hodge, Mrs L. R. Lawson, Mrs K. A. McGladdery, Mr A. M. Mitchell, Mrs Rosemary Moszkowicz.

Jockey (Flat): J Tate (8-0). **Amateur:** Miss Joanna Rees (9-0).

---

186   MR. M D. J. EVANS, Lydiate
Postal: **Oaklea Racing Stables, Southport Road, Lydiate, Merseyside, L31 4HH.**
Contact: **OFFICE/FAX** (01515) 200299 **MOBILE** (07860) 599101 **PARTNER** (07748) 630685

1 5, Ch m Environment Friend—Four Friends **Mr Paul Green (Oaklea)**
2 5, Ch m Sabrehill (USA)—Loch Quest (USA) **Mr Paul Green (Oaklea)**
3 **REAL TING**, 8, br g Forzando—St Helena **Mr Paul Green (Oaklea)**
4 **YORKER (USA)**, 6, b g Boundary (USA)—Shallows (USA) **Men Behaving Badly**
5 **ZIGGY DAN**, 4, b g Slip Anchor—Nikatino **Mr B. T. O'Sullivan**

THREE-YEAR-OLDS

6 **AMBER LEGEND**, b f Fraam—Abstone Queen **Mr J. E. Abbey**
7 **CARNT SPELL**, b g Wizard King—Forever Shineing **Mr Paul Green (Oaklea)**
8 **HOME FRONT (IRE)**, b g Intikhab (USA)—Felicita (IRE) **Mr B. T. O'Sullivan**
9 **JILLY WHY (IRE)**, b f Mujadil (USA)—Ruwy **Mr Paul Green (Oaklea)**
10 **ROYALTEA**, ch f Desert King (IRE)—Come To Tea (IRE) **Highly Sociable Syndicate**
11 **SHAYMEE'S GIRL**, b f Wizard King—Mouchez Le Nez (IRE) **B. & B. Hygiene Limited**
12 **SUITCASE MURPHY (IRE)**, b g Petardia—Noble Rocket **Mr Paul Green (Oaklea)**

MR. M D. J. EVANS—continued
TWO-YEAR-OLDS

13 B f 6/2 Fraam—Abstone Queen (Presidium) (10000) **Mr J. E. Abbey**
14 B c 7/3 Fraam—Classy Cleo (IRE) (Mujadil (USA)) **Mr Keith Ascot**
15 Gr f 8/5 Atraf—Demolition Jo (Petong) (741) **Mr Paul Green (Oaklea)**
16 **DESERT FERN (IRE)**, b f 8/4 Desert Style (IRE)—Lady Fern (Old Vic) (6500) **Mr Alan Williams**
17 B f 25/3 Mujadil (USA)—Kilcsem Eile (IRE) (Commanche Run) (4946) **Cannon, Grundy & Harris**
18 Ch f 23/4 Bahhare (USA)—Lady Ellen-M (IRE) (Ballad Rock) (4328) **Mr Paul Green (Oaklea)**
19 B g 19/4 King's Theatre (IRE)—Promising Lady (Thunder Gulch (USA)) (8000) **Mr Mike Nolan**
20 B f 31/3 Bachir (IRE)—Ruwy (Soviet Star (USA)) (5256) **Mr Paul Green (Oaklea)**

Assistant Trainer: Mr W McLaughlin

Jockey (NH): Antony Evans (10-0). **Conditional:** Anthony Evans (10-0). **Amateur:** Mr W McLaughlin (10-0).

---

187 MR H. J. EVANS, Chipping Campden
Postal: **Nineveh Farm, Campden Road, Mickleton, Chipping Campden, Gloucestershire, GL55 6PS.**
Contact: **PHONE (01386) 438921**

1 **SHAVA**, 4, b g Atraf—Anita Marie (IRE) **Mrs Jane Evans**
2 **STAR CONTROL (IRE)**, 10, gr m Phardante (FR)—Greystar **Mrs Jane Evans**
3 **TIME FOR ACTION (IRE)**, 12, b g Alzao (USA)—Beyond Words **Mrs Jane Evans**

THREE-YEAR-OLDS

4 Ch f Sir Harry Lewis (USA)—Friendly Fairy **Mrs Jane Evans**

---

188 MRS M. EVANS, Haverfordwest
Postal: **Hengoed, Clarbeston Road, Pembrokeshire, SA63 4QL.**
Contact: **PHONE (01437) 731336**

1 **FLORANZ**, 8, br m Afzal—Tuesday Member **Mr W. J. Evans**
2 **LYPHARITA'S RISK (FR)**, 9, b g Take Risks (FR)—Patissima (FR) **Mr W. J. Evans**

Assistant Trainer: W J Evans

Amateur: Mr Evan Williams (10-10).

---

189 MR M. J. M. EVANS, Kidderminster
Postal: **The Hawthorns, Hurcott Lane, Kidderminster, Worcestershire, DY10 3PJ.**
Contact: **PHONE (01562) 60970 MOBILE (07814) 631731 E-MAIL martinjohnmorgan@aol.com**

1 **ADVANCE EAST**, 12, b g Polish Precedent (USA)—Startino **Mrs J. Z. Munday**
2 **BAIE DES SINGES**, 10, b g Royal Vulcan—Mikey's Monkey **Mr M. J. M. Evans**
3 **BOLD HUNTER**, 10, b g Polish Precedent (USA)—Pumpona (USA) **Mr M. J. M. Evans**
4 **MICHIGAN BLUE**, 12, b g Rakaposhi King—Starquin (IRE) **Mrs J. Z. Munday**
5 **RED OASSIS**, 13, ch g Rymer—Heron's Mirage **Mrs J. Z. Munday**

Assistant Trainer: Jeanette Zoe Munday

Jockeys (NH): R Johnson (10-0), W Marston (10-0), O McPhail.

---

190 MR P. D. EVANS, Abergavenny
Postal: **Ty Derlywn Farm, Pandy, Abergavenny, NP7 8DR.**
Contact: **PHONE (01873) 890837**

1 **ADALAR (IRE)**, 4, b g Grand Lodge (USA)—Adalya (IRE) **Mr M. W. Lawrence**
2 **ALAFZAR (IRE)**, 6, b g Green Desert (USA)—Alasana (IRE) **Waterline Racing Club**
3 **AND TOTO TOO**, 4, br f Averti (IRE)—Divina Mia **Mrs S. J. Lawrence**
4 **BANDINI (SAF)**, 4, b g Zafonic (USA)—Estime (FR) **Mr P. D. Evans**
5 **BEST BEFORE (IRE)**, 4, b g Mujadit (USA)—Miss Margate (IRE) **Mr M. W. Lawrence**
6 **BOAVISTA (IRE)**, 4, b f Fayruz—Florissa (FR) **Mr D. Healy**

MR P. D. EVANS—continued

7 **CROSSWAYS**, 6, b g Mister Baileys—Miami Dancer **Mr T. Gailienne**
8 **DIAMOND MAX (IRE)**, 6, b g Nicolotte—Kawther **Diamond Racing Ltd**
9 **DIAMOND ORCHID (IRE)**, 4, gr f Victory Note (USA)—Olivia's Pride (IRE) **Diamond Racing Ltd**
10 **FEN GYPSY**, 6, b g Nashwan—Didicoy (USA) **Mr P. D. Evans**
11 **FLORENZAR (IRE)**, 6, b m Inzar (USA)—Nurse Tyra (USA) **Mr D. Healy**
12 **GALLANT BOY (IRE)**, 5, ch g Grand Lodge (USA)—Damerela (IRE) **Mr M. W. Lawrence**
13 **GOLD GUEST**, 5, ch g Vettori (IRE)—Cassilis (IRE) **Diamond Racing Ltd**
14 **INTELLIBET ONE**, 4, b f Compton Place—Safe House **Mr G. E. Amey**
15 5, B m Saddlers' Hall (IRE)—Katie Scarlett **Mr M. Murray**
16 **MISS CHAMPERS (IRE)**, 4, b br f Grand Lodge (USA)—Katherine Gorge (USA) **Mrs S. J. Lawrence**
17 **NASHAAB (USA)**, 7, b g Zafonic (USA)—Tajannub (USA) **Mr M. W. Lawrence**
18 **NAUGHTY GIRL (IRE)**, 4, b f Dr Devious (IRE)—Mary Magdalene **Mrs S. Lawrence**
19 **PAS DE SURPRISE**, 6, b g Dancing Spree (USA)—Supreme Rose **Mr D. Healy**
20 **RISK FREE**, 7, ch g Risk Me (FR)—Princess Lily **Thats Racing Partnership**
21 **SPRINGALONG (USA)**, 4, ch g Gone West (USA)—Seven Springs (USA) **Mr M. W. Lawrence**
22 **SUPER SONG**, 4, b g Desert Prince (IRE)—Highland Rhapsody (IRE) **Mr M. W. Lawrence**
23 **THEATRE LADY (IRE)**, 6, b m King's Theatre (IRE)—Littlepace **Waterline Racing Club**
24 **THE KIDDYKID**, 4, b g Danetime (IRE)—Mezzanine **Mrs C. Massey**
25 **TOP OF THE CLASS (IRE)**, 7, b m Rudimentary (USA)—School Mum **Mr P. D. Evans**
26 **WATERLINE DANCER (IRE)**, 4, b br f Danehill Dancer (IRE)—Thrill Seeker (IRE) **Waterline Racing Club**
27 **WATERLINE SPIRIT**, 4, b g Piccolo—Gina of Hithermoor **Waterline Racing Club**
28 **ZAFARSHAH (IRE)**, 5, b g Danehill (USA)—Zafarana (FR) **Waterline Racing Club**

THREE-YEAR-OLDS

29 **DANIFAH (IRE)**, b f Perugino (USA)—Afifah **Mr E. A. R. Morgans**
30 **DIAMOND RIBBY (IRE)**, br f Desert Sun—Kathleen's Dream (USA) **Diamond Racing Ltd**
31 **EMARADIA**, ch f Emarati (USA)—Rewardia (IRE) **Treble Chance Partnership**
32 **FLEETFOOT MAC**, b g Fleetwood (IRE)—Desert Flower **Mr M. W. Lawrence**
33 **GO GREEN**, ch f Environment Friend—Sandra Mac **Mr M. Murray**
34 **GO YELLOW**, b g Overbury (IRE)—Great Lyth Lass (IRE) **Mr G. R. Price**
35 **HARRY LAD**, ch g Then Again—Silly Sally **Mr T. Jarvis**
36 **HAZEWIND**, gr g Daylami (IRE)—Fragrant Oasis (USA) **Mr M. W. Lawrence**
37 **KILCULLEN LASS (IRE)**, ch f Fayruz—Foretell **Ms Ann Cully**
38 **LADY PISTE (IRE)**, b f Ali-Royal (IRE)—Alpine Lady (IRE) **Mrs S. J. Lawrence**
39 **LIGNE D'EAU**, ch c Cadeaux Genereux—Miss Waterline **Mr M. W. Lawrence**
40 **MELODY KING**, b g Merdon Melody—Retaliator **Treble Chance Partnership**
41 **ODDSMAKER (IRE)**, b g Barathea (IRE)—Archipova **Mr S. Rudolf**
42 **PARALLEL LINES (IRE)**, ch g Polish Precedent (USA)—Phone Booth (USA) **Mr M. W. Lawrence**
43 **QUARRY ISLAND (IRE)**, b f Turtle Island (IRE)—Last Quarry **Mr G. E. Amey**
44 **RED ACER (IRE)**, b g Shinko Forest (IRE)—Another Babyers **Threepenny Bits**
45 **UNDER MY SPELL**, b f Wizard King—Gagajulu **Mr R. Salter**
46 **WATERLINE BLUE (IRE)**, b g Mujadil (USA)—Blues Queen **Mr M. W. Lawrence**

TWO-YEAR-OLDS

47 B f 2/3 Lear Fan (USA)—Aranda (Fairy King (USA) **Mr P. D. Evans**
48 **DARTANIAN**, b c 6/4 Jurado (USA)—Blackpool Mamma's (Merdon Melody)
49 Ch f 21/4 Efisio—Food of Love (Music Boy) (18000) **Mr M. W. Lawrence**
50 Ch f 8/4 Timeless Times (USA)—Marfen (Lochnager) (3400) **Mr D. Hilton**
51 B f 18/4 Compton Place—Miss Waterline (Rock City) **Mr M. W. Lawrence**
52 B g 13/4 Magic Ring—My Bonus (Cyrano de Bergerac) (9000) **Mr R. Salter**
53 B f 16/4 Primo Dominie—Petrikov (In The Wings) (3000)
54 B f 20/4 Vettori (IRE)—Rewardia (IRE) (Petardia) (6200) **Treble Chance Partnership**
55 B f 22/4 Mujadil (USA)—Tintinara (Selkirk (USA)) (4000) **Mr M. W. Lawrence**

Other Owners: Mr P. Brazier, Mr Christopher Chell, Mr M. E. Hughes, Mr D. Maloney, Mr G. Weaver, Mr P. T. Williams.

Assistant Trainer: Jeremy Salter

Jockey (Flat): Joanne Badger (7-12). **Jockey (NH):** Antony Evans (10-0). **Apprentice:** S Donohue (8-0). **Conditional:** Antony Evans (10-0). **Amateurs:** Miss M Bryan (8-12), Miss E Folkes (8-7).

191	**MR A. FABRE, Chantilly**

Postal: **14 Avenue de Bourbon, 60500 Chantilly, France.**
Contact: **PHONE 03 44 57 04 98 FAX 03 44 58 14 15**

1 **BAILADOR (IRE)**, 4, b c Alzao (USA)—Alymatrice (USA) **Mr E. Rothschild**
2 **BORGES (GER)**, 4, b c Sadler's Wells (USA)—Britannia (GER) **Gestut Ammerland**
3 **CLEAR THINKING**, 4, b c Rainbow Quest (USA)—Coraline **Prince Khalid Abdullah**
4 **MARTALINE**, 5, b m Linamix (FR)—Coraline **Prince Khalid Abdullah**
5 **MYSTIC MELODY (USA)**, 4, b f Seattle Slew (USA)—Munnaya (USA) **Maktoum Al Maktoum**
6 **PHOENIX HILL**, 4, b f Sadler's Wells (USA)—Park Appeal **Sheikh Mohammed al Maktoum**
7 **POLISH SUMMER**, 7, b h Polish Precedent—Hunt The Sun **Prince Khalid Abdullah**
8 **REAL TRUST (USA)**, 4, b f Danzig (USA)—True Flare (USA) **Prince Khalid Abdullah**
9 **RUSSIAN HILL**, 4, b f Indian Ridge—Dievotchka **Mr E. Rothschild**
10 **SHORT PAUSE**, 5, b h Sadler's Wells (USA)—Interval **Prince Khalid Abdullah**
12 **VISORAMA**, 4, b br f Linamix (FR)—Visor (USA) **Mr J. L. Lagardere**

THREE-YEAR-OLDS

12 **ACHAMBRA (FR)**, b f Desert Prince (IRE)—Armarama **Mr J. L. Lagardere**
13 **ADVICE**, b c Seeking The Gold (USA)—Anna Palariva (IRE) **Sheikh Mohammed al Maktoum**
14 **ALIYESKA (IRE)**, b f Fasliyev (USA)—Armilina (FR) **Mme Elisabeth Fabre**
15 **AMIE DE MIX (FR)**, b f Linamix (FR)—Amen (USA) **Mr J. L. Lagardere**
16 **APSIS**, b c Barathea (IRE)—Apogee **Prince Khalid Abdullah**
17 **ART AMERICAN (USA)**, b c Quiet American (USA)—Artistique (IRE) **J. L. Lagardere**
18 **ART MASTER (USA)**, b c Royal Academy (USA)—True Flare (USA) **Prince Khalid Abdullah**
19 **BARRANCO (IRE)**, b c Sadler's Wells (USA)—Belize Tropical (IRE) **Sheikh Mohammed Al Maktoum**
20 **BERMUXA (FR)**, gr f Linamix (FR)—Bernique (USA) **Mr J. L. Lagardere**
21 **BITS OF PARADISE (FR)**, b f Desert Prince (IRE)—Don't Worry Me (IRE) **Anne Marie Springer**
22 **BOLIVAR (GER)**, b c Sadler's Wells (USA)—Brogia (GER) **Gestut Ammerland**
23 **BRITIX (FR)**, gr c Linamix (FR)—Bright Tessa (USA) **Mr J. L. Lagardere**
24 **CACIQUE (IRE)**, b c Danehill (USA)—Hasili (IRE) **Prince Khalid Abdullah**
25 **CHERRY MIX (FR)**, gr c Linamix (FR)—Cherry Moon (USA) **Mr J. L. Lagardere**
26 **CRESTA**, b f Sadler's Wells (USA)—Comme d'Habitude (USA) **Gestut Ammerland**
27 **DIAMOND FOR EVER (FR)**, gr c Linamix (FR)—Diamond Seal **Mr J. L. Lagardere**
28 **DIAMOND GREEN (FR)**, b c Green Desert (USA)—Diamonaka (FR) **J. L. Lagardere**
29 **DIAMOND TANGO (FR)**, b c Acatenango (GER)—Diamond Dance (FR) **J. L. Lagardere**
30 **DIEGO CAO (IRE)**, b c Cape Cross (IRE)—Lady Moranbon (USA) **Sheikh Mohammed Al Maktoum**
31 **DREAM PLAY (FR)**, b f In The Wings—Lustre (USA) **Sheikh Mohammed al Maktoum**
32 **DRESS SWORD (UAE)**, b c Theatrical—Queen's Dagger (USA) **Sheikh Mohammed Al Maktoum**
33 **ECOLE D'ART (USA)**, b c Theatrical—Colour Chart (USA) **Sheikh Mohammed Al Maktoum**
34 **ETENDARD INDIEN (FR)**, b c Selkirk (USA)—Danseuse Indienne (IRE) **Mr E. Rothschild**
35 **FAIRLY RUN (FR)**, b c Cherokee Run (USA)—Fairly Grey (FR) **J. L. Lagardere**
36 **FAR SHORES (USA)**, b f Distant View (USA)—Razyana (USA) **Prince Khalid Abdullah**
37 **FRACASSANT (IRE)**, b c Linamix (FR)—Fragrant Hill **Mr J. L. Lagardere**
38 **GLANLEAM (IRE)**, b c Indian Ridge—Durrah (USA) **Maktoum al Maktoum**
39 **GREY LILAS (IRE)**, b f Danehill (USA)—Kenmist **Gestut Ammerland**
40 **GROSGRAIN (USA)**, b f Diesis—Green Lady (IRE) **Maktoum al Maktoum**
41 **ILES MARQUISES (IRE)**, ch f Unfuwain (USA)—Good To Dance (IRE) **Mme Paul Moussac**
42 **JAILHOUSE ROCK (IRE)**, ch c Soviet Star (USA)—Adjacent (IRE) **Bob Lalemant**
43 **JARREER (IRE)**, b c Dynaformer (USA)—Flaxen Wells (USA) **Prince Sultan Al Kabeer**
44 **JUST FOR CHANCE (IRE)**, b f Danehill (USA)—Don't Rush (IRE) **Maktoum al Maktoum**
45 **KAMARITA (IRE)**, b f Octagonal (NZ)—Reine de Neige (IRE) **Maktoum al Maktoum**
46 **KARELIAN**, gr c Linamix (FR)—Kalikala **Sheikh Mohammed Al Maktoum**
47 **KENTUCKY CHARM (FR)**, gr c Linamix (FR)—Kentucky Kaper (USA) **Mr J. L. Lagardere**
48 **LINGUIST (IRE)**, gr f Linamix (FR)—Persian Secret (FR) **Sheikh Mohammed Al Maktoum**
49 **LIXIAN**, gr f Linamix (FR)—New Abbey **Prince Khalid Abdullah**
50 **LORD DARNLEY (IRE)**, b c Darshaan—Ghariba **Sheikh Mohammed Al Maktoum**
51 **LORENTZ (JPN)**, b c Carnegie (IRE)—Prestigious (USA) **Sheikh Mohammed al Maktoum**
52 **LOUVE DE SARON (FR)**, b f Loup Solitaire (USA)—Luth de Saron (FR) **Mme Paul Moussac**
53 **LUNA CELTICA (IRE)**, b f Celtic Swing—Luna Caerla (IRE) **Mr J. L. Lagardere**
54 **LUNA GULCH (IRE)**, b f Gulch (USA)—Luna Mareza **Mr J. L. Lagardere**
55 **MADHYA (USA)**, b f Gone West—Khumba Mela (IRE) **Mme Paul Moussac**
56 **MAJLIS (JPN)**, b c Commander In Chief—Prayer Wheel (CAN) **Sheikh Mohammed al Maktoum**
57 **MARCHING WEST (USA)**, b f Gone West—Zaizafon (USA) **Price Khalid Abdullah**
58 **MILADY'S PRIDE**, b f Machiavellian (USA)—Ideal Lady (IRE) **Maktoum al Maktoum**
59 **MISTER WELLS (FR)**, b c Sadler's Wells (USA)—Miss Satamixa (FR) **J. L. Lagardere**
60 **MOUNTAIN TOP**, b c Zafonic (USA)—Monroe (USA) **Prince Khalid Abdullah**

MR A. FABRE—continued

61 B f Peintre Celebre (USA)—My Secret (GER) **Gestut Ammerland**
62 **RAIN ON MIX (FR)**, gr c Linamix (FR)—Resless Rain (IRE) **Mr J. L. Lagardere**
63 **REEFSCAPE**, gr c Linamix (FR)—Coraline **Prince Khalid Abdullah**
64 **ROSA RAISA (FR)**, b f Rainbow Quest (USA)—Ring of Music **Sheikh Mohammed al Maktoum**
65 **RUSSIAN BEAUTY (USA)**, b f Diesis—Berine (IRE) **Mr E. Rothschild**
66 **RUSSIAN LOVE (IRE)**, ch f Machiavellian (USA)—Dievotchka **Mr E. Rothschild**
67 **RUSSIAN MUSE (FR)**, bl f Machiavellian (USA)—Sinueuse (FR) **Mr E. Rothschild**
68 **SADDLER'S GIRL (FR)**, b f Sadler's Wells (USA)—Taffety **Mr E. Rothschild**
69 **SAVE ME THE WALTZ (FR)**, b f Halling (USA)—Flawlessly (FR) **Anne Marie Springer**
70 **SAVILLE ROW (USA)**, b c Gone West (USA)—Style Setter (USA) **Sheikh Mohammed al Maktoum**
71 **SCARLET MIX (FR)**, gr c Linamix (FR)—Scarlet Raider (USA) **Mr J. L. Lagardere**
72 **SIERRA LEONE**, b f Polish Precedent (USA)—African Peace (USA) **Sheikh Mohammed al Maktoum**
73 **STAFF NURSE (USA)**, b f Arch (USA)—Medicine Woman (USA) **Sheikh Mohammed al Maktoum**
74 **SWEET PROTECTION (FR)**, b f Hector Protector (USA)—Sweet Opera (FR) **J. L. Lagardere**
75 **TANNENBERG (IRE)**, b c Polish Precedent (USA)—Upper Strata **Sheikh Mohammed Al Maktoum**
76 **TELEMANN (IRE)**, b br c Singspiel (IRE)—Diamond Field (USA) **Sheikh Mohammed al Maktoum**
77 **TOP OF THE BILL (USA)**, b c Lear Fan (USA)—Note Musicale **Maktoum al Maktoum**
78 **VAILLANT PRINCE (FR)**, b c Desert Prince (IRE)—Vadlava (FR) **Mr J. L. Lagardere**
79 **VALIXIR (IRE)**, b c Trempolino (USA)—Vadlamixa (FR) **J. L. Lagardere**
80 **VELVET QUEEN**, b f Singspiel (IRE)—Velvet Moon (IRE) **Sheikh Mohammed al Maktoum**
81 **VIMY RIDGE (FR)**, b f Indian Ridge—Maximoa (FR) **Maktoum al Maktoum**
82 **VOLISIX (IRE)**, gr c Linamix (FR)—Vadsa Honor (FR) **Mr J. L. Lagardere**
83 **WATERMARK**, b f Rainbow Quest (USA)—Wajd (USA) **Sheikh Mohammed Al Maktoum**
84 **WEST HILL (IRE)**, b c Gone West (USA)—Altamura (USA) **Sheikh Mohammed al Maktoum**
85 **WINDYX (FR)**, b c Linamix (FR)—Windy Gulch (USA) **Mr J. L. Lagardere**

TWO-YEAR-OLDS

86 **ASAGILD (FR)**, b c 10/3 Gilded Time—Ashaninka (USA) (Woodman (USA)) **Mr J. L. Lagardere**
87 B f 14/2 King's Best (USA)—Barger (USA) (Riverman (USA)) **Sheikh Mohammed al Maktoum**
88 **BERNABEU (USA)**, ch c 27/4 Kris S (USA)—Set In Motion (USA) (Mr Prospector (USA)) **Maktoum al Maktoum**
89 **BRIXA (FR)**, gr f 19/3 Linamix (FR)—Broad And High (USA) (Broad Brush (USA)) **Mr J. L. Lagardere**
90 B c 19/2 Danehill (USA)—Brush Strokes (Cadeaux Genereux) (360000) **Sheikh Mohammed al Maktoum**
91 **CARLIX (FR)**, gr c 27/2 Linamix (FR)—Carlitta (USA) (Olympio (USA)) **Mr J. L. Lagardere**
92 **CLOVERTE (IRE)**, b f 2/4 Green Desert (USA)—Clodora (FR) (Linamix (FR)) **Mr J. L. Lagardere**
93 Ch f 5/5 Seeking The Gold—Colorado Dancer (FR) (Shareef Dancer (USA)) **Sheikh Mohammed al Maktoum**
94 **DESIDERATUM**, b c 8/3 Darshaan—Desired (Rainbow Quest (USA)) **Sheikh Mohammed al Maktoum**
95 **DIAMPILINA (FR)**, b f 14/4 Trempolino (USA)—Diamond Dance (FR) (Dancehall (USA)) **Mr J. L. Lagardere**
96 B c 10/5 Danehill (USA)—Dievotchka (Dancing Brave (USA)) **Mr E. Rothschild**
97 **DILAG (IRE)**, b f 3/2 Almutawakel—Terracotta Hut (Habitat) (105132) **Anne Marie Springer**
98 **DOCUMENTARY (USA)**, b c 22/2 Storm Cat (USA)—
 Honest Lady (USA) (Seattle Slew (USA)) **Prince Khalid Abdullah**
99 B f 14/3 Sadler's Wells (USA)—Elegant As Always (USA) (Nashwan (USA)) (160791) **Gestut Ammerland**
100 **FAIRBATHE (FR)**, b c 16/5 Barathea (IRE)—Fairlee Wild (USA) (Wild Again (USA)) **Mr J. L. Lagardere**
101 **FAIRWUALA (IRE)**, b f 19/2 Unfuwain (USA)—Fairly Grey (FR) (Linamix (FR)) **Mr J. L. Lagardere**
102 **FRALOGA (IRE)**, b f 20/3 Grand Lodge (USA)—Fragrant Hill (Shirley Heights) **Mr J. L. Lagardere**
103 **GALILANI (USA)**, b f 17/2 Storm Creek (USA)—Cognac Lady (USA) (Olympio (USA)) **Mme Elisabeth Fabre**
104 Ch c 25/1 Grand Lodge (USA)—Goodwood Blizzard (Inchinor) (20000) **Bob Lalemant**
105 B f 5/3 Go For Gin (USA)—Gretel (Hansel) (USA) **Sheikh Mohammed al Maktoum**
106 B f 15/3 Diktat—High Hawk (Shirley Heights) **Sheikh Mohammed al Maktoum**
107 **HIGH IS THE MOON (FR)**, gr c 2/4 Highest Honor (FR)—
 Ambassadrice (FR) (Be My Guest (USA)) (64935) **Bob Lalemant**
108 **HURRICANE RUN (IRE)**, b c 13/4 Montjeu (IRE)—Hold On (GER) (Surumu (GER)) **Gestut Ammerland**
109 B c 7/3 King's Best (USA)—Intrepidity (Sadler's Wells (USA)) **Sheikh Mohammed al Maktoum**
110 **JUMP FOR YOU (FR)**, b c 16/5 Montjeu (FR)—Polly's Wika (FR) (Miswaki (USA)) (24737) **Bob Lalemant**
111 **KING KASYAPA (IRE)**, b c 4/3 Darshaan—Ezana (Ela-Mana-Mou) (600000) **Maktoum al Maktoum**
112 Ch c 7/4 Sunday Silence (USA)—Laiyl (IRE) (Nureyev (USA)) **Sheikh Mohammed al Maktoum**
113 Ch c 29/4 Kingmambo (USA)—
 Lily O'Gold (USA) (Slew O' Gold (USA)) (199405) **Shiekh Mohammed al Maktoum**
114 **LUNATHEA (IRE)**, b f 20/3 Barathea (IRE)—Luna Caerla (IRE) (Caerleon (USA)) **Mr J. L. Lagardere**
115 B c 2/2 King's Best (USA)—Manureva (USA) (Nureyev (USA)) (278293) **Sheikh Mohammed al Maktoum**
116 **MATHEMATICIAN (IRE)**, br c 11/3 Machiavellian (USA)—
 Zibilene (Rainbow Quest (USA)) (525000) **Sheikh Mohammed al Maktoum**
117 **MINIMIZE (USA)**, b c 28/2 Chester House (USA)—Jolypha (USA) (Lyphard (USA)) **Prince Khalid Abdullah**
118 **MIRABILIS (USA)**, b f 9/2 Lear Fan (USA)—Media Nox (Lycius (USA)) **Prince Khalid Abdullah**

MR A. FABRE—continued

119 B f 9/3 Horse Chestnut (SAF)—
      Muskoka Command (CAN) (Top Command (USA)) (160000) **Sheikh Mohammed al Maktoum**
120 **NO GREATER LOVE (FR)**, b c 12/4 Take Risks (FR)—Desperate Virgin (BEL) (Chief Singer) **Bob Lalemant**
121 **NOT FOR TURNING (USA)**, b f 18/5 Deputy Minister (USA)—
      Vana Turns (USA) (Wavering Monarch (USA)) **Maktoum al Maktoum**
122 B br c 6/3 Highest Honor (FR)—Numidie (FR) (Baillamont (USA)) (98948) **Sheikh Mohammed al Maktoum**
123 **OISEAU RARE (FR)**, ch f 12/5 King's Best (USA)—Oiseau de Feu (USA) (Nijinsky (CAN)) **Mr J. L. Lagardere**
124 **PACHELLO (IRE)**, b c 19/1 Priolo (USA)—Most Charming (FR) (Darshaan) **Maktoum al Maktoum**
125 **POEMOANA**, br f 14/3 Dansili—Proud Douna (FR) (Kaldoun (FR)) **Mme Elisabeth Fabre**
126 **QUIET ISLE (IRE)**, ch c 9/3 Sunday Silence (USA)—
      Island of Silver (USA) (Forty Niner (USA)) **Maktoum al Maktoum**
127 **RAINBOW ARCH**, b f 25/3 Rainbow Quest (USA)—Dream Ticket (USA) (Danzig (USA)) **Maktoum al Maktoum**
128 **RAZZLE (USA)**, b f 7/5 Danzig (USA)—Razyana (USA) (His Majesty (USA)) **Prince Khalid Abdullah**
129 B c 26/2 King's Best (USA)—
      Reine Wells (IRE) (Sadler's Wells (USA)) (123685) **Sheikh Mohammed al Maktoum**
130 **ROSAWA (FR)**, gr f 13/2 Linamix (FR)—Rose Quartz (Lammtarra (USA)) **Mr J. L. Lagardere**
131 B br c 18/2 Singspiel (IRE)—Rosia (FR) (Mr Prospector (USA)) **Sheikh Mohammed al Maktoum**
132 **ROUNDEL (USA)**, b f 15/3 Kingmambo (USA)—
      Ring of Music (Sadler's Wells (USA)) **Sheikh Mohammed al Maktoum**
133 B c 6/2 Singspiel (IRE)—Rum Cay (USA) (Our Native (USA)) **Sheikh Mohammed al Maktoum**
134 **SANTIAGA (FR)**, b f 11/1 Deputy Commander—Santiago Blue (USA) (Relaunch (USA)) **Mr J. L. Lagardere**
135 **SCARTARA (FR)**, gr f 13/2 Linamix (FR)—Scarlet Raider (USA) (Red Ransom (USA)) **Mr J. L. Lagardere**
136 Ch c 20/3 Dubai Millennium—Serengeti Day (Alleged (USA)) **Sheikh Mohammed al Maktoum**
137 **SHADUF (USA)**, b f 7/2 Pleasant Tap (USA)—
      Shade Dance (USA) (Nureyev (USA)) **Sheikh Mohammed al Maktoum**
138 B f 30/3 Darshaan—Shinko Hermes (IRE) (Sadler's Wells (USA)) **Sheikh Mohammed al Maktoum**
139 B c 26/2 Fasliyev (USA)—Sinueuse (FR) (Fabulous Dancer (USA)) **Mr E. Rothschild**
140 **STOP MAKING SENSE**, b c 19/2 Lujain (USA)—
      Freeway (FR) (Exit To Nowhere (USA)) (37105) **Anne Marie Springer**
141 **SUN BOAT**, b c 27/4 Machiavellian (USA)—
      One So Wonderful (Nashwan (USA)) (525000) **Sheikh Mohammed al Maktoum**
142 B c 18/3 Anabaa (USA)—Sweet Story (IRE) (Green Tune (USA)) **Mr E. Rothschild**
143 **SWIFT GASCON (FR)**, b c 1/4 Highest Honor (FR)—Sweet Opera (FR) (Linamix (FR)) **Mr J. L. Lagardere**
144 B c 23/2 Montjeu (IRE)—Termania (IRE) (Shirley Heights) **Sheikh Mohammed al Maktoum**
145 **THRIFT (IRE)**, b f 30/1 Green Desert (USA)—Fawaayid (USA) (Vaguely Noble) **Maktoum al Maktoum**
146 B f 11/3 Saint Ballado (USA)—True Glory (IRE) (In The Wings) **Sheikh Mohammed al Maktoum**
147 **VADASIN (IRE)**, b c 20/3 Sinndar (IRE)—Vadlamixa (FR) (Linamix (FR)) **Mr J. L. Lagardere**
148 **VADAWINA (IRE)**, b f 7/2 Unfuwain (USA)—Vadaza (FR) (Zafonic (USA)) **Mr J. L. Lagardere**
149 Ch f 6/5 Halling (USA)—Wajd (USA) (Northern Dancer) **Sheikh Mohammed al Maktoum**
150 **WINNING SEQUENCE (FR)**, b f 1/2 Zafonic (USA)—Cracovie (Caerleon (USA)) (154607) **Anne Marie Springer**
151 **WITHOUT A TRACE (IRE)**, b f 4/2 Darshaan—Star Profile (IRE) (Sadler's Wells (USA)) **Maktoum al Maktoum**

---

192 **MR R. A. FAHEY, Malton**
Postal: **RF Racing Ltd, Mews House, Musley Bank, Malton, North Yorkshire, YO17 6TD.**
Contact: **PHONE** (01653) 698915 **FAX** (01653) 699735 **MOBILE** (07713) 478079
E-MAIL richard.fahey@virgin.net

1   **ALRIDA (IRE)**, 5, b g Ali-Royal (IRE)—Ride Bold (USA) **Mark Russell & Partners**
2   **ALTAY**, 7, b g Erins Isle—Aliuska (IRE) **Mr R. M. Jeffs & Mr J. Potter**
3   **ANGEL ISA (IRE)**, 4, b f Fayruz—Isa **Yorkshire Racing Club Owners Group 1990**
4   **BALL O MALT (IRE)**, 8, b g Star Quest—Vera Dodd (IRE) **Mr Declan Kinahan & Syndicate**
5   **BESEIGED (USA)**, 7, ch g Cadeaux Genereux—Munnaya (USA) **Mr Mike Caulfield**
6   **BLYTHE SPIRIT**, 5, b g Bahamian Bounty—Lithe Spirit (IRE) **R F Racing Limited**
7   **BRAMANTINO (IRE)**, 4, b g Perugino (USA)—Headrest **Mrs Kenyon, A Rhodes Haulage, P Timmins**
8   **CALL OF THE WILD**, 4, ch g Wolfhound—Biba (IRE) **Lets Go Racing 1**
9   **CLASSICAL BEN**, 6, ch g Most Welcome—Stoproveritate **J. D. Clark and Partners**
10 **CUMWHITTON**, 5, b m Jumbo Hirt (USA)—Dominance **Mr J. Roundtree**
11 **CYCLONIC STORM**, 5, b m Catrail (USA)—Wheeler's Wonder (IRE) **Galaxy Racing**
12 **DANELOR (IRE)**, 6, b g Danehill (USA)—Formulate **Mr Mark A. Leatham**
13 **DARK CHARM (FR)**, 5, b g Anabaa (USA)—Wardara **Mr G. H. Leatham**
14 **DEFINITE GUEST (IRE)**, 6, gr g Definite Article—Nicea (IRE) **Mr G. H. Leatham**
15 **DENE VIEW (IRE)**, 9, br g Good Thyne (USA)—The Furnituremaker **Mr C. H. Stevens**
16 **DHAUDELOUP (FR)**, 9, ch g Mister Sicy (FR)—Debolouve (FR) **Mr G. H. Leatham**
17 4, Ch f Emerati (USA)—Don't Be Late **Mr Tim Kilroe**
18 **EXSTOTO**, 7, b g Mtoto—Stoproveritate **J. D. Clark and Partners**

IF YOU WANT TO TAKE ON THE WORLD, IT HELPS TO START WITH A WORLD CHAMPION
HAWK WING
WORLD CHAMPION OF 2003
NEW FOR 2004
ROCK OF GIBRALTAR
WORLD CHAMPION OF 2002
CRACKING FIRST FOALS IN 2004
MONTJEU
WORLD CHAMPION OF 1999
FIRST 2-Y-O'S TO RUN IN 2004
PEINTRE CELEBRE
WORLD CHAMPION OF 1997
EUROPEAN CHAMPION SECOND CROP SIRE.
COOLMORE

MR R. A. FAHEY—continued

19 **FENWICKS PRIDE (IRE)**, 6, b g Imperial Frontier (USA)—Stunt Girl (IRE) **Mr J. H. Tattersall**
20 **FIROZI**, 5, b m Forzando—Lambast **Galaxy Racing**
21 **FOOLISH THOUGHT (IRE)**, 4, b g Green Desert (USA)—Trusted Partner (USA) **Mr P. Macklam & Syndicate**
22 **FRIEDHELMO (GER)**, 8, ch g Dashing Blade—Fox For Gold **Mr G. H. Leatham**
23 **GIOCOMO (IRE)**, 6, ch g Indian Ridge—Karri Valley (USA) **Mugsrus**
24 **HAZE BABYBEAR**, 4, b f Mujadil (USA)—River's Rising (FR) **A K Lingerie Holdings Ltd**
25 **HOUT BAY**, 7, ch g Komaite (USA)—Maiden Pool **Mr P. Macklin**
26 **HUMID CLIMATE**, 4, ch g Desert King (IRE)—Pontoon **J. E. M. Hawkins Ltd**
27 **INDIAN SOLITAIRE (IRE)**, 5, b g Bigstone (IRE)—Terrama Sioux **P. D. Smith Holdings Ltd**
28 **KINGS COLLEGE BOY**, 4, b g College Chapel—The Kings Daughter **The Dandy Dons Partnership**
29 **KING'S CREST**, 6, b g Deploy—Classic Beauty (IRE) **Seamus Farrey & Partners**
30 **MAFRUZ**, 5, ch g Hamas (IRE)—Braari (USA) **Mr C. Rosbottom**
31 **MARKET AVENUE**, 5, b m Factual (USA)—The Lady Vanishes **Market Avenue Racing Club**
32 **MARSHALLSPARK (IRE)**, 5, b g Fayruz—Lindas Delight **Mr J. J. Staunton**
33 **MILLIGAN (FR)**, 9, b g Exit To Nowhere (USA)—Madigan Mill **Mr G. H. Leatham & Syndicate**
34 **MR LEAR (USA)**, 5, b g Lear Fan (USA)—Majestic Mae (USA) **Phoenix Racing**
35 **MR PERTEMPS**, 6, b g Primo Dominie—Amber Mill **Kingdom Racing**
36 5, B m King's Ride—My Lovely Rose (IRE) **Mr M. Hurst**
37 **NAMROUD (USA)**, 5, b g Irish River (FR)—Top Line (FR) **Mr D. M. Knaggs**
38 **NECKAR VALLEY (IRE)**, 5, b g Desert King (IRE)—Solar Attraction (IRE) **Mr G. Morrill**
39 **NO GROUSE**, 4, b c Pursuit of Love—Lady Joyce (IRE) **Valley Paddocks Racing**
40 **OLDENWAY**, 5, b g Most Welcome—Sickle Moon **Mr J. J. Staunton**
41 **OPENING CEREMONY (USA)**, 5, br m Quest For Fame—Gleam of Light (IRE) **Mr H. Hurst**
42 **PERTEMPS MAGUS**, 4, b f Silver Wizard (USA)—Brilliant Future **Sue Wilox**
43 **QUINTOTO**, 4, b g Mtoto—Ballet **Mr P. Timmins**
44 **RISKA KING**, 4, b g Forzando—Artistic Licence **Market Avenue Racing Club**
45 **SABREFLIGHT**, 4, ch f Sabrehill (USA)—Little Redwing **Mr D. S. Coates**
46 **SHAROURA**, 8, ch m Inchinor—Kinkajoo **Mr K. Hind**
47 **SIR SANDROVITCH (IRE)**, 8, b g Polish Patriot (USA)—Old Downie **R F Racing Limited & Syndicate**
48 **SUALDA (IRE)**, 5, b g Idris (IRE)—Winning Heart **Mr J. H. Tattersall**
49 **SWAN KNIGHT (USA)**, 8, b br g Sadler's Wells (USA)—Shannkara (IRE) **Mr J. J. Staunton**
50 **TURN OF PHRASE (IRE)**, 5, b g Cadeaux Genereux—
    Token Gesture (IRE) **Jacksons Transport (West Riding) Ltd**
51 **VINTAGE PREMIUM**, 7, b g Forzando—Julia Domna **Mr J. C. Parsons**
52 **WING COMMANDER**, 5, b g Royal Applause—Southern Psychic (USA) **Bee Health Ltd**
53 **WUXI VENTURE**, 9, b g Wolfhound (USA)—Push A Button **Mr R. G. Leatham**

THREE-YEAR-OLDS

54 **ABELARD (IRE)**, b g Fasliyev (USA)—Half-Hitch (USA) **Mr Aidan J. Ryan**
55 **ARIESANNE (IRE)**, ch f Primo Dominie—Living Legend (ITY) **Mr Bill Walker**
56 **BO MCGINTY (IRE)**, ch g Fayruz—Georges Park Lady (IRE) **R F Racing Limited**
57 **CHIMES EIGHT**, b f Octagonal (NZ)—Bell Toll **Mr Giles W. Pritchard-Gordon**
58 **FLYING BANTAM (IRE)**, b g Fayruz—Natural Pearl **The Matthewman Partnership**
59 **HARRISON'S FLYER (IRE)**, b g Imperial Ballet (IRE)—Smart Pet **P. D. Smith Holdings Ltd**
60 **IO CALLISTO**, br f Hector Protector (USA)—Queen Shirley (IRE) **Spartans Racing Syndicate**
61 **KAMENKA**, ch f Wolfhound (USA)—Aliuska (IRE) **Mr R. M. Jeffs & Mr J. Potter**
62 **KING'S SILVER (IRE)**, b g King of Kings (IRE)—Almi Ad (USA) **Let's Go Racing 2**
63 **LITTLE JIMBOB**, b g Desert Story (IRE)—Artistic Licence **Mr A. Tattersall**
64 **MR LEWIN**, ch g Primo Dominie—Fighting Run **Market Avenue Racing Club**
65 **PHILHARMONIC**, b g Victory Note (USA)—Lambast **Mr R. Cowie**
66 **PRINCES GRANT**, b c Compton Place—Penny Dip **Mr D. R. Brotherton**
67 **PURE VINTAGE (IRE)**, b g Fasliyev (USA)—Tootling (IRE) **Mr J. C. Parsons**
68 **RICHTEE (IRE)**, ch f Desert Sun—Santarene (IRE) **Terence Elsey and Richard Mustill**
69 **RISING SHADOW (IRE)**, b g Efisio—Jouet **Mr G. Morrill**
70 **SIOUX RYDER (IRE)**, gr f Intikhab (USA)—Street Lina (FR) **Mrs Una Towell**
71 **STARCROSS VENTURE**, b f Orpen (USA)—Maculatus (USA) **Mr D. M. Beresford & Partners**
72 **WILLJOJO**, br f Mind Games—Millie's Lady (IRE) **The Yorkshire Lancashire Alliance**
73 **WONDER WOLF**, b f Wolfhound (USA)—Wrangbrook **The Tom Mix Partners**
74 **WRENLANE**, ch g Fraam—Hi Hoh (IRE) **Mr Keith Taylor**
75 **XPRESSIONS**, b g Turtle Island (IRE)—Make Ready **Mr J. C. Parsons**

TWO-YEAR-OLDS

76 B c 19/2 Forzando—Artistic Licence (High Top) (13000) **The Matthewman Partnership**
77 Ch f 1/2 Desert Story (IRE)—Bird In My Hand (IRE) (Bluebird (USA)) (9276) **Mr Aidan J. Ryan**
78 **BISSPHILLY**, b f 25/3 Primo Dominie—Majalis (Mujadil (USA)) (15500) **Mr Phillip Lawton**

MR R. A. FAHEY—continued

79 **BURNLEY AL (IRE)**, ch c 30/4 Desert King (IRE)—
Bold Meadows (Persian Bold) (6000) **The Mathewman Partnership**
80 B c 9/3 Lend—Cantata (IRE) (Saddler's Hall (IRE)) (7000) **J. C. Parsons Esq.**
81 **CHOREOGRAPHIC (IRE)**, b c 24/4 Komaite (USA)—Lambast (Relkino) (35000) **Mr Ray Cowie**
82 Br c 24/5 Danehill Dancer (IRE)—Crimbourne (Mummy's Pet) (12000) **Re-New Windows (G. Morrill)**
83 B f 4/4 Rossini (USA)—Dissidentia (IRE) (Dancing Dissident (USA)) **Mr Glen Devlin**
84 B c 14/4 Sinndar (IRE)—Fancy Wrap (Kris) (9000) **Mr Aidan J. Ryan**
85 **KARASHINO (IRE)**, ch f 31/1 Shinko Forest (IRE)—Karisal (Persian Bold) (26000) **J. E. M. Hawkins Ltd**
86 **LOUP SIFFLET (IRE)**, b c 22/4 Loup Sauvage (USA)—Bee-Bee-Gee (IRE) (Lake Coniston (IRE)) **Mr Ray Cowie**
87 B f 25/2 Bahamian Bounty—Lunar Ridge (Indian Ridge) (4500) **Valley Paddocks Racing**
88 **MASTER BEAR (IRE)**, b c 26/5 Bluebird (USA)—Kunuz (Ela-Mana-Mou) (17315) **J. A. Campbell Esq.**
89 B c 7/2 Shinko Forest (IRE)—Notley Park (Wolfhound (USA)) (10000) **Syndicate led by A. Rhodes Haulage Ltd**
90 Ch c 1/4 Fayruz—Peace Dividend (IRE) (Alzao (USA)) (6500) **The Rumpole Partnership**
91 **PECANWOOD (IRE)**, ch g 5/3 Bluebird (USA)—Baccara (IRE) (Sri Pekan (USA)) (14500) **D. Brotherton Esq.**
92 **PETERS DELITE**, b c 10/3 Makbul—Steadfast Elite (IRE) (Glenstal (USA)) (31000) **Mr E. P. Foden**
93 **PLENTY CRIED WOLF**, b c 2/3 Wolfhound (USA)—
Plentitude (FR) (Ela-Mana-Mou) (10500) **The Definitely Maybe Partnership**
94 B c 14/3 Soviet Star (USA)—She's The Tops (Shernazar) (14000) **Syndicate led by Market Avenue Racing**
95 **SUMMER SILKS**, ch f 31/3 Bahamian Bounty—
Sadler's Song (Saddlers' Hall (IRE)) (500) **Syndicate led by Falcon Assets Ltd**
96 B f 12/4 Mark of Esteem (IRE)—Sunflower Seed (Mummy's Pet) (4638) **Mrs A. Mallinson**
97 **TAGULA SUNRISE (IRE)**, ch f 22/2 Tagula (IRE)—
Lady From Limerick (IRE) (Rainbows For Life (CAN)) (35000) **Yorkshire Lancashire All'**
98 B c 4/4 Second Empire (IRE)—Vax Lady (Millfontaine) (5000) **Valley Paddocks Racing**

Other Owners: Mrs Helena Ashworth, Mrs Angie Bailey, Mr D. Barnett, Mr Jim Blair, Mr Jim Browne, Mr J. A. Campbell, Mrs K. Campbell, Mr David Craggs, Mrs Rachel Denny, Mr Terence Elsey, Mr John Fieldus, Mr F. Firzmaurice, Mr C. R. Galloway, Mr J. J. Gilmartin, Mr Peter Greaves, Mr Martin Green, Mr W. E. Gruber, Mr J. P. Hames, Mr J. Hilton, Mr T. Hynes, Mr R. M. Jeffs, Mr A. Jones, Miss S. Kelly, Mr J. McGarr, Mr C. H. McGhie, Mr P. McGinty, Mr W. G. Moore, Mrs P. A. Morrison, Mr Brian Morton, Mr George Murray, Mrs Kathleen Murray, Mr Richard Mustill, Mrs M. S. Nelson, Mr R. W. North, Mr Pierce O'Sullivan, Mr G. J. Paver, Mr N. D. Peppiatt, Mr J. Potter, Ms J Rainer-Thomas, Mr G. Ralph, Mr Mel Roberts, Mr D. J. Robertson, Mrs B. Roger, Mr E. Roger, Mr Richard Stimson, Mr N. A. Swales, Mr Peter Tingey, Mr Bo Turnbull, Mr Nigel Vaulkhard, Mr J. Waddington, Mr G. H. M. Walker, Mr M. Wassall, Mr Tim Watts, Mr John Wicks, Mr G. R. Winton.

Assistant Trainer: Pat Brilly

Jockey (Flat): P Hannagan (7-12). **Apprentice:** C Poste (7-3). **Conditional:** P Whelan (9-11).

---

193 MR C. W. FAIRHURST, Middleham

Postal: **Glasgow House, Middleham, Leyburn, North Yorkshire, DL8 4QG.**
Contact: PHONE **(01969) 622039** FAX **(01969) 622039** MOBILE **(07889) 410840**
WEBSITE **www.chrisfairhurstracing.com** E-MAIL **cfairhurst@tiscali.co.uk**

1 **ABBAJABBA**, 8, b g Barrys Gamble—Bo' Babbity **North Cheshire Trading & Storage Ltd**
2 **CAPTAINTWOTHOUSAND**, 9, b g Milieu—Royal Scarlet **Mrs A. M. Leggett**
3 **DUE DILIGENCE**, 5, ch g Entrepreneur—Kerry Project (IRE) **Mrs P. J. Taylor Garthwaite & H. Taylor**
4 **GILOU**, 8, b m Midyan (USA)—Lunagraphe (USA) **P. Richmond & Partners**
5 **KING'S WELCOME**, 6, b g Most Welcome—Reine de Thebes (FR) **G. H. & S. Leggott**
6 **M FOR MAGIC**, 5, ch g First Trump—Celestine **M. J. & Mrs D. Grace**
7 **OOS AND AHS**, 4, b f Silver Wizard (USA)—Hot Feet **Mr C. W. Fairhurst**
8 **PRIMITIVE JEAN**, 5, b m Primitive Rising (USA)—Gemma Jean **Mr David Bartlett**
9 **PRIX STAR**, 9, ch g Superpower—Celestine **M. J. & Mrs D. Grace**
10 **QUINN**, 4, ch g First Trump—Celestine **Grace Arnold Partnership**
11 **RADICAL JACK**, 7, b g Presidium—Luckifosome **Mrs B. J. Boocock**
12 **RAHWAAN (IRE)**, 5, b g Darshaan—Fawaakeh (USA) **The Six Iron Partnership**
13 **RINGSIDE JACK**, 8, b g Batshoof—Celestine **M. J. G. Partnership**
14 **STRONG WILL**, 4, b g Primo Dominie—Reine de Thebes (FR) **G. H. & S. Leggott**
15 **TOMORROWS TREASURE**, 4, ch f Bahamian Bounty—Yesterday's Song **Mr David Hawes**
16 **WARRLIN**, 10, b g Warrshan (USA)—Lahin **Glasgow House Racing Syndicate**

THREE-YEAR-OLDS

17 **CHARLIE CHAN**, gr g Paris House—Vindictive Lady (USA) **John Jackson Racing Partnership**
18 **LUCKY PISCEAN**, b g River Falls—Celestine **Grace Arnold Partnership**
19 **PASSION FRUIT**, b f Pursuit of Love—Reine de Thebes (FR) **G. H. & S. Leggott**

MR C. W. FAIRHURST—continued

20 **POLAR GALAXY**, br f Polar Falcon (USA)—June Brilly (IRE) **John Jackson Racing Partnership**
21 **RIVER LINE (USA)**, b g Keos (USA)—Portio (USA) **Mrs B. J. Boocock**
22 **YORKE'S FOLLY (USA)**, b f Stravinsky (USA)—Tommelise (USA) **Mrs A. M. Leggett**

TWO-YEAR-OLDS

23 B f 4/2 Fraam—River Maiden (USA) (Riverman (USA)) (2500) **Thornton Racing Partnership**
24 **SPECTRUM OF LIGHT**, b f 2/2 Spectrum (IRE)—Express of Light (Emperor Jones (USA)) **Mr J. Jackson**

Other Owners: Mrs C. Arnold, Mr D. M. Gardner, Barry Kitching, Derek Latham, Shirley Makin, Alistair Robertson, Mr B. M. Saumtally, H. Spence, Mr M. Williams, Mr S. C. Wrightson.

---

194   **MR J. R. FANSHAWE, Newmarket**
Postal: **Pegasus Stables, Snailwell Road, Newmarket, Suffolk, CB8 7DJ.**
Contact: **PHONE (01638) 664525/660153 FAX (01638) 664523**
E-MAIL james.fanshawe@virgin.net WEBSITE www.jamesfanshawe.com

1 **ABLE BAKER CHARLIE (IRE)**, 5, b g Sri Pekan (USA)—Lavezzola (IRE) **David Croft & Partners**
2 **ARRESTING**, 4, b g Hector Protector (USA)—Misbelief **Mrs Andrew Wates & Mr Tim Vestey**
3 **BELUGA BAY**, 5, b g Millkom—Bellyphax **Beluga Bay Partnership**
4 **CURFEW**, 5, b m Marju (IRE)—Twilight Patrol
5 **DEFINING**, 5, b g Definite Article—Gooseberry Pie **Mrs V. Shelton**
6 **DUBROVSKY**, 4, ch g Hector Protector (USA)—Reuval **Dr Catherine Wills**
7 **ETCHING (USA)**, 4, b f Groom Dancer (USA)—Eternity **Dr Catherine Wills**
8 **EYECATCHER**, 7, b g Green Desert (USA)—Reuval **Dr Catherine Wills**
9 **FLAMINGO FLOWER (USA)**, 4, ch f Diesis—Fabula Dancer (USA) **Lael Stable**
10 **FRIZZANTE**, 5, b m Efisio—Juliet Bravo **Mrs Jan Hopper & Mrs Elizabeth Grundy**
11 **GIFT HORSE**, 4, ch g Cadeaux Genereux—Careful Queen **Exors of the Late Anne Church**
12 **HERETIC**, 6, b g Bishop of Cashel—Barford Lady **Barford Bloodstock**
13 **ICE PLACE**, 4, b f Polar Falcon (USA)—White Palace **Cheveley Park Stud**
14 **I'LL FLY**, 4, ch g Polar Falcon (USA)—I'll Try **Mrs K Fraser Mrs D Strauss Mrs R Hambro**
15 **LOUP (FR)**, 5, b g Cyborg (FR)—Quintessence III (FR) **Mr Paul Green**
16 **MORNING AFTER**, 4, b f Emperor Jones (USA)—Onefortheditch (USA) **The Nightcaps**
17 **PERSARIO**, 5, b m Bishop of Cashel—Barford Lady **Barford Bloodstock**
18 **POLAR BEN**, 5, b g Polar Falcon (USA)—Woodbeck **Mr Simon Gibson**
19 **POLE STAR**, 6, b g Polar Falcon (USA)—Ellie Ardensky **Mr D. I. Russell**
20 **PRINS WILLEM (IRE)**, 5, b g Alzao (USA)—American Garden (USA) **Mr Chris van Hoorn**
21 **REVEILLEZ**, 5, gr g First Trump—Amalancher (USA) **Exors of the Late Anne Church**
22 **RUMOUR**, 4, b f Lion Cavern (USA)—Thea (USA) **T. & J. Vestey**
23 **SATINE (IRE)**, 4, b f Danehill (USA)—Shahtoush (IRE)
24 **SOLDERA (USA)**, 4, b f Polish Numbers (USA)—La Pepite (USA) **Woodhall Stud**
25 **SOVIET SONG (IRE)**, 4, b f Marju (IRE)—Kalinka (IRE) **Elite Racing Club**
26 **ULTIMATA**, 4, ch f Unfuwain (USA)—Last Look **J. H. Richmond-Watson**
27 **UNSCRUPULOUS**, 5, ch g Machiavellian (USA)—Footlight Fantasy (USA) **Lancen Farm Partnership**
28 **VINDICATION**, 4, ch g Compton Place—Prince's Feather (IRE) **B & F Mechanical SVCCS**
29 **WELCOME SIGNAL**, 4, ch g Most Welcome—Glenfinlass **Mr Simon Gibson**
30 **ZONIC BOOM (FR)**, 4, b br c Zafonic (USA)—Rosi Zambotti (USA) **Mrs V. Shelton**

THREE-YEAR-OLDS

31 **ALEXEI**, ch g Ashkalani (IRE)—Sherkova (USA) **Mrs V. Shelton**
32 **ANTHOS (GER)**, b f Big Shuffle (USA)—Anemoni (GER) **Cheveley Park Stud**
33 **ASPIRED (IRE)**, b f Mark of Esteem (IRE)—Dreams **Nigel & Caroline Elwes**
34 **AZAROLE (IRE)**, b c Alzao (USA)—Cashew **Lord Vestey**
35 **BABOOSH (IRE)**, b f Marju (IRE)—Slipper **Lord Halifax**
36 **CASHBAR**, b f Bishop of Cashel—Barford Sovereign **Barford Bloodstock**
37 **CATHERINE WHEEL**, b f Primo Dominie—Prancing **Cheveley Park Stud**
38 **CESARE**, b c Machiavellian (USA)—Tromond **Cheveley Park Stud**
39 **CHANTELOUP**, ch f Grand Lodge (USA)—Nibbs Point (IRE) **Lord Halifax**
40 **CONVICTION**, b g Machiavellian (USA)—Beldarian (IRE) **Mr M. Fisch**
41 **DISPARITY (USA)**, b f Distant View (USA)—Eternity **Dr Catherine Wills**
42 **FIFTH COLUMN (USA)**, b g Allied Forces (USA)—Miff **Miff**
43 **FIRENZE**, ch f Efisio—Juliet Bravo **Mrs Jan Hopper**
44 **FLING**, b f Pursuit of Love—Full Orchestra **Cheveley Park Stud**
45 **HIGH CHARTER**, b c Polish Precedent (USA)—By Charter **Colin Davey Racing**
46 **HIGH RESERVE**, b f Dr Fong (USA)—Hyabella **Helena Springfield Ltd**

MR J. R. FANSHAWE—continued

47 **KAURI FOREST (USA)**, ch c Woodman (USA)—Kentucky Fall (FR) **Mr D. I. Russell**
48 Ch c Peintre Celebre (USA)—Kotama (USA) **Mr Ivan Allan**
49 **LADY GEORGINA**, gr f Linamix (FR)—Georgia Venture **Byerley Turf**
50 **LA TURQUE (IRE)**, ch f Diesis—Queen's Music (USA) **Woodhall Stud**
51 **MARBLE GARDEN (USA)**, b br g Royal Academy (USA)—Maria de La Luz **Mrs Robert G. Ehrnrooth**
52 **MOANING MYRTLE**, br f Desert King (IRE)—Grinning (IRE)
53 **MRS SHILLING**, b f Dr Fong (USA)—Papaha (IRE) **Exors of the Late Anne Church**
54 **MUSICANNA**, b f Cape Cross (IRE)—Upend **Mr Abdulla BuHaleeba**
55 **MUSLIN**, ch f Bien Bien (USA)—Moidart **Dr Catherine Wills**
56 **PASS THE PORT**, ch g Docksider (USA)—One of The Family **Lancen Farm Partnership**
57 **PENDING (IRE)**, b g Pennekamp (USA)—Dolcezza (FR) **Eildon Racing Partnership**
58 **PENZANCE**, ch c Pennekamp (USA)—Kalinka (IRE) **Elite Racing Club**
59 **POLAR MAGIC**, ch c Polar Falcon (USA)—Enchant **Mr R. C. Thompson**
60 **POLAR SUN**, b g Polar Falcon (USA)—Barford Lady **Barford Bloodstock**
61 **PRIMUS INTER PARES (IRE)**, b c Sadler's Wells (USA)—Life At The Top **Colin Davey Racing**
62 **PRIVATE JESSICA**, ch f Cadeaux Genereux—Rose Bay **Eildon Racing Partnership**
63 **RACHEL'S VERDICT**, b f Royal Applause—Shady Street (USA) **Mr M. Fisch**
64 **RAINBOW COLOURS (IRE)**, br f Linamix (FR)—Mill Rainbow (FR) **Cheveley Park Stud**
65 **RED SAIL**, ch f Dr Fong (USA)—Manhattan Sunset (USA) **Mrs David Russell**
66 **ROYAL PRINCE**, gr c Royal Applause—Onefortheditch (USA) **Mr Abdulla BuHaleeba**
67 **SOLAR POWER (IRE)**, b f Marju (IRE)—Next Round (IRE) **Deln Ltd**
68 **SOVIET SPIRIT**, ch f Soviet Star (USA)—Kristina **Mr J. H. Richmond-Watson**
69 **SPRING JIM**, b g First Trump—Spring Sixpence **Andrew & Julia Turner**
70 **THE VESEYAN (USA)**, ch g Atticus (USA)—Mother Courage
71 **TREASON TRIAL**, b g Peintre Celebre (USA)—Pampabella (IRE) **Elite Racing Club**
72 **VERVAIN**, b br f Vettori (IRE)—Princess Nawaal (USA) **Dr Catherine Wills**
73 **WARDEN COMPLEX**, b g Compton Place—Miss Rimex (IRE) **Park Farm Racing**
74 **YORKSHIRE OWL**, b br c Marju (IRE)—Rosa Canina

TWO-YEAR-OLDS

75 B f 29/1 Deploy—Blane Water (USA) (Lomond (USA)) (8500)
76 **BOUQUET**, ch f 10/5 Cadeaux Genereux—Bayadere (USA) (Green Dancer (USA)) **Mrs Dennis Haynes**
77 **BUSTER HYVONEN (IRE)**, b c 5/4 Dansili—Serotina (IRE) (Mtoto) (25000) **Mr Simon Gibson**
78 B f 16/2 Zilzal (USA)—Cavernista (Lion Cavern (USA)) (10000) **Mrs D. Swinburn**
79 **DAWN AT SEA**, b f 20/3 Slip Anchor—Finger of Light (Green Desert (USA)) (22000)
80 **DREADNOUGHT**, b c 21/4 Slip Anchor—Fleet Amour (USA) (Afleet (CAN)) **Mrs Denis Haynes**
81 **EGERIA (IRE)**, b f 1/5 Daylami (IRE)—Spring (Sadler's Wells (USA)) **Cheveley Park Stud**
82 **EMBARK**, b f 7/3 Soviet Star (USA)—Shore Line (High Line) **Cheveley Park Stud**
83 B c 26/4 Inchinor—First Fantasy (Be My Chief (USA))
84 B f 2/4 Unfuwain (USA)—Hyperspectra (Rainbow Quest (USA)) (100000) **Helena Springfield Ltd**
85 **ICELANDIC**, b c 21/4 Selkirk (USA)—Icicle (Polar Falcon (USA)) **Cheveley Park Stud**
86 **KAZATZKA**, ch f 1/4 Groom Dancer (USA)—Kalinka (IRE) (Soviet Star (USA)) **Kazatzka**
87 Ch c 25/3 Nashwan (USA)—Kissogram (Caerleon (USA)) **Lancen Farm Partnership**
88 **KRISTINOR (FR)**, ch c 28/3 Inchinor—Kristina (Kris) **J. H. Richmond Watson**
89 **LIGHT SPEED**, b c 30/1 Green Desert (USA)—
Elle Questro (Rainbow Quest (USA)) (80000) **Mr Abdulla BuHaleeba**
90 **MANTLE**, b f 7/5 Loup Sauvage (USA)—Kyle Rhea (In The Wings)
91 **NOBELIX (IRE)**, gr c 14/3 Linamix (FR)—Nataliana (Surumu (GER)) (30921) **Mr Rupert Hambro**
92 **NOR'WESTER**, br c 19/3 Inchinor—Princess Nawaal (USA) (Seattle Slew (USA)) **J. H. Richmond-Watson**
93 **PENNY WEDDING (IRE)**, b f 6/2 Pennekamp (USA)—Eilean Shona (Suave Dancer (USA)) **Dr Catherine Wills**
94 **PRIMONDO (IRE)**, b c 25/2 Montjeu (IRE)—Tagiki (IRE) (Doyoun) (60000) **Nicolas Kairis**
95 Br c 28/3 Pivotal—Rainy Day Song (Persian Bold) (40000) **Mr Chris van Hoorn**
96 **RIVER MIST IMAGE (USA)**, ch f 3/2 Swain (USA)—
Cat's Image (CAN) (Storm Cat (USA)) (80000) **Mr Abdulla BuHaleeba**
97 B f 8/5 Diktat—Selvi (Mummy's Pet) (30000)
98 **SOAR**, b f 4/2 Danzero (AUS)—Splice (Sharpo) **Cheveley Park Stud**
99 B g 23/3 Mind Games—Tattinger (Prince Sabo) (4000)
100 B g 7/3 Singspiel (IRE)—Thea (USA) (Marju (IRE)) (42000) **T. Vestey**
101 Br c 22/2 Docksider (USA)—Threatening (Warning) (19000) **Colin Davey**
102 **THREE STRIKES (IRE)**, b f 14/4 Selkirk (USA)—Special Oasis (Green Desert (USA)) (85000)
103 **TILT**, b c 30/4 Daylami (IRE)—Tromond (Lomond (USA)) **Cheveley Park Stud**
104 **TOOTSY**, b f 2/5 Dansili—Totom (Mtoto)

MR J. R. FANSHAWE—continued

105 WONDEROUS, b c 10/2 Danzero (AUS)—Glorious (Nashwan (USA))
106 ZIDANE, b c 7/5 Danzero (AUS)—Juliet Bravo (Glow (USA)) **Mrs Jan Hopper**

Other Owners: Mrs Amanda Brudenall, Mrs D. Cantillon, Mr D. M. B. Croft, Mr Simon De Zoete, Mrs J. Fanshawe, Mrs Elizabeth Grundy, Mr Tony Hill, Dr A. Kerr, Mr S. Lane, Mr & Mrs Leach, A. Massen, Mr S. D. Swaden, Mr & Mrs P. Underwood, Mr T. R. G. Vestey, Julie Walmsley, Mrs Andrew Wates, Miss Helena Weinfeld, Mr M. Weinfeld, Mrs S. M. Willson, Mr J. D. Younger, Mr W. G. R. Younger.

Assistant Trainer: Emma Candy

---

195 MR. M LUCINDA FEATHERSTONE, Melton Mowbray
Postal: **Largesse Stud, Gated Road, Kirby Bellars, Leicestershire, LE14 2TH.**
Contact: **PHONE (01664) 812234 MOBILE (07946) 403147 E-MAIL largessestud@virgin.net**

1 ANNIVERSARY GUEST (IRE), 5, b br m Desert King (IRE)—Polynesian Goddess (IRE) **Largesse Racing**
2 BID SPOTTER (IRE), 5, b g Eagle Eyed (USA)—Bebe Auction (IRE) **Heart Of England Racing**
3 COURTCARD, 5, b m Persian Bold—Hafhafah **Heart Of England Racing**
4 KELTIC FLUTE, 5, b g Piccolo—Nanny Doon **Largesse Racing**
5 ROMAN CANDLE (IRE), 7, b g Sabrehill (USA)—Penny Banger (IRE) **Largesse Racing**
6 SILENT ANGEL, 4, b f Petong—Valls d'Andorra **Largesse Racing**
7 YOUNG WILL, 5, b g Keen—Barkston Singer **Largesse Racing**

THREE-YEAR-OLDS

8 LA VIGNA (IRE), ch g Woodborough (USA)—Bona Fide **Largesse Racing**
9 RIVER IRIS, ch f Riverhead (USA)—Barkston Singer
10 B f Riverhead (USA)—Tallulah **Heart of England Racing**
11 ZOOMIEZANDO, b g Forzando—Zarah **Largesse Racing**

Other Owners: Mr E. A. Buckley, Mr P. R. Featherstone, Pat Green, The Hon Cherry King, Indian Ocean Partnership, Mr Reg Parnham, Ms Diana Wilder.

Assistant Trainer: Simon Maplekoft

---

196 MR D. B. FEEK, Robertsbridge
Postal: **2 Street Cottage, Brightling, Robertsbridge, East Sussex, TN32 5HH.**
Contact: **PHONE (01424) 838557 MOBILE (07884) 387798**
E-MAIL dfeek@brightlingracing.co.uk WEBSITE www.brightlingracing.co.uk

1 ARCTIC RAINBOW (IRE), 6, b g King's Ride—Arctic Chatter **The Hon Mrs C. Cameron**
2 GREEN GAMBLE, 4, gr g Environment Friend—Gemma's Wager (IRE) **Mr Barry & Baroness Noakes**
3 HERCULES MORSE (IRE), 8, b g Spanish Place (USA)—Pragownia **Mr D. M. Grissell**
4 LITTLE ROSS, 9, b g St Ninian—Little Katrina **Mr Barry & Baroness Noakes**
5 MR BOO (IRE), 5, b g Needle Gun (IRE)—Dasi **The Hon Mrs C. Cameron**
6 MYSON (IRE), 5, ch g Accordion—Ah Suzie (IRE) **R. Winchester & Son**
7 PARTY GAMES (IRE), 7, b g King's Ride—Shady Miss **Mr Gregory Barker**
8 SPANISH POINT (IRE), 7, br g Un Desperado (FR)—Molly Murphy (IRE) **Mrs R. M. Hepburn**

THREE-YEAR-OLDS

9 MR DINGLAWI (IRE), b g Danehill Dancer (IRE)—Princess Leona (IRE) **Brightling Folly Partnership**
10 PRINCE VALENTINE, b g My Best Valentine—Affaire de Coeur **Mr D. R. Hunnisett**

TWO-YEAR-OLDS

11 DREAM OF LOVE, b f 13/5 Pursuit of Love—Affaire de Coeur (Imperial Fling (USA)) **Mr D. R. Hunnisett**

Other Owners: Mr D. Curtis, Mr Tony Feek, Mr J. Hills, Baroness Noakes, Mr C. B. Noakes, Mr M. D. Winchester, Mr R. F. Winchester.

197 MISS J. D. FEILDEN, Newmarket

Postal: **Harraton Stables, Chapel Street, Exning, Newmarket, Suffolk, CB8 7HA.**
Contact: **MOBILE (07974) 817694 E-MAIL hoofbeatstours@aol.com**

1 **DANCE WORLD**, 4, b g Spectrum (IRE)—Dansara **Stowstowquickquickstow Partnership**
2 **FIFE AND DRUM (USA)**, 7, b br g Rahy (USA)—Fife (IRE) **Hoofbeats Racing Club**
3 **GARW VALLEY**, 5, b m Mtoto—Morgannwg (IRE) **Mr Steven Rees**
4 **HALCYON MAGIC**, 6, b g Magic Ring (IRE)—Consistent Queen **The Magic Partnership**
5 **INDRAPURA STAR (USA)**, 4, b g Foxhound (USA)—Royal Recall (USA) **City Racing Club**
6 **KING FLYER (IRE)**, 8, b g Ezzoud (IRE)—Al Guswa **Mr J. Jenkins**
7 **LOADED GUN**, 4, ch g Highest Honor (FR)—Woodwardia (USA) **Mr J. F. Thomas**
8 **MAID FOR A MONARCH**, 4, b f King's Signet (USA)—Regan (USA) **Mr Steven Rees**
9 **MISTY MAN (USA)**, 6, ch g El Gran Senor (USA)—Miasma (USA) **Mr R. J. Creese**
10 **MOONGLADE (USA)**, 4, ch f Carson City (USA)—Moonshine Girl (USA) **Mrs J A Howell**
11 **NAJAABA (USA)**, 4, b f Bahhare (USA)—Ashbilya (USA) **Mrs A. Sparks**
12 **SHAYDEYLAYDEH (IRE)**, 5, b m Shaddad (USA)—Spirito Libro (USA) **Mr Steven Rees**
13 **SYLVIAJAZZ**, 5, b m Alhijaz—Dispol Princess (IRE) **Mr J. Jenkins**
14 **TEAM-MATE (IRE)**, 6, b g Nashwan (USA)—Ustka **Mr G. Gooden & Mrs P. Gooden**
15 **TERN INTERN (IRE)**, 5, b g Dr Devious (IRE)—Arctic Bird (USA) **Miss F. A. Brown**

THREE-YEAR-OLDS

16 **BLAKE HALL LAD (IRE)**, b g Cape Cross (IRE)—Queen of Art (IRE) **Blake Hall Partnership**
17 **ESSEX STAR (IRE)**, b f Revoque (IRE)—Touch of White **Essex Partnership**
18 **LAND ARMY (IRE)**, b f Desert Style (IRE)—Family At War (USA) **Mr S. Gibson**
19 **MISS HOOFBEATS**, b f Unfuwain (USA)—Oiselina (FR) **Miss J. Feilden**

TWO-YEAR-OLDS

20 B c 25/3 Lujain (USA)—About Face (Midyan (USA)) (11000) **Rosewood Racing Partnership**
21 B c 7/3 Revoque (IRE)—Columbian Sand (IRE) (Salmon Leap (USA)) **Mr A. Sparks**
22 **ORPEN ANNIE (IRE)**, b f 21/4 Orpen (USA)—Nisibis (In The Wings) **Hoofbeats Racing Club Syndicate**
23 B f 19/4 Second Empire (IRE)—Touch of White (Song) **Mr A. Sparks**

Other Owners: Mr F. G. Amondson, Mr J. Birkett, Mr J. L. Bonfield, Mr G. V. Jukes, Miss H. M. A. Omersa, Mr P. R. Truett.

Assistant Trainer: Poppy Feilden

Amateurs: Miss F Brown (9-0), Mr S Rees (9-0).

198 MR D. J. S. FFRENCH DAVIS, Lambourn

Postal: **Gordon Cottage, Parsonage Lane, Lambourn, Hungerford, Berkshire, RG17 8PA.**
Contact: **HOME (01488) 72342 YARD (01488) 73675 MOBILE (07831) 118764**
E-MAIL ffrenchdavis@supanet.com WEBSITE www.ffrenchdavis.com

1 **BOTTOM DRAWER**, 4, b g My Best Valentine—Little Egret **Mr M. Duthie**
2 **GEESPOT**, 5, b m Pursuit of Love—My Discovery (IRE) **B. Barrett A. Creighton P. Gallagher**
3 **HEAD TO KERRY (IRE)**, 4, b g Eagle Eyed (USA)—
                     The Poachers Lady (IRE) **Blueprint Construction Supplies Ltd**
4 **MAJIK**, 5, ch g Pivotal—Revoke (USA) **Mr Andrew Stimpson**
5 **NASSAU STREET**, 4, gr g Bahamian Bounty—Milva **Mrs Patrick McCarthy**
6 **SWAIN DAVIS**, 4, b f Swain (IRE)—Exclusive Davis (USA) **B. Barrett A. Creighton P. Gallagher**
7 **YDRAVLIS**, 6, ch m Alflora (IRE)—Levantine Rose **Mr D. Ffrench Davis**

THREE-YEAR-OLDS

8 **ASK THE DRIVER**, b g Ashkalani (IRE)—Tithcar **Mrs F. Houlihan**
9 **CRAFTY FANCY (IRE)**, ch f Intikhab (USA)—Idle Fancy **Mrs F. Houlihan**
10 **ENGLISH ROCKET (IRE)**, b c Indian Rocket—Golden Charm (IRE) **Hargood Limited**
11 B f Polish Precedent (USA)—Feather Bride (IRE) **Mr D. J. ffrench Davis**
12 **KERRISTINA**, b f So Factual (USA)—Arch Angel (IRE) **Mr P. H. Wafford**
13 **LADY ELLENDUNE**, b f Piccolo—Eileen's Lady **Wroughton Racing Partnership**

MR D. J. S. FFRENCH DAVIS—continued

TWO-YEAR-OLDS

14 B g 10/4 Desert King (IRE)—Broken Spirit (IRE) (Slip Anchor) **Woodview Racing**
15 B c 4/2 Sri Pekan (USA)—Evergreen (IRE) (Lammtarra (USA)) (8000)
16 **FLYING PASS**, b c 11/4 Alzao (USA)—Complimentary Pass (Danehill (USA)) (17000) **Woodview Racing**
17 B f 30/4 Orpen—Haajra (IRE) (Polish Precedent (USA)) (2782) **Hyperion Bloodstock**

Other Owners: Mr B. Barrett, Mr K. Blyth, Mr A. W. Creighton, Mr P. B. Gallagher, Mr Jaideep Mhajan, Mr Michael Pearl, Mr R. J. Stratford, Mrs F. A. Veasey.

Assistant Trainer: Avery Ffrench Davis

Jockey (Flat): T Quinn.

---

199 **MR R. FIELDER, Cranleigh**
Postal: 15 Clappers Meadow, Alfold, Cranleigh, Surrey, GU6 8HH.
Contact: **PHONE (01403) 752144 MOBILE (07711) 024054 E-MAIL** valerie.h.fielder@talk21.com

1 **HILLS OF RAKAPOSHI**, 5, ch m Rakaposhi King—Hilly Path **Mr R. Fielder**
2 **MY RETREAT (USA)**, 7, b g Hermitage (USA)—My Jessica Ann (USA) **Mr R. Fielder**

Amateurs: Mr C Gordon (11-0), Mr P York (10-7).

---

200 **MR G. FIERRO, Hednesford**
Postal: "Woodview", Hazel Slade Racing Stables, Rugeley Road, Hazel Slade, Staffordshire, WS12 5PH.
Contact: **HOME/YARD (01543) 879611 MOBILE (07976) 321468**

1 **ABBIEJO (IRE)**, 7, b m Blues Traveller (IRE)—Chesham Lady (IRE) **Mr G. Fierro**
2 **CROMER PIER**, 9, b g Reprimand—Fleur du Val **Mr G. Fierro**
3 **FRENCH CAT (USA)**, 6, b br g Storm Cat (USA)—Shannkara (IRE) **Mr G. Fierro**
4 **GO ON JACK**, 6, ch g Saint Keyne—Swift Messenger **Mr G. Fierro**
5 **JUST BETH**, 8, ch m Carlingford Castle—One For The Road **Mr G. Fierro**
6 **SILVER GIFT**, 7, b m Rakaposhi King—Kellsboro Kate **Mr G. Fierro**
7 **SOUTHERN DUNES**, 8, b g Ardkinglass—Leprechaun Lady **Mr G. Fierro**
8 **TODDEANO**, 8, b g Perpendicular—Phisus **Mr G. Fierro**

THREE-YEAR-OLDS

9 **GREEN CONVERSION (IRE)**, ch c Desert King (IRE)—Blue Bangor (IRE)

Assistant Trainer: M Fierro

Conditional: Shaun Lycett (10-0).

---

201 **MR R. F. FISHER, Ulverston**
Postal: Great Head House, Priory Road, Ulverston, Cumbria, LA12 9RX.
Contact: **PHONE (01229) 585664 FAX (01229) 585079 MOBILE (07779) 609068**
E-MAIL elliefisher@btinternet.com **WEBSITE** www.roger-fisher.com

1 **COERCION (IRE)**, 6, b g Ilium—Nicholas Ferry **Great Head House Estates Limited**
2 **EURYALUS (IRE)**, 6, ch g Presenting—New Talent **Great Head House Estates Limited**
3 **LAZY BUT LIVELY (IRE)**, 8, br g Supreme Leader—Oriel Dream **Mr S. P. Marsh**
4 **LOUIS CSASZAR (IRE)**, 6, b g Arctic Lord—Satlan's Treasure (IRE) **Great Head House Estates Limited**
5 **MIKASA (IRE)**, 4, b g Victory Note (USA)—Resiusa (ITY) **Great Head House Estates Limited**
6 **OUBUS HILL (IRE)**, 8, b g Zaffaran (USA)—Garnerstown Queen **Great Head House Estates Limited**
7 **STOIC LEADER (IRE)**, 4, b g Danehill Dancer (USA)—Starlust **Great Head House Estates Limited**
8 **TONI ALCALA**, 5, b g Ezzoud (IRE)—Etourdie (USA) **Mr Alan Willoughby**
9 **ZYGOMATIC**, 6, ch g Risk Me (FR)—Give Me A Day **Mr S. P. Marsh**

THREE-YEAR-OLDS

10 **DUNCANBIL (IRE)**, b f Turtle Island (IRE)—Saintly Guest **Mr W. M. Ballantyne**
11 **KYBER**, ch g First Trump—Mahbob Dancer (FR) **Great Head House Estates Limited**

MR R. F. FISHER—continued

12 **MENAI STRAIGHTS,** ch g Alhaarth (IRE)—Kind of Light **Mr M. Maclennan**
13 **RARE COINCIDENCE,** ch g Atraf—Green Seed (IRE) **Great Head House Estates Limited**
14 **TEUTONIC (IRE),** b f Revoque (IRE)—Classic Ring (IRE) **Great Head House Estates Limited**

TWO-YEAR-OLDS

15 **BECKERMET (IRE),** b g 3/5 Second Empire (IRE)—
    Razida (IRE) (Last Tycoon) (7729) **Great Head House Estates Limited**
16 **CALDERBRIDGE (IRE),** b g 10/4 Trans Island—
    Premier Amour (Salmon Leap (USA)) (4946) **Great Head House Estates Limited**
17 **ESKDALE (IRE),** b g 15/3 Perugino (USA)—
    Gilding The Lily (IRE) (High Estate) (11000) **Great Head House Estates Limited**
18 **HARDKNOTT (IRE),** ch g 11/2 Intikhab (USA)—
    Danita (IRE) (Roi Danzig (USA)) (17315) **Great Head House Estates Limited**
19 **MOUNT EPHRAM (IRE),** b g 4/4 Entrepreneur—
    Happy Dancer (Seattle Dancer (USA)) (12368) **Great Head House Estates Limited**
20 **NO COMMISSION (IRE),** b g 7/2 General Monash (USA)—
    Price of Passion (Dolphin Street (FR)) (18000) **Great Head House Estates Limited**
21 **PROCRASTINATE (IRE),** ch g 19/4 Rossini (USA)—
    May Hinton (Main Reef) (10512) **Great Head House Estates Limited**
22 **VERSTONE (IRE),** b g 27/3 Brave Act—
    Golden Charm (IRE) (Common Grounds) (12000) **Great Head House Estates Limited**

Other Owners: Mrs D. Miller.

Jockeys (Flat): J Fanning (8-1), L Fletcher, S Richton. **Jockeys (NH):** D Elsworth, C McCormack (10-0). **Apprentice:** L Fletcher (8-0).

---

202   MR T. J. FITZGERALD, Malton
Postal: **Norton Grange, Norton, Malton, North Yorkshire, YO17 9EA.**
Contact: **OFFICE (01653) 692718 MOBILE (07950) 356437 E-MAIL** fitzgeraldracing@aol.com

1 **CAMPBELL'S TALE (IRE),** 5, gr g Lake Coniston (IRE)—Fair Tale (USA) **Mrs R. A. G. Haggie**
2 **COUNT FOSCO,** 6, b g Alflora (IRE)—Carrikins **Lady Lloyd Webber**
3 **COY LAD (IRE),** 7, ch g Be My Native—Don't Tutch Me **Mr & Mrs Raymond Anderson Green**
4 **FATHER PADDY,** 9, ch g Minster Son—Sister Claire **Mr P. McMahon**
5 **FRONTIS,** 7, ch g Be My Chief—Heavy Rock (IRE) **Marquesa de Moratalla**
6 **INCHNADAMPH,** 4, b g Inchinor—Pelf (USA) **Mr R. N. Cardwell**
7 **KINGSDON (IRE),** 7, b g Brief Truce (USA)—Richly Deserved (IRE) **Mr Mike Browne**
8 **MOMENT OF MADNESS (IRE),** 6, ch g Treasure Hunter—Sip of Orange **Mrs R. A. G. Haggie**
9 **MR NO MAN,** 8, b g Cosmonaut—Christmas Show **Mr J. G. Fitzgerald**
10 **MUQARRAR (IRE),** 5, ch h Alhaarth (IRE)—Narjis (USA) **Mr N. H. T. Wrigley**
11 **NEEDWOOD BRAVE,** 6, b g Lion Cavern (USA)—Woodcrest **Mr Tim Kilroe**
12 **RANDOM NATIVE (IRE),** 6, br g Be My Native (USA)—Random Wind **Mr Jim Ennis**
13 **STAR JACK (FR),** 9, b g Epervier Bleu—Little Point (FR) **Mr & Mrs Raymond Anderson Green**
14 **VICENTIO,** 5, br g Vettori (IRE)—Smah **Shaw Thing Partnership**

THREE-YEAR-OLDS

15 **BALLIN ROUGE,** ch f Dr Fong (USA)—Bogus John (CAN) **The Three Putt Partnership**
16 **GOLDEN BOY (IRE),** b g Fayruz—Figini **Mr Don Eason**
17 **LAWGIVER (IRE),** b c Definite Article—Marylou Whitney (USA) **Marquesa de Moratalla**
18 **SEAPIN,** b g Double Trigger (IRE)—Four-Legged Friend **Marquesa de Moratalla**

TWO-YEAR-OLDS

19 **BREEDER'S FOLLY,** b f 11/2 Mujahid (USA)—Wynona (IRE) (Cyrano de Bergerac) (15000) **Mr Mike Browne**
20 B f 4/2 Bien Bien (USA)—Fair Test (Fair Season) (2500)
21 Br c 30/3 Deploy—Smooth Princess (IRE) (Roi Danzig (USA))

Other Owners: Mr S. J. Atkinson, Mrs Peter Corbett, Mrs Anita Green, Mr J. S. Murdoch, Mr J. G. Porthouse.

203 MR J. L. FLINT, Bridgend
Postal: **Cherry Tree, 71 Woodlands Park, Kenfig Hill, Bridgend, Mid-Glamorgan, CF33 6EB.**
Contact: **PHONE (01656) 744347 MOBILE (07713) 053626**

1 **SENNA DA SILVA**, 4, gr f Prince of Birds (USA)—Impulsive Decision (IRE) **Mr J. L. Flint**

Assistant Trainer: Mrs Martine Louise Flint

204 MR DAVID FLOOD, Lingfield
Postal: **21 Cedar Mews, High Street, Edenbridge, Kent, TN8 5AB.**
Contact: **PHONE (01732) 863449 FAX (01732) 863490**

1 **AMYROSEISUPPOSE**, 5, b m Classic Cliche (IRE)—Fishki
2 **GOLDEN OLDIE (IRE)**, 6, b g Old Vic—Misty Gold **Mr A. M. McArdle**
3 **HURRICANE COAST**, 5, b g Hurricane Sky (AUS)—Tread Carefully **Mrs Ruth M. Serrell**
4 **NIGHT WARRIOR (IRE)**, 4, b g Alhaarth (IRE)—Miniver (IRE) **Rowfield Racing & The Warriors**
5 **ONEFORTHEBOYS (IRE)**, 5, b g Distinctly North (USA)—Joyful Prospect **Rowfield Racing**
6 **SECOND MINISTER**, 5, ch g Lion Cavern (USA)—Crime of Passion **Rowfield Racing**

THREE-YEAR-OLDS
7 **FOLEY PRINCE**, b g Makbul—Princess Foley (IRE) **Rowfield Racing**
8 **JAYCEE STAR (IRE)**, ch f Idris (IRE)—Shantung (IRE) **Mrs J. Coombs**

TWO-YEAR-OLDS
9 **HIGGYS PRINCE**, b c 16/3 Prince Sabo—
              Themeda (Sure Blade (USA)) (3500) **Ian Higginson & Cheryl Flood Racing Ltd**
10 **LORD CHALFONT (IRE)**, ch c 25/2 Daggers Drawn (USA)—
              Byproxy (IRE) (Mujtahid (USA)) (1800) **Mr Malcolm O'Hair**

Other Owners: Cheryl Flood Racing Ltd, Mr I. Higginson, Mr P. Kingsbury, Mrs J. A. Leeper, Mr P. R. Leeper.

Assistant Trainer: Mrs Cheryl Flood

Jockey (Flat): P Doe (8-2, w.a.). **Jockey (NH):** A. P. McCoy (w.a.). **Apprentices:** D Fox, S Valentine. **Conditional:** J Gray, O Kozak.

205 MR F. FLOOD, Grangecon
Postal: **Ballynure, Grangecon, Co. Wicklow, Ireland.**
Contact: **PHONE +353 (0) 45 403136 FAX +353 (0) 45 403214 MOBILE +353 (0) 872 590919**

1 **ADONIA (IRE)**, 6, b m Beneficial—Suny Castle (IRE) **Mr S. Reilly**
2 **AIMEES MARK (IRE)**, 8, br g Jolly Jake (NZ)—Wee Mite **Mr R. McConn**
3 **AMBER SKY (IRE)**, 4, b g Lycius (USA)—Mine Hostess (IRE) **Mr R. Deane**
4 **ANOTHER NATIVE (IRE)**, 9, b g Be My Native (USA)—Lancastrians Wine (IRE) **Mr P. Sheridan**
5 **AVEC PLAISIR (GER)**, 5, b m Acatenango (GER)—Aminata (GER) **Kildare Racing Club**
6 **BE MY LEADER (IRE)**, 5, b m Supreme Leader—Try Your Case **Mr P. Costigan**
7 **BESSINA (IRE)**, 4, b f King's Theatre (IRE)—Ballycuirke **Mrs H. McParland**
8 **BIRCHALL (IRE)**, 5, b m Priolo (USA)—Ballycuirke **Mrs H. McParland**
9 **BLAME THE REF (IRE)**, 7, ch g Aahsaylad—Nags Head (IRE) **Mr S. Murphy**
10 **CARA MO CHROI (IRE)**, 5, b g Broken Hearted—Kambaya (IRE) **Mr C. Falls**
11 **COLONEL GUN (IRE)**, 4, ch g Catrail (USA)—Return Again (IRE) **Mr G. Martin**
12 **DANSE MACABRE (IRE)**, 5, b g Flemensfirth—My Romance **Mr R. P. Behan**
13 **FLAGOFCONVENIENCE (IRE)**, 6, ch m Old Vic—Bella Velutina **Mr G. Martin**
14 **FREIWIND (GER)**, 7, b g Local Suitor (USA)—Frei Geboren (GER) **Mr W. A. Browne**
15 **GEORGES GIRL (IRE)**, 6, b m Montelimar (USA)—Keshia **Mr G. Martin**
16 **GIOLLA DE (IRE)**, 5, b g Glacial Storm (USA)—Deep Inagh **Mr C. Falls**
17 **GONE DANCING (IRE)**, 4, b g Key of Luck (USA)—French Lady (IRE) **Mr D. Reddan**
18 **GRANGEBEG (IRE)**, 5, b g Shernazar—Coolmoonan **Mrs H. McParland**
19 **G V A IRELAND (IRE)**, 6, br g Beneficial—Dippers Daughter **Mr D. O'Buachalla**
20 **HUDSON HOPE (IRE)**, 6, b m Topanoora—Be My Hope (IRE) **Mr G. Mannion**
21 **LANMIRE GLEN (IRE)**, 7, b g Jurado—Cool Glen **Mr W. A. Browne**
22 **LITTLE THEATRE (IRE)**, 4, b f Old Vic—Indian Project (IRE) **Mr J. D. Flood**
23 **LORNA'S STAR (IRE)**, 5, b m Fourstars Allstar (USA)—Lorna's Beauty (IRE) **Mr J. M. O'Brien**

MR F. FLOOD—continued

24 **MAGIC MARK**, 6, b g King's Ride—South Quay Lady **Mr R. McConn**
25 **MIJAS LADY (IRE)**, 5, b m Jolly Jake (NZ)—South Quay Lady **Mr A. Doyle**
26 **NEWHALL (IRE)**, 6, b m Shernazar—Graffogue (IRE) **Mrs H. McParland**
27 **O'CONNELL (IRE)**, 7, b m Erins Isle—Book Choice **Mrs T. Deane**
28 **OUR FELLA (IRE)**, 6, b g Be My Native (USA)—Bon Retour **Mr C. McDonnell**
29 **SATOHA (IRE)**, 6, b g Zaffaran (USA)—Whackers World **Never Despair Syndicate**
30 **SHIVERMETIMBER (IRE)**, 6, b m Arctic Lord—Cherry Dancer **Abbey Rose Syndicate**
31 **STAR STORM (IRE)**, 10, br g Glacial Storm (USA)—Star Whistler **Mr H. James**
32 **SUPREME PEACE (IRE)**, 6, b m Supreme Leader—Peace Time Girl (IRE) **Mr L. Kelly & Mr P. McAteer**
33 **THE CULDEE (IRE)**, 8, ch g Phardante (FR)—Deep Inagh **Mr C. Falls**
34 **THE PENITENT MAN (IRE)**, 6, b g Corrouge (USA)—Swift Glider (IRE) **Mr M. Holly**
35 **TONENILI (IRE)**, 4, b f Old Vic—Kokopelli (IRE) **Mrs N. O'Reilly**
36 **VEGAS VIC (IRE)**, 6, b m Old Vic—Princess Breda (IRE) **Mr S. Maguire**
37 **WALK OVER (IRE)**, 6, b g Welsh Term—Black-Crash **Mr J. P. McManus**
38 **WINDMILL FLYER (IRE)**, 6, ch g Old Vic—Clahada Rose (IRE) **Elphin Racing Syndicate**

Jockey (NH): F J Flood (9-12). **Apprentice:** A B Joyce (8-0). **Amateurs:** Mr D Macauley, J P McKeown.

---

206 **MR A. L. FORBES, Uttoxeter**
Postal: **Hill House Farm, Poppits Lane, Stramshall, Uttoxeter, Staffordshire, ST14 5EX.**
Contact: **PHONE (01889) 568145 FAX (01782) 599041 MOBILE (07812) 350991**
E-MAIL tony@thimble.net

1 **ASCARI**, 8, br g Presidium—Ping Pong **Mr Ernie Jackson**
2 **DOUCEUR DES SONGES (FR)**, 7, b m Art Francais (USA)—Ma Poetesse (FR) **Mr Tony Forbes**
3 **MOON COLONY**, 11, b g Top Ville—Honeymooning (USA) **Mr Tony Forbes**

Jockey (NH): X Aizpury.

---

207 **MRS P. M. FORD, Hereford**
Postal: **Stone House Stables, Preston Wynne, Hereford, Herefordshire, HR1 3PB.**
Contact: **HOME & FAX (01432) 820604 MOBILE (07733) 152051**
E-MAIL Pam@fordracing.fsnet.co.uk

1 **ALFIE VALENTINE**, 8, b g Alflora (IRE)—My Aisling **Mr K. R. Ford**
2 **ALWAYS BELIEVE (USA)**, 8, b g Carr de Naskra (USA)—Wonder Mar (USA) **Mr R. S. Herbert**
3 **BEN KENOBI**, 6, ch g Accondy (IRE)—Nour El Sahar (USA) **Mr K. Marritt**
4 7, B m Minster Son—Cheeny's Brig **Mr K. R. Ford**
5 **ELEGANT ACCORD (IRE)**, 6, b m Accordion—Swan Bridge (IRE) **Mr J. T. Jones**
6 **FRIENDLY REQUEST**, 5, br m Environment Friend—Who Tells Jan **Mr W. E. Donohue**
7 **GREENBOROUGH (IRE)**, 6, b g Dr Devious (IRE)—Port Isaac (USA) **Mr W. E. Donohue**
8 **HAYLEY'S PEARL**, 5, b m Nomadic Way (USA)—Pacific Girl (IRE) **Mr P. Martin**
9 **LITTLETON AMETHYST (IRE)**, 5, ch m Revoque (IRE)—Sept Roses (USA) **Mr W. E. Donohue**
10 **MR PERRY (IRE)**, 8, b g Perugino (USA)—Elegant Tune (USA) **R. Champken & A. Petrie**
11 **MURPHY'S ANGEL**, 10, br m Derrylin—Just A Tipple (IRE) **Mr K. R. Ford**
12 **NEW DIAMOND**, 5, ch g Bijou d'Inde—Nannie Annie **Mr R. S. Herbert**
13 **OUR MAN DENNIS**, 10, b g Arzanni—Pendocks Polly **Mrs S. J. Williams**

Assistant Trainer: Kenny Ford

Jockeys (Flat): R Ffrench, Lisa Jones. **Jockeys (NH):** S Stronge, Sam Stronge. **Amateur:** Mr K R Ford (9-10).

---

208 **MR R. FORD, Tarporley**
Postal: **Folly Farm, Forest Road, Little Budworth, Tarporley, Cheshire, CW6 9ES.**
Contact: **PHONE (01829) 760095 FAX (01829) 760895 MOBILE (07976) 522768**
E-MAIL richardfordracing.co.uk

1 **BAMFORD CASTLE (IRE)**, 9, b g Scenic—Allorette **Mr Mick Coulson and Mr John Bull**
2 **BLACK STRIPE LADY**, 6, b m Karinga Bay—Garvenish **Black Stripe Racing**
3 **BLUES STORY (FR)**, 6, b g Pistolet Bleu (IRE)—Herbe Sucree (FR) **Mr D. F. Price**
4 **BROMLEY ABBEY**, 6, ch m Minster Son—Little Bromley **Mrs A. Eubank**
5 **BROWN TEDDY**, 7, b g Afzal—Quadrapol **Mr G. B. Barlow**
6 **CHABRIMAL MINSTER**, 7, b g Minster Son—Bromley Rose **B. Mills, C. Roberts, M & M Burrows**

MR R. FORD—continued

7 **COPPERMALT (USA)**, 6, b g Affirmed (USA)—Poppy Carew (IRE) **Mr N. Morgan**
8 **DENNEY'S WELL (IRE)**, 9, ch g Good Thyne (USA)—Julias Well **Black Stripe Racing**
9 **DORANS GOLD**, 10, b g Gildoran—Cindie Girl **Mr D. Harrison**
10 **DOUBLE WHIRL**, 8, ch g Destroyer—Priceless Peril **Mrs David Marshall**
11 **FOREST GUNNER**, 10, ch g Gunner B—Gouly Duff **Mr J. Gilsenan**
12 **GOLDENAVOUR (FR)**, 5, b g Endeavour (USA)—Golden Moon (FR) **Miss M. Burrows**
13 **HAVIT**, 6, b g Lucky Wednesday—Gouly Duff **Black Stripe Racing**
14 **KEBREYA (USA)**, 5, ch g Affirmed (USA)—Minifah (USA) **The Haydock Badgeholders**
15 **KING-FOR-LIFE (IRE)**, 6, ch g Rainbows For Life (CAN)—Fair Song **Mr & Mrs T. D. Williams**
16 **KING HALLING**, 5, b g Halling (USA)—Flower Fairy (FR) **D. F. Price & A. Eyres**
17 **LANOS (POL)**, 6, ch g Special Power—Lubeka (POL) **Mr D. W. Watson**
18 **LANTERN LAD (IRE)**, 8, b g Yashgan—Lantern Lass **Tarporley Turf Club**
19 **LITTLE BROWN BEAR (IRE)**, 10, b g Strong Gale—Gladtogetit **Mr G. B. Barlow**
20 **LUCKY NOMAD**, 8, b g Nomadic Way (USA)—Daleena **Mr N. Morgan**
21 **MONTESSORI MIO (FR)**, 5, b g Robellino (USA)—Child's Play (USA) **Dantom Production Solutions Ltd**
22 **OCEAN TIDE**, 7, b g Deploy—Dancing Tide **D. F. Price & A. Eyres**
23 **OLD KING COAL**, 8, b g Miner's Lamp—Mill Shine **Mr G. B. Barlow**
24 **OULTON BROAD**, 8, b g Midyan (USA)—Lady Quachita (USA) **Haydock Badge Holders**
25 **OWENABUE VALLEY (IRE)**, 8, b g Yashgan—Lek-Lady (USA) **Barking Mad Syndicate 2**
26 **PISTE BLEU (FR)**, 4, b f Pistolet Bleu (IRE)—Thamissia (FR) **Mr M. Dunlevy & Mr N. Morgan**
27 **RENDARI (IRE)**, 9, b g Shardari—Reneagh **Mr D. C. Fillingham**
28 **ROYAL WHISPER**, 5, b g Prince of Birds (USA)—Hush It Up **Haydock Badge Holders**
29 **RUSSELL HOUSE (IRE)**, 8, b br g Roselier (FR)—Salufair **Mr L. A. E. Hopkins**
30 **SAMSON DES GALAS (FR)**, 6, br g Agent Bleu (FR)—Sarema (FR) **J. & G. Sporting Partners**
31 **SMUDGE (IRE)**, 7, br g Be My Native (USA)—Crash Call **Mrs Brenda Siddall**
32 **THE ALLEYCAT (IRE)**, 13, b g Tidaro (USA)—Allitess **Mr David Bostock**
33 **TREGASTEL (FR)**, 9, b g Tel Quel (FR)—Myrtlewood (FR) **Mr D. W. Watson**
34 **UNDERLEY PARK (IRE)**, 10, ch g Aristocracy—Even Bunny VII
35 **YAIYNA TANGO (FR)**, 9, br g Fijar Tango (FR)—Yaiyna (FR) **Mr D. W. Watson**

THREE-YEAR-OLDS

36 Ch f Opening Verse (USA)—Fleur d'Or **Mrs Carrie Ford**

Other Owners: Mr Paul Clarkson, Mr T. J. Crehan, Mr V. Harvey, Mr C. P. Jones, Mr S. Ledbrooke, Mr S. A. Stokes, Mr M. Waterfall, Mr C. G. Wilson.

Assistant Trainer: Carrie Ford

Jockeys (NH): G Lee (10-0, w.a.), Richard McGrath (10-0, w.a.). **Amateur:** Mr S Hughes (10-0).

---

209 MR D. M. FORSTER, Darlington
Postal: **Todd Fall Farm, Heighington, Darlington, Co. Durham, DL2 2XG.**
Contact: **PHONE (01388) 772441**

1 **ATOMIC BREEZE (IRE)**, 10, b br g Strong Gale—Atomic Lady **Mr D. M. Forster**
2 4, B g Zaffaran (USA)—Blue Rinse **Mr D. M. Forster**
3 5, B g Accordion—Cool Virtue (IRE) **Mr D. M. Forster**
4 **JIMMYS DUKY (IRE)**, 6, b g Duky—Harvey's Cream (IRE) **Mr D. M. Forster**
5 **OSSMOSES (IRE)**, 7, gr g Roselier (FR)—Sugarstown **Mr D. M. Forster**
6 **SHINING FOUNTAIN (IRE)**, 15, b g Royal Fountain—Ever Shining **Mr D. M. Forster**

THREE-YEAR-OLDS

7 B g Zaffaran (USA)—Parson's Run (IRE) **Mr D. M. Forster**

Jockey (NH): Richard McGrath.

---

210 MISS S. E. FORSTER, Kelso
Postal: **Halterburn Head, Yetholm, Kelso, Roxburghshire, TD5 8PP.**
Contact: **PHONE (01573) 420615 MOBILE (07880) 727877**
E-MAIL **c.storey.pt-to-pt@tinyworld.co.uk**

1 **AMERAS (IRE)**, 6, b b m Hamas (IRE)—Amerindian **Mr A. G. & Mrs E. J. Bell**
2 **BOLTON FOREST (IRE)**, 11, b g Be My Native (USA)—Tickenor Wood **Mrs A. Strang-Steel**

MISS S. E. FORSTER—continued

3 **CARNACRACK**, 10, b g Le Coq d'Or—Carney **Mr C. Storey**
4 **DREAM KING (IRE)**, 4, b g Petardia—Barinia **Should Be Fun Racing**
5 **LADY JANAL**, 6, gr m Sir Harry Lewis (USA)—Mrs Dawson **Mr A. G. & Mrs E. J. Bell**
6 **MIKE STAN (IRE)**, 13, b g Rontino—Fair Pirouette **Miss H. Crichton**
7 **MOMENTS MADNESS (IRE)**, 5, br m Corrouge (USA)—Treble Clef (IRE) **Miss S. Forster**
8 **NOBLE TEVIOT**, 6, b g Lithgie-Brig—Polly Peril **Mr R. J. Kyle**
9 **PRIMITIVE WAY**, 6, b g Primitive Rising (USA)—Potterway **The Hon Gerald Maitland-Carew**
10 **RADAR (IRE)**, 9, b g Petardia—Soignee **Mr C. Storey**
11 **RUBYLUV**, 5, ch m Rock Hopper—Hunting Cottage **Mrs J. Cadzow**
12 **SHADY GREY**, 6, gr m Minster Son—Yemaail (IRE) **Mr A. Dawson**
13 **SKENFRITH**, 5, b g Atraf—Hobbs Choice **Mr C. Storey**
14 **STAR TROOPER (IRE)**, 8, b br g Brief Truce (USA)—Star Cream **Mr C. Storey**
15 **THE MINER**, 6, ch g Hatim (USA)—Glen Morvern **The Wellconnected Partnership**
16 **TREASURED MEMORIES**, 4, b f Cloudings (IRE)—Glen Morvern **Mr C. Storey**
17 **WELSH DREAM**, 7, b g Mtoto—Morgannwg (IRE) **Should Be Fun Racing**

Other Owners: Mr R. Adamson, Mr Alan G. Bell, Mrs E. J. Bell, Mr F. Berry, Mr A. Black, Mr J. M. Crichton, Mr P. Dyson, Mr G. McGuinness, Mrs B. O'Donnell, Mrs C. Rettie, Mr D. Skeldon.

Assistant Trainer: C Storey

Jockeys (NH): J Crowley (w.a.), G Lee (w.a.). **Amateurs:** Miss J Riding (9-7), Mr C Storey (10-0).

---

211 **MR J. R. H. FOWLER, Summerhill**
Postal: **Rahinston, Summerhill, Co. Meath, Ireland.**
Contact: **PHONE (046)9557014 FAX (046) 9557537**

1 **BACK ON CONCORDE (IRE)**, 6, br g Executive Perk—Kitty Cullen **James McQuaid**
2 7, B g Forstars Allstar (USA)—Ballybree **Lady J. Fowler**
3 **BALLYRONAN (IRE)**, 7, ch g Be My Native (USA)—Blue Rainbow **S.P. Tindall**
4 **BIRAS CREEK (IRE)**, 5, ch m Most Welcome—Orange Hill **S. P. Tindall**
5 **FIERY RING (IRE)**, 9, b g Torus—Kakemona **S. P. Tindall**
6 **HEARTBREAK HILL (IRE)**, 5, b m Synefos (FR)—Knockea Hill **Lady J. Fowler**
7 **HOUDUNIT**, 9, br g Houmayoun (FR)—Super Leg **B. D. Smith**
8 **HURADA (IRE)**, 6, b m Jurado (USA)—Knockea Hill **Lady J. Fowler**
9 **JENNIFERS DIARY (IRE)**, 6, b m Supreme Leader—Chattering **Lady J. Fowler**
10 **MARMALADE SKY (IRE)**, 6, ch g Be My Native (USA)—Armagale (IRE) **Miss D. Duggan**
11 **NATIVE BEAT (IRE)**, 9, b g Be My Native (USA)—Deeprunonthepound (IRE) **Mrs D. Duggan**
12 **RENVYLE SOCIETY (IRE)**, 6, ch m Moscow Society (USA)—Great Outlook (IRE) **March Hares Syndicate**
13 **RUSSIAN MASTER (IRE)**, 8, b g Moscow Society (USA)—Little Sloop **Virginia Lady Petersham**
14 **SEA VOYAGER (USA)**, 5, b m High Roller (IRE)—Little Sloop **Virginia Lady Petersham**
15 **SELOUS SCOUT (IRE)**, 7, ch g Be My Native (USA)—Lady Leona **Lady J. Fowler**
16 **SHIMMINIE (IRE)**, 5, b m Bob Back (USA)—Shining Willow **S. P. Tindall**
17 **SIMPLE DAME (IRE)**, 5, b m Simply Great (FR)—Three Lucky (IRE) **R. J. Wilson**
18 **SUMMERTIME BLUES (IRE)**, 5, b m Blues Traveller—Ennel Lady (IRE) **Mrs C. A. Waters**
19 **SUPREME TADGH (IRE)**, 7, b g Supreme Leader—Mariaetta (IRE) **Roger Brockerick**
20 **TENA TENA (IRE)**, 7, b g Fourstars Allstar (USA)—Ballybree **Mrs C. A. Waters**
21 **TSARETTA (IRE)**, 5, b m Supreme Leader—Pharetta (IRE) **G. H. Briscoe**
22 **TSESSEBE (IRE)**, 7, b m Fourstars Allstar (USA)—Daraheen Pearl **Lady J. Fowler**

Jockey (NH): R Geraghty (9-0). **Conditional:** A P Fagan (8-7). **Amateurs:** Mr S Burke (10-7), Mr D O'Brien (11-7).

---

212 **MR J. C. FOX, Marlborough**
Postal: **Highlands Farm Stables, Herridge, Collingbourne Ducis, Marlborough, Wiltshire, SN8 3EG.**
Contact: **PHONE (01264) 850218 MOBILE (07702) 880010**

1 **BUSINESS MATTERS (IRE)**, 4, b f Desert Style (IRE)—Hear Me **Ms I. Bristow**
2 **CAMROSS**, 8, b g Teenoso (USA)—Arizona Belle **Shannon Racing Partnership**
3 **DREAMING DIVA**, 5, ch m Whittingham (IRE)—Any Dream (IRE) **Mrs Alicia Aldis and Mr Simon Caunce**
4 **KILMEENA LAD**, 6, b g Minshaanshu Amad (USA)—Kilmeena Glen **Mrs J. A. Cleary**
5 **KILMEENA ROSE**, 4, ch f Compton Place—Kilmeena Glen **Mrs J. A. Cleary**
6 **KILMEENA STAR**, 6, b h So Factual (USA)—Kilmeena Glen **Mrs J. A. Cleary**
7 **MAGIC WARRIOR**, 4, b g Magic Ring (IRE)—Clarista (USA) **Miss H. J. Flower**
8 **NEPTUNE**, 8, b g Dolphin Street (FR)—Seal Indigo (IRE) **S J V Construction**

MR J. C. FOX—continued

9 **SAORSIE**, 6, b g Emperor Jones (USA)—Exclusive Lottery **Lord Mutton Racing Partnership**
10 **SILVER WOOD**, 4, b f Silver Wizard (USA)—Eastwood Heiress **Mrs J. A. Cleary**
11 **SUNSET KING (USA)**, 4, b c King of Kings (IRE)—Sunset River (USA) **Mr Mitchell Block**
12 **TE-DEUM (IRE)**, 7, ch g Ridgewood Ben—Tabessa (USA) **The Slaney Partnership**
13 **WALKER BAY (IRE)**, 6, ch m Efisio—Lalandria (FR) **Mr Mitchell Block**

THREE-YEAR-OLDS

14 **RUE DE VERTBOIS (USA)**, ch f King of Kings (IRE)—Tea Cozzy (USA) **Mr Mitchell Block**
15 **SOLAR PRINCE (IRE)**, b g Desert Prince (IRE)—Quiche **Double Jay Syndicate**

Other Owners: Mrs A. Doyle, Mr P. F. Doyle, Mr J. Farrar, Mr C. Fiford, Mr P. G. Haran, Mr J. Kearns, Mr S. Kearns, Mr Anthony Kelly, Mr P. G. O'Leary, Miss A. Poplar.

Assistant Trainer: Sarah-Jane Durman

Jockey (NH): S Fox (10-0). **Amateur:** Miss Sarah-Jane Durman (8-7).

---

213 **MR M. E. D. FRANCIS, Lambourn**
Postal: **Folly House, Upper Lambourn Road, Lambourn, Hungerford, Berkshire, RG17 8QG.**
Contact: **PHONE (01488) 71700 MOBILE (07836) 244988 E-MAIL Merrick@LRTltd.demon.co.uk**

1 **FARD DU MOULIN MAS (FR)**, 11, b br g Morespeed—Soiree d'Ex (FR) **Mrs Merrick Francis III**
2 **TAILLEFER (FR)**, 8, b g Cyborg (FR)—Tourka (FR) **Mrs Merrick Francis III**

---

214 **MR J. D. FROST, Buckfastleigh**
Postal: **Hawson Stables, Buckfastleigh, Devon, TQ11 0HP.**
Contact: **YARD (01364) 642267 HOME (01364) 642332 MOBILE (07860) 220229**

1 **ACCESS OVERSEAS**, 7, b m Access Ski—Access Advantage **Miss Elaine D. Williams**
2 **BALOO**, 8, b g Morpeth—Moorland Nell **Cloud Nine-Premier Cru**
3 **BEYONDTHEREALM**, 6, b g Morpeth—Workamiracle **Mr J. D. Frost**
4 **CANCUN CARIBE (IRE)**, 7, ch g Port Lucaya—Miss Tuko **Dapper Racing Syndicate**
5 **DEER DANCER**, 4, b g Tamure (IRE)—Anatomic **Mrs J. F. Bury**
6 **DEVOTE**, 6, b g Pennekamp (USA)—Radiant Bride **The Welsh Valleys Syndicate**
7 **DUN AN DORAS (IRE)**, 8, b g Glacial Storm (USA)—Doorslammer **Cloud Nine-Premier Cru**
8 **FIRE RANGER**, 8, ch m Presidium—Regal Flame **Mr P. A. Tylor**
9 **FROSTY JAK**, 6, b g Morpeth—Allied Newcastle **Mr Jack Joseph**
10 **HONEYSTREET (IRE)**, 4, b f Woodborough (USA)—Ring of Kerry (IRE) **Mr W. A. Edginton**
11 **KATIES HERO**, 6, b g Pontevecchio Notte—Kindly Lady **D. C. & Mrs T. M. Fisher**
12 **KEETCHY (IRE)**, 5, b g Darshaan—Ezana **The Tuesday Syndicate**
13 **KILDEE LASS**, 5, gr m Morpeth—Pigeon Loft (IRE) **Mr J. F. O'Donovan**
14 **KING'S TRAVEL (FR)**, 8, gr g Balleroy (USA)—Travel Free **Mr C. Johnston**
15 **KNIGHT OF SILVER**, 7, gr g Presidium—Misty Rocket **Mr C. Johnston**
16 **LESDREAM**, 7, b g Morpeth—Lesbet **Mrs L. W. Carlson**
17 **LESPRIDE**, 6, b g Morpeth—Lesbet **Mrs L. W. Carlson**
18 **LITTLE LIL**, 5, ch m Sula Bula—Sherzine **Mr Martin Hill**
19 **MISS WOODPECKER**, 7, b m Morpeth—Pigeon Loft (IRE) **Mr R. G. Frost**
20 **MISS WOODPIGEON**, 8, b m Landyap (USA)—Pigeon Loft (IRE) **Christine and Aubrey Loze**
21 **MOORLAND MONARCH**, 6, b g Morpeth—Moorland Nell **Peninsula Racegoers**
22 **MR WOODLAND**, 10, br g Landyap (USA)—Wood Corner **Mr P. A. Tylor**
23 **OJAYS ALIBI (IRE)**, 8, b g Witness Box (USA)—Tinkers Lady **Mrs C. Irish**
24 **PEGGY'S PRINCE**, 6, b g Morpeth—Prudent Peggy **Mrs J. McCormack**
25 **QUIET DESPERATION**, 8, b g Supreme Leader—Wing On **Mr Arthur Watling**
26 **SAFFRON SUN**, 9, b g Landyap (USA)—Saffron Bun **Mrs J. F. Bury**
27 **SARENA PRIDE (IRE)**, 7, b m Persian Bold—Avidal Park **Sarena Mfg Ltd**
28 **SILENT GUEST (IRE)**, 11, b g Don't Forget Me—Guest House **Mr R. C. Burridge**
29 **TYRRELLSPASS (IRE)**, 7, b g Alzao (USA)—Alpine Chime (IRE) **Dead Loss Racing**

MR J. D. FROST—continued

30 **WORKING GIRL**, 7, b m Morpeth—Workamiracle **Mr R. G. Frost**
31 **WRAGS TO RICHES (IRE)**, 7, b g Tremblant—Clonea Lady (IRE) **No Illusions Partnership**

Other Owners: Mr S. Adams, Mr J. E. Blake, Mr Iain Carruth, Mrs Marion Christmas, Mr P. Collins, Mr P. M. Evans, Mrs M. Mitchell, Mr G. N. Noye, Mrs D. M. Philpott, Mr D. P. Pope, Mr R. J. Pritchard, Mrs M. A. Simpson, Mrs Peggy Smallbone, Mr G. Thompson, Ms H. Vernon-Jones, Mr Michael H. Watt, Mrs J. A. Williams.

Assistant Trainer: G. Frost

Conditional: C Honour (10-0). **Amateur:** Mr A Glasonbury (10-0).

MR JOHN GALLAGHER, Moreton-In-Marsh
Postal: Little Grove, Chastleton, Moreton In Marsh, Gloucestershire, GL56 0SZ.
Contact: **PHONE (01608) 674492 MOBILE (07780) 972663 FAX (01608) 674492**
E-MAIL gallagher.racing@virgin.net WEBSITE www.gallagherracing.com

1 **BENEKING**, 4, b b g Wizard King—Gagajulu **Dr & Mrs Why, S. Brandreth, D. Chubb**
2 **BOSWORTH GYPSY (IRE)**, 6, b m Aahsaylad—Googly **J. L. Marriott and A. L. Marriott**
3 **BREATHOFFRESHAIR (IRE)**, 7, ch g Fresh Breeze (USA)—Carl Louise **G. Ivall**
4 **CLASSIC SIGHT**, 4, ch f Classic Cliche (IRE)—Speckyfoureyes **Dr & Mrs Why & Miss A. Storrs**
5 **COLCA'S DATE**, 5, br m Sovereign Water (FR)—Rabdanna **Smith Wadley Homes Ltd**
6 **MISS ISSY (IRE)**, 4, b f Victory Note (USA)—Shane's Girl (IRE) **C. R. Marks (Banbury)**
7 **MOON GLOW (IRE)**, 8, b g Fayruz—Jarmar Moon **Mrs V. W. Jones**
8 **MURZIM**, 5, b g Salse (USA)—Guilty Secret (IRE) **C. R. Marks (Banbury)**
9 **MY SHARP GREY**, 5, gr m Tragic Role (USA)—Sharp Anne **Mr Bob Bevan**
10 **WHITE PARK BAY (IRE)**, 4, b f Blues Traveller (IRE)—Valiant Friend (USA) **Mr Tony Absolom**

THREE-YEAR-OLDS

11 **KILLING ME SOFTLY**, b g Kingsinger (IRE)—Slims Lady **Mr Stuart Prior**
12 **RED ROCKY**, b f Danzero (AUS)—Post Mistress (IRE) **Mr John L. Marriott**

TWO-YEAR-OLDS

13 B f 18/4 Wizard King—Aonia (Mummy's Pet) (800) **J. Gallagher**
14 **GOGETTER GIRL**, b f 10/4 Wolfhound (USA)—Square Mile Miss (IRE) (Last Tycoon) (800) **Mr R. A. Newman**

Other Owners: Mrs B. A. Long, Mr J. F. Long.

Assistant Trainer: Mrs R J Gallagher

Jockey (Flat): N Callan. **Jockeys (NH):** R Johnson (w.a.), J Mogford.

MRS E. J. GALPIN, Wincanton
Postal: Church Farm, Bratton Seymour, Wincanton, Somerset, BA9 8BY.
Contact: **HOME (01963) 32179 YARD (01963) 33276 MOBILE (07929) 184132**

1 **ALFIE PLUNKETT**, 5, b g Mind Games—River of Fortune (IRE) **The Artemis Partnership**
2 **LADY MATADOR**, 5, b m El Conquistador—Slashing **Mr Glenn Moore**
3 **PREACHER'S FANCY**, 6, ch m Alflora (IRE)—Preachers Popsy **Mr T. Seegar**
4 **PRINCE SANDROVITCH (IRE)**, 10, b g Camden Town—Devon Royale **Mrs C. D. Farmer**
5 **RIVER BANN (USA)**, 7, ch g Irish River (FR)—Fairy Crown (USA) **Mrs C. D. Farmer**
6 **VITO ANDOLINI**, 6, br g Faustus (USA)—Sunshine Gal **Mrs Jane Galpin**

Other Owners: Mrs L. J. Dowson, Bonny Jarvis, Mrs Annabel Kerby.

Assistant Trainer: Guy Galpin

Jockeys (NH): L Aspell (10-0, w.a.), Philip Hide. **Conditional:** T O'Connor. **Amateur:** Mr Johnathan Barnes (10-0).

217 MR D. R. GANDOLFO, Wantage

Postal: **Downs Stables, Manor Road, Wantage, Oxfordshire, OX12 8NF.**
Contact: **PHONE (01235) 763242 FAX (01235) 764149 E-MAIL david.gandolfo@virgin.net**

1 ANZAL (IRE), 6, b g Kahyasi—Anazara (USA) **Mr Peter Melotti & Mr Andy Chalmers**
2 BANIPOUR (IRE), 4, b g Marju (IRE)—Baniyka (IRE) **D. R. Gandolfo Ltd**
3 BELL TOR (IRE), 7, b m King's Ride—Shannon Juliette **Starlight Racing**
4 CANDARLI (IRE), 8, ch g Polish Precedent (USA)—Calounia (IRE) **Mr A. E. Frost**
5 COULDN'T BE PHAR (IRE), 7, ch g Phardante (FR)—Queenford Belle **Starlight Racing**
6 DEEP SIGH, 7, b g Weld—At Long Last **Mrs John Lee**
7 DIPLOMATIC DAISY (IRE), 5, b m Afflora (IRE)—Landa's Counsel **Mr James Blackshaw**
8 GLENGARRA (IRE), 7, ch g Phardante (FR)—Glengarra Princess **Mr T. J. Whitley**
9 GRAY'S EULOGY, 6, b g Presenting—Gray's Ellergy **Mr M. A. Dore**
10 GUNNERBLONG, 11, ch g Gunner B—At Long Last **Mrs John Lee**
11 LEGAL SPY, 6, ch g Weld—Run Lady Run **D. R. Gandolfo Ltd**
12 4, B f Afflora—Miss Wrensborough **Mr G. C. Hartigan**
13 5, B g Un Desperado (FR)—Pearltwist **Mr G. C. Hartigan**
14 PERCIPIENT, 6, b g Pennekamp (USA)—Annie Albright (USA) **Mr Nigel Stafford**
15 PHAR FAR AWAY, 6, b m Phardante (FR)—Shannon Juliette **Stephen Freud & Friends**
16 QUATRAIN (IRE), 4, ch g Anshan—Gray's Ellergy **Starlight Racing**
17 RAINBOWS AGLITTER, 7, ch g Rainbows For Life (CAN)—Chalet Waldegg **Mr Nigel Stafford**
18 RED SOCIALITE (IRE), 7, ch g Moscow Society (USA)—Dees Darling (IRE) **Starlight Racing**
19 ROOSTER'S REUNION, 5, gr g Presenting—Court Town **Mr Terry Warner**
20 SHIRAZI, 6, b g Mtoto—Al Shadeedah (USA) **Starlight Racing**
21 SOVEREIGN GOLD, 7, b g Rakaposhi King—Page of Gold **K. W. Bell & Son Ltd**
22 WINGED HUSSAR, 11, b g In The Wings—Akila (FR) **Mr A. E. Frost**

THREE-YEAR-OLDS

23 B f Silver Patriarch (IRE)—Lotschberg Express **Mr A. W. F. Clapperton**

Other Owners: Mrs D. E. Blackshaw, Mr J. P. Carrington, Mr M. F. Cartwright, Mr G. Clarke, Mr E. Hance, Mrs A. D. Jackson, Mr P. J. Kennedy, Mr John S. Lee, Mr C. Mackenzie, Mr P. Renahan, Mr M. Robinson, Mr P. J. Slade, Mr A. E. Smith, Mrs J. Snell, Mr V. R. Vyner-Brooks, Mr H. J. M. Webb, Mr J. Webb.

Assistant Trainer: Miss E A Gandolfo

218 MR N. A. GASELEE, Upper Lambourn

Postal: **Saxon Cottage, Upper Lambourn, Hungerford, Berkshire, RG17 8QN.**
Contact: **PHONE (01488) 71503 FAX (01488) 71585**

1 BALLYROBERT (IRE), 7, b br g Bob's Return (IRE)—Line Abreast **The Saxon Partnership**
2 BALLYWALTER (IRE), 8, ch g Commanche Run—Call Me Honey **Mr Barry Marsden**
3 CHATEAU ROSE (IRE), 8, b g Roselier (FR)—Claycastle (IRE) **The Southern Set**
4 EURADREAM (IRE), 6, ch g Eurobus—Its All A Dream **Lady Eliza Mays-Smith**
5 FOXES FANDANGO, 7, br g Munjarid—The Pride of Pokey **Mr Dean Woodley & Mr Mark Fiander**
6 FRANCOLINO (FR), 11, b g Useful (FR)—Quintefeuille II (FR) **Mr Barry Marsden**
7 PLENTY, 5, b m Terimon—Mrs Moneypenny **Mr P. T. Fenwick**
8 REPUNZEL, 9, b m Carlingford Castle—Hi-Rise Lady **Mr Michael Watt**
9 ROMANTIC HERO (IRE), 8, b g Supreme Leader—Right Love **Miss F. M. Fletcher**
10 SPINAROUND, 6, br g Terimon—Re-Spin **Mr D. R. Stoddart**
11 SWAZI PRINCE, 5, b g Rakaposhi King—Swazi Princess (IRE) **Mrs P. T. Orchart**
12 THE LOCAL, 4, b g Selkirk (USA)—Finger of Light **Mr Barry Marsden**

Other Owners: Lady Aitken, Mrs R. W. S. Baker, Lady Bevan, Mrs M. A. Boddington, Mr C. R. Buttery, Mrs P. T. Fenwick, Mr Mark Fiander, Mr G. R. Furse, Mr Simon Harrap, Mrs Patrick McCarthy, Mr R. E. Morris-Adams, Mrs J. K. Newton, Mrs A. Peel Cross, Mrs Tim Perkins, Mr Michael Stoddart, Mr I. R. Taylor, Mrs P. T. Walwyn, Mr Dean Woodley.

Jockeys (NH): C Llewellyn (10-0, w.a.), A Thornton (w.a.).

219 MR T. R. GEORGE, Slad
Postal: **Springbank, Slad, Stroud, Gloucestershire, GL6 7QE.**
Contact: **PHONE (01452) 814267 FAX (01452) 814246 MOBILE (07850) 793483**

1 ALPINE FOX, 7, b g Risk Me (FR)—Hill Vixen **Mrs A. D. Williams**
2 ASHLEY MARSH, 6, b g Alflora (IRE)—Annapuma **Mr M. J. Hoskins**
3 ATLASTABOY (IRE), 8, b g Phardante (FR)—Corcaigh **Mr Timothy N. Chick**
4 BACARDI BOY (IRE), 8, b g Lord Americo—Little Welly **Allan Stennett & Terry Warner**
5 BATON CHARGE (IRE), 6, b g Gildoran—Frizzball **Mr John Dyson**
6 BEE AN BEE (IRE), 7, b g Phardante (FR)—Portia's Delight **Mr Stan Moore**
7 BRAZIL (IRE), 6, b g Germany (USA)—Alberta Rose (IRE) **Mrs Sharon C. Nelson**
8 BURWOOD BREEZE (IRE), 8, b g Fresh Breeze (USA)—Shuil Le Cheile **David & Lesley Byrne**
9 CALVIC (IRE), 6, ch g Old Vic—Calishee (IRE) **The Alchabas Partnership**
10 CURTINS HILL (IRE), 5, b g Roi Guillaume (FR)—Kinallen Lady (IRE) **Mrs Elizabeth Pitman**
11 DANTE CITIZEN (IRE), 6, ch g Phardante (FR)—Boreen Citizen **Ryder Racing Ltd**
12 DAWTON (POL), 6, br h Greinton—Da Wega (POL) **Mr B. A. Kilpatrick**
13 DON VALENTINO (POL), 5, ch g Duke Valentino—Dona (POL) **Sir Stanley Clarke**
14 DROM WOOD (IRE), 8, ch g Be My Native (USA)—Try Your Case **Mrs M. Devine**
15 FLOWER OF PITCUR (IRE), 7, b g Alflora (IRE)—Coire Vannich **Mrs Strachan,L-Palmer,Parkinson,J.Morris**
16 GALILEO (POL), 8, b g Jape (USA)—Goldika (POL) **Mrs S.Nelson,Allan Stennett,Terry Warner**
17 HISTORIC (IRE), 8, b g Sadler's Wells (USA)—Urjwan (USA) **Mrs R. E. R. Rumboll**
18 IRISH DISTINCTION (IRE), 6, b g Distinctly North (USA)—Shane's Girl (IRE) **Ryder Racing Ltd**
19 ISHKA BAHA (IRE), 5, ch m Shernazar—Briongloid **Miss Judith Wilson**
20 JETOWA DU BOIS HUE (FR), 7, b g Kadrou (FR)—Vaika (FR) **Mr B. A. Kilpatrick**
21 JOE DEANE (IRE), 8, ch g Alphabatim (USA)—Craic Go Leor **Mr & Mrs D. A. Gamble**
22 JULIES BOY (IRE), 7, b g Toulon—Chickmo (IRE) **Mr R. P. Foden**
23 KOMBINACJA (POL), 6, ch m Jape (USA)—Komancza (POL) **C.Davies,S.Nelson,A.Stennett,T.Warner**
24 4, Ch f Anshan—La Bise **Mr T. R. George**
25 LORD OF ILLUSION (IRE), 7, b g Mister Lord (USA)—Jellaride (IRE) **Mr P. J. Kennedy**
26 MADGE CARROLL (IRE), 7, b m Hollow Hand—Spindle Tree **Madge At Slad Partnership**
27 MALLORY, 10, b g North Col—Veritate **Mr D. J. Price**
28 MAMIDEOS (IRE), 7, br g Good Thyne (USA)—Heavenly Artist **Silkword Racing Partnership**
29 MANDY'S ROSE (IRE), 8, b br m Mandalus—Rookery Lady (IRE) **Mr & Mrs D. A. Gamble**
30 MISTER MAGPIE, 8, gr g Neltino—Magic **Mr Timothy N. Chick**
31 MYSTERY (GER), 6, br g Java Gold (USA)—My Secret (USA) **Mr P. J. Kennedy**
32 NATIVE BUCK (IRE), 11, ch g Be My Native (USA)—Buckskins Chat **The One Over Par Partnership**
33 NOWATOR (POL), 7, ch g Jape (USA)—Naradka (POL) **Mrs Sharon C. Nelson**
34 PADDY THE OPTIMIST (IRE), 8, b g Leading Counsel (USA)—Erne Duchess (IRE) **Mr M. R. C. Opperman**
35 PHARAWAY CITIZEN (IRE), 9, ch g Phardante (FR)—Boreen Citizen **Pharaway Partnership**
36 POLISH CLOUD (FR), 7, gr g Bering—Batchelor's Button (FR) **Mrs Grace Frankel & Partners**
37 REDSKIN RAIDER (IRE), 8, b g Commanche Run—Sheltered (IRE) **Mrs Christine Davies**
38 RIVER SLAVE (IRE), 10, b br g Over The River (FR)—Sally Slave **Mrs P. Miller**
39 ROSETOWN (IRE), 6, gr g Roselier (FR)—Railstown Cheeky (IRE) **Mr Timothy N. Chick**
40 ROYAL BELUGA (USA), 7, b g Rahy (USA)—Nravitalovna (USA) **Mr M. R. C. Opperman**
41 RYDERS STORM (USA), 5, b br g Dynaformer (USA)—Justicara **Ryder Racing Ltd**
42 SEARCH AND DESTROY (USA), 6, b br g Sky Classic (CAN)—Hunt The Thimble (USA) **Mrs R. E. R. Rumboll**
43 STACK THE PACK (IRE), 7, ch g Good Thyne (USA)—Game Trix **Mrs Christine Davies**
44 TOULOUSE-LAUTREC (IRE), 8, ch g Toulon—Bucks Slave **Mr John French**
45 TRAVEL (IRE), 4, gr g Freedom's Choice (USA)—Transylwania (POL) **Mrs Sharon C. Nelson**
46 TREMALLT (IRE), 13, b g Henbit (USA)—Secret Romance **Silkword Racing Partnership**
47 TRENANCE, 6, b g Alflora (IRE)—Carmel's Joy (IRE) **Mr & Mrs D. A. Gamble**
48 TURTLE SOUP (IRE), 8, b g Turtle Island (IRE)—Lisa's Favourite **Mr M. K. George**

Other Owners: Mr A. A. Bamboye, Mr Richard J. B. Blake, Mr B. Corrigan, Mr R. C. Cox, Mr R. A. Dalton, Mrs S. P. George, Mr H. Harford, Mr Crispin Hodges, Mr John B. Lawson, Mr A. R. Lewers, Mr Roy Neal, Mr David Seed, Mr R. F. Tromans.

Jockey (NH): Jason Maguire (10-2). Conditional: Paul C O'Neill (9-10), Z L Owen (9-7). Amateur: Mr Paul Callaghan (9-7).

220 MR V. Y. GETHIN, Stoke Prior
Postal: **Sunny Bank Farm, Stoke Prior, Leominster, Herefordshire, HR6 0NF.**
Contact: **PHONE (01568) 760485 MOBILE (07718) 051394**

1 CRACK ON CHERYL, 10, b m Rakaposhi King—Furstin **Mrs C. Gethin**
2 ESKLEYBROOK, 11, b g Arzanni—Crystal Run VII **Mr V. Y. Gethin**

MR V. Y. GETHIN—continued

3 **QUEEN OF JAZZ**, 7, b m Sovereign Water (FR)—When The Saints **Mr V. Y. Gethin**
4 **THE WELDER**, 10, b g Buckley—Crystal Run VII **Mr V. Y. Gethin**

Assistant Trainer: Mrs Christine Gethin

---

221 **MR RICHARD GIBSON, Chantilly**
Postal: 7, Avenue Montpensier, 60500 Chantilly, France.
Contact: **PHONE +33 (0) 44 57 53 00 FAX +33 (0) 44 58 15 48 MOBILE 0608 61 57 88**
E-MAIL richard.gibson@wanadoo.fr

1 **CUT QUARTZ (FR)**, 7, b h Johann Quatz—Cutlass **Mrs A. G. Kavanagh**
2 **ECLAIR D'IRLANDE (FR)**, 4, b br c Zieten (USA)—Valixa (FR) **Mr T. Stewart**
3 **LADY YING (FR)**, 5, b m Kendor (FR)—Super Vite (USA) **Mr T. Yoshida**
4 **LA SABANA (FR)**, 4, b f Loup Solitaire (USA)—La Peregrina (FR) **Mr M. Randelli**
5 **PRINCE CHARMANT**, 4, gr c Wolfhound (USA)—Plume Bleu Pale (USA) **Ecurie Wildenstein**
6 **SWEDISH SHAVE (FR)**, 6, b g Midyan (USA)—Shavya **Mr S. Thynell**

THREE-YEAR-OLDS

7 **ANYONE FOR TENNIS (IRE)**, b f Night Shift (USA)—Lame de Fond (FR) **Mr J. Livock**
8 **AUSTRALIE (IRE)**, b f Sadler's Wells (USA)—Asnieres (USA) **Ecurie J. L. Bouchard**
9 **BERROSCOBERRO (FR)**, b f Octagonal (NZ)—Muramixa (FR) **Haras Saint Pair du Mont**
10 **BRADAMANTE**, b f Sadler's Wells (USA)—Balisada **Mr A. E. Oppenheimer**
11 **CATTIVA GENEROSA**, b f Cadeaux Genereux—Signorina Cattiva (USA) **Haras Saint Pair du Mont**
12 **DREAMS COME TRUE (FR)**, b f Zafonic (USA)—Moonlight Dreams (IRE) **Mrs E. Soderberg**
13 **DROP SHOT**, ch c Groom Dancer (USA)—Three Greens **Mr J. Livock**
14 **GEORDIELAND (FR)**, gr c Johann Quatz (FR)—Aerdee (FR) **Mr R. Elbaz**
15 **GOLUBITSA (IRE)**, b f Bluebird (USA)—Bolshaya **Mr T. Stewart**
16 **HECTOLUN (FR)**, b c Hector Protector—Lunata (IRE) **Mr F. Mani**
17 **ICKNIELD**, b c Polish Precedent—Ingozi **Mr A. Oppenheimer**
18 **KALKARA (IRE)**, gr f Desert King (IRE)—Valnerina (IRE) **Mr G. A. Oldham**
19 **KYLE AKIN**, b f Vettori (IRE)—Kyle Rhea **Mrs A. G. Kavanagh**
20 **LAND BRIDGE (FR)**, b f Bering—Miss Ebene (FR) **Mr W. Baumann**
21 **LE MAREYEUR**, b c Fasliyev (USA)—Green Rosy **Mrs G. Forien**
22 **LUNE D'OR (FR)**, b f Green Tune (USA)—Luth d'Or (FR) **Mrs P. de Moussac**
23 **LURE OF THE MOON (USA)**, b f Lure (USA)—Moonlit (CAN) **Mr R. Barnes**
24 **OLONELLA**, b f Selkirk (USA)—Zinarelle (FR) **Mrs V. Riva**
25 **PETIT CALVA (FR)**, b f Desert King (IRE)—Jimkana (FR) **Mrs A. G. Kavanagh**
26 **PLEASE BE GOOD (IRE)**, ch f Prince of Birds (USA)—Adultress (IRE) **Mr D. Adams**
27 **ROSE OF AFRICA (FR)**, gr f Verglas (IRE)—Oh Lucky Day **Mr T. Stewart**
28 **SKY GIFT (USA)**, ch f Stravinsky (USA)—Wedding Gift (FR) **Mrs G. Duval Lemonnie**
29 **STEEL PRINCESS (IRE)**, b f Danehill (USA)—Champaka (IRE) **Mr R. Barnes**
30 **TRITONA (IRE)**, b f Barathea (IRE)—Piacenza (IRE) **Mr G. A. Oldham**
31 **VERTE VALLEE (FR)**, b f Septieme Ciel (USA)—Valleyrose (IRE) **M. O. Lecerf**
32 **VIVE LA VIE (USA)**, ro c Cozzene (USA)—Kiyo Amy (USA) **Mr L. Robbins**
33 **VOCATAINE (IRE)**, b f Royal Applause—Voltage (USA) **Mrs A. Gibson**

TWO-YEAR-OLDS

34 **AISIN (IRE)**, ch f 22/1 Giant's Causeway—Angelina Carolina (IRE) (Kris) (89672) **Haras Saint Pair du Mont**
35 B f 9/4 Inchinor—Amnesia (USA) (Septieme Ciel (USA)) (18552) **Mrs A. Gibson**
36 **AMOROSA BRI**, b f 10/3 Bering—Ampelopsis (FR) (Night Shift (USA)) (49474) **Mr J. Crowley**
37 **ANESTASIA (IRE)**, b f 12/4 Anabaa (USA)—
　　　　　Spectacular Joke (USA) (Spectacular Bid (USA)) (197897) **Mr F. Mani**
38 B f 15/3 Sadler's Wells (USA)—Animatrice (USA) (Alleged (USA)) **Mr A. E. Oppenheimer**
39 **ANNEE LUMIERE (IRE)**, ch f 29/3 Giant's Causeway—Luminosity (Sillery (USA)) (75000) **Mrs G. Forlen**
40 **APACHE HOGAN (FR)**, ch c 23/5 Indian Lodge (IRE)—Lisheba (USA) (Alysheba (USA)) (28427) **Mr J. Wallinger**
41 **ASPOLINA (IRE)**, b f 6/3 Trempolino (USA)—Astonishing (BRZ) (Vacilante (ARG)) **Mr M. Randelli**
42 B c 17/4 Red Ransom (USA)—Balenciaga (USA) (Gulch (USA)) (50000) **Mr M. Tololi**
43 B f 27/1 Pennekamp (USA)—Brother (FR) (Dolphin Street (FR)) **Mrs A. G. Kavanagh**
44 **CATTIVO LEONARDO**, ch c 15/1 Machiavellian (USA)—
　　　　　Signorina Cattiva (USA) (El Gran Senor (USA)) **Haras Saint Pair du Mont**
45 **COONAWARRA (FR)**, b c 15/3 Septieme Ciel (USA)—
　　　　　Champion's Sister (USA) (Spence Bay (IRE)) **Mr A. Al Maddah**
46 B f 9/3 Xaar—Cootamundra (FR) (Double Bed (FR)) (34013) **Mr H. de Burgh**
47 **DOCTOR DINO (FR)**, ch c 16/3 Muhtathir—Logica (IRE) (Priolo (USA)) (23500) **Mr M. Salmean**

MR RICHARD GIBSON—continued

48 **EGYPT MOON,** b f 8/4 Zieten (USA)—Ile Mamou (IRE) (Ela-Mana-Mou) (22263) **Mrs E. Soderberg**
49 B f 8/2 Sinndar (IRE)—Flanders (IRE) (Common Grounds) (28000) **Mrs A. G. Kavanagh**
50 B f 22/5 Inchinor—Gai Bulga (Kris) **Mr A. E. Oppenheimer**
51 B f 21/2 Capote (USA)—Glasgow's Gold (USA) (Seeking The Gold (USA)) (83333) **Skymarc Farm**
52 Ch f 20/4 King's Best (USA)—Glenarff (USA) (Irish River (FR)) (21644) **Mr H. de Burgh**
53 **GRAZIA BELLA,** b f 23/1 Green Desert (USA)—Zinarelle (FR) (Zino) (71119) **Mrs V. Riva**
54 **HIDEAWAY (FR),** b f 29/4 Cape Cross (IRE)—Hint of Silver (USA) (Alysheba (USA)) **Skymarc Farm**
55 **HIGHEST LOVER (FR),** gr c 12/1 Highest Honor (FR)—Distant Lover (Distant Relative (IRE)) (37105) **Mr F. Mani**
56 Gr f 26/4 Kahyasi—Kaldevees (FR) (Kaldoun (FR)) (27210) **Mr I. Blance**
57 B f 5/4 Horse Chestnut (SAF)—Lady Ilsley (USA) (Trempolino (USA)) (86580) **Mr A. E. Oppenheimer**
58 B f 4/3 Highest Honor (FR)—Lady Winner (FR) (Fabulous Dancer (USA)) **Skymarc Farm**
59 **LE TIGRE D'OR (FR),** ch c 3/5 Indian Ridge (IRE)—La Panthere (USA) (Pine Bluff (USA)) (126777) **Mr J. Livock**
60 **LEVENTINA (IRE),** b f 21/2 Anabaa (USA)—Perugina (FR) (Highest Honor (FR)) (11750) **Mr H. de Burgh**
61 **LISTEN DADDY (FR),** b f 4/5 Piccolo—Torreglia (IRE) (Elmaamul (USA)) (11750) **Mr S. Thynell**
62 **LOVE FIFTEEN (IRE),** ch f 18/2 Grand Lodge (USA)—
                                   Tresor Russe (IRE) (Soviet Star (USA)) (40197) **Mr J. Livock**
63 **LUCERA (IRE),** b f 15/3 Fasliyev—Lunata (USA) (Marju (IRE)) **Mr J. L. Bouchard**
64 **MADRID BEAUTY (FR),** ch f 17/3 Sendawar (IRE)—Kate Marie (Bering) (40197) **Mr F. Mani**
65 B f 9/4 Barathea—Mrs Ting (USA) (Lyphard (USA)) (37105) **Mr H. de Burgh**
66 **NONNO LIBERO,** bc 8/4 Anabaa (USA)—Graceful Bering (Bering) (24737) **Mrs V. Riva**
67 Ch f 5/3 Distant View (USA)—Nunatak (USA) (Bering) (20000) **Ecurie Wildenstein**
68 **PARIS AT NIGHT (FR),** b f 23/4 In The Wings—Rigoureuse (USA) (Septieme Ciel (USA)) (123685) **Mr R. Barnes**
69 **PATERNO (IRE),** b c 25/5 Marju (IRE)—Piacenza (IRE) (Darshaan) **Mr G. A. Oldham**
70 **PRETREVAL (FR),** ch c 1/5 Barathea (IRE)—Touville (USA) (Shadeed (USA)) (24737) **Mr O. Lecerf**
71 **ROYAL MISTRESS (IRE),** b f 16/3 Fasliyev (USA)—
                                   Regal Peace (Known Fact (USA)) (60000) **Ecurie Wildenstein**
72 **SALTINO (IRE),** b c 31/1 Daylami (IRE)—Mahalia (IRE) (Danehill (USA)) **Mr G. A. Oldham**
73 B f 23/3 Vettori (IRE)—Salvinaxia (FR) (Linamix (FR)) (64935) **Mr L. Robbins**
74 **SEGESTA (IRE),** bf 25/4 Vettori (IRE)—Mistra (FR) (Rainbow Quest (USA)) **Mr G. A. Oldham**
75 Ch f 4/4 Aljabr (USA)—Shamisen (Diesis) (37105) **Mr H. de Burgh**
76 B f 1/5 Verglas (IRE)—Sixty Six (IRE) (Exit To Nowhere (USA)) (11750) **Skymarc Farm**
77 **THE JEWEL (IRE),** b f 12/3 Octagonal (NZ)—The Blade (GER) (Sure Blade (USA)) **Mr Stein**
78 **VALBUENA (FR),** bl f 20/4 Highest Honor (FR)—Desert Victory (Green Desert (USA)) **Mrs M. Campbell**
79 **VOVAN (IRE),** ch c 8/3 Indian Ridge—Mistreat (Gay Mecene (USA)) (105132) **Mr F. Mani**
80 **YASMARA (IRE),** gr f 22/2 Kendor (FR)—Muirfield (FR) (Crystal Glitters (USA)) (37105) **Mr H. de Burgh**

Other Owners: Mr W. Baumann, Mr S. Boucheron, Mr A. Crawford, Mr M. Flaherty, Mr M. Lind, Mrs A. Redfern, Mrs J. Sanders, Mr R. Stephenson.

Assistant Trainer: Eric Gandon

Jockey (Flat): T Jarnet. **Apprentice:** T Richer.

---

222   MR N. J. G. GIFFORD, Findon
Postal: **The Downs, Stable Lane, Findon, West Sussex, BN14 0RR.**
Contact: **OFFICE (01903) 872226 FAX (01903) 877232 MOBILE (07940) 518077**
        E-MAIL downs.stables@btconnect.com

1 **ALPINE SLAVE,** 7, ch g Alflora—Celtic Slave **Mrs J. T. Gifford**
2 **ALPINE STAR,** 7, ch g Alflora (IRE)—Northwood Star (IRE) **Mr S. N. J. Embiricos**
3 **CAMDENATION (IRE),** 8, b g Camden Town—Out The Nav (IRE) **Unstable Companions**
4 **CARLOTTA,** 7, b m Carlingford Castle—Baryta **Lime Street Racing Syndicate**
5 **CHICAGO CITY (IRE),** 11, br g Strong Gale—Orchardstown **Mr S. N. J. Embiricos**
6 **FELIXRDOTCOM,** ch g Gran Alba (USA)—Golden Curd (FR) **Felix Rosenstiel's Widow & Son**
7 **GALAXY SAM (USA),** 5, ch g Royal Academy (USA)—Istiska (USA) **Mr S. Munir**
8 **GLANDORE MOON,** 5, br g Presenting—My Gonny (IRE) **Mr Chris Keeley**
9 **INDEED (IRE),** 9, ch g Camden Town—Pamrina **Pell-mell Partners**
10 **JOLY BEY (FR),** 7, ch g Beyssac—Rivolie (FR) **Mr David Dunsdon**
11 **KOPECK (IRE),** 6, ch g Moscow Society (USA)—Cashla (IRE) **Mr P. H. Betts**
12 **LADY HARRIET,** 5, b m Sir Harry Lewis (USA)—Forever Together **The Brabourne Partnership**
13 **MAJOR CATCH (IRE),** 5, b g Safety Catch (USA)—Inch Tape **Martin & Valerie Slade**
14 **MONSIEUR ROSE,** 8, gr g Roselier (FR)—Derring Slipper **Martin & Valerie Slade**
15 **MR MARKHAM (IRE),** 12, b g Naheez (USA)—Brighter Gail **Felix Rosenstiel's Widow & Son**
16 **MULLIGATAWNY (IRE),** 10, b g Abednego—Mullangale **Pell-mell Partners**
17 **NARWHAL (IRE),** 6, b br g Naheez (USA)—Well Why (IRE) **Mrs S. N. J. Embiricos**

MR N. J. G. GIFFORD—continued

18 **PETER'S DEBT**, 5, b g Arzanni—Another Debt **Miss J. Semple**
19 **POUNSLEY MILL (IRE)**, 11, b g Asir—Clonroche Abendego **Mrs John Shipley**
20 5, B g Lord Americo—Red Dusk **Mrs J. T. Gifford**
21 **RED GUARD**, 10, ch g Soviet Star (USA)—Zinzara (USA) **The Marvellous Partnership**
22 **SAFE ENOUGH (IRE)**, 8, ch g Safety Catch (USA)—Godfreys Cross (IRE) **D. S. Norden & R. S. Norden**
23 **SENOR SEDONA**, 5, b g Royal Vulcan—Star Shell **Felix Rosenstiel's Widow & Son**
24 **SILVER STREAK (IRE)**, 10, gr g Roselier (FR)—Vulcash (IRE) **Mrs Timothy Pilkington**
25 **SKYCAB (IRE)**, 12, b g Montelimar (USA)—Sams Money **P. H. Betts (Holdings) Ltd**
26 **WEE ROBBIE**, 4, b g Bob Back (USA)—Blast Freeze (IRE) **P. H. Betts (Holdings) Ltd**

Other Owners: Mr Jon Baldwin, Mr J. Bayer, Mr. G. H. L. Bird, Mr D. H. C. Boath, Mr Nigel Chamberlain, Mr M. Chandler, Mr J. Chromiak, Mr G. K. Duncan, Mr Ian Gibson, Mr Richard Gilder, Mr Raymond Anderson Green, Mr S. Hurst, Mr A. Mason, Mr D. S. Norden, Mr R. Norden, Mr D. M. Slade, Mrs V. J. M. Slade, Mr Ian Fenton White, Mr T. H. White.

Jockeys (NH): L Aspell (10-0), P Hide (10-0). **Conditional:** D Laverty (9-7). **Amateur:** Mr David Dunsdon (10-0).

---

223 MR J. A. GILBERT, Bury St Edmunds
Postal: **Albion House, Birds End, Hargrave, Bury St Edmunds, Suffolk, IP29 5HE.**
Contact: **PHONE (01284) 850908 MOBILE (07702) 189086**

1 **ANGEL ANNIE**, 4, b f Alzao (USA)—Pure **Mr Terry Connors**
2 **FANTASY CRUSADER**, 5, ch g Beveled (USA)—Cranfield Charger **The Fantasy Fellowship**
3 **LAW BREAKER (IRE)**, 6, ch g Case Law—Revelette **Mr Terry Connors**
4 **MISS JINGLES**, 5, b m Muhtarram (USA)—Flamingo Times **Mr James A. Gilbert**
5 **OUR OLD BOY (IRE)**, 4, br g Petorius—Minzal Legend (IRE) **Mr Bill Diaper**
6 **SARGENTS DREAM**, 4, b f Regal Embers (IRE)—Dance Lady **Mr K. Sargent**

THREE-YEAR-OLDS

7 **FOOLS ENTIRE**, ch g Fraam—Poly Blue (IRE) **Mr Terry Connors**

Other Owners: Mr A. M. Blewitt, Exors Of The Late Mr N. J. Hagan, Mr Nick Lane, Mr. S. Williams.

Assistant Trainer: A. C. Buckley

---

224 MR M. J. GINGELL, Saxmundham
Postal: **2 The Old Post Office, Saxtead Green, Framlingham, Suffolk, IP13 9QU.**
Contact: **HOME (01728) 621193 TRAINER (07831) 623624 SECRETARY (07770) 533488
YARD (01728) 602537 E-MAIL gingell@ukonline.com**

1 **CAPTAIN SMOOTHY**, 4, b g Charmer—The Lady Captain **Mr P. Cranney**
2 **CIRCLE OF WOLVES**, 6, ch g Wolfhound (USA)—Misty Halo **Mrs J. M. Penney**
3 **DUNRAVEN**, 9, b g Perpendicular—Politique **Fare Dealing Partnership**
4 **EMERALD GREEN (GER)**, 5, br g Goofalik (USA)—Elaine (GER) **Mr B. M. Gray**
5 **GLADYS GRACE**, 4, ch f Double Trigger (IRE)—Try For Gold **T. Alexander and G. S. Plastow**
6 **HARRY THE HOOVER (IRE)**, 4, b g Fayruz—Mitsubishi Style **W. Stanger, P. Whittall and G. Plastow**
7 **LUNAR LEADER (IRE)**, 4, b f Mujadil (USA)—Moon River (FR) **Mrs L. Bangs**
8 **NEW PERK (IRE)**, 6, b g Executive Perk—New Chello (IRE) **Mr A. White**
9 **NORTON SAPPHIRE**, 5, ch m Karinga Bay—Sea of Pearls (IRE) **Gentlemen Don't Work on Mondays**
10 **NUTCRACKER LAD (IRE)**, 6, ch g Duky—Allercashin Moon (IRE) **C. N. & A. V. Roberts**
11 **ORIENTAL MOON (IRE)**, 5, ch m Spectrum (IRE)—La Grande Cascade (USA) **Mr M. J. Gingell**
12 **REMEMBRANCE**, 4, b g Sabrehill (USA)—Perfect Poppy **W. Stanger, P. Whittall and G. Plastow**
13 **SMOKIN GREY**, 4, gr f Terimon—Wollow Maid **Gingells Disciples**
14 **STEPPES**, 9, b g Jendali (USA)—Asoness **T. Alexander and G. S. Plastow**

THREE-YEAR-OLDS

15 **GLADYS GERTRUDE**, ch f Double Trigger (IRE)—Nour El Sahar (USA)

Other Owners: Dr Tom Alexander, Mr P. A. Burling, Mr C. Cole, Mr N. P. Haley, Dr G. S. Plastow, Mrs A. V. Roberts, Mr C. N. Roberts, Mrs Wendy Stanger, Mr A. Stanton, Miss S. L. White, Mr Pete Whittall, Mr J. M. Williams.

Assistant Trainer: Mrs A Gingell

Jockey (NH): S Fox (10-4). **Conditional:** B Murphy (10-2), C Williamson (9-8).

225 MR JAMES GIVEN, Gainsborough

Postal: **Mount House Stables, Long Lane, Willoughton, Gainsborough, Lincolnshire, DN21 5SQ.**
Contact: **PHONE** (01427) 667618 **FAX** (01427) 667734 **MOBILE** (07801) 100496
E-MAIL james.given@edgfoot.com

1 **AIMEE'S DELIGHT**, 4, b f Robellino (USA)—Lloc **Mr D. Hilton**
2 **BRANSTON TIGER**, 5, b h Mark of Esteem (IRE)—Tuxford Hideaway **Mr J. D. Abell**
3 **BURLEY FIREBRAND**, 4, b g Bahamian Bounty—Vallauris **Burley Appliances Ltd**
4 **CADEAUX DES MAGES**, 4, b g Cadeaux Genereux—On Tiptoes **Mr J. Rowles**
5 **CHANTRY FALLS (IRE)**, 4, b g Mukaddamah (USA)—Woodie Dancer (USA) **White Rose Poultry**
6 **COPLEY PLACE**, 4, b f Piccolo—Bangles **Mrs Susan M. Lee**
7 **CROW WOOD**, 5, b h Halling (USA)—Play With Me (IRE) **Mr J. Hardy**
8 **DAME DE NOCHE**, 4, b f Lion Cavern (USA)—Goodnight Kiss **The G-Guck Group**
9 **GRAMPIAN**, 5, b h Selkirk (USA)—Gryada **Mr M. J. Dawson**
10 **HIGHLAND GAMES (IRE)**, 4, b g Singspiel (IRE)—Highland Gift (IRE) **K. Bailey, P. Booth & D. Boorer**
11 **I CRIED FOR YOU**, 9, b g Statoblest—Fall of The Hammer (IRE) **One Stop Partnership**
12 **KILLING JOKE**, 4, b c Double Trigger (IRE)—Fleeting Vision (IRE) **Mr A. Clarke**
13 **MALLARD (IRE)**, 6, b g Tagula (IRE)—Frill **Audrey Scotney & Malcolm Joyce**
14 **MARITIME BLUES**, 4, b c Fleetwood (IRE)—Dixie d'Oats **Downlands Racing**
15 **MING THE MERCILESS**, 4, b g Hector Protector (USA)—Sundae Girl (USA) **Mr A. Clarke**
16 **MORVERN (IRE)**, 4, ch g Titus Livius (FR)—Scotia Rose **Mrs D. Given**
17 **PENNY CROSS**, 4, b f Efisio—Addaya (IRE) **Mr & Mrs G. Middlebrook**
18 **PURI**, 5, b g Mujadil (USA)—Prosperous Lady **Mrs Doreen Swinburn**
19 **RECALL (IRE)**, 4, b f Revoque (IRE)—Toffee **Mrs M. V. Chaworth-Musters**
20 **ROCK'N COLD (IRE)**, 6, b g Bigstone (IRE)—Unalaska (IRE) **Mr A. Clarke**
21 **SIR SIDNEY**, 4, b g Shareef Dancer (USA)—Hattaafeh (IRE) **Becky & Sidney Stones**
22 **SKYE'S FOLLY (USA)**, 4, b g Kris S (USA)—Bittersweet Hour (USA) **Audrey Scotney & Malcolm Joyce**
23 **SUERTE**, 4, b f Halling (USA)—Play With Me (IRE) **Mr Cyril Humphris**
24 **SUMMITVILLE**, 4, b f Grand Lodge (USA)—Tina Heights **Mountain High Partnership**
25 **TELEMACHUS**, 4, b c Bishop of Cashel—Indian Imp **The Travellers**
26 **TERDAD (USA)**, 11, ch g Lomond (USA)—Istiska (FR) **Tremousser Partnership**
27 **TETCHY**, 4, b f Robellino (USA)—Putout **Bloomsbury Stud**

THREE-YEAR-OLDS

28 **APPETINA**, b f Perugino (USA)—Tina Heights **Great Escape Partnership**
29 **BE WISE GIRL**, ch f Fleetwood (IRE)—Zabelina (USA) **Be Wise Racing**
30 **BURLEY FLAME**, b g Marju (IRE)—Tarsa **Burley Appliances Ltd**
31 **COCO POINT BREEZE**, b f Great Dane (IRE)—Flying Colours (IRE) **Mrs R. W. S. Baker**
32 **COMMEMORATION DAY (IRE)**, b g Daylami (IRE)—Bequeath (USA) **Reg Griffin & Jim McGrath**
33 **CRATHES**, ch f Zilzal (USA)—Sweet Dreams **Mr B. H. Farr**
34 **CTESIPHON (USA)**, b f Arch (USA)—Beautiful Bedouin (USA) **The Socrates Partnership**
35 **DAKOTA BLACKHILLS**, b c Singspiel (IRE)—Lady Blackfoot **M. S. Anderson & R.S.G. Jones**
36 **DANZIG'S HEIRESS**, b f Danzig Connection (USA)—Zielana Gora **Skeltools Ltd**
37 **EUIPPE**, b f Air Express (IRE)—Myth **Mr C. G. Rowles Nicholson**
38 **FIRST CANDLELIGHT**, b f First Trump—No Candles Tonight **Skeltools Ltd**
39 **FISHLAKE FLYER (IRE)**, b f Desert Style (IRE)—Millitrix **Fishlake Commercial Motors**
40 **FOUR AMIGOS (USA)**, b c Southern Halo—Larentia **Bailey Booth Boorer Nelson**
41 **FREDDIE FRECCLES**, ch g Komaite (USA)—Leprechaun Lady **The Secret Seven Partnership**
42 **GIVEN A CHANCE**, b g Defacto (USA)—Milly Molly Mango **D. S. Arnold and M. W. Horner**
43 **GRANDE TERRE (IRE)**, b f Grand Lodge (USA)—Savage (IRE) **Mr & Mrs G. Calder**
44 **HARRY UP**, ch c Piccolo—Faraway Lass **Mr J. E. Rose**
45 **HAVVA DANZ**, b f Danzero (AUS)—Possessive Lady **Mrs P. A. Barrett**
46 **HUGS DESTINY (IRE)**, b f Victory Note (USA)—Embracing **Mr J. G. White & Mr D. Maloney**
47 **ISAAC POINT (IRE)**, br g Desert Style (IRE)—Mettlesome **Moneyleague Ltd**
48 **KEN SHABBY**, b g Forzando—Secret Dance **Mr A. Clarke**
49 **LISTEN TO REASON (IRE)**, b c Mukaddamah (USA)—Tenalist (IRE) **Mike Beadle & John Furness**
50 **MAGARI**, b f Royal Applause—Thatcher's Era (IRE)
51 **MARITA**, ch f Dancing Spree (USA)—Maria Cappuccini **Mr D. Bass**
52 **MILLIBIEN**, b g Bien Bien (USA)—Mill Thyme **Mr R. Meredith**
53 **MISS LADYBIRD (USA)**, b br f Labeeb—Bird Dance (CAN) **Mrs R. Morley & Mr M. S. Anderson**
54 **MOLEHILL**, b f Salse (USA)—Mountain Lodge **Lord Halifax**
55 **MOUNT COTTAGE**, b f Cape Cross (USA)—Brecon Beacons (IRE) **Mrs G. A. Jennings**
56 **MUNGO JERRY (GER)**, b c Tannenkonig (IRE)—Mostly Sure (IRE) **Mrs Ann Harrison**
57 **NESSEN DORMA (IRE)**, b g Entrepreneur—Goldilocks (IRE) **Hokey Cokey Partnership**
58 **ONE ALONE**, b f Atraf—Songsheet **Realistic Racing**
59 **PAPPY (IRE)**, b f Petardia—Impressive Lady **Mr John McMahon**

MR JAMES GIVEN—continued

60 **POSH SHEELAGH**, b f Danzero (AUS)—Button Hole Flower (IRE) **Mr I. Jackson & Mr A. Clarke**
61 **QUEEN LUCIA (IRE)**, b f Pursuit of Love—Inquirendo (USA) **Mr H. J. P. Farr**
62 **QUEENSLANDER (IRE)**, b f Inchinor—Royal Subject **Mr J. D. Abell**
63 **REDMARLEY (IRE)**, b g Croco Rouge (IRE)—Dazzling Fire (IRE) **Tweenhills Racing/Queenhill Syndicate**
64 **REIDIES CHOICE**, b g Royal Applause—Fairy Ring (IRE) **Mr M. J. Dawson**
65 **RILEY BOYS (IRE)**, ch g Most Welcome—Scarlett Holly **Mr Paul Riley**
66 **ROCK LOBSTER**, b c Desert Sun—Distant Music **Mr A. Clarke**
67 **SAINT LAZARE (IRE)**, b c Peintre Celebre—Height of Passion **Mr Chris Watson**
68 **SATSU (IRE)**, ch f Shinko Forest (IRE)—Cap And Gown (IRE) **Mr J. D. Abell**
69 **SCOTS GUARD (IRE)**, b g Selkirk (USA)—Island Race **Car Colston Hall Stud/Hamill**
70 **SHIPSHAPE**, ch f Docksider (USA)—Toffee **Mrs M. V. Chaworth Musters**
71 **SONG KOI**, b f Sri Pekan (USA)—Eastern Lyric **Mr R. Meredith**
72 **STILETTO LADY (IRE)**, b f Daggers Drawn (USA)—Nordic Pride **JJP Partnership**
73 **THADEA (IRE)**, b br f Grand Lodge (USA)—Kama Tashoof **Hanibel Racing Partnership**
74 **THROUGH THE SLIPS (USA)**, ch f Boundary (USA)—Fast Selection (USA) **Mr A. M. Warrender & Partners**
75 **TROUBLEINPARADISE (IRE)**, b f Pursuit of Love—Sweet Holland (USA) **Mr R. Jennings**
76 **TRUE TO YOURSELF (USA)**, b g Royal Academy (USA)—Romily **Mike Beadle**
77 **TYZACK (IRE)**, b g Fasliyev (USA)—Rabea (USA) **Mr A. Clarke**
78 **VIOLET AVENUE**, ch f Muhtarram (USA)—Ivoronica **The Exors of the late Mr H. Key**
79 Ch c Hector Protector (USA)—You Make Me Real (USA) **Mr Peter Onslow**

TWO-YEAR-OLDS

80 **AFRICAN GIFT**, b f 19/3 Cadeaux Genereux—African Light (Kalaglow) **Mr & Mrs G. Middlebrook**
81 Ch c 20/2 Bluebird (USA)—Antinnaz (IRE) (Thatching) (15460)
82 Ch f 2/3 Pursuit of Love—Arminda (Blakeney) (17000) **Mr H. J. P. Farr**
83 B f 25/2 Montjeu (IRE)—Autumn Fall (USA) (Sanglamore (USA)) **Mr & Mrs G. Middlebrook**
84 B f 11/3 Zaha (CAN)—Bay Bianca (IRE) (Law Society (USA)) (8000) **Zaha Racing Partnership**
85 B c 17/4 Celtic Swing—Baylands Sunshine (IRE) (Classic Secret (USA)) (11749)
86 **BESTBYFAR (IRE)**, b c 11/4 King's Best (USA)—Pippas Song (Reference Point) (50000) **Pentakan Ltd**
87 **BE WISE BOY**, ch c 24/1 Monashee Mountain—Much Ado (Mujtahid (USA)) (6000) **Be Wise Racing**
88 Gr c 24/4 Highest Honor (FR)—Black Tulip (FR) (Fabulous Dancer (USA)) **4th Middleham Partnership**
89 **BRANSTON PENNY**, ch f 2/3 Pennekamp (USA)—Branston Jewel (IRE) (Prince Sabo) (13000) **Mr J. David Abell**
90 **BURTON ASH**, b br f 19/4 Diktat—Incendio (Siberian Express (USA)) **Mrs Susan Lee**
91 **CAVA BIEN**, b c 7/2 Bien Bien (USA)—Bebe de Cham (Tragic Role (USA)) (2000) **Lovely Bubbly Racing**
92 B f 10/5 Bahamian Bounty—Creeking (Persian Bold) (7000) **Moneyleague Ltd**
93 **CRIMSON BOW (GER)**, ch f 4/2 Night Shift (USA)—Carma (IRE) (Konigsstuhl (GER)) (20000) **Swann Racing**
94 **DARRINGTON**, b c 8/4 Vitus—Masirah (Dunphy) **The G-Guck Group**
95 B f 21/3 Atraf—Desert Dawn (Belfort (FR)) **Mr P. Onslow**
96 **E BRIDE (USA)**, gr f 26/4 Runaway Groom (CAN)—
                              Fast Selection (USA) (Talinum (USA)) **Anthony Warrender & Rosemary Morley**
97 **ELLERAY (IRE)**, b f 2/4 Docksider (USA)—Saint Ann (USA) (Geiger Counter (USA)) **Mr & Mrs G. Middlebrook**
98 B f 25/4 Petardia—Fall of The Hammer (Auction Ring (USA)) **One Stop Partnership**
99 B f 3/3 Lahib (USA)—Fervent Fan (Soviet Lad (USA)) (8000) **Mrs C. P. Lees-Jones**
100 Gr f 28/2 Timeless Times (USA)—Fort Vally (Belfort (FR)) (2200) **Mrs R. Morley**
101 **GIVEN A CHOICE (IRE)**, b c 29/3 Trans Island—
                              Miss Audimar (USA) (Mr Leader (USA)) (40197) **The G-Guck Group**
102 **GLOVED HAND**, b f 26/3 Royal Applause—Fudge (Polar Falcon (USA)) **Mrs M. V. Chaworth Musters**
103 Ch f 12/4 Diesis—Gossamer (USA) (Seattle Slew (USA))
104 **GREATCOAT**, ch c 27/5 Erhaab (USA)—Vaula (Henbit (USA)) **Mrs M. V. Chaworth Musters**
105 B f 29/1 Lujain (USA)—Gymcrak Flyer (Aragon) (13000) **David Maloney & Graham White**
106 **HARBOUR LEGEND**, b f 24/3 Dansili—
                              English Harbour (Sabrehill (USA)) (4946) **Living Legend Racing Partnership**
107 **HIGH TREASON (USA)**, ch c 14/2 Diesis—Fabula Dancer (USA) (Northern Dancer) (50000) **Mr S. Rudolf**
108 **JESSICA'S STYLE (IRE)**, b f 26/2 Desert Style (IRE)—Mugello (Emarati (USA)) (17315) **Mr Derek Hilton**
109 B f 1/5 Polish Precedent—Kinchenjunga (Darshaan) (7000) **Eastwell Manor Racing Ltd**
110 **KRISTALCHEN**, b f 10/3 Singspiel (IRE)—Crystal Flite (IRE) (Darshaan)
111 B f 16/3 Fraam—Libretta (Highest Honor (FR)) (3000)
112 **MISTERS SISTER**, b f 6/4 Robellino (USA)—
                              Baileys On Line (Shareef Dancer (USA)) **G. R. Bailey Ltd (Baileys Horse Feeds)**
113 **QUEUE UP**, b c 12/2 Royal Applause—Faraway Lass (Distant Relative) **Mr John E. Rose**
114 B br c 1/3 Dansili—Radiancy (IRE) (Mujtahid (USA))
115 **ROSABLANCA (IRE)**, b f 15/5 Sinndar (IRE)—
                              Elegant Bloom (IRE) (Be My Guest (USA)) (34013) **The G-Guck Group**
116 **SHAMROCK BAY**, b f 9/4 Celtic Swing—Kabayil (Dancing Brave (USA)) **Elite Racing Club**
117 **SI SI SI**, b f 13/3 Lomitas—Notturna (Diu Star) **The G-Guck Group**

MR JAMES GIVEN—continued

118 Ch f 9/3 Halling (USA)—South Shore (Caerleon (USA)) **Mr H. J. P. Farr**
119 **SUNNYDALE (IRE)**, ch f 26/1 Shahrastani (USA)—Golden Cay (Habitat) (21000) **Mr D. Allan**
120 **THEOSONY**, b f 21/1 Singspiel (IRE)—
        New Fortune (FR) (Exit To Nowhere (USA)) (5000) **Templeton Stud & Jared Bernstein**
121 **UNION JACK JACKSON (IRE)**, b c 18/1 Daggers Drawn (USA)—
        Beechwood Quest (IRE) (River Falls) (17000) **Mr A. Clarke**
122 **VANADIUM**, b c 19/2 Dansili—Musianica (Music Boy) (70000) **Bolton Grange**
123 **VETTORIOUS**, ch c 28/2 Vettori (IRE)—
        Sleepless (Night Shift (USA)) (35000) **Audrey Scotney, Malcolm Joyce & Partners**
124 B f 2/4 Mister Baileys—Woodbeck (Terimon) **Mr B. H. Farr**
125 **ZORIPP (IRE)**, b c 16/1 Spectrum IRE)—Allspice (Alzao (USA)) **P. A. Morton & A. Britcliffe**

Other Owners: Mr D. S. Arnold, Mr N. Collins, Mr G. W. Dalton, Mr P. Dalton, Mr N. J. Forman Hardy, Mrs N. J. Forman Hardy, Mr John Furness, Mr B. Gaunt, Mr D. M. Gibbons, Mr Keith Hogg, Mr M. W. Horner, Mr Ian Jackson, Mr R. S. G. Jones, Mr D. J. P McWilliams, Mr A. S. Robertson, Mr D. A. Smeaton, Mr J. Stark, Mr Trevor C. Stewart, Mr H. A. B. Stroud, Tessona Racing, Mrs J. M. Turner, Mr Richard Venn.

Assistant Trainer: Chris Nash

Jockey (Flat): Michael Fenton (8-4).

---

226 MR J. A. GLOVER, Worksop
Postal: **Pinewood Stables, Carburton, Worksop, Nottinghamshire, S80 3BT.**
Contact: **OFFICE (01909) 475962 MOBILE (07802) 362909**

1 **CHICO GUAPO (IRE)**, 4, b g Sesaro (USA)—Summer Queen **2nd Carlton Partnership**
2 **FIELD SPARK**, 4, b g Sillery (USA)—On The Top **G. Taylor & J. P. Burton**
3 **KELSEAS KOLBY (IRE)**, 4, b g Perugino (USA)—Notre Dame (IRE) **Mr J. A. Glover**
4 **MUSICAL FAIR**, 4, b f Piccolo—Guarded Expression **P. and S. Partnership**
5 **TAGULA BLUE (IRE)**, 4, b g Tagula (IRE)—Palace Blue (IRE) **Boston R. S. Ian Bennett**

THREE-YEAR-OLDS

6 **BLUETORIA**, b f Vettori (IRE)—Blue Birds Fly **Advanced Brickwork Ltd**
7 **FIELD POWER (USA)**, b g Gulch (USA)—Dreamy Jovite (USA)
8 **GLADTOBEE**, b f Deploy—Cabaret Artiste **Mr Kenneth Paul Beecroft**
9 **JUNGLE JIM**, b g Atraf—Enchanting Melody **Countrywide Classics Limited**
10 **MIDNIGHT PROMISE**, b g Aragon—Uninvited **Countrywide Classics Limited**
11 **RENE BARBIER (IRE)**, b c Desert Style (IRE)—Sweet Decision (IRE) **Mrs Janis MacPherson**

TWO-YEAR-OLDS

12 **BEDTIME BLUES**, b f 22/3 Cyrano de Bergerac—
        Boomerang Blade (Sure Blade (USA)) (15000) **Mr Adrian Swingler**
13 **CHAMPAGNE IN PARIS**, gr f 2/3 Paris House—Ashleen (Chilibang) **Mr David Jenkins**
14 **FORTUNE'S FAIR**, b g 26/4 Forzando—River's Rising (FR) (Mendez (FR)) (27000) **P. and S. Partnership**
15 **INN FOR THE DANCER**, b g 23/4 Groom Dancer (USA)—
        Lady Joyce (FR) (Galetto (FR)) (5500) **The Dovecote Inn Racing Partnership**
16 **INSIDER**, ch f 9/3 Docksider (USA)—Inquirendo (Roberto (USA)) (1000) **Mr R. W. Metcalfe**
17 **ITALIAN TOUCH (IRE)**, b g 25/4 Rossini (USA)—Attached (IRE) (Forest Wind (USA)) (6000) **Mr Clive Buckle**
18 **KIMBERLEY HALL**, ch f 4/3 Bachir (IRE)—Sedna (FR) (Bering (3091) **The Wilthorpe Racing Partnership**
19 **MALINSA BLUE (IRE)**, b f 29/3 Desert Style (IRE)—
        Talina's Law (IRE) (Law Society (USA)) (12368) **Mrs Andrea M. Mallinson**
20 B g 16/2 Perryston View—Martine (Clantime) (1800) **Mr J. A. Glover**
21 **MERMAID'S CRY**, b f 11/2 Danzero (AUS)—Little Tramp (Trempolino (USA)) **Mrs M. Slater**
22 B f 19/5 Unfuwain (USA)—Oops Pettie (Machiavellian (USA)) (22000) **Mrs M. Slater**
23 **SAM'S SECRET**, b f 30/4 Josr Algarhoud (IRE)—Twilight Time (Aragon) (13000) **Copskam Partnership**
24 **STEVMARIE STAR**, b f 23/4 Muhtarram (USA)—Cabaret Artiste (Shareef Dancer (USA)) (5700) **Mr S. J. Beard**

Other Owners: Mr J. A. Beckitt, Mr Ian Bennett, Mr Derrick Bloy, Mr J. A. Bower, Mr P. Burdett, Mr J. P. Burton, Mr P. Copson, Mr G. W. Cowburn, Mr T. A. Farrin, Mr P. R. Nodder, Mr John Pumfrey, Mr Andrew Roy, Mr S. Shepherd, Exors Of The Late P. B. Short, Mr N. D. Skinner, Mr Glenn Taylor, Mr Steve Whelbourn.

227 MR J. S. GOLDIE, Glasgow
Postal: **Libo Hill Farm, Uplawmoor, Glasgow, Lanarkshire, G78 4BA.**
Contact: **PHONE (01505) 850212 MOBILE (07778) 241522**

1 **ANDREYEV (IRE)**, 10, ch g Presidium—Missish **Mr J. S. Goldie**
2 **BALLYHURRY (USA)**, 7, b g Rubiano (USA)—Balakhna (FR) **Mr John Breslin**
3 **COLLEGE MAID (IRE)**, 7, b m College Chapel—Maid of Mourne **Mrs S. E. Bruce**
4 **COSMIC CASE**, 9, b m Casteddu—La Fontainova (IRE) **The Cosmic Cases**
5 **DOUBLE YOU CUBED**, 10, b g Destroyer—Bright Suggestion **Mrs D. I. Goldie**
6 **GARGOYLE GIRL**, 7, b m Be My Chief (USA)—May Hills Legacy (IRE) **Mrs C. Brown**
7 **HIGHLAND WARRIOR**, 5, b h Makbul—Highland Rowena **Frank & Annette Brady**
8 **INDIAN SPARK**, 10, ch g Indian Ridge—Annes Gift **Mr Frank Brady**
9 **KUNG HEI FAT CHOI (IRE)**, 9, b g Roselier (FR)—Gallant Blade **Strathayr Publishing Ltd**
10 **MIDDLEMARCH (IRE)**, 4, ch c Grand Lodge (USA)—Blanche Dubois **Mr W. M. Johnstone**
11 **MOUNT PEKAN (IRE)**, 4, b c Sri Pekan (USA)—The Highlands (FR) **Mrs S. E. Bruce**
12 **ORIENTOR**, 6, b h Inchinor—Orient **Mr S. Bruce**
13 **PIPS MAGIC (IRE)**, 8, b g Pips Pride—Kentucky Starlet (USA) **Mr Frank Brady**
14 **REGENT'S SECRET (USA)**, 4, br c Cryptoclearance (USA)—Misty Regent (CAN) **Mr J. S. Goldie**
15 **STING LIKE A BEE (IRE)**, 5, b g Ali-Royal (IRE)—Hidden Agenda (FR) **Mrs C. Brown**
16 **TONY TIE**, 8, b g Ardkinglass—Queen of The Quorn **Mr Frank Brady**

THREE-YEAR-OLDS

17 **GLENCAIRN STAR**, b c Selkirk (USA)—Bianca Nera **Mr Frank Brady**
18 **INSUBORDINATE**, ch c Subordination (USA)—Manila Selection (USA) **Mr J. S. Goldie**
19 **KELUCIA (IRE)**, ch f Grand Lodge (USA)—Karachi (SPA) **B. Scanlon & F. Brady**

TWO-YEAR-OLDS

20 B c 12/3 Compton Place—Ayr Classic (Local Suitor (USA)) (16000) **Mr J. S. Goldie**
21 Ch f 2/3 Rainbow Quest (USA)—Gaily Royal (IRE) (Royal Academy (USA)) (65000) **B. Scanlon & F. Brady**

Other Owners: Mr E. Bruce, Mr I. T. Buchanan, Mr Mike Flynn.

Jockeys (Flat): A Culhane (8-3), K Dalgleish, K Fallon, W Supple. **Jockeys (NH):** A Dobbin, G Lee, C McCormack, R McGrath, K Renwick. **Apprentices:** Jonathan Currie (7-10), Nick Mackay (7-5). **Conditional:** P Whelan (9-11). **Amateurs:** Q George Goldie, Mrs Carol Williams.

228 MR R. H. GOLDIE, Kilmarnock
Postal: **Harpercroft, Old Loans Road, Dundonald, Kilmarnock, Ayrshire, KA2 9DD.**
Contact: **PHONE (01292) 317222 FAX (01292) 313585 MOBILE (07801) 922552**

1 **CHIEF SEATTLE (IRE)**, 6, b g Glacial Storm (USA)—Jubilaire **R. H. Goldie**
2 **MISS NEL**, 9, b m Denel (FR)—Ice Lass **R. H. Goldie**
3 **SUNY HENRY**, 7, ch g Henbit (USA)—Suny Zeta **R. H. Goldie**
4 4, B g Warcraft (USA)—Wanjib's Song (IRE) **R. H. Goldie**

THREE-YEAR-OLDS

5 B f Old Vic—Easter Oats **R. H. Goldie**
6 B f Florida Son—Ice Nel **R. H. Goldie**
7 B g Florida Son—Miss Cavo **R. H. Goldie**

TWO-YEAR-OLDS

8 B f 3/6 Rakaposhi King—Easter Oats (Oats) **R. H. Goldie**
9 B f 20/5 Terimon—Ice Nel (Denel (FR)) **R. H. Goldie**
10 B g 18/6 Terimon—Miss Cavo (Ovac (ITY)) **R. H. Goldie**

Assistant Trainer: Mrs R H Goldie

229 MR S. GOLLINGS, Louth
Postal: **Highfield House, Scamblesby, Louth, Lincolnshire, LN11 9XT.**
Contact: **HOME/YARD (01507) 343204 FAX (01507) 343213 MOBILE (07860 218910**
E-MAIL stevegollings@aol.com

1 4, B f King's Theatre (IRE)—Adjacent (IRE) **Mr P. Winfrow**
2 **ALMNADIA (IRE)**, 5, b m Alhaarth (IRE)—Mnaafa (IRE) **Mr J. Hennessy**
3 **BALHAM LADY (IRE)**, 7, ch m Mister Lord (USA)—Jodi's Money **Mr Nick Robey**
4 **BEYOND BORDERS (USA)**, 6, b br g Pleasant Colony (USA)—Welcome Proposal **Quickfall Racing**
5 **CASTLESHANE (IRE)**, 7, b g Kris—Ahbab (IRE) **W.Hobson,J.King,G.King,P.Winfrow**
6 **COLLEGE QUEEN**, 6, b m Lugana Beach—Eccentric Dancer **The Swallow Inn Racing Club**
7 **DANCE OF LIFE**, 5, b m Shareef Dancer (USA)—Regan (USA) **Mrs Shirley Brasher**
8 **DIMITRI (IRE)**, 7, b g Roselier (FR)—Treidlia **Mr J. B. Webb**
9 **FREYDIS (IRE)**, 6, b m Supreme Leader—Lulu Buck **The Highfield House Partnership**
10 **IBERUS (GER)**, 6, b g Monsun (GER)—Iberica (GER) **Mr D. A. Johnson**
11 **JACK MARTIN (IRE)**, 7, ch g Erins Isle—Rolling Penny (IRE) **Mr J. B. Webb**
12 **JIDIYA (IRE)**, 5, b g Lahib (USA)—Yaqatha (IRE) **Holmes Court Securities Ltd**
13 **KING'S ECHO**, 6, b g Rakaposhi King—Welgenco **Mr J. B. Webb**
14 **KING'S THOUGHT**, 5, b h King's Theatre (IRE)—Lora's Guest **Mrs E. Houlton**
15 **KITSKI (FR)**, 6, b g Perrault—Macyrienne (IRE) **Mr J. B. Webb**
16 **LANMIRE TOWER**, 10, b g Celio Rufo—Lanigans Tower **Mrs Debbie Dukes**
17 **LUCKY LARGO**, 4, b br g Key of Luck (USA)—Lingering Melody (IRE) **Mr J. B. Webb**
18 **MOVIE KING (IRE)**, 5, ch g Catrail (USA)—Marilyn (IRE) **The High Five Partnership**
19 **RIVER MARSHAL**, 6, b g Synefos (USA)—Marshallstown **Mr Robert L. Houlton**
20 **ROYAL SHAKESPEARE (FR)**, 5, b g King's Theatre (IRE)—Persian Walk (FR) **Mr J. B. Webb**
21 **RUTLAND CHANTRY (USA)**, 10, b g Dixieland Band (USA)—Christchurch (FR) **Mrs Allison L. Bottomley**
22 **SALHOOD**, 5, b g Capote (USA)—Princess Haifa (USA) **Mr J. B. Webb**
23 **SEANIETHESMUGGLER (IRE)**, 6, b g Balla Cove—Sharp Shauna **Mr J. B. Webb**
24 **SEATTLE PRINCE (USA)**, 6, gr g Cozzene (USA)—Chicken Slew (USA) **Mr D. J. Butler**
25 **SENOR EDUARDO**, 7, gr g Terimon—Jasmin Path **Mr R. L. Houlton**
26 **SILVER SECRET**, 10, ro g Absalom—Secret Dance **Mrs Jayne M. Gollings**
27 **SISTER CINNAMON**, 6, ch m Karinga Bay—Cinnamon Run **Mrs M. A. Hall**
28 **SISTER SUPERIOR (IRE)**, 9, b m Supreme Leader—Nicat **The High Five Partnership**
29 **SPRINGFIELD GILDA (IRE)**, 6, b m Gildoran—Ledee **Mrs M. A. Hall**
30 **SPRINGFIELD SCALLY**, 11, ch g Scallywag—Ledee **Mrs M. A. Hall**
31 **STONEYFORD BEN**, 5, b g Beneficial—Rosie Rock **Mr John B. Webb**
32 **VIGOUREUX (FR)**, 5, b g Villez (USA)—Rouge Folie (FR) **Ian Hesketh & John Webb**
33 **WICKED UNCLE**, 5, b g Distant Relative—The Kings Daughter **Mr D. A. Johnson**
34 **WILL HE WISH**, 8, b g Winning Gallery—More To Life **Mrs D. Dukes**

THREE-YEAR-OLDS

35 **TRINAREE (IRE)**, b g Revoque (IRE)—Ball Cat (FR) **Mr Bill Hobson**

Other Owners: Mr Richard Abbott, Mr J. D. Chilton, Mrs V. Chilton, Mr M. J. Quickfall, Mr L. M. Robinson, Mr M. Stavrou, Mr Ken Sweales, Mr R. Wilson.

Assistant Trainer: Mrs Jayne M Gollings

Jockeys (Flat): K Fallon, D Holland, J Quinn. **Jockeys (NH):** J Culloty, S Durack, M A Fitzgerald, P Flynn, D Gallagher (10-0), T Murphy, T Scudamore. **Conditional:** Stefan Karnicnik (10-0). **Amateur:** Mrs Jayne M Gollings (9-0).

230 MRS H. O. GRAHAM, Jedburgh
Postal: **Brundeanlaws Cottage, Camptown, Jedburgh, Roxburghshire, TD8 6NW.**
Contact: **PHONE (01835) 840354 MOBILE (07919) 363900 E-MAIL robdgraham@hotmail.com**

1 **BENO (IRE)**, 5, b h Ridgewood Ben—Future Romance **Mrs H. O. Graham**
2 **INDY MOOD**, 5, ch g Endoli (USA)—Amanta (IRE) **Mr R. D. Graham**
3 **ROSALYONS (IRE)**, 10, gr g Roselier (FR)—Coffee Shop **Mrs H. O. Graham**
4 **RUSSIAN SKY**, 5, gr g Endoli (USA)—Anzarra **Mrs H. O. Graham**

Assistant Trainer: R D Graham

Jockey (NH): M H Naughton. **Conditional:** D C Costello. **Amateur:** Miss Laura Hislop.

231 MR N. A. GRAHAM, Newmarket

Postal: **Coronation Stables, Newmarket, Suffolk, CB8 9BB.**
Contact: **PHONE (01638) 665202 MOBILE (07770) 321571 E-MAIL coronationstables@virgin.net**

1 **HABSHAN (USA)**, 4, ch g Swain (IRE)—Cambara **Alan & Jill Smith**
2 **KALANISHA (IRE)**, 4, ch g Ashkalani (IRE)—Camisha (IRE) **Three Blind Mice**
3 **KING'S MILL (IRE)**, 7, b g Doyoun—Adarika **First Millennium Racing**
4 **MASJOOR**, 4, ch g Unfuwain (USA)—Mihnah (IRE) **Mr Paul G. Jacobs**
5 **ROSE TEA (IRE)**, 5, ro m Alhaarth (IRE)—Shakamiyn **Mr Paul G. Jacobs**
6 **SECOND PAIGE (IRE)**, 7, b g Nicolotte—My First Paige (IRE) **Coronation Partnership**
7 **SIRAJ**, 5, b g Piccolo—Masuri Kabisa (USA) **Hermione Scrope,Tom Chadney,Paul Jacobs**
8 **SPINNING DOVE**, 4, ch f Vettori (IRE)—Northern Bird **Hermione Scrope,Tom Chadney,Paul Jacobs**
9 **TOMINA**, 4, b g Deploy—Cavina **Mr Paul G. Jacobs**

THREE-YEAR-OLDS

10 **BUKHOOR (IRE)**, b f Danehill (USA)—Touch of Magic (IRE) **Mr Hamdan Al Maktoum**
11 **DHEHDAAH**, b c Alhaarth (IRE)—Carina Clare **Mr Hamdan Al Maktoum**

TWO-YEAR-OLDS

12 **DHAKAA (IRE)**, gr c 9/2 Mujadil (USA)—Severa (GER) (Kendor (FR)) (30000) **Mr Hamdan Al Maktoum**
13 **ETAAR**, b c 12/3 Zafonic (USA)—Hawayah (IRE) (Shareef Dancer (USA)) (36000) **Mr Hamdan Al Maktoum**
14 **GHABESH (USA)**, gr c 15/3 Dumaani (USA)—Dish Dash (Bustino) **Mr Hamdan Al Maktoum**
15 **QAWAASEM (IRE)**, b c 21/4 Soviet Star (USA)—Harmless Albatross (Pas de Seul) **Mr Hamdan Al Maktoum**

Other Owners: Mr A. M. Briam, Mrs J. A. Cross, Mr P. A. Deal, Mr J. Henwood, Mr M. Jones, Mr Brian March, Mr T. Scott, Mr R. A. Smith, Mr D. Tibbetts, Mr G. Triefus, Mrs A. Wade, Mr R. A. Wade, Mr T. Wells.

232 MR C. GRANT, Billingham

Postal: **Low Burntoft Farm, Wolviston, Billingham, Cleveland, TS22 5PD.**
Contact: **PHONE (01740) 644054 MOBILE (07860) 577998 FAX (01740) 644054**
E-MAIL chris@chrisgrantracing.fsnet.co.uk

1 **ATLANTICUS (IRE)**, 8, b g Kings Lake (USA)—Amazonia (GER) **Paul & Anne Sellars**
2 **BERRYWHITE (IRE)**, 6, ch g Barathea (IRE)—Berryville (USA) **Mrs A. Meller**
3 **BEXLEY (IRE)**, 6, b g Torus—Regency Charm (IRE) **Mr Trevor Hemmings**
4 **BOLD CLASSIC (IRE)**, 11, b g Persian Bold—Bay Street **Mr Chris Grant**
5 **CLASSIC KEY**, 4, ch g Classic Cliche—Natural Key **Dingley Dell Racing Ltd**
6 **COLONNADE**, 5, b m Blushing Flame (USA)—White Palace **Mr Ian W. Glenton**
7 **CRUISE LEADER (IRE)**, 9, b g Supreme Leader—Ormskirk Mover **Mr Trevor Hemmings**
8 **CRYSTAL DANCE (FR)**, 4, gr g Loup Solitaire (USA)—Somptueuse **Lord Daresbury**
9 **DANABU (IRE)**, 6, b g Un Desperado (FR)—Ishtar Abu **Mr Trevor Hemmings**
10 **FARINGTON LODGE (IRE)**, 6, b g Simply Great (FR)—Lodge Party (IRE) **Mr Trevor Hemmings**
11 5, B m Overbury (IRE)—Flo-Jo (DEN) **Dingley Dell Racing Ltd**
12 **GUNNER DREAM**, 8, b g Gunner B—Star Route **The Hon Mrs M. Faulkner**
13 **HALF OF NOTHING**, 8, b g Hatim (USA)—Lucy's Brig
14 **KAPPILLAN (IRE)**, 5, b g Flemensfirth (USA)—Snuggle **Mr J. Henderson (Co Durham)**
15 **LEAP YEAR LASS**, 4, ch f Fleetwood (IRE)—Lady Phyl **Dingley Dell Racing Ltd**
16 **LOST AND FOUND**, 4, ch g Master Willie—Top Cover **Lord Daresbury**
17 **MASTER WOOD**, 13, b g Wonderful Surprise—Miss Wood **Mr Chris Grant**
18 **MINSTER SHADOW**, 5, b g Minster Son—Polar Belle **Panther Racing Ltd**
19 **OLD ROLLA (IRE)**, 6, b g Old Vic—Criswood (IRE) **Mr A. Dawson**
20 **RED HUSTLER (IRE)**, 8, ch g Husyan (USA)—Isoldes Tower **Mr W. Raw**
21 **REGAL VINTAGE (USA)**, 4, ch g Kingmambo—Grapevine (IRE) **Mr J. C. Garbutt**
22 **ROOBIHOO (IRE)**, 5, b g Norwich—Griffinstown Lady **Mrs H. E. Aitkin**
23 **ROYAL BLAZER (IRE)**, 4, b g Barathea (IRE)—Royale (IRE) **Club 4 Racing**
24 **SACHSENWALZER (GER)**, 6, ch g Top Waltz (FR)—Stairway To Heaven (GER) **Mrs A. Meller**
25 **SHARP'S THE WORD**, 5, b g Keen—Scally's Girl **Mr W. Raw**
26 **TIME SPIN**, 4, b g Robellino (USA)—Chiltern Court (USA) **Mr J. C. Garbutt**
27 **TRIBAL RUN (IRE)**, 9, ch g Be My Native (USA)—Queen's Run (IRE) **Mr Trevor Hemmings**
28 **WASHINGTON PINK (IRE)**, 5, b g Tagula (IRE)—Little Red Rose **Mr Ian W. Glenton**
29 **WEB MASTER (FR)**, 6, b g Arctic Tern (USA)—Inesperada **Miss S. J. Turner**
30 **ZESTA FIESTA**, 4, b g El Conquistador—Little Lemon **Lord Daresbury**

MR C. GRANT—continued
THREE-YEAR-OLDS

31 **THIRD EMPIRE,** b g Second Empire (IRE)—Tahnee **Mr C. F. Bellwood**

Other Owners: Mr A. Clark, Mr J Moodie, Mr Walter Morris, Mr D. M. Robinson, Mrs Anne Sellars, Mr Paul Sellars, Mrs Linda Swainston, Mr B. T. Woods.

Assistant Trainer: Mrs S Grant

Jockey (NH): Richard McGrath (10-0). **Amateurs:** Mr T Greenall (10-4), Mr P Kinsella (9-7).

---

233 | **MR L. P. GRASSICK, Cheltenham**
Postal: **Postlip Racing Stables, Winchcombe, Cheltenham, Gloucestershire, GL54 5AQ.**
Contact: **HOME (01242) 603124 YARD (01242) 603919 MOBILE (07816) 930423 FAX (01242) 603602 E-MAIL billy.grassick@btopenworld.com**

1 **COUNTING,** 9, ch m Minster Son—Elitist **Mr Graham Brookhouse**
2 **FELONY (IRE),** 9, ch g Pharly (FR)—Scales of Justice **Baskerville Racing Club**
3 **MIDNIGHT GOLD,** 4, ch g Midnight Legend—Yamrah **Nettleton Harts**
4 **MIKE SIMMONS,** 8, b g Ballacashtal (CAN)—Lady Crusty **Mr L. P. Grassick**
5 **SANDYWELL GEORGE,** 9, ch g Zambrano—Farmcote Air **David Lloyd & Mrs Carole Lloyd**
6 **SIMON THE POACHER,** 5, br g Chaddleworth (IRE)—Lady Crusty **Mr N. Goodger & Postlip Racing**

THREE-YEAR-OLDS

7 Br c Chaddleworth (IRE)—Lady Crusty **Mr L. P. Grassick**

Other Owners: Mr P. F. D. Badham, Mr K Carpenter, Mr Nigel Goodger, Mrs C. J. Lloyd, Mr D. V. Lloyd, Ms G. E. Morgan, Mr Nick Stephens.

Jockey (Flat): V Slattery (8-7). **Jockey (NH):** D Laverty (9-7). **Conditional:** D Laverty (9-7). **Amateur:** Mr T Malone (9-0).

---

234 | **MR M. J. GRASSICK, Curragh**
Postal: **Fenpark Stables, Pollardstown, Curragh, Co. Kildare, Ireland.**
Contact: **HOME (+353 (0) 45 436956 YARD (045) 434483 FAX (+353 (0) 45 437895 MOBILE +353 (0) 87 2431923**

1 **ALEXANDER EURO,** 5, b m Cadeaux Genereux—Mistle Thrush (USA) **Mr N. O'Callaghan**
2 **ALICUDI (IRE),** 4, b c Ali-Royal (IRE)—Nawadder **R. Weiss**
3 **ARCTIC ICE (IRE),** 4, gr f Zafonic (USA)—Oskarberg **J. A. Higgins**
4 **BOCACCIO (IRE),** 6, b g Brief Truce (USA)—Idara **Mrs C. Grasswick**
5 **CALIFORNIA SPIRIT (IRE),** 4, b c Perugino (USA)—Rising Spirits **Mrs C. Grassick**
6 **CAYTEVA,** 4, ch f Hernando (FR)—Cupira (GER) **A. Bish**
7 **ECKBEAG (USA),** 5, b m Trempolino (USA)—Stormin Jane (USA) **J. Clarke**
8 **GEMINI DIAMOND (IRE),** 4, b br f Desert King (IRE)—Wakria (IRE) **Mrs A. Higgins**
9 **GOLOVIN (GER),** 7, b h Bering—Guilnin (IRE) **Mrs H. Focke**
10 **GRANTSHOUSE (IRE),** 4, b c College Chapel—Indian Honey **Mrs C. Grassick**
11 **GRAVIERES,** 6, ch g Mujtahid (USA)—Jumairah Sunset **Mrs S. Grassick**
12 **IRISH EMPIRE (IRE),** 6, b h Tirol—Hazy Image **R. Weiss**
13 **KEITHARA (IRE),** 4, b f Entrepreneur—Princesse Sharpo (USA) **Ms C. Tsui**
14 **KING'S OPERA (IRE),** 6, b m King's Theatre (IRE)—Thrifty's Best **Mrs C. Grassick**
15 **LITTLE RORT,** 5, b g Ali-Royal (IRE)—Florinda (CAN) **Mrs C. Grassick**
16 **LORD PATCHY (USA),** 4, b br c Lord Avie (USA)—Teeming Shore (USA) **Mrs C. Grassick**
17 **LOVE TOKEN (IRE),** 5, b m Mark of Esteem (IRE)—Percy's Lass **Mr Albert Finney**
18 **MADAME MARJOU (IRE),** 4, b f Marju (IRE)—Sudeley **Mrs S. Grasswick**
19 **MAJOR TITLE (IRE),** 5, b g Brief Truce (USA)—Dariyba (IRE) **Tour Syndicate**
20 **MALTHOUSE MASTER (IRE),** 4, b c Sadler's Wells (USA)—Miss Arizona (IRE) **M. Stewkesbury**
21 **MOORE'S LAW (USA),** 6, b g Technology (USA)—Brass Needles (USA) **Mrs S. Grassick**
22 **MR SMOOTH (USA),** 4, b g Dieis—Recoleta (USA) **J. Higgins**
23 **MY RENEE (USA),** 4, b br f Kris S (USA)—Mayenne (USA) **Miss P. F. O'Kelly**
24 **PIXIE DUST (IRE),** 4, b f Desert King (IRE)—Turkansa (FR) **Ms C. Tsui**
25 **PRINCE MAY (IRE),** 9, ch g Houmayoun (FR)—Creative Princess (IRE) **D. Swan**
26 **PRINCESS DARIYBA (IRE),** 4, b f Victory Note—Dariyba (IRE) **Mr Andrew S. Bradley**
27 **SISSY SLEW (USA),** 4, b f Unbridled's Song (USA)—Missy Slew (USA) **J. Higgins**

MR M. J. GRASSICK—continued

28 **SKY TO SEA (FR)**, 6, b g Adieu Au Roi (IRE)—Urban Sky (FR) **Ms C. Tsui**
29 **SORANNA (IRE)**, 4, b f Compton Place—White-Wash **S. Mullins**
30 **SOUTHERN COMMAND (IRE)**, 4, b c In Command (IRE)—Pretoria **E. Cogan**
31 **SOUTHERN STYLE (IRE)**, 4, b f Southern Halo (USA)—Stately Bid (USA) **A. Finney**
32 **SUNSHINE GUEST (IRE)**, 4, b f Be My Guest (USA)—Arrow Field (USA) **H. Sweeney**
33 **TIME DISCLOSES ALL**, 4, b c Polar Falcon (USA)—Take Charge **Mrs S. Grassick**
34 **TRITON DANCE (IRE)**, 4, b f Hector Protector (USA)—Dancing Drop **J. Higgins**

THREE-YEAR-OLDS

35 **CATILINE (IRE)**, b c Nashwan (USA)—Mild Intrigue (USA) **S. Rogers**
36 **CAYTINGA**, ch f Docksider (USA)—Cupira (GER) **Mrs S. Fox**
37 B g Seeking The Gold (USA)—Dearest (USA) **Mrs C. Grasswick**
38 **DESERT OF GOLD (IRE)**, ch f Desert Prince (IRE)—Camisha (IRE) **M. Duffy**
39 **FINEENA (IRE)**, br f Titus Livius (FR)—Silhouette (IRE) **S. Mullins**
40 **FLAMING EYES (GER)**, b f Imperial Ballet (IRE)—Fantastic Flame (IRE) **D. Swan**
41 **INDIAN'S FEATHER (IRE)**, ch f Indian Ridge—Mashmoum **Ms C. Tsui**
42 **INDIGO SKY (IRE)**, br c Adieu de Roi (IRE)—Urban Sky (FR) **Ms C. Tsui**
43 **LA GAMBA (IRE)**, b f Alhaarth (IRE)—Aglaia (SWI) **R. Weiss**
44 **LAKE TAHOE (IRE)**, ch f Grand Lodge (USA)—Ar Hyd Y Knos **M. C. Grasswick**
45 **LAMON BAY (IRE)**, b f Perugino (USA)—Blue Jazz (IRE) **M. C. Grasswick**
46 **LOST SHOES (USA)**, ch f Old Trieste (USA)—Beating The Buzz (IRE) **D. Swan**
47 **MAJORITY DECISION (IRE)**, b f Second Empire (IRE)—Implicit View **Pentagon Syndicate**
48 **MISS UNIACKE (IRE)**, b f Pennekamp (USA)—Dafwan **H. Hyland**
49 **NIGHT FAIRY (IRE)**, b f Danehill (USA)—Sassenach (IRE) **Ms C. Tsui**
50 **PELAGIAS STAR (IRE)**, b f Darshaan—Wakria (IRE) **J. Higgins**
51 **PINE VALLEY (IRE)**, ch f Entrepreneur—Blue Valley (FR) **M. C. Grasswick**
52 **POETICAL (IRE)**, ch f Croco Rouge (IRE)—Abyat (USA) **Mrs S. Grasswick**
53 **RED BELLS**, b g Magic Ring (IRE)—Redgrave Devil **A. Bish**
54 **SATIN RISKS (FR)**, b f Take Risks (FR)—Kiri Lou (FR) **Ms C. Tsui**
55 **SIDECAR (IRE)**, gr f Spectrum (IRE)—Streetcar (IRE) **D. Grant**
56 **SIGN OF AFFECTION (IRE)**, b f Mark of Esteem (IRE)—Tafrah (IRE) **S. Taylor**
57 **SKYHAWK (IRE)**, b c In The Wings—Babushka (IRE) **Highclere Stud**
58 **SPRING OPERA (IRE)**, b f Sadler's Wells (USA)—Spring Easy (IRE) **J. Higgins**
59 **STYLISH BOB (IRE)**, br c Derest Style (IRE)—Bobbella (IRE) **A. Finney**
60 **TRIKIRK (IRE)**, b c Selkirk (USA)—Shastri (USA) **S. Taylor**

TWO-YEAR-OLDS

61 B c 23/4 Turtle Island (IRE)—Aglaia (SWI) (Aguarico (GER)) **R. Weiss**
62 B f 20/5 Rainbow Quest (USA)—Akarita (IRE) (Akarad (FR)) (64934) **Barouche Stud**
63 **ASHDALI (IRE)**, b f 30/3 Grand Lodge (USA)—Sidama (FR) (Top Ville) (43289) **M. Quirke**
64 B f 29/3 Tagula (IRE)—Bobbella (IRE) (Bob Back (USA)) **A. Finney**
65 Ch f 11/5 Ashkalani (IRE)—Feather River (USA) (Strike The Gold (USA)) **Mr A. Clarke**
66 **FLAME'S LAST (IRE)**, b f 22/4 Montjeu (IRE)—Flame of Tara (Artaius (USA)) **Miss P. F. O'Kelly**
67 B c 10/5 Intikhab (USA)—Ghassak (USA) (Persian Bold) (7420) **Tour Syndicate**
68 B f 21/3 Zafonic (USA)—Grail (USA) (Quest For Fame) (135000) **J. Higgins**
69 **GRANDFIELD (IRE)**, b f 18/4 Fasliyev (USA)—Vernonhills (Hard Fought) **B. Cooke**
70 B f 5/4 Indian Lodge (IRE)—K S Sunshine (USA) (Sunshine Forever (USA)) **Mr K. Takada**
71 B f 30/3 Monashee Mountain—Lady Anna Livia (Ahonoora) **T. Ward**
72 B c 5/5 Giant's Causeway—Mayenne (USA) (Nureyev (USA)) (61842) **Miss P. F. O'Reilly**
73 B f 28/5 Night Shift (USA)—Oariyba (IRE) (Kahyasi) **A. Bradley**
74 **SAPELE (USA)**, ch f 7/2 Marquetry (USA)—River Fairy (USA) (Irish River (FR)) (23810) **D. Dundon**
75 Br f 14/4 Gone West (USA)—Seattle Summer (USA) (Seattle Slew (USA)) (52565) **D. Swan**
76 **SEHOYA (IRE)**, br f 7/1 Second Empire (IRE)—Blue Jazz (IRE) (Bluebird (USA)) (2473) **M. C. Grasswick**
77 **SHABU (IRE)**, b c 17/3 Revoque (IRE)—Shajara (FR) (Kendor (FR)) **Cuadra Madronos**
78 B f 23/3 Giant's Causeway—Shastri (USA) (Alleged (USA)) **S. Taylor**
79 Ch f 19/1 Machiavellian (USA)—Spring Easy (IRE) (Alzao (USA)) (98948) **J. Higgins**
80 B f 24/1 Darshaan—Star Crystal (FR) (Brief Truce (USA)) (222634) **J. Higgins**
81 Gr f 5/2 Desert Style (IRE)—Stately Bid (USA) (Stately Don) **A. Finney**
82 B c 1/5 Zafonic (USA)—Sudeley (Dancing Brave (USA)) **D. Swan**

MR M. J. GRASSICK—continued

83 **THICK AND EASY (IRE),** b f 7/5 Welsh Lion (IRE)—Fast And Straight (IRE) (Shirley Heights) **D. Sheahan**
84 B f 13/4 Revoque (IRE)—Traumerei (GER) (Surumu (GER)) (8039) **Mrs M. J. Grasswick**

Assistant Trainer: Mr M C Grassick

Jockey (Flat): N G McCullagh (8-0) **Apprentices:** Michael Fahy (7-0), Michael O'Connel (8-4).

---

235 MR C. J. GRAY, Bridgwater
Postal: **Horlake, Moorland, Bridgwater, Somerset, TA7 0AT.**
Contact: **HOME (01278) 691359 MOBILE (07989) 768163**

1 **ALLER MOOR (IRE),** 13, b g Dry Dock—Boggy Peak **Mr G. Keirle**
2 **ANNIE DIPPER,** 9, ch m Weld—Honey Dipper **Mr P. F. Popham**
3 **BAILEYS PRIZE (USA),** 7, ch g Mister Baileys—Mar Mar (USA) **Mrs Elizabeth Heal**
4 **CHAKRA,** 10, gr g Mystiko (USA)—Maracuja (USA) **Mr R. L. Squire**
5 **CHARM OFFENSIVE,** 6, b m Zieten (USA)—Shoag (USA) **What Racing**
6 **DECO STAR (IRE),** 5, b g Dolphin Street (FR)—Ecco Mi (IRE) **Mr A. C. Heal**
7 **LE FOREZIEN (FR),** 5, b g Gunboat Diplomacy (FR)—Diane du Forez (FR) **Mr S. C. Botham**
8 4, B g Sovereign Water (FR)—My Purple Prose **Mr D. J. Staddon**
9 **OUDALMUTEENA (IRE),** 9, b g Lahib (USA)—Roxy Music (IRE) **Riverdance Consortium**

Other Owners: Mr T. Bartlett, Mr M. J. Colenutt, Mr A. P. Hayne, Mr A. P. Helliar, Mr A. J. W. Hill, Mr F. D. Popham, Ms T. S. Wilson.

Assistant Trainer: Mrs C M L Gray

---

236 MR S. G. GRIFFITHS, Carmarthen
Postal: **Rwyth Farm, Nantgaredig, Carmarthen, Dyfed, SA32 7LG.**
Contact: **PHONE (01267) 290321/290120**

1 **SOLVE IT SOBER (IRE),** 10, b br g Carefree Dancer (USA)—Haunted Lady **Mr S. G. Griffiths**
2 **TIRIKUMBA,** 8, ch m Le Moss—Ntombi **Mr S. G. Griffiths**

Assistant Trainer: Martyn Roger Griffiths

---

237 MR S. P. GRIFFITHS, Easingwold
Postal: **Longbridge House, Stillington Road, Easingwold, York, YO61 3ET.**
Contact: **PHONE (01347) 823589 MOBILE (07967) 039208 E-MAIL elizabeth@svsl.net**

1 **BABY BE,** 10, b m Bold Arrangement—B Grade **Mr M. Grant**
2 **COUNT COUGAR (USA),** 4, b g Sir Cat (USA)—Gold Script (USA) **Mr M. Grant**
3 **DIAMOND VEIN,** 5, b g Green Dancer (USA)—Blushing Sunrise (USA) **Mr J. Lavelle**
4 **HOT GIRL,** 6, b m State Diplomacy (USA)—Hundred Islands **Mr M. Grant**

THREE-YEAR-OLDS

5 **WHITKIRK STAR (IRE),** b g Alhaarth (IRE)—Three Stars **Mr M. Grant**

Assistant Trainer: Elizabeth Grant

---

238 MR R. C. GUEST, Brancepeth
Postal: **Brancepeth Manor Farm, Brancepeth, Nr Crook, Durham, Co. Durham, DL15 9AS.**
Contact: **PHONE (0191) 373 5220/6277 FAX (0191) 373 9655 MOBILE (07860) 883303**
E-MAIL richard.guest@tiscali.co.uk

1 **ALL ROCK HARD (NZ),** 6, ch g Bigstone (IRE)—My Lady Gray (NZ) **Mr Paul Beck**
2 **APADI (USA),** 8, ch g Diesis—Ixtapa (USA) **Mrs Anna Kenny**
3 **ARCHIAS (GER),** 5, b g Darshaan—Arionette **Miss C. Metcalf**
4 **ASSUMETHEPOSITION (FR),** 4, gr g Cyborg (FR)—Jeanne Grey (FR) **D. V. Racing**
5 **BERNARDON (GER),** 8, b g Suave Dancer (USA)—Berjaria (GER) **The Macca and Growler Partnership**
6 **BILLS ECHO,** 5, br g Double Eclipse (IRE)—Bit On Edge **Burns Partnership**

MR R. C. GUEST—continued

7 **BLACK SMOKE (IRE)**, 7, gr g Ala Hounak—Korean Citizen (IRE) **R & H Burridge & Bard Entertainment**
8 **BOLTON BARRIE (IRE)**, 6, b g Broken Hearted—Ballyduggan Queen (IRE) **Mr Glenn Roberts**
9 **CERESFIELD (NZ)**, 8, b m Westminster (NZ)—Audrey Rose (NZ) **Mr K. Middleton**
10 **COLLEGE CITY (IRE)**, 5, b g College Chapel—Polish Crack (IRE) **Mrs A. Kenny**
11 **DONOVAN (NZ)**, 5, b g Stark South (USA)—Agent Jane (USA) **Concertina Racing Too**
12 **FIDALUS (IRE)**, 11, b g Mandalus—Fifi L'Amour **Miss S. Howell**
13 **GABLA (NZ)**, 8, b g Prince of Praise (NZ)—Dynataine (NZ) **Mr T. N. Siviter**
14 **JAHIA (NZ)**, 5, br m Jahafil—Lana (NZ) **DDB Racing**
15 **JERICHO III (FR)**, 7, b g Lute Antique (FR)—La Salamandre (FR) **Sir Robert Ogden**
16 **JUST THE JOBE**, 6, gr g Roselier (FR)—Radical Lady **Mr N. B. Mason**
17 **LES ARCS (USA)**, 4, br g Arch (USA)—La Sarto (USA) **Mr W. McKay**
18 **LIBRE**, 4, b g Bahamian Bounty—Premier Blues (FR) **Mr W. McKay**
19 **LIK WOOD POWER (NZ)**, 7, b g Bigstone (IRE)—Lady Paloma (USA) **Bache Silk**
20 **LOST SOLDIER TWO**, 4, b g Kris—Hejraan (USA) **Mr B. V. Ward**
21 **MERSEY MIRAGE**, 7, b g King's Signet (USA)—Kirriemuir **The Friar Tuck Racing Club**
22 **MONTESINO**, 5, b g Bishop of Cashel—Sutosky **DDB Racing**
23 **MOSCOW LEADER (IRE)**, 6, ch g Moscow Society (USA)—Catrionas Castle (IRE) **Miss P. Overy**
24 **MR BOSSMAN (IRE)**, 11, b g Jolly Jake (NZ)—Imperial Greeting **Mr T. N. Siviter**
25 **MULGA BILL (NZ)**, 6, br g Carolingian (AUS)—Replica (NZ) **DDB Racing**
26 **NOSAM**, 14, b g Idiot's Delight—Socher **Mr N. B. Mason**
27 **ONE DAY (NZ)**, 6, ch g Stark South (USA)—Dragon Pearl (USA) **Mr Paul Beck**
28 **OTTOMAN (AUS)**, 8, br g Grand Lodge (USA)—Cushti (AUS) **Mr Leslie John Garrett**
29 **OUR ARMAGEDDON (NZ)**, 7, b g Sky Chase (NZ)—Monte d'Oro (NZ) **Mr Leslie John Garrett**
30 **POLISHED**, 5, ch g Danzig Connection (USA)—Glitter (FR) **The Cherry Blossom Partnership**
31 **PRINCE OF PERSIA**, 4, b g Turtle Island (IRE)—Sianiski **DDB Racing**
32 **RAJAM**, 6, b g Sadler's Wells (USA)—Rafif (USA) **A. A. Bloodstock Ltd**
33 **RED ARK**, 11, ch g Gunner B—Minim **Mr N. B. Mason**
34 **RED MARSALA**, 6, b g Tragic Role (USA)—Southend Scallywag **Mr N. B. Mason**
35 **RED MINSTER**, 7, b g Minster Son—Minty Muncher **Mr N. B. Mason**
36 **RED PERK (IRE)**, 7, b g Executive Perk—Supreme View **Mr N. B. Mason**
37 **RED STRIKER**, 10, ch g Gunner B—Cover Your Money **Mr N. B. Mason**
38 **SCARBOROUGH FAIR (IRE)**, 7, b g Synefos (USA)—Hue 'n' Cry (IRE) **Sir Robert Ogden**
39 **SPECTROMETRE**, 7, ch g Rainbow Quest (USA)—Selection Board **Concertina Racing**
40 **TEN PAST SIX**, 12, ch m Kris—Tashinsky (USA) **Mr J. Kennerly & Miss J. Hall**
41 **TIGER FROG (USA)**, 5, b g French Deputy (USA)—Woodyoubelieveit (USA) **Miss C. Metcalfe**
42 **TYNEANDTHYNEAGAIN**, 9, b g Good Thyne (USA)—Radical Lady **Mr N. B. Mason**
43 **VALUABLE GIFT**, 7, ch g Cadeaux Genereux—Valbra **London Gold (Fanway Limited)**
44 **VIDI CAESAR (NZ)**, 9, b g Racing Is Fun (USA)—Vidi Vici (NZ) **Mr Mark Barrett**
45 **VULCAN LANE (NZ)**, 7, ch g Star Way—Smudged (NZ) **Miss C. Metcalfe**
46 **WALLY WONDER (IRE)**, 6, ch g Magical Wonder (USA)—Sally Gap **Mr Richard Long**
47 **WET LIPS (AUS)**, 6, ch g Grand Lodge (USA)—Kissing (AUS) **Concertina Racing Three**
48 **WHAT'S A FILLY**, 4, b f Bob's Return (IRE)—Pearly-B (IRE) **The Don't Tell Pat Partnership**
49 **WHISPERED SECRET (GER)**, 5, b g Selkirk (USA)—Wells Whisper (FR) **Mr D. Levine**
50 **WHY THE LONG FACE (NZ)**, 7, ch g Grosvenor (NZ)—My Charm (NZ) **Mr N. H. Oliver**
51 **XAIPETE (IRE)**, 12, b g Jolly Jake (NZ)—Rolfete (USA) **Mr N. B. Mason**
52 **YORK RITE (AUS)**, 8, ch g Grand Lodge (USA)—Amazaan (NZ) **Miss C. Metcalf**

Other Owners: Mr Peter Bache, Miss F. Baker, Mr T. Delaney, Mr R. Fowler, Mr N. Lennon, Mr B. J. P. McLeavy, Mr S. McManaman, Mr C. K. Byers, Mr E.O'Sullivan, Mr Danny O'Sullivan, Mr M. Phylakti, Mr J. M. Rogers, Mr J. W. Ryan, Mr G. Hampson Silk, Mr J. Tyrrell, Mr C. Varley, Mr L. Vettraino.

Jockeys (NH): Richard Guest (10-7), L McGrath (9-9), H Oliver (10-0). **Apprentice:** Andrew Cooper (7-0).
Amateur: Miss C Metcalfe (10-0).

---

239 MR RAE GUEST, Newmarket
Postal: **Chestnut Tree Stables**, Hamilton Road, Newmarket, Suffolk, CB8 0NY.
Contact: PHONE **(01638) 661508** FAX **(01638) 667317** MOBILE **(07711) 301095**
E-MAIL **raeguest@totalise.co.uk**

1 **CADEAU SPECIALE**, 4, b f Cadeaux Genereux—Pat Or Else **Matthews Breeding and Racing**
2 **ELEGANT GRACIE (IRE)**, 4, ch f Desert Prince (IRE)—Elegant Fragrant (IRE) **Mr C. J. Murfitt**
3 **LADY LAKSHMI**, 4, ch f Bahhare—Polish Honour (USA) **Mr Graham Robinson**
4 **MIDNIGHT MAMBO (USA)**, 4, b f Kingmambo—Witching Hour (FR) **Bradmill Ltd**
5 **MILLYBAA (USA)**, 4, b f Anabaa (USA)—Millyant **Mr C. J. Mills**
6 **MIMIC**, 4, b f Royal Applause—Stripanoora **Mr C. J. Mills**

MR RAE GUEST—continued

7 **MOMENTS OF JOY**, 4, b f Darshaan—My Emma **Matthews Breeding and Racing**
8 **MONTECRISTO**, 11, br g Warning—Sutosky **Mr Rae Guest**
9 **RUBY WEDDING**, 6, b m Blushing Flame (USA)—First Sapphire **Ms E. Reffo & Mr B. Cooper**
10 **SIR DESMOND**, 6, gr g Petong—I'm Your Lady **The Quintessentials**
11 **SPARTAN PRINCIPLE**, 4, b f Spartan Monarch—Altar Point **Broomdown Racing 3**
12 **TAHIRAH**, 4, b f Green Desert (USA)—Kismah **Mr C. J. Murfitt**
13 **YOMALO (IRE)**, 4, ch f Woodborough (USA)—Alkariyh (USA) **Mr F. Nowell**

THREE-YEAR-OLDS

14 **AL JOUDHA (FR)**, b f Green Desert (USA)—Palacegate Episode (IRE) **Mr C. J. Murfitt**
15 **BIRD KEY**, b f Cadeaux Genereux—Portelet **Matthews Breeding and Racing**
16 **BLUE OASIS (IRE)**, b f Sadler's Wells—Humble Eight (USA) **E. Duggan & D. Churchman**
17 **COME WHAT JULY (IRE)**, b g Indian Rocket—Persian Sally (IRE) **The Storm Again Syndicate**
18 **CORNWALLIS**, b c Forzando—Up And Going (FR) **The Bricklayers Partnership**
19 **GIGANTES**, b c Nashwan (USA)—Mahasin (USA) **E. Duggan & D. Churchman**
20 **HAPPY BOY (IRE)**, b c Victory Note (USA)—Pepper And Salt (IRE) **Dragonchain Partnership**
21 **KARASHINKO (IRE)**, b g Shinko Forest (IRE)—Kayoko (IRE) **Mr Jon Carr**
22 **KENSINGTON (IRE)**, b c Cape Cross (IRE)—March Star (IRE) **Mr M. Sakal**
23 **LADY LEXIE**, b f Cape Cross (IRE)—Lady of The Land **Mr Graham Robinson**
24 **LA PETITE CHINOISE**, ch f Dr Fong (USA)—Susi Wong (IRE) **Mr N. Elsass**
25 **LIGHT OF MORN**, gr f Daylami (IRE)—My Emma **Matthews Breeding and Racing**
26 **MAGIC VERSE**, ch f Opening Verse (USA)—Festival Sister **Mr Eugene Lismonde**
27 **MALUTI**, ch g Piccolo—Persian Blue **Mrs Jane Poulter**
28 **MILLINSKY (USA)**, ch f Stravinsky (USA)—Millyant **Mr C. J. Mills**
29 **MINDFULNESS**, b f Primo Dominie—My Cadeaux **Bradmill Ltd**
30 **MISS INKHA**, b f Intikhab (USA)—Santi Sana **Mrs J. E. Lury and Mr O. T. Lury**
31 **NOBLE DESERT (FR)**, b f Green Desert (USA)—Sporades (USA) **Mr C. J. Murfitt**
32 **NOBLE MOUNT**, b g Muhtarram (USA)—Our Poppet (IRE) **Mr Graham Robinson**
33 **PEARL OF YORK (DEN)**, b f Richard of York—Laser Show (IRE) **Mr N. Elsass**
34 **PETONG'S PET**, br f Petong—What A Pet **Mr C. J. Murfitt**
35 **PETRION**, b f Petong—Rion River (IRE) **Mr C. J. Murfitt**

TWO-YEAR-OLDS

36 **ALL A DREAM**, br f 29/1 Desert Story (IRE)—Alioli (Nishapour (FR)) **Miss K. Rausing**
37 **DIAMOND KATIE (IRE)**, b f 2/3 Night Shift (USA)—
              Fayrooz (Gulch (USA)) (16000) **Matthews Breeding and Racing**
38 **EASY MOVER (IRE)**, ch f 7/2 Bluebird (USA)—Top Brex (FR) (Top Ville) (13000)
39 Ch f 3/3 Night Shift (USA)—Gaelic's Fantasy (IRE) (Statoblest) (15000) **Mr N. Elsass**
40 **GENERAL JIST**, ch c Opening Verse (USA)—Pharling (Pharly (FR))
41 **GRAND COURSE (IRE)**, ch f 30/1 Grand Lodge (USA)—
              Star of The Course (Theatrical) (29000) **Matthews Breeding and Racing**
42 **GRANDMA'S GIRL**, b f 30/3 Desert Style (IRE)—Sakura Queen (IRE) (Woodman (USA)) **Mr Barry Stewart**
43 **PRETTY AS CAN BE**, b f 8/5 Giant's Causeway—Pato (High Top) **Matthews Breeding and Racing**
44 **REGAL AFFECTION (USA)**, ch f King of Kings (IRE)—
              Blush With Love (Mt Livermore (USA)) (14000) **Mr D. G. Jones**
45 **ROMA VALLEY (FR)**, gr f 23/3 Linamix (FR)—Lois (IRE) (Be My Guest (USA)) (17316) **Mrs Jane Poulter**
46 Ch f 13/3 Tagula (IRE)—Ruby Heights (Shirley Heights) **Mrs J. E. Lury and Mr O. T. Lury**
47 **TRAFALGAR SQUARE**, b c 7/4 King's Best (USA)—Pat Or Else (Alzao (USA)) **Matthews Breeding and Racing**

Other Owners: Miss L. J. Balcombe, Mr D. Churchman, Mr Brian Cooper, Mr E. W. Dale, Mr A. P. Davies, Mr E. P. Duggan, Mr B. J. Flahive, Mr John Fullick, Mr R. T. Goodes, Mrs J. E. Lury, Mr O. T. Lury, Prof M. M. A. McCabe, Mr W. R. Milner, Mr D. G. Raffel, Ms Elaine Reffo, Mrs Diane Robinson, Mr Michael G. T. Stokes, Mrs R. J. Stoop, Mr Paul Thorman, Mr L. J. Vaessen.

Assistant Trainer: Colin Campbell

240

MR E. HADDOCK, Tewkesbury

Postal: **Slades Green Farm, Slades Green, Nr Longdon, Tewkesbury, Gloucestershire, GL20 6AN.**
Contact: **PHONE (01684) 833167 FAX (01684) 833114 E-MAIL edmund@aceine.fsbusiness.co.uk**

1 **BOREHILL JOKER**, 8, ch g Pure Melody (USA)—Queen Matilda **Miss H. M. Newell**
2 **FANION DE NOURRY (FR)**, 11, ch g Bad Conduct (USA)—Ottomane (FR) **Miss H. M. Newell**
3 **IACACIA (FR)**, 7, b g Silver Rainbow—Palencia (FR) **Mr E. Haddock**
4 **NATIVE COVE (IRE)**, 12, b g Be My Native (USA)—Down All The Coves **Miss H. M. Newell**

MR E. HADDOCK—continued
THREE-YEAR-OLDS

5 B g I'm Supposin (IRE)—Millie Million **Miss H. M. Newell**

Assistant Trainer: Miss H M Newell

Amateurs: Mr L Hicks (10-7), Miss S Sharratt (9-7).

---

241 **MR W. J. HAGGAS, Newmarket**
Postal: **Somerville Lodge, Fordham Road, Newmarket, Suffolk, CB8 7AA.**
Contact: **PHONE (01638) 667013 FAX (01638) 660534 E-MAIL william@somerville-lodge.co.uk**

1 **ALNAJA (USA)**, 5, b g Woodman (USA)—Cursory Look (USA) **Mr & Mrs J. Caplan**
2 **CHORIST**, 5, ch m Pivotal—Choir Mistress **Cheveley Park Stud**
3 **CLASSIC VISION**, 4, b f Classic Cliche (IRE)—Orient **The Chosen Few Partnership**
4 **DEL MAR SUNSET**, 5, b g Unfuwain (USA)—City of Angels **Mr R. A. Dawson**
5 **ENCHANTED PRINCESS**, 4, b f Royal Applause—Hawayah (IRE) **Mrs S. Jensen**
6 **ESCAYOLA (IRE)**, 4, b g Revoque (IRE)—First Fling (IRE) **Mrs M. Findlay**
7 **FLOWERDRUM (USA)**, 4, b f Mister Baileys—Norelands (USA) **Mr & Mrs J. Caplan**
8 **OBRIGADO (USA)**, 4, b g Bahri (USA)—Glorious Diamond (USA) **B. Haggas**
9 **POLAR BEAR**, 4, ch g Polar Falcon (USA)—Aim For The Top (USA) **B. Haggas**
10 **PRINCE HECTOR**, 5, ch h Hector Protector (USA)—Ceanothus (IRE) **David Heath**
11 **SHARPLAW VENTURE**, 4, b f Polar Falcon (USA)—Breakaway **Tina Miller**
12 **SUGGESTIVE**, 6, b g Reprimand—Pleasuring **Mrs B. Bassett**

THREE-YEAR-OLDS

13 **ACE CLUB**, ch g Indian Rocket—Presently **Mr C. G. Donovan**
14 **ALI DEO**, ch c Ali-Royal (IRE)—Lady In Colour (IRE) **Mrs J. J. Dye**
15 **APERITIF**, ch c Pivotal—Art Deco Lady **Stretton Manor Stud**
16 **ARKHOLME**, b g Robellino (USA)—Free Spirit (IRE) **Mr & Mrs G. Middlebrook**
17 **ATLANTIC CITY**, ch g First Trump—Pleasuring **The Slosh Partnership**
18 **BRUNEL (IRE)**, b c Marju (IRE)—Castlerahan (IRE) **Highclere Thoroughbred Racing X**
19 **BYGONE DAYS**, ch g Desert King (IRE)—May Light **Mr J. Hanson**
20 **CHOIR LEADER**, b c Sadler's Wells (USA)—Choir Mistress **Cheveley Park Stud**
21 **COBALT BLUE (IRE)**, b g Bluebird (USA)—Amy Hunter (USA) **Peter S. Jensen**
22 **CROWBERRY**, b g Orpen (USA)—Cloudberry **Mrs S. P. Davis & Mrs A. M. Green**
23 **FIVE YEARS ON (IRE)**, b g Desert Sun—Snowspin **Surf N'Turf Racing**
24 **FYODOR (IRE)**, b c Fasliyev (USA)—Royale Figurine (IRE) **The Fyodor Partnership**
25 **HEVERSHAM (IRE)**, b c Octagonal (NZ)—Saint Ann (USA) **Mr & Mrs G. Middlebrook**
26 **JELLY BABY**, b f Marju (IRE)—Daisy May **Mr B. Haggas**
27 **JUST DANCE ME (FR)**, gr f Linamix (FR)—Reine de La Ciel (USA) **Maurice Teboul**
28 **KSCHESSINKA (USA)**, br f Nureyev (USA)—Gran Dama (USA) **Lael Stable**
29 **LOVERS WALK (USA)**, b f Diesis—Starlight Way (USA) **Lael Stable**
30 **MAJESTIC MISSILE (IRE)**, b c Royal Applause—Tshusick **Flying Tiger Partnership**
31 **MALVERN LIGHT**, b f Zieten (USA)—Michelle Hicks **Tweenhills Racing (Summerhill)**
32 **MOON DAZZLE (USA)**, b f Kingmambo (USA)—June Moon (USA) **Wentworth Racing (Pty) Ltd**
33 **NEW YORK (IRE)**, b f Danzero (AUS)—Council Rock **A. Hirschfeld & L. K. Piggott**
34 **PERLE D'OR (IRE)**, b f Entrepreneur—Rose Society **The Perle D'Or Partnership**
35 **POKER**, ch g Hector Protector (USA)—Clunie **The Poker Partnership**
36 **RAMPAGE**, ch f Pivotal—Noor El Houdah (IRE) **Cheveley Park Stud**
37 **RED SAHARA (IRE)**, ch f Desert Sun—Red Reema (IRE) **Shortgrove Manor Stud**
38 **RED SKELTON (IRE)**, ch c Croco Rouge (IRE)—Newala **Mr J. D. Ashenheim**
39 **RESERVOIR (IRE)**, b g Green Desert (USA)—Spout **Highclere Thoroughbred Racing**
40 **SECRET FLAME**, b f Machiavellian (USA)—Secret Obsession (USA) **Cheveley Park Stud**
41 **SHARPLAW DESTINY (IRE)**, br f Petardia—Coolrain Lady (IRE) **Tina Miller**
42 **SPES BONA (USA)**, b c Rakeen (USA)—Novelette **Wentworth Racing (Pty) Ltd**
43 **SUCCUMB**, ch f Pursuit of Love—Doctor Bid (USA) **Cheveley Park Stud**
44 **VONADAISY**, b f Averti (IRE)—Vavona **B. Smith & Partners**
45 **WITCHCRAFT**, b c Zilzal (USA)—Witch of Fife (USA) **Cheveley Park Stud**
46 **WYVERN (GER)**, b c Unfuwain (USA)—Wladinova (GER) **Highclere Thoroughbred Racing XIII**

TWO-YEAR-OLDS

47 **ALABAMA TWIST**, b c 31/3 Magic Ring (IRE)—Glass (Bering) (30000) **A. Duke & Partners**
48 **BEAUNE**, b c 4/2 Desert Prince (IRE)—Tipsy (Kris) **Cheveley Park Stud**

MR W. J. HAGGAS—continued

49 **BLUFF**, b c 19/2 Bluebird (USA)—Show Off (Efisio) (34000) **Mr & Mrs A. Peskin**
50 **BROCKHOLE (IRE)**, gr c 7/3 Daylami (IRE)—Free Spirit (IRE) (Caerleon) **Mr & Mrs G. Middlebrook**
51 **CENTRE POINT**, ch f 23/4 Pivotal—Ink Pot (USA) (Green Dancer (USA)) **Cheveley Park Stud**
52 **CLUELESS**, b c 4/2 Royal Applause—Pure (Slip Anchor) (26000) **W. J. Gredley**
53 **CONFETTI**, ch f 19/2 Groom Dancer (USA)—Fabulous (Fabulous Dancer (USA)) **Cheveley Park Stud**
54 **CRETE (IRE)**, b c 19/2 Montjeu (IRE)—
    Paesanella (Seattle Song (USA)) (125000) **Highclere Thoroughbred Racing**
55 **DISCIPLE**, b c 14/3 Polar Falcon (USA)—Sparkling (Kris) (25000) **B. Haggas**
56 **ESKIMO'S NEST**, b f 1/3 Polar Falcon (USA)—White House (Pursuit of Love) **J. M. Greetham**
57 **FIRST GENERATION**, b c 1/4 Primo Dominie—My Cadeaux (Cadeaux Genereux) (75000) **Peter S. Jensen**
58 **FLORINO**, b f 26/1 Polish Precedent—Flourish (Selkirk (USA)) **Wyck Hall Stud**
59 **GINGER SPICE (IRE)**, ch f 27/2 Cadeaux Genereux—Pop Queen (Nashwan (USA)) (22000)
60 **ICING**, br f 21/2 Polar Falcon (USA)—Dance Steppe (Norwick (USA)) **Cheveley Park Stud**
61 **LANGDALE**, ch c 11/2 Dr Fong (USA)—Ciboure (Norwick (USA)) **Mr & Mrs G. Middlebrook**
62 B f 15/3 Vettori (IRE)—La Piazza (IRE) (Polish Patriot (USA)) (7000) **Jolly Farmers Racing & Steve De Martino**
63 Ch f 9/2 Indian Ridge—Likely Story (IRE) (Night Shift (USA)) (68000) **A. Hirschfeld**
64 Br c 5/2 Pivotal—Lucky Arrow (Indian Ridge) (42000) **G. Roberts & F. M. Green**
65 **NEFERURA**, b f 24/3 Mister Baileys—Boadicea's Chariot (Commanche Run) **Mrs Fiona Williams**
66 **PHI PHI (IRE)**, b f 25/2 Fasliyev (USA)—Council Rock (General Assembly (USA)) **A. Hirschfeld & L. K. Piggott**
67 Gr f 20/4 Linamix (FR)—Reine de La Ciel (USA) (Conquistador Cielo (USA)) **John-Henri Metzger**
68 **ROWAN WARNING**, b c 11/5 Diktat—
    Golden Seattle (IRE) (Seattle Dancer (USA)) (40000) **Rowan Stud Partnership**
69 **SEA LARK**, b g 27/1 Green Horizon—Fiora (IRE) (Sri Pekan (USA)) **Mrs Robert Armstrong**
70 **SHARPLAW STAR**, b f 2/4 Xaar—Hamsah (IRE) (Green Desert (USA)) (92000) **Tina Miller**
71 **SILVER SWING**, gr c 11/2 Celtic Swing—Poetry In Motion (IRE) (Ballad Rock) (5238) **D. H. Armitage & Partner**
72 **SKIRINGSAAL (GER)**, b f 20/4 Kornado—
    Second Game (GER) (Second Set (IRE)) (4638) **Good Ordinary Clarets**
73 **STAKHANOV**, b c 22/5 Dr Fong (USA)—Russian Grace (IRE) (Soviet Star (USA)) (8500) **B. Smith & Partners**
74 **TRACTOR BOY**, b c 25/3 Mind Games—
    Day Star (Dayjur (USA)) (30000) **Mr Simon Turner & Mrs Holly Bellingham**
75 **VERY WISE**, b c 2/5 Pursuit Of Love—With Care (Warning) **J. M. Greetham**

Other Owners: Mr T. Bannister, Mr M. Braddell, Mr Ian Brown, Mr P. A. Deal, Mr G. Eaton, Mr S. Ellis, Mr C. Feather, Mr J. Fildes, Mr S. Haggas, Mr S. Hope, Mrs G. S. Jackson, Mr R. Jackson, Mrs H. Morss, Mr & Mrs J. Ridout, Mr D. I. Scott, Mr Brian Wallace, Mr Dudley White, Mr T. Wickham, Mr J. Worboys.

Assistant Trainer: Michael Denaro

---

242 **MISS V. HAIGH**, Bawtry
Postal: **Martin Grange, Bawtry, Doncaster, South Yorkshire, DN10 6DD.**

1 **BINT ROYAL (IRE)**, 6, ch m Royal Abjar (USA)—Living Legend (USA) **Miss V. Haigh**
2 **GUNS BLAZING**, 5, b g Puissance—Queen of Aragon (USA) **Miss V. Haigh**
3 **MR LOVERMAN (IRE)**, 4, ch g Spectrum (IRE)—Soviet Artic (FR) **Miss V. Haigh**
4 **SCRAPPY DOO**, 4, b g Petong—Maziere **Miss V. Haigh**

THREE-YEAR-OLDS

5 **SALUT SAINT CLOUD**, b c Primo Dominie—Tiriana **Miss V. Haigh**

Amateurs: Miss F Bramley (8-7), Miss V Haigh (10-0).

---

243 **MR J. S. HALDANE**, Mindrum
Postal: **The Yard Cottage, Mindrum, Northumberland, TD12 4QN.**
Contact: **PHONE (01890) 850382**

1 **BIG LUGS**, 8, ch g Rakaposhi King—Winnowing (IRE) **Mr J. S. Haldane**
2 **BLACK BOB (IRE)**, 7, b g Good Thyne (USA)—Midsummer Blends (IRE) **Mr J. S. Haldane**
3 **CAMP HILL**, 10, gr g Ra Nova—Baytino **Mrs Hugh Fraser**
4 **DARK MANDATE (IRE)**, 6, b br m Mandalus—Ceoltoir Dubh **Mrs Hugh Fraser**
5 **HIGH EXPECTATIONS (IRE)**, 9, ch g Over The River (FR)—Andy's Fancy (IRE) **Mr J. S. Haldane**
6 **HUGHIE**, 9, ch g Super Sunrise—Clarilaw **Mrs Hugh Fraser**

MR J. S. HALDANE—continued

7 **MIRABAD**, 5, b g Pursuit of Love—Shemaleyah **Mr J. S. Haldane**
8 **MITEY PERK (IRE)**, 5, b g Executive Perk—More Dash (IRE) **Mrs A. Tullie**
9 **ORANGINO**, 6, b g Primo Dominie—Sweet Jaffa **Mr J. S. Haldane**
10 **PRINCE OF PERILS**, 10, b g Lord Bud—Kumari Peril **Mr J. S. Haldane**
11 **TRINLEY MOSS (IRE)**, 6, b m Executive Perk—Rosmere (IRE) **Mr J. S. Haldane**
12 **WELCOME ARCHIE**, 4, ch g Most Welcome—Indefinite Article (IRE) **Mr D. Young**

244 MR ALEXANDER HALES, Wendover Dean
Postal: **The Coach House Stables, Cobblers Hill, Wendover Dean, Buckinghamshire, HP22 6QD.**
Contact: **OFFICE (01296) 621116 FAX (01296) 621117 MOBILE (07771) 511652**

1 **BEETLE BUG**, 4, b f Robellino (USA)—Special Beat **Mr A. M. Hales**
2 **FULL ON**, 7, b g Le Moss—Flighty Dove **Coach House Racing**
3 **GO CLASSIC**, 4, b f Classic Cliche (IRE)—Edraianthus **The Chalfont Partnership**
4 **GRAND FOLLY (FR)**, 4, ch f Grand Lodge (USA)—Folmanie (USA) **Mr Adrian Smith**
5 **HIGH TOWER**, 7, b g Lycius (USA)—Sedova (USA) **The Cornish 'Crac' Partnership**
6 **MULLIGANS FOOL (IRE)**, 7, ch m Torus—Miss Mulligan **William Rowley**
7 **MURDINGA**, 5, br g Emperor Jones (USA)—Tintinara **The Cornish 'Crac' Partnership**
8 **NO FORECAST (IRE)**, 10, b g Executive Perk—Guess Twice **Coach House Racing**
9 **PERCHCOURT STEEL (IRE)**, 8, b g Grand Lodge (USA)—Scaravie (IRE) **Mr J. Smith**
10 **SALTANGO (GER)**, 5, b h Acatenango (GER)—Salde (GER) **Mr A. M. Hales**
11 **SEAL OF OFFICE**, 5, ch g Mark of Esteem (IRE)—Minskip (USA) **The West One Partnership**
12 **SHARP RIGGING (IRE)**, 4, b g Son of Sharp Shot (IRE)—In The Rigging (USA) **Mr A. M. Hales**
13 **VERY VERY NOBLE (IRE)**, 10, ch g Aristocracy—Hills Angel (IRE) **Coach House Racing**
14 **VIVA FOREVER (FR)**, 5, br m Lando (GER)—Very Mighty (FR) **Mr P. A. Deal**

Other Owners: Mr Andrew L. Cohen, Mr M. Dragisic, Mr D. Jones, Mr Gary Marquard, Mr C. J. McGale, Mr K. M. Mortimore, Mr T. D. O'Sullivan, Mr I. H. Stephenson, Mr John Tyndall, Mrs T. Yates.

Amateur: Mr D Lowe (9-7).

245 MR L. MONTAGUE HALL, Epsom
Postal: **Ermyn Lodge Stables, Shepherds Walk, Headley, Epsom, Surrey, KT18 6DF.**
Contact: **PHONE (01372) 279308**

1 **BADOU**, 4, b g Averti (IRE)—Bint Albadou (IRE) **Mr J. Daniels**
2 **FAST FORWARD FRED**, 13, gr g Sharrood (USA)—Sun Street
3 **LYSANDER'S QUEST (IRE)**, 6, br g King's Theatre (IRE)—Haramayda (FR) **Mrs E. N. Nield**
4 **MADRASEE**, 6, b m Beveled (USA)—Pendona **Mr J. Daniels**
5 4, B f Parthian Springs—My Lifetime Lady (IRE) **Grenian Farm**
6 **RIVIERA RED (IRE)**, 4, b g Rainbow Quest—Banquise (IRE) **Mr Michael S. Green**
7 **ZAFORUM**, 11, b g Deploy—Beau's Delight (USA) **Mr L. Montague Hall**

THREE-YEAR-OLDS

8 Ch c Pursuit of Love—Glow Forum **Mr L. Montague Hall**
9 **JOMUS**, b g Soviet Star (USA)—Oatey **Mr J. Daniels**
10 **MISS MILLIETANT**, b f Up And At 'em—Annie Hall **Grenian Farm**

Other Owners: Mr S. R. Finlay, Mr A. Minhinnick, Ms Helen Mulholland, Omni Colour Presentations Ltd, Mr B. Page, Mr R. Pain, Mr K. J. Quinn, Mr M. Wallinger.

246 MISS S. E. HALL, Middleham
Postal: **Brecongill, Coverham, Leyburn, North Yorkshire, DL8 4TJ.**
Contact: **PHONE (01969) 640223 FAX (01969) 640567 E-MAIL** sally@brecongill.co.uk

1 **CHARLOTTE LAMB**, 4, gr f Pharly (FR)—Caroline Lamb **Miss S. E. Hall**
2 **FRENCH TUNE (FR)**, 6, ch g Green Tune (USA)—Guerre de Troie **Mr C. Platts**
3 **KATY O'HARA**, 5, b m Komaite (USA)—Amy Leigh (IRE) **Mr C. Platts**
4 4, B f Alderbrook—Knowing **Miss S. E. Hall**
5 **SECOND AFFAIR (IRE)**, 7, b m Pursuit of Love—Startino **Miss S. E. Hall**
6 **SIR LAMB**, 8, gr g Rambo Dancer (CAN)—Caroline Lamb **Mr C. Platts**
7 **THAT'S FOR SURE**, 4, b g Forzando—Sure Flyer (IRE) **Mrs Joan Hodgson**

MISS S. E. HALL—continued

THREE-YEAR-OLDS

8 **STARBRIGHT,** b g Polar Falcon (USA)—Treasure Hunt **Miss S. E. Hall**
9 **WEAKEST LINK,** b g Mind Games—Sky Music **Miss S. E. Hall**
10 **ZERO POINT,** b g Danzero (AUS)—Uniform **Mr C. Platts**

TWO-YEAR-OLDS

11 B g 8/4 Namaqualand (USA)—Belamcanda (Belmez (USA)) (5000)
12 B f 27/5 Kayf Tara—Caroline Lamb (Hotfoot)
13 B f 15/3 Bold Edge—Second Affair (IRE) (Pursuit of Love)

Assistant Trainer: Colin Platts

Jockeys (NH): Richard Johnson (10-0, w.a.), J P McNamara (10-0, w.a.). **Amateur:** Mrs Diane Wilkinson (8-0).

---

247 MR G. A. HAM, Axbridge
Postal: **Rose Farm, Rooksbridge, Axbridge, Somerset, BS26 2TH.**
Contact: **HOME (01934) 750331 FAX (01934) 750331 MOBILE (07732) 979962**
E-MAIL info@rosefarmdevelopments.co.uk

1 **BLACK SWAN (IRE),** 4, b g Nashwan (USA)—Sea Spray (IRE) **Mr Colin B. Taylor**
2 **BOSS ROYAL,** 7, ch g Afzal—Born Bossy **The Holmes Office**
3 **BOXER'S DOUBLE,** 7, b g Petoski—Grayrose Double **Mr K. C. White**
4 **BROADWAY BAY,** 6, b g Karinga Bay—Brownscroft **Mrs W. D. Smith**
5 **CODY,** 5, ch g Zilzal (USA)—Ibtihaj (USA) **Mr P. A. Dales**
6 **DYLAN THE VILLAIN,** 5, b g Overbury (IRE)—Radmore Brandy **J. R. Salter**
7 **GEORGIC BLAZE,** 10, b g Petoski—Pooka **Mr E. Simmons**
8 **GORDY'S JOY,** 4, b f Cloudings (IRE)—Beatle Song **Sally & Tom Dalley**
9 **JACK DURRANCE (IRE),** 4, b g Polish Precedent (USA)—Atlantic Desire (IRE) **The Jack Durrance Partnership**
10 **MIGHTY MAX,** 6, b g Wellbeloved—Jokers High (USA) **Max Pro Bets Partnership**
11 **PRIDE OF PENNKER (IRE),** 11, b m Glacial Storm (USA)—Quitrentina **Mr C. F. Caple**
12 **RADMORE SPIRIT,** 4, b f Whittingham (IRE)—Ruda (FR) **J. R. Salter**
13 **REGAL ALI (IRE),** 5, ch g Ali-Royal (IRE)—Depeche (FR) **Mr N. G. Ahier**
14 **RESISTANCE (IRE),** 7, br g Phardante (FR)—Shean Hill (IRE) **Tom Dalley & David Derbin**
15 **SAXE-COBURG (IRE),** 7, b g Warning—Saxon Maid **Sally & Tom Dalley**
16 **SNINFIA (IRE),** 4, b f Hector Protector (USA)—Christmas Kiss **The Sninfia Partnership**
17 **UNDER CONSTRUCTION (IRE),** 6, b g Pennekamp (USA)—Madame Nureyev (USA) **Sally & Tom Dalley**
18 7, b g Homo Sapien—Val's Jem **J. R. Salter**

TWO-YEAR-OLDS

19 **INDIAN SAGE,** b c 25/6 Awesome—Angharad Lyn (Perpendicular) **Mr Jim Thomas**

Other Owners: Mr D. M. Drury, Mr Corey Gardner, Mr P. A. Terrett, Mr S. Thorne.

Jockeys (Flat): J Quinn, V Slattery. **Jockey (NH):** S Curran (10-0). **Conditional:** S Elliott (9-7).
Amateur: Mr Gerard Denvir (9-3).

---

248 MRS M. C. HAMBRO, Cheltenham
Postal: **Cotswold Stud, Sezincote, Moreton-In-Marsh, Gloucestershire, GL56 9TB.**
Contact: **PHONE (01386) 700700 FAX (01386) 700701 MOBILE (07860) 632990**
E-MAIL maryhambro@cotswoldstud.com

1 **BEECHY BANK (IRE),** 6, b m Shareef Dancer (USA)—Neptunalia **Mr Richard Hambro**
2 **BRUERN (IRE),** 7, b g Aahsaylad—Bob's Girl (IRE) **Mr Richard Hambro**
3 **DOVEDALE,** 4, b f Groom Dancer (USA)—Peetsie (IRE) **Mr Richard Hambro**
4 **KINGHAM,** 4, ch g Desert Prince (IRE)—Marie de Flandre (FR) **Mr Richard Hambro**
5 **SPRINGHILL,** 9, b g Relief Pitcher—Early Call **Mr Richard Hambro**
6 **STANWAY,** 5, b g Presenting—Nicklup **Mr Richard Hambro**

MRS M. C. HAMBRO—continued

THREE-YEAR-OLDS

7 HUMBLEBEE, b f Mtoto—d'Azy **Mr Richard Hambro**
8 KITEBROOK, b f Saddlers' Hall (IRE)—Neptunalia **Mr Richard Hambro**
9 OAT HILL, b g Mtoto—Chaloupe **Mr Richard Hambro**

TWO-YEAR-OLDS

10 BECKY'S HILL, b f 23/4 Mtoto—Neptunalia (Slip Anchor) **Mr Richard Hambro**
11 DIDBROOK, b f 19/2 Alzao (USA)—Nedaarah (Reference Point) **Mr Richard Hambro**
12 DORN HILL, b f 20/4 Lujain (USA)—Benedicite (Lomond (USA)) **Mr Richard Hambro**

Jockey (Flat): Vince Slattery (8-9).

249 **MRS A. HAMILTON, Newcastle Upon Tyne**
Postal: **Claywalls Farm, Capheaton, Newcastle Upon Tyne, NE19 2BP.**
Contact: **PHONE (01830) 530219**

1 BACYAN (IRE), 7, ch g Denel (FR)—Naycab **Mr Ian Hamilton**
2 DIVET HILL, 10, b g Milieu—Bargello's Lady **Mr Ian Hamilton**
3 5, B m Primitive Rising (USA)—Lady Manello **Mr Ian Hamilton**
4 LUCKY DUCK, 7, ch g Minster Son—Petroc Concert **Mr Ian Hamilton**
5 MISS ROYELLO, 7, b m Royal Fountain—Lady Manello **Mr Ian Hamilton**
6 SUPERIOR WEAPON (IRE), 10, b g Riverhead (USA)—Ballytrustan Maid (IRE) **Mr Ian Hamilton**
7 TYNEDALE (IRE), 5, b g Good Thyne (USA)—Book of Rules (IRE) **Mr Ian Hamilton**

Assistant Trainer: Ian Hamilton

250 **MRS A. C. HAMILTON, Minto**
Postal: **Old Orchard Cottage, Cavers, Hawick, TD9 9ST.**
Contact: **(01450) 376399**

1 BAY OF DREAMS, 5, ch g Salse (USA)—Cantico **Mr G. Hamilton**
2 RED GAUNTLET, 11, b g Wonderful Surprise—Border Minstrel **Mr G. Hamilton**
3 WHAT A NIGHT, 5, gr g Environment Friend—Misty Night **Mr & Mrs G. Hamilton**

Assistant Trainer: Mr G. Hamilton

251 **MRS A. J. HAMILTON-FAIRLEY, Hook**
Postal: **Moor Place, Plough Lane, Bramshill, Hook, Hampshire, RG27 0RF.**
Contact: **PHONE (0118) 932 6269 MOBILE (07798) 577761 E-MAIL mouse@hamilton-fairley.co.uk**

1 EXPENSIVE FOLLY (IRE), 6, b g Satco (FR)—Tarasandy (IRE) **Hamilton-Fairley Racing**
2 FRENCH MANNEQUIN (IRE), 5, b br m Key of Luck (USA)—Paris Model (IRE) **Runs In The Family**
3 NELLY MOSER, 7, gr m Neltino—Boreen's Glory **Hamilton-Fairley Racing**
4 PERUVIA (IRE), 4, b f Perugino (USA)—Dane's Lane (IRE) **Hamilton-Fairley Racing**
5 STANDING APPLAUSE (USA), 6, b g Theatrical—Pent (USA) **Hamilton-Fairley Racing**

Other Owners: Mr Geoffrey Hamilton-Fairley, Mrs Richard Plummer.

252 **MR M. D. HAMMOND, Middleham**
Postal: **Oakwood Stables, East Witton Road, Middleham, Leyburn, North Yorkshire, DL8 4PT.**
Contact: **(01969) 625223 FAX (01969) 625224 E-MAIL mdhammondracing@aol.com**

1 ASHGAR (USA), 8, ch g Bien Bien (USA)—Ardisia (USA) **Jay Dee Bloodstock Limited**
2 DEEPASTHEOCEAN, 5, b h Kris—Dance On A Cloud (USA)
3 DEEP WATER (USA), 10, b g Diesis—Water Course (USA) **The County Set**
4 HOMBRE, 9, ch g Shernazar—Delray Jet (USA) **Mr R. D. Bickenson**
5 JOHN THE MOLE (IRE), 6, ch g Glacial Storm (USA)—City Dame **Mr M. T. McCarthy and Mr L. Ibbotson**
6 KEPI DE KERFELLEC (FR), 6, b g Valanjou (FR)—Ulfica (FR) **Mr Mike Newbould**
7 KING PLATO (IRE), 7, b g King's Ride—You Are A Lady (IRE) **Jay Dee Bloodstock Limited**
8 MANBOW (IRE), 6, b g Mandalus—Treble Base (IRE) **Hope Springs Eternal**

MR M. D. HAMMOND—continued

9 MANIATIS, 7, b h Slip Anchor—Tamassos **Mr Andy Peake**
10 MEXICAN (USA), 5, b h Pine Bluff (USA)—Cuando Quiere (USA) **Mr L. Ibbotson and Mr M. McCarthy**
11 MINSTER YORK, 10, ch g Minster Son—Another Treat **The Adbrokes Partnership**
12 SHOGOON (FR), 5, b h Rangoon (FR)—Touranlad (FR) **The County Set**
13 TEE-JAY (IRE), 8, ch g Un Desperado (FR)—N T Nad **T. J. Equestrian Ltd**

TWO-YEAR-OLDS

14 MCCORMACK (IRE), b c 25/4 Desert Story (IRE)—La Loba (IRE) (Treasure Kay) (12000) **Mr R. D. Bickenson**

Other Owners: Mr Bobby Anderson, Mr John Bell, Mr A. Cadger, Mr Paul Elborn, Mr Douglas Godsman, Mr George Godsman, Mr E. D. Haggart, Mr Tony Harding, Mrs Christine McGuiness, Mrs M. Powney-Jones, Mr B. Raper, Mr A. W. Sinclair, Mr James Thomson, Mr H. W. Voigt, Mr O. R. Weeks.

Assistant Trainer: Ernie Patterson

Conditional: A Hopkins, K Renwick.

---

253 MR B. HANBURY, Newmarket
Postal: **Diomed Stables, Hamilton Road, Newmarket, Suffolk, CB8 0PD.**
Contact: **OFFICE** (01638) 663193 **YARD** 664799 **FAX** 667209 **HOME** (01440) 820396
MOBILE (07733) 322324 **E-MAIL** ben.hanbury@virgin.net **WEBSITE** www.benhanburyracing.co.uk

1 DHABYAN (USA), 4, ch c Silver Hawk (USA)—Fleur de Nuit (USA)
2 FOREST TUNE (IRE), 6, b g Charnwood Forest (IRE)—Swift Chorus **The Acorn Partnership**
3 LIQUID FORM, 4, b g Bahhare (USA)—Brogan's Well (IRE)

THREE-YEAR-OLDS

4 EMTILAAK, b c Marju (IRE)—Just A Mirage **Mr Hamdan Al Maktoum**
5 HAWAAJES, b g Royal Applause—Aegean Blue
6 IFTERADH, b c Bahhare (USA)—Matila (IRE)
7 KHAFAYIF (USA), b f Swain (USA)—Copper Play (USA)
8 LADY BLADE (IRE), b f Daggers Drawn (USA)—Singhana (IRE) **Pink Elephant Racing**
9 NADAYEM (USA), ch f Gulch (USA)—Tajannub (USA) **Mr Hamdan Al Maktoum**
10 NEQAAWI, br f Alhaarth (IRE)—Jinsiyah (USA) **Mr Hamdan Al Maktoum**
11 REWAYAAT, b f Bahhare (USA)—Alumisiyah (USA) **Mr Hamdan Al Maktoum**
12 SHARAAB (USA), b br c Erhaab (USA)—Ghashtah (USA) **Mr Hamdan Al Maktoum**
13 STANLEY CRANE (USA), b g Bahri (USA)—Grey Starling
14 STOCKING ISLAND, ch f Desert King (IRE)—Rawya (USA)

TWO-YEAR-OLDS

15 ALGHARB, b c 25/4 Mujahid (USA)—Actress (Known Fact (USA)) (110000)
16 B f 28/4 Unfuwain (USA)—Alshakr (Bahri (USA))
17 DHEFAAF (IRE), b c 20/2 Lujain (USA)—Paparazza (IRE) (Arazi (USA)) (25000)
18 ESWARAH, b f 21/4 Unfuwain (USA)—Midway Lady (Alleged (USA))
19 INTAAJ (IRE), b f 19/3 Machiavellian (USA)—Jinsiyah (USA) (Housebuster (USA))
20 B f 1/1 Shawaf (USA)—Istinad (USA) (Kris S (USA))
21 B c 23/3 Definite Article—Liege (IRE) (Night Shift (USA)) (20407)
22 B c 14/4 Bold Edge—Multi-Sofft (Northern State (USA)) (13000)
23 MURHEF, b c 18/2 Royal Applause—Petit Point (Petorius)
24 TADLIL, b c 24/4 Pivotal—Pretty Poppy (Song) (105000)
25 B f 14/4 Linamix (FR)—Tarhhib (Danzig (USA))
26 TUJJAAR (IRE), ch f 27/2 Cadeaux Genereux—Meshhed (USA) (Gulch (USA))

Assistant Trainer: Frank Crozier

254 **MR R. HANNON, Marlborough**
Postal: **East Everleigh Stables, Everleigh, Marlborough, Wiltshire, SN8 3EY.**
Contact: **PHONE (01264) 850 254 FAX (01264) 850 820**

1 **BARON'S PIT**, 4, b c Night Shift (USA)—Incendio **J. T. & K. M. Thomas**
2 **BINT MAKBUL**, 5, b m Makbul—Victoria Sioux **Mr Malih L. Al Basti**
3 **BONUS (IRE)**, 4, b c Cadeaux Genereux—Khamseh **Highclere Thoroughbred Racing VII**
4 **CAPE TOWN (IRE)**, 7, gr h Desert Style (IRE)—Rossaldene **Mr A. F. Merritt**
5 **CAPTAIN SAIF**, 4, b c Compton Place—Bahawir Pour (USA) **Mr Malih L. Al Basti**
6 **CARROWDORE (IRE)**, 4, b c Danehill (USA)—Euromill **Stonethorn Stud Farms Limited**
7 **COSMO (IRE)**, 4, b c Turtle Island (IRE)—Ewan **Mr Louis Stalder**
8 **DASH FOR COVER (IRE)**, 4, b g Sesaro (USA)—Raindancing (IRE) **Lady Davis**
9 **DORIS SOUTER (IRE)**, 4, b br f Desert Story (IRE)—Hope And Glory (USA) **Mr A. F. Merritt**
10 **GOLDEN BOUNTY**, 5, b h Bahamian Bounty—Cumbrian Melody **Mr George E. K. Teo**
11 **HURRICANE ALAN (IRE)**, 4, b c Mukaddamah (USA)—Bint Al Balad (IRE) **Mr I. A. N. Wight**
12 **NYSAEAN (IRE)**, 5, b h Sadler's Wells (USA)—Irish Arms (FR) **Fieldspring Racing**
13 **OH BOY (IRE)**, 4, b c Tagula (IRE)—Pretty Sally (IRE) **Mr A. F. Merritt**
14 **REBATE**, 4, b g Pursuit of Love—Aigua Blava (USA) **Mr R. Gander**
15 **ROCKETS 'N ROLLERS (IRE)**, 4, b c Victory Note (USA)—Holly Bird **Mr M. Mulholland**
16 **TIZZY MAY (FR)**, 4, ch c Highest Honor—Forentia **Mr J. R. May**
17 **TYCOON HALL (IRE)**, 4, ch c Halling (USA)—Tycooness (IRE) **Mr Cathal M. Ryan**

THREE-YEAR-OLDS

18 **BAKER OF OZ**, b c Pursuit of Love—Moorish Idol **The Mystery Partnership**
19 **BENTLEY'S BALL (USA)**, b br c Stravinsky (USA)—Slide By **On Trak Partnership**
20 **BINNION BAY (IRE)**, b c Fasliyev (USA)—Literary **Mr Jim Horgan**
21 **BOHOLA FLYER (IRE)**, b f Barathea (IRE)—Sharp Catch (IRE) **Mr William Durkan**
22 **BOOGIE STREET**, b c Compton Place—Tart And A Half **Hippodrome Racing**
23 **BOSCO (IRE)**, br c Petardia—Classic Goddess (IRE) **Mr Louis Stalder**
24 **CAVERAL**, ch f Ashkalani (IRE)—Melting Gold **Mr Louis Stalder**
25 **CELLO**, gr c Pivotal—Raffelina (USA) **Mr Louis Stalder**
26 **COCONUT COOKIE**, ch f Bahamian Bounty—Spicy Manner (USA) **Mrs Anna Doyle**
27 **CORKY (IRE)**, b c Intikhab—Khamseh **Robert Whitworth & Jane Whitworth**
28 **CREDIT (IRE)**, b c Intikhab (USA)—Tycooness (IRE) **Highclere Thoroughbred Racing**
29 **CUSCO (IRE)**, ch f Titus Livius (FR)—John's Ballad (IRE) **Family Amusements Ltd**
30 **DAFORE**, b c Dr Fong (USA)—Aquaglow **Fieldspring Racing**
31 **DARN GOOD**, ch c Bien Bien (USA)—Thimbalina **Mr J. E. Garrett**
32 **DEE GEE GIRL (IRE)**, b f Primo Dominie—Chapel Lawn **J. B. R. Leisure Ltd**
33 **DESERT HAWK**, b c Cape Cross (IRE)—Milling (IRE) **Mr D. Boocock**
34 **DOWAGER**, b f Groom Dancer (USA)—Rose Noble (USA) **Plantation Stud**
35 **EMSAM BALLOU (IRE)**, ch f Bluebird (USA)—Persian Tapestry **The Gold Partnership**
36 **ENFORD PRINCESS**, b f Pivotal—Expectation (IRE) **Major A. M. Everett**
37 **EPAMINONDAS (USA)**, ch c Miswaki (USA)—Nora Nova **Mr Michael Pescod**
38 **EUGENIE**, ch f Primo Dominie—Misty Goddess (IRE) **Mr J. R. Good**
39 **FANTASTIC VIEW (USA)**, ch c Distant View (USA)—Promptly (IRE) **Mr Malih L. Al Basti**
40 **FAREWELL GIFT**, b c Cadeaux Genereux—Daring Ditty **Lady Whent & Friends**
41 **FUEL CELL (IRE)**, b c Desert Style (IRE)—Tappen Zee **A. F. M. (Holdings) Ltd**
42 **HABANERO**, b c Cadeaux Genereux—Queen of Dance (IRE) **The Waney Racing Group Inc.**
43 **HOT LIPS PAGE (FR)**, b f Hamas (IRE)—Salt Peanuts (IRE) **Mr Bob Lalemant**
44 **HUNTER'S VALLEY**, b f Nicolotte—Down The Valley **Mr J. R. Shannon**
45 **IF PARADISE**, b c Compton Place—Sunley Stars **Mrs J. Wood**
46 **INSTINCT**, b c Zafonic (USA)—Gracious Gift **Mr Jim Horgan**
47 **INSTRUCTOR**, ch c Groom Dancer (USA)—Doctor's Glory (USA) **Highclere Thoroughbred Racing IX**
48 **I WON'T DANCE (IRE)**, b c Marju (IRE)—Carnelly (IRE) **Mr Bob Lalemant**
49 **JAOLINS**, b f Groom Dancer (USA)—On The Top **Allen & Associates**
50 **JUST TIM (IRE)**, ch c Inchinor—Simply Sooty **Mr D. J. Walker**
51 **KING CARNIVAL (USA)**, ch c King of Kings—Miss Waki Club (USA) **Mr J. A. Lazzari**
52 **KING OF CASHEL (IRE)**, b c King of Kings—Jaya (USA) **Dr A. Haloute**
53 **KINGS POINT (IRE)**, b c Fasliyev (USA)—Rahika Rose **Mr J. R. May**
54 **KUNDA (IRE)**, b f Intikhab (USA)—Ustka **Mr James Wigan**
55 **LORD LINKS (IRE)**, ch c Daggers Drawn (USA)—Lady From Limerick (IRE) **Coriolan Links Partnership VI**
56 **LUCAYAN LEGEND (IRE)**, b c Docksider (USA)—Capo di Monte **Lucayan Stud**
57 **MAC THE KNIFE (IRE)**, b c Daggers Drawn (USA)—Icefern **The Roman Road Partnership**
58 **MAN AT ARMS (IRE)**, b c Daggers Drawn (USA)—Punta Gorda (IRE) **The Waney Racing Group Inc.**
59 **MISSION MAN**, b c Revoque (IRE)—Opopmil (USA) **Lady Davis**
60 **MISSUS LINKS (USA)**, b f Lure (USA)—Cozisaidso (USA) **Coriolan Partnership II**

A unique sports story
A unique sports book

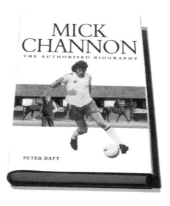

MR R. HANNON—continued

61 **MISTER SAIF (USA)**, ch c Miswaki (USA)—Shawgatny (USA) **Mr Malih L. Al Basti**
62 **MOONLIGHT MAN**, ch c Night Shift (USA)—Fleeting Rainbow **Mr J. A. Lazzari**
63 **NIGHT WORKER**, b c Dracula (AUS)—Crystal Magic **Mr T. A. Daniels**
64 **ORO VERDE**, ch c Compton Place—Kastaway **Mr I. A. N. Wight**
65 **PICCLEYES**, b g Piccolo—Dark Eyed Lady (IRE) **Mr Paul J. Dixon**
66 **PLANTERS PUNCH (IRE)**, b c Cape Cross (IRE)—Jamaican Punch (IRE) **Major A. M. Everett & Lucayan Stud**
67 **PRESTO SHINKO (IRE)**, b c Shinko Forest (IRE)—Swift Chorus **Major A. M. Everett & Lucayan Stud**
68 **PSYCHIATRIST**, ch g Dr Devious (IRE)—Zahwa **Mr Raymond Tooth**
69 **RED SPELL (IRE)**, ch c Soviet Star (USA)—A-To-Z (IRE) **Mrs John Lee**
70 **RED TOP (IRE)**, b f Fasliyev (USA)—Petite Epaulette **Mr William Durkan**
71 **RENDORO (USA)**, ch c Crafty Prospector (USA)—Renge (IRE) **Park Walk Racing**
72 **RINNEEN (IRE)**, b f Bien Bien (USA)—Sparky's Song **Denis Barry**
73 **SCARLET EMPRESS**, b f Second Empire (IRE)—Daltak **T.J.Dale,J.A.Leek,M.Pescod and Partners**
74 **SGT PEPPER (IRE)**, b c Fasliyev (USA)—Amandine **Mr A. T. Macdonald**
75 **SIGNOR PANETTIERE**, b c Night Shift (USA)—Christmas Kiss **The Mystery Partnership**
76 **SOLIPSIST (IRE)**, ch c Grand Lodge (USA)—Mijouter (IRE) **Fieldspring Racing**
77 **TOP SPEC (IRE)**, b c Spectrum (IRE)—Pearl Marine (IRE) **The Hill Top Partnership**
78 **TOTAL FORCE (IRE)**, b c Night Shift (USA)—Capegulch (USA) **Stonethorn Stud Farms Limited**
79 **TREGARRON**, br c Efisio—Language of Love **Mr J. R. Good**
80 **TURNSTILE**, gr c Linamix (FR)—Kissing Gate (USA) **The Queen**
81 **VENABLES (USA)**, ch c Stravinsky (USA)—Hope For A Breeze (CAN) **Team Havana**
82 **VERMILLIANN (IRE)**, b f Mujadil (USA)—Refined (IRE) **Mr M. Olden**
83 **VIENNA'S BOY (IRE)**, b c Victory Note (USA)—Shinkoh Rose (FR) **Mr M. Sines**
84 **VOILE (IRE)**, b f Barathea (IRE)—Samriah (IRE) **De La Warr Racing**
85 **WHIPLASH (IRE)**, b c Orpen (USA)—La Colombari (ITY) **Dr Thomas & Mrs Thelma Wade**
86 **WHY DUBAI (USA)**, br f Kris S (USA)—Highest Goal (USA) **Mr Malih L. Al Basti**
87 **WIZARD LOOKING**, b c Wizard King—High Stepping (IRE) **Mr J. G. Phillips**
88 **ZUMA (IRE)**, b c Grand Lodge (USA)—Paradise Waters **The Waney Racing Group Inc.**

TWO-YEAR-OLDS

89 **AASTRAL MAGIC**, b f 19/4 Magic Ring (IRE)—Robanna (Robellino (USA)) (2600) **Green Pastures Partnership**
90 **ALWAYS MINE**, ch f 21/3 Daylami (IRE)—Mamoura (IRE) (Lomond (USA)) (50000) **Mr J. G. Davis**
91 Ch f 30/3 Pivotal—Ariadne (GER) (Kings Lake (USA)) (30000) **Highclere Thoroughbred Racing**
92 **ASIAN TIGER (IRE)**, b c 12/4 Rossini (USA)—
                Dry Lightning (Shareef Dancer (USA)) (32000) **Waney Racing Group**
93 **AUNT JULIA**, b f 3/2 In The Wings—Original (Caerleon (USA)) (21000) **Mr J. Dowley & M. Pescod**
94 **BALTIC DIP (IRE)**, br f 18/2 Benny The Dip (USA)—
                Drei (USA) (Lyphard (USA)) (38000) **Thurloe Thoroughbreds VIII**
95 **BENTLEY'S BUSH (IRE)**, ch f 5/4 Barathea (IRE)—
                Veiled Threat (IRE) (Be My Guest (USA)) (45000) **Off Trak Partnership**
96 B c 28/4 Lujain (USA)—Bold Gem (Never So Bold) (25000) **Darley Stud Management Co.**
97 **CANTON (IRE)**, b c 1/2 Desert Style (IRE)—Thirlmere (Cadeaux Genereux) (30000) **Louis Stadler**
98 B f 4/3 Almutawakel—Capella (IRE) (College Chapel) **Malcolm Olden**
99 **CAYMAN COLONY (IRE)**, b c 20/2 Namid—Imperialist (IRE) (Imperial Frontier (USA)) (46381) **Ian Knight**
100 B c 29/4 Stravinsky (USA)—Celtic Shade (Lomond (USA)) (38000) **D. Barry & K. Trowbridge**
101 **CHALISON (IRE)**, b c 22/2 Anabaa (USA)—Raincloud (Rainbow Quest (USA)) (42000) **N. R. Hodges**
102 **LOVE AFFAIR (IRE)** B f 4/4 Tagula (IRE)—Changing Partners (Rainbow Quest (USA)) (26000) **Speedlith Group**
103 **CHAPTER (IRE)**, ch c 12/3 Sinndar (IRE)—
                Web of Intrigue (Machiavellian (USA)) (100000) **Highclere Thoroughbred Racing**
104 **CLOANN (IRE)**, b f 27/5 Danetime (IRE)—Rustic Lawn (Rusticard (FR)) (4328) **Mr M. A. Dunleavy**
105 **COME GOOD**, ch c 25/3 Piccolo—The Frog Lady (IRE) (Al Hareb (USA)) (30000) **R. Barby & Partners**
106 **CORNUS**, ch c 8/4 Inchinor—Demerger (Distant View (USA)) (16000) **D. Mort & Partners**
107 **CRESCENT LADY**, ch f 15/3 Kris—Prima Cominna (Unfuwain (USA)) (5000) **Mrs J. A. Daniels**
108 **DAVIAN**, b c 3/3 Robellino (USA)—Silver Purse (Interrex (CAN)) (36000) **David Bannon**
109 **DAVID'S SYMPHONY (IRE)**, ch c 29/3 Anabaa—Habemus (FR) (Bluebird (USA)) (19000) **Mr A. P. Patey**
110 **DESTINATE (IRE)**, b c 19/3 Desert Style (IRE)—
                Double Eight (IRE) (Common Grounds) (28447) **Mr Michael Pescod & J. Dowley**
111 B f 6/4 Robellino (USA)—Down The Valley (Kampala) **J. R. Shannon**
112 Ch c 2/2 Diesis—Elle Est Marie (IRE) (Night Shift (USA)) (55658) **F. Sines**
113 **ENCOURAGEMENT**, b f 5/3 Royal Applause—Gentle Persuasion (Bustino) **The Queen**
114 **FORTNUM**, b c 7/4 Forzando—Digamist Girl (Digamist (USA)) (35000) **Mrs J. Wood**
115 **FORWARD MOVE (IRE)**, ch c 8/5 Dr Fong (USA)—Kissing Gate (USA) (Easy Goer (USA)) **The Queen**
116 **GALEOTA (IRE)**, b c 5/4 Mujadil (USA)—Refined (IRE) (Statoblest) (150000) **Mr J. A. Lazzari**
117 **GARANCE**, b f 27/1 Zafonic (USA)—Arletty (Rainbow Quest (USA)) **Plantation Stud Ltd**

MR R. HANNON—continued

118 **GEOMETRIC**, b c 14/4 Octagonal (NZ)—
　　　　　　　　Liska's Dance (USA) (Riverman (USA)) (35000) **Royal Ascot Racing Club**
119 **GODSEND**, b f 13/3 Royal Applause—Gracious Gift (Cadeaux Genereux) **The Queen**
120 **GRAND MARQUE (IRE)**, ch c 23/2 Grand Lodge (USA)—
　　　　　　　　Royal Fizz (IRE) (Royal Academy (USA)) (50000) **Hoodles Racing**
121 **HALLUCINATE**, b c 13/4 Spectrum (IRE)—Swift Spring (FR) (Bluebird (USA)) (14000) **T. S. Events**
122 **HE'S A STAR**, ch c 28/1 Mark Of Esteem (IRE)—
　　　　　　　　Sahara Belle (USA) (Sanglamore (USA)) (10000) **T. S. M. Cunningham**
123 **HIDDEN CHANCE**, ch f 28/2 Hernando (FR)—
　　　　　　　　Catch (USA) (Blushing Groom (FR)) (15000) **N. R. Hodges & Partners**
124 　B c 15/5 Orpen (USA)—Indian Jubilee (Indian King (USA)) (5000) **Mrs T. S. M. Cunningham**
125 **ISLAND AIR**, b g 5/2 Desert Style (IRE)—Island Story (Shirley Heights) **The Queen**
126 　B c 31/3 Mujadil (USA)—Kahla (Green Desert (USA)) **Pat Eddery Racing**
127 **KAMAKIRI (IRE)**, b c 18/2 Trans Island—Alpine Flair (IRE) (Tirol) (35000) **Mr Michael Pescod**
128 　Ch c 28/3 Bachir (IRE)—Kentmere (FR) (Galetto (FR)) (30000) **N. A. Woodcock**
129 **KINGS QUAY**, b c 4/2 Montjeu (IRE)—Glen Rosie (IRE) (Mujtahid (USA)) (32000) **J. R. May**
130 **LADRUCA**, br f 26/4 Dracula (AUS)—Promissory (Caerleon (USA)) **Plantation Stud Ltd**
131 **LINDBERG**, b c 10/2 Bold Edge—Halland Park Girl (IRE) (Primo Dominie) (135000) **Cathal M. Ryan**
132 　B c 4/5 Entrepreneur—Lust (Pursuit of Love) (30000) **Mr Raymond Tooth**
133 　B c 23/3 Mark Of Esteem (IRE)—L-Way First (IRE) (Vision (USA)) (20000) **Ms R. Z. Shephenson & Partners**
134 **MADHAVI**, gr f 30/1 Diktat—Grey Galava (Generous (IRE)) (24000) **White Beech Farm**
135 　B f 29/3 Diktat—Maid To Dance (Pyramus (USA)) (17500) **Malih L Al Basti & Partners**
136 **MARCHING SONG**, b c 23/2 Royal Applause—Marl (Lycius (USA)) **The Queen**
137 　B f 14/2 Compton Place—Miller's Melody (Cheif Singer) (42000) **W. Durkan**
138 　B c 22/3 Spinning World (USA)—Miss Woodchuck (USA) (Woodman (USA)) (43289) **Mrs Dermot O'Rourke**
139 **MONEY MARKET (IRE)**, b g 13/5 Machiavellian (USA)—
　　　　　　　　Trying For Gold (USA) (Northern Baby (CAN)) **The Queen**
140 **MONTECITO**, b f 24/2 Montjeu (IRE)—Dancing Fire (USA) (Dayjur (USA)) (34000) **Mr R. J. McCreery**
141 　B c 10/4 Night Shift (USA)—New Tycoon (IRE) (Last Tycoon) (18552) **Ian Night**
142 **NORTH SHORE (IRE)**, b c 26/4 Soviet Star (USA)—
　　　　　　　　Escape Path (Wolver Hollow) (37000) **D. Boocock & K. Ivory**
143 　B c 5/3 Pennekamp (USA)—Pinkstone (FR) (Bigstone (IRE)) **F. Sines**
144 　B c 14/4 Royal Academy (USA)—Premier Peak (USA) (Mt Livermore (USA)) (92763) **Fieldspring Racing**
145 　Br c 11/2 Xaar—Prima Mat (IRE) (Primo Domonie) (15460) **J. R. May**
146 **PRINCE SAMOS (IRE)**, b c 22/4 Mujadil (USA)—Sabaniya (IRE) (Lashkari) (40197) **Mrs S. Costello-Haloute**
147 **PRINCESS LINKS**, b f 12/3 Bahamian Bounty—Miss Prism (Niniski (USA)) (35000) **Coriolan Partnership II**
148 **QUEEN OF THE PALMS (IRE)**, ch f 30/4 King Of Kings (IRE)—
　　　　　　　　Slip Ashore (IRE) (Slip Anchor) (12368) **Mrs V. Hubbard**
149 **RAGGED GLORY (IRE)**, br c 11/2 Foxhound (USA)—
　　　　　　　　Resurgence (Polar Falcon (USA)) (25000) **Mr Michael Pescod**
150 **REFERENCE (IRE)**, b c 1/4 Almutawakel (USA)—
　　　　　　　　Uffizi (IRE) (Royal Academy (USA)) (30000) **Royal Ascot Racing Club**
151 　Ch f 15/3 Tomba—Risk The Witch (Risk Me (FR)) (1500) **J. R. Good**
152 **SERENADE BLUE**, gr f 20/3 Linamix (FR)—Bimbola (FR) (Bikala) (52566) **Bob Alemant**
153 **SIR BLUEBIRD (IRE)**, ch c 12/4 Bluebird (USA)—Persian Tapestry (Tap On Wood) (38000) **D. J. Walker**
154 **SOLANICH**, ch c 4/5 Inchinor—Gussy Marlowe (Final Straw) (40000) **N. R. Hodges**
155 **SOLENT (IRE)**, b c 18/3 Montjeu (IRE)—Stylish (Anshan) (60000) **Mrs J. Wood**
156 **SPREE (IRE)**, gr f 3/2 Dansili—Ibiza (GER) (Linamix (FR)) (18552) **A. F. Merritt & Partners**
157 　B c 21/2 Gilded Time (USA)—Sudden Storm Birm (USA) (Storm Bird (CAN)) **Highclere Thoroughbred Racing**
158 **TAKE IT THERE**, ch f 24/1 Cadeaux Genereux—Feel Free (IRE) (Generous (IRE)) **The Queen**
159 　B f 25/2 Night Shift (USA)—Talena (Zafonic (USA)) (18552) **Speedlith Group**
160 **THE COIRES (IRE)**, b c 18/3 Green Desert (USA)—Purple Heather (USA) (Rahy (USA)) **The Queen**
161 **THE KEEP**, ch f 24/4 Shinko Forest—Poyle Amber (Sharrood (USA)) (7800) **The One Short Partnership**
162 **TRANSGRESS (IRE)**, b c 11/2 Trans Island—
　　　　　　　　Ned's Contessa (IRE) (Persian Heights) (35000) **Mr Raymond Tooth**
163 　B f 14/2 Montjeu (IRE)—Velvet Appeal (IRE) (Petorius) (45000) **Mrs Sue Brendish**
164 **VENEER (IRE)**, b c 9/5 Woodborough (USA)—Sweet Lass (Belmez (USA)) (12500) **A. F. Merritt & Partners**
165 　B c 6/5 Imperial Ballet (USA)—Victim of Love (Damister (USA)) (18552) **Mrs T. M. Moriarty**
166 **WAATHEB (IRE)**, b c 1/4 Barathea (IRE)—Bally Souza (USA) (Alzao (USA)) (27828) **Haif Al-Qatani**
167 　B f 16/3 Efisio—Well Proud (IRE) (Sadler's Wells (USA)) **W. J. Gredley**

MR R. HANNON—continued

168 XACOBEO (IRE), b c 24/4 Montjeu (IRE)—Afistak (Efisio) **A. T. Macdonald**
169 B f 14/2 Dansili—Zinnia (Zilzal (USA)) (12368) **Mrs T. M. Moriarty**

Other Owners: Mr David Allen, Mr Michael Baker, Mr K. A. Bentley, Mr R. A. Bernard, Mr C. Bowen, Mr P. Burgoyne, Mr J. A. Cover, Mr James Creed, Mrs D. Dawes, Dr K. P. Dunleavy, Mr Jonathon East, Mrs Barrie Gallop, Mr R. F. U. Gaskell, Mr Conal Kavanagh, Mr Joe Kelliher, Mr A. F. Leighton, Mrs A. Lovat, Ms K. Lowe, Mr J. Newsome, Mrs Caroline Parker, Mr E. John Perry, Mr R. A. Simmons, Mr Barrie Tankel, Mr G. P. Triefus.

Assistant Trainer: Richard Hannon Jnr

Jockeys (Flat): P Dobbs (8-2), R Hughes (8-6), Dane O'Neill (8-4), R Smith (8-0). **Apprentices:** Wayne Burton (8-4), P Gallagher (8-0), Ryan Moore (8-0).

---

255 MR G. A. HARKER, Middleham
Postal: **The Winning Post, Bolton Hall, Wensley, Leyburn, North Yorkshire, DL8 4UF.**
Contact: **(01969) 624507 (07803) 116412 (07930) 125544 E-MAIL gandjhome@aol.com**

1 **ATLANTIC QUEST (USA),** 5, b g Woodman (USA)—Pleasant Pat **Mr P. Savignano**
2 **BOLTON CASTLE,** 7, b g Royal Fountain—Elegant Mary **Mr P. I. Harker**
3 **BONNY GROVE,** 4, b g Bonny Scot (IRE)—Binny Grove **Mr D. Holmes**
4 **BRIOS BOY,** 4, ch g My Best Valentine—Rose Elegance **Mr P. Savignano**
5 **ENZO DE BAUNE (FR),** 7, b g En Calcat (FR)—Pure Moon (FR) **Lord Bolton**
6 **EXPRESS LILY,** 5, b m Environment Friend—Jaydeeglen **Mr A. P. Muir**
7 **FAIRY SKIN MAKER (IRE),** 6, ch g Nomadic Way (USA)—Malvern Madam **The Four S**
8 **FARNE ISLE,** 5, ch m Midnight Legend—Biloela **Mr M. F. Spence**
9 **JAY BE JUNIOR,** 4, br g J B Quick—Staggering (IRE) **Mr Geoff Bonson**
10 **PATRIARCH EXPRESS,** 7, b g Noble Patriarch—Jaydeeglen **Mr A. P. Muir**
11 **PEBBLE BAY,** 9, br g Perpendicular—Milly L'Attaque **Mr M. F. Spence**
12 **PRESENTING ROXY (IRE),** 6, br m Presenting—Two Hills Folly (IRE) **Mr David Adair**
13 **ROUGE BLANC (USA),** 4, b f King of Kings (IRE)—Style N' Elegance (USA) **Mr John J. Maguire**
14 **SWEET CHAMPAGNE,** 5, ch m Mazaad—Pink Sensation **Mr P. I. Harker**
15 **THE MASARETI KID (IRE),** 7, b g Commanche Run—Little Crack (IRE) **Mr R. Ward**

Other Owners: Mr S. B. Elphee, Mr S. F. Peel, Miss S. M. Smith, Mr Stephen John Smith.

Assistant Trainer: Jenny Harker

Conditional: N Hannity.

---

256 MR R. C. HARPER, Banbury
Postal: **Home Farm, Kings Sutton, Banbury, Oxfordshire, OX17 3RY.**
Contact: **PHONE (01295) 810997 MOBILE (07970) 223481 E-MAIL rharper@freeuk.com**

1 **CASH 'N CARROTS,** 5, b g Missed Flight—Rhiannon **Mr R. C. Harper**
2 **CHEEKY LAD,** 4, b g Bering—Cheeky Charm (USA) **Mr R. C. Harper**
3 **NAFSIKA (USA),** 4, b f Sky Classic (CAN)—Exotic Beauty (USA) **Mr R. C. Harper**
4 5, ch m Presidium—Sister Claire **Mr R. C. Harper**
5 **WOT NO CASH,** 12, gr g Ballacashtal (CAN)—Madame Non **Mr R. C. Harper**

---

257 MRS JESSICA HARRINGTON, Kildare
Postal: **Commonstown Stables, Moone, Co. Kildare.**
Contact: **PHONE +353 (0) 598624153 FAX +353 (0) 598624292 MOBILE +353 (0) 872566129 E-MAIL jessicaharrington@eircom.net**

1 **ANOTHER DOLLAR (IRE),** 6, br m Supreme Leader—Deep Dollar **Godfery Deacon**
2 **ARCHES BAR (IRE),** 4, b g Needle Gun (IRE)—Kovalevskia **Joe Doyle**
3 **AYE AYE POPEYE (IRE),** 6, ch g Imperial Frontier (USA)—Boscovice (IRE) **Mr Vincent Clynch**
4 **BE QUIET (IRE),** 7, b g Be My Native (USA)—Cool Mist (IRE) **Mr James Parkinson**
5 4, b g Needle Gun (IRE)—Bininoo (IRE) **Ian Morgan**
6 **BLACK ISLE (IRE),** 7, b m Supreme Leader—Black Gayle (IRE) **Mr John Peutherer**
7 **BRASYA (FR),** 5, gr m Baryshnikov (AUS)—La Toscanella (FR) **Commonstown Syndicate**
8 **BRUTTO FACIE (IRE),** 5, b g Old Vic—Elas Image (IRE) **Paul Maher & Kevin Norton**
9 **BUST OUT,** 8, ch g Bustino—Nordic Beauty (USA) **The BB Horse Racing Club**

MRS JESSICA HARRINGTON—continued

10 **CARDINAL VALLEY (IRE)**, 7, b g Shardari—Who Says **Sean Dalton**
11 **CEART GO LEOR (IRE)**, 7, b m Montelimar (USA)—Bold Empress **The Craic Syndicate**
12 6, Ch g Carroll House—Chantecler **John Tyndall Racing Syndicate**
13 6, B g Toulon—Clerical Lady (IRE) **Mr Paul Cooke**
14 **CLOSED ORDERS (IRE)**, 7, b g Phardante (FR)—Monks Lass (IRE) **Brian Smith & James Osborne**
15 **COLCA CANYON (IRE)**, 7, br g Un Desperado (FR)—Golden Flats **P. Myerscough**
16 4, B br c Scribano—Coolafinka (IRE) **Paid Thru The Nose Syndicate**
17 **COPPERVEGA (IRE)**, 5, b m Toulon—Friars Pass **Sean O'Regan**
18 **DESIGN TO WIN (IRE)**, 5, b m Flemensfirth (USA)—Miss Brecknell (IRE) **John Quigley**
19 **DEVERED (IRE)**, 5, ch g Desert King (IRE)—Tea House **H. McCalmont, H.de Burgh & P. Myerscough**
20 **DJANGO (IRE)**, 5, ch g Glacial Storm (USA)—Rathtrim **Brian Keoghan**
21 **EL FORESTAL (IRE)**, 6, b g King's Ride—Lady Conductor **Patrick McAvey**
22 **EXPRESS EXIT**, 6, b h Exit To Nowhere (USA)—Jasminola (FR) **The Shiners Syndicate**
23 **FIRE QUEEN (IRE)**, 4, b f Perugino (USA)—El Pina **The Star Syndicate**
24 **FORSAIL (IRE)**, 7, b g Good Thyne (USA)—Off You Sail (IRE) **Commonstown Syndicate**
25 **FOUR ACES**, 7, b g Forzando—Anhaar **Lakeside Racing Syndicate**
26 **FRANK MOSS BENNETT (IRE)**, 4, b g Bahhare (USA)—Despondant (IRE) **DJMP Syndicate**
27 **GREEN BELT FLYER (IRE)**, 6, b g Leading Counsel (USA)—Current Liability **The Green Belter Syndicate**
28 **HUME CASTLE (IRE)**, 8, b g Religiously (USA)—Clyde Avenue **Castle Hume Syndicate**
29 **HUME THEATRE (IRE)**, 5, b g Old Vic—Carrig Con (IRE) **Castle Hume Syd**
30 **I'LL CALL YOU BACK**, 5, b g Zaffaran (USA)—Ben Tack **Eammon McEntee**
31 **ILARON (FR)**, 8, b g April Night (FR)—Rousseliere (FR) **L. Quinn**
32 **IMAZULUTOO (IRE)**, 4, b c Marju (IRE)—Zapata (IRE) **Eamonn Salmon**
33 **INTELLIGENT (IRE)**, 9, b g Religiously (USA)—Arctic Laura **N. Moore**
34 **IRISH TZAR (IRE)**, 7, b g Moscow Society (USA)—The Real Gael (IRE) **Emer Purcell, Mark Sheeran**
35 **JACKIE CULLEN (IRE)**, 7, b g Lord Americo—Rose Hand (IRE) **Andies Syndicate**
36 **JEFF DE CHALAMONT (FR)**, 7, b g Abary (GER)—Clio de Chalamont (FR) **Mr Joe Dennigan**
37 **KILMOORLAND (IRE)**, 6, b g Hollow Hand—Becky's Angel (IRE) **Mr Tom Gray**
38 **KILROSSANTY (IRE)**, 5, b g Accordion—Baby Clair **Ron Shaw**
39 **LANDING RIGHTS (IRE)**, 7, b g Good Thyne (USA)—Raise Our Hopes (IRE) **Mr James Parkinson**
40 **MACS JOY (IRE)**, 5, b g Religiously (USA)—Snob's Supreme (IRE) **The Macs J Syn**
41 **MAHIRA (IRE)**, 7, b m Be My Native (USA)—Arumah **Mr David Pierce**
42 4, B Eagle Eyed (USA)—Mean To Me **Favourites Racing Ltd**
43 **MONT PUTTENS (IRE)**, 6, b m Montelimar (USA)—River Puttens (IRE) **Silver Lining Syndicate**
44 **MOSCOW COURT (IRE)**, 6, b g Moscow Society (USA)—Hogan Stand **James Parkinson**
45 **MOSCOW FLYER (IRE)**, 10, b g Moscow Society (USA)—Meelick Lady (IRE) **B. Kearney**
46 **MOUNT PROSPECT (IRE)**, 5, ch g Anshan—Rustic Court (IRE) **Brian Kearney**
47 **MR WONG (IRE)**, 8, b g Be My Native (USA)—Adare Boreen **Gerry Byrne, Sean Hussey & J. Hussey**
48 **NAN CHORO (IRE)**, 7, b h Jurado (USA)—Monksville **Mr Mark O'Reilly**
49 **NEON STAR (IRE)**, 5, b g Fourstars Allstar (USA)—Mandy's Treasure **Sean Harrington**
50 **NO BIG RUSH (IRE)**, 7, b g Be My Native (USA)—Cash It In (IRE) **In And Out Syndicate**
51 **OLD VAL (IRE)**, 6, b g Old Vic—Kilkilrun **Alan O'Neill & Brian Moore**
52 **OUTONACALL (IRE)**, 5, b m King Persian—E-Augh (IRE) **Nigle Floyd & John Bell**
53 5, B m Bob Back (USA)—Pachamama **Mr Dan Lenihan**
54 **PASSIONATE KNIGHT (IRE)**, 5, ch g Semillon—Knight's Maid **Ron MacDonald**
55 **PAY IT FORWARD**, 6, b g Anshan—Kellsboro Kate **Paid Thru The Nose Syndicate**
56 **PESCOTTO LADY**, 6, b m Toulon—Glenpatrick Peach (IRE) **Peter Queally & Mrs J. Harrington**
57 **POLAR (IRE)**, 5, ch g Good Thyne (USA)—Winter Cherry **Lorainne O'Brien**
58 **PRESIDENTE (IRE)**, 5, ch g Presenting—Lepida **Tom Curran**
59 **PRIVATE BEN (IRE)**, 6, b g Ridgewood Ben—Timeless **Seven Good Reasons Syndicate**
60 **PURE N SIMPLE (IRE)**, 5, ch m Presenting—Kept In The Dark **J. Maxwell & D. Maxwell**
61 **QUARRYLAND MAGIC**, 8, b m Toulon—Last Act **John O'Keeffee**
62 **QUEST FOR A STAR (IRE)**, 7, b g Rainbow Quest (USA)—Ridgewood Pearl **Mr Albert Crowley**
63 **RINGTOWN MINE (IRE)**, 7, ch g Grand Plaisir (IRE)—Your Mine **The Cool Ring Syn**
64 **RITA'S STAR**, 5, b m Moshaajir (USA)—Masirah **Lyon Den Syd**
65 **ROOSKA (IRE)**, 7, ch g Good Thyne (USA)—Night Blade **Paddy Musgrave & Peter Leonard**
66 **ROSSBROOK (IRE)**, 5, b m Presenting—Euroblend (IRE) **Pat O'Meara**
67 **SATCO'S LADY (IRE)**, 7, b m Satco (FR)—Back To Black (IRE) **Martin White**
68 **SIMPLY DA BEST (IRE)**, 6, b g Lake Coniston (IRE)—Sakala (NZ) **Mr Joe Rafferty**
69 **SLANEY FOX (IRE)**, 7, br m Foxhound (USA)—Mean To Me **Kinvale Partners**
70 **SOCIETY BREEZE (IRE)**, 5, ch m Moscow Society (USA)—Just A Breeze (IRE) **Empty Pockets Syndicate**
71 **SPANISH GUEST (IRE)**, 5, b g Be My Guest (USA)—Cabcharge Princess (IRE) **Dunboy Syndicate**
72 **SPIRIT LEADER (IRE)**, 8, b m Supreme Leader—That's The Spirit **Dil Thompson**
73 **STANAFOSS (IRE)**, 5, b g Synefos (USA)—Northern Elation (IRE) **Favourites RAcing Ltd**
74 **STAR HORSE (IRE)**, 6, b g Toulon—Clerical Lady (IRE) **Des O'Connell & Emma Harrington**
75 **STRIKE BACK (IRE)**, 6, b g Bob Back (USA)—First Strike (IRE) **Commonstown Syndicate**

MRS JESSICA HARRINGTON—continued

76 **SUPREME REBEL (IRE)**, 6, b g Supreme Leader—Corcaigh **Peter Thompson**
77 **THE LONG INCH (IRE)**, 5, b g College Chaple—Leola (IRE) **Dr J. O'Connell**
78 **ULAAN BATAAR (IRE)**, 7, b g Jacksons Drift (USA)—Leinster Lady (IRE) **Joe O'Flaherty**
79 **WATERLILY (IRE)**, 5, b m Revoque (IRE)—Cochineal (USA) **Dermot Cox & James Osbourne**
80 **WELL PRESENTED (IRE)**, 6, b g Presenting—Casualty Madame **The BB Horse Racing Club**
81 5, B g Flying Legend (USA)—Well Trucked (IRE) **Mark Kerr & Barney O'Rourke**
82 **WINDY SPIRIT (IRE)**, 9, br g Religiously (USA)—Golden Gale **Favourites Racing Ltd**
83 **YOU NEED LUCK (IRE)**, 4, b g Key of Luck (IRE)—Cathy Garcia (IRE) **Liam Brady & Jerry Shevlin**
84 **YOUNEVERTOLDME (IRE)**, 8, b m Simply Great (FR)—Royal Daisy **Mr C. Power**
85 **YOUNG LORD (IRE)**, 7, b h Leading Counsel (USA)—Cromore Princess **Mr Kevin Lee**
86 **YOUTH CUTHBERT**, 6, b h Homo Sapien—Deirdres Dream **Oh Goram Syndicate**

THREE-YEAR-OLDS

87 **CORRAN ARD (IRE)**, b g Imperial Ballet (IRE)—Beeper The Great (USA) **Mr Eamonn Salmon**
88 **MARJO (IRE)**, b f Marju (IRE)—Joleah (IRE) **R. Wood**
89 **VISSI D'ARTE (IRE)**, ch f Peintre Celebre (USA)—Shunaire (USA) **Margurite Clifford Racing LLC**

Jockey (NH): B Geraghty (w.a.). **Conditional:** A D Leigh, R Power. **Amateur:** Mr Ross O'Sullivan.

258

MR J. A. HARRIS, Melton Mowbray
Postal: **Eastwell Hall Stables, Eastwell, Melton Mowbray, Leicestershire, LE14 4EE.**
Contact: **YARD** (01949) 860671 **HOME** (01400) 282819 **MOBILE** (07989) 947712

1 **AQUILINE**, 6, ch g Sanglamore (USA)—Fantasy Flyer (USA) **Risley Hall Partnership**
2 **ESTIMATE**, 4, b f Mark of Esteem (IRE)—Mistle Thrush (USA)
3 **FRANK'S QUEST (IRE)**, 4, b g Mujadil (USA)—Questuary (IRE) **Mr M. F. Schofield**
4 **HAUNT THE ZOO**, 9, b m Komaite (USA)—Merryhill Maid (IRE) **Mrs A. E. Harris**
5 **JUNGLE LION**, 6, ch g Lion Cavern (USA)—Star Ridge (USA) **M. Rowley**
6 **KAMA'S WHEEL**, 5, ch m Magic Ring (IRE)—Tea And Scandals (USA) **Mr Paddy Barrett**
7 **LUCKY UNO**, 8, b g Rock City—Free Skip **Mr H. G. Norman**
8 **PALAIS (IRE)**, 9, b g Darshaan—Dance Festival **Mr J. South**
9 **RENZO (IRE)**, 11, b g Alzao (USA)—Watership (USA) **Cleartherm Ltd**
10 **SERAPH**, 4, ch g Vettori (IRE)—Dahlawise (IRE) **Mr M. F. Schofield**
11 **SHARP BELLINE (IRE)**, 7, b g Robellino (USA)—Moon Watch **Townville C. C. Racing Club**
12 **SHEER GUTS (IRE)**, 5, b g Hamas (IRE)—Balakera (FR) **Cleartherm Ltd**
13 **SOPHOMORE**, 10, b g Sanglamore—Livry (USA) **Mr D. Wilcox**
14 **THEME PARK**, 4, b g Classic Cliche (IRE)—Arcady **Mr J. H. Henderson**
15 **VINCENT**, 9, b g Anshan—Top-Anna (IRE) **Mrs A. E. Harris**
16 **ZIGALI**, 5, b g Zilzal (USA)—Alilisa (USA) **Ms Annie Glanfield**

THREE-YEAR-OLDS

17 **BROTHER CADFAEL**, ch g So Factual (USA)—High Habit **Mrs R. Morley**
18 **INDRANI**, b f Bijou d'Inde—Tea And Scandals (USA) **Mr Paddy Barrett**
19 **SES SELINE**, b f Salse (USA)—Absentee **J. H. Henderson**

TWO-YEAR-OLDS

20 B f 5/4 Diktat—Tahilla **Mr P. Barrett**

Other Owners: Mr M. Crosbie, Mr Len Green, Mr D. Jackson, Miss Janine L. Mann.

Assistant Trainer: Miss Vicki M Harris, Mrs A E Harris

Jockeys (Flat): Dean McKeown (w.a.), Seb Sanders (w.a.). **Jockey (NH):** Paul Flynn.

259 MR PETER W. HARRIS, Berkhamsted
Postal: **Sallow Copse, Ringshall, Berkhamsted, Hertfordshire, HP4 1LZ.**
Contact: **OFFICE/FAX** (01442) 851134/851063 **HOUSE/FAX** (01442) 842480/842521

1 **ALBAVILLA**, 4, b f Spectrum (IRE)—Lydia Maria
2 **BALTIC BLAZER (IRE)**, 4, b g Polish Precedent (USA)—Pine Needle
3 **BAROLO**, 5, b g Danehill (USA)—Lydia Maria
4 **BEST BE GOING (IRE)**, 4, b g Danehill (USA)—Bye Bold Aileen (IRE)
5 **BLUE MARINER**, 4, b c Marju (IRE)—Mazarine Blue
6 **CAMZO (USA)**, 6, ch g Diesis—Cary Grove (USA)
7 **FLIGHT OF ESTEEM**, 4, b g Mark of Esteem (IRE)—Miss Up N Go
8 **GAELIC ROULETTE (IRE)**, 4, b f Turtle Island (IRE)—Money Spinner (USA)
9 **GLIMMER OF LIGHT (IRE)**, 4, b g Marju (IRE)—Church Light
10 **GROOMS AFFECTION**, 4, b c Groom Dancer (USA)—Love And Affection (USA)
11 **KERNEL DOWERY (IRE)**, 4, b g Sri Pekan (USA)—Lady Dowery (USA)
12 **LEPORELLO (IRE)**, 4, b c Danehill (USA)—Why So Silent
13 **MONTECASSINO ABBEY (IRE)**, 5, b g Danehill (USA)—Battle Mountain (IRE)
14 **NORTHSIDE LODGE (IRE)**, 6, b g Grand Lodge (USA)—Alongside
15 **PALAMEDES**, 5, b g Sadler's Wells (USA)—Kristal Bridge
16 **PERSIAN MAJESTY (IRE)**, 4, b c Grand Lodge (USA)—Spa
17 **POLISH EMPEROR (USA)**, 4, ch g Polish Precedent (USA)—Empress Jackie (USA)
18 **RESPLENDENT CEE (IRE)**, 5, ch h Polar Falcon (USA)—Western Friend (USA)
19 **REZZAGO (USA)**, 4, b c Night Shift (USA)—Western Friend (USA)
20 **RING OF DESTINY**, 5, b g Magic Ring (IRE)—Canna
21 **SABALARA (IRE)**, 4, b f Mujadil (USA)—Sabaniya (FR)
22 **SERBELLONI**, 4, b g Spectrum (IRE)—Rose Vibert
23 **SHOT TO FAME (USA)**, 5, b g Quest For Fame—Exocet (USA)
24 **SKY QUEST (IRE)**, 4, b g Spectrum (IRE)—Rose Vibert
25 **STAR SENSATION**, 4, b br f Sri Pekan (USA)—Dancing Sensation (USA)
26 **SUPREME HONOUR**, 4, b g Highest Honor (FR)—Killgham (IRE)

THREE-YEAR-OLDS

27 **ALEKHINE (IRE)**, b g Soviet Star (USA)—Alriyaah
28 **ALINDA (IRE)**, b f Revoque (IRE)—Gratclo
29 **ALPINE REEL (IRE)**, b c Danehill Dancer (IRE)—Alpine Flair (IRE)
30 **ANNA PALLIDA**, b f Sadler's Wells (USA)—Masskana (IRE)
31 **BARANOOK (IRE)**, b c Barathea (IRE)—Gull Nook
32 **BARATHEA BLUE**, ch c Barathea (IRE)—Empty Purse
33 **CANNI THINKAAR (IRE)**, b g Alhaarth (IRE)—Cannikin (IRE)
34 **CAPTAIN MARRYAT**, ch g Inchinor—Finlaggan
35 **CAZISA STAR (USA)**, ch f Mister Baileys—Placer Queen
36 **CHARNWOOD PRIDE (IRE)**, gr g Charnwood Forest (IRE)—Pride of Pendle
37 **CHRISTINA'S DREAM**, b f Spectrum (IRE)—Christine Daae
38 **COOL HUNTER**, ch c Polar Falcon (USA)—Seabound
39 **CUTTING CREW (USA)**, ch c Diesis—Poppy Carew (IRE)
40 **DAN DI CANIO (IRE)**, b g Bahri (USA)—Khudud
41 **DANZOLIN**, b f Danzero (AUS)—Howlin' (USA)
42 **GRACIOUS**, b f Grand Lodge (USA)—Clincher Club
43 **HALICARDIA**, br f Halling (USA)—Pericardia
44 **HILLS SPITFIRE (IRE)**, b br c Kahyasi—Questina (FR)
45 **MAGIC MERLIN**, b g Magic Ring (IRE)—St James's Antigua (IRE)
46 **MAJESTIC VISION**, ch g Desert King (IRE)—Triste Oeil (USA)
47 **MASTERMAN READY**, b g Unfuwain (USA)—Maria Isabella (FR)
48 **MIDSHIPMAN EASY (USA)**, ch g Irish River (FR)—Winger
49 **MISS POLARIS**, b f Polar Falcon (USA)—Sarabah (IRE)
50 **MISTER MUJA (IRE)**, gr g Mujadil (USA)—Remiss (IRE)
51 **NORDWIND (IRE)**, b c Acatenango (GER)—Narola (GER)
52 **OASIS STAR (IRE)**, b f Desert King (IRE)—Sound Tap (IRE)
53 **PERSIAN BELLE**, b f Machiavellian (USA)—Nicola Bella (IRE)
54 **ROSINGS**, ch f Grand Lodge (USA)—Hajat
55 **SHERGAEL (IRE)**, b g Barathea (IRE)—Shergress
56 **SILK FAN (IRE)**, b f Unfuwain (USA)—Alikhlas
57 **STORMY NATURE (IRE)**, b br f Mujadil (USA)—Ossana (USA)
58 **SUSIEDIL (IRE)**, b f Mujadil (USA)—Don't Take Me (IRE)
59 **TORLEY GRANGE (IRE)**, b c Grand Lodge (USA)—Eliza Acton
60 **ZILMY (IRE)**, ch g Zilzal (USA)—My Lewicia (IRE)

MR PETER W. HARRIS—continued
TWO-YEAR-OLDS

61 B c 11/3 Piccolo—Abundance (Cadeaux Genereaux) (18000)
62 B f 10/2 Royal Applause—Alarming Motown (Warning) (18000)
63 B c 28/1 Pivotal—Alessia (GER) (Warning) (24737)
64 B c 20/4 Singspiel (IRE)—Auenlust (GER) (Surumu (GER)) (35000)
65 B f 27/3 Danehill (USA)—Breyani (Commanche Run) (111317)
66 B c 25/4 Efisio—Christine Daae (Sadler's Wells (USA))
67 Ch f 22/2 Komaite (USA)—Clara Barton (Youth (USA))
68 B c 12/2 Mind Games—Dane Dancing (IRE) (Danehill (USA)) (15000)
69 EDICT, br f 27/2 Diktat—Pericardia (Petong)
70 B f 18/4 Spectrum (IRE)—Eliza Acton (Shirley Heights)
71 B c 8/6 Mark Of Esteem (IRE)—Fetlar (Pharly (FR)) (30000)
72 Ch c 20/4 Pivotal—Fleur Rouge (Pharly (FR)) (50000)
73 Ch c 23/4 Grand Lodge (USA)—Gold Mist (Darshaan) (68026)
74 HANDEL WITH CARE (IRE), b c 28/4 King Of Kings (IRE)—La Pepite (USA) (Mr Prospector (USA)) (6183)
75 B f 20/2 Desert Story (IRE)—Hope And Glory (USA) (Well Decorated) (21000)
76 B c 1/3 Spectrum (IRE)—Juno Marlowe (IRE) (Danehill (USA))
77 Ch f 23/4 Primo Dominie—Kristal Bridge (Kris)
78 B c 16/4 Primo Dominie—Lydia Maria (Dancing Brave (USA))
79 B f 22/1 Fraam—Magic Moment (Magic Ring (IRE)) (17000)
80 B c 8/5 Danehill Dancer—Mahabba (Elocutionist (USA)) (15460)
81 B c 22/2 Grand Lodge (USA)—March Hare (Groom Dancer (USA)) (86580)
82 B f 25/3 Primo Dominie—Martha Stevens (Super Concorde (USA))
83 B g 10/2 Anabaa (USA)—Maskunah (IRE) (Sadler's Wells (USA)) (70000)
84 B f 1/2 Spectrum (IRE)—Mazarine Blue (Bellypha) (26000)
85 B f 8/5 Fraam—Medina de Rioseco (Puissance) (10000)
86 MISS PROVVIDENCE (IRE), b f 8/5 Grand Lodge (USA)—
                                    My Southern Love (ITY) (Southern Arrow (USA)) (24737)
87 Br c 5/4 Compton Place—Miss Up N Go (Gorytus (USA)) (40000)
88 B f 23/4 Mujadil—My Lewicia (IRE) (Taufan (USA))
89 B c 26/3 Polar Falcon—Once Removed (Distant Relative) (5500)
90 Gr c 29/4 Linamix (FR)—Palavera (FR) (Bikala) (28000)
91 PERSIAN RUBY (IRE), b f 16/3 Grand Lodge (USA)—Spa (Sadler's Wells (USA)) (111317)
92 B f 28/5 Sadler's Wells (USA)—Petroleuse (Habitat) (98948)
93 B c 16/4 Mind Games—Play The Game (Mummy's Game) (10000)
94 B c 20/3 Grand Lodge (USA)—Red Tiara (USA) (Mr Prospector (USA)) (55000)
95 RESPLENDENT NOVA, b c 6/4 Pivotal—Santiburi Girl (Casteddu) (22000)
96 RESPLENDENT PRINCE, ch c 27/4 Primo Dominie—Last Result (Northern Park (USA)) (17000)
97 B f 24/5 Zilzal (USA)—Rose Vibert (Caerleon (USA))
98 Ch f 23/3 Polar Falcon—Sand Grouse (USA) (Arctic Tern (USA)) (42000)
99 B f 7/4 Desert Prince (IRE)—Seasonal Blossom (IRE) (Fairy King (USA)) (18000)
100 B c 21/2 Desert Prince (IRE)—Sheer Spirit (IRE) (Caerleon (USA)) (46000)
101 B c 22/3 Mujadil (USA)—Snap Crackle Pop (IRE) (Statoblast) (24000)
102 Ch c 23/2 Nashwan (USA)—Susi Wong (IRE) (Selkirk (USA)) (11000)
103 SWEET SIOUX, ch f 5/2 Halling (USA)—Mohican Girl (Dancing Brave (USA)) (40000)
104 B f 7/5 Fasliyev (USA)—Thaidah (CAN) (Vice Regent (CAN)) (34013)
105 Ch f 22/4 Grand Lodge (USA)—Why So Silent (Mill Reef (USA))

---

260 MR. M M E. HARRISON, Carlisle
Postal: **Cobble Hall, Aldoth, Silloth, Carlisle, Cumbria, CA7 4NE.**
Contact: **PHONE (016973) 61753 MOBILE (07803) 179023**

1 **JUSTUPYOURSTREET (IRE),** 8, b g Dolphin Street (FR)—Sure Flyer (IRE) **Mr David Alan Harrison**
2 **SOLWAY BREEZE (IRE),** 11, b m King's Ride—Spicey Cut **Mr David Alan Harrison**
3 **SOLWAY GALE (IRE),** 7, b m Husyan (USA)—Some Gale **Mr David Alan Harrison**
4 **SOLWAY LARKIN (IRE),** 6, b m Supreme Leader—In Any Case (IRE) **Mr David Alan Harrison**
5 **SOLWAY MINSTREL,** 7, ch g Jumbo Hirt (USA)—Spicey Cut **Mr David Alan Harrison**
6 **SOLWAY RAIDER,** 6, ch g Jumbo Hirt (USA)—Lady Mag **Mr David Alan Harrison**
7 **SOLWAY ROSE,** 10, ch m Minster Son—Lady Mag **Mr David Alan Harrison**

Assistant Trainer: W Harrison

Taking Your Horse To Water...

If you've ever had a dream of owning a racehorse but thought you'd never be able to afford it - think again.

We can make it reality for you.

Unlike other anonymous clubs and syndicates, Peter Harris Racing Stables' partnership scheme and easy payment terms has made it possible for racing enthusiasts to live their dream.

When you join a partnership, you join eleven like minded individuals in your chosen horse, each of you recognised as an owner. And as an owner you also get

to name your thoroughbred, choose your racing colours and are welcome to visit your horse anytime you like.

To gain entry to this racing paradise you don't need to invest any capital - a simple monthly payment is all it takes (which you can even pay by credit card).

It covers all costs, horse purchase, training, farrier, jockey, vet and race entry fees, plus ALL other expenses. There are no hidden extras.

THE JOY OF OWNERSHIP!
WITH

Call 01442 851328
or email enquiries@
peterharrisracing.co.uk

261   MRS G. HARVEY, Kingston Lisle
Postal: **Blowing Stone Stables, Kingston Lisle, Wantage, Oxfordshire, OX12 9QL.**
Contact: **PHONE (01367) 820215 MOBILE (07780) 951634**

1 **FELIX DARBY (IRE)**, 9, b g Buckskin (FR)—Cool Anne **Ms Pat Treacy**
2 4, B g Norwich—Gleann Oisin (IRE) **Mr A. Scrimgeor & Mr R. Kanter**
3 **JAKE THE JUMPER (IRE)**, 7, b g Jolly Jake (NZ)—Princess Tino (IRE) **Mrs Rosalinde Elsbury**
4 **LADY BLAZE**, 5, ch m Afflora (IRE)—Lady Elle (IRE) **Ms Pat Treacy**
5 **MILL EMERALD**, 7, b m Old Vic—Milinetta **The Mill Emerald Partnership**
6 **MR MUSIC MAN (IRE)**, 11, b g Accordion—A New Rose (IRE) **Brig C. K. Price**
7 **NOMADIC ICE**, 7, b g Nomadic Way (USA)—Icelolly **Blowing Stone Quartet**
8 **REDWOOD GROVE (USA)**, 8, b g Woodman (USA)—Ikebana (IRE) **Mr B. Mathieson**
9 **ROY MCAVOY (IRE)**, 6, b g Danehill (USA)—Decadence **Mr M. Maplesden**
10 **SEGSBURY BELLE**, 9, b m Petoski—Rolling Dice **Mr R. A. Instone**
11 **THE BAR MAID**, 6, b m Alderbrook—Corny Story **Brig C. K. Price**

THREE-YEAR-OLDS

12 **THE FOOTBALLRESULT**, b f The West (USA)—Bunny Gee **Mr M. Maplesden & Mr R. Digance**

Other Owners: Mr I. Bone, Mr Barry J. McClean.

262   MR PATRICK HASLAM, Middleham
Postal: **Manor House Stables, Middleham, Leyburn, North Yorkshire, DL8 4QL.**
Contact: **PHONE (01969) 624351 FAX (01969) 624463**
E-MAIL **haslamracing@rapidial.co.uk WEBSITE www.patrickhaslamracing.com**

1 **BLUE VENTURE (IRE)**, 4, ch g Alhaarth (IRE)—September Tide (IRE) **Blue Lion Racing 1**
2 **BUSTLING RIO (IRE)**, 8, b g Up And At 'em—Une Venitienne (FR) **Rio Stainless Engineering Limited**
3 **CALL ME SUNSHINE**, 4, b f Robellino (USA)—Kirana **Mr P. C. Haslam**
4 **CHINA CASTLE**, 11, b g Sayf El Arab (USA)—Honey Plum **Middleham Park Racing I & Others**
5 **FIORI**, 8, b g Anshan—Fen Princess (IRE) **Wilson Imports I**
6 **KING REVO (IRE)**, 4, b g Revoque (IRE)—Tycoon Aly (IRE) **Dick Renwick & Mrs C. Barclay**
7 **LOOKING DOWN**, 4, ch f Compton Place—High Stepping **Mr S. A. B. Dinsmore**
8 **MAUNBY ROCKER**, 4, ch g Sheikh Albadou—Bullion **Mr P. A. Hill-Walker & Mrs C. Barclay**
9 **MIDDLEHAM PARK (IRE)**, 4, b g Revoque (IRE)—
                                                     Snap Crackle Pop (IRE) **Middleham Park Racing VIII & J.McCarthy**
10 **MR MISCHIEF**, 4, b g Millkom—Snow Huntress **Middleham Park Racing**
11 **POSITIVE PROFILE (IRE)**, 6, b g Definite Article—Leyete Gulf (IRE) **Chelgate Public Relations Ltd**
12 **RED FLYER (IRE)**, 5, br g Catrail (USA)—Marostica (ITY) **Mrs C. Barclay**
13 **ROSTI**, 4, b g Whittingham (IRE)—Uae Flame (IRE) **Exors of Late B.M Hawkins/Lord Downshire**
14 **YOU'RE SPECIAL (USA)**, 7, b g Northern Flagship (USA)—Pillow Mint (USA) **Mr Les Buckley**

THREE-YEAR-OLDS

15 **ABROGATE (IRE)**, b g Revoque (IRE)—Czarina's Sister **Mr R. Millican**
16 **ALPINE SPECIAL (IRE)**, gr g Orpen (USA)—Halomix **Mr Les Buckley**
17 **BLUE EMPIRE (IRE)**, b g Second Empire (IRE)—Paleria (USA) **Blue Lion Racing II**
18 **CEASAR (IRE)**, b g Orpen (USA)—Fen Princess (IRE) **Wilson Imports**
19 **COURANT D'AIR (IRE)**, b g Indian Rocket—Red River Rose (IRE) **Mr M. Buckley**
20 **DALIDA**, ch f Pursuit of Love—Debutante Days **Exors of the Late Mrs B. M. Hawkins**
21 **DAME NOVA (IRE)**, b f Definite Article—Red Note **Blue Lion Racing II**
22 **DIFFERENTGEAR**, b g Robellino (USA)—Garconniere **Vyas Ltd**
23 **DRUID**, b g Magic Ring (IRE)—Country Spirit **Exors of the Late Mrs B. M. Hawkins**
24 **KINNAIRD (IRE)**, ch f Dr Devious (IRE)—Ribot's Guest (IRE) **Mrs R. I. Jacobs**
25 **MAJOR PROJECT (IRE)**, ch g General Monash (USA)—Mini Project (IRE) **Mrs S. V. Milner**
26 **MAUNBY RAVER**, ch g Pivotal—Colleen Liath **Maunby Investment Management**
27 **MIDDLEHAM ROSE**, b f Dr Fong (USA)—Shallop **Middleham Park Racing III**
28 **NOCATEE (IRE)**, b g Vettori (IRE)—Rosy Sunset (IRE) **Middleham Park Racing**
29 **RESTART (IRE)**, b g Revoque (IRE)—Stargard **Mr J. Roundtree**
30 **RUN DOCTOR RUN (IRE)**, ch g Dr Devious (IRE)—True Freedom (IRE) **Mr J. Millican**
31 **SOLEIL D'HIVER**, b f Bahamian Bounty—Catriona **Mr P. C. Haslam**
32 **TURKS AND CAICOS (IRE)**, b br g Turtle Island (IRE)—Need You Badly **Middleham Park Racing**
33 **TWO OF CLUBS**, b g First Trump—Sulaka **Blue Lion Racing II**
34 **YANKEEDOODLEDANDY (IRE)**, b g Orpen (USA)—Laura Margaret **Mr. K. Tyre**

MR PATRICK HASLAM—continued

TWO-YEAR-OLDS

35 **AIRE DE MOUGINS (IRE)**, b c 15/3 Pennekamp (USA)—
  Colouring (IRE) (Catrail (USA)) (26000) **Mr S. A. B. Dinsmore**
36 B f 28/4 Groom Dancer (USA)—Bird of Time (IRE) (Persian Bold) (12000) **Kary-On Racing Partnership**
37 **BLUSHING RUSSIAN (IRE)**, b c 8/3 Fasliyev (USA)—Ange Rouge (Priolo) (6801) **Blue Lion Racing III**
38 **CHICAGO NIGHTS (IRE)**, ch f 11/2 Night Shift (USA)—
  Enclave (USA) (Woodman (USA)) (10000) **Mr Michael Cook**
39 **DANE'S ROCK (IRE)**, b c 24/3 Indian Danehill (IRE)—
  Cutting Ground (IRE) (Common Grounds) (6801) **Blue Lion Racing III**
40 **DENNICK**, b c 16/2 Nicolotte—Branston Dancer (Rudimentary (USA)) (10000) **Mr D. Browne**
41 **DRAMATIC REVIEW (IRE)**, b c 22/2 Indian Lodge (IRE)—
  Dramatic Shift (IRE) (Night Shift (USA)) (10000) **Blue Lion Racing III**
42 **FRANSISCAN**, ch c 17/2 Fraam—Ordained (Mtoto) (6000) **Northern Lights Racing**
43 **GOOD INVESTMENT**, b c 5/3 Silver Patriarch—Bundled Up (Sharpen Up) (12500) **Blue Lion Racing III**
44 **HIGHBURY LASS**, ch f 18/3 Entrepreneur—Princess Victoria (Deploy) (6801) **Mr A. Peachey**
45 **HOPELESSLY DEVOTED**, b f 14/4 Compton Place—Alpi Dora (Valiyar) **Mr R. Pocock**
46 **IMPASSE CARRAIRE**, ch f 14/4 Piccolo—Magical Dancer (IRE) (Magical Wonder (USA)) **Mr S. A. B. Dinsmore**
47 **INDIBRAUN (IRE)**, b c 9/4 Indian Rocket—The Aspecto Girl (IRE) (Alzao (USA)) (10500) **Mr D. Browne**
48 B c 10/3 Imperial Ballet—L'Harmonie (USA) (Bering) (9894) **Rio Stainless Engineering Ltd**
49 **LIGHTNING PROSPECT**, ch f 31/3 Zaha (CAN)—Lightning Blaze (Cosmonaut) (12000) **Middleham Park Racing**
50 **MAUNBY REVELLER**, b c 6/3 Benny The Dip (USA)—
  Aunt Tate (Tate Gallery (USA)) (16000) **Maunby Investment Management**
51 Ch f 23/4 Grand Lodge (USA)—Merci (IRE) (Cadeaux Genereux) (12368) **Blue Lion Racing IV**
52 B c 18/1 Dansili—Million Heiress (Auction Ring (USA)) (4500) **Mr P. C. Haslam**
53 **MIST OPPORTUNITY (IRE)**, b c 11/4 Danetime (IRE)—
  Lady of The Mist (IRE) (Digamist (USA)) (15000) **Blue Lion Racing III**
54 B c 23/3 Spectrum (IRE)—Newala (Royal Academy (USA)) (11000) **Blue Lion Racing IV**
55 **NORTHERNSAIL (IRE)**, b c 14/3 Indian Lodge (IRE)—
  Folk Riviera (IRE) (Shareef Dancer (USA)) (9000) **Mr D. Browne**
56 **NOVA TOR (IRE)**, b f 24/4 Trans Island—Nordic Living (IRE) (Nordico (USA)) (3091) **Blue Lion Racing III**
57 B c 9/2 Forzando—Rockin' Rosie (Song) (10500) **Blue Lion Racing IV**
58 B c 26/4 Loup Sauvage (USA)—Secret Waters (Pharly (FR)) (22000) **Blue Lion Racing IV**
59 **SINNBARA**, b f 25/3 Sinndar (IRE)—Souk (IRE) (Ahonoora) (12000) **Mrs C. Barclay**
60 B f 17/3 Revoque (IRE)—Stargard (Polish Precedent (USA)) (6183) **Mr P. C. Haslam**
61 **STRATHTAY**, ch f 23/3 Pivotal—Cressida (Polish Precedent (USA)) (20000) **Mr S. A. B. Dinsmore**
62 **TIFFIN BROWN**, br c 1/3 Erhaab (USA)—Cockatrice (Petong) (31000) **Lord Clyde Racing**
63 **TIFFIN DEANO (IRE)**, b c 28/2 Mujadil (USA)—Xania (Mujtahid (USA)) (10000) **Lord Clyde Racing**
64 B c 27/3 Soviet Star (USA)—To The Skies (Sky Classic (CAN)) (11500) **Mr P. C. Haslam**
65 **VOCATIVE (GER)**, gr f 25/1 Acatenango (GER)—Vadinaxa (FR) (Linamix (FR)) (19000) **Mr S. A. B. Dinsmore**

Other Owners: Mr G. Chapman, Mr J. Corbally, Mr G. Craig, Mr A. Dixon (Leyburn), Mr A. Gleadall, Mrs M. Haslam, Sir George Meyrick, Mr T. S. Palin, Mr I. Wilson, Mr R. Young.

Apprentices: L Enstone (8-3), Rory Moore (7-9), D Wakenshaw (8-3). **Conditional:** T Burton-Pye (9-7). **Amateurs:** Mr Ben Haslam, Ms C Williams.

---

263 **MR N. J. HAWKE, Woolminstone**
Postal: Blackmore Farm, Woolminstone, Crewkerne, Somerset, TA18 8QP.
Contact: PHONE (01460) 271124 MOBILE (07899) 922827

1 **DOUBLE TEE (IRE)**, 8, br g Jurado (USA)—Monkeylane **Mr N. J. Hawke**
2 **HONNEUR FONTENAIL (FR)**, 5, ch g Tel Quel (FR)—Fontanalia (FR) **Wags To Riches Partnership**
3 **INVESTOR RELATIONS (IRE)**, 6, b g Goldmark (USA)—Debach Delight **N. J. McMullan and N. R. Packer**
4 **JENAVIVE**, 4, b f Danzig Connection (USA)—Promise Fulfilled (USA) **Mr Trevor Heayns**
5 **KIM FONTENAIL (FR)**, 4, b f Kaldounevees (FR)—Fontanalia (FR) **Mr Bryan Fry**
6 **LAW UNTO HIMSELF**, 6, b g Contract Law (USA)—Malacanang **The Fairway Boys**
7 **PHAZAR**, 4, b g Zamindar (USA)—Ypha (USA) **Set To Stun Partnership**
8 **PRESIDIO (GER)**, 9, b g Konigsstuhl (GER)—Pradera (GER) **The Fairway Boys**
9 **REVERSO (FR)**, 4, b g Kaldounevees (FR)—Sweet Racine (FR) **R. J. & Mrs J. A. Peake**
10 **SILKEN THOMAS**, 9, b g King's Ride—Padykin **Mr N. J. Hawke**
11 **TUTTONS**, 6, ch m Whittingham (IRE)—Avonmouthsecretary **Mrs Jackie Tutton**

MR N. J. HAWKE—continued

12 **WHOSE LINE IS IT**, 6, gr g Sharp Deal—Madame Ruby (FR) **Mrs D. A. Wetherall**
13 **ZIMBABWE (FR)**, 4, b g Turgeon (USA)—Razzamatazz (FR) **R. J. & Mrs J. A. Peake**

Other Owners: Mr R. Clifton, Mr S. M. Lambert, Mr Michael Lawrence, Mr V. B. Lewer, Mr D. A. Little, Mr N. J. McMullan, Mr Keith Myall, Mr N. R. Packer, Mrs J. A. Peake, Mr Russell J. Peake, Mr K. Scutt.

Assistant Trainer: Mrs S Hawke

Amateur: Miss T Newman.

264
MR JOHN C HAYDEN, Kildare
Postal: **Castlemartin Abbey House Stables, Kilcullen, Co. Kildare, Ireland.**
Contact: **PHONE** +353 (0) 45 481598 **FAX** +353 (0) 045 481598 **MOBILE** +353 (0) 86 8226717
E-MAIL hayden-jj@yahoo.com **WEBSITE** jchayden.com

1 **ALONE HE STANDS (IRE)**, 4, b g Flying Spur (AUS)—Millennium Tale (FR)
2 **MORNING (IRE)**, 5, gr m Ali-Royal (IRE)—Island Goddess
3 **QUAKER GIRL (IRE)**, 5, b m Mujadil (USA)—Roundstone Dancer (IRE)
4 **SONG OF SIXPENCE (IRE)**, 4, ch f Among Men (USA)—Golden Leap
5 **VALENTINE'S PET**, 4, b f My Best Valentine—Fabulous Pet

THREE-YEAR-OLDS

6 B g Desert Style (IRE)—Millennium Tale (FR)
7 **NOK TWICE (IRE)**, b c Second Empire (IRE)—Bent Al Fala (IRE)

TWO-YEAR-OLDS

8 Ch f 3/4 Almutawakel—Ilia (USA) (Shadeed (USA)) (16000)
9 Ch f 20/4 Lahib (USA)—Island Goddess (Godswalk (USA)) (2473)
10 Ch f 14/4 Night Shift (USA)—Eleanor Antoinette (IRE) (Double Schwartz) (18552)
11 B f 28/3 Lahib (USA)—Roundstone Dancer (IRE) (Dancing Dissident (USA))
12 **SIGHTSEER (USA)**, b f 21/2 Distant View—Lady of Vision (Vision (USA))

Other Owners: Castlemartin Racing Club, Mr P. Crimin, Mr J. Hardiman, Mrs Ann P. Hayden, Mr S. Hayden, Mr J. Keeling, Mr S. Kistler, Mr E. McAllister, Mr P. McCutcheon, Sir A. J. O'Reilly, Lady O'Reilly, Mr F. O'Toole, Mr S. Ridgeway.

Assistant Trainer: J. J. Hayden.

Jockeys (Flat): M J Kinane (w.a.), J P Murtagh (w.a.). **Jockey (NH):** D Casey (w.a.). **Amateur:** Mr Mark Hayden.

265
MR D. HAYDN JONES, Pontypridd
Postal: **Garth Paddocks, Efail Isaf, Pontypridd, Mid-Glamorgan, CF38 1SN.**
Contact: **PHONE** (01443) 202515 **FAX** (01443) 201877 **MOBILE** (07967) 680012

1 **ASHTREE BELLE**, 5, b m Up And At 'em—Paris Babe **Mason Gill Racing**
2 **BONNY RUAN**, 5, b m So Factual (USA)—Sans Diablo (IRE) **Mr Mick White**
3 **CONSIGNIA (IRE)**, 5, ch m Definite Article—Coppelia (IRE) **Mr I. Jerrard**
4 **CRIMSON SILK**, 4, ch g Forzando—Sylhall **Mick White Partnership**
5 **FOREVER LOVED**, 5, ch m Deploy—Truly Madly Deeply **The Preseli Partnership**
6 **HEATHERS GIRL**, 5, ch m Superlative—Kristis Girl **Trio Racing**
7 **HOW'S THINGS**, 4, b g Danzig Connection (USA)—Dim Ots **Mrs D. J. Hughes**
8 **LADY NATILDA**, 4, ch f First Trump—Ramajana (USA) **Mr L. M. Baker**
9 **MONTE MAYOR LAD (IRE)**, 4, b g Sesaro (USA)—Alcalali (USA) **Mrs E. M. Haydn Jones**

THREE-YEAR-OLDS

10 **BROWN DRAGON**, ch g Primo Dominie—Cole Slaw **Jack Brown (Bookmaker) Ltd**
11 **CHICKADO (IRE)**, b f Mujadil (USA)—Arcevia (IRE) **Monolithic Refractories Ltd**
12 **COMIC GENIUS**, b f Comic Strip (USA)—Itsy Bitsy Betsy (USA) **Mr J. Runeckles**
13 **CORNISH BELLE**, b f Slip Anchor—Sans Diablo (IRE) **L. Lockwood, S. Marsh, M. Burne**
14 **ERMINE GREY**, gr g Wolfhound (USA)—Impulsive Decision (IRE) **Mr L. M. Baker**
15 **KELTIC MAIDEN (IRE)**, b f Spectrum (IRE)—Secrets of Honour **Miss Gillian Byrne**
16 **LOVE IS ALL (IRE)**, b f Second Empire (IRE)—Sellette (IRE) **The Lamorran Partnership**
17 **PETITE COLLEEN (IRE)**, b f Desert Sun—Nishiki (USA) **Mr D. M. Richards**

MR D. HAYDN JONES—continued

18 **QUEENS FANTASY**, ch f Grand Lodge (USA)—Alcalali (USA) **Mr Mick White**
19 **SABLE 'N SILK**, b f Prince Sabo—Sibilant **Mrs M. L. Parry**
20 **UNITED UNION (IRE)**, b br g Imperial Ballet (IRE)—Madagascar **Monolithic Refractories Ltd**

TWO-YEAR-OLDS

21 **ALVARINHO LADY**, b f 8/3 Royal Applause—Jugendliebe (IRE) (Persian Bold) (13000) **Mr Mick White**
22 **CASTEROSSA**, ch f 11/2 Rossini (USA)—First Musical (First Trump) (52000) **Mr D. P. Barrie & Mr M. J. Rees**
23 **IS THAT RIGHT**, b f 20/3 Josr Algarhoud (IRE)—Dim Ots (Alhijaz) (4500) **Mrs D. J. Hughes**
24 Ch f 11/4 Daggers Drawn (USA)—
          Leitrim Lodge (IRE) (Classic Music (USA)) (15000) **Boniface, Llewellyn & Runeckles**
25 **LISTEN TO ME**, gr g 3/2 Petong—Time Clash (Timeless Times (USA)) (5200) **Mrs D. J. Hughes**
26 Ch f 20/4 Daggers Drawn (USA)—Missed Opportunity (IRE) (Exhibitioner) (4638) **Mr L. M. Baker**
27 B g 6/4 First Trump—Risalah (Marju (IRE))
28 **SOLO LADY (IRE)**, br f 3/4 Namid—Casaveha (IRE) (Persian Bold) (12000) **P. A. Mason**
29 B f 10/4 Soviet Star (USA)—Victoria Regia (IRE) (Lomond (USA)) (26000) **Monolithic Refractories Ltd**

Other Owners: Mr A. J. Biggs, Mr R. T. Drage, Mr J. R. Gill, Mr R. W. Hacker, Mr D. Llewelyn, Mrs C. A. R. Mason, Mrs M. Mason, Mr R. E. Mason, Mrs Judy Mihalop, Dr P. B. Mihalop, Mrs Deirdre Mobbs, Mr Edgar Mobbs, Mr. P. Steele-Mortimer.

Assistant Trainer: Mrs E M Haydn-Jones

Jockey (Flat): Paul Eddery.

266
MR H. E. HAYNES, Highworth
Postal: **Red Down Farm, Highworth, Wiltshire, SN6 7SH.**
Contact: **PHONE (01793) 762437 FAX (01793) 762437**

1 **BROWN HOLLY**, 6, br g So Factual (USA)—Scarlett Holly **Miss Sally R. Haynes**
2 **CHOISTY (IRE)**, 14, ch g Callernish—Rosemount Rose **Mr H. Edward Haynes**
3 **FREDERICK JAMES**, 10, b g Efisio—Rare Roberta (USA) **Miss Sally R Haynes**
4 **IRISH CHAPEL (IRE)**, 8, b g College Chapel—Heart of Flame **Miss Sally R. Haynes**
5 **MR JAKE**, 11, b g Safawan—Miss Tealeaf (USA) **Mrs H. E. Haynes**
6 **RICKHAM GLORY**, 6, b g Past Glories—Rickham Bay **Miss Alison Joy**
7 **SINGLE TRIGGER (IRE)**, 6, ch m Ela-Mana-Mou—Tycoon Aly (IRE) **Miss Sally R. Haynes**
8 **SOMETHING SPECIAL**, 6, b g Petong—My Dear Watson **Miss Sally R. Haynes**
9 **WORTH A GAMBLE**, 6, ch g So Factual (USA)—The Strid (IRE) **Miss Sally R. Haynes**

Other Owners: Mr J. Curtis, Reddwon High Explosive Partnership, Mr G. Hunt, Mr T. Hunt, Mr R. H. Trotman.

Assistant Trainer: Sally R Haynes

Jockeys (Flat): D Allan, M Savage, R Winston. **Amateur:** Miss Fiona Haynes (9-5).

267
MR J. C. HAYNES, Brampton
Postal: **Cleugh Head, Low Row, Brampton, Cumbria, CA8 2JB.**
Contact: **PHONE (01697) 746253 MOBILE (07771) 511471 (08451) 249715**

1 **FIFTEEN REDS**, 9, b g Jumbo Hirt (USA)—Dominance **Mr J. C. Haynes**
2 **FLASHY FILLY**, 4, b f Puissance—Tempted (IRE) **Mr J. C. Haynes**
3 **MOONLIGHT GOLD**, 8, b g Jupiter Island—Moonlight Bay **Mr J. C. Haynes**
4 **NORTHERN FLASH**, 10, b g Rambo Dancer (CAN)—Spinster **Mr J. C. Haynes**

TWO-YEAR-OLDS

5 B f 15/5 Polar Prince (IRE)—Tempted (IRE) (Invited (USA)) **Mr J. C. Haynes**

Jockey (NH): C McCormack.

268 MR M. J. HAYNES, Epsom
Postal: **21 Chantry Hurst, Epsom, Surrey, KT18 7BW.**
Contact: HOME (013727) 22664 STABLES (01737) 351140

1 **EL HAMRA (IRE)**, 6, gr g Royal Abjar (USA)—Cherlinoa (FR) **Porthilly Partners**
2 **LADY FRANPALM (IRE)**, 4, b f Danehill Dancer (IRE)—Be Nimble **Frank Palmer and Friends**
3 **LADY JEANNIE**, 7, b m Emarati (USA)—Cottonwood **G. R. Sanford & Partners**
4 **MISS CELERITY**, 4, b f Compton Place—Film Buff **Mr David M. Butler**

THREE-YEAR-OLDS

5 **EUNICE CHOICE**, b g College Chapel—Aquiletta **Mr F. Palmer**
6 **FOX HOLLOW (IRE)**, b c Foxhound (USA)—Soignee **Chantry Partnership**
7 **THANK MICHAEL**, ch g In Command (IRE)—Hat Hill **Mr F. Palmer**

Other Owners: Mr M. A. Evans, Mr J. Kitson, Mr W. E. Moore, Mr D. C. G. Ollis, Mr Bob Pettis, Mr G. R. Sanford, Mr P. J. Wiggins.

Assistant Trainer: Miss Y Haynes

Amateur: Miss Y Haynes (9-7).

269 MRS C. HEAD, Chantilly
Postal: **32 Avenue du General Leclerc, 60500 Chantilly, France.**
Contact: PHONE +33 (0) 3 44 57 01 01 FAX +33 (0) 3 44 58 53 33 MOBILE +33 (0) 6 07 31 05 05
E-MAIL christiane.head@wanadoo.fr

1 **FLYING HOST (USA)**, 4, b c Silver Hawk (USA)—Fabulous Hostess (USA) **Wertheimer et Frere**
2 **MAGNESIUM (USA)**, 4, b c Kris S (USA)—Proflore (USA) **Prince Khalid Abdulla**
3 **MORNING ECLIPSE**, 4, b c Zafonic (USA)—Hunt The Sun **Prince Khalid Abdulla**
4 **MURMURER (JPN)**, 4, b c Sunday Silence (USA)—Pas de Reponse (USA) **Wertheimer et Frere**
5 **SALYDORA (FR)**, 4, b f Peintre Celebre (USA)—Silwana (FR) **Wertheimer et Frere**
6 **SILVER RAIN (FR)**, 4, b f Rainbow Quest (USA)—Riviere d'Argent (USA) **Wertheimer et Frere**
7 **THE LAST SOLDIER (USA)**, 4, b c Nureyev (USA)—Fresa (USA) **Mrs Cyril Morange**
8 **TORNO (IRE)**, 4, b c Darshaan—Lambada (USA) **Gilles Maarek**
9 **TOUT SEUL (USA)**, 4, b c Gone West (USA)—Only Seule (USA) **Wertheimer et Frere**
10 **UNDERWATER (USA)**, 4, b f Theatrical—Sea Hill (USA) **Wertheimer et Frere**

THREE-YEAR-OLDS

11 **AMERICAN POST**, b c Bering—Wells Fargo **Prince Khalid Abdulla**
12 **ANYWHO**, b c Barathea (IRE)—Anysheba (USA) **Wertheimer et Frere**
13 **ATTICUS BOY (USA)**, ch c Atticus (USA)—Ring Beaune (USA) **Wertheimer et Frere**
14 **BOBOMAN (USA)**, b c Kingmambo (USA)—Slewvera (USA) **Wertheimer et Frere**
15 **BOLDINI (USA)**, ch c Atticus (USA)—Bold Bold **Wertheimer et Frere**
16 **BOUTIQUE**, b f Selkirk (USA)—Bolas **Prince Khalid Abdulla**
17 **BRILLIANTE**, b f Sillery (USA)—Riviere d'Argent (USA) **Wertheimer et Frere**
18 **BUBBLING RING (FR)**, ch c Bering—Arazina **Wertheimer et Frere**
19 **CLASS KING**, b c Royal Academy (USA)—Krissante (USA) **Wertheimer et Frere**
20 **COLONY BAND (USA)**, b f Dixieland Band (USA)—Hostessante (USA) **Wertheimer et Frere**
21 **DANCING STARLIGHT (USA)**, b c Atticus (USA)—Night And Dreams (USA) **Gainsborough Stud**
22 **DAZZLING MOMENT (USA)**, b f Southern Halo (USA)—Capricorn Moon (USA) **Gainsborough Stud**
23 **DELIGHTFUL LADY (USA)**, b f Cozzene (USA)—Fife **Gainsborough Stud**
24 **DORIC (USA)**, b c Distant View (USA)—Doree (USA) **Prince Khalid Abdulla**
25 **DRISSE (FR)**, b f Octagonal (NZ)—Composition (USA) **Mme Morange**
26 **ESNEH**, b f Sadler's Wells (USA)—Egyptown (FR) **Wertheimer et Frere**
27 **EXIMIUS**, ch f Atticus (USA)—Gorgeous (USA) **Wertheimer et Frere**
28 **FABULOUS SPEED (USA)**, b f Silver Hawk (USA)—Fabulous Hostess (USA) **Wertheimer et Frere**
29 **FOR CRIQUETTE (IRE)**, b f Barathea (IRE)—Winsome **Bates Mewton**
30 **GOGOPOGO (USA)**, b f Dare And Go (USA)—La Groupie (FR) **Wertheimer et Frere**
31 **GREEN ROVER**, gr c Green Desert (USA)—Mabrova **Wertheimer et Frere**
32 **HUE**, ch c Peintre Celebre (USA)—Quandary (USA) **Prince Khalid Abdulla**
33 **I HAD A DREAM**, b f Bering—Dirigeante (FR) **Mme Anne-Marie Springer**
34 **JAZZ DRUMMER (USA)**, b f Dixieland Band (USA)—Kinema (USA) **Prince Khalid Abdulla**
35 **LINDA REGINA (FR)**, gr f Linamix (FR)—Altamira (FR) **G. B. Torrealba**
36 **LIVING ON MY OWN (GER)**, b f Rainbow Quest (USA)—Lea (GER) **Mrs Focke**
37 **LONDRA (IRE)**, b f Sadler's Wells (USA)—Lady Ambassador **Mme Hildegard Focke**

BALLYLINCH STUD

SIRES FOR 2004

SOVIET STAR
by Nureyev ex Veruschka

European Champion with **5 Group 1 wins**.
Proven sire of **5 individual Group 1 winners**.
Sire of Sires and a top broodmare Sire.

KING'S THEATRE
by Sadler's Wells ex Regal Beauty

Champion 3yo & Gr.1 winner at 2 and 3.
A leading European sire of Black Type winners
**Royal Code, (Gr.2 x 2), I Rock My World (Gr.2),
Kings Ironbridge (Gr.3 x 2), Red Rioja (Gr.3 x 2),
King's Drama, (Gr.3)** and Stakes winners
Alinga, Great Pretender, Messager Du Roi
and **Sagarmatha.**

TRADITIONALLY
by Mr. Prospector ex Personal Ensign

Group 1 winner by **Mr. Prospector** out of
Champion **Personal Ensign**. Full-brother to **Our Emblem**.
Excellent first book of mares in 2003.
First crop foals 2004.

*Other services offered: Boarding, Foaling,
Sales Preparation, Breaking, Resident Vet and Laboratory*

BALLYLINCH STUD, Thomastown, County Kilkenny, Ireland.
Tel: 056-7724217 Fax: 056-7724624 E-mail: joc@ballylinchstud.ie
www.ballylinchstud.com

MRS C. HEAD—continued

38 **NIGHT CHAPTER**, b c Night Shift (USA)—Context **Prince Khalid Abdulla**
39 **NOCAUSEFORCONCERN (USA)**, b f Red Ransom (USA)—Barad **Gainsborough Stud**
40 **NO SOUND (FR)**, b f Exit To Nowhere (USA)—Sound Hill (FR) **Wertheimer et Frere**
41 **ONLY ALONE (USA)**, ch f Rahy (USA)—Only Seule (USA) **Wertheimer et Frere**
42 **PAUILLAC (GER)**, b c Machiavellian (USA)—Pelagic **Wertheimer et Frere**
43 **PLECTRUM (USA)**, b c Awesome Again (CAN)—Berceau (USA) **Prince Khalid Abdulla**
44 **POLYFIRST (FR)**, b f Poliglote—First Turn (USA) **Wertheimer et Frere**
45 **PRIMAXIS**, gr c Linamix (FR)—Ring Pink (USA) **Wertheimer et Frere**
46 **QUIET NAME**, b f Danehill (USA)—Quiet Dream (USA) **Wertheimer et Frere**
47 **RED MO**, b c Red Ransom (USA)—Moiava (USA) **Wertheimer et Frere**
48 **RED RUNNER (USA)**, ch c Storm Cat (USA)—Blushing Away (USA) **Wertheimer et Frere**
49 **RED TUNE (FR)**, ch c Green Tune (USA)—Born Gold (USA) **Wertheimer et Frere**
50 **ROCK SALT**, ch f Selkirk (USA)—Kamkova (USA) **Prince Khalid Abdulla**
51 **ROSEANNA (FR)**, b f Anabaa (USA)—Dancing Rose (FR) **Mr P. D. Savill**
52 **SEAMAMBO**, b g Kingmambo (USA)—Sea Hill (USA) **Wertheimer et Frere**
53 **SEAMIX (FR)**, b g Bering—Beautimix (FR) **Wertheimer et Frere**
54 **SOFT PLEASURE (USA)**, b f Diesis—Vintage (CAN) **Wertheimer et Frere**
55 **SOMBRERO**, ch c Trempolino—High Summer (USA) **Prince Khalid Abdulla**
56 **SOUTHERN QUEEN (USA)**, b f Anabaa (USA)—Due South **Gainsborough Stud**
57 **SPACECRAFT (USA)**, b f Distant View (USA)—Willstar (USA) **Prince Khalid Abdulla**
58 **STUPENDOUS MISS (USA)**, b f Dynaformer (USA)—Subeen **Gainsborough Stud**
59 **SUNDAY DOUBT (USA)**, b c Sunday Silence (USA)—Pas de Reponse (USA) **Wertheimer et Frere**
60 **SWANDOR (USA)**, b f Swain (IRE)—Louis d'Or (USA) **Prince Khalid Abdulla**
61 **SWEET GO (USA)**, b f Dare And Go (USA)—Bravalma (USA) **Wertheimer et Frere**
62 **THROUGH ENDEAVOUR (USA)**, b g Gulch (USA)—Amirati (USA) **Gainsborough Stud**
63 **TRESPASS**, b f Entrepreneur—Infringe **Prince Khalid Abdulla**
64 **TRUE TO THE FACT (USA)**, b g Quiet American (USA)—Yousefia (USA) **Gainsborough Stud**
65 **VULNERABLE**, b f Hector Protector (USA)—Beleaguer **Prince Khalid Abdulla**
66 **WAKIRED (USA)**, b f Red Ransom (USA)—Waki Decree (USA) **Wertheimer et Frere**
67 **WESTCOTE (USA)**, b f Gone West (USA)—Kingscote **Prince Khalid Abdulla**
68 **WHITBY (FR)**, ch f Gold Away—Eloura (FR) **Wertheimer et Frere**

TWO-YEAR-OLDS

69 **ANYNAME (IRE)**, b c 6/5 Danehill (USA)—Anysheba (USA) **Wertheimer et Frere**
70 **ARABICA (USA)**, b f 19/5 Red Ransom (USA)—Moiava (FR) **Wertheimer et Frere**
71 **ARTIC SAND (USA)**, ch c 16/5 Dixieland Band (USA)—Hostessante (USA) **Wertheimer et Frere**
72 **ATTIRINA**, ch f 25/3 Atticus (USA)—Ring Beaune (USA) **Wertheimer et Frere**
73 **BABBLING ON (FR)**, b f 18/4 Poliglote—Sky Bibi (FR) (2164) **Wertheimer et Frere**
74 **BOLITHO (FR)**, b c 28/4 Poliglote—Red Vintage (USA) **Wertheimer et Frere**
75 **BORN FRIENDLY (IRE)**, ch c 30/1 Selkirk (USA)—Gold Round (IRE) **Wertheimer et Frere**
76 **CELINDE (FR)**, b f 4/5 Anabaa (USA)—Carelaine (USA) (123685) **Ecurie des Charmes**
77 Ch f 5/5 Stravinsky—Conical **Prince Khalid Abdulla**
78 B f 17/2 Dansili—Dockage (CAN) **Prince Khalid Abdulla**
79 **EIGHTY SIX (FR)**, b f 21/5 Octagonal (NZ)—Sound Hill (FR) **Wertheimer et Frere**
80 **ELLE ET TOI (FR)**, bl f 24/2 Octagonal (NZ)—Toi Et Moi (USA) **Wertheimer et Frere**
81 Br c 28/1 Dansili—Emplane (USA) **Prince Khalid Abdulla**
82 **FIREJACK (USA)**, b c 2/3 Dixieland Band (USA)—Partygoer (USA) **Wertheimer et Frere**
83 **FLAMENBA (USA)**, b f 26/5 Kingmambo (USA)—Sadler's Flag (IRE) **Wertheimer et Frere**
84 **GANAGO (FR)**, ch c 12/4 Kingmambo (USA)—Ganasheba (USA) **Wertheimer et Frere**
85 **GOLDEN PALACE (USA)**, ch c 14/2 Chester House (USA)—Doree (USA) **Prince Khalid Abdulla**
86 **GOLDINA (USA)**, b f 4/5 Rahy (USA)—Natural Gold (USA) **Wertheimer et Frere**
87 B f 22/4 Anabaa (USA)—Gorgeous (USA) **Robert Clay**
88 **HAIRBALL**, b c 21/3 Highest Honor (FR)—Sail Storm (USA) **Wertheimer et Frere**
89 **HAWKSBURY HEIGHTS**, ch c 20/3 Nashwan (USA)—Gentle Dame **Maktoum Al Maktoum**
90 Ch c 26/1 Theatrical—Ixtapa (USA) **Prince Khalid Abdulla**
91 **KERJOUANNO (FR)**, ch c 7/3 Gold Away (IRE)—Star du Rhuis (FR) (21645) **Wertheimer et Frere**
92 **KICKAHEAD (USA)**, b c 22/2 Danzig (USA)—Krissante (USA) **Wertheimer et Frere**
93 **KLAIRONNETTE (FR)**, bl f 6/2 Goldneyev (USA)—Saint Gig (FR) **Wertheimer et Frere**
94 **LE REVEUR (USA)**, ch c 23/4 Machiavellian (USA)—Brooklyn's Dance (FR) **Wertheimer et Frere**
95 B f 6/2 Sadler's Wells (USA)—Monevassia (USA) (197897) **Ecurie des Charmes**
96 **MOUNT PAGET (USA)**, ch f 27/1 Atticus (USA)—Garza **Maktoum Al Maktoum**
97 **MYDARSHAAN**, b f 9/4 Darshaan—Mypreciousprospect (USA) **Wertheimer et Frere**
98 **NANABANANA (IRE)**, b f 8/2 Anabaa (USA)—Tanabata (FR) (58750) **Mr Savill**
99 Ch f 16/2 Giant's Causeway—Net Worth (USA) (310000) **Ecurie des Charmes**
100 **NEW LEGEND (USA)**, ch c 16/3 Rahy (USA)—Regal Star **Maktoum Al Maktoum**

MRS C. HEAD—continued

101 B c 8/3 Stravinsky (USA)—Night Risk (USA) (27829) **Bettina Jenney**
102 **NO DANZIG (USA),** b c 31/3 Danzig (USA)—Juvenia (USA) **Wertheimer et Frere**
103 B c 4/2 Bering—Pan Galactic (USA) **Prince Khalid Abdulla**
104 **PARAMOUNT (FR),** b c 7/2 Octagonal (NZ)—Passionnee (USA) **Wertheimer et Frere**
105 **POLIGLOTTI (FR),** b c 7/3 Poliglote—Loretta Gianni (FR) (55658) **Wertheimer et Frere**
106 **SABLONNE (USA),** b f 30/3 Silver Hawk (USA)—Desert Jewel (USA) **Wertheimer et Frere**
107 **SAPHIRE (USA),** ch f 27/2 Silver Hawk (USA)—Fabulous Hostess (USA) **Wertheimer et Frere**
108 B c 24/3 Anabaa (USA)—Shining Molly (FR) (46382) **Prince Khalid Abdulla**
109 **SILENT NAME (JPN),** b c 1/1 Sunday Silence (USA)—Danzigaway (USA) **Wertheimer et Frere**
110 **SILVER FASHION (IRE),** b f 17/1 Unfuwain (USA)—Silver Fun (FR) **Wertheimer et Frere**
111 **SOUTHERN SUNSET,** b f 25/4 Polish Precedent—Due South **Maktoum Al Maktoum**
112 B f 4/3 King Of Kings (IRE)—Statistic (USA) (29683) **Ecurie des Charmes**
113 **STORM AVERTED (USA),** b c 15/3 Summer Squall (USA)—Averti (USA) **Prince Khalid Abdulla**
114 **STRADIVARI (USA),** b c 6/3 Silver Hawk (USA)—Vibrant **Robin Swily**
115 **STRETCHING (USA),** b f 29/3 Red Ransom (USA)—Broad Pennant (USA) **Wertheimer et Frere**
116 **SWINGSKY (IRE),** b f 3/3 Indian Ridge—Plissetskaia (FR) **Wertheimer et Frere**
117 **TAKENDO,** b c 27/2 Acatenango (GER)—Tiyi (FR) **Wertheimer et Frere**
118 Ch c 19/2 Bering—Thermal Spring **Prince Khalid Abdulla**
119 **TOUT ROUGE (USA),** b c 7/3 Red Ransom (USA)—Ecoute (USA) **Wertheimer et Frere**
120 **TRANSPARENCY (USA),** b f 7/2 Rahy (USA)—Hang The Moon (USA) **Mrs Ann Jones**
121 **VIOLET LANE,** b f 2/3 Danzero (AUS)—Banafsajee (USA) **Maktoum Al Maktoum**
122 Ch f 23/2 Diesis—Willstar (USA) **Prince Khalid Abdulla**
123 B f 5/3 Anabaa (USA)—Xaymara (USA) **Prince Khalid Abdulla**
124 **ZIZARING,** b c 2/5 Bering—Arazina **Wertheimer et Frere**

Assistant Trainer: D Boulard

Jockeys (Flat): N Guesdon, O Peslier, R Thomas. **Amateur:** Miss Isabelle Got.

---

270 MR P. R. HEDGER, Chichester

Postal: **Eastmere Stables, Eastergate Lane, Eastergate, Chichester, West Sussex, PO20 3SJ.**
Contact: PHONE (01243) 543863 FAX 543913 MOBILE (07860) 209448

1 **BUSHIE BILL,** 6, ch g Captain Webster—Mistress Royal **Mr Bill Broomfield**
2 **FORCE TWELVE (IRE),** 6, b g Magical Wonder (USA)—Gale Force Nine **Mrs A. Trigg**
3 **GATHERING STORM (IRE),** 6, gr g Roselier (FR)—Queen of The Rock (IRE) **Mr Howard Spooner**
4 **JACK FULLER (IRE),** 7, b g Be My Native (USA)—Jacks Sister (IRE) **The Brightling Club 1997**
5 **KILDARE CHILLER (IRE),** 10, ch g Shahrastani (USA)—Ballycuirke **Mr P. R. Hedger**
6 **KING DARSHAAN,** 4, b g Darshaan—Urchin (IRE) **Mr J. J. Whelan**
7 **LISSAHANELODGE,** 5, b g Grand Lodge—Lissahane Lass **J. J. Whelan**
8 **MICKLEY (IRE),** 7, b g Ezzoud (IRE)—Dawsha (FR) **Jay Dee Bloodstock**
9 **MISSION TO MARS,** 5, b g Muhtarram (USA)—Ideal Candidate **Mr Ian Hutchins**
10 **OLIVER CROMWELL (IRE),** 9, br g Mandalus—Gemini Gale **Mr Howard Spooner**
11 **PICATRIP,** 4, b f Piccolo—Transylvania **Mr M. McD. Hooker**
12 **RECYCLING RITA,** 5, ch m Karinga Bay—Gaynor Goodman (IRE) **Mr Ian Hutchins**
13 **RODIAK,** 5, b g Distant Relative—Misty Silks **P. Iron Ltd**
14 **ROLLSWOOD (USA),** 4, ch g Diesis—Spit Curl (USA) **Mr Howard Spooner**
15 **STOCKERS PRIDE,** 9, b g Sula Bula—Fille de Soleil **Mr J. D. Sells**
16 **SYSTEM,** 5, ch g Nashwan (USA)—Vivid Imagination **Simon Cross & P. R. Hedger**
17 **TAI LASS,** 4, b br f Taipan (IRE)—Kerry's Oats **Mr J. J. Whelan**
18 **WAIMEA BAY,** 5, b m Karinga Bay—Smart In Sable **Mr M. McD. Hooker**

THREE-YEAR-OLDS

19 **IMTOUCHINGWOOD,** b f Fleetwood (IRE)—Shanuke (IRE) **Mr R. Howitt**

Other Owners: Mrs D. M. Grissell, Mr Christopher Newport, Mr Chris Silverthorne.

Jockey (Flat): S Whitworth. **Jockeys (NH):** L Aspell, M A Fitzgerald (w.a.). **Amateur:** Miss E Kemp (9-0).

271 MR C. J. HEMSLEY, Witney
Postal: **Watermans Lodge Staples, Cornbury Park, Charlbury, Oxon OX7 3HN.**
Contact: **YARD (01608) 810615 HOME/FAX (01993) 844554 MOBILES (07971) 205503**
Assistant Trainer (07974) 660223

1 AEGEAN PIRATE (IRE), 7, b g Polykratis—Rusheen Na Corra (IRE) **Mr Keith McKay**
2 BOBAWAY (IRE), 7, br g Bob Back (USA)—Baybush **Mr Keith McKay**
3 EQUAL BALANCE, 6, ch g Pivotal—Thatcher's Era (IRE) **Mr Andrew King**
4 SHARVIE, 7, b g Rock Hopper—Heresheis **Mrs Sandra Rodney & Mrs Jill Hemsley**
5 SINNERMAN (IRE), 8, gr g Roselier (FR)—Madam Beau **Mr Keith McKay**
6 WINGS OF HOPE (IRE), 8, b g Treasure Hunter—She's Got Wings **Mrs M. L. Sell**

Other Owners: Exors Of The Late Miss P A. Watson.

Assistant Trainer: Mr Keith McKay

Jockeys (NH): B Fenton (w.a.), J Mogford (w.a.), S Stronge (w.a.).

272 MR N. J. HENDERSON, Lambourn
Postal: **Seven Barrows, Lambourn, Hungerford, Berkshire, RG17 8UH.**
Contact: **PHONE (01488) 72259 FAX (01488) 72596**

1 AIN TECBALET (FR), 6, b g Riverquest (FR)—La Chance Au Roy (FR) **The French Connection**
2 ALPHABETIC, 7, ch g Alflora (IRE)—Incamelia **Mrs D. A. Henderson**
3 AMBITION ROYAL (FR), 4, ch g Cyborg (FR)—Before Royale (FR) **Mr A. K. Collins**
4 ARCTIC SKY (IRE), 7, b g Arctic Lord—Lake Garden Park **Mrs Christopher Pugh**
5 BACK TO BEN ALDER (IRE), 7, b br g Bob Back (USA)—Winter Fox **Mrs Christopher Hanbury**
6 BALLYLYNCH (IRE), 7, b g Lashkari—Tasmania Star **Mr Lynn Wilson**
7 BED BUG (FR), 6, b g Double Bed (FR)—Cotation (FR) **The Barrow Boys IV**
8 BERNINI (IRE), 4, b g Grand Lodge (USA)—Alsabah (IRE) **Mrs Maureen Buckley**
9 BRANKLEY BOY, 6, ch g Afzal—Needwood Fortune **Mr Gary Stewart**
10 CALLING BRAVE (IRE), 8, ch g Bob Back (USA)—Queenie Kelly **Sir Robert Ogden**
11 CA NA TRONA (IRE), 5, b g Accordion—Sterna Star **Lady Lloyd Webber**
12 CANDELLO, 8, b m Supreme Leader—Oubava (FR) **Mr Erik Thorbek**
13 CAPPADRUMMIN (IRE), 7, ch g Bob Back (USA)—Out And About **Lady Lloyd Webber**
14 CARACCIOLA (GER), 7, b g Lando (GER)—Capitolina (FR) **Mr P. J. D. Pottinger**
15 CEANANNAS MOR (IRE), 10, b br g Strong Gale—Game Sunset **Major Christopher Hanbury**
16 CHAPELTOWN (IRE), 12, b g Denel (FR)—Lady Dunsford **Newbury Racecourse Owners Group**
17 CHAUVINIST (IRE), 9, b g Roselier (FR)—Sacajawea **Mrs E. Roberts & Nick Roberts**
18 COPSALE LAD, 7, ch g Karinga Bay—Squeaky Cottage **Swallow Racehorse**
19 CRYSTAL CHOIR, 4, b f Singspiel (IRE)—Crystal Ring (IRE) **Mr & Mrs Peter Orton**
20 DANCING BAY, 7, b g Suave Dancer (USA)—Kabayil **Elite Racing Club**
21 DEOCH AN DORAIS (IRE), 9, b g Supreme Leader—General Rain **Park Lane Racing AG Switzerland**
22 DIAMOND MONROE (IRE), 8, ch g Treasure Hunter—Star of Monroe **Newbury Racehorse Owners Group**
23 DUNGARVANS CHOICE (IRE), 9, ch g Orchestra—Marys Gift **Elite Racing Club**
24 ESHBRAN LAD, 7, b g Golden Lahab (USA)—Lansdowne Lady **Mr P. J. Harle**
25 FAR HORIZON (IRE), 10, b g Phardante (FR)—Polly Puttens **Lady Tennant**
26 FIRST LOVE, 8, br g Bustino—First Romance **The Queen**
27 FLEET STREET, 5, ch g Wolfhound (USA)—Farmer's Pet **Mr W. H. Ponsonby**
28 FLORAL DREAM, 5, b br m Alflora (IRE)—Cauchemar **Mrs G. M. Tregaskes**
29 FONDMORT (FR), 8, b g Cyborg (FR)—Hansie (FR) **Mr W. J. Brown**
30 FOXCHAPEL QUEEN (IRE), 6, b br m Over The River (FR)—Glencairn Lass **Mr Paul Green**
31 FOXTON BROOK (IRE), 5, br g Presenting—Martins Times (IRE) **Mr Lynn Wilson**
32 FULL OF MICHEL (FR), 5, gr g Michel Georges—Quinte Royale (FR) **ROA Dawn Run Partnership**
33 GEOS (FR), 9, b br g Pistolet Bleu (IRE)—Kaprika (FR) **Thurloe Finsbury**
34 GLENCOYLE (IRE), 4, b g In The Wings—Lucky State (USA) **Raymond Tooth**
35 GO FOR BUST, 5, b g Sabrehill (USA)—Butsova **Mrs E. Roberts & Nick Roberts**
36 GOT ONE TOO (FR), 7, ch g Green Tune (USA)—Gloria Mundi (FR) **Sir Eric Parker & Mary Anne Parker**
37 GRANDE JETE (SAF), 7, ch g Jallad (USA)—Corps de Ballet (SAF) **L. Westwood A. Chandler J. J. Hindley**
38 GREENHOPE (IRE), 6, b g Definite Article—Unbidden Melody (USA) **Lynn Wilson Giles Wilson Martin Landau**
39 HERSOV (IRE), 8, gr g Roselier (FR)—Higher Again (IRE) **Mr Michael H. Watt**
40 HIS SONG (IRE), 11, ch g Accordion—Pampered Finch VII **Mr David Lloyd**
41 IAMBE DE LA SEE (FR), 8, b m Useful (FR)—Reine Mati (SWI) **Elite Racing Club**
42 IFNI DU LUC (FR), 8, b br m Chamberlin (FR)—Acca du Luc (FR) **Mary-Anne Parker,Sir Eric Parker,P.White**
43 IKRENEL ROYAL (FR), 8, b g Bricassar (USA)—Kreneldore (FR) **Mr Lynn Wilson**
44 INSHARANN (FR), 5, b g Sheyrann—My Last Chance (FR) **Mr W. H. Ponsonby**

MR N. J. HENDERSON—continued

45 **IRIS COLLONGES (FR)**, 8, b g Luchiroverte (IRE)—Soubrette Collonge (FR) **The Barrow Boys II**
46 **IRISH HUSSAR (IRE)**, 8, b g Supreme Leader—Shuil Ard **Major Christopher Hanbury**
47 **IRIS ROYAL (FR)**, 8, b g Garde Royale—Tchela (FR) **Sir Robert Ogden**
48 **ISIO (FR)**, 8, b g Silver Rainbow—Swifty (FR) **Sir Peter And Lady Gibbings**
49 **JOHANN DE VONNAS (FR)**, 7, b g Cadoudal (FR)—Diana de Vonnas (FR) **B. T. M. Racing**
50 **KEN'TUCKY (FR)**, 6, b g Video Rock (FR)—La Salamandre (FR) **Sir Robert Ogden**
51 **KERCABELLEC (FR)**, 6, b br g Useful (FR)—Marie de Geneve (FR) **Sir Peter And Lady Gibbings**
52 **KING EIDER**, 5, b g Mtoto—Hen Harrier **Mr & Mrs Peter Orton**
53 **LADY OF FORTUNE (IRE)**, 5, b m Sovereign Water (FR)—Needwood Fortune **Gary Stewart**
54 **LADY TERIMOND**, 7, br m Terimon—Kitty Come Home **R. J. Parish**
55 **LANDING LIGHT (IRE)**, 9, b g In The Wings—Gay Hellene **Mr & Mrs John Poynton**
56 **LIBERIA (FR)**, 5, b g Kadalko (FR)—Unica IV (FR)
57 **LIBERTHINE (FR)**, 5, b m Chamberlin (FR)—Libertina (FR) **Mr Robert Waley-Cohen**
58 **LILIUM DE COTTE (FR)**, 5, b g Ragmar (FR)—Vanille de Cotte (FR) **Mr J. P. McManus**
59 **LONG SHOT**, 7, b m Sir Harry Lewis (USA)—Kovalevskia **Mr W. H. Ponsonby**
60 **LORD BUCKINGHAM**, 6, ch g Carroll House—Lady Buck **Mrs Hugh Maitland-Jones**
61 **LORD JOSHUA (IRE)**, 6, b g Harry's Theatre (IRE)—Lady Joshua (IRE) **Mrs William S. Farish**
62 **LORD OF THE RIVER (IRE)**, 12, b g Lord Americo—Well Over **B. T. Stewart-Brown**
63 **LUSTRAL DU SEUIL (FR)**, 5, b g Sassanian (USA)—Bella Tennise (FR) **Mr W. J. Brown**
64 **MAGIC MISTRESS**, 5, b m Magic Ring—Sight'n Sound **Brian Two Johns Partnership**
65 **MAHARBAL (FR)**, 4, b g Assessor (IRE)—Cynthia (FR) **The Pheasant Inn Partnership**
66 **MAMBO (IRE)**, 8, b g Ashkalani (IRE)—Bold Tango (FR) **Mrs Belinda Harvey**
67 **MARDELLO**, 6, b m Supreme Leader—Clonmello **Mr R. D. Chugg**
68 **MARLBOROUGH (IRE)**, 12, br g Strong Gale—Wrekenogan **Sir Robert Ogden**
69 **MIGHTY STRONG**, 10, b g Strong Gale—Muffet's Spider **Exors of the Late Mr J. R. Henderson**
70 **MONTPELIER (IRE)**, 11, b g Montelimar (USA)—Liscarton **The 2020 Droxford Partnership**
71 **MONTY'S SALVO (USA)**, 5, b g Supreme Leader—Likeashot **Mr W. H. Ponsonby**
72 **MON VILLEZ (FR)**, 5, ch g Villez (FR)—Europa (SPA) **Million in Mind Partnership**
73 **MOONSTREAM**, 4, b g Terimon—Lunabelle **The Queen**
74 **MORE HANKY PANKY (IRE)**, 6, b g King's Ride—Melarka **Mrs Christopher Hanbury**
75 **NAS NA RIOGH (IRE)**, 5, b m King's Theatre (IRE)—Abstraite **Brian Twojohns Partnership**
76 **NIGHTWATCHMAN (IRE)**, 5, b g Hector Protector (USA)—Nightlark (IRE) **Sir Eric Parker**
77 **NON SO (FR)**, 6, b g Definite Article—Irish Woman (FR) **ROA Dawn Run Partnership**
78 **NO SHENANIGANS (IRE)**, 7, b g King's Ride—Melarka **Mrs Christopher Hanbury**
79 **OLD BEAN (IRE)**, 8, b g Eurobus—Princess Petara (IRE) **Wrestlers Racing**
80 **OLD ROWLEY**, 5, br g Supreme Leader—Teeno Nell **Gibson, Goddard, Hamer & Hawkes**
81 **OURISA (IRE)**, 5, b m Supreme Leader—Knockaday (IRE) **David Sumpter and John Hornsey**
82 **PEARLIWHIRL**, 5, b m Alflora (IRE)—Pearlossa (IRE) **P. J. Hughes Developments Ltd**
83 **PETANQUE (IRE)**, 8, b g King's Ride—Phargara (IRE) **Mr P. J. D. Pottinger**
84 **PRIDE OF THE RIVER (IRE)**, 9, b g Executive Perk—Ardglass Pride **Riverwood Racing**
85 **QUEENS HARBOUR (IRE)**, 10, b g Brush Aside (USA)—Queenie Kelly **Phillip Matton**
86 **RARE QUALITY**, 6, b m Chaddleworth (IRE)—Pink Mex **Magno-Pulse Ltd**
87 **RED LION**, 7, ch g Lion Cavern (USA)—Mahogany River **Mr W. H. Ponsonby**
88 **REGAL EXIT (FR)**, 8, ch g Exit To Nowhere (USA)—Regalante **Mr Brian Buckley**
89 **RICO HOMBRE (FR)**, 5, b g Cadoudal (FR)—Lady Carolina **Sir Robert Ogden**
90 **RIVER PIRATE (IRE)**, 7, b g Un Desperado (FR)—Kigali (IRE) **Riverwood Racing II**
91 **ROYAL KATIDOKI (FR)**, 4, b g Rochesson (FR)—Miss Coco (FR) **Mr Anthony Speelman**
92 **SAINTSAIRE (FR)**, 5, b g Apeldoorn (FR)—Pro Wonder (FR) **Mr Anthony Speelman**
93 **SANGATTE (IRE)**, 6, b g Un Desperado (FR)—Mad House **Mr Trevor Hemmings**
94 **SCOTS GREY**, 9, gr g Terimon—Misowni **Mr W. H. Ponsonby**
95 **SEA CAPTAIN**, 4, b g Oscar (IRE)—Calabria **The Queen**
96 **SHAMDIAN (IRE)**, 4, b g Indian Ridge—Shamadara (IRE) **Thurloe Thoroughbreds XI**
97 **SHINING STRAND**, 5, ch h Karinga Bay—First Romance **The Queen**
98 **SLEEP BAL (FR)**, 5, b g Sleeping Car (FR)—Balle Six (FR) **Mrs M. O. Bryant**
99 **SPREAD THE DREAM**, 6, ch g Alflora (IRE)—Cauchemar **Mrs G. M. Tregaskes**
100 **SPRING DAWN**, 9, gr g Arzanni—Another Spring **Mr W. H. Ponsonby**
101 **STARELLO**, 5, b m Supreme Leader—Oubava (FR) **Mr R. A. Ballin**
102 **STORMYFAIRWEATHER (IRE)**, 12, b g Strong Gale—Game Sunset **Mrs Christopher Hanbury**
103 **TANIKOS (FR)**, 5, b g Nikos—Tamana (USA) **Studwell Two Partnership**
104 **THAMES (IRE)**, 6, b g Over The River (FR)—Aon Dochas (IRE) **Mr Trevor Hemmings**
105 **THE BUSHKEEPER (IRE)**, 10, b g Be My Native (USA)—Our Little Lamb **Mr B. T. Stewart-Brown**
106 **THE THUNDERER**, 5, gr g Terimon—By Line **Mr Tom Wilson**
107 **TIQUET**, 5, b g Bedford (USA)—Lady Kay-Lee **The T. K. Partnership**
108 **TOLLBRAE (IRE)**, 7, gr g Supreme Leader—Miss Henrietta (IRE) **Mr R. A. Bartlett**
109 **TRABOLGAN (IRE)**, 6, b g King's Ride—Derrella **Mr Trevor Hemmings**
110 **TWIST OF FAITH (IRE)**, 5, b g Fresh Breeze (USA)—Merry And Bright **Studwell Three Partnership**

MR N. J. HENDERSON—continued

111 TYSOU (FR), 7, b br g Ajdayt (USA)—Pretty Point **Mr W. J. Brown**
112 WATER NYMPH (IRE), 4, ch f Be My Guest (USA)—Justitia **Paul Murphy**
113 WILBERFORCE, 7, ch g Elegant Monarch—Eskimo Slave **S. An. S. Racing**

Other Owners: Mr V. A. Auer, Mr Barry J. Bailey, Mr S. W. Barnett, Mr Ronnie Beevor, Mr Peter Bentley, Mr Gerald Blackwell, Mr Nick Blair, Mr C. H. Bothway, Executrix Of The Late C. W. Brasher, Mr A. R. Bromley, Mr Martin Broughton, Mr B. G. Brown, T. G. S. Busher, Mr B. Cartmell, Mr Andrew Charity, Mr N. C. Clark, Mrs Tracey Cook, Mr Pat Cornell, Mr Bill Cummings, Mrs J. M. Cummings, Mr R. Dingley, Mrs D. M. Douglas-Pennant, Mrs G. J. Edwards, Miss M. L. Edwards M.B.E., Mr A. T. Eggleton, Mr Philip Ellick, Mr D. G. Ellis, Mrs Judy England, Mr Tony Fox, Mr D. A. Godfrey, Mr Graham Goode, Mr Peter Goode, Mrs N. J. G. Green, Mr Brian J. Griffiths, Mr Brian Hague, Mr Ray Harding, Mr M. J. Harley, Mr Tony Hill, Ms J. Holloway, Mrs E. S. Hoskins, Mr E. J. Hounslow, Mr David Howse, Mr D. Humphreys, Mr John Ibbotson, Mrs Nicholas Jones, Mr G. Kennington, Mr M. B. J. Kimmins, Miss E. A. Lake, Mrs Martin Lowe, Mr C. Mackenzie, Mrs A. Marshall, Mr Ed McCormack, Mr D. Minton, Mr C. J. L. Moorsom, Mr I. Moss, Mr D. S. Mossman, Mr Paul Murphy, Mr Ian Murray, Mr David Nash, Mr David Nicholson, Mr J. M. Nicholson, Miss M. Noden, Mr D. R. Painter, Mr J. Palmer-Brown, Mr A. C. Parker, Mr Brian Parker, Mr D. Parsons, Mr Oliver Pawle, Lord Pembroke, Mr Stephen Pollard, Mrs Anne Poynton, Mr John Poynton, Mr John Quorn, Mrs Johnny Reed, Mr David M. Richards, Mrs F. C. Saint Jean, Mrs Ruth M. Serrell, Mr Navin Shah, Mrs M. E. Slade, Mr John Smith (Roehampton), Mr C. F. D. Staddon, Mr J. A. B. Stafford, Mrs S. Stirling, Mr A. Taylor, Mr B. A. Taylor, Mr Peter Truman, Mr Peter Verity, Mr Noel Wabe, Mr Marcus Waley Cohen, Mr R. K. Watson, Ms L. Whitehorn, Mr M. J. F. T. Wilson.

Jockeys (NH): M A Fitzgerald (10-0), M Foley. **Conditional:** A Tinkler. **Amateur:** Mr Ben King.

---

273 LADY HERRIES, Littlehampton
Postal: **Angmering Park, Littlehampton, West Sussex, BN16 4EX.**
Contact: **HOME (01903) 871421 YARD (01903) 871460 FAX (01903) 871609**
MOBILE **(07785) 282996**

1 AUTHORITY (IRE), 4, b g Bluebird (USA)—Persian Tapestry **Seymour Bloodstock (Uk) Ltd**
2 CAPTAIN CRUSOE, 6, b g Selkirk (USA)—Desert Girl **Mr Andrew Baker**
3 CLOTH OF GOLD, 7, b g Barathea (IRE)—Bustinetta **Mrs H. A. Cameron-Rose**
4 LAND OF FANTASY, 5, ch g Hernando (FR)—Height of Folly **Lady Herries**
5 LASANGA, 5, ch g Zamindar (USA)—Shall We Run **Mr Charles Green**
6 NAROOMA, 4, b f Emperor Jones (USA)—Cassilis (IRE) **Mr D. K. R. & Mrs J. B. C. Oliver**
7 POLAR TRYST, 5, ch m Polar Falcon (USA)—Lovers Tryst **Lady Herries and Friends**
8 RIPCORD (IRE), 6, b g Diesis—Native Twine **Lady Herries**
9 RUDOOD (USA), 4, b g Theatrical—Kardashina (FR) **Lady Herries**
10 RUE DU RIVOLI, 6, ch g Rudimentary (USA)—Lovers Tryst **Lady Herries**
11 SEA PLUME, 5, b m Slip Anchor—Fine Quill **Mrs E. F. Griffiths**
12 SECRET JEWEL (FR), 4, b f Hernando (FR)—Opalette **Lady Herries and Friends**
13 SHAMROCK, 7, ch m Sanglamore (USA)—Rockfest (USA) **Lady Herries**
14 STAR OF LOVE (FR), 5, b m Celtic Swing—Meant To Be **Lady Mary Mumford**
15 WUNDERWOOD (USA), 5, b g Faltaat (USA)—Jasoorah (IRE) **Mr Tony Perkins**
16 ZONERGEM, 6, ch g Zafonic (USA)—Anasazi (IRE) **Lady Herries**

THREE-YEAR-OLDS

17 ARGENTUM, b g Sillery (USA)—Frustration **Lady Herries and Friends**
18 HERON'S WING, ch g Hernando (FR)—Celtic Wing **Angmering Park Stud**
19 LUNAR EXIT (IRE), gr g Exit To Nowhere (USA)—Moon Magic **Angmering Park Stud**
20 MARIDAY, br g Trifolio—Classic Hand **Mr Chris Hardy**
21 NUKHBAH (USA), b f Bahri (USA)—El Nafis (USA) **Seymour Bloodstock (Uk) Ltd**
22 TARTOUCHE, b f Pursuit of Love—Megan's Flight **Lady Herries**
23 WARNINGCAMP (GER), b g Lando (GER)—Wilette (GER) **Lady Sarah Clutton**

TWO-YEAR-OLDS

24 HONOUR HIGH, gr g 18/2 Cloudings (IRE)—Meant To Be (Morston (FR)) **Lady Mary Mumford**
25 B f 19/3 Fraam—Megan's Flight (Welsh Pageant) **Lady Herries**

Other Owners: Sir Roger G. Gibbs, Mr R. Turner.

274 MR J. HETHERTON, Malton

Postal: **The Old Farmhouse, Highfield, Beverley Road, Malton, North Yorkshire, YO17 9PJ.**
Contact: **OFFICE/FAX (01653) 696778 MOBILE (07801) 441991**

1 BLUE MAEVE, 4, b g Blue Ocean (USA)—Louisville Belle (IRE) **Mr R. G. Fell**
2 BYGONE, 6, b g Past Glories—Meltonby **Mr N. Hetherton**
3 CALL ME JACK (IRE), 8, b g Lord Americo—Tawney Rose **Mr R. G. Fell**
4 CYBER SANTA, 6, b g Celtic Swing—Qualitair Ridge **Qualitair Holdings Limited**
5 DASH OF MAGIC, 6, b m Magic Ring (IRE)—Praglia (IRE) **21st Century Racing**
6 DIVA DANCER, 4, ch f Dr Devious (IRE)—Catina **21st Century Racing 2**
7 ENCOUNTER, 8, b g Primo Dominie—Dancing Spirit (IRE) **Qualitair Holdings Limited**
8 GINNER MORRIS, 9, b g Emarati (USA)—Just Run (IRE) **Mrs C. A. Brown**
9 GOOD TIMING, 6, gr g Timeless Times (USA)—Fort Vally **Mrs Jean Stapleton**
10 MELROSE, 5, b m Past Glories—Meltonby **James Hetherton**
11 MICHAELS DREAM (IRE), 5, b g Spectrum (IRE)—Stormswept (USA) **Mrs Michael John Paver**
12 OWN LINE, 5, b g Classic Cliche (IRE)—Cold Line **Mr N. Hetherton**
13 PHASE EIGHT GIRL, 8, b m Warrshan (USA)—Bugsy's Sister **Peter Urquhart**
14 PRIDE OF KINLOCH, 4, ch f Dr Devious (IRE)—Stormswept (USA) **Mrs Michael John Paver**
15 4, B f Slip Anchor—Qualitair Ridge **Qualitair Holdings Limited**
16 QUALITAIR WINGS, 5, b g Colonel Collins (USA)—Semperflorens **Qualitair Holdings Limited**
17 SWYNFORD PLEASURE, 8, b m Reprimand—Pleasuring **Qualitair Holdings Limited**
18 THAT'S RACING, 4, ch g Classic Cliche—All On **Mr N. Hetherton**
19 TYNDARIUS (IRE), 13, b g Mandalus—Lady Rerico **Mr Alex Shaw**
20 VALEUREUX, 6, ch g Cadeaux Genereux—La Strada **Eureka Racing**

THREE-YEAR-OLDS

21 MIND THE TIME, b g Mind Games—Rare Indigo **21st Century Racing 3**

TWO-YEAR-OLDS

22 DESERT BUZZ (IRE), b c 24/1 Desert Story (IRE)—Sugar (Hernando (FR)) (1855) **21st Century Racing**
23 GALLOPING GERTIE, b f 30/3 Aragon—Meltonby (Sayf El Arab (USA)) **James Hetherton**

Assistant Trainer: John Bottomley

275 MR P. W. HIATT, Banbury

Postal: **Six Ash Farm, Hook Norton, Banbury, Oxfordshire, OX15 5DB.**
Contact: **PHONE (01608) 737255 FAX (01608) 730641 MOBILE (07973) 751115**

1 BUNDABERG, 4, b c Komaite (USA)—Lizzy Cantle **Mr Brian D. Cantle**
2 DANCING KING (IRE), 8, b g Fairy King (USA)—Zariysha (IRE) **Mr P. W. Hiatt**
3 GIUST IN TEMP (IRE), 5, b h Polish Precedent (USA)—Blue Stricks **River Side Partnership**
4 HAJEER (IRE), 6, b g Darshaan—Simouna **Mr Phil Kelly**
5 ISA'AF (IRE), 5, b g Darshaan—Shauna's Honey (IRE) **Miss Maria McKinney**
6 KOSSIES MATE, 5, b m Cosmonaut—Pola Star (IRE) **Mr P. W. Hiatt**
7 LAZZAZ, 6, b g Muhtarram (USA)—Astern (USA) **Mr Phil Kelly**
8 LEOPHIN DANCER (USA), 6, b g Green Dancer (USA)—Happy Gal (FR) **Mr Clive Roberts**
9 LORD TRIX (IRE), 5, b g Lord Americo—Up To Trix **Mr K. Hutsby**
10 LOST SPIRIT, 8, b g Strolling Along (USA)—Shoag (USA) **Mr P. W. Hiatt**
11 MEXICAN PETE, 4, b g Atraf—Eskimo Nel (IRE) **First Chance Racing**
12 PIPS SONG (IRE), 9, ch g Pips Pride—Friendly Song **Mrs Lucia Stockley & Ken Read**
13 PRESIDENTS LADY, 7, b m Superpower—Flirty Lady **Mrs J. Harmsworth**
14 REALISM (FR), 4, b g Machiavellian (USA)—Kissing Cousin (IRE) **Miss Maria McKinney**
15 SOMETHINGABOUTHER, 4, b f Whittingham (IRE)—Paula's Joy **Mr P. W. Hiatt**
16 SUNDRIED TOMATO, 5, b g Lugana Beach—Little Scarlett **Mr Clive Roberts**
17 TERMONFECKIN, 6, b g Runnett—Crimson Sol **Mr Phil Kelly**
18 THE NUNS SONG, 4, b f Sir Harry Lewis (USA)—The Nuns Story **Mrs T. W. H. Dancer**
19 TIGHT SQUEEZE, 7, br m Petoski—Snowline **Mr Anthony Harrison**

MR P. W. HIATT—continued

THREE-YEAR-OLDS

20 **IPHIGENIA (IRE)**, b br f Orpen (USA)—Silver Explosive **Mr Clive Roberts**

Other Owners: Mr Peter Cousins, Mr J. D. Groves, Mr N. B. Manning, Mr H. E. Peachey, Miss J. L. Peachey, Mr J. S. Sterry, Mr M. Walker, Mr R. Walker.

Assistant Trainer: Mrs E Hiatt

Jockeys (Flat): Joanna Badger, R Winston. **Apprentices:** D Allan, L Fletcher. **Amateurs:** Miss E J Jones, Mrs M King (9-0), Miss N McKim.

---

276 **MISS E. HILL, Flyford Flavell**
Postal: **Dobbins Farm, Colwall Road, Mathon, Malvern, Worcestershire, WR13 5PH.**
Contact: **PHONE (01684) 540407 MOBILE (07866) 532722**

1 **MR FISHER (IRE)**, 7, ch g Toulon—Parthian Opera **Mr R. G. Langley**
2 **RAISE A GALE (IRE)**, 10, b br m Strong Gale—Raise A Rose (IRE) **Mr R. G. Langley**
3 **RIVER GROUND (IRE)**, 9, br g Lord Americo—Rapid Ground **Mr R. G. Langley**
4 4, Ch f Executive Perk—Rosie Ring (IRE) **Mr R. G. Langley**
5 **SEA SQUIRT (IRE)**, 7, b g Fourstars Allstar (USA)—Polynesian Goddess (IRE) **Mr R. G. Langley**
6 **TANK BUSTER**, 4, b g Executive Perk—Macfarly (IRE) **Mr R. G. Langley**
7 **TOP GUARD (IRE)**, 6, b g Topanoora—Garter Royale (IRE) **Mr R. G. Langley**
8 **WAVE BACK (IRE)**, 8, b m Bob Back (USA)—Stormy Wave **Mr R. G. Langley**
9 4, B f Oscar (IRE)—Winter Ground (IRE) **Mr R. G. Langley**

Assistant Trainer: Mr R G Langley

Amateur: Mr R G Langley (10-4).

---

277 **MR B. W. HILLS, Lambourn**
Postal: **Wetherdown House, Lambourn, Hungerford, Berkshire, RG17 8UB.**
Contact: **OFFICE (01488) 71548 FAX (01488) 72823 E-MAIL info@barryhills.com**
WEBSITE www.barryhills.com

1 **BEST FLIGHT**, 4, gr g Sheikh Albadou—Bustling Nelly **Mr J. Hanson**
2 **CALCUTTA**, 8, b h Indian Ridge—Echoing **The Hon Mrs J. M. Corbett & Mr C. Wright**
3 **CRAIOVA (IRE)**, 5, b h Turtle Island (IRE)—Velvet Appeal (IRE) **Mr Ahmed BuHaleeba**
4 **DUBAI SUCCESS**, 4, b c Sadler's Wells (USA)—Crystal Spray **Maktoum Al Maktoum**
5 **DUNHILL STAR (IRE)**, 4, b c Danehill (USA)—Sueboog (USA) **Mr Mohamed Obaida**
6 **FAITHFUL WARRIOR (USA)**, 6, ch g Diesis—Dabawyaaa **Mr Mohamed Obaida**
7 **FLYING EXPRESS**, 4, ch c Air Express (IRE)—Royal Loft **Mr Mohamed Obaida**
8 **MAKHLAB (USA)**, 4, b c Dixieland Band (USA)—Avasand (USA) **Mr Hamdan Al Maktoum**
9 **PABLO**, 5, b h Efisio—Winnebago **Mr Guy Reed**
10 **PRAIRIE FALCON (IRE)**, 10, b g Alzao (USA)—Sea Harrier **Mrs B. W. Hills**
11 **PRIVATE CHARTER**, 4, b c Singspiel (IRE)—By Charter **Mr R. E. Sangster**
12 **SAN ANTONIO**, 4, b g Efisio—Winnebago **Mr Guy Reed**
13 **SPLENDID ERA (UAE)**, 4, b c Green Desert (USA)—Valley of Gold (FR) **Maktoum Al Maktoum**
14 **SUCCESSOR**, 4, ch c Entrepreneur—Petralona (USA) **Mr K. Abdulla**
15 **TO WIT TO WOO**, 4, b g Efisio—Sioux **Mr Guy Reed**
16 **TRUST RULE**, 4, b c Selkirk (USA)—Hagwah (USA) **Mr Abdulla BuHaleeba**
17 **TURN AROUND**, 4, b g Pivotal—Bemuse **Gryffindor (www.racingtours.co.uk)**
18 **YAWMI**, 4, ch c Zafonic (USA)—Reine Wells (IRE) **Mr Hamdan Al Maktoum**

THREE-YEAR-OLDS

19 **ALFONSO**, ch c Efisio—Winnebago **Mr Guy Reed**
20 **AQUALUNG**, b c Desert King (IRE)—Aquarelle **Mr K. Abdulla**
21 **ASIA WINDS (IRE)**, b f Machiavellian (USA)—Ascot Cyclone (USA) **Mr Mohamed Obaida**
22 **BRINDISI**, b f Dr Fong (USA)—Genoa **Mr M. H. Dixon**
23 **CAUSE CELEBRE (IRE)**, gr f Peintre Celebre (USA)—
　　　　　　　　　　　　　　　　　Madame Belga (USA) **The Hon Mrs J. M. Corbett & Mr C. Wright**
24 **CHAPLIN**, b c Groom Dancer (USA)—Princess Borghese (USA) **Mr K. Abdulla**
25 **CHINA EYES (IRE)**, b f Fasliyev (USA)—Limpopo **Mr Rick Barnes**

MR B. W. HILLS—continued

26 **CITY PALACE**, ch c Grand Lodge (USA)—Ajuga (USA) **Mr K. Abdulla**
27 **COMING AGAIN (IRE)**, b c Rainbow Quest (USA)—Hagwah (USA) **Mr Abdulla BuHaleeba**
28 **CRYSTAL CURLING (IRE)**, ch f Peintre Celebre (USA)—State Crystal (IRE) **Mr Urs E. Schwarzenbach**
29 **DANCING PARTNER (USA)**, b c Distant View (USA)—Bold Ballerina **Mr K. Abdulla**
30 **DANZIG RIVER (IRE)**, b c Green Desert (USA)—Sahara Breeze **Mr R. J. Arculli**
31 **DASHIKI (USA)**, ch f Distant View (USA)—Musicanti (USA) **Mr K. Abdulla**
32 **DAYTIME GIRL (IRE)**, gr f Daylami (IRE)—Snoozeandyoulose (IRE) **Bonnycastle, Concord Racing, Morton**
33 **DELIGHTFULLY**, b f Definite Article—Kingpin Delight **Mr Stephen Crown**
34 **DESERT DREAMER (IRE)**, b g Green Desert (USA)—Follow That Dream **Maktoum Al Maktoum**
35 **DEVIL'S BITE**, ch c Dracula (AUS)—Niggle (USA) **Mrs H. T. Jones**
36 **DREAM VALLEY (IRE)**, b f Sadler's Wells (USA)—Vallee des Reves (USA) **Lady Richard Wellesley**
37 **EXCLUSIVE DANIELLE**, ch f Thunder Gulch (USA)—Hasta (USA) **Mr John C. Grant**
38 **FAHLAWI (IRE)**, gr c Daylami (IRE)—Dancing Sea (USA) **Mr Ahmed BuHaleeba**
39 **FATAYAAT (IRE)**, b f Machiavellian (USA)—Maraatib (IRE) **Mr Hamdan Al Maktoum**
40 **FIZZY LADY**, b f Efisio—The Frog Lady (IRE) **Baydon House Stud**
41 **FLAMBOYANT LAD**, ch c Nashwan (USA)—Cheeky Charm (USA) **Maktoum Al Maktoum**
42 **FOKINE (USA)**, b c Royal Academy (USA)—Polar Bird **Mr R. E. Sangster**
43 **FOUR PENCE (IRE)**, b c Rainbow Quest (USA)—American Queen (FR) **Mr Rick Barnes**
44 **FUN TO RIDE**, ch f Desert Prince (IRE)—Zafaaf **Mr Abdulla BuHaleeba**
45 **GALVANISE (USA)**, b c Run Softly (USA)—Shining Bright **Mr K. Abdulla**
46 **GAME DAME**, ch f Nashwan (USA)—Gentle Dame **Maktoum Al Maktoum**
47 **GAY ROMANCE**, ch f Singspiel (IRE)—Gaijin **Wickfield Stud and Hartshill Stud**
48 **GO SOLO**, b c Primo Dominie—Taza **Mr Guy Reed**
49 **GRAND BUT ONE (IRE)**, ch c Grand Lodge (USA)—Unscathed **Enton Thoroughbred Racing 2**
50 **GUSTAVO**, b c Efisio—Washita **Mr Guy Reed**
51 **HAAFHD**, ch c Alhaarth (IRE)—Al Bahathri (USA) **Mr Hamdan Al Maktoum**
52 **HAVE FAITH (IRE)**, b f Machiavellian (USA)—Fatefully (USA) **Maktoum Al Maktoum**
53 **HEART'S DESIRE (IRE)**, b f Royal Applause—Touch And Love (IRE) **Maktoum Al Maktoum**
54 **HONEST INJUN**, b c Efisio—Sioux **Mr Guy Reed**
55 **INDIAN MYTH (USA)**, b f Lear Fan (USA)—Navarene (USA) **Mr K. Abdulla**
56 **INTIMATE FRIEND (USA)**, b f Expelled (USA)—Intimate (USA) **Mr K. Abdulla**
57 **ISIDORE BONHEUR (IRE)**, b c Mtoto—Way O'Gold (USA) **Mr W. J. Gredley & Matthew Green**
58 **IVY LEAGUE STAR (IRE)**, b f Sadler's Wells (USA)—Ivy (USA) **Mr D. M. James**
59 **JOKING APART**, b f Rainbow Quest (USA)—Jood (USA) **Maktoum Al Maktoum**
60 **KAMANDA LAUGH**, ch g Most Welcome—Kamada (USA) **Mr John Sillett**
61 **KASKA (IRE)**, b f King of Kings (IRE)—Antiguan Jane **Mrs E. Roberts**
62 **KEY IN**, ch f Unfuwain (USA)—Fleet Key **Mr E. D. Kessly and Mrs A. Jenkins**
63 **LA CUCARACHA**, b f Piccolo—Peggy Spencer **Mr Guy Reed**
64 **LINE DRAWING**, b c Unfuwain (USA)—Fine Detail (IRE) **Mr K. Abdulla**
65 **LORIEN HILL (IRE)**, b f Danehill (USA)—Lothlorien (USA) **Mr D. M. James**
66 **LUCKY PIPIT**, b f Key of Luck (USA)—Meadow Pipit (CAN) **Maktoum Al Maktoum**
67 **LUXURY LAUNCH (USA)**, b f Seeking The Gold (USA)—Ocean Ridge (USA) **Maktoum Al Maktoum**
68 **LYCA BALLERINA**, b f Marju (IRE)—Lovely Lyca **Letitia Lucas & Mr R. J. McCreery**
69 **MASHIE**, ch f Selkirk (USA)—Nashmeel (USA) **Mr K. Abdulla**
70 **MISS ADELAIDE (IRE)**, b f Alzao (USA)—Sweet Adelaide (USA) **Mr R. E. Sangster & Mrs B. W. Hills**
71 **MODEL FIGURE (USA)**, b f Distant View (USA)—Sylph (USA) **Mr K. Abdulla**
72 **MOORS MYTH**, b c Anabaa (USA)—West Devon (USA) **Mr K. Abdulla**
73 **MOSS VALE (IRE)**, b c Shinko Forest (IRE)—Wolf Cleugh (IRE) **Mr John C. Grant**
74 **MOUFTARI (USA)**, b c Miswaki (USA)—Nature's Magic (USA) **Mr Ahmed BuHaleeba**
75 **MRS PANKHURST**, b f Selkirk (USA)—Melodist (USA) **Mr W. J. Gredley**
76 **MUNAAHEJ (IRE)**, b c Soviet Star (USA)—Azyaa **Mr Hamdan Al Maktoum**
77 **MUTAWAFFER**, b c Marju (USA)—Absaar (USA) **Mr Hamdan Al Maktoum**
78 **MUTAWASSEL (USA)**, b c Kingmambo (USA)—Danzig Darling (CAN) **Mr Hamdan Al Maktoum**
79 **MY SUNSHINE (IRE)**, b f Alzao (USA)—Sunlit Ride **The Hon Mrs J. M. Corbett & Mr C. Wright**
80 **NEWS SKY (USA)**, b c Gone West (USA)—Dubian **Mr Mohamed Obaida**
81 **NINE RED**, b f Royal Applause—Sarcita **Enton Thoroughbred Racing 2**
82 **OMAN GULF (USA)**, b c Diesis—Dabaweyaa **Mr Mohamed Obaida**
83 **OMAN SEA (USA)**, b f Rahy (USA)—Ras Shaikh (USA) **Mr Mohamed Obaida**
84 **OPERA STAR (IRE)**, b f Sadler's Wells (USA)—Adjalisa (USA) **Mr Urs E. Schwarzenbach**
85 **OVER THE RAINBOW (IRE)**, b c Rainbow Quest (USA)—Dimakya (USA) **Harrison, Jamieson, Parker, Snowden**
86 **PRIMO WAY**, b c Primo Dominie—Waypoint **Mr D. M. James**
87 **RIVER NUREY (IRE)**, gr c Fasliyev (USA)—Dundel (IRE) **Mr R. J. Arculli**
88 **SAHARAN SONG (IRE)**, ch f Singspiel (IRE)—Sahara Baladee **Mr N. N. Browne**
89 **SECRET CHARM (IRE)**, b f Green Desert (USA)—Viz (USA) **Maktoum Al Maktoum**
90 **SHAZANA**, gr f Key of Luck (USA)—Shawanni **Maktoum Al Maktoum**
91 **SI SI AMIGA (IRE)**, b f Desert Style (IRE)—No Hard Feelings (IRE) **Mr R. A. N. Bonnycastle**

MR B. W. HILLS—continued

92 **SOUTHERN BAZAAR (USA)**, ch c Southern Halo (USA)—Sunday Bazaar (USA) **Mr K. Abdulla**
93 **SPRING SURPRISE**, b f Hector Protector (USA)—Tender Moment (IRE) **Mr Ray Richards**
94 **STATE DILEMMA (IRE)**, b c Green Desert (USA)—Nuriva (USA) **Maktoum Al Maktoum**
95 **STEPHANO**, ch g Efisio—Polo **Mr Guy Reed**
96 **SUNISA (IRE)**, b f Daggers Drawn (USA)—Winged Victory (IRE) **Mr Ray Richards**
97 **SWIFT SAILING (USA)**, b c Storm Cat (USA)—Saytarra (USA) **Mr Saeed Maktoum Al Maktoum**
98 **SYDNEY STAR**, b f Machiavellian (USA)—Sena Desert **Mr Mohamed Obaida**
99 **TABLEAU (USA)**, ch c Marquetry (USA)—Model Bride (USA) **Mr K. Abdulla**
100 **TAROT CARD**, b f Fasliyev (USA)—Well Beyond (IRE) **Mr K. Abdulla**
101 **TENNY'S GOLD (IRE)**, b f Marju (IRE)—Itatinga (USA) **Mr Rick Barnes**
102 **THREE SHIPS**, ch c Dr Fong (USA)—River Lullaby (USA) **Mr K. Abdulla**
103 **UNSHOODA**, ch f Machiavellian (USA)—Rawaabe (USA) **Mr Hamdan Al Maktoum**
104 **WARED (USA)**, gr c El Prado (IRE)—My Shafy **Mr Hilal Salem**
105 **ZONUS**, b c Pivotal—Jade Mistress **Concord Racing,Bonnycastle,Grant,Morton**

TWO-YEAR-OLDS

106 Ch f 13/5 Bering—Action de Grace (USA) (Riverman (USA)) **Mr Guy Reed**
107 **ALEXANDER CAPETOWN (IRE)**, b f 25/2 Fasliyev (USA)—
Hawas (Mujtahid (USA)) (111317) **Mrs N. O'Callaghan & Mrs Carol Kennedy**
108 **ALL THAT AND MORE (IRE)**, ch c 21/2 Unfuwain (USA)—
Ideal Lady (IRE) (Seattle Slew (USA)) **Maktoum Al Maktoum**
109 **ALMANSOOR (IRE)**, b c 29/4 Sadler's Wells (USA)—
Groom Order (Groom Dancer (USA)) (300000) **Mr Hamdan Al Maktoum**
110 **ALUMNI**, ch f 10/5 Selkirk (USA)—Ajuga (USA) (The Minstrel (CAN)) **Mr K. Abdulla**
111 **AMIRA**, b f 14/4 Efisio—Princess Athena (Ahonoora) (120000) **David Powell & Partners**
112 **ART ELEGANT**, b c 11/4 Desert Prince (IRE)—Elegant (IRE) (Marju (IRE)) (58000) **Matthew Green**
113 **ASK FOR RAIN**, gr f 4/4 Green Desert (USA)—Requesting (Rainbow Quest (USA)) **Maktoum Al Maktoum**
114 **ASRAR**, b f 2/4 King's Theatre (IRE)—Zandaka (FR) (Doyoun) **Mr Abdulla BuHaleeba**
115 **ASTRONOMICAL (IRE)**, b c 13/4 Mister Baileys—Charm The Stars (Roi Danzig (USA)) (14000) **Mr J. Hanson**
116 **AU REVOIR**, ch f 3/2 Efisio—Blow Me A Kiss (Kris) **Mr Guy Reed**
117 **BALLETOMAINE (IRE)**, b f 21/4 Sadler's Wells (USA)—Ivy (USA) (Sir Ivor) **Mr & Mrs Peter Orton**
118 **BASSERAH (IRE)**, b f 16/2 Unfuwain (USA)—Blueberry Walk (Green Desert (USA)) **Mr Hamdan Al Maktoum**
119 **BOBO**, ch f 12/4 Efisio—Taza (Persian Bold) **Mr Guy Reed**
120 **BON BON**, b f 16/2 Efisio—Polo (Warning) **Mr Guy Reed**
121 **BORN FOR DIAMONDS (IRE)**, b f 1/3 Night Shift (USA)—Kirri (IRE) (Lycius (USA)) (40197) **Mr Paul McNamara**
122 **BRANDEXE (IRE)**, b f 15/5 Xaar—Tintara (IRE) (Caerleon (USA)) (14841) **Mr R. A. N. Bonnycastle**
123 B f 26/3 Sadler's Wells (USA)—Brigid (USA) (Irish River (FR)) (750000) **Lady Bamford**
124 **CAVALARRA**, b c 20/1 Green Desert (USA)—Ya Tarra (Unbridled (USA)) **Mr Saeed Maktoum Al Maktoum**
125 **CEIRIOG VALLEY**, b f 14/2 In The Wings—Bodfari Quarry (Efisio) **Mr R. J. McAlpine**
126 **CIEL BLEU**, ch f 14/3 Septieme Ciel (USA)—
Valthea (FR) (Antheus (USA)) (80000) **The Hon Mrs J. M. Corbett & Mr C. Wright**
127 **CLOVE (USA)**, b f 2/3 Distant View (USA)—Nidd (USA) (Known Fact (USA)) **Mr K. Abdulla**
128 B c 10/2 Red Ransom (USA)—Country Garden (Selkirk (USA)) (133929) **Mr Ahmed BuHaleeba**
129 **DABBERS RIDGE (IRE)**, b c 5/5 Indian Ridge—Much Commended (Most Welcome) (47000) **Maurice Mogg**
130 B c 10/3 Grand Lodge (USA)—Daftiyna (IRE) (Darshaan) (70000)
131 B c 15/1 Spectrum (IRE)—Decrescendo (IRE) (Polish Precedent (USA)) (30000)
132 **DESERT DEMON (IRE)**, b c 26/3 Unfuwain (USA)—
Baldemosa (FR) (Lead On Time (USA)) **Maktoum Al Maktoum**
133 **DHAULAR DHAR (IRE)**, b c 6/5 Indian Ridge—Pescara (IRE) (Common Grounds) **Maktoum Al Maktoum**
134 **DIAMOND CIRCLE**, br f 18/3 Halling (USA)—Canadian Mill (USA) (Mill Reef (USA)) **Maktoum Al Maktoum**
135 **DIXIEANNA**, ch f Night Shift (USA)—Dixielake (IRE) (Lake Coniston (IRE)) **Mr C. G. P. Wyatt**
136 **DUNYA**, b f Unfuwain (USA)—Tithcar (Cadeaux Genereux) **Mr Abdulla BuHaleeba**
137 **EJAABI (USA)**, ch c 1/4 Aljabr (USA)—Ruznama (USA) (Forty Niner (USA)) **Mr Hamdan Al Maktoum**
138 **EMPTY GESTURE**, b c 27/1 Cadeaux Genereux—Broken Spectre (Rainbow Quest (USA)) **Mr K. Abdulla**
139 **ETLAALA**, ch c 23/3 Selkirk (USA)—Portelet (Night Shift (USA)) (160000) **Mr Hamdan Al Maktoum**
140 B c 7/4 Zafonic (USA)—Fame At Last (USA) (Quest For Fame) **Mr K. Abdulla**
141 B f 8/3 Fasliyev (USA)—Fancy Boots (IRE) (Salt Dome (USA)) (27828) **Mrs Simon Polito**
142 Ch f 3/3 Nashwan (USA)—Fine Detail (IRE) (Shirley Heights) **Mr K. Abdulla**
143 **FOLLOW MY LEAD**, b f 2/3 Night Shift (USA)—Launch Time (USA) (Relaunch (USA)) (50000) **Mr D. M. James**
144 **FOREST OF LOVE**, br f 17/3 Charnwood Forest—
Touch And Love (IRE) (Green Desert (USA)) **Maktoum Al Maktoum**
145 **FORTUNATE ISLE (USA)**, ch c 2/5 Swain (IRE)—Isla Del Rey (USA) (Nureyev (USA)) **Maktoum Al Maktoum**
146 B c 21/4 Efisio—Gecko Rouge (Rousillon (USA)) (18552)
147 **GRANDE ROCHE (IRE)**, b c 17/5 Grand Lodge (USA)—
Arabian Lass (SAF) (Al Mufti (USA)) (46381) **Mr R. J. Arculli**

MR B. W. HILLS—continued

148 **GROUND RULES (USA),** b c 31/3 Boundary (USA)—Gombeen (USA) (Private Account (USA)) **Mr K. Abdulla**
149 **GUADIARO (USA),** b c 25/3 El Prado (IRE)—
  Splendid (IRE) (Mujtahid (USA)) (98948) **P. D. Savill, R. A. N. Bonnycastle & R. E. Sangster**
150 B c 8/3 Fasliyev—Hasty Words (IRE) (Polish Patriot (USA)) **Mr W. J. Gredley**
151 **HEART STOPPING (USA),** b f 20/1 Chester House (USA)—Clog Dance (Pursuit of Love) **Mr K. Abdulla**
152 **HEWARAAT (IRE),** b c 22/5 Fasliyev (USA)—Maraatib (IRE) (Green Desert (USA)) **Mr Hamdan Al Maktoum**
153 B f 14/2 Dansili—Illusory (Kings Lake (USA)) **Mr K. Abdulla**
154 B f 8/3 Cape Cross (IRE)—In The Highlands (Petong) (19789)
155 B c 4/4 Kingmambo (USA)—Isle de France (USA) (Nureyev (USA)) (238095) **Mr Ahmed BuHaleeba**
156 **JACK THE GIANT (IRE),** b c 4/5 Giant's Causeway—State Crystal (IRE) (High Estate) **Mr Urs E. Schwarzenbach**
157 **JE SUIS BELLE,** ch f 15/3 Efisio—Blossom (Warning) **Mr Guy Reed**
158 Ch c 23/5 Giant's Causeway—Kotama (USA) (Shahrastani (USA)) (50000)
159 **MADEMOISELLE,** b f 18/2 Efisio—Shall We Dance (Rambo Dancer (CAN)) **Mr Guy Reed**
160 B c 20/3 Benny The Dip (USA)—Melodist (USA) (The Minstrel (CAN)) **Mr W. J. Gredley**
161 **MIDCAP (IRE),** b f 9/3 Entrepreneur—Tis Juliet (USA) (Alydar (USA)) **Mr & Mrs Peter Orton**
162 **MISS PARTICULAR (IRE),** b f 20/4 Sadler's Wells (USA)—Viz (USA) (Kris S (USA)) **Maktoum Al Maktoum**
163 **MUSAHIM (USA),** b c 10/3 Dixieland Band (USA)—Tabheej (IRE) (Mujtahid (USA)) **Mr Hamdan Al Maktoum**
164 B c 14/2 El Prado (IRE)—My Hansel (USA) (Hansel (USA)) **Mr Hilal Salem**
165 **NAWAAEM (USA),** b f 21/3 Swain (IRE)—Alattrah (USA) (Shadeed (USA)) **Mr Hamdan Al Maktoum**
166 B c 15/4 Pursuit Of Love (USA)—Nullarbor (Green Desert (USA)) **Mr K. Abdulla**
167 **ORANMORE CASTLE (IRE),** b c 29/1 Giant's Causeway—
  Twice The Ease (Green Desert (USA)) (92763) **R. E. Sangster, R. A. N. Bonnycastle & P. D. Savill**
168 B c 14/3 Darshaan—Our Queen of Kings (Arazi (USA)) (30000) **Mr John C. Grant & Mr A. L. R. Morton**
169 **PAPER TALK (USA),** b c 4/3 Unbridled's Song—Journalist (IRE) (Night Shift (USA)) **Maktoum Al Maktoum**
170 **PERFECT BLEND,** gr f 2/3 Linamix (FR)—Picture Princess (Sadler's Wells (USA)) **Maktoum Al Maktoum**
171 B f 12/4 Honour And Glory—Polar Bird (IRE) (Thatching (USA)) **Mr R. E. Sangster & Lady Bamford**
172 **PONENTE,** b f 8/4 Robellino (USA)—Polmara (IRE) (Polish Precedent (USA)) **Burton Agnes Bloodstock**
173 B c 28/1 Dansili—Post Modern (USA) (Nureyev (USA)) **Mr K. Abdulla**
174 B c 5/2 Indian Lodge (IRE)—Priyanka (Last Tycoon) (50000)
175 B f 31/1 Dansili—Questionable (Rainbow Quest (USA)) **Mr K. Abdulla**
176 **RAINBOW SKY,** b f 1/4 Rainbow Quest (USA)—Safayn (USA) (Lyphard (USA)) (52565) **Mr D. M. James**
177 B c 14/5 Mujadil (USA)—Rakli (Warning) **Mr K. Abdulla**
178 **RIGHTFUL RULER,** b c 21/3 Montjoy (USA)—Lady of The Realm (Prince Daniel (USA)) **Mr G. J. Hicks**
179 **SELF DISCIPLINE,** b c 10/2 Dansili—Cosh (USA) (A P Indy (USA))
180 B f 10/3 Cape Cross (IRE)—Sevres (USA) (Lyphard's Wish (FR)) (34000) **Mr R. A. N. Bonnycastle**
181 **TAHRIR (IRE),** gr f 13/5 Linamix (FR)—Miss Sacha (Last Tycoon) (350000) **Mr Hamdan Al Maktoum**
182 **TOUCH OF SILK (IRE),** ch f 1/4 Night Shift (USA)—
  Blew Her Top (USA) (Blushing John (USA)) (68026) **Mr Rick Barnes**
183 Ch f 11/3 Giant's Causeway—Vallee des Reves (USA) (Kingmambo (USA)) (25000) **Lady Richard Wellesley**
184 B c 12/3 Compton Place—Watheeqah (USA) (Topsider (USA)) (38000) **Mr John C. Grant**
185 **WHAZZAT,** b f 2/2 Daylami (IRE)—Wosaita (Generous (IRE)) (30000) **Mr W. J. Gredley**
186 **WITWATERSRAND (IRE),** b f 22/4 Unfuwain (USA)—Valley of Gold (FR) (Shirley Heights) **Maktoum Al Maktoum**

Other Owners: Mr R. Barnett, Norton Brookes, Mr James E. S. Colling, Mrs Sheila Crown, Mr Rubin Gruber, Lady Harrison, Mrs Eileen Jamieson, David Jenks, Flora Lane, Mrs John Magnier, Mr A. L. R. Morton, Lady Parker, Miss F. R. Smith, Mrs Diane Snowden.

Assistant Trainer: K Mooney, C Hills, T Sturgis & S Savva

Apprentice: K May (7-6).

---

278 MR J. W. HILLS, Lambourn
Postal: **The Croft, Upper Lambourn, Newbury, Berkshire, RG17 8QH.**
Contact: PHONE (01488) 73144 FAX (01488) 73099 MOBILE (07836) 283091
E-MAIL john@johnhills.com

1 **BLAZING THE TRAIL (IRE),** 4, ch g Indian Ridge—Divine Pursuit **Sir John Robb**
2 **BOUNDLESS PROSPECT (USA),** 5, b g Boundary (USA)—
  Cape (USA) **M. Wauchope, Sir Simon Dunning, R. Cottam**
3 **FREELOADER (IRE),** 4, b g Revoque (IRE)—Indian Sand **Scott Hardy Partnership**
4 **HIGH FINANCE (IRE),** 4, b br f Entrepreneur—Phylella **Mr N. Brunskill and Mr D. M. Kerr**
5 **INTERCEPTOR,** 4, ch c Hector Protector (USA)—Moorish Idol **M. Kerr-Dineen, W. Eason, M. Smith**
6 **INTO THE BREEZE (IRE),** 4, b g Alzao (USA)—Catalane (USA) **Eric Whitehouse and Partners**
7 **KARATHAENA (IRE),** 4, b f Barathea (IRE)—Dabtara (USA) **Mr D. M. Kerr**
8 **PONT NEUF (IRE),** 4, b f Revoque (IRE)—Petite Maxine **Peter Fenwick (Dan Abbott Racing P/S 2)**

MR J. W. HILLS—continued

  9 ROYAL ADVOCATE, 4, b g Royal Applause—Kept Waiting **Nick Hubbard and Partners**
10 **SAY WHAT YOU SEE (IRE),** 4, b c Charnwood Forest (IRE)—
                                Aster Aweke (IRE) **Mr Ken Wilkinson & Mr Richard Tufft**
11 **WATERSIDE (IRE),** 5, ch g Lake Coniston (IRE)—Classic Ring (IRE) **Sir John Robb**

THREE-YEAR-OLDS

12 **ARCHERFIELD (IRE),** ch f Docksider (USA)—Willow River (CAN) **Team Havana**
13 **CARRY ON DOC,** b c Dr Devious (IRE)—Florentynna Bay **Stuart Whitehouse & Abbott Racing Partne**
14 B f Barathea (IRE)—Chocolate Box **Mr J. W. Hills**
15 **DANCING LYRA,** b c Alzao (USA)—Badaayer (USA) **Mr N. N. Browne**
16 **DIFFERENT PLANET,** b c Inchinor—Take Heart **The Phantom Partnership**
17 **FIRST CENTURION,** b c Peintre Celebre (USA)—Valley of Hope (USA) **Mr D. M. Kerr and Mr N. Brunskill**
18 **GOLDEN ISLAND (IRE),** ch f Selkirk (USA)—Daftiyna (IRE) **Mr D. M. Kerr and Mr N. Brunskill**
19 **GREEN FALCON,** b c Green Desert (USA)—El Jazirah **F. Bienstock, M. Boase, M. Kerr-Dineen**
20 **KARMA CHAMELIAN (USA),** b f Diesis—Wild Rumour (IRE) **Mr Christopher Wright**
21 **LANDUCCI,** b c Averti (IRE)—Divina Luna **Mr R. J. Tufft**
22 **MASKED (IRE),** b c Soviet Star (USA)—Moon Masquerade (IRE) **The Phantom Partnership**
23 **NIGHT FROLIC,** b f Night Shift (USA)—Miss d'Ouilly (FR) **The Wandering Stars**
24 **NIKIFOROS,** b c Inchinor—Putout **Mr Lukis Joakim**
25 **ON THE WATERFRONT,** ch c Docksider (USA)—Film Buff **Freddy Bienstock and Martin Boase**
26 **REHIA,** b f Desert Style (IRE)—Goes A Treat **Mr G. and Mrs L. Woodward**
27 **SCARLETT BREEZE,** b f Shinko Forest (IRE)—La Suquet **Mr G. and Mrs L. Woodward**
28 **SONG OF THE SEA,** ch f Bering—Calypso Run **Mr M. Wauchope and Mr R. Cottam**
29 **TROIS ETOILES (IRE),** ch f Grand Lodge (USA)—Stardance (USA) **The Wandering Stars**
30 **TURNBERRY (IRE),** b c Petardia—Sunrise (IRE) **Mr Kenneth Wilkinson**

TWO-YEAR-OLDS

31 **BEAUTIFUL MOVER (USA),** ch f 30/3 Spinning World (USA)—
                    Dancer's Glamour (USA) (Danzig Connection (USA)) (19048) **Whitehouse, Morrison, Christie**
32 **CAPE ENTERPRISE (USA),** b c 22/4 Cape Canaveral—
                    Principessa (USA) (Alydeed (CAN)) (35714) **Mr D. M. Kerr & Mr N. Brunskill**
33 B c 29/3 Trans Island—Christoph's Girl (Efisio) (27000) **The Phantom Partnership**
34 **DIAMOND HOMBRE,** gr c 24/2 Two Punch (USA)—
                    Flowing (USA) (El Gran Senor (USA)) (62500) **Mr D. M. Kerr & Mr N. Brunskill**
35 B c 22/3 Unfuwain—Flame Valley (USA) (Gulch (USA)) (35000) **The Croft Partnership**
36 B c 13/2 Sadler's Wells (USA)—Highest Accolade (Shirley Heights) **The Croft Partnership**
37 B c 8/5 Namid—Lovely Me (IRE) (Vision (USA)) (26000) **The Croft Partnership**
38 B f 4/4 Xaar—Miss Golden Sands (Kris) **Crandon Park Stud**
39 **NOBBLER,** b c 3/3 Classic Cliche—Nicely (IRE) (Bustino) **Mrs Claire Smith**
40 Ch f 14/5 Night Shift (USA)—Play The Queen (King of Clubs) **Abbott Racing Partners**
41 B c 6/4 Piccolo—Presently (Cadeaux Genereaux) (16000) **The Phantom Partnership**
42 Ch c 12/3 Woodman—Shalabia (USA) (Fast Topaze (USA)) (26786) **The Croft Partnership**
43 B f 23/1 Almutawakel—Shaping Up (USA) (Storm Bird (CAN)) (17000)
44 B c 11/3 Mark of Esteem (IRE)—Surf Bird (Shareef Dancer (USA)) (6000)
45 **SWEET NAMIBIA (IRE),** ch f 1/4 Namid—Almond Flower (IRE) (Alzao (USA)) (130000) **Mountgrange Stud**
46 B c 20/4 Docksider (USA)—Thakhayr (Sadler's Wells (USA)) (14000)
47 B f 12/4 Danehill Dancer (IRE)—Vieux Carre (Pas de Seul) (12000) **Mr G. & Mrs L. Woodward**
48 **WINDSCREAMER,** b f 20/4 Josr Algarhoud (IRE)—
                    St James's Antigua (IRE) (Law Society (USA)) (10000) **Mr N. N. Browne**
49 **WINGMAN (IRE),** b c 18/5 In The Wings—Precedence (IRE) (Polish Precedent (USA)) (16079) **Mr D. M. Kerr**

Other Owners: Mr Daniel Abbott, Amity Finance Ltd, Mr T. W. Bailey, Mr A. H. Bartlett, Mr R. J. Bolam, Mr A. M. Fairbairn, Mr P. T. Fenwick, Miss L. M. Gold, Mr H. C. Hardy, Mr Stewart R. Hunt, Mr R. Hunter, Mrs M. Kingham, Mr David Klein, Mrs T. Maitland, Mr M. C. Moutray-Read, Mr David Murrell, Mr J. D. Murtagh, Mr C. New, Mr M. J. Pallett, G. D. Peck, Mr Jerry Quinn, Mr Campbell Ross, Mr G. C. Rothwell, Mr A. Scott, Mr Andy J. Smith, Miss E. L. Smith, Mr Brian J. Standing, Mr M. A. Styles, Mrs M. A. Townsend, Mr Gordian Troeller, Mr R. P. Tullett, Mr F. C. W. Whitehouse, Mr G. Woodward, Mrs Linnet Woodward.

Assistant Trainer: Colin Gorman

Jockeys (Flat): M Hills (8-4), R Hills (8-4), S Whitworth (8-2). **Apprentice:** H Gemberlu (8-4).

279 **MR M. R. HOAD, Lewes**
Postal: **Windmill Lodge Stables, Spital Road, Lewes, East Sussex, BN7 1LS.**
Contact: **PHONE** (01273) 477124/(01273) 480691 **MOBILE** (07742) 446168

1 **ADELPHIE LASS**, 4, b f Theatrical Charmer—Miss Adventure **Mrs Julie Hoad**
2 **CORONADO FOREST (USA)**, 5, b g Spinning World (USA)—Desert Jewel (USA) **Mr Ken Webb**
3 **LADY HECCLES**, 5, b m Sayaarr (USA)—Rae Un Soleil **Mr P. Collins**
4 **ROLLING TIDE (IRE)**, 8, b g Alphabatim—St Cristoph **Mr G. Brice**
5 **THE STAGGERY BOY (IRE)**, 8, b g Shalford (IRE)—Murroe Star **Foray Racing**
6 **WILOM (GER)**, 6, ch g Lomitas—Whispering Willows **Mrs Julie Hoad**

TWO-YEAR-OLDS

7 B c 26/4 Pyramus (USA)—Dolphin Beach (IRE) (Dolphin Street (FR))
8 **JUSTCALLMEHANDSOME**, ch c 4/3 Handsome Ridge—Pearl Dawn (IRE) (Jareer (USA)) **Mrs J. E. Taylor**
9 B c 3/4 Pyramus (USA)—Nordesta (IRE) (Nordico (USA))

Other Owners: Mr D. Dunworth, Mr N. Potter, Mr A. Styles.

Jockey (Flat): Dane O'Neill. **Jockey (NH):** L Aspell.

280 **MR P. J. HOBBS, Minehead**
Postal: **Sandhill, Bilbrook, Minehead, Somerset, TA24 6HA.**
Contact: **PHONE** (01984) 640366 **CAR** (07860) 729795 **FAX** (01984) 641124
E-MAIL racing@pjhobbs.freeserve.co.uk

1 **ALDIRUOS (IRE)**, 4, ch c Bigstone (IRE)—Ball Cat (FR) **Aramis Racing Syndicate**
2 **ALLUMEE**, 5, ch g Alflora (IRE)—Coire Vannich **High Spirits**
3 **AMPLIFI (IRE)**, 7, b g Phardante (FR)—Season's Delight **Mr C. K. Watkins**
4 **ANDY GIN (FR)**, 5, b g Ski Chief (USA)—Love Love Kate (FR) **Mr Terry Warner**
5 **BERTIEBANOO (IRE)**, 6, ch g Be My Native (USA)—Gemeleks Gem (IRE) **Mr P. A. Newey**
6 **BLUE DERBY (IRE)**, 6, b g Supreme Leader—Minigirls Niece (IRE) **Mrs Angela Tincknell**
7 **BOW STRADA**, 7, ch g Rainbow Quest (USA)—La Strada **Mr M. J. Tuckey**
8 **BREKNEN LE NOIR (FR)**, 6, b g Pelder (IRE)—Roziyna **Mr P. A. Deal**
9 **CAMERON BRIDGE (IRE)**, 8, b g Camden Town—Arctic Raheen **The Country Side**
10 **CASTLEBOY (IRE)**, 6, b g King's Ride—Bissie's Jayla **Mrs D. L. Whateley**
11 **CASTLEFORD (IRE)**, 6, b g Be My Native (USA)—
        Commanche Bay (IRE) **Mrs D.Whateley,Mrs L.Field & Mr D.Green**
12 **CASTLEMORE (IRE)**, 6, b g Be My Native (USA)—Parsonetta **Castlemore Securities Limited**
13 **CHIVITE (IRE)**, 5, b g Alhaarth (IRE)—Laura Margaret **Mr I. Russell**
14 **CHRISTOPHER**, 7, gr g Arzanni—Forest Nymph (NZ) **Mr Allan Stennett**
15 **CIRRUS (FR)**, 5, gr g Saint Preuil (FR)—Cirta de Champfeu (FR) **Sir Robert Ogden**
16 **CLARENDON**, 8, ch g Forest Wind (USA)—Sparkish (IRE) **The Plus Fours**
17 **CODE SIGN (USA)**, 5, b g Gulch (USA)—Karasavina (IRE) **Denise Winton and Elizabeth Hodgson**
18 **COOL SPICE**, 7, b m Karinga Bay—Cool Run **Celtic Racing**
19 **CORRIB LAD (IRE)**, 6, b br g Supreme Leader—Nun So Game **Ms C. Hehir**
20 **DAMARISCO (FR)**, 4, b g Scribe (IRE)—Blanche Dame (FR) **The Kingpins**
21 **DEUX DROS AMIS**, 6, gr g Roselier (FR)—Rippling Melody **Celtic Racing**
22 **DO L'ENFANT D'EAU (FR)**, 5, ch g Minds Music (USA)—L'Eau Sauvage **Mr Terry Warner**
23 **DOUBLE HONOUR (FR)**, 6, gr g Highest Honor (FR)—Silver Cobra (USA) **The 4th Middleham Partnership**
24 **DUNKERRON**, 7, b g Pursuit of Love—Top Berry **Mr Jack Joseph**
25 **ENRIQUE (GER)**, 9, ch g Niniski (USA)—Eicidora (GER) **Sir Robert Ogden**
26 **EVERREADY**, 6, b g Afzal—Sister Shot **Ms C. Hehir**
27 **FARMER JACK**, 8, b g Alflora (IRE)—Cheryls Pet (IRE) **Mr Peter Partridge**
28 **FLAGSHIP UBERALLES (IRE)**, 10, b g Accordion—Fourth Degree **Mr J. P. McManus**
29 **FLYING FUSELIER**, 5, ch g Gunner B—Wing On **Mrs Z. S. Clark**
30 **FOOL ON THE HILL**, 7, b g Reprimand—Stock Hill Lass **Louisville Syndicate**
31 **FOREVER DREAM**, 6, b g Afzal—Quadrapol **Mr W. McKibbin & Mr A. Stevens**
32 **FREDDY CRYSTAL (FR)**, 5, b g Northern Crystal—Native Times (FR) **Mr Terry Warner**
33 **FREDERIC FOREVER (IRE)**, 6, b g Exit To Nowhere (USA)—Sarooh's Love (USA) **Mrs D. A. Winton**
34 **GALLANT HERO**, 5, b g Rainbow Quest (USA)—Gay Gallanta (USA) **Mrs David Thompson**
35 **GAMBLERS DREAM (IRE)**, 7, b g Executive Perk—Tinkers Lady **Mrs L. R. Lovell**
36 **GENTLE BEAU**, 6, b g Homo Sapien—Tapua Taranata (IRE) **Mr Rod Hamilton**
37 **GIORGIO (IRE)**, 6, b g Presenting—Billys Pet **Sir Robert Ogden**
38 **GOOD LORD LOUIS (IRE)**, 6, br g Presenting—Ash Queen (IRE) **The Country Side**
39 **GREY REPORT (IRE)**, 7, gr g Roselier (FR)—Busters Lodge **Mrs D. A. La Trobe**

MR P. J. HOBBS—continued

40 **GUNTHER MCBRIDE (IRE)**, 9, b g Glacial Storm (USA)—What Side **Mr M. J. Tuckey**
41 **HANDYMAN (IRE)**, 10, b g Hollow Hand—Shady Ahan **Elizabeth Hodgson and Denise Winton**
42 **HARRY'S DREAM**, 7, b g Aflora (IRE)—Cheryls Pet (IRE) **Mr Peter Partridge**
43 **ILE DE PARIS (FR)**, 5, b g Cadoudal (FR)—Sweet Beauty (FR) **Sir Robert Ogden**
44 **IN CONTRAST (IRE)**, 8, b br g Be My Native (USA)—Ballinamona Lady (IRE) **Mr Tony Staple**
45 **IN THE FRAME (IRE)**, 5, b g Definite Article—Victorian Flower **The Gascoigne Brookes Partnership**
46 **JAHASH**, 6, ch g Hernando (FR)—Jalsun **Mr J. Hawkins**
47 **JAROD (FR)**, 6, b g Scribe (IRE)—Somnambula (IRE) **Network Training**
48 **JUST IN TIME**, 9, b g Night Shift (USA)—Future Past (USA) **Mr B. K. Peppiatt**
49 **KALCA MOME (FR)**, 6, b g En Calcat (FR)—Belle Mome (FR) **Miss I. D. Du Pre**
50 **KOQUELICOT (FR)**, 6, ch g Video Rock (FR)—Ixia des Saccarts (FR) **Mr Alan Peterson**
51 **LEABURN (IRE)**, 11, b g Tremblant—Conderlea **The Guiburn Set**
52 **LIMERICK LEADER (IRE)**, 6, b g Supreme Leader—View of The Hills **Mr D. R. Peppiatt**
53 **LINCOLN PLACE (IRE)**, 9, ch g Be My Native (USA)—Miss Lou **Mr A. J. Scrimgeour**
54 **LORD VILLE (FR)**, 5, b g Useful (FR)—Triaina **Mr Rod Hamilton**
55 **LOUP BLEU (USA)**, 5, b g Nureyev (USA)—Louve Bleue (USA) **Richard Green (Fine Paintings)**
56 **MADE IN JAPAN (JPN)**, 4, b g Barathea (IRE)—Darrery **Terry Evans**
57 **MASTER GEORGE**, 7, b g Mtoto—Topwinder (USA) **Mr David R. Watson & Mr Duncan Lofts**
58 **MISTER FLINT**, 6, b g Petoski—National Clover **Mr Alan Peterson**
59 **MONKERHOSTIN (FR)**, 7, b g Shining Steel—Ladoun (FR) **Mr M. G. St Quinton**
60 **MOSCOW WHISPER (IRE)**, 7, b g Moscow Society (USA)—Native Woodfire (IRE) **Mr Yusof Sepiuddin**
61 **MOUNSEY CASTLE**, 7, ch g Carlingford Castle—Gay Ticket **Mr Alan Peterson**
62 **MR FLUFFY**, 7, br g Charmer—Hinton Bairn **The Cockpit Crew**
63 **MRS PHILIP**, 5, b m Puissance—Lightning Legacy (USA) **Mr Jack Joseph & Mrs Philip Hobbs**
64 **NATIVE STAR**, 6, b g Be My Native (USA)—Star Chamber (FR) **Mr M. J. Tuckey**
65 **NIGHT DRIVER (IRE)**, 5, b g Night Shift (USA)—Highshaan **Colin Brown Racing II**
66 **ONE KNIGHT (IRE)**, 8, ch g Roselier (FR)—Midnights Daughter (IRE) **Mr R. Gibbs**
67 **ORSWELL CREST**, 10, b g Crested Lark—Slave's Bangle **The Mane Chance Partnership**
68 **PARSONS LEGACY (IRE)**, 6, b g Leading Counsel (USA)—The Parson's Girl (IRE) **Mr R. A. S. Offer**
69 **PER AMORE (IRE)**, 6, ch g General Monash (USA)—Danny's Miracle **Mrs J. F. Deithrick**
70 **PILGRIMS PROGRESS (FR)**, 4, b c Entrepreneur—Rose Bonbon (FR) **Mr P. A. Newey**
71 **POSSIBLE PARDON (NZ)**, 10, b g Iades (FR)—Wonderful Excuse (NZ) **Mr B. Pike**
72 **QUIET WATER (IRE)**, 8, br g Lord Americo—Sirana **Network Training**
73 **RAGDALE HALL (USA)**, 7, b g Bien Bien—Gift of Dance (USA) **Mr Jack Joseph**
74 **RAOUL DUFY (USA)**, 4, gr g El Prado (USA)—Parrish Empress (USA) **Richard Green (Fine Paintings)**
75 **REIZIGER (FR)**, 8, gr g Balleroy (USA)—Dany Ohio (FR) **D. Jones & B. Thomas**
76 **RIFT VALLEY (IRE)**, 9, b g Good Thyne (USA)—Necochea **Mrs Kathy Stuart**
77 **ROBBER (IRE)**, 7, ch g Un Desperado (FR)—Christy's Girl (IRE) **The Hedonists**
78 **ROOSTER BOOSTER**, 10, gr g Riverwise (USA)—Came Cottage **Mr Terry Warner**
79 **ROSCHAL (IRE)**, 6, gr g Roselier (FR)—Sunday World (USA) **Mr Brian Walsh**
80 **ROSS MINSTER (IRE)**, 10, ro gr g Roselier (FR)—Face To Face **The Country Side**
81 **SABY (FR)**, 6, b g Sassanian (USA)—Valy Flett (FR) **Setsquare Recruitment**
82 **SARAGANN (IRE)**, 9, b g Danehill (USA)—Sarliya (IRE) **Jay Dee Bloodstock Limited**
83 **SHADOW RIVER (IRE)**, 6, b g Over The River (FR)—Society Belle **Ian David Ltd & Byrne Bros (FWK) Ltd**
84 **SHALAKO (USA)**, 6, ch g Kingmambo (USA)—Sporades (USA) **Mr D. J. Jones**
85 **SHAMSAN (IRE)**, 7, ch g Night Shift (USA)—Awayil (USA) **Mr Jack Joseph**
86 **SHE'S OUR NATIVE (IRE)**, 6, b m Be My Native (USA)—More Dash (IRE) **Mr Ian Brice**
87 **SILVER CHIEFTAN (IRE)**, 6, gr g Be My Native (USA)—Mystery Rose **Mr P. A. Newey**
88 **SIMBER HILL (IRE)**, 10, ch g Phardante (FR)—Princess Wager **C. de P. Berry, C. Moore, P. Rowe**
89 **STERLING DOT COM (IRE)**, 8, b g Roselier (FR)—Daddy's Folly **Sterling Racing Syndicate**
90 **SUNNYLAND**, 5, b m Sovereign Water (FR)—Quadrapol **Mr C. D. Harrison**
91 **SUPREME PIPER (IRE)**, 6, b g Supreme Leader—Whistling Doe **Mrs Karola Vann**
92 **SUPREME PRINCE (IRE)**, 7, b g Supreme Leader—Strong Serenade (IRE) **Mrs Karola Vann**
93 **SUPREME SERENADE (IRE)**, 5, b m Supreme Leader—Strong Serenade (IRE) **Mrs Karola Vann**
94 **TAMANGO (FR)**, 7, ch g Klimt (FR)—Tipmosa (FR) **The Brushmakers**
95 **TASKMASTER**, 7, b g Aflora (IRE)—Travail Girl **Andrew & Philippa Wyer**
96 **TENSILE (IRE)**, 9, b g Tenby—Bonnie Isle **Mr D. Charlesworth**
97 **TESIO**, 6, b g Danehill (USA)—Pale Grey **Ms C. Hehir**
98 **TOI EXPRESS (IRE)**, 8, ch g Phardante (FR)—Toi Figures **D. F. P. Racing**
99 **TRESOR PREZINIERE (FR)**, 6, b br g Grand Tresor (FR)—Rose de Martine (FR) **Mr Bob Jevon**
100 **TURAATH (IRE)**, 8, b g Sadler's Wells (USA)—Diamond Field (USA) **Mrs Kathy Stuart**
101 **TUXEDO JUNCTION (NZ)**, 9, br g Little Brown Jug (NZ)—Just Kay (NZ) **Mr D. A. Gascoigne**
102 **UNDER THE SAND (IRE)**, 7, b g Turtle Island (USA)—Occupation **R Triple H**
103 **UNLEASH (USA)**, 5, ch g Benny The Dip (USA)—Lemhi Go (USA) **Mrs David Thompson**
104 **UNLOCKED (IRE)**, 6, b g Supreme Leader—Shunnagh Lass (IRE) **Capt. E. J. Edwards-Heathcote**
105 **VILLAGE KING (IRE)**, 11, b g Roi Danzig (USA)—Honorine (USA) **Capt. E. J. Edwards-Heathcote**

MR P. J. HOBBS—continued

106 **WALSINGHAM (IRE)**, 6, b g Presenting—Let's Compromise **Sir Robert Ogden**
107 **WAVE ROCK**, 9, br g Tragic Role (USA)—Moonscape **Sterling Racing Syndicate**
108 **WIDEMOUTH BAY (IRE)**, 6, br g Be My Native (USA)—Lisaleen River **Mrs J. F. Deithrick**
109 **WILD OATS**, 6, b g Primitive Rising (USA)—Miss Nosey Oats **J & B Gibbs & Sons Ltd**
110 **WILLIE JOHN DALY (IRE)**, 7, b g Mister Lord (USA)—Murphy's Lady (IRE) **Mr D. R. Peppiatt**
111 **XELLANCE (IRE)**, 7, b g Be My Guest (USA)—Excellent Alibi (USA) **The Five Nations Partnership**
112 **ZAFARABAD (IRE)**, 10, gr g Shernazar—Zarafa **Mrs Elaine Baines**

Other Owners: Mr A. J. Allright, Mr Kerry Barker, Mr P. Bateman, Mr C. De P. Berry, Mr J. Blain, Mr N. Brookes, Byrne Bros (Formwork) Ltd, Mr Colin Brown, Mr C. J. Butler, Mr D. F. P. Callaghan, Mr A. M. Carding, Mr T. Connop, Mr J. P. Cooper, Hilary Cope, Ian David Limited, Mrs J. Edwards-Heathcote, Mrs J Gibbs, Mr Bill Gibson, Mrs Glenda Giles, Mr I. Gould, Mr Tim Hailstone, Mr J. R. Hall, Mr J. F. Hanna, Mr M. Hill, Mr R. W. Hills, Mrs S. L. Hobbs, Mrs J. R. Holmes, Mrs B. J. House, Mr Richard B. Huckerby, Mr R. W. Huggins, Mr Gordon E. Innes, Mr R. M. Kellow, K. D. Kerslake, Mr S. C. Lee, Mr Duncan Lofts, D. P. J. Lyons, Mr B. J. Malone, Mr W. McKibbin, Mr Bob Millen, Mr C. Moore, Mr G. R. Penbertys, Mr M. C. Sarsent, Dr R. D. P. Newland, Mrs L. M. Northover, Mr M. J. Ogborne, Mr Joe Parslow, Mr T. Peckham, Mr V. J. Pennington, Nick Peppiatt, Mrs B. S. Port, Mr R. G. Pritchard, Oakview Racing, Mrs E. N. Reed-Daunter, Mr D. A. Rees, Mr S. D. Reeve, Mr Michael Rice, Mrs Jean E Richards, Sir John Robb, Mr J. Robinson, Mrs Patrick Ross, Seamus Ross, Miss Nicole Rossa, Mr Philip Rowe, Mr T. J. R. Sanders, Mr R. Sansom, Mr N. C. Savery, Mr Trevor Sharman, Mrs B. Shaw, Mr I. L. Shaw, Mr D. Sheldon, Brian Shrubsall, Mr R. K. Simmons, Mr Clive D. Smith, Mrs R. O. Steed, Mr Ian S. Steers, Mr A. Stevens, Mr B, H, Thomas, Mr W. Tincknell, Mr C. R. Trembath, Mr R. Trow, Mr C. J. M. Walker, Mr David R. Watson, Miss Lar Whateley, Mr Peter Wiles, Mr David J. Wood.

Assistant Trainer: Richard White & Ben Woodhouse

Jockeys (NH): Paul Flynn (9-7), Richard Johnson (10-0). **Conditional:** P Brennan (9-11). **Amateur:** Mr R Stephens (9-7).

---

281 MR R. J. HODGES, Somerton

Postal: **Footsteps, Cedar Lodge, Charlton Adam, Somerton, Somerset, TA11 7AR.**
Contact: **PHONE (01458) 223922 FAX (01458) 223969 MOBILE (07770) 625846**

1 **ALLERTON BOY**, 5, ch g Beveled (USA)—Darakah **A. Midgley**
2 **ANOTHER DEAL (FR)**, 5, ch g Barathea (IRE)—Mill Rainbow (FR) **Mr R. J. Hodges**
3 **ARABIAN KNIGHT (IRE)**, 4, ch g Fayruz—Cheerful Knight (IRE) **D. F. P. Partnership**
4 **BALI-STAR**, 9, b g Alnasr Alwasheek—Baligay **Mr E. W. Carnell**
5 **BLUE GALE (IRE)**, 6, b m Be My Native (USA)—Riancoir Alainn **Mrs Angela Tincknell**
6 **CASTLE PRINCE (IRE)**, 10, b g Homo Sapien—Lisaleen Lady **Miss R. Dobson**
7 **DEVON MAID**, 5, ch m Fraam—Sharp Dance **Mrs Angela Tincknell**
8 **DREAM FALCON**, 4, b g Polar Falcon (USA)—Pip's Dream **Mr P. E. Axon**
9 **HAZY MORN**, 5, gr m Cyrano de Bergerac—Hazy Kay (IRE) **Mr R. J. Hart**
10 **INDOUX (FR)**, 8, b g Useful (FR)—Pin'hup (FR) **Mr Frank E. Crumpler**
11 **JUPON VERT (FR)**, 7, b g Lights Out (FR)—Danse Verte (FR) **Mrs J. B. Jenkins**
12 **KINGS CASTLE (IRE)**, 9, b g King's Ride—Kilmana (IRE) **Fieldspring Racing**
13 **LA MARETTE**, 6, ch m Karinga Bay—Persistent Gunner **Miss R. Dobson**
14 **MOBO-BACO**, 7, ch g Bandmaster (USA)—Darakah **Frome Racing**
15 **MOUNTS BAY**, 5, ch m Karinga Bay—Sweet On Willie (USA) **D. F. P. Racing**
16 **NOBLE CALLING (FR)**, 7, b h Caller I D (USA)—Specificity (USA) **Nineways**
17 **NOBLE JUSTICE (IRE)**, 8, b g Jurado (USA)—Furry Hope **Fieldspring Racing**
18 **PENTHOUSE MINSTREL**, 10, b br g Seven Hearts—Pentameron **Mr Bob Andrews**
19 **PHAR JEFFEN (IRE)**, 9, ch g Phardante (FR)—Clever Milly **Fieldspring Racing**
20 **ROBERT ELLIS**, 8, ch g Anshan—Susie's Baby **Mr Bob Andrews**
21 **ROYAL PRODIGY (USA)**, 5, ch g Royal Academy (USA)—Prospector's Queen (USA) **Mr D. Charlesworth**
22 **SECOND GENERATION (IRE)**, 7, ch g Cadeaux Genereux—Title Roll (IRE) **Mr Graham Dalziel**
23 **SON OF FLIGHTY**, 6, b g Then Again—Record Flight **Mr Frank E. Crumpler**
24 **TENDER FALCON**, 4, b g Polar Falcon (USA)—Tendresse (IRE) **P. E. Axon**
25 **THE GENE GENIE**, 9, b g Syrtos—Sally Maxwell **Mrs Carol Taylor**
26 **TIKI TAPU**, 6, b m Karinga Bay—Hy Wilma **Mrs C. J. Cole**
27 **TRAVELLERS JOY**, 4, b f The West (USA)—Persian Fortune **Miss R. Dobson**
28 **VINCENT VAN GOGH (IRE)**, 9, b g Executive Perk—Rare Picture **The Trojan Partnership**

THREE-YEAR-OLDS

29 **BARABELLA (IRE)**, gr f Barathea (IRE)—Thatchabella (IRE) **Miss R. Dobson**
30 **ITS ALEX (IRE)**, ch g Tagula (IRE)—Shrewd Girl (USA) **J. W. Mursell**

MR R. J. HODGES—continued

TWO-YEAR-OLDS

31 **INDIAN PEARL (IRE)**, gr f 24/4 Indian Lodge (IRE)—Thatchabella (IRE) (Thatching) (16000) **Miss R. Dobson**

---

282 **MR M. J. HOGAN, Findon**
Postal: **2 New Cottages, Gallops Farm, Findon, West Sussex, BN14 0RQ.**

1 **GREAT CRUSADER**, 12, ch g Deploy—Shannon Princess **Mrs Barbara Hogan**
2 **ISAM TOP (FR)**, 8, b g Siam (USA)—Miss Sic Top (FR) **Mrs Barbara Hogan**
3 **MYSTICAL STAR (FR)**, 7, b g Nicolette—Addaya (IRE) **Mrs Barbara Hogan**

---

283 **MR H. P. HOGARTH, Stillington**
Postal: **New Grange Farm, Stillington, York, YO61 1LR.**
Contact: **(01347) 811168**

1 **ALLFRIENDS**, 5, b br g Alflora (IRE)—Three Friends (IRE) **Hogarth Racing**
2 **CRARAE JACK**, 6, gr g Gran Alba (USA)—Double Dose **Hogarth Racing**
3 7, B m Perpendicular—Distant Cherry
4 **HENRY PEARSON (USA)**, 6, ch g Distant View (USA)—Lady Ellen (USA) **Hogarth Racing**
5 **JURALAN (IRE)**, 9, b g Jurado (USA)—Boylan **Hogarth Racing**
6 **KEIRAN (IRE)**, 10, b g Be My Native (USA)—Myra Gaye **Hogarth Racing**
7 **PRIMITIVE REBEL**, 5, gr g Primitive Rising (USA)—Distant Cherry **Hogarth Racing**
8 **RED RAMPAGE**, 9, b g King's Ride—Mighty Fly **Hogarth Racing**
9 **THE SLEEPER**, 8, b g Perpendicular—Distant Cherry **Hogarth Racing**

Other Owners: Mr J. Hogarth, Mr J. L. Hogarth, Mr P. H. Hogarth.

Jockey (NH): D O'Meara (10-0).

---

284 **MR A. S. T. HOLDSWORTH, Abbotskerswell**
Postal: **By The Way, Abbotskerswell, Devon, TQ12 5NL.**
Contact: **HOME (01626) 334584**

1 **OFF MY TOES**, 4, b f Relief Pitcher—On My Toes **Mr N. J. Holdsworth**
2 **UMISTA (IRE)**, 5, b m Tagula (IRE)—Nishiki (USA) **Mr N. J. Holdsworth**

TWO-YEAR-OLDS

3 **BARHAM BROOK**, b f Bandmaster (USA)—Time To Move (IRE) (Cyrano de Bergerac) **Mr N. J. Holdsworth**

Assistant Trainer: E M Vince

Jockey (NH): G Supple. **Amateur:** Mr D Alers Hanky.

---

285 **MR A. F. HOLLINGSWORTH, Feckenham**
Postal: **Lanket House, Crofts Lane, Feckenham, Redditch, Worcestershire, B96 6PU.**
Contact: **PHONE (01527) 68644/892054 MOBILE (07775) 670644**

1 **BLACKANBLUE**, 5, b g Alflora (IRE)—Emmabella **A. Hollingsworth**
2 **GALLIK DAWN**, 6, ch g Anshan—Sticky Money **Mr Perry Adams**
3 **GEMSTER**, 6, b m Alflora (IRE)—Gemmabel **Kombined Motor Services Ltd**
4 **HIJACKED**, 10, b g True Song—Scamper **A. Hollingsworth**
5 **LOOSE NUT**, 6, b m Alflora (IRE)—Emmabella **Kombined Motor Services Ltd**
6 **MAKE IT PLAIN**, 5, b m Alflora (IRE)—Gemmabel **A. Hollingsworth**
7 **MILDAN GRACE**, 8, b m Afzal—An Bothar Dubh **A. Hollingsworth**
8 **QUARTERMASS**, 8, b g Karinga Bay—Panchellita (USA) **A. Holingsworth**

Assistant Trainer: Sharon Smith

Jockey (NH): A Thornton. **Conditional:** D R Dennis. **Amateurs:** Mr T Greenway, Mr J Newbould, Mr T Stephenson.

286 MR R. HOLLINSHEAD, Upper Longdon
Postal: **Lodge Farm, Upper Longdon, Rugeley, Staffordshire, WS15 1QF.**
Contact: **PHONE (01543) 490298 FAX (01543) 490490**

1 **AMBITIOUS ANNIE**, 5, b m Most Welcome—Pasja (IRE) **Mr Kieron P. Grealis**
2 **CASTLE RING**, 5, b g Sri Pekan (USA)—Understudy **Mr R. Hollinshead**
3 **CHICKASAW TRAIL**, 6, ch m Be My Chief (USA)—Maraschino **Mr Anthony White**
4 **COMMANDER FLIP (IRE)**, 4, ch g In Command (IRE)—Boldabsa **Mr Tim Leadbeater**
5 **CROSS ASH (IRE)**, 4, ch g Ashkalani (IRE)—Priorite (IRE) **Mr Tim Leadbeater**
6 **DANGER BIRD (IRE)**, 4, ch f Eagle Eyed (USA)—Danger Ahead **The C H F Partnership**
7 **DANUM**, 4, b c Perpendicular—Maid of Essex **Clarke, Lawrence and Hollinshead**
8 **DORA CORBINO**, 4, b f Superpower—Smartie Lee **Mrs Norman Hill**
9 **GILDED COVE**, 4, b c Polar Prince (IRE)—Cloudy Reef **Mr M. Johnson**
10 **GOLDEVA**, 5, gr m Makbul—Gold Belt (IRE) **Mr M. Pyle & Mrs T. Pyle**
11 **HEATHYARDSBLESSING (IRE)**, 7, b g Unblest—Noble Nadia **Mr L. A. Morgan**
12 **HEATHYARDS PRIDE**, 4, b g Polar Prince (IRE)—Heathyards Lady (USA) **Mr L. A. Morgan**
13 **HIGH POLICY (IRE)**, 8, ch g Machiavellian (USA)—Road To The Top **Mrs Susy Haslehurst**
14 **JUST RED**, 6, ch h Meqdaam (USA)—Orchard Bay **Mr J. Holcombe**
15 **MAI TAI (IRE)**, 9, b m Scenic—Oystons Propweekly **Mr Keith Nicholson**
16 **MARGOLD (IRE)**, 4, ch f Goldmark (USA)—Arcevia (IRE) **L & R Roadlines**
17 **NICKEL SUNGIRL (IRE)**, 4, b f Petorius—Sharp Hint **Mr Keith Nicholson**
18 **NORTHERN NYMPH**, 5, b g Makbul—Needwood Sprite **Mr Tim Leadbeater**
19 **PRINCE OF GOLD**, 4, b c Polar Prince (IRE)—Gold Belt (IRE) **Horne, Hollinshead, Johnson**
20 **RED MOOR (IRE)**, 4, gr g Eagle Eyed (USA)—Faakirah **The C H F Partnership**
21 **ROYAL CAVALIER**, 7, b g Prince of Birds (USA)—Gold Belt (IRE) **The Three R's**
22 **SASHAY**, 6, b m Bishop of Cashel—St James's Antigua (IRE) **E Young, D Short, M Board**
23 **SILVER MASCOT**, 5, gr g Mukaddamah (USA)—Always Lucky **Mr R. Hollinshead**
24 **STRAVMOUR**, 8, ch h Seymour Hicks (FR)—La Stravaganza **Mr E. Bennion**
25 **SUPER DOMINION**, 7, ch g Superpower—Smartie Lee **Mrs Norman Hill**
26 **THEATRE TINKA (IRE)**, 5, b g King's Theatre (IRE)—Orange Grouse (IRE) **Mr Tim Leadbeater**
27 **THINK QUICK (IRE)**, 4, b f Goldmark (USA)—Crimson Ring **Mr R. Hollinshead**
28 **VERMILION CREEK**, 5, b m Makbul—Cloudy Reef **Mr M. Johnson**
29 **VICTORY FLIP (IRE)**, 4, b f Victory Note (USA)—Two Magpies **Mr Tim Leadbeater**
30 **WEET FOR ME**, 8, b g Warning—Naswara (USA) **Ed Weetman (Haulage & Storage) Ltd**

THREE-YEAR-OLDS

31 B g Wolfhound (USA)—Anthem Flight (USA)
32 **BRETTON**, b g Polar Prince (IRE)—Understudy **Mr J. D. Graham**
33 **FOOLISH GROOM**, ch g Groom Dancer (USA)—Scared **Mr J. D. Graham**
34 **GRELE (USA)**, gr f Loup Sauvage (USA)—Fiveblushingroses (USA) **Mr J. D. Graham**
35 **HEATHYARDS JOY**, ch f Komaite (USA)—Heathyards Lady (USA) **Mr L. A. Morgan**
36 **KUKA**, b g Polar Prince (IRE)—Crissem (IRE) **Mrs Christine Johnson**
37 **MR MIDASMAN (IRE)**, b c Entrepreneur—Sifaara (IRE) **Mr Tim Leadbeater**
38 **MRS GEE (IRE)**, b f Desert Story (IRE)—My Gloria (IRE) **Mr J. D. Graham**
39 **NANNA (IRE)**, b f Danetime (IRE)—Pre Catelan **Mrs G. A. Weetman**
40 **NORMA HILL**, b f Polar Prince (IRE)—Smartie Lee **Mrs Norman Hill**
41 **PEPE (IRE)**, b f Bahhare (USA)—Orange And Blue **Mr J. D. Graham**
42 **SAFFRON RIVER**, b c Polar Prince (IRE)—Cloudy Reef **Mr M. Johnson**
43 **WEET A HEAD (IRE)**, b c Foxhound (USA)—Morale **Mr Ed Weetman**
44 **WEET AN STORE (IRE)**, gr c Spectrum (IRE)—Karmisymixa (FR) **Ed Weetman (Haulage & Storage) Ltd**
45 **WOOLLY BACK (IRE)**, b g Alzao (USA)—Hopping Higgins (IRE) **Mr J. D. Graham**

TWO-YEAR-OLDS

46 Br f Nomination—Barachois Princess (USA) (Barachois (CAN)) **Mr J. D. Graham**
47 Br c Nomination—Cutlass Princess (USA) (Cutlass (USA)) **Mr J. D. Graham**
48 B c Polar Prince (IRE)—Etma Rose (IRE) (Fairy King (USA)) (4000) **Mr R. Hollinshead**
49 **LEGAL LOVER (IRE)**, b c Woodborough (USA)—
　　　　　　　　　　　Victoria's Secret (IRE) (Law Society (USA)) (9894) **Mr Tim Leadbeater**
50 B c Rossini (USA)—Lonely Brook (USA) (El Gran Senor (USA)) (12986)
51 **MALAIKA**, b f Polar Prince (IRE)—Gold Belt (IRE) (Bellypha) **Mr M. Pyle & Mrs T. Pyle**
52 Ch f Spectrum (IRE)—Minstrels Folly (USA) (The Minstrel (CAN)) (3710) **Mr R. Hollinshead**
53 B f Desert Story (IRE)—My Gloria (IRE) (Saint Estephe (FR)) (3091) **Mr J. D. Graham**
54 B c Entrepreneur—Nom de Plume (USA) (Nodouble (USA)) (3400) **Mr R. Hollinshead**
55 **POLAR PASSION**, b f Polar Prince (IRE)—Priorite (IRE) (Kenmare (FR)) **Mr Tim Leadbeater**
56 B f Mark of Esteem (IRE)—Pounelta (Tachypous) (22262) **Mr R. Hollinshead**

MR R. HOLLINSHEAD—continued

57 B f Polar Prince (IRE)—Understudy (In The Wings) **Mr R. Hollinshead**
58 WEET N MEASURES, b c Weet-A-Minute (IRE)—
Weet Ees Girl (IRE) (Common Grounds) **Ed Weetman (Haulage & Storage) Ltd**

Other Owners: Mr M. J. Board, Mr S. R. Clarke, Mr C. H. Fischer, Mr K. H. Fischer, Mr D. R. Horne, Mr Andrew Lawrence, Mr M. Pyle, Mrs T. Pyle, Mr Ray Robinson, Mr D. Short, Mr E. J. G. Young.

Assistant Trainer: A N Hollinshead

Apprentices: A Hawkins (8-0), Stephanie Hollinshead (7-12), S Sayer. **Amateur:** Mrs Jane Galpin (8-7).

---

287 MR CON HORGAN, Marlborough
Postal: **Pond Cottage, Uffcott, Swindon, Wiltshire, SN4 9NB.**
Contact: **OFFICE (01793) 731676 FAX (01793) 731889 MOBILE (07850) 365459**

1 ALZOLA (IRE), 7, b m Alzao (USA)—Polistatic **Mr C. A. Horgan**
2 ARTZOLA (IRE), 4, b f Alzao (USA)—Polistatic **Mrs B. Sumner**
3 BLUE QUIVER (IRE), 4, b c Bluebird (USA)—Paradise Forum **Mrs B. Sumner**
4 HALLINGS OVERTURE (USA), 5, b g Halling (USA)—Sonata **Mrs B. Sumner**
5 OCEAN AVENUE (IRE), 5, b g Dolphin Street (FR)—Trinity Hall **Mr A. Kinghorn**
6 POLANSKI MILL, 5, b g Polish Precedent (USA)—Mill On The Floss **Mrs B. Sumner**
7 REGAL GALLERY (IRE), 6, b m Royal Academy (USA)—Polistatic **Mrs B. Sumner**

THREE-YEAR-OLDS

8 FUTURE DEAL, b f First Trump—Katyushka (IRE) **Mr Mohammed Al-Gaoud**
9 KAJUL, b f Emperor Jones (USA)—Andbell **Mr Mohammed Al-Gaoud**
10 OCEAN ROCK, b c Perugino (USA)—Polistatic **Mrs B. Sumner**
11 PARADISE BREEZE, b f Perugino (USA)—Paradise Forum **Mrs B. Sumner**
12 PEARL FARM, b f Foxhound (USA)—Trinity Hall **Miss Katie Kinghorn**

---

288 MR M. HOURIGAN, Limerick
Postal: **Lissaleen, Patrickswell, Limerick, Ireland.**
Contact: **+353 (0) 61 396603 +353 (0) 86 8226655 FAX +353 (0) 61 396812**

1 ALMIER (IRE), 6, gr g Phardante (FR)—Stepfaster
2 AMERICAN DUCHESS (IRE), 7, b m Lord Americo—Dukes Darling
3 A NEW STORY (IRE), 6, b g Fourstars Allstar (USA)—Diyala (FR)
4 ARCTIC WARRIOR (IRE), 5, b m Arctic Lord—Ye Little Daisy
5 ARTEEA (IRE), 5, b g Oscar (IRE)—Merric (IRE)
6 BEEF OR SALMON (IRE), 8, ch g Cajetano (USA)—Farinella (IRE)
7 BLACK CHURCH LAD (IRE), 8, gr g Ashmolean (USA)—Petit Guest
8 BOUGHT HIMIN, 6, b g Alderbrook—Reperage (USA)
9 BROWN PADDY, 12, b g Buckley—Another Rumour
10 CASINI, 5, b g Slip Anchor—Ower (IRE)
11 CASLAIN OG (IRE), 6, b m Supreme Leader—Caslain Nua
12 CEOL TIRE (IRE), 9, gr m Roselier (FR)—Banna's Lady (IRE)
13 CHANGE THE PLAN (IRE), 6, ch g Bob Back (USA)—Dysart Lass
14 CLARIDGE (IRE), 5, b g Aahsaylad—Bucks Serenade (IRE)
15 COURT CLONAGH (IRE), 8, b g Governor General—Tarka
16 CRATLOE CASTLE (IRE), 6, b g Aahsaylad—Miss Paleface
17 DASHER'S CHOICE, 4, b f Defacto (USA)—Skiddaw Bird
18 DENMARK, 5, b h Danehill (USA)—Shamarra (FR)
19 DROMHALE LADY (IRE), 11, gr m Roselier (FR)—Miss Minella
20 ELBOWS MAGUINESS (IRE), 7, br g Lord Americo—Anmaca (IRE)
21 EMER'S CHOICE, 4, b f Moscow Society (USA)—Time O'Day (IRE)
22 EURO FLYER (IRE), 6, b m Muharib (USA)—Tranquila
23 FAITHEN GRAND (IRE), 6, b m Lucky Guest—Tangle Thorn
24 GARSINGTON (IRE), 7, ch m Over The River (FR)—Apicat
25 HAILY BABY (IRE), 9, b m Ilium—Bellavard
26 HAPPENSTANCE (IRE), 4, b c Ali-Royal (IRE)—Viking Dream (IRE)
27 HAVE A SHARE (IRE), 9, b m Husyan (USA)—Tell A Tale
28 HI CLOY (IRE), 7, b g Be My Native (IRE)—Thomastown Girl
29 HORIZON HILL (USA), 4, b g Distant View (USA)—Accardia Rocket (USA)

MR M. HOURIGAN—continued

30 **HORNER ROCKS (IRE)**, 8, b g Phardante (FR)—Horner Water (IRE)
31 **HOW SPLENDID (IRE)**, 6, b g Hubbly Bubbly (USA)—Peter's Sister (IRE)
32 **IT ECHOES SISTER (IRE)**, 7, ch m Executive Perk—Nicenames (IRE)
33 **JOHNJOE'S EXPRESS (IRE)**, 7, gr g Moscow Society (USA)—Abigails Dream
34 **JUST (IRE)**, 5, ch g Great Marquess—Gerdando Lady (IRE)
35 **KELLYS LEADER (IRE)**, 7, b m Supreme Leader—Nora Dante (IRE)
36 **KERRYHEAD WINDFARM (IRE)**, 6, br g Bob Back (USA)—Kerryhead Girl (IRE)
37 **KILBEGGAN LAD (IRE)**, 6, b g Doyoun—Pamala (USA)
38 **KILLONE MOONLIGHT (IRE)**, 5, b m Moonax (IRE)—Killone Brae
39 **KING KARACKACUS (IRE)**, 5, b g Flemensfirth (USA)—Supreme Alliance (IRE)
40 **KNOCKNABROGUE (IRE)**, 6, b m Afzal—Just Precious
41 **LEAVEITSO (IRE)**, 6, b g Gothland (FR)—C P V Lady
42 **LEMAGURT (IRE)**, 4, b f Mukaddamah (USA)—Fervent Fan (IRE)
43 **MAVERICK DANCER (IRE)**, 6, ch g Goldmark (USA)—Lili Bengam
44 **MINELLA VIC (IRE)**, 5, b g Old Vic—The Race Fly
45 **MOSCOW PARADE (IRE)**, 6, b g Moscow Society (USA)—Corrie Laugh (IRE)
46 **MR GROUSE (IRE)**, 5, b g Maramouresh (USA)—French Lady (IRE)
47 **OLD KILMINCHY (IRE)**, 8, b br g Cashel Court—Janeyway
48 **OLIVERJOHN (IRE)**, 7, ch g Denel (FR)—Graeme's Gem
49 **ON THE BALL (IRE)**, 5, b m Zaffaran (USA)—Khazna
50 **RABBLE RUN (IRE)**, 5, b m Zaffaran (USA)—Ribble Rabble
51 **RAJOE (IRE)**, 5, b m Lord Americo—Blackbushe Place (IRE)
52 **ROCKHOLM BOY (IRE)**, 11, b g Eve's Error—Rockholm Rosie
53 **SARGON**, 5, b h Oscar (IRE)—Syrian Queen
54 **SHADE ME SHAUNY (IRE)**, 9, b g Phardante (FR)—Sleeven Lady
55 **SHE'LL BE LUCKY**, 6, ch m Arctic Cider (USA)—Johnnys Girl
56 **SIMON VAUGHAN (IRE)**, 6, ch g Montelimar (USA)—Arakeepa
57 **SOCRATES**, 6, b g Hernando (FR)—Kamada (USA)
58 **SPANISH ATHLETE**, 5, b m Relief Pitcher—Kings Athlete (IRE)
59 **SURPRISE MILLION (IRE)**, 5, b g Semillon—Surprise Packet
60 **TAKE THE OATH (IRE)**, 7, b g Big Sink Hope (USA)—Delgany Chimes (IRE)
61 **TAP THE BARREL (IRE)**, 6, b m Roselier (FR)—Dear Limousin
62 **THE PARISHIONER (IRE)**, 6, ch m Glacial Storm (USA)—Phairy Miracles (FR)
63 **THE REAL SOLARA (IRE)**, 7, b g Aahsaylad—Arctic Brief
64 **THE SPACER (IRE)**, 6, ch g Florida Sun—Tacova's Gift (IRE)
65 **THE TAILER CAREY (IRE)**, 5, b g Kadeed (IRE)—Secret Tryst (IRE)
66 **VICTORIAN LADY**, 7, b m Old Vic—Semperflorens
67 **VIC VILLE (IRE)**, 5, b g Old Vic—N T Nad
68 **WHOWOULDYOUASK (IRE)**, 4, ch g Ridgewood Ben—Generali Contadini
69 **WILLIESDREAM (IRE)**, 5, b g Kadeed (IRE)—Eye In The Sky
70 **WILLIE THE SHOE**, 7, b g Pyramus—Me Neither

---

289 **MR H. S. HOWE, Tiverton**
Postal: **Ringstone Stables, Oakford, Tiverton, Devon, EX16 9EU.**
Contact: **PHONE (01398) 351224 MOBILE (07802) 506344**
FAX (01938) 351153 **E-MAIL** stuarthoweracing@yahoo.co.uk

1 **BOOZY DOUZ**, 4, ch f Abou Zouz (USA)—Ackcontent (USA) **Mr R. J. Sage**
2 **CLIFTON MIST**, 8, gr m Lyphento (USA)—Brave Maiden **Mr Richard Garrard**
3 **MADAMOISELLE JONES**, 4, b f Emperor Jones (USA)—Tiriana **Horses Away Racing Club**
4 **MUSIC MAID (IRE)**, 6, b m Inzar—Richardstown Lass (IRE) **R. J. Parish**
5 **REPLACEMENT PET (IRE)**, 7, b m Petardia—Richardstown Lass (IRE) **Mr R. J. Sage**
6 **SHAKE EDDIE SHAKE (IRE)**, 7, b g Blues Traveller (IRE)—Fortune Teller **Mr C. I. A. Slocock**
7 **SILVER CHARMER**, 5, b m Charmer—Sea Dart **Mr John Bull**
8 **SILVER CHARTER (USA)**, 5, b g Silver Hawk (USA)—Pride of Darby (USA) **Mr M. J. Moore**
9 **SUNDAY GOLD**, 4, b f Lion Cavern (USA)—Sunday Night (GER) **Ms A. Williams**

THREE-YEAR-OLDS

10 **BAHAMA BELLE**, b f Bahamian Bounty—Barque Bleue (USA) **The Trojan Partnership**
11 **DELPHINIUM (IRE)**, b f Dr Massini (IRE)—Lunulae **Mrs M. O'Sullivan**
12 **GONE LOCO**, b f Piccolo—Missed Again **B. Griffith**
13 **LADY REDERA (IRE)**, b f Inzar (USA)—Era **Horses Away Racing Club**
14 **OPERA BABE (IRE)**, b f Kahyasi—Fairybird (FR) **Mr Kevin Daniel Crabb**
15 **UIG**, ch f Bien Bien (USA)—Madam Zando **Mr Stuart Howe**

MR H. S. HOWE—continued
TWO-YEAR-OLDS

16 B f 24/2 King's Theatre (IRE)—Duly Elected (Persian Bold) (2500) **R. J. Parish**
17 B f 28/4 Josr Algarhoud—Slava (USA) (Diesis) (2200)
18 B f 18/2 Perryston View—Tonic Chord (La Grange Music) (800)

Other Owners: Mrs Ruth Egan, Mr Ian Forster, Mr C. J. Harris, Mr C. R. Hollands, Mr Jonathan Leigh, A. F. O'Callaghan, J. S. Tackley.

Jockeys (Flat): S Drowne (w.a.), D Kinsella. **Jockeys (NH):** P Flynn, R. P. McNally.

---

290   MR P. HOWLING, Newmarket
Postal: **Wellbottom Lodge, Moulton Paddocks, Bury Road, Newmarket, Suffolk, CB8 7PJ.**
Contact: **PHONE (01638) 668503 MOBILE (07866) 674469 E-MAIL billichang@aol.com**

1 ARTISTRY, 4, b f Night Shift (USA)—Arriving **Wyck Hall Stud**
2 A TEEN, 6, ch h Presidium—Very Good **Mrs A. K. Petersen**
3 BELLESOEUR, 4, ch f Whittingham (IRE)—Trina's Pet **Mr Paul Howling**
4 BELLS BEACH (IRE), 6, b m General Monash (USA)—Clifton Beach **Mr Paul Howling**
5 FABRANESE, 4, b f Dr Devious (USA)—Babsy Babe **Mr I. Pattle**
6 FEAST OF ROMANCE, 7, b g Pursuit of Love—June Fayre **Mr D. C. Patrick**
7 ITS ECCO BOY, 6, ch g Clantime—Laena **Mr J. Hammond**
8 LAHOB, 4, ch c First Trump—Mystical Song **Arkland International (UK) Ltd**
9 MADIBA, 5, b g Emperor Jones (USA)—Priluki **Eastwell Manor Racing Ltd**
10 MANNORA, 4, b f Prince Sabo—Miss Bussell **Arkland Interntional (UK) Ltd**
11 SECOND VENTURE, 6, b g Petardia—Hilton Gateway **Mr Richard Berenson**
12 SHAMROCK CITY (IRE), 7, b g Rock City—Actualite **Mr Liam Sheridan**
13 SURDOUE, 4, b g Bishop of Cashel—Chatter's Princess **Les Amis Partners**
14 THE LAST MOHICAN, 5, b g Common Grounds—Arndilly **Mr P. Woodward**
15 TOPTON (IRE), 10, b g Royal Academy (USA)—Circo **Mr Liam Sheridan**
16 TROJAN WOLF, 9, ch g Wolfhound (USA)—Trojan Lady (USA) **Mr Max Pocock**
17 WARLINGHAM (IRE), 6, b g Catrail (USA)—Tadjname (USA) **Mr D. Brown**

THREE-YEAR-OLDS

18 ALTARES, b c Alhaarth (IRE)—Reach The Wind (USA) **Mrs A. K. Petersen**
19 ANOUSA (IRE), b c Intikhab (USA)—Annaletta **Arkland International (UK) Ltd**
20 B g Polar Falcon (USA)—Bowden Rose **Mr M. Boreham**
21 DIAL SQUARE, b g Bluegrass Prince (IRE)—Honey Mill **Mr Rory Murphy**
22 MY PENSION (IRE), b g Orpen (USA)—Woodenitbenice (USA) **Mr D. Brown**
23 MYRIAD, ch f Amfortas (IRE)—Spriolo **Wyck Hall Stud**
24 NADIR, b c Pivotal—Amid The Stars **Mr Liam Sheridan**
25 PENWAY, b c Groom Dancer (USA)—Imani **Mr R. Khan**

TWO-YEAR-OLDS

26 B c 20/2 Komaite (USA)—Blossoming (Vague Shot) **Mr M. Boreham**
27 B c 17/5 Lake Coniston (IRE)—Daynabee (Common Grounds) (1800) **Mr Paul Howling**
28 B c 22/4 Lugana Beach—Double Rock (Rock Hopper) **Mr Alfred Walls**
29 B c 27/4 Bluegrass Prince—Lowrianna (Cyrano de Bergerac) (800) **Mr C. Hammond**

Other Owners: Mr Christopher Hammond, Mrs J. C. Lewis, Mr Steve Pugh, Mrs E. Reid, Mrs Harry Sawyer, Mrs Lily Smith, Mr C. N. Wright.

Assistant Trainer: Mrs J Howling

Jockeys (Flat): K Fallon, J Quinn (7-7), R Winston. **Amateur:** Miss Francoise Guillambert.

291 **MR J. S. HUBBUCK, Hexham**
Postal: High House Farm, Highford Lane, Hexham, Northumberland, NE46 2LZ.
Contact: PHONE (01434) 602913

1 BRIDGEND BLUE (IRE), 8, b g Up And At 'em—Sperrin Mist **Mr J. S. Hubbuck**

292 **MR D. T. HUGHES, Kildare**
Postal: Osborne Lodge, Kildare, Co. Kildare, Ireland.
Contact: PHONE +353 (0) 45 521490 FAX +353 (0) 45 521643 MOBILE +353 (0) 862 534098

1 ADMIRAL BROWN (IRE), 8, b g Supreme Leader—Light The Lamp **K. McNulty**
2 ALLSUN (IRE), 4, b g Eagle Eyed (USA)—Be Crafty (USA) **Peter Brady**
3 AQUEDUCT (IRE), 5, b g Alflora (IRE)—Mrs Barty (IRE) **Glen Devlin**
4 ARDAN GLASS (IRE), 7, ch g Safety Catch (USA)—Jude's Hollow (IRE) **James J. Gleeson**
5 BALLYELLERY BOY (IRE), 5, ch g Fayruz—Mabsouta **D. T. Hughes**
6 BAMMERS (IRE), 6, ch m Zaffaran (USA)—Glaskerbeg Lady (IRE) **Mrs K. Leech**
7 CARDINAL VALLEY (IRE), 7, b g Shardari—Who Says **Sean Dalton**
8 CELESTIAL LIGHT (IRE), 7, b m Archway (IRE)—Lady Heather **Michael B. Moore**
9 CENTRAL HOUSE, 7, b g Alflora (IRE)—Fantasy World **Francis G. Kenny**
10 CHAIN, 7, b g Last Tycoon—Trampship **James Kelly**
11 COLONEL BRAXTON (IRE), 9, b g Buckskin (FR)—Light The Lamp **Mrs John Magnier**
12 COLUMBA (IRE), 8, b g Lord Americo—Jackson Miss **Brian MacMahon**
13 COPPERVEGA (IRE), 5, b m Toulon—Friars Pass **Sean O'Regan**
14 CUPLA CAIRDE, 4, b c Double Eclipse (IRE)—Four Legged Friend **Ceathrar Le Ceile Syndicate**
15 DEE MAN (IRE), 7, b g Posen (USA)—Suttonian (IRE) **Gary McCausland**
16 DEMOPHILOS, 6, b g Dr Devious (IRE)—Graecia Magna (USA) **Athos Christodoulou**
17 DERAMORE (IRE), 7, b g Hollow Hand—Leaney Kamscourt **Busted Sofa Syndicate**
18 DESIGN TO WIN (IRE), 5, b m Flemensfirth (USA)—Miss Brecknell (IRE) **John Quigley**
19 DEVERED (IRE), 5, ch g Desert King (IRE)—Tea House **H. McCalmot, H de Burgh & P. Myerscough**
20 DJANDO (IRE), 5, ch g Glacial Storm (USA)—Rathtrim **Brian Keoghan**
21 DON AMECHIE (IRE), 8, gr g Roselier (FR)—Miss Pitpan **T. J. Culhane/Brian McMahon**
22 DUBLIN HUNTER (IRE), 8, b g Treasure Hunter—Cutty Sark **Woodland Racing Syndicate**
23 ELIZABETH TUDOR (IRE), 6, b m Supreme Leader—Tudor Dawn **Mrs J. Magnier**
24 5, B m Dilum (USA)—Fantasy World **John Kenny**
25 FIRE QUEEN (IRE), 4, b f Perugino (USA)—El Pina **The Star Syndicate**
26 FRENCH STYLE (IRE), 8, b m Archway—Rustic Stile **Brian MacMahon**
27 5, B h Glacial Storm (USA)—Gale Choice (IRE) **M. Kane**
28 GLENANNAAR, 6, b g Supreme Leader—Miss Dunbrody **Declan O'Keeffe**
29 GONEFORALLTIME (IRE), 6, b m Lord Americo—Jackson Miss **Mrs Nancy Doyle**
30 GUILT, 4, b g Mark of Esteem (IRE)—Guillem (USA) **T C D D Syndicate**
31 HARD WINTER (IRE), 7, b g Arctic Lord—Lucycello **D. A. Pim**
32 HARDY DUCKETT (IRE), 5, br g Key of Luck (USA)—Bramdean **Laurence Byrne**
33 HARDY EUSTACE (IRE), 7, b g Archway (IRE)—Sterna Star **Laurence Byrne**
34 HARDY OLIVER (IRE), 5, b h Flemensfirth—Lucky Appeal **Laurence Byrne**
35 HEADS ONTHE GROUND (IRE), 7, br g Be My Native—Strong Wings **John P. McManus**
36 IRISH STREAM (USA), 6, ch g Irish River (FR)—Euphonic (USA) **James T. Barton**
37 5, Ch h Presenting—Isodes Tower **A. Hanahoe**
38 I'VEHADIT (IRE), 10, ch g Treasure Hunter—Had Enough **D. A. Pim**
39 KHAIRAMRAR (IRE), 7, gr g Persian Bold—Khairkana (IRE) **S. Mulryan**
40 KILDARE (IRE), 7, b g Supreme Leader—Fairly Deep **Cathal Ryan**
41 KILDARE MINOR (IRE), 5, b g Old Vic—Fairly Deep **Cathal M. Ryan**
42 LEINSTER (IRE), 7, b g Supreme Leader—Jennycomequick **Cathal Ryan**
43 LISCANNOR LAD (IRE), 6, b g Nicolotte—Tinerana Memories (IRE) **C. P. O'Brien**
44 LORNA'S LADY (IRE), 8, b m Be My Native (USA)—Gales Chariot **Breda Brady & M. P. Whelan**
45 MARK THE SHARK (IRE), 4, b g Entrepreneur—Danse Royale (IRE) **D. T. Hughes**
46 5, B h Carroll House—Matinee Theatre **Tony O'Meara**
47 4, B g Eagle Eyed (USA)—Mean To Me **Favourites RAcing Ltd**
48 MERRIE CHAPEL (IRE), 5, b g College Chapel—Merrie Moment (IRE) **Three To One Syndicate**
49 MICKEY CUMBA (IRE), 5, ch g Shernazar—Scarlet Lane **A. Hanahoe**
50 5, B h King's Ride—Mossey Tune **H. A. Campbell**
51 MUTINEER (IRE), 5, gr g Highest Honor (FR)—Miss Amy R (USA) **Seven To Eleven Syndicate**
52 NEVER AWOL (IRE), 7, ch g John French—Lark Lass **Peter S. Thompson**
53 NIGHT BUSKER (IRE), 6, b g Accordian—Toca Time (IRE) **Gigginstown House Stud**
54 NOBLE PRINCE (IRE), 7, ch g Nucleon (USA)—Burnished Gold **T. J. Culhane**
55 O'DRISCOLL (IRE), 6, b g Bob Back (USA)—Winter Fox **Cathal M. Ryan**
56 OUR HANDYMAN (IRE), 6, b g Nucleon (USA)—Burnished Gold **Peter S. Thompson**

MR D. T. HUGHES—continued

57 PAKIEFROMATHLEAGUE (IRE), 6, b h Namaqualand (USA)—Krisdaline (USA) **B. Connaughton**
58 PASSING INTEREST (USA), 5, br h Defensive Play (USA)—Intimate (USA) **K. F. McNulty**
59 PATHUGHKENJO (IRE), 4, ch g Eagle Eyed (USA)—Deirdre's Music **Irish Racing Syndicate**
60 POR CHABLIS (IRE), 5, b g Key of Luck (USA)—State Princess (IRE) **K. McNulty**
61 PUNTA CANA (IRE), 5, b h Moonax (IRE)—Aliceion **Pakie Cummins**
62 RACHEL'S CHOICE (IRE), 5, b m Ela-Mana-Mou—Kutaisi (USA) **Sean Mulryan**
63 SPY GAME (IRE), 4, b g Definite Article—Postie **Sean Dunne**
64 SUPREME JUSTICE (IRE), 8, br g Supreme Leader—Flashey Blonde **Donald King**
65 TATENDA (IRE), 6, b g Accordion—Loughloone (IRE) **Declan Hyland**
66 THE JESUIT (IRE), 5, b g Key of Luck (USA)—Henrietta Street (IRE) **Cathal M. Ryan**
67 TIMBERA (IRE), 10, br g Commanche Run—Morry's Lady **Mrs J. M. Breen**
68 TIPP TOP (IRE), 7, b g Brief Truce (USA)—Very Sophisticated **Francis G. Kenny**
69 TODANEKI (IRE), 7, b g Leading Counsel (USA)—Miss Polumer **T. Brassil**
70 TROTSKY (IRE), 6, b g Jurado (USA)—Make Me An Island **Horseplay Syndicate**
71 WINE MERCHANT (IRE), 6, b g Montelimar (USA)—Fly Fuss **James Nicholson**

THREE-YEAR-OLDS

72 CORRAN ARD (IRE), b g Imperial Ballet (IRE)—Beeper The Great (USA) **Mr Eammon Salmon**
73 IRON HAGUE (IRE), b g Among Men (USA)—Conditional Sale (IRE) **John Duignam**

Apprentice: Paul Gallagher (8-0). **Conditional:** Patrick Flood (9-0). **Amateurs:** Mr Robert Hennessy (10-0), Mr Roger Loughran (10-0).

---

293   DON E. INCISA, Middleham
Postal: Thorngill House, Coverham, Middleham, Leyburn, North Yorkshire, DL8 4TJ.
Contact: PHONE (01969) 640653 FAX (01969) 640694

1 CRIPSEY BROOK, 6, ch g Lycius (USA)—Duwon (IRE) **Don Enrico Incisa**
2 EAST CAPE, 7, b g Bering—Reine de Danse (USA) **Don Enrico Incisa**
3 JESSIE, 5, ch m Pivotal—Bold Gem **Don Enrico Incisa**
4 LUFERTON LANE (IRE), 7, b m Ela-Mana-Mou—Saddle 'er Up (IRE) **Don Enrico Incisa**
5 MATRIARCHAL, 4, ch f Presidium—Mayor **Mrs Christine Cawley**
6 MCGILLYCUDDY REEKS (IRE), 13, b m Kefaah (USA)—Kilvarnet **Don Enrico Incisa**
7 SIMPLE IDEALS (USA), 10, b g r g Woodman (USA)—Comfort And Style **Don Enrico Incisa**
8 SIMPLY THE GUEST (IRE), 5, b g Mujadil (USA)—Ned's Contessa (IRE) **Don Enrico Incisa**
9 SKYLARK, 7, ch m Polar Falcon (USA)—Boozy **Don Enrico Incisa**
10 STAFF NURSE (IRE), 4, b f Night Shift (USA)—Akebia (USA) **Don Enrico Incisa**
11 TURFTANZER (GER), 5, b g Lomitas—Tower Bridge (GER) **Don Enrico Incisa**
12 UNO MENTE, 5, b m Mind Games—One Half Silver (CAN) **Don Enrico Incisa**

THREE-YEAR-OLDS

13 CHEVERAK FOREST (IRE), ch g Shinko Forest (IRE)—Meranie Girl (IRE) **Don Enrico Incisa**
14 FRANCESCHIELLA (ITY), gr f Beat of Drums—Filicaia **Don Enrico Incisa**
15 LOVEISDANGEROUS, b f Pursuit of Love—Brookhead Lady **Don Enrico Incisa**
16 SPEED RACER, b f Zieten (USA)—Sharenara (USA) **Don Enrico Incisa**

TWO-YEAR-OLDS

17 CUT TO THE CHASE, b g 4/3 Fraam—Chasetown Cailin (Suave Dancer (USA)) (2200) **Don Enrico Incisa**

Jockey (Flat): Kim Tinkler (7-10). **Apprentice:** Janice E Webster (7-11). **Amateur:** Mrs Rebecca Howell.

---

294   MR R. INGRAM, Epsom
Postal: Wendover Stables, Burgh Heath Road, Epsom, Surrey, KT17 4LX.
Contact: PHONE (01372) 748505 or (01372) 749157 MOBILE (0777) 3665980
E-MAIL roger.ingram.racing@btconnect.com

1 ALPH, 7, b g Alflora—Royal Birthday **G. Anvil**
2 BALERNO, 5, b g Machiavellian (USA)—Balabina (USA) **The Three Amigos**
3 CLASSIC ROLE, 5, b g Tragic Role (USA)—Clare Island **Pillar To Post Racing**
4 FIGURA, 6, b m Rudimentary (USA)—Dream Baby **Cricketers Club**
5 HIGH PADDY, 5, b g Master Willie—Ivy Edith **G. Anvil**
6 ITSONLYAGAME, 4, b c Ali-Royal (IRE)—Mena **Mrs Gina Brown**

MR R. INGRAM—continued

7 **JUNIKAY (IRE)**, 10, b g Treasure Kay—Junijo **Ellangowen Racing Partnership**
8 **MY MAITE (IRE)**, 5, b g Komaite (USA)—Mena **The Stargazers 2nd XI**
9 **ROYALE PEARL**, 4, gr f Cloudings (IRE)—Ivy Edith **Mr Glen Antill**
10 **SUDDEN FLIGHT (IRE)**, 7, b g In The Wings—Ma Petite Cherie (USA) **Norbury Ten**
11 **WILD WILD WES**, 4, ch g The West (USA)—Dam Certain (IRE) **Global Trio Partnership**

THREE-YEAR-OLDS

12 **BOULE D'OR (IRE)**, b c Croco Rouge (IRE)—Saffron Crocus **Friends and Family**
13 **DEVINE COMMAND**, b g In Command (IRE)—Adriya **Mr Luke Devine**
14 B f Charnwood Forest (IRE)—High Flying Adored (IRE) **Friends of the Turf**
15 **HULLABALOO (IRE)**, b c Princley Heir (IRE)—Lomalou (IRE) **Hullbran Bros**
16 **PRINCESS KAI (IRE)**, b f Cayman Kai (IRE)—City Princess **Brannigan Bros**

TWO-YEAR-OLDS

17 B f 1/1 Komaite (USA)—Dam Certain (IRE) (Damister (USA)) **Roger Ingram**
18 B f 25/5 Piccolo—Raffelina (USA) (Carson City (USA) (4500)) **M. Maurio**
19 B f 15/2 Tomba—Scottish Royal (IRE) (Night Shift (USA)) **Friends Of The Turf**

Other Owners: Mr J. Brannigan, Mr J. A. Brannigan, Mr J. Bunyer, Mr G. S. Collis, Mr A. J. Cousins, Mr J. Dwight, Mr L. E. Edwards, Mr Michael Joy, Mr W. E. Maund, Mr H. G. Newell, Mr D. Ross-Watt, Mr K. Santana, Mr G. Scott, Mr Peter Thompkins.

Assistant Trainer: Sharon Ingram

Jockey (Flat): N Day.

---

295 **MR D. K. IVORY, Radlett**
Postal: **Harper Lodge Farm, Harper Lane, Radlett, Hertfordshire, WD7 7HU.**
Contact: PHONE **(01923) 855337** MOBILE **(07785) 118658**
E-MAIL **deanivoryracing.horses@virgin.net** WEBSITE **deanivoryracing.co.uk**

1 **BUCKS**, 7, b g Slip Anchor—Alligram (USA) **Mr M. Murphy**
2 **CEDRIC COVERWELL**, 4, ch g Charmer—Marsara **John Waterfall**
3 **DANCING FOREST (IRE)**, 4, br g Charnwood Forest (IRE)—Fauna (IRE) **Mr K. T. Ivory**
4 **EL CHAPARRAL (IRE)**, 4, b g Bigstone (IRE)—Low Line **Mr K. T. Ivory**
5 **FURTHER OUTLOOK (USA)**, 10, gr g Zilzal (USA)—Future Bright (USA) **Mr K. T. Ivory**
6 **HARD TO CATCH (IRE)**, 6, b g Namaqualand (USA)—Brook's Dilemma **Karen Graham**
7 **HIGH FINALE**, 5, b m Surf Blade (USA)—High Velocity **Mr K. T. Ivory**
8 **IVORY VENTURE**, 4, b f Reprimand—Julietta Mia (USA) **Mr Dean Ivory**
9 **JOOLS**, 6, b g Cadeaux Genereux—Madam Crecy (USA) **Mr Anthony W. Parsons**
10 **KINDLELIGHT DEBUT**, 4, b f Groom Dancer (USA)—Dancing Debut **Kindlelight Ltd**
11 **LUCRETIUS**, 5, b g Mind Games—Eastern Ember **Mr R. D. Hartshorn**
12 **MISS GEORGE**, 6, b m Pivotal—Brightside (IRE) **Mrs A. Shone**
13 **MISTER CLINTON (IRE)**, 7, ch g Lion Cavern (USA)—Thewaari (USA) **Mr J. B. Waterfall**
14 **PANCAKEHILL**, 5, ch m Sabrehill (USA)—Sawlah **Sapphire Racing**
15 **SUMMER JOY**, 4, b f Myfontaine—Marycee (IRE) **Mr D. O'Connor**

THREE-YEAR-OLDS

16 **BERESFORD BOY**, b c Easycall—Devils Dirge **Beresford Pumps Ltd**
17 **EMILYS DAWN**, b f Komaite (USA)—Spice And Sugar **Mr Dean Ivory**
18 **GENTLEMAN GEORGE**, b g Kingsinger (IRE)—Miss Bigwig **Mr K. T. Ivory**
19 **IMPERIAL PRINCESS (IRE)**, b f Imperial Ballet (IRE)—Rose Tint (IRE) **Mr L. M. Baker**
20 **IVORY LACE**, b f Atraf—Miriam **Mr K. T. Ivory**
21 **MIRASOL PRINCESS**, ch f Ali-Royal (IRE)—Yanomami (USA) **Mr Anthony W. Parsons**
22 **RADLETT LADY**, ch f Wolfhound (USA)—Royal Dream **Radlett Racing**
23 **SAPPHIRE SKY**, b br f Compton Place—Jewel (IRE) **Sapphire Racing**
24 **SILVER PRELUDE**, gr c Prince Sabo—Silver Blessings **Mrs A. Shone**
25 **SON OF REMBRANDT (IRE)**, b g Titus Livius (FR)—Avidal Park **Radlett Racing**
26 **TIKITANO (IRE)**, b f Dr Fong (USA)—Asterita **Mr K. T. Ivory**

TWO-YEAR-OLDS

27 **BEAUFORT**, b c 20/5 Yaheeb (USA)—Royal Blaze (Scallywag) **R. & M. Bright**
28 B f 9/4 Tagula (IRE)—Dioscorea (IRE) (Pharly (FR)) (3710) **Kindlelight Ltd**

MR D. K. IVORY—continued

29 B f 25/3 Soviet Star (USA)—Gold Prospector (IRE) (Spectrum (IRE)) (7000) **Mr D. K. Ivory**
30 B f 9/2 Opening Verse (USA)—Indian Wardance (ITY) (Indian Ridge) **Mr D. K. Ivory**
31 **LIMONIA (GER)**, b f 2/5 Perugino (USA)—Limoges (GER) (Konigsstuhl (GER)) (6000) **Mr M. Murphy**
32 Ch f 12/4 Opening Verse (USA)—Peperonata (IRE) (Cyrano de Bergerac) **Mr D. K. Ivory**
33 **VISCOUNT ROSSINI**, b br c 2/3 Rossini (USA)—Spain (Polar Falcon (USA)) (20000) **Mr L. M. Baker**

Other Owners: Mr H. D. Shaw.

Assistant Trainer: Chris Scally

296
MR E. L. J. D. JAMES, Hungerford
Postal: **Mask Cottage, Front Street, East Garston, Hungerford, Berkshire, RG17 7EU.**
Contact: **HOME/OFFICE (01488) 648077 MOBILE (07802) 886307 FAX (01488) 649781**
E-MAIL edward@racing9.fsnet.co.uk

1 **ALFANO (IRE)**, 6, b g Priolo (USA)—Sartigila **Lilburn Estates**
2 **DOLI CYGNUS**, 6, gr m Bedford (USA)—Damsong **Exors of the Late Mrs D. Hardy**
3 **FIRST DAN**, 6, b g Gildoran—Danny Rhy **Mr C. James**
4 **ISARD DU BUARD (FR)**, 8, b g April Night (FR)—Upsala du Buard (FR) **Lady Thompson**
5 **LORD O'ALL SEASONS (IRE)**, 11, b br g Mister Lord (USA)—Autumn News **Miss R. P. Davidson**
6 **SELBERRY**, 10, b g Selkirk (USA)—Choke Cherry **Mr & Mrs D. W. H. Bell**
7 **STARRY MARY**, 6, b m Deploy—Darling Splodge **Mr A. Von Westenholz**

Assistant Trainer: C James

Amateur: Miss R Davidson.

297
MR L. R. JAMES, Malton
Postal: **The Seven, Norton Grange Stables, Park Road, Norton, Malton, N. Yorks YO17 9EA**
Contact: **PHONE (01653) 691455 MOBILE (07732) 556322**

1 4, B g Vettori (IRE)—Cailin Ciarrai (IRE) **Mrs Carol Lloyd-James**
2 **MODULOR (FR)**, 12, gr g Less Ice—Chaumontaise (FR) **Mr L. R. James Ltd**
3 **SHE WHO DARES WINS**, 4, b f Atraf—Mirani (IRE) **Nelson Unit Ltd**
4 **TIOGA GOLD (IRE)**, 5, b g Goldmark (USA)—Coffee Bean **Nelson Unit Ltd**

THREE-YEAR-OLDS

5 **ATTACK MINDED**, ch g Timeless Times (USA)—French Ginger **Mr L. R. James Ltd**
6 **MISS TIDDLYPUSH**, gr f Defacto (USA)—Misty Rocket **Mrs M. L. Lingwood**
7 **SECRET OF SECRETS**, b g Timeless Times (USA)—Sophisticated Baby **Mr C. Raine**

Assistant Trainer: Carol James

298
MR A. P. JARVIS, Twyford
Postal: **Mill Race Stables, Twyford Mill, Twyford, Buckingham MK18 4HA.**
Contact: **PHONE (01296) 730707 FAX (01296) 733572 MOBILE (07770) 785551**
E-MAIL alan@alanjarvis.co.uk

1 **BLUE KNIGHT (IRE)**, 5, ch g Bluebird (USA)—Fer de Lance (IRE) **Jarvis Associates**
2 **BOUMAHOU (IRE)**, 4, b c Desert Story (IRE)—Kilbride Lass (IRE) **Mrs B. A. Headon**
3 **EFFECTIVE**, 4, ch g Bahamian Bounty—Efficacy **Eurostrait Ltd**
4 **FATHER JUNINHO (IRE)**, 7, b g Distinctly North (USA)—Shane's Girl (IRE) **Haleray Ltd**
5 **JARDINES LOOKOUT (IRE)**, 7, b g Fourstars Allstar (USA)—
Foolish Flight (IRE) **Morton Bamford Caird and Jarvis Partners**
6 **STAR MEMBER (IRE)**, 5, b g Hernando (FR)—Constellation (IRE) **Jarvis Associates**

THREE-YEAR-OLDS

7 **DANCING PRINCE (IRE)**, b g Imperial Ballet (IRE)—Eastern Aura (IRE) **Mr Christopher Shankland**
8 **DESERT REIGN**, ch c Desert King (USA)—Moondance **Mr Allen B. Pope**
9 **DISTANT CONNECTION (IRE)**, b c Cadeaux Genereux—Night Owl **Mrs Ann Jarvis**
10 **LATIN REVIEW (IRE)**, ch f Titus Livius (FR)—Law Review (IRE) **Mrs Ann Jarvis**
11 **MELINDA'S GIRL**, b f Intikhab (USA)—Polish Honour (USA) **Melinda Racing**

MR A. P. JARVIS—continued

12 **MIKATI MAID**, ch f Piccolo—Dame Helene (USA) **HK Dublin Jackers**
13 **ON THE WING**, b f Pivotal—Come Fly With Me **Grant & Bowman Limited**
14 **ROYAL AWAKENING (IRE)**, b g Ali-Royal (IRE)—Morning Surprise **Wellmet Partners**
15 **SPRING DANCER**, b f Imperial Ballet (IRE)—Roxy Music (IRE) **Hibiscus**
16 **SPRING GODDESS (IRE)**, b f Daggers Drawn (USA)—Easter Girl **Grant & Bowman Limited**
17 **SWEEP THE BOARD (IRE)**, b c Fasliyev (USA)—Fun Board (FR) **Eurostrait Ltd**
18 **TRISHAY**, gr f Petong—Marjorie's Memory (IRE) **Mr Allen B. Pope**
19 **WINNERS DELIGHT**, ch g First Trump—Real Popcorn (IRE) **Breckland Bingo**

TWO-YEAR-OLDS

20 B f 4/4 Fumo di Londra (IRE)—Acebo Lyons (IRE) (Waajib) **Mr Terence P. Lyons II**
21 B f 5/2 Danzero (AUS)—Audition (Machiavellian (USA)) (30920) **Mrs Ann Jarvis**
22 B c 4/4 Cape Cross (IRE)—Baalbek (Barathea (IRE)) (34000) **Mrs Ann Jarvis**
23 B c 11/4 Polar Falcon (USA)—Bowden Rose (Dashing Blade) **Morton Bamford Caird and Jarvis Partners**
24 B c 12/2 Indian Ridge—Chauncy Lane (IRE) (Sadler's Wells (USA)) (43289) **Mrs Ann Jarvis**
25 B c 30/4 Namid—Daltak (Night Shift (USA)) (26000) **Mrs Ann Jarvis**
26 B f 24/2 Danehill Dancer (IRE)—Finnegans Dilemma (IRE) (Marktingo) (2473) **Mr A. P. Jarvis**
27 B f 23/3 Prince Sabo—Frisson (Slip Anchor) (13000) **Mr Christopher Shankland**
28 B c 16/1 Barathea (IRE)—Handora (IRE) (Hernando) (19789)
29 B c 21/4 Mujadil (USA)—Law Review (IRE) (Case Law) (16000) **Mrs Ann Jarvis**
30 B f 10/2 Raise A Grand (IRE)—Locorotondo (IRE) (Broken Hearted) (36000) **Mr Allen B. Pope**
31 B c 6/3 Lujain (USA)—Lonesome (Night Shift (USA)) (14000) **Mrs Ann Jarvis**
32 B c 11/3 Mujadil (USA)—Lunadine (FR) (Bering) (6500) **Mrs Ann Jarvis**
33 B f 24/2 Indian Lodge (IRE)—Milady Lillie (IRE) (Distinctly North (USA)) (12000) **Mrs Ann Jarvis**
34 Ch f 18/2 Dr Fong (USA)—My Valentina (Royal Academy) (46381) **Mrs Ann Jarvis**
35 B br c 19/4 Awad (USA)—Night Duja (USA) (Dayjur (USA)) (27828) **Mrs Ann Jarvis**
36 B f 4/2 Dr Fong (USA)—Opera Lover (IRE) (Sadler's Wells (USA)) **Mr Christopher Shankland**
37 B f 3/2 Lujain (USA)—Quiz Show (Primo Dominie) (25000) **Mr Christopher Shankland**
38 B f 20/3 Josr Algarhoud (IRE)—Rushing River (USA) (Irish River (FR)) (13000) **Mrs Ann Jarvis**
39 B f 31/2 Diktat—Scared (Royal Academy) (11000) **Mrs Ann Jarvis**
40 B c 25/4 Barathea (IRE)—Starlight Smile (USA) (Green Dancer (USA)) (21644) **Mrs Ann Jarvis**
41 Ch f 9/4 Dr Fong (USA)—Tahara (IRE) (Caerleon (USA)) (10000) **Mrs Ann Jarvis**
42 B c 14/4 Orpen (USA)—Woodenitbenice (USA) (Nasty And Bold (USA)) (14000)
43 B c 19/2 Bachir (IRE)—Zest (USA) (Zilzal (USA)) (15000) **Mrs Ann Jarvis**

Other Owners: Mrs C. O. Bamford, Mr Nick Coverdale, Mr Colin Jones, Ms L. T. Korsak, Mrs D. C. Mills, Mr A. L. R. Morton, Mr Ian A. Robinson, Mrs L. C. Sutton, Mr M. F. Sutton, Mr W. Ward.

Assistant Trainer: T O Jarvis, M A Jarvis, S E Simmons

Jockeys (Flat): N Callan, Pat Eddery, J Quinn. **Apprentices:** Leon Harman (7-10), Ben Nishart (7-5).

---

299 MR M. A. JARVIS, Newmarket

Postal: **Kremlin House Stables, Fordham Road, Newmarket, Suffolk, CB8 7AQ.**
Contact: **OFFICE (01638) 661702 HOME 662519 FAX 667018 MOBILE (07836) 649280**
E-MAIL majarvis@hotmail.com

1 **ANAK PEKAN**, 4, ch g In The Wings—Trefoil (FR) **H.R.H. Sultan Ahmad Shah**
2 **FRUHLINGSSTURM**, 4, b c Unfuwain (USA)—Fruhlingswachen (USA) **Mr Gary A. Tanaka**
3 **MAKTUB (ITY)**, 5, b h Love The Groom (USA)—Carmen The Best (IRE) **Mr Gary A. Tanaka**
4 **MASTER ROLE (IRE)**, 4, ch c Master Willie—Calaloo Sioux (USA) **Lord Harrington**
5 **MILLVILLE**, 4, ch g Millkom—Miss Top Ville (FR) **Mr T. G. Warner**
6 **OFARABY**, 4, b g Sheikh Albadou—Maristax **Mr T. G. Warner**
7 **PUTRA KUANTAN**, 4, b c Grand Lodge (USA)—Fade **H.R.H. Sultan Ahmad Shah**
8 **PUTRA PEKAN**, 6, b h Grand Lodge (USA)—Mazarine Blue **H.R.H. Sultan Ahmad Shah**
9 **RAKTI**, 5, b h Polish Precedent (USA)—Ragera (IRE) **Mr Gary A. Tanaka**
10 **RANVILLE**, 6, ch g Deploy—Kibitka (FR) **Mr K. G. Powter**
11 **RED FORT (IRE)**, 4, gr c Green Desert (USA)—Red Bouquet **The Red Fort Partnership**
12 **SHAHZAN HOUSE (IRE)**, 5, b h Sri Pekan (USA)—Nsx **H.R.H. Sultan Ahmad Shah**
13 **SOYUZ (IRE)**, 4, ch g Cadeaux Genereux—Welsh Mist **Mr N. R. A. Springer**
14 **ST ANDREWS (IRE)**, 4, b c Celtic Swing—Viola Royale (IRE) **Team Havana**

MR M. A. JARVIS—continued

THREE-YEAR-OLDS

15 **ART NAIF (IRE),** br f Desert King (IRE)—Mistress Thames **Mrs O. Razzini**
16 **ASHTANZA,** gr g Ashkalani (IRE)—Poetry In Motion (IRE) **Thurloe Thoroughbreds IX**
17 **BAYHIRR,** b c Selkirk (USA)—Pass The Peace **Sheikh Ahmed Al Maktoum**
18 **BUCKEYE WONDER (USA),** b c Silver Hawk (USA)—Ameriflora (USA) **Mr John W. Phillips**
19 **CAYMAN CALYPSO (IRE),** ro g Danehill Dancer (USA)—Warthill Whispers **Mr John E. Sims**
20 **CELTIC HEROINE (IRE),** ch f Hernando (FR)—Celtic Fling **Mr P. D. Savill**
21 **CLOSE REGARDS (IRE),** b f Danehill (USA)—La Luna (GER) **Mr N. R. A. Springer**
22 B c Orpen (USA)—Cresalin **Team Havana**
23 **DALLOOL,** b c Unfuwain (USA)—Sardonic **Sheikh Ahmed Al Maktoum**
24 **DIVINE GIFT,** b c Groom Dancer (USA)—Child's Play (USA) **Mr B. E. Nielsen**
25 **FIRST OF MAY,** b f Halling (USA)—Finger of Light **Mr Saif Ali**
26 **HENNDEY (IRE),** b g Indian Ridge—Del Deya (IRE) **Sheikh Ahmed Al Maktoum**
27 **IFFRAAJ,** b c Zafonic (USA)—Pastorale **Sheikh Ahmed Al Maktoum**
28 **KEELUNG (USA),** b c Lear Fan (USA)—Miss Universal (IRE) **Mr Norman Cheng**
29 **KIBRYAA (USA),** ch c Silver Hawk (USA)—Fleur de Nuit (USA) **Sheikh Ahmed Al Maktoum**
30 **MAGANDA (IRE),** b f Sadler's Wells (USA)—Minnie Habit **Mr N. R. A. Springer**
31 **MARBUSH (IRE),** ro c Linamix (FR)—Fig Tree Drive (USA) **Sheikh Ahmed Al Maktoum**
32 **MARINE CITY (JPN),** b f Carnegie (IRE)—Marienbad (FR) **Mr Saif Ali**
33 **MONTE MAJOR (IRE),** b g Docksider (USA)—Danalia (IRE) **The C H F Partnership**
34 **NEW MORNING (IRE),** b f Sadler's Wells (USA)—Hellenic **Mr N. R. A. Springer**
35 **OBSERVATION,** ch f Polish Precedent (USA)—Search Party **Jumeirah Racing**
36 **PEAK OF PERFECTION (IRE),** b g Deploy—Nsx **H.R.H. Sultan Ahmad Shah**
37 **QASIRAH (IRE),** b f Machiavellian (USA)—Altaweelah (IRE) **Sheikh Ahmed Al Maktoum**
38 **RICHIE BOY,** b c Dr Fong (USA)—Alathezal (USA) **R. & G. Marchant & H. & A. Richenberg**
39 **SILVER SATIRE,** ch f Dr Fong (USA)—Love of Silver (USA) **Mr Saif Ali**
40 **SOUTH AFRICA,** b f Cape Cross (IRE)—Breakaway **Mr Mohammed Rashid**
41 **TANNOOR (USA),** b c Miswaki (USA)—Iolani **Sheikh Ahmed Al Maktoum**
42 **ZAMEYLA (IRE),** b f Cape Cross (IRE)—Angelic Sounds (IRE) **Sheikh Ahmed Al Maktoum**

TWO-YEAR-OLDS

43 **ANAAMIL,** b f 15/2 Darshaan—Noushkey (Polish Precedent (USA)) **Sheikh Ahmed Al Maktoum**
44 **ARAB SEA,** b f 4/2 Singspiel (IRE)—Baaderah (IRE) (Cadeaux Genereux) **Sheikh Ahmed Al Maktoum**
45 **ARIANE STAR (IRE),** b f 1/3 Marju (IRE)—Northgate Raver (Absalom) (12368) **Ariane Star Partnership**
46 **A THOUSAND SMILES (IRE),** b f 8/3 Sadler's Wells (USA)—
                                  Bluffing (IRE) (Darshaan) (220000) **Mr N. R. A. Springer**
47 Ch c 24/2 Grand Lodge (USA)—Ballet (Sharrood (USA)) (170000) **H.R.H. Sultan Ahmad Shah**
48 **CELTICELLO (IRE),** b br c 14/2 Celtic Swing—Viola Royale (IRE) (Royal Academy (USA)) **Mr P. D. Savill**
49 **CHARADE (IRE),** b f 6/5 Danehill (USA)—Actoris (USA) (Diesis) **Sheikh Mohammed**
50 **CONSULAR,** br c 28/4 Singspiel (IRE)—Language of Love (Rock City) **Mr J. R. Good**
51 B f 10/3 Xaar—Cyclone Flyer (College Chapel) (60000) **Mr Saif Ali**
52 **DONYANA,** b f 9/2 Mark of Esteem (IRE)—Albarsha (Mtoto) **Sheikh Ahmed Al Maktoum**
53 B f 31/2 Machiavellian (USA)—El Opera (IRE) (Sadler's Wells (USA)) (130000) **Mr Saif Ali**
54 Ch c 20/2 Grand Lodge (USA)—Flower Girl (Pharly (FR)) (100000) **Mr W. J. Gredley**
55 B f 5/2 King's Best (USA)—Gilah (IRE) (Saddlers' Hall (IRE)) (70000) **Mr Saif Ali**
56 **GOLD GUN (USA),** b c 5/3 Seeking The Gold (USA—
                          Possessive Dancer (Shareef Dancer (USA)) **Sheikh Ahmed Al Maktoum**
57 **GOLO GAL,** b c 8/5 Mark of Esteem (IRE)—Western Sal (Salse (USA)) (100000) **Sheikh Ahmed Al Maktoum**
58 **GONE FISHING (IRE),** ch f 21/2 Cadeaux Genereux—
                             Dabbing (USA) (Cure The Blues (USA)) (68027) **Mr N. R. A. Springer**
59 **HAUNTING MEMORIES (IRE),** b c 1/2 Barathea (IRE)—
                                   King of All (IRE) (King of Clubs) (30000) **Mr Lawrence Wosskow**
60 **HELEN SHARP,** ch f 10/4 Pivotal—Sunny Davis (USA) (Alydar (USA)) (115000) **Cheveley Park Stud**
61 **HINTERLAND (IRE),** b br c 14/4 Danzig (USA)—
                            Electric Society (IRE) (Law Society (USA)) (142857) **Sheikh Mohammed**
62 Ch f 20/2 Singspiel (IRE)—India Atlanta (Ahonoora) (160000) **Sheikh Mohammed**
63 B gr c 29/1 Green Desert (USA)—Indian Skimmer (USA) (Storm Bird (CAN)) **Sheikh Mohammed**
64 **JOSH,** b c 3/2 Josr Algarhoud (IRE)—Charlie Girl (Puissance) (16000) **Mr M. A. Jarvis**
65 B f 10/2 Soviet Star (USA)—Jouet (Reprimand) (20000) **Mr R. P. Marchant**
66 B f 8/2 Montjeu (IRE)—Kardashina (FR) (Darshaan) (58750) **Mr Saif Ali**
67 **KARRNAK,** b c 12/3 Hernando (FR)—Maiden Aunt (IRE) (Distant Relative) (80000) **Sheikh Ahmed Al Maktoum**
68 **KHE SANH,** b f 23/2 Mtoto—Hoh Chi Min (Efisio) (49474) **Mr N. R. A. Springer**
69 **MISS TRIAL,** b f 3/5 Zafonic (USA)—Perfect Alibi (Law Society (USA)) (20000) **Mr & Mrs Kevan Watts**
70 **MODARAB,** b c 10/2 Barathea (IRE)—Jathaabeh (Nashwan (USA)) **Sheikh Ahmed Al Maktoum**

MR M. A. JARVIS—continued

71 B c 2/02 Mark of Esteem (IRE)—Nassma (IRE) (Sadler's Wells (USA)) (60000) **Mr Raymond Anderson Green**
72 NATIVE AMERICAN, b c 27/1 Indian Lodge (IRE)—Summer Siren (FR) (Saint Cyrien (FR)) (86580)
73 NOTABILITY (IRE), b c 20/2 King's Best (USA)—Noble Rose (IRE) (Caerleon (USA)) **Sheikh Mohammed**
74 B c 9/3 Montjeu (IRE)—Pacific Grove (Persian Bold) (170000) **Mr M. A. Jarvis**
75 B c 26/4 Cape Cross (IRE)—Party Dress (Lahib (USA)) (75000) **Sheikh Mohammed**
76 PEARL KING (IRE), gr c 2/4 Daylami (IRE)—
 Regal Opinion (USA) (Gone West (USA)) (80000) **Sheikh Mohammed**
77 PROFICIENT, b f 25/1 Primo Dominie—Penthouse Lady (Last Tycoon) **Cheveley Park Stud**
78 B f 17/4 Grand Lodge (USA)—Proskona (USA) (Mr Prospector (USA)) (280000) **Mr B. E. Nielsen**
79 QAADMAH (IRE), b f 23/2 Dubai Millennium—Zahrat Dubai (Unfuwain (USA)) **Sheikh Ahmed Al Maktoum**
80 B f 21/2 Green Desert (USA)—Repeat Warning (Warning) (480000) **Sheikh Mohammed**
81 RICHELIEU, b c 18/4 Machiavellian (USA)—Darling Flame (USA) (Capote (USA)) **Sheikh Mohammed**
82 Ch c 24/2 Cadeaux Genereux—Ring The Relatives (Bering) (220000) **Sheikh Mohammed**
83 Ch f 13/2 Polish Precedent (US—Rose Bourbon (USA) (Woodman (USA)) (42000) **Mr W. J. Gredley**
84 SAADIGG (IRE), b c 8/4 Indian Danehill (IRE)—
 White Caps (Shirley Heights) (105000) **Sheikh Ahmed Al Maktoum**
85 B c 4/3 Desert Prince (IRE)—Soeur Ti (FR) (Kaldoun (FR)) (49474) **Mr B. E. Nielsen**
86 SUBPOENA, b c 8/5 Diktat—Trefoil (Kris) **Sheikh Mohammed**
87 TAAKEED, b c 9/5 Mark of Esteem (IRE)—Walimu (USA) (Top Ville) **Sheikh Ahmed Al Maktoum**
88 TALLIAR, br c 28/3 Indian Ridge—Mill Rainbow (FR) (Rainbow Quest (USA)) **Sheikh Mohammed**
89 B c 3/2 Indian Ridge—Triomphale (USA) (Nureyev (USA)) (200000) **H.R.H. Sultan Ahmad Shah**
90 VISTA BELLA, b f 20/4 Diktat—Cox Orange (USA) (Trempolino (USA)) **Sheikh Mohammed**
91 WELL ESTABLISHED (IRE), b c 22/2—Riveryev (USA) (Irish River (FR)) (210000) **Mr M. A. Jarvis**
92 WIND IN MY HEART (IRE), b f 1/2 Grand Lodge (USA)—
 Zooming (IRE) (Indian Ridge) (324675) **Mr N. R. A. Springer**
93 ZAVILLE, gr f 22/1 Zafonic (USA)—Colleville (Pharly (FR)) (40000) **Mr K. G. Powter**
94 ZAYN ZEN, ch f 30/1 Singspiel (IRE)—Roshani (IRE) (Kris) **Sheikh Ahmed Al Maktoum**

Other Owners: Mr J. J. Fellows, Mr C. H. Fischer, Mr K. H. Fischer, Mrs Greta Sarfaty Marchant, Sqdn Ldr R. A. Milsom, Mr M. C. Moutray-Read, Mr Richard Nunn, Mr Oliver Pawle, Hon Philip Remnant, Mrs A. K. Richenberg, Mr H. A. Richenberg, Mr Ali Saeed, Mr Andy J. Smith, Mr L. Straszewski, Mr Michael Swinburn, Mr Kevan Watts, Mrs Prudence Watts.

Assistant Trainer: Roger Varian

300 MR W. JARVIS, Newmarket

Postal: **Phantom House Stables, Fordham Road, Newmarket, Suffolk, CB8 7AA.**
Contact: **HOME (01638) 662677 OFFICE (01638) 669873 FAX (01638) 667328**
E-MAIL **william.jarvis@virgin.net**

1 FREE WHEELIN (IRE), 4, b c Polar Falcon (USA)—Farhana **Canisbay Bloodstock Ltd**
2 GRAND WIZARD, 4, b c Grand Lodge (USA)—Shouk **J. H. Slade & Partners**
3 LADY JUSTICE, 4, b f Compton Place—Zinzi **Mr Raymond Tooth**
4 LOVED UP, 4, b f Bin Ajwaad (IRE)—To Love With Love **Mr William Jarvis**
5 MACARONI GOLD (IRE), 4, b g Rock Hopper—Strike It Rich (FR) **Dr J. Walker**
6 MISSCOSTALOT, 4, b f Hernando (FR)—Glamour Game **Mr William Jarvis**
7 PHANTOM STOCK, 4, b g Alzao (USA)—Strike Alight (USA) **The L E H Partnership**
8 TAWNY WAY, 4, b f Polar Falcon (USA)—Ma Petite Anglaise **Rams Racing Club**

THREE-YEAR-OLDS

9 BLOFELD, b g Royal Applause—Bliss (IRE) **Byculla Thoroughbreds**
10 CLEAVER, ch c Kris—Much Too Risky **Mr J. M. Greetham**
11 ENHANCE, b f Entrepreneur—Charming Life (NZ) **Plantation Stud**
12 FUSS, b f Unfuwain (USA)—First Sapphire **Mr Brian Cooper**
13 B f Charnwood Forest (IRE)—Glashedy Rose **Dr Conor O'Doherty**
14 LA PERSIANA, gr f Daylami (IRE)—La Papagena **Plantation Stud**
15 LATE NIGHT (GER), b f Groom Dancer (USA)—Laurencia **Mr Manfred Ostermann**
16 MANNYMAN (IRE), b f Dr Devious (IRE)—Lithe Spirit (IRE) **W. Jarvis & W. Haggas**
17 MARSH ORCHID, b g Lahib—Majalis **Mr M. C. Banks**
18 MOMTIC (IRE), ch c Shinko Forest (IRE)—Uffizi (IRE) **Heath, Keenan & Verrier**
19 MOON LEGEND (USA), ch f Gulch (USA)—Highland Legend (USA) **Mr Eugene Lismonde**
20 Ch g Cadeaux Genereux—Nwaahil (IRE) **Mr Richard McDonnell**
21 RESHUFFLE, ch f Compton Place—Prince's Feather (IRE) **The Phantom House Partnership**
22 ST BARCHAN (IRE), ch g Grand Lodge (USA)—Moon Tango (IRE) **The Phantom House Partnership**
23 THE FUN MERCHANT, b g Mind Games—Sinking **Mr A. K. Collins**

MR W. JARVIS—continued

24 **THE VIOLIN PLAYER (USA)**, b g King of Kings (IRE)—
Silk Masque (USA) **Peter Webb, David Milne & Jim Walker**
25 **TORQUEMADA (IRE)**, ch c Desert Sun—Gaelic's Fantasy (IRE) **Canisbay Bloodstock**
26 **TRIVIAL PURSUIT**, b c Mind Games—Chushan Venture **The Phantom House Partnership**
27 **WEAKEST LINK**, b g Mind Games—Sky Music **Miss S. E. Hall**
28 **YLANG YLANG (IRE)**, ch f Hennessy (USA)—Princess Alydar (USA) **Mr R. Scarborough**

TWO-YEAR-OLDS

29 B br c 26/2 Elnadim (USA)—Attasliyah (IRE) (Marju (IRE)) (30000) **Dr J. Walker**
30 **BEDLAM**, b f 8/2 Dracula (AUS)—La Tiziana (Rudimentary (USA)) **A Partnership**
31 **CHILLIN OUT**, ch c 2/2 Bahamian Bounty—Steppin Out (First Trump) **Canisbay Bloodstock Ltd**
32 B f 20/4 Mark Of Esteem (IRE)—
Classic Colleen (IRE) (Sadler's Wells (USA)) (5000) **Henry Marsh & Richard Milner**
33 **DIZZY FUTURE**, b c 5/4 Fraam—Kara Sea (USA) (River Special (USA)) (8000) **A. K. Collins & Partners**
34 **FAIR ALONG (GER)**, b c 23/3 Alkalde (GER)—Fairy Tango (FR) (Acatenango (GER)) (6184) **A Partnership**
35 **FOLLOWING FLOW (USA)**, b br c 4/3 King Of Kings (IRE)—
Sign Here (USA) (Private Terms (USA)) (42000) **Sales Race 2001 Syndicate**
36 **FORT ASSOS**, b c 20/1 Grand Lodge (USA)—Cephalonia (Slip Anchor) **Plantation Stud**
37 B c 17/3 Imperial Ballet (IRE)—Habaza (Shernazar) (9500) **Capel CS Ltd**
38 Gr c 26/4 Highest Honor (FR)—Land of Ivory (USA) (The Minstrel (CAN)) (15000) **N. S. Yong & Partners**
39 **LET SLIP**, b f 13/3 Second Empire (USA)—Loose Talk (Thatching) **Mrs Susan Davis**
40 B c 8/5 Zaha (CAN)—Mo Stopher (Sharpo) **Canisbay Bloodstock Ltd**
41 B c 6/4 Vettori (IRE)—Never Diss Miss (Owington) **Mr T. Fenner**
42 **PAPALITY**, b f 10/2 Giant's Causeway—Papabile (USA) (Chief's Crown (USA)) (100000) **Plantation Stud**
43 B c 18/3 Bachir (IRE)—Profit Alert (IRE) (Alzao (USA)) (20000) **A Partnership**
44 B f 17/5 Dansili—Regent's Folly (Touching Wood (USA))
45 **SANDBAT**, b c 3/4 Vettori (IRE)—Desert Flower (Green Desert (USA)) (18000) **Sales Race 2001 Syndicate**
46 **SLIP CATCH (IRE)**, b f 27/4 Intikhab (USA)—Buckle (IRE) (Common Grounds) (7000) **Noodles Racing**
47 **THREE BOARS**, ch c 8/5 Most Welcome—Precious Poppy (Polish Precedent (USA)) **Mr J. M. Greetham**
48 B c 30/3 Winged Love (IRE)—Vangelis (Gorytus) (11131) **Ian David Ltd & Mr P. Byrne**
49 Ch f 14/4 Zaha (CAN)—Vrennan (Suave Dancer (USA)) **Canisbay Bloodstock Ltd**
50 B f 8/2 First Trump—Zinzi (Song) (25000) **Mr Raymond Tooth**

Other Owners: Mr A. K. Collins, Mr Joss Collins, Mr Brian Cooper, Mr A. Donald, Mr N. Donald, Mr A. Foster, Mr R. A. C. Furber, Mr Nigel Glaister, The Hon R. T. A. Goff, Mr A. L. Harrison, Mr Andy Hood, Mr R. F. Kilby, Mr B. J. Leaver, Mr F. H. Lee, Mr Yaser Martini, Mr R. McDonald, Mr B. McLaughlin, Mrs Paula Moody, Mr D. Murrell, Mrs Victoria Pakenham, Mr M. Paviten, Mr John Phizackerley, Miss Elaine Reffo, Mr Ian Robertson, Mr P. D. N. Robertson, Mr Willie W. Robertson, Mrs I. A. C. Slade, Mrs J. Stockbridge, Miss Maureen Stopher, Mr G. W. Turnbull, Mrs J. Watts-Farmer, Mrs Nigel Watts-Farmer, Mr Peter Webb.

Assistant Trainer: Mrs J Cecil

---

301   ## MR J. M. JEFFERSON, Malton
Postal: **Newstead Cottage Stables, Norton, Malton, North Yorkshire, YO17 9PJ.**
Contact: **PHONE (01653) 697225 MOBILE (07710) 502044**

1 **AGAIN JANE**, 4, ch f Then Again—Janie-O **Mr P. Nelson**
2 **ALTAREEK (USA)**, 7, b g Alleged (USA)—Black Tulip (FR) **Dean Bostock and Raymond Bostock**
3 **ANOTHER CHANCE**, 9, b g Golden Heights—Lapopie **North South Partnership**
4 4, B f Good Thyne (USA)—Another Grouse **Mrs K. S. Gaffney**
5 **BERTIE ARMS**, 4, b f Cloudings (IRE)—Pugilistic **Mr P. Birch**
6 **BEST OF THE BLUES**, 4, b c Whittingham (IRE)—Gold And Blue (IRE) **Mr J. R. Salter**
7 **BIG TREE (FR)**, 6, ch g Apple Tree (FR)—Maria Cara (FR) **Mr & Mrs Raymond Anderson Green**
8 **BLAZING FIDDLE (IRE)**, 5, b g Anshan—Second Violin (IRE) **P. Gaffney & J. N. Stevenson**
9 **BORDER STAR (IRE)**, 7, b g Parthian Springs—Tengello **Mrs Kathleen Campey**
10 **BROOKLYN BROWNIE (IRE)**, 5, b g Presenting—In The Brownies (IRE) **P. Gaffney & J. N. Stevenson**
11 **CALATAGAN (IRE)**, 5, ch g Danzig Connection (USA)—Calachuchi **Mr & Mrs J. M. Davenport**
12 **CLARINCH CLAYMORE**, 8, b g Sabrehill (USA)—Salu **Mr John Donald**
13 **CLASSIC CAPERS**, 5, ch g Classic Cliche (IRE)—Jobiska **Mr R. Collins**
14 **CLEAR DAWN**, 9, b g Clearly Bust—Cobra Queen **Mr & Mrs J. M. Davenport**
15 **CUMBRIAN KNIGHT (IRE)**, 6, b g Presenting—Crashrun **Cumbrian Industrials Ltd**
16 **DEWASENTAH (IRE)**, 5, b m Supreme Leader—Our Sioux (IRE) **Mrs J. U. Hales**
17 **ELVIS RETURNS**, 6, b g Alhaatmi—Buckmist Blue (IRE) **Mr J. Cleeve**
18 5, B g Primitive Rising (USA)—Enkindle **Ashleybank Investments Limited**
19 **FLUR NA H ALBA**, 5, b g Atraf—Tyrian Belle **The Matheson Partnership**

MR J. M. JEFFERSON—continued

20 **HILLS OF VIEW**, 6, b g Sea Raven (IRE)—Hardwick Sun **Mr R. G. Marshall**
21 **HONEST ENDEAVOUR**, 5, b g Alflora (IRE)—Isabeau **Mr T. R. Pryke**
22 **INNOCENT BYSTANDER**, 5, ch g Rudimentary (USA)—Right To The Top **Ashleybank Investments Limited**
23 **JACK WEIGHELL**, 5, b g Accordion—Magic Bloom **Mr P. Nelson**
24 **KIDS INHERITANCE (IRE)**, 6, b g Presenting—Princess Tino (IRE) **Mr & Mrs J. M. Davenport**
25 **LAMBHILL STAKES (IRE)**, 6, gr g King's Ride—Summerhill Express (IRE) **Ashleybank Investments Limited**
26 **LOI DE MARTIALE (IRE)**, 6, br g Presenting—Thresa-Anita (IRE) **Mr R. G. Marshall**
27 **MOSS HARVEY**, 9, ch g Le Moss—Wings Ground **Mr A. R. Salter**
28 **OSCAR THE BOXER (IRE)**, 5, b g Oscar (IRE)—Here She Comes **The New Phoenix Racing Club**
29 **PERTINO**, 8, b g Terimon—Persian Fountain (IRE) **W. Fouracres, T. Pryke & D. Willis**
30 **POILU**, 6, ch g Fearless Action (USA)—Marielou (FR) **Mr Richard Collins**
31 **POLAR GUNNER**, 7, b g Gunner B—Polar Belle **Mrs M. E. Dixon**
32 **RED NOSE LADY**, 7, b m Teenoso (USA)—Red Rambler **Mrs M. E. Dixon**
33 **ROMAN ARK**, 6, b g Terimon—Larksmore **Mr Richard Collins**
34 **RUTLEDGE RED (IRE)**, 8, gr g Roselier (FR)—Katebeaujolais **Ashleybank Investments Limited**
35 **RYMON**, 4, b g Terimon—Rythmic Rymer **Mrs M. Barker**
36 **SEA COVE**, 4, b f Terimon—Regal Pursuit (IRE) **W. A. Developments Ltd**
37 **SHARED EXPECTATION (IRE)**, 8, ch g Husyan (USA)—Calmount (IRE) **Mr. R. E. Williams**
38 **SHUIL TSARINA (IRE)**, 6, b m King's Ride—Shuil Realt (IRE) **Mrs K. S. Gaffney & Mrs Alix Stevenson**
39 **STAMPARLAND HILL**, 9, b g Gildoran—Woodland Flower **Ashleybank Investments Limited**
40 **THE FROSTY FERRET (IRE)**, 6, b g Zaffaran (USA)—Frostbite **Ashleybank Investments Limited**
41 **THE MANSE BRAE (IRE)**, 8, b g Roselier (FR)—Decent Preacher **Ashleybank Investments Limited**
42 **THE MERRY MASON (IRE)**, 8, gr g Roselier (FR)—Busters Lodge **Ashleybank Investments Limited**
43 **THE YELLOW EARL (IRE)**, 6, b g Topanoora—Sweet Innocence (IRE) **Boundary Garage (Bury) Ltd**
44 **TULLYNAGARDY (IRE)**, 4, ch g Sabrehill (USA)—Moorefield Girl **David Bamber**
45 **TURTLE QUEST (IRE)**, 5, b g Turtle Island (IRE)—

Brooks' Quest (IRE) **Mrs T.H.Barclay/Mrs F.D.McInnes Skinner**
46 **WILLIE THE FISH (IRE)**, 7, b g King's Ride—Bricon Lady **Ashleybank Investments Limited**
47 5, B g Rakaposhi King—Woodland Flower **Ashleybank Investments Limited**
48 **WUCHOWSEN (IRE)**, 6, b m King's Ride—Our Sioux (IRE) **Yorkshire Racing Club Owners Group**

THREE-YEAR-OLDS

49 **DUSKY DAWN (IRE)**, b c Desert Style (IRE)—Kaaba **Mrs J. Pallister**
50 **I'LL DO IT TODAY**, b g Mtoto—Knayton Lass **Mr & Mrs J. M. Davenport**
51 B g Accordian—Pugiliste
52 **SCHINKEN OTTO (IRE)**, ch g Shinko Forest (IRE)—Athassel Rose (IRE) **Mr John Donald**
53 **TOO KEEN**, ch f Keen—Janie-O **Mr P. Nelson**

Other Owners: Mr Dean Graham Bostock, Mr J. R. Bostock, Mr W. Butterworth, Mrs Anita Green, Mr J. Parkin, Pryke Hygiene Group, Mr Harold E. St. Quinton, Mr M. Thompson, Mr R. G. Tilbrook, Mr Brian Wade, Mr Phil Wilkinson.

Jockey (NH): Graham Lee (10-0).

302 MR J. R. W. JENKINS, Royston
Postal: **Kings Ride, Baldock Road, Royston, Hertfordshire, SG8 9NN.**
Contact: **PHONE** (01763) 241141 **FAX** (01763) 248223 **HOME** (01763) 246611
MOBILE (07802) 750855 **E-MAIL** john@johnjenkinsracing.co.uk **WEBSITE** www.johnjenkinsracing.co.uk

1 **AFADAN (IRE)**, 6, br g Royal Academy (USA)—Afasara (IRE) **St. Albans Chasers**
2 **AMIR ZAMAN**, 6, ch g Salse (USA)—Colorvista **The B. C. W. Partnership**
3 **AMWELL STAR (USA)**, 6, gr m Silver Buck (USA)—Markham Fair (CAN) **Amwell Racing**
4 **ANGELS VENTURE**, 8, ch g Unfuwain (USA)—City of Angels **Mrs Wendy Jenkins & Sandra Yuill**
5 **COOLING OFF (IRE)**, 7, b m Brief Truce (USA)—Lovers' Parlour **Mrs Wendy Jenkins & Sandra Yuill**
6 **DOMENICO (IRE)**, 6, b g Sadler's Wells (USA)—Russian Ballet (USA) **American Horse Racing Club Ltd**
7 **EMPRESS JOSEPHINE**, 4, b f Emperor Jones (USA)—Valmaranda (USA) **Mrs Olive Meddle**
8 **ENVIRONMENT AUDIT**, 5, ch g Kris—Bold And Beautiful **American Horse Racing Club Ltd**
9 **ERRIS EXPRESS (IRE)**, 6, ch g Definite Article—Postie **Erris Boys**
10 **EVIYRN (IRE)**, 8, b g In The Wings—Evrana (USA) **S. C. Finance Limited**
11 **EZZ ELKHEIL**, 5, b g Benny—Numidie (FR) **Mr Kevin Hudson**
12 **HARRY ANCHOR**, 4, b g Slip Anchor—Subtle One (IRE) **Mrs P. J. Rowland**
13 **HOLLOW JO**, 4, b g Most Welcome—Sir Hollow (USA) **Ms Sandra Yuill**
14 **ISLAND STREAM (IRE)**, 5, b g Turtle Island (IRE)—Tilbrook (IRE) **Mr Mark Apps**
15 **JACK DORAN**, 4, ch g Gildoran—Faustelerie **Nolan's Bar Racing Syndicate**
16 **JAWWALA (USA)**, 5, b m Green Dancer (USA)—Fetch N Carry (USA) **Skullduggery**
17 **JEM'S LAW**, 5, b m Contract Law (USA)—Alnasr Jewel (USA) **Mrs P. J. Rowland**

MR J. R. W. JENKINS—continued

18 **JOSHUA'S BAY**, 6, b g Karinga Bay—Bonita Blakeney **Mr & Mrs Leon Shack**
19 **JULIA'S CHOICE**, 5, ch m Elmaamul (USA)—Daarat Alayaam (IRE) **Mr M. Ng & Mr G. R. Hattle**
20 **LIVELY LADY**, 8, b m Beveled (USA)—In The Papers **Mrs Wendy Jenkins**
21 **MADDIE'S A JEM**, 4, b f Emperor Jones (USA)—Royal Orchid (IRE) **Mrs Wendy Jenkins**
22 **MOON EMPEROR**, 7, b g Emperor Jones (USA)—Sir Hollow (USA) **Robert Ellis & Christopher Shankland**
23 **NEWKIDONTHEBLOCK (IRE)**, 9, b g Be My Native (USA)—Jenny's Child **The Beaver Group**
24 **NOWBYTHEWAY (IRE)**, 7, b g Wakashan—Gilded Empress **Mr Jack McGrath**
25 **ON THE VERGE (IRE)**, 6, ch g Alphabatim (USA)—Come On Lis **Mr James Roche**
26 **PRINCE DU SOLEIL (FR)**, 8, b g Cardoun (FR)—Revelry (FR) **S. C. Finance Limited & Partners**
27 **QUEST ON AIR**, 5, b g Star Quest—Stormy Heights **Mr David Morris & Mr T. H. Ounsley**
28 **REN'S MAGIC**, 6, gr g Petong—Bath **Mr H. Thomas & Mrs Wendy Jenkins**
29 **SIR HAYDN**, 4, ch g Definite Article—Snowscape **Ms Ellen R. M. Sowle**
30 **SPLENDID TOUCH**, 4, b f Distinctly North (USA)—Soft Touch (GER) **Kingsland Bloodstock**
31 **THUNDERING SURF**, 7, b g Lugana Beach—Thunder Bug (USA) **Mr C. N. & Mrs J. C. Wright**
32 **TOUCH OF SPIRIT**, 5, b m Dancing Spree (USA)—Soft Touch (GER) **Kingsland Bloodstock**
33 **VANILLA MOON**, 4, b f Emperor Jones (USA)—Daarat Alayaam (IRE) **Mrs Irene Hampson**
34 **WESTMEAD ETOILE**, 4, b f Unfuwain (USA)—Glossary **Westmead**
35 **WESTMEAD TANGO**, 4, b f Pursuit of Love—Tango Teaser **Westmead**
36 **WHO CARES WINS**, 8, ch g Kris—Anne Bonny **The B. C. W. Partnership**

THREE-YEAR-OLDS

37 **AFTER THE SHOW**, b c Royal Applause—Tango Teaser **Mr M. Ng & Miss L. Thompson**
38 **AMWELL BRAVE**, b c Pyramus—Passage Creeping (IRE) **Amwell Racing**
39 **BOOKIESINDEXDOTCOM**, b f Great Dane (IRE)—Fifth Emerald **Bookmakers Index Ltd**
40 **CHARA**, ch f Deploy—Subtle One (IRE) **Mr M. Ng**
41 **HILLY BE**, ch f Silver Patriarch (IRE)—Lolita (FR) **S. C. Finance Limited**
42 **IMTALKINGGIBBERISH**, ch c Pursuit of Love—Royal Orchid (IRE) **Mr M. Ng**
43 **JESSE SAMUEL**, ch c First Trump—Miss Kellybell **Mr C. N. & Mrs J. C. Wright**
44 **MAGIC AMIGO**, ch g Zilzal (USA)—Emaline (FR) **Mr Kevin Reddington**
45 **MUY BIEN**, ch c Daggers Drawn (USA)—Primula Bairn **Mr Kevin Reddington**
46 **MYSTIC MOON**, br f First Trump—Misty Moon **Kingsland Bloodstock**
47 **PICK OF THE CROP**, ch c Fraam—Fresh Fruit Daily **Buy and Sell Partnership**
48 **SECOND USER**, b g Zilzal (USA)—Glossary **The Dough Boys**
49 **VELVET TOUCH**, b f Danzig Connection (USA)—Soft Touch (GER) **Kingsland Bloodstock**

TWO-YEAR-OLDS

50 **BRADDERS**, b c 25/2 Silver Patriarch—Lolita (FR) (Hellios (USA)) **S. C. Finance Ltd**
51 B g 6/3 Lujain (USA)—Fifth Emerald (Formidable (USA)) **Mr M. Ng**
52 B f 18/4 Classic Cliche (IRE)—Five And Four (IRE) (Green Desert (USA)) **Mr M. Ng**
53 B f 15/4 Fraam—Fresh Fruit Daily (Reprimand)
54 **LIGHTHORNE LAD**, ch c 13/4 Hornbeam—Give Me A Day **Mr K. C. Payne**
55 B c 12/4 Wolfhound (USA)—Peggys Rose (IRE) (Shalford) (4000) **Mr M. O'Donovan**
56 **POLISH INDEX**, b c 13/4 Polish Precedent—Glossary (Reference Point) **Mrs Stella Peirce & Mr A. E. Peirce**
57 B f 25/4 Most Welcome—Sir Hollow (USA) (Sir Ivor)
58 Ch c 26/2 Lake Coniston (IRE)—Soft Touch (GER) (Horst-Herbert) (1500) **Kingsland Bloodstock**

Conditional: T Bailey, C Harris.

---

303 MR W. P. JENKS, Bridgnorth
Postal: **Wadeley Farm, Glazeley, Bridgnorth, Shropshire, WV16 6AD.**
Contact: **OFFICE (01746) 789288 FAX (01746) 789535**

1 **AUBURN DUKE**, 4, ch g Inchinor—Dakota Girl **Mr B. Perkins**
2 **AUDITTY (IRE)**, 11, b g Montelimar (USA)—Tax Code **Mr Michael Stoddart**
3 **FENNEY SPRING**, 4, b f Polish Precedent (USA)—Sliprail (USA) **Mr Michael Stoddart**
4 **FORREST TRIBE (IRE)**, 11, b br g Be My Native (USA)—Island Bridge **Mrs Douglas Graham**
5 **FULL PITCH**, 8, ch g Cadeaux Genereux—Tricky Note **Mr W. Jenks**
6 **HAILE SELASSIE**, 4, b g Awesome—Lady of The Realm **The Glazeley Partnership**
7 6, Br g Gold Brose (AUS)—Hey Paula (NZ) **Mr W. Jenks**
8 **MAGICAL LIAISON (IRE)**, 6, b g Mujtahid (USA)—Instant Affair (USA) **The Glazeley Partnership 2**
9 **MUSALLY**, 7, ch g Muhtarram (USA)—Flourishing (IRE) **The Glazeley Partnership**
10 **SLEIGHT**, 5, ch m Bob's Return (IRE)—Jolejester **The Wadeley Partnership**
11 4, Br g Senor Pete (USA)—Stapleton Row (NZ) **Mr W. Jenks**

MR W. P. JENKS—continued
THREE-YEAR-OLDS

  12 **CHAGA**, b f Hector Protector (USA)—Santarem (USA) **Mr W. Jenks**

Other Owners: Dr B. Alexander, Mr J. Beasley, Mrs Beatrice Grant, Mr Richard Mapp, Mrs G. Pugie, Mr J. Scarrett.

Jockey (NH): C Llewellyn (10-0). **Amateur:** Mr R Burton.

---

304 | **MR A. E. M. JESSOP, Chelmsford**
Postal: **Flemings Farm, Warren Road, South Hanningfield, Chelmsford, Essex, CM3 8HU.**
Contact: **PHONE (01268) 710210 MOBILE (07718) 736482**

  1 **L'ARCHER**, 6, b g Lancastrian—Sailors Joy **Mr A. Jessop**
  2 **LEVRET BLEU (FR)**, 5, b g Panoramic—Azur Bleue (FR)
  3 **MISS COLMESNIL (FR)**, 4, b f Dear Doctor (FR)—Princesse Dolly (FR) **Mrs Gloria Jessop**
  4 **MOSS RUN (IRE)**, 10, b g Commanche Run—Glenreigh Moss **Mrs Gloria Jessop**
  5 4, B f Old Vic—Sailors Joy **Mrs Gloria Jessop**

Assistant Trainer: Alison Jessop

---

305 | **MR B. R. JOHNSON, Epsom**
Postal: **Little Woodruffe Racing Stable, Headley Road, Epsom, Surrey, KT18 6BH.**
Contact: **YARD (01372) 270199 MOBILE (07768) 697141**
E-MAIL juliereeves@outofoffice73freeserve.co.uk

  1 **BEYOND THE POLE (USA)**, 6, b g Ghazi (USA)—North of Sunset (USA) **Tann Racing**
  2 **HIGH DIVA**, 5, b m Piccolo—Gifted **Tann Racing**
  3 **JAHANGIR**, 5, b g Zamindar (USA)—Imperial Jade **Mr A. A. Lyons**
  4 **MANDOOB**, 7, b g Zafonic (USA)—Thaidah (CAN) **Mr J. L. Guillambert & Mr B. R. Johnson**
  5 **MISS PEBBLES (IRE)**, 4, ch f Lake Coniston (IRE)—Sea of Stone (USA) **Mr A. A. Lyons**
  6 **SUMMER RECLUSE (USA)**, 5, gr g Cozzene (USA)—Summer Retreat (USA) **P M C Racing**
  7 **TEDZAR (IRE)**, 4, b g Inzar (USA)—Chesham Lady (IRE) **Mr P. Clark**
  8 **TOP TENOR (IRE)**, 4, b c Sadler's Wells (USA)—Posta Vecchia (USA) **Mr B. R. Johnson**
  9 **TREETOPS HOTEL (IRE)**, 5, ch g Grand Lodge (USA)—Rousinette **Tann Racing**
 10 **WHAT'S THE COUNT**, 8, gr g Theatrical Charmer—Yankee Silver **The Twenty Five Club**

THREE-YEAR-OLDS

 11 **MONASH GIRL (IRE)**, b f General Monash (USA)—Maricica **Mrs Beryl Williams & Mr B. Johnson**
 12 B f Grand Lodge (USA)—Mysterious Plans (IRE) **Mr A. A. Lyons**
 13 **PAT'S NEMISIS (IRE)**, b f Sri Pekan (USA)—Exemplaire (FR) **Mr A. A. Lyons**

Other Owners: Mr P. Grimes, Miss N. J. Holmwood, Mr R. D. Jenrick, Mr P. Morley, Mr B. A. Rolls, Mrs E. Tann, Mr Gary Tann, Mr M. C. Trevena, Mr B. A. Whittaker.

Assistant Trainer: Julie Reeves

---

306 | **MR J. H. JOHNSON, Crook**
Postal: **White Lea Farm, Crook, Co. Durham, DL15 9QN.**
Contact: **PHONE (01388) 762113 CAR (07914) 691017 FAX (01388) 768278**
MOBILE (07714) 691016/(07714) 691017 E-MAIL directroute1@aol.com

  1 **ALBANY (IRE)**, 4, ch g Alhaarth (IRE)—Tochar Ban (USA) **Andrea & Graham Wylie**
  2 **ANOTHER DUDE (IRE)**, 7, br g Shardari—Gemma's Fridge **Mr Maurice Hutchinson**
  3 **ARMAGH SOUTH (IRE)**, 5, ch g Topanoora—Mogen **Mr M. McKernan**
  4 **ASTRONOMIC**, 4, b g Zafonic (USA)—Sky Love (USA) **Andrea & Graham Wylie**
  5 **BACK ON SONG (IRE)**, 5, b m Bob Back (USA)—No Blues (IRE) **Dr B. Mayoh**
  6 **BAHLINO (IRE)**, 4, gr g Bahhare (USA)—Azulino (IRE) **Andrea & Graham Wylie**
  7 **BALLYBOUGH RASHER (IRE)**, 9, b g Broken Hearted—Chat Her Up **Comtake-Welding Engineering Specialists**
  8 **BEAU ARTISTE**, 4, ch g Peintre Celebre (USA)—Belle Esprit **Mr G. F. Bear**
  9 **BEAUCHAMP GIGI (IRE)**, 6, b m Bob Back (USA)—Beauchamp Grace **Andrea & Graham Wylie**
 10 **BIG SMOKE (IRE)**, 4, gr g Perugino (USA)—Lightning Bug **Mr M. McKernan**
 11 **BOY'S HURRAH (IRE)**, 8, b g Phardante (FR)—Gorryelm **Mr R. Gurney**

MR J. H. JOHNSON—continued

12 **CHEVET BOY (IRE)**, 6, b g Welsh Term—Sizzle **Mr D. M. Gibbons**
13 **CHEVET GIRL (IRE)**, 9, ch m Roselier (FR)—Vulcash (IRE) **Mr D. M. Gibbons**
14 **CHIVALRY**, 5, b g Mark of Esteem (IRE)—Gai Bulga **Andrea & Graham Wylie**
15 **COVENT GARDEN**, 6, b g Sadler's Wells (USA)—Temple Row **ADA Partnership**
16 **DALARAM (IRE)**, 4, b g Sadler's Wells (USA)—Dalara (IRE) **Andrea & Graham Wylie**
17 **DEJA VU (IRE)**, 5, b g Lord Americo—Khalkeys Shoon **The SGS Partnership**
18 **DEL TROTTER (IRE)**, 9, b g King Luthier—Arctic Alice **Group Captain J. A. Prideaux**
19 **DIONN RIGH**, 9, b g Asir—Happy Eliza **Gordon Brown/Bert Watson**
20 **EURO CAT (IRE)**, 5, b g Anshan—Bailey House (IRE) **Mr Roy Campion**
21 **FACTOR FIFTEEN**, 5, gr g Hector Protector (USA)—Catch The Sun **Andrea & Graham Wylie**
22 **FARLINGTON**, 7, b g Aflora (IRE)—Annapuma **Mr John Smart**
23 **FIELDS OF HOME (IRE)**, 6, b m Synefos (USA)—Homefield Girl (IRE) **Mrs Lucy Forbes**
24 **FLOWNAWAY**, 5, b g Polar Falcon (USA)—No More Rosies **Andrea & Graham Wylie**
25 **FORTUNA FAVENTE (IRE)**, 4, b f Supreme Leader—La Grande Dame **Andrea & Graham Wylie**
26 **GIULIANI**, 4, b c Sadler's Wells (USA)—Anka Germania **Mr J. R. McAleese**
27 **GRATTAN LODGE (IRE)**, 7, gr g Roselier (FR)—Shallow Run **Mr W. M. G. Black**
28 **GREY ABBEY (IRE)**, 10, gr g Nestor—Tacovaon **Ken Roper,Elinor M. Roper,Norman Furness**
29 **HUNCHEON SISS (IRE)**, 7, b m Phardante (FR)—Parsons Term (IRE) **Mr J. R. McAleese**
30 **INCHING CLOSER**, 7, b g Inchinor—Maiyaasah **Andrea & Graham Wylie**
31 **INGLIS DREVER**, 5, b g In The Wings—Cormorant Creek **Andrea & Graham Wylie**
32 **INTERSKY NATIVE (IRE)**, 8, ch g Be My Native (USA)—Creative Music **Interskyracing.com**
33 **INTERSKY SOVEREIGN (IRE)**, 6, b g Aristocracy—Queen's Prize **Interskyracing.com**
34 **IT'S ALL A CHANCE (IRE)**, 9, ch g Eve's Error—Butlers Pier **Mr Roy Campion**
35 **KASTHARI (IRE)**, 5, gr g Vettori (IRE)—Karliyka (USA) **Elliott Brothers**
36 **KATMANDU**, 5, b g Sadler's Wells (USA)—Kithanga (IRE) **ADA Partnership**
37 **KILLULTAGH DAWN (IRE)**, 6, b m Phardante (FR)—Rostrevor Lady **Frank Boyde**
38 **KINBURN (IRE)**, 5, gr g Roselier (FR)—Leadaro (IRE) **Mr W. M. G. Black**
39 **KING OF ARMS**, 6, b g Rakaposhi King—Herald The Dawn **Mr M. McKernan**
40 **KINGS HILL LEADER (IRE)**, 5, b g Supreme Leader—Mary Kate Finn **Mr J. R. McAleese**
41 4, ch f Classic Cliche (IRE)—Kiniohio (FR) **Mr Jim Buchanan**
42 **LA PERROTINE (FR)**, 4, b f Northern Crystal—Haratiyna **Mrs M. W. Bird**
43 **LOCH 'N' LAIRD (IRE)**, 5, b g Supreme Leader—Parsons Term **Mr M. McKernan**
44 **LOG ON INTERSKY (IRE)**, 8, ch g Insan (USA)—Arctic Mo (IRE) **Interskyracing.com**
45 **LORD CAPITAINE (IRE)**, 10, b g Mister Lord (USA)—
　　　　　　Salvation Sue **The Scottish Steeplechasing Partnership**
46 **LORD TRANSCEND (IRE)**, 7, gr g Aristocracy—Capincur Lady **Transcend (Hair and Beauty) Limited**
47 **LOUSTIC COLLONGES (FR)**, 5, b g Kadalko (FR)—Altesse Collonges (FR) **Andrea & Graham Wylie**
48 **LUTHELLO (FR)**, 5, b g Marchand de Sable (USA)—Haudello (FR) **Mrs M. W. Bird**
49 **MELMOUNT STAR (IRE)**, 6, b br g Rashar (USA)—Bucktina **Mrs Lucy Forbes**
50 **MONTMARTRE (IRE)**, 4, br f Grand Lodge (USA)—French Quarter **Andrea & Graham Wylie**
51 **NAMELESS WONDER (IRE)**, 8, b g Supreme Leader—Miss Kylogue (IRE) **Group Captain J. A. Prideaux**
52 **NORTHERN GALAXY (IRE)**, 12, b g Pennine Walk—Etoile Grise **Mr J. Howard Johnson**
53 **RAYSHAN (IRE)**, 4, b g Darshaan—Rayseka (IRE) **Andrea & Graham Wylie**
54 **RIGHT ON TARGET (IRE)**, 6, b m Presenting—Owenageera (IRE) **Dr B. Mayoh**
55 **ROSS PARK (IRE)**, 8, b g Roselier (FR)—La Christyana (IRE) **Gordon Brown/Bert Watson**
56 **ROYAL ROSA (FR)**, 5, ch g Garde Royale—Crystalza (FR) **Andrea & Graham Wylie**
57 **SAN PEIRE (FR)**, 7, b g Cyborg (FR)—Shakapoura (FR) **Comtace-Welding Engineering Specialists**
58 **SCOTMAIL BOY (IRE)**, 11, b g Over The River (FR)—Princess Paula **Mr George Tobitt**
59 **SHADY MERLIN (IRE)**, 6, b g Shardari—Merillion **Cathal McCarthy**
60 **SILVER SEDGE (IRE)**, 5, br g Aristocracy—Pollyfaster **Mr W. M. G. Black**
61 **SOUTHBOUND (IRE)**, 5, ch g Zaffaran (USA)—Soxess (IRE) **Mr R. J. Crake**
62 **SPANCHIL HILL**, 4, b g Sabrehill (USA)—War Shanty **Mr J. Howard Johnson**
63 **SQUEEZE BOX (IRE)**, 5, b m Accordion—Spread Your Wings (IRE) **Hoggy, Hammy, Hendy and Howy**
64 **TEME VALLEY**, 10, br g Polish Precedent (USA)—Sudeley **Mr Chris Heron**
65 **TREYBOR (IRE)**, 5, br g Bob Back (USA)—Ballyvooney **Andrea & Graham Wylie**
66 **VALLEY HENRY (IRE)**, 9, b g Step Together (USA)—Pineway VII **Andrea & Graham Wylie**
67 **VALLUM (IRE)**, 4, ch g Master Willie—Tracker **Andrea & Graham Wylie**
68 **WISEGUY (IRE)**, 5, b g Darshaan—Bibliotheque (USA) **Andrea & Graham Wylie**
69 **YOUNG WHACK (IRE)**, 10, br g Phardante (FR)—Flash Parade **Gordon Brown/Bert Watson**

THREE-YEAR-OLDS

70 Ch f Commanche Run—Zajira (IRE) **Zagira Partnership**

MR J. H. JOHNSON—continued
TWO-YEAR-OLDS

71 **MELODY QUE (IRE)**, b f 24/3 Sadler's Wells (USA)—
Bex (USA) (Explodent (USA)) (247371) **Andrea & Graham Wylie**
72 **PARCHMENT (IRE)**, ch c 20/1 Singspiel (IRE)—
Hannalou (FR) (Shareef Dancer (USA)) (100000) **Andrea & Graham Wylie**
73 **POIROT**, b c 14/3 Montjeu (IRE)—Opari (IRE) (Night Shift (USA)) (185528) **Andrea & Graham Wylie**
74 **RAINBOW RISING (IRE)**, b br c 8/3 Desert King (IRE)—
Fantastic Bid (USA) (Auction Ring (USA)) (36000) **Andrea & Graham Wylie**
75 **RENADA**, b f 9/2 Sinndar (IRE)—Asterita (Rainbow Quest (USA)) (290660) **Andrea & Graham Wylie**
76 **ROCKPILER**, b c 16/2 Halling (USA)—Emma Peel (Emarati (USA)) (185528) **Andrea & Graham Wylie**
77 **SANDYSNOWING (FR)**, b c 1/3 Sendawar (IRE)—
Snow White (Polar Falcon (USA)) (123685) **Andrea & Graham Wylie**
78 **TSAROXY (IRE)**, b c 27/2 Xaar—Belsay (Belmez (USA)) (259740) **Andrea & Graham Wylie**

Other Owners: Mr Gordon Brown, Mrs Lucy Forbes, Mr David M. Fulton, Mr Norman Furness, Mrs Tracey Gaunt, Mr Ian Hamilton, Mr John Henderson, Mr John Hogg, Mrs S. Johnson, Mr R. M. Kirkland, Mr Terry McDermott, Mr W. Murphy, Mr David Parry, Mr Brian Rafferty, Mrs Elinor M. Roper, Mr Ken Roper, Mr A. Shearer, Mr A. Shield, Mr Robert Watson, Mrs Andrea Wylie, Mr Graham Wylie.

Jockey (NH): Graham Lee (w.a.). **Conditional:** Peter Buchanan.

307 MR ROBERT W. JOHNSON, Newcastle Upon Tyne
Postal: **Grange Farm, Newburn, Newcastle Upon Tyne, NE15 8QA.**
Contact: **PHONE (01912) 674464 MOBILE (07774) 131133**

1 **AELRED**, 11, b g Ovac (ITY)—Sponsorship **Mr J. L. Gledson**
2 **BABY JANE**, 10, b m Old Vic—Sutosky **Mr Geoff Pickering**
3 **BOB'S BUSTER**, 8, b g Bob's Return (IRE)—Saltina **Mrs Geraldine Jones**
4 **CESARE BORGIA (IRE)**, 4, ch c Dr Devious (IRE)—Prospering **Mr Robert Johnson**
5 **IMPERIAL MAN (IRE)**, 9, b g Mandalus—The Foalicule **Mr Robert Johnson**
6 **JACCOUT (FR)**, 6, b g Sheyrann—Jacottiere (FR) **Mr Alan Kidd and Mr Andrew Johnson**
7 **KATIES DOLPHIN (IRE)**, 6, ch m Dolphin Street (FR)—Kuwah (IRE) **Mr Foster Watson**
8 **SANDS RISING**, 7, b g Primitive Rising (USA)—Celtic Sands **Mr T. L. A. Robson**
9 **SHINING TYNE**, 10, b g Asir—Twice Regal **Mr C. H. P. Bell**
10 **SIRERIC (IRE)**, 14, b g Asir—Twice Regal **Mr C. H. P. Bell**
11 **STORMY BEECH**, 8, b g Glacial Storm (USA)—Cheeny's Brig **Peter & Paul Kelly**
12 **UPSWING**, 7, b g Perpendicular—Moorfield Lady **Mr C. H. P. Bell**
13 **UPTOWN LAD (IRE)**, 5, b g Definite Article—Shoka (FR) **Mr C. Grindell**
14 **VALUABLE (IRE)**, 7, b m Jurado (USA)—Can't Afford It (IRE) **The Jolly Boys Partnership**

Other Owners: Mr B. Weir, Mr D. Weir.

Jockey (NH): K Johnson (10-0). **Amateur:** Mr P Johnson (10-9).

308 MRS S. M. JOHNSON, Madley
Postal: **Carwardine Farm, Madley, Hereford, HR2 9JQ.**
Contact: **PHONE (01981) 250214**

1 **AMBER GOLD**, 6, b m Tragic Role (USA)—Dark Amber **Evans, Compton, Matthews & Matthews**
2 5, Ch g High Roller (IRE)—Captain's Covey **Mr I. K. Johnson**
3 **DERRING BRIDGE**, 14, b g Derring Rose—Bridge Ash **Mr I. K. Johnson**
4 **FOREVER POSH**, 6, b m Rakaposhi King—B Final **Mr P. J. Allen**
5 **KILLALONGFORD (IRE)**, 7, b g Tenby—Queen Crab **Mrs M. E. Mason**
6 **LYRICAL LILY**, 6, b m Alflora (IRE)—Music Interpreter **Mr I. K. Johnson**
7 **OVER BRIDGE**, 6, b g Overbury (IRE)—Celtic Bridge **Mr I. K. Johnson**
8 **THREEPENNY BIT**, 6, b m Safawan—Tuppence In Clover **J. P. and Mrs M. A. Skues**

Other Owners: Mrs M. Chinn, Mr W. Chinn, Mr C. B. Compton, Mr David F. Evans, Mr J. E. Matthews, Mr W. D. Matthews, Mr J. P. Skues, Mrs M. A. Skues.

Jockey (NH): Richard Johnson (10-0, w.a.). **Amateurs:** Miss Sam Beddoes, Mr Richard Burton.

309 MR R. F. JOHNSON HOUGHTON, Didcot

Postal: **Woodway, Blewbury, Didcot, Oxfordshire, OX11 9EZ.**
Contact: **PHONE** (01235) 850480 **FAX** (01235) 851045 **MOBILE** (07836) 599232
E-MAIL fulke@johnsonhoughton.com

1 **AWARDING**, 4, ch g Mark of Esteem (IRE)—Monaiya **Anthony Pye-Jeary And Mel Smith**
2 **BARABBAS (USA)**, 5, b g Royal Academy (USA)—Kamsi **Mr Philip Newton**
3 **IMBIBING (IRE)**, 5, ch g Halling (USA)—Polar Fizz **Anthony Pye-Jeary And Mel Smith**
4 **MAGIC SPIN**, 4, b f Magic Ring (IRE)—Moon Spin **Mr G. C. Stevens**
5 **PHECKLESS**, 5, ch g Be My Guest (USA)—Phlirty **Mrs R. F. Johnson Houghton**
6 **PHRED**, 4, ch g Safawan—Phlirty **Mrs R. F. Johnson Houghton**
7 **PONDERON**, 4, ch g Hector Protector (USA)—Blush Rambler (IRE) **Mrs P. Robeson**
8 **REMINISCENT (IRE)**, 5, b g Kahyasi—Eliza Orzeszkowa (IRE) **Mr R. F. Johnson Houghton**
9 **ROCK GARDEN (IRE)**, 5, br m Bigstone (IRE)—Woodland Garden **Mr R. F. Johnson Houghton**
10 **ROHAN**, 8, gr g Norton Challenger—Acushla Macree **Mrs R. F. Johnson Houghton**
11 **TOUT SEUL (IRE)**, 4, b c Ali-Royal (IRE)—Total Aloof **Eden Racing**

THREE-YEAR-OLDS

12 **ALCHERA**, b c Mind Games—Kind of Shy **Mr G. C. Stevens**
13 **BLUEFIELD (IRE)**, b c Second Empire (IRE)—Imco Reverie (IRE) **Mrs C. J. Hue Williams**
14 **DREAMING WATERS**, ch f Groom Dancer (USA)—Faraway Waters **T. P. Ronan & M. J. W. McKinley**
15 **MACCHIATO**, br f Inchinor—Tereyna **Fyfield Racing**
16 **MALLING**, ch c Halling (USA)—Queens Way (FR) **Anthony Pye-Jeary and Mel Smith**
17 **MIDNIGHT BALLARD (USA)**, b br c Mister Baileys—Shadow Music (USA) **Mr C. W. Sumner**
18 **OFF BEAT (USA)**, ch g Mister Baileys—Off Off (USA) **Eden Racing (II)**
19 **PHLUKE**, b g Most Welcome—Phlirty **Mrs R. F. Johnson Houghton**
20 **VELVET WATERS**, br f Unfuwain (USA)—Gleaming Water **Mr R. Crutchley**

TWO-YEAR-OLDS

21 **AMPITHEATRE (IRE)**, b c 26/4 Titus Livius (FR)—Crimson Ring (Persian Bold) (3000)
22 **ASTEEM**, b c 30/4 Mark Of Esteem (IRE)—Amidst (Midyan (USA)) (9000) **Eden Racing**
23 **BEAVER PATROL (IRE)**, ch c 18/4 Tagula (IRE)—
Erne Project (IRE) (Project Manager) (11131) **Mr G. C. Stevens**
24 **BRIDGE T'THE STARS**, b f 15/2 Josr Algarhoud (IRE)—Petra's Star (Rock City) **Mrs Zara Campbell-Harris**
25 **JUDDSTREET**, b c 21/2 Compton Place—
Pudding Lane (IRE) (College Chapel) (2500) **Mr R. F. Johnson Houghton**
26 **KRYENA**, b f 8/4 Kris—Tereyna (Terimon) **Mrs P. Robeson**
27 Br c 7/4 Daylami (IRE)—Mawhiba (USA) (Dayjur (USA)) (11131) **Anthony Pye-Jeary & Mel Smith**
28 **PEACE LILY**, b f 25/4 Dansili—Shall We Run (Hotfoot) (24000) **Mrs R. F. Johnson Houghton**
29 B f 24/2 Namid—Petomi (Presidium) (10000) **Eden Racing**
30 **PHLAUNT**, b f 24/2 Faustus (USA)—Phlirty (Pharly (FR)) (952) **Mrs R. F. Johnson Houghton**
31 **PICKAPEPPA**, ch f 20/1 Piccolo—Cajole (IRE) (Barathea (IRE)) **Mrs C. J. Hue Williams**
32 **ROODEYE**, b f 13/2 Inchinor—Roo (Rudimentary) (USA)) **Mrs H. & Mrs R. F. Johnson Houghton**
33 **RUBIES**, ch f 5/2 Inchinor—Fur Will Fly (Petong) **Mrs M. McCalmont**
34 B c 27/4 Mujahid (USA)—Salalah (Lion Cavern (USA)) (20000) **Anthony Pye-Jeary And Mel Smith**
35 B c 15/4 Namid—Socialite (IRE) (Alzao (USA)) (21644) **Mrs Mangan**
36 **THORNY MANDATE**, b c 26/1 Diktat—Rosa Canina (Bustino) (16000) **Christopher Naylor**

Other Owners: Miss E Johnson Houghton, Mr W. H. Ponsonby, Mr N. R. Pullan.

Assistant Trainer: Eve Johnson Houghton

Jockey (Flat): S Carson. **Jockey (NH):** M Bradburne. **Amateur:** Miss E A Johnson Houghton (9-7).

310 MR A. E. JONES, Sparsholt

Postal: **8 Hawthorn Way, Blakeney Fields, Great Shefford, Hungerford, Berkshire, RG17 7BT.**
Contact: **MOBILE** (07901) 505064 **E-MAIL** wannahorse@heritageracing.fslife.co.uk

1 **ALEEMDAR (IRE)**, 7, b g Doyoun—Aleema **Mr John Spence**
2 **CARNANEY GIRL**, 6, ch m Primitive Rising (USA)—Mossberry Fair **Whisper Club Syndicate**
3 **GREY CISEAUX (IRE)**, 9, gr g Mujtahid (USA)—Inisfail **Mr John Spence**
4 **THRASHING**, 9, b g Kahyasi—White-Wash **Mr Graham Brown**

Other Owners: Mr W. Kelly, Mr P. Martin.

Jockey (Flat): K Fallon (w.a.). **Jockey (NH):** R Johnson (w.a.). **Amateurs:** Mr K Culligan, Miss S Parmentier.

311 MR A. P. JONES, Upper Lambourn

Postal: **Hill House Stables, Sherwood, Folly Road, Lambourn, Berkshire, RG17 8QE.**
Contact: **OFFICE (01488) 670245 MOBILE (07771) 553242 E-MAIL apjonesracing@aol.co.uk**

1 BEAUCHAMP Q, 5, b g Inchinor—Beauchamp Buzz **Mrs K. T. Pilkington**
2 BEDFORD LEADER, 6, b m Bedford (USA)—Neladar **Mr B. W. Bedford**
3 BRANDYWINE BAY (IRE), 4, b f Mujadil (USA)—Ned's Contessa (IRE) **Mrs K. T. Pilkington**
4 BRAVE PROTECTOR, 4, ch g Hector Protector (USA)—Brave Revival **Mrs K. T. Pilkington**
5 CAROLINE'S ROSE, 6, br m Fraam—Just Rosie **The Lambourn Racing Club**
6 FIN BEC (FR), 11, b g Tip Moss (FR)—Tourbrune (FR) **Mr P. Newell**
7 FIRE CAT, 5, ch g Beveled (USA)—Noble Soul **The Lambourn Racing Club**
8 FULL ENGLISH, 5, b m Perugino (USA)—Grown At Rowan **Mr T. G. N. Burrage**
9 GOLDEN FIELDS (IRE), 4, b f Definite Article—Quickstep Queen (FR) **Mrs K. T. Pilkington**
10 GOODENOUGH STAR, 4, b f Stronz (IRE)—Goodenough Girl **Mrs T. Lewis**
11 HARRY'S GAME, 7, gr g Emperor Jones (USA)—Lady Shikari **Mr T. G. N. Burrage**
12 INDULGENT WAY (IRE), 13, gr g Roselier (FR)—Glenmore Lady **Mrs T. Lewis**
13 INTRICAT, 4, ch g Bluegrass Prince (IRE)—Noble Soul **The Lambourn Racing Club**
14 JESSINCA, 8, b m Minshaanshu Amad (USA)—Noble Soul **The Lambourn Racing Club**
15 MR WHIZZ, 7, ch g Manhal—Panienka (POL) **The Milk Sheiks**
16 PLURALIST (IRE), 8, b g Mujadil (USA)—Encore Une Fois (IRE) **Mr G. Last**
17 RIMOSA, 9, b m Miner's Lamp—Crosa **Mr A. P. Jones**
18 RUBY RAINNE, 5, gr m Perugino (USA)—Lady Shikari **Mr T. G. N. Burrage**
19 SURPRISE GUNNER, 14, b g Gunner B—Heckley Loch **Mrs T. Lewis**
20 THINK IT OVER (IRE), 5, ch m Bijou d'Inde—Good News (IRE) **Mr T. G. N. Burrage**
21 TOP SON, 5, b h Komaite (USA)—Top Yard **Mr George W. Smith**
22 VICTORY BELL, 6, b g Komaite (USA)—Shikabell **Mr George W. Smith**
23 WANSFORD LADY, 8, b m Michelozzo (USA)—Marnie's Girl **Mrs T. Lewis**

THREE-YEAR-OLDS

24 AVOCET (IRE), b f Desert Style (IRE)—Grown At Rowan **Mr T. G. N. Burrage**
25 BEAUCHAMP SPARK, ch g Pharly (FR)—Beauchamp Buzz **Mrs K. T. Pilkington**
26 CONFUZION (IRE), b f Inzar (USA)—Fernlea (USA) **Mrs K. T. Pilkington**
27 DARK RAIDER (IRE), br gr f Definite Article—Lady Shikari **Mr T. G. N. Burrage**
28 GOOD ARTICLE (IRE), b c Definite Article—Good News (IRE) **Mr T. G. N. Burrage**
29 JUST FILLY (IRE), ch f Woodborough (USA)—Good Aim (IRE) **Mrs K. T. Pilkington**
30 MISS JUDGED, b f Case Law—Marie's Crusader (IRE) **Mrs K. T. Pilkington**
31 Ch c Bluegrass Prince (IRE)—Noble Soul **P. Newell & A. P. Jones**
32 VENETIAN ROMANCE (IRE), ch f Desert Story (IRE)—Cipriani **Mrs K. T. Pilkington**

TWO-YEAR-OLDS

33 Ch c 10/4 Bluegrass Prince (IRE—Bless (Beveled (USA)) **Mrs K. T. Pilkington**
34 B f 21/3 Bluegrass Prince (IRE—Madam Marash (IRE) (Astronef)) **Mrs K. T. Pilkington**
35 Ch c 14/4 Fumo di Londra (IRE)—Noble Soul (Sayf Elarub (USA)) **P. Newell & A. P. Jones**
36 Ch c 30/4 Fumo di Londra (IRE)—Try The Duchess (Try My Best (USA)) **Mrs K. T. Pilkington**

Other Owners: Mr W. A. Edgington, Mr J. A. Herbert, Mr A. A. King, K. D. Linsley, Mr D. R. Mead.

Assistant Trainer: K T Pilkington, G Hannon

Jockeys (Flat): G Hannon, F Norton, D Sweeney, S Whitworth. **Jockeys (NH):** L Aspell, T Doyle, M Foley, A Thornton. **Apprentice:** Liam Keniry. **Amateurs:** Mr Wayne Lewis (9-7), Mr Ashley Price (9-7).

312 MR G. ELWYN JONES, Lampeter

Postal: **Lluestnewydd, Bettws, Lampeter, Dyfed, SA48 8PB.**
Contact: **PHONE (01570) 493291 MOBILE (07817) 885504**

1 BLUE CASCADE (IRE), 5, b g Royal Academy (USA)—Blaine (USA) **Mr G. Elwyn Jones**
2 DESERT SPA (USA), 9, b g Sheikh Albadou—Healing Waters (USA) **Mr G. Elwyn Jones**
3 PRIME MINISTER, 10, ch g Be My Chief (USA)—Classic Design **Mr G. Elwyn Jones**

Amateur: Mr D Turner (9-7).

313   MRS M. A. JONES, Lambourn
Postal: **Felstead Court Stables, Lambourn, Hungerford, Berkshire, RG17 8QE.**
Contact: **PHONE (01488) 72409 MOBILE (07798) 641478 FAX (01488) 72409**
E-MAIL merrita_jones@hotmail.com

1 **AULD THYNES SAKE (IRE)**, 7, b g Good Thyne (USA)—La Fairy (IRE) **Speed 2911 Ltd**
2 **KING'S CHAMPION (IRE)**, 8, br g King's Ride—Decent Slave **Speed 2911 Ltd**
3 **LITE THE WAY**, 7, b m Miner's Lamp—Polly Tix **Mrs D. J. Hughes**
4 **SHILO (IRE)**, 10, ch g Roselier (FR)—Cathedral Street **Mrs D. J. Hughes**

Assistant Trainer: Louis Jones

314   MR R. W. JONES, Newmarket
Postal: **Boyden End House, Wickhambrook, Newmarket, Suffolk, CB8 8XX.**
Contact: **PHONE (01440) 820342 FAX (01440) 820958 MOBILE (07932) 164641**

1 **ANTONIO CANOVA**, 8, ch g Komaite (USA)—Joan's Venture **The Antonio Canova Partnership**
2 **BALLARE (IRE)**, 5, b g Barathea (IRE)—Raindancing (IRE) **The Ballare Partnership**
3 **COLD CLIMATE**, 9, ch g Pursuit of Love—Sharpthorne (USA) **The Cold Climate Partnership**
4 **UNSHAKABLE (IRE)**, 5, b g Eagle Eyed (USA)—Pepper And Salt (IRE) **Unshakable Partnership**

THREE-YEAR-OLDS

5 B g Great Dane (IRE)—Bettynouche **Mr Bob Jones & Partners**
6 **INCHCONNEL**, b g Inchinor—Sharanella **Mrs Joanne Baines**

Other Owners: Mr J. R. Abraham, Mrs Daphne Downey, Mrs S. A. Jones, Mr T. J. Law, Mr C. F. Monticolombi, Mrs L. C. Monticolombi, Mr T. Newman, Mrs A. J. F. Perry, Mr Gordon Stead, Mrs C. M. Stewart, Mr Richard W. D'A Stoop, Mr J. S. Taylor, Mr B. A. Wilson.

Assistant Trainer: Diana Carroll

Jockey (Flat): F Norton (w.a.). Jockey (NH): J Goldstein (w.a.).

315   MR T. M. JONES, Guildford
Postal: **Brook Farm, Albury, Guildford, Surrey, GU5 9DJ.**
Contact: **PHONE (01483) 202604/(01483) 203749 MOBILE (07785)915762**
E-MAIL buck@brookfarmalbury.freeserve.co.uk

1 **ALBURY HEATH**, 4, b g Mistertopogigo (IRE)—Walsham Witch **Mr T. M. Jones**
2 **WARAQA (USA)**, 5, b m Red Ransom (USA)—Jafn **Mr T. M. Jones**

THREE-YEAR-OLDS

3 **OUT OF MY WAY**, ch f Fraam—Ming Blue **Mr T. M. Jones**

TWO-YEAR-OLDS

4 **NEVER BOLDER**, b f Bold Edge—Nevita (Never So Bold) (1500) **Mr T. M. Jones**
5 **TIME TRAVELLER**, b g Timeless Times (USA)—Belltina (Belfort (FR)) (1500) **Mr T. M. Jones**

Assistant Trainer: Miss K. Windsor-Luck

316   MR A. G. JUCKES, Abberley
Postal: **Cherry Ash, Worsley Farm, Abberley, Worcester, WR6 6BQ.**
Contact: **PHONE (01299) 896471/(01299) 896522**

1 **ASADOR (FR)**, 8, ch g Kadounor (FR)—Apos (FR) **Mr Dennis Skinner**
2 **CAMARADERIE**, 8, b g Most Welcome—Secret Valentine **Mrs K. C. Price**
3 **FLEMMING (USA)**, 7, ch g Green Dancer (USA)—La Groupie (FR) **Ten Out Of Ten Racing Partnership**
4 **I TINA**, 8, b m Lycius (USA)—Tintomara (IRE) **Mr R. Axford**
5 **MANTLES PRINCE**, 10, ch g Emarati (USA)—Miami Mouse **Emlyn Hughes' Cleobury Golfers**
6 **MEDELAI**, 8, b m Marju (IRE)—No Islands **Mr M. P. Tokley**
7 **MOON SHOT**, 8, gr g Pistolet Bleu (IRE)—La Luna (USA) **Mr R. T. Juckes**
8 **MY COUNTRY CLUB**, 7, b h Alzao (USA)—Merry Rous **Mr R. T. Juckes**

MR A. G. JUCKES—continued

9 NANDOO, 5, b m Forzando—Ascend (IRE) **Mrs K. C. Price**
10 PRINCE NASSEEM (GER), 7, b h Neshad (USA)—Penola (GER) **Mr R. T. Juckes**
11 WALTER PLINGE, 8, b g Theatrical Charmer—Carousel Zingira **Mr Tony Cocum**
12 WINGED LADY (GER), 5, b m Winged Love (IRE)—Wonderful Lady (GER) **Whistlejacket Partnership**

Other Owners: Mr Shaun Bannister, Mr Emlyn Hughes, Dr D. Woodhouse, Mr J. Woodhouse.

Assistant Trainer: N R Juckes

Jockey (Flat): D Sweeney (w.a.). **Jockey (NH):** O McPhail.

317 MR H. M. KAVANAGH, Llandrindod Wells
Postal: **Midway Villa, Crossgates, Llandrindod Wells, Powys, LD1 5SL.**

1 LOVERS TALE, 6, b g Pursuit of Love—Kintail **Mrs S. Kavanagh**
2 PENNY'S CROWN, 5, b m Reprimand—Two And Sixpence (USA) **Mrs S. Kavanagh**

Jockey (NH): L Aspell.

318 MR D. P. KEANE, Limpley Stoke
Postal: **220 Conkwell, Conkwell Grange Stud, Limpley Stoke, Bath, Avon, BA2 7FD.**
Contact: PHONE (01225) 722806 MOBILE (07764) 200012 E-MAIL conkwell@aol.com

1 ALL IN THE STARS (IRE), 6, ch g Fourstars Allstar (USA)—Luton Flyer **Avon Thoroughbreds Ltd**
2 BARTON BARON (IRE), 6, b g Phardante (FR)—Boolavogue (IRE) **Sir Stanley Clarke**
3 BARTON GATE, 6, b g Rock Hopper—Ruth's River **Sir Stanley Clarke**
4 BARTON NIC, 11, b g Nicholas Bill—Dutch Majesty **Conkwell Grange Stud Ltd**
5 BATHWICK ANNIE, 8, ch m Sula Bula—Lily Mab (FR) **Mr W. Clifford**
6 BROWN BEN, 10, b g General Gambul—City Sunset **Mrs H. R. Cross**
7 4, B g Arctic Cider (USA)—Clonminch Lady **Avon Thoroughbreds Ltd**
8 4, Ch f Beneficial—Coronea Sea Queen (IRE) **Avon Thoroughbreds Ltd**
9 DIAMOND DAZZLER, 6, br g Sula Bula—Dancing Diamond (IRE) **Dajam Ltd**
10 GREY SHARK (IRE), 5, gr g Roselier (FR)—Sharkezan (IRE) **Robert M. Feak**
11 GUN'N ROSES II (FR), 10, gr g Royal Charter (FR)—Offenbach II (FR) **Lady Clarke**
12 5, B m Midnight Legend—Home From The Hill (IRE) **Sir Stanley Clarke**
13 5, B m Beneficial—Index Lady
14 LE TURK (FR), 5, br g Baby Turk—Valse de Sienne (FR) **W. Clifford & P. Rose**
15 MAGALINA (IRE), 5, br m Norwich—Pike Review **Dajam & Damian Burbidge**
16 MCHATTIE (NZ), 13, ch g Tom's Shu (USA)—Kittain (NZ) **Sir Stanley Clarke**
17 OYSTERHAVEN (IRE), 6, b g Mister Lord (USA)—Haven's Glory (IRE) **Avon Thoroughbreds Ltd**
18 PENNILLION, 4, b g Pennekamp (USA)—Brave Princess **Avon Thoroughbreds Ltd**
19 PLASTIC PADDY (IRE), 7, b g Beau Sher—Vultang Lady **Mrs S. Clifford**
20 ROOFING SPIRIT (IRE), 6, b g Beneficial—Vulcash (IRE) **Clifford/Matthews**
21 SEMI PRECIOUS (IRE), 6, ch g Semillon—Precious Petra **Richard & Carol Stainer**
22 SIR BATHWICK (IRE), 5, b g Oscar (IRE)—Karenda **Mrs S. Clifford**
23 5, Ch m Midnight Legend—Yamrah **Sir Stanley Clarke**

319 MR T. KEDDY, Newmarket
Postal: **Heyward Place, Hamilton Road, Newmarket, Suffolk, CB8 7JQ.**
Contact: PHONE (01638) 561498 MOBILE (07710) 450982

1 DANEHILL LAD (IRE), 4, b g Danehill (USA)—River Missy (USA) **Epsom's Dream Team**
2 HEYWARD PLACE, 4, b f Mind Games—Ginny Binny **Abbeygate Estates Limited**
3 JADE'S TREASURE, 5, b m Zamindar (USA)—Jade Venture **Treasure Seekers Limited**
4 ODDLYDODD (IRE), 8, b g Tremblant—Poor Times (USA) **Mrs H. Keddy**
5 SHAPE UP (IRE), 4, b g Octagonal (NZ)—Bint Kaldoun (IRE) **Mr Andrew Duffield**
6 SILVALINE, 5, gr g Linamix (FR)—Upend **Exoteric Partnership**
7 SOVEREIGN NATION (IRE), 5, b g Ashkalani (IRE)—Sovereign Dona **Mr Andrew Duffield**
8 SPIDERS WEB, 4, gr c Linamix (FR)—Cattermole (USA) **Mr Andrew Duffield**
9 TAJAR (USA), 12, b g Slew O' Gold (USA)—Mashaarif (USA) **Mrs H. Keddy**
10 URSA MAJOR, 10, b g Warning—Double Entendre **NewmarketConnections.com**

MR T. KEDDY—continued
THREE-YEAR-OLDS
11 **ABBEYGATE**, b c Unfuwain (USA)—Ayunli **Abbeygate Estates Limited**
12 **LITTLE FLUTE**, b c Piccolo—Nordic Victory (USA) **Mrs H. Keddy**
13 **MISTER CHALK**, gr c Silver Patriarch (IRE)—B B Glen **OK Partnership**

TWO-YEAR-OLDS
14 **WIZ IN**, gr g 29/3 Wizard King—Great Intent (Aragon) (9000) **Epsom's Dream Team**

Other Owners: Eclipse Management (Newmarket) Ltd, Mr Howard Fielding, Mr P. Karanjia, Mr Peter Newman, Mr Jeff O'Leary, Mrs S. F. O'Leary, Mr I. A. Southcott.

Assistant Trainer: Hayley Keddy

Jockeys (Flat): Gary Carter, M Fenton. **Jockeys (NH):** S Curran, B Murphy. **Apprentice:** Lisa Jones. **Amateur:** Mrs Hayley Keddy (8-0).

---

320 MR S. L. KEIGHTLEY, Newmarket
Postal: **Racecourse Farm, Bescaby Lane, Waltham On The Wolds, Melton Mowbray, Leicestershire, LE14 4AB.**
Contact: **OFFICE (01664) 464251 FAX (01664) 464564 MOBILE (07989) 322654**

1 **ALASTAIR SMELLIE**, 8, ch g Sabrehill (USA)—Reel Foyle (USA) **Mrs C. C. Regalado-Gonzalez**
2 **BYINCHKA**, 4, br g Inchinor—Bystrouska **The Blue Group**
3 **MARAVEDI (IRE)**, 4, ch f Hector Protector (USA)—Manuetti (IRE) **Mrs C. C. Regalado-Gonzalez**
4 **OUR GLENARD**, 5, b g Royal Applause—Loucoum (FR) **Ormonde Racing**
5 **TOLEDO STAR**, 5, br g Petong—Shafir (IRE) **Mrs C. C. Regalado-Gonzalez**
6 **ZAGALA**, 4, b f Polar Falcon (USA)—Whittle Woods Girl **Mrs C. C. Regalado-Gonzalez**
7 **ZARIANO**, 4, b c Emperor Jones (USA)—Douce Maison (IRE) **Mrs C. C. Regalado-Gonzalez**

THREE-YEAR-OLDS
8 **DANDOUCE**, b f Danzero (AUS)—Douce Maison (IRE) **Mr Colin Mercer**
9 **DIVINA**, b f King's Theatre (IRE)—Heuston Station (IRE) **Ms C. C. Regalado Gonzalez**
10 **FABUCO (IRE)**, b f Mujadil (USA)—Beechwood (USA) **Mrs C. C. Regalado-Gonzalez**
11 **IT MUST BE SPEECH**, b c Advise (FR)—Maiden Speech **The Speech Partnership**
12 **ZULOAGA (USA)**, b f Stravinsky (USA)—Attitre (FR) **Mrs C. C. Regalado-Gonzalez**

TWO-YEAR-OLDS
13 **GALLEGO**, br c 20/4 Danzero (AUS)—Shafir (IRE) (Shaadi (USA) (20000) **Mrs C. C. Regalado-Gonzalez**
14 **JOYEAUX**, b f 18/3 Mark Of Esteem (IRE)—Divine Street (Hernando (FR)) **Mrs C. C. Regalado-Gonzalez**
15 B f 28/4 Desert Style (IRE)—Mettlesome (Lomond (USA)) (5256) **S K Bloodstock**
16 Ch c 24/4 Muhtarram (USA)—Miss Bussell (Sabrehill (USA)) (8000) **S K Bloodstock**
17 Ch c 27/1 General Monash (USA)—Racing Brenda (Faustus (USA)) (3091) **S K Bloodstock**

Other Owners: Mr D. Burrows, Mr P. A. Coleman, Mr Michael Mercer, Mr J. Reed, Miss C. A. Salmon, Miss K. C. Salmon, Mr P. D. Silvester, Mr David Smith.

Jockeys (Flat): A Culhane (8-6), R Winston (8-4). **Amateur:** Miss A L Turner (9-0).

---

321 MR G. P. KELLY, Sheriff Hutton
Postal: **3 Church End Cottages, Sheriff Hutton, North Yorkshire, YO60 6SY.**
Contact: **HOME (01347) 878770 MOBILE (07866) 285187**

1 **CASTLE FLOWER**, 4, b f Bal Harbour—Tinkle **Mr G. P. Kelly**
2 **DERRY ANN**, 8, b m Derrylin—Ancat Girl **Mr C. I. Ratcliffe**
3 **DISTANT KING**, 11, b g Distant Relative—Lindfield Belle (IRE) **Mr A. Barrett**
4 **HOWSHAM LAD**, 5, b g Perpendicular—Sherwood Hope **Mrs J. M. Fox**
5 **NARCISO (GER)**, 4, ch g Acatanango (GER)—Notturna **Mr G. P. Kelly**

THREE-YEAR-OLDS
6 B g Presidium—Pro-Token **Mr C. I. Ratcliffe**

MR G. P. KELLY—continued

TWO-YEAR-OLDS

7 Ch c 25/5 Doubletour (USA)—Morcat (Morston (FR)) **Mr C. I. Ratcliffe**
8 Ch c 10/4 The Again—Primitive Light (Primitive Rising (USA)) **Mr C. I. Ratcliffe**

Assistant Trainer: Ian Ratcliffe

Apprentice: Paul Mulrennan. Conditional: Gino Carenza (10-2). Amateurs: Miss Sarah Brotherton (9-7), Mr T Greenall (10-4), Mr C Mulhall (10-9), Mr M Walford (10-7).

---

322   MR P. KELSALL, Leominster
Postal: **Gallop View House, Risbury, Leominster, Herefordshire, HR6 0NQ.**
Contact: **PHONE (01568) 760396 FAX (01568) 760373 MOBILE (07802) 160584**

1 **RUFIUS (IRE)**, 11, b g Celio Rufo—In View Lass **Mr Peter Kelsall**
2 **SHAH (IRE)**, 11, b g King Persian—Gay And Sharp **Mr Peter Kelsall**
3 **TUMBLEWEED GLEN (IRE)**, 8, ch g Mukaddamah (USA)—Mistic Glen (IRE) **Mr Peter Kelsall**

THREE-YEAR-OLDS

4 **FASHION SHOOT**, b g Double Trigger (IRE)—Paris Fashion (FR) **Mr Peter Kelsall**

TWO-YEAR-OLDS

5 B c 15/3 Double Trigger (IRE)—Paris Fashion (FR) (Northern Fashion (USA)) **Mr Peter Kelsall**

Assistant Trainer: Miss J Kelsall

Jockey (NH): C Llewelyn (10-0, w.a.).

---

323   MRS C. J. KERR, Aberfeldy
Postal: **Balnacraig Farm, Fortingall, Aberfeldy, Perthshire, PH15 2LJ.**
Contact: **PHONE (01887) 830354 MOBILE (07768) 682841**

1 **AMBER MOSS**, 9, ch g Phardante (FR)—Queen's Darling **Mrs C. J. Kerr**
2 **APACHE IRELAND (IRE)**, 7, b m Mandalus—Brisbee **Mrs C. J. Kerr**
3 **FISHER STREET**, 9, gr g Tigani—Pricket Walk **Mrs C. J. Kerr**
4 **MACKENZIE (IRE)**, 8, b g Mandalus—Crinkle Lady **Mrs C. J. Kerr**
5 **MCCRINKLE (IRE)**, 7, b rg Mandalus—Crinkle Lady **Mrs C. J. Kerr**
6 **MISS ELLIE**, 8, b m Elmaamul—Jussoli **Mrs C. J. Kerr**
7 **PHARAGON (IRE)**, 6, b g Phardante (FR)—Hogan (IRE) **Mrs C. J. Kerr**
8 **PHARLETTA (IRE)**, 9, b m Phardante (FR)—Vibrant Hue (USA) **Mrs C. J. Kerr**

Amateur: Mr David Da Silva (10-0).

---

324   MRS A. L. M. KING, Stratford-on-Avon
Postal: **Ridgeway House, Moor Farm, Wilcote, Stratford-upon-Avon, Warwickshire, CV37 9XG.**
Contact: **OFFICE (01789) 205087 HOME 298346 FAX 263260 E-MAIL anabelking.racing@virgin.net**

1 **ASTRAC (IRE)**, 13, b g Nordico (USA)—Shirleen **Mr Clive Titcomb**
2 **DANCES WITH ANGELS (IRE)**, 4, b f Mukaddamah (USA)—
Lady of Leisure (USA) **Mr S. J. Harrison & Mr P. Charlesworth**
3 **GREAT VIEW (IRE)**, 5, b g Great Commotion (USA)—Tara View (IRE) **All The Kings Horses**
4 **HELLO HOLLY**, 7, b m Lake Coniston (IRE)—Amandine (IRE) **Mr Aiden Murphy**
5 **IMPERIAL ROCKET (USA)**, 7, b br g Northern Flagship (USA)—
Starsawhirl (USA) **Lynda Lovell and Aiden Murphy**
6 **JACARANDA (IRE)**, 4, ch g Bahhare (USA)—Near Miracle **Mrs A. L. M. King**
7 **JEWEL OF INDIA**, 5, ch g Bijou d'Inde—Low Hill **Mrs A. L. M. King**
8 **KING'S MOUNTAIN (USA)**, 4, b g King of Kings (IRE)—Statistic (USA) **All The Kings Horses**
9 **LITTLE TAO**, 4, ch g Theatrical Charmer—Madam Brady (USA) **Mr L. Sherwood**
10 **OPEN ARMS**, 8, ch g Most Welcome—Amber Fizz (USA) **Mr Aiden Murphy**

MRS A. L. M. KING—continued
THREE-YEAR-OLDS

11 RABBIT, b f Muhtarram (USA)—Ninia (USA) **Mr Clive Titcomb**

TWO-YEAR-OLDS

12 GOLDEN APPLAUSE (FR), b f 18/3 Royal Applause—Golden Circle (USA) (Theatrical) (26000) **Mrs L. Field**
13 Ch f 22/2 Desert Prince (IRE)—Helianthus (Groom Dancer (USA)) (38000) **Mrs L. Field**
14 ROSIE MUIR, br f 14/2 Mind Games—Step On Degas (Superpower) **Mrs Pennie Muir**

Other Owners: Mr & Mrs Cobley, Mr & Mrs P. Hepworth, Mr T. Hilliam, Mr D. King, Mr G. Martin, Mr J. Martin, Mrs P. Muir, Mr G. Titcomb.

---

325   **MR ALAN KING, Barbury Castle**
Postal: **Barbury Castle Stables, Wroughton, Wiltshire, SN4 0QZ.**
Contact: **PHONE** (01793) 815009 **FAX** (01793) 845080 **MOBILE** (07973) 461233
E-MAIL alanking.racing@virgin.net

1 ALF LAUREN, 6, b g Alflora (IRE)—Gokatiego **Helen Loggin & Richard Preston**
2 ALLEGED SLAVE (IRE), 9, ch g Husyan (USA)—Lek Dawn **Mrs Peter Prowting**
3 ANSHABIL (IRE), 5, br g Anshan—Billeragh Thyne (IRE) **Mr Jerry Wright**
4 ARTEMISE (FR), 6, b m Cyborg (FR)—Articule (FR) **Mr J. A. H. West**
5 BEAR ON BOARD (IRE), 9, b g Black Monday—Under The River **Mr J. E. Brown**
6 BORN LEADER (IRE), 6, b g Supreme Leader—Real Lace **Nigel Bunter & Jules Sigler**
7 BOURBON MANHATTAN, 6, b g Alflora (IRE)—Vanina II (FR) **A Longman, T. Warner, R Devereux & Ptnrs**
8 CALCOT FLYER, 6, br g Anshan—Lady Catcher **Miss J. M. Bodycote**
9 5, B g El Conquistador—Call For Taylor **Mr Alan King**
10 CHANCE MEETING, 6, b m Overbury (IRE)—Pepper Star (IRE) **The Golden Anorak Partnership**
11 CHICAGO BULLS (IRE), 6, b g Darshaan—Celestial Melody (USA) **Mr A. M. Armitage**
12 CRYSTAL D'AINAY (FR), 5, b g Saint Preuil (FR)—Guendale (FR) **Mr Tony Fisher & Mrs Jeni Fisher**
13 D'ARGENT (FR), 7, gr g Roselier (FR)—Money Galore (IRE) **Mr Nigel Bunter**
14 DIAMOND MERCHANT, 5, ch g Vettori (IRE)—Tosca **Mr T. J. & Mrs H. Parrott**
15 DOCE VIDA (IRE), 6, b m Montelimar (USA)—Miss The Post **Mrs R. J. Skan**
16 ECCENTRICITY, 6, b m Emarati (USA)—Lady Electric **Mr A. J. Coombes & Mr J. L. Frampton**
17 ECHO DU LAC (FR), 8, b g Matahawk—Love Dream (FR) **Mr Jerry Wright**
18 EMANIC (FR), 4, b g Video Rock (FR)—Una Volta (FR) **Million in Mind Partnership**
19 FLEETWOOD FOREST, 4, b g Fleetwood (IRE)—Louise Moillon **A. King & A. R. Bromley**
20 FLYING LYRIC (IRE), 6, b g Definite Article—Lyric Junction (IRE) **Mr Nigel Bunter**
21 FORK LIGHTNING (IRE), 8, gr g Roselier (FR)—Park Breeze (IRE) **Mr & Mrs F. C. Welch**
22 GOLA CHER (IRE), 10, b g Beau Sher—Owen Money **Mr & Mrs F. C. Welch**
23 GUTHRIE (IRE), 6, ch g Mister Lord (USA)—Nephin Far (IRE) **Mrs J. K. Powell**
24 HALF AN HOUR, 7, b g Alflora (IRE)—Country Mistress **Mr C. W. Lane**
25 HOME JAMES (IRE), 7, b g Commanche Run—Take Me Home **Mrs Stewart Catherwood**
26 HOWLE HILL (IRE), 4, b g Ali-Royal (IRE)—
Grandeur And Grace (USA) **J.E.Brown,R.Benton,R.Devereux,R.A.Lucas**
27 HURRICANE LAMP, 13, b g Derrylin—Lampstone **Mr & Mrs F. C. Welch & Mr Alan King**
28 ITSA LEGEND, 5, b g Midnight Legend—Onawing Andaprayer **The We're A Legend Partnership**
29 JABOUNE (FR), 7, ch g Johann Quatz (FR)—Seasonal Pleasure (USA) **Mrs R. J. Skan**
30 JAC AN REE (IRE), 8, b g Supreme Leader—Nic An Ree (IRE) **C. Newport, J. Draper & T. Edmonds**
31 JAHASH, 6, ch g Hernando (FR)—Jalsun **Mr J. Hawkins**
32 JAY BEE ELL, 7, b g Pursuit of Love—On Request (IRE) **J. M. & A. L. Longman**
33 KADOUNT (FR), 6, b g Our Account (USA)—Une de Lann (FR) **Elite Racing Club**
34 KIMONO ROYAL (FR), 6, b br g Garde Royale—Alizane (FR) **Mr Nigel Bunter**
35 KING OF BARBURY (IRE), 7, b g Moscow Society (USA)—Aine's Alice (IRE) **Miss J. M. Bodycote**
36 KOBAI (IRE), 5, b g Florida Son—Helens Birthday **Mrs M. C. Sweeney**
37 4, B g Alflora (IRE)—Lady Solstice **Mr Barry Winfield**
38 LALAGUNE (FR), 5, b m Kadalko (FR)—Donatella II (FR) **Mrs A. J. Davies**
39 LAMP'S RETURN, 5, ch m Bob's Return (IRE)—Lampstone **Mr & Mrs F. C. Welch**
40 LANTAUR LAD (IRE), 10, b g Brush Aside (USA)—Gleann Oge **Mrs A. A. Shutes**
41 LORDS BEST (IRE), 8, b g Mister Lord (USA)—Ballinlonig Star **Jerry Wright, Peter Smith & Jules Sigler**
42 MIKADO MELODY (IRE), 5, b g Supreme Leader—Double Symphony (IRE) **Mrs M. C. Sweeney**
43 MISTRESS BANJO, 4, b f Start Fast (FR)—Temperance (IRE) **The Banjo Players**
44 MUGHAS (IRE), 5, b g Sadler's Wells (USA)—Quest of Passion (FR) **B. Winfield, C. Fenton & A. Longman**
45 NATTERJACK (IRE), 6, b g Roselier (FR)—Hansel's Lady (IRE) **Elite Racing Club**
46 OFF BROADWAY (IRE), 6, b g Presenting—Mona Curra Gale (IRE) **The Presenters**

MR ALAN KING—continued

47 **PEDDARS WAY**, 5, b g Nomadic Way (USA)—Deep Selection (IRE) **Mrs Peter Mason**
48 **PRECIOUS MYSTERY (IRE)**, 4, ch f Titus Livius (FR)—Ascoli **The Dunnkirk Partnership**
49 **REGAL CHANCE**, 11, b g Cisto (FR)—Regal Flutter **Mrs A. A. Shutes**
50 **ROWLEY HILL**, 6, b g Karinga Bay—Scarlet Dymond **Mr J. E. Brown & Mrs S. Faccenda**
51 **SALSALINO**, 4, ch c Salse (USA)—Alicedale (USA) **Mr Nigel Bunter**
52 **SAMANDARA (FR)**, 4, b f Kris—Samneeza (USA) **Miss J. M. Bodycote**
53 **SAXON MIST**, 5, b g Slip Anchor—Ruby Venture **Mr C. W. Lane**
54 **SEAL HARBOUR (FR)**, 4, b g Vertical Speed (FR)—Maraxalou (FR) **Mr W. A. Harrison-Allan**
55 **SENTO (IRE)**, 6, ch g Persian Bold—Esclava (USA) **Mrs M. C. Sweeney**
56 **SHAADIVA**, 6, b m Shaamit (IRE)—Kristal Diva **Cheltenham Racing Ltd**
57 **SHARAJAN (IRE)**, 4, b g Desert King (IRE)—Balakera (FR) **Mr Tony Fisher & Mrs Jeni Fisher**
58 **SHAREEF (FR)**, 7, b g Port Lyautey (FR)—Saralik **Mr Tony Fisher & Mrs Jeni Fisher**
59 **SHOSEN (IRE)**, 8, b g Persian Mews—Lugnagullagh **Mrs M. C. Sweeney**
60 **SPECIAL RATE (IRE)**, 7, br g Grand Plaisir (IRE)—
Clerical Artist (IRE) **J.Brown,Mrs Bunter,M.Deeley&Mrs Faccenda**
61 **STROMNESS (USA)**, 7, ch g Trempolino (USA)—Caithness (USA) **Lady Harris**
62 **SUNNE LORD (IRE)**, 7, b g Mister Lord (USA)—Happy Party **Mrs S. Warren**
63 **SUPREME RETURN**, 9, b g Bob's Return (IRE)—Supreme Wonder (IRE) **Lady Harris**
64 **TROUBLE AT BAY (IRE)**, 4, b g Slip Anchor—Fight Right (FR) **Mr Nigel Bunter**
65 **VISTA VERDE**, 6, b g Alflora (IRE)—Legata (IRE) **Mrs L. Field**
66 **WESTBOURNE (IRE)**, 6, b m King's Ride—Give Me Hope (IRE) **Mr Aiden Murphy**
67 **WHATASHOCK**, 9, b g Never So Bold—Lady Electric **Mr J. L. Frampton & Mr A. J. Coombes**
68 **WHISPERING STORM (IRE)**, 6, br g Good Thyne (USA)—
Ballybride Gale (IRE) **Mrs A.Shutes,Mr A.Sheppard,Mr A.Humbert**
69 **WINDROSS**, 12, b g Ardross—Dans Le Vent **Mrs Peter Prowting**

THREE-YEAR-OLDS

70 **GARNETT (IRE)**, b c Desert Story (IRE)—In Behind (IRE) **Mrs J. K. Powell**
71 **HIGH ALTITUDE (IRE)**, b c Alhaarth (IRE)—Delphini (IRE) **Mr Nigel Bunter**
72 **INCURSION**, b c Inchinor—Morgannwg (IRE) **Mr Nigel Bunter**
73 **RAINSBOROUGH HILL**, b c Groom Dancer (USA)—Ellebanna **J.Wright,J.E.Brown,R.Preston,J.Sigler**
74 **SILENCIO (IRE)**, b g Sillery (USA)—Flabbergasted (IRE) **Let's Live Racing**
75 **ZAZOUS**, b c Zafonic (USA)—Confidentiality (USA) **Mr Nigel Bunter**

TWO-YEAR-OLDS

76 **COPPER BAY (IRE)**, b c 20/3 Revoque (IRE)—Bahia Laura (FR) (Bellypha) (19000) **Four Mile Racing**
77 **GRAPHEX**, b c 29/4 Inchinor—Allegra (Niniski) (35000) **Four Mile Racing**
78 B br f 14/3 Lear Fan (USA)—Juliet's Jewel (Houston (USA)) (30000) **Miss Janet Menzies**
79 **MYSTERY LOT (IRE)**, b f 18/3 Revoque (IRE)—Mystery Bid (Auction Ring (USA)) (9500) **Four Mile Racing**
80 B c 10/2 Pursuit of Love—Persuasion (Batshoof) (16000) **Mr Andrew Longman**
81 Ch f 29/2 Dr Fong (USA)—Pine Needle (Kris) (31000) **Miss Janet Menzies**
82 **PRINCE VECTOR**, b c 19/2 Vettori (IRE)—
The In-Laws (IRE) (Be My Guest (USA)) (31000) **Nigel Bunter & Jules Sigler**
83 **RUSSIAN CONSORT (IRE)**, ch c 18/1 Groom Dancer (USA)—
Ukraine Venture (Slip Anchor) (52000) **Four Mile Racing**
84 **SECRET AFFAIR**, b c 10/4 Piccolo—Secret Circle (Magic Ring (IRE)) (34000) **Four Mile Racing**
85 B c 2/2 Trans Island—Sparklingsovereign (Sparkler) (18552) **Mr Alan King**

Other Owners: Mr Robert Benton, Mr A. R. Bromley, Mrs Penny Bunter, Mrs C. E. Caddick, Mr A. J. Coombes, Mr P. A. Deal, Mr M. R. Deeley, Mr J. Draper, Mr Roy Dunnett, Mr T. W. Edmonds, Mr Richard Edwards, Mrs Sue Faccenda, Mr Clive Fenton, Mr Anthony D. Fisher, Mrs Jeni Fisher, Mr J. L. Frampton, Mr Graham Goode, Mrs K. M. Graham, Mr D. N. Green, Mr P. M. Hill, Mr Simon Hill, Mr Tony Hill, Mr D. Holpin, Mr Arthur Humbert, Mr Ian Kirkham, Knightsbridge Bc, Ms Helen Loggin, Mr Mark Longman, Mr R. Lucas, Mrs D. C. Meech, Mr D. Minton, Mr Christopher Newport, Mr David Nicholson, Miss M. Noden, Mrs L. H. Oakley, Mrs H. Parrott, Mr T. J. Parrott, Mr A. D. Potts, Mr G. M. Powell, Mrs Mark Powell, Mr R. J. Preston, Mr J. P. L. Reynolds, Mr A. N. Sheppard, Mr Jules Sigler, Mr James P. Smith, Mr Terry Warner, Mr F. Welch, Mrs S. C. Welch, Mrs Anthony West.

Assistant Trainer: Mark Douglas & Noel Williams

Jockey (NH): R Thornton. **Conditional:** W Hutchinson. **Amateur:** Mr Gerard Tumelty.

326 MR J. S. KING, Swindon
Postal: **Elm Cross House, Broad Hinton, Swindon, Wiltshire, SN4 9PF.**
Contact: **PHONE (01793) 731481 FAX (01793) 739001 MOBILE (07890) 444135**
E-MAIL trishking1@hotmail.com

1 BEN MORE, 6, b g Seymour Hicks (FR)—Stac-Pollaidh **Miss S. Douglas-Pennant**
2 BIT OF A SNOB, 13, b g St Columbus—Classey **Miss S. Douglas-Pennant**
3 BREAKING BREEZE (IRE), 9, b g Mandalus—Knockacool Breeze **W. Askew, N. Rich & H. Porter**
4 FLUFF 'N' PUFF, 10, ch g Nicholas Bill—Puff Puff **Dajam Ltd**
5 FOXTROT YANKEE (IRE), 5, b g Lord Americo—Derby Fox (IRE)
6 GOODENOUGH MOVER, 8, ch g Beveled (USA)—Rekindled Flame (IRE) **D. Goodenough Removals & Transport**
7 GWYLAN, 9, b g Crested Lark—Flopsy Mopsy **Mr W. J. Lee**
8 LANCASHIRE LASS, 8, b m Lancastrian—Chanelle **Mrs R. M. Hill**
9 LORD NELLSSON, 8, b g Arctic Lord—Miss Petronella **Dajam Ltd**
10 NICK THE JEWEL, 9, b g Nicholas Bill—Bijou Georgie **Marlborough Racing Partnership**
11 PETOLINSKI, 6, b g Petoski—Olnistar (FR) **Mr R. B. Denny**
12 SEEF, 10, b g Slip Anchor—Compton Lady (USA) **Mrs S. Horton**
13 SILENT GUNNER, 6, ch g Gunner B—Quiet Dawn **Mr T. L. Morshead**
14 TINO (IRE), 8, ch g Torus—Delphic Thunder **Mr Robert Skillen**
15 TUDOR KING (IRE), 10, br g Orchestra—Jane Bond **Mr J. R. Kinloch**
16 WARTORN (IRE), 9, b g Warcraft (USA)—Alice Minkthorn **Miss S. Douglas-Pennant**

THREE-YEAR-OLDS

17 ROOD BOY (IRE), b c Great Commotion (USA)—Cnocma (IRE) **Dajam Ltd**
18 THEVENIS, ch c Dr Fong (USA)—Pigeon Hole **Dajam Ltd**

Other Owners: Mr Howard Booty, Mr Michael P. Hill, Mrs P. M. King, Mr Jim McCarthy, Mr P. W. Murphy.

Assistant Trainer: Mrs P M King

327 MR N. B. KING, Newmarket
Postal: **St Gatien Cottage, Vicarage Road, Newmarket, Suffolk, CB8 8HP.**
Contact: **PHONE (01638) 666150 FAX (01638) 666150 MOBILE (07880) 702325**
E-MAIL neil.king@st-gatien-racing.co.uk

1 COMBE CASTLE, 9, gr g Carlingford Castle—Silver Cirrus **Major R. G. Wilson**
2 FITZ THE BILL (IRE), 4, b f Mon Tresor—In The Sky (IRE) **The Greyhound Partnership**
3 GOT NO SHADOW, 5, b g Terimon—Run On Stirling **Mr J. L. Rowsell**
4 MONDEED, 7, b m Terimon—House Deed **Mr Neil King**
5 PANGERAN (USA), 12, ch g Forty Niner (USA)—Smart Heiress (USA) **Mr R. Oliver Smith**
6 REGAL CUSTOM, 6, ch g Royal Vulcan—Rural Custom
7 SALMON FLY (IRE), 8, b g Leading Counsel—Lola Sharp **Mr Neil King**
8 TRUDI BAY, 7, b m Terimon—Letterewe **Mrs E. H. Vestey**
9 VALIGAN (IRE), 11, gr g Roselier (FR)—Wonderful Lilly **Mr Martin Bailey**

Assistant Trainer: Caroline Fryer

328 MR F. KIRBY, Northallerton
Postal: **High Whinholme Farm, Danby Wiske, Northallerton, North Yorkshire, DL7 0AS.**
Contact: **PHONE (01325) 378213 FAX (01325) 378213 MOBILE (07976) 294214**

1 FOREST DANTE (IRE), 11, ch g Phardante (FR)—Mossy Mistress (IRE) **Mr Fred Kirby**
2 HEROICUS (NZ), 7, ch g Heroicity (AUS)—Glenford (NZ) **Mr Fred Kirby**
3 MAGIC BENGIE, 5, b g Magic Ring (IRE)—Zinzi **Mr Fred Kirby**
4 SOUND OF CHEERS, 7, br g Zilzal (USA)—Martha Stevens (USA) **Mr Fred Kirby**
5 TOPPING TIME (IRE), 6, b g Topanoora—Vampirella (FR) **Mr Fred Kirby**

Assistant Trainer: N A Kirby

Jockey (NH): K Johnson (10-0). **Conditional:** J P Byrne (9-4).

329 MR S. A. KIRK, Upper Lambourn
Postal: **Cedar Lodge Stables, Upper Lambourn, Hungerford, Berkshire, RG17 8QT.**
Contact: **PHONE/OFFICE (01488) 73215 FAX (01488) 73826 MOBILE (07768) 855261**

1 **BLUE TROJAN (IRE)**, 4, b g Inzar (USA)—Roman Heights (IRE) **The Ex Katy Boys**
2 **BOLD RIDGE (IRE)**, 4, b g Indian Ridge—Cutting Ground (IRE) **Mrs Chris Harrington**
3 **DANGEROUS BEANS**, 4, b gr g Bluegrass Prince (IRE)—A Little Hot **Mr G. W. Witheford**
4 **GLENCOE SOLAS (IRE)**, 4, ch f Night Shift (USA)—Boranwood (IRE) **Mr Eddie Tynan**
5 **HEIDELBURG (IRE)**, 4, b f Night Shift (USA)—Solar Attraction (IRE) **Mr Eddie Tynan**
6 **JUST FLY**, 4, b g Efisio—Chrysalis **Ascot Brew Racing**
7 **KARAOKE (IRE)**, 4, b g Mujadil (USA)—Kayoko (IRE) **Speedhith Group**
8 **MERSEY SOUND (IRE)**, 6, b g Ela-Mana-Mou—Coral Sound (IRE) **Alec Lackerman**
9 **MICHELLE MA BELLE (IRE)**, 4, b f Shareef Dancer (USA)—April Magic **Bill Allan & Michelle Collins**
10 **SECRET FORMULA**, 4, b f So Factual (USA)—Ancient Secrets **J. G. Smith**
11 **SIR NINJA (IRE)**, 7, b g Turtle Island (IRE)—The Poachers Lady **Hargood Limited**
12 **SRI DIAMOND**, 4, b g Sri Pekan (USA)—Hana Marie **Ascot Brew Racing**
13 **TREASURE TRAIL**, 5, b g Millkom—Forever Shineing **Mr T. Neill & Mrs John Lee**
14 **TRUE HOLLY**, 4, b f Bishop of Cashel—Polly's Teahouse **Tina Lock**

THREE-YEAR-OLDS

15 **ALEXANDER AMBITION (IRE)**, b f Entrepreneur—Lady Alexander (IRE) **Mrs N. O'Callaghan**
16 **BALLYLIFFIN (IRE)**, b c Daggers Drawn (USA)—Blues Quartet **The South Western Partnership III**
17 **BURLINGTON PLACE**, b g Compton Place—Wandering Stranger **Mr J. G. Lambton**
18 **FISBY**, ch c Efisio—Trilby **Mr P. Valentine**
19 **FIT TO FLY (IRE)**, b c Lahib (USA)—Maid of Mourne **Morris Magowan**
20 **FLIP FLOP AND FLY (IRE)**, b g Woodborough (USA)—Angelus Chimes **Mike Browne**
21 **GENERAL FEELING (IRE)**, b c General Monash (USA)—Kamadara (IRE) **The So Long Partnership**
22 **HOH BLEU DEE**, b g Desert Style (IRE)—Ermine (IRE) **Mr D. F. Allport**
23 **INCISOR**, b g Dracula (AUS)—Last Night's Fun (IRE) **Ron Gander**
24 **MUSTANG ALI (IRE)**, ch g Ali-Royal (IRE)—Classic Queen (IRE) **Ascot Brew Racing**
25 **PREGNANT PAUSE (IRE)**, b c General Monash (USA)—Dissidentia (IRE) **Mr A. W. Nielsen**
26 **REGAL PERFORMER (IRE)**, b g Ali-Royal (IRE)—Khatiynza **Mr I. A. N. Wight**
27 **SWORN TO SECRECY**, ch f Prince Sabo—Polly's Teahouse **Ascot Brew Racing**
28 **UNCLE JOHN**, b g Atraf—Bit O' May **Mrs John Lee**
29 **WEE DINNS (IRE)**, b f Marju (IRE)—Tir-An-Oir (IRE) **F.B.O.T Racing**
30 **ZWEIBRUCKEN (IRE)**, b f Alhaarth (IRE)—Solar Attraction (IRE) **Mr Eddie Tynan**

TWO-YEAR-OLDS

31 **AFRICAN STORM (IRE)**, b c 11/2 Fasliyev (USA)—Out of Africa (IRE) (Common Grounds) (68027) **Cathal Ryan**
32 B c 16/4 Dr Fong (USA)—Alusha (Soviet Star (USA)) (12000) **Speedlith Group**
33 B f 14/3 Tagula (IRE)—Auriga (Belmez (USA)) (8000) **Elaine Power, Mary Kavanagh**
34 B c 30/3 Monashee Mountain—Big Fandango (Bigstone (IRE)) (18000) **Pedro Rosas**
35 **CLEO COLLINS (IRE)**, b f 8/4 General Monash (USA)—Madrina (Waajib) (7420) **Tim Collins**
36 Ch c 15/5 Inchinor—Fair Verona (USA) (Alleged (USA)) (12500)
37 B c 9/3 Mujahid (USA)—Gracious Beauty (USA) (Nijinsky (CAN)) (22000) **Bjorn E. Nielson**
38 **HURSLEY HOPE**, b f 20/2 Compton Place—Kilcoy (USA) (Secreto (USA)) **J. C. Smith**
39 **IVANA ILLYICH (IRE)**, ch f 29/4 Tipsy Creek (USA)—Tolstoya (Northfields (USA)) (15460) **Mr N. Pickett**
40 B f 28/4 Fasliyev (USA)—Jamaican Punch (IRE) (Shareef Dancer (USA)) (27828) **Thurloe Thoroughbreds VI**
41 B c 23/3 Mind Games—Millie's Lady (IRE) (Common Grounds) (15000) **Pat Eddery Racing Ltd**
42 B c 8/4 Indian Lodge (IRE)—Pride of Pendle (Grey Desire) (6000) **R. Louth**
43 B c 9/5 Night Shift (USA)—Quiche (Formidable (USA)) (16079) **Alan Merritt & Friends**
44 Br c 24/3 Lend A Hand—Romora (FR) (Sillery (USA)) (34000) **J. Breslin**
45 **RUM CREEK**, ch c 10/4 Tipsy Creek (USA)—Carnbrea Belle (IRE) (Kefaah (USA)) (21000) **Vernon Carl Makalon**
46 **SALAMANCA**, b c 6/2 Pivotal—Shanara (IRE) (Persian Heights) (28000) **Wood Street Syndicate**
47 **SEA MAP**, ch c 24/3 Fraam—
                              Shehana (USA) (The Minstrel (CAN)) (12000) **The www.mortgages.tv. Partnership**
48 B c 8/4 Lear Fan (USA)—Sharp Flick (USA) (Sharpen Up) (11131) **D. J. Dundon**
49 B f 20/4 Indian Lodge (IRE)—Skerray (Soviet Star (USA)) (22000) **Frank Brady, Robert Whitworth**
50 B c 27/3 Piccolo—St Helena (Monsanto (FR)) (4000)
51 **ST JAMES GATE (IRE)**, ch c 28/1 Spectrum (IRE)—
                              Fay (IRE) (Polish Precedent (USA)) (10512) **Martin White & Partners**

MR S. A. KIRK—continued

52 B c 19/3 Danzig Connection—The Fugative (Nicholas (USA)) (13000) **J.B.R.Leisure Ltd**
53 VERITABLE, br f 11/3 So Factual (USA)—Madam Trilby (Grundy) **J. C. Smith**

Other Owners: Mrs S. Z. Bates, Mrs D. Crow, Mr E. Dolan, M. A. Dunleavy, K. P. Dunleavy, Mr A. East, Mr M. East, Mr Peter Guntrip, Mr Jim Horgan, Mr D. Kavanagh, Mr S. McCay, Mrs P. McHugh, Mr Oliver Pawle, Mr Dennis Potter, Miss E. Power, Mr D. Revell, Mr J. Sanders, Mr R. Scott, Mrs N. H. Stafford.

Assistant Trainer: Fanny Kirk

Apprentices: Jon Daly (8-5), Joey Walsh (8-0).

---

330 MR WILLIAM S. KITTOW, Cullompton
Postal: **Haynefield Farm, Blackborough, Cullompton, Devon, EX15 2JD.**
Contact: **HOME (01823) 680183 FAX (01823) 680601 MOBILE (07714) 218921**
E-MAIL stuartkittowracing@hotmail.com

1 DILYS, 5, b m Efisio—Ramajana (USA) **Mrs Jenny Hopkins**
2 GUILDED FLYER, 5, b g Emarati (USA)—Mo Ceri **The Racing Guild**
3 LADY WURZEL, 5, b m Dilum (USA)—Fly The Wind **Mrs Pam Pengelly**
4 LILY OF THE GUILD (IRE), 5, ch m Lycius (USA)—Secreto Bold **The Racing Guild**
5 MAGGIE MAQUETTE, 4, ch f Atraf—Bronze Maquette (IRE) **Mr & Mrs Owen Flynn**
6 ONLY FOR SUE, 5, ch g Pivotal—Barbary Court **Ms Susan Arnesen**
7 SKYLARKER (USA), 6, b g Sky Classic (CAN)—O My Darling (USA) **Midd Shire Racing**
8 TARSKI, 10, ch g Polish Precedent (USA)—Illusory **Midd Shire Racing**
9 TIGER BABY, 4, b c Averti (IRE)—Risky Baby **Mr & Mrs Owen Flynn**
10 TOP TREES, 6, b g Charnwood Forest (IRE)—Low Line **Mrs P. E. Hawkings**

THREE-YEAR-OLDS

11 MAIDSTONE MIDAS (IRE), b c Nashwan (USA)—Be Mine **Mr F. G. Wilson**
12 VEVERKA, b f King's Theatre (IRE)—Once Smitten (IRE) **Mr Gary B. Watts**

TWO-YEAR-OLDS

13 DOVE COTTAGE (IRE), b c 3/2 Great Commotion (USA)—Pooka (Dominion) (20000) **Mr Reg Gifford**
14 IN THE SHADOWS, b f 2/3 Lujain (USA)—
        Addicted To Love (Touching Wood (USA)) (13000) **Mrs Jenny Hopkins**
15 PINK BAY, b f 4/4 Forzando—Singer On The Roof (Chief Singer) (5000) **Mr T. Jones**
16 B c 18/2 Erhaab (USA)—Sadaka (Kingmambo (USA)) (8000) **Mr Eric Gadsden**
17 B c 22/2 Alzao (USA)—Serenity (Selkirk (USA)) (46000) **Mr Eric Gadsden**

Other Owners: Mr D. W. Arnesen, Mrs June K. Flynn, Mr Owen G. Flynn, Mrs Judy Kittow, Mr B. G. Middleton, Mrs Ruth Perry, Mr A. J. Shire, Ms W. A. Stoker, Mr R. A. Stoker.

Assistant Trainer: Mrs Judy Kittow

Jockeys (Flat): M Fenton (w.a.), I Mongan (w.a.). **Jockey (NH):** R Johnson (w.a.). **Amateur:** Mr L Jefford.

---

331 MISS H. C. KNIGHT, Wantage
Postal: **West Lockinge Farm, Wantage, Oxfordshire, OX12 8QF.**
Contact: **PHONE (01235) 833535 FAX 820110 MOBILE (07860) 110153 CAR (07808) 290898**

1 ALLIMAC (IRE), 7, b g Alphabatim (USA)—Firewood (IRE) **Mrs T. P. Radford**
2 4, B g Old Vic—All Set (IRE) **Mrs T. P. Radford**
3 ALVINO, 7, b g Alflora (IRE)—Rose Ravine **Mr Martin Broughton**
4 ARCTIC FANCY (USA), 11, ch g Arctic Tern (USA)—Fit And Fancy (USA) **Another Chance Partnership**
5 BALLADEER (IRE), 6, b g King's Theatre (IRE)—Carousel Music **Scott Hardy Partnership**
6 BEECHWOOD, 6, b g Fraam—Standard Rose **Mr Peter Taplin**
7 BEST MATE (IRE), 9, b g Un Desperado (FR)—Katday (FR) **Mr Jim Lewis**
8 BLAZING GUNS (IRE), 5, ch g Un Desperado (FR)—Quefort **Mr Jim Lewis**
9 BOYTJIE (IRE), 4, b g Un Desperado (FR)—Miss Cali **Mr Jim Lewis**
10 CAPTAIN FLINDERS (IRE), 7, b g Satco (FR)—Auburn Queen **Mr P. M. Warren**
11 CARIBBEAN COVE (IRE), 6, gr g Norwich—Peaceful Rose **Mr Trevor Hemmings**
12 CHASE THE SUNSET (IRE), 6, ch g Un Desperado (FR)—Cherry Chase (IRE) **Mr Jim Lewis**
13 CHELSEA BRIDGE (IRE), 6, b g Over The River (FR)—Anguillita (IRE) **The Earl Cadogan**

MISS H. C. KNIGHT—continued

14 **CHIVES (IRE)**, 9, b g Good Thyne (USA)—Chatty Actress **Mr Trevor Hemmings**
15 **CREATIVE TIME (IRE)**, 8, b g Houmayoun (FR)—
Creative Princess (IRE) **Mrs G. M. Sturges & H. Stephen Smith**
16 **EASTER PRESENT (IRE)**, 5, br g Presenting—Spring Fiddler (IRE) **Mrs R. A. Humphries**
17 **EDREDON BLEU (FR)**, 12, b g Grand Tresor (FR)—Nuit Bleue III (FR) **Mr Jim Lewis**
18 **EL VAQUERO (IRE)**, 6, ch g Un Desperado (FR)—Marble Fontaine **Mr T. M. Curtis**
19 **EVA SO CHARMING**, 6, ch g Karinga Bay—Charming Gale **Eva so Charming Partnership**
20 **FOLY PLEASANT (FR)**, 10, ch g Vaguely Pleasant (FR)—Jeffologie (FR) **Jim Lewis & Friends**
21 **FOSSE HILL**, 7, b g Bustino—Amber's Image **Lord Vestey**
22 **FRAGRANT ROSE**, 8, b m Aflora (IRE)—Levantine Rose **Mr David Jenks**
23 **GENERAL GREY (IRE)**, 4, gr g Fourstars Allstar (USA)—Tara The Grey (IRE) **Mr Martin Broughton**
24 **GREAT BENEFIT (IRE)**, 5, ch g Beneficial—That's Lucy (IRE) **Senate Racing Partnership**
25 **HARRIS BAY**, 5, b g Karinga Bay—Harristown Lady **Mrs G. M. Sturges & H. Stephen Smith**
26 **HOWRWENOW (IRE)**, 6, b g Commanche Run—Maythefifth **Mr Toby Cole**
27 **IMPEK (FR)**, 8, b g Lute Antique (FR)—Attualita (FR) **Mr Jim Lewis**
28 **IMPERIAL DREAM (IRE)**, 6, b g Roselier (FR)—Royal Nora (IRE) **Hogarth Racing**
29 **INCA TRAIL (IRE)**, 8, br g Un Desperado (FR)—Katday (FR) **Mr Philip F. Myerscough**
30 **IRISH GROUSE (IRE)**, 5, b g Anshan—Another Grouse **Mrs R. A. Humphries**
31 **JACK DASH (IRE)**, 6, b g Teamster—Gathering Moss **Mr Philip Newton**
32 **JEFERTITI (IRE)**, 7, ch g Le Nain Jaune (FR)—Nefertiti (FR) **Mr Jim Lewis**
33 **KICASSO**, 5, b g Environment Friend—Merry Jane **Mr D. J. Smith and Mr D. J. Ellis**
34 **KICK FOR TOUCH (IRE)**, 7, ch g Insan (USA)—Anns Nun **Mr Trevor Hemmings**
35 **KRZYSZKOWIAK (IRE)**, 6, b g Polish Precedent (USA)—Overdrive **Mrs Shirley Brasher**
36 **LORD JAY JAY (IRE)**, 4, b g Lord of Appeal—Mesena **Mrs Jan Johnson**
37 **LORD LUKER (IRE)**, 8, b g Lord Americo—Canon's Dream **Luker Bros (Removals & Storage) Ltd**
38 **LOUGH RYNN (IRE)**, 6, b g Beneficial—Liffey Lady **Carfield.Baxter**
39 **MAGNIFICENT SEVEN (IRE)**, 5, ch g Un Desperado (FR)—Seven Hills (FR) **Lady Vestey**
40 **MALJIMAR (IRE)**, 4, b g Un Desperado (FR)—Marble Miller (FR) **Mr Jim Lewis**
41 **MELFORD (FR)**, 6, br g Presenting—Echo Creek (IRE) **Mr John Melville**
42 **MIDLAND FLAME (IRE)**, 9, b g Un Desperado (FR)—Lathanona **Mr Trevor Hemmings**
43 **MILLER'S BAY**, 6, ch g Karinga Bay—Millers Action **Carfield Partners**
44 4, B g Ilium—Miss Cynthia **Mrs V. Griffiths & Partners**
45 **MISS QUICKLY (IRE)**, 5, b m Anshan—Shari Owen (IRE) **Mrs Nicola Moores**
46 **MOSCOW FIELDS (IRE)**, 6, ch g Moscow Society (USA)—Cloverlady **Mr J. D. N. Tillyard**
47 **MY PAL VAL (IRE)**, 4, b g Classic Cliche (IRE)—Lessons Lass (IRE) **Mr Harold Winton**
48 **NOBLE DEED (IRE)**, 7, b g Lord Americo—Legal Statement (IRE) **Winter Madness**
49 **NO MORE MONEY**, 6, b m Aflora (IRE)—Cover Your Money **Mr David Jenks**
50 **O CINZA (IRE)**, 6, gr g Norwich—Queenlier (IRE) **Mr Martin Broughton**
51 **ONE NATION (IRE)**, 9, br g Be My Native (USA)—Diklers Run **The Earl Cadogan**
52 **OUR PRIMA DONNA (IRE)**, 6, ch m Be My Native (USA)—Stage Debut **GPS Racing**
53 **OVER THE STORM (IRE)**, 7, b g Over The River (FR)—Naas **Hogarth Racing**
54 **PERFECT FELLOW**, 10, b g Teamster—G W Supermare **Unlucky For Some Partnership**
55 **PIN HIGH (IRE)**, 5, b g Needle Gun (IRE)—Eva's Fancy **M.B.J.Kimmins & Mr & Mrs D.Anderson**
56 **POINTALISM (IRE)**, 5, gr g Roselier (FR)—Ballinahowna Dream (IRE) **The Hon Mrs Peter Tower**
57 **QUEEN SORAYA**, 6, b m Persian Bold—Fairlead **Mrs Oliver Fox-Pitt**
58 **RARE VINTAGE (IRE)**, 6, b m Germany (USA)—Tatlock **Mr Trevor Hemmings**
59 **RATHBARN PRINCE (IRE)**, 12, ch g All Haste (USA)—Ellis Town **Miss S. Samworth**
60 **RED BLAZER**, 13, ch g Bustino—Klewraye **Miss H. Knight**
61 **RED DAWN (IRE)**, 5, b g Presenting—West Tour **Mr Jim Lewis**
62 **REGAL BANDIT (IRE)**, 6, b g Un Desperado (FR)—Rainbow Alliance (IRE) **The Bandits**
63 **RIVER TRAPPER (IRE)**, 5, b g Over The River (FR)—Mousa **Mrs C. A. Waters**
64 **ROMANTIC AFFAIR (IRE)**, 7, ch g Persian Bold—Broken Romance (IRE) **The Earl Cadogan**
65 **ROSSLEA (IRE)**, 6, b g Roselier (FR)—Burren Gale **Mr Jim Lewis**
66 **ROYAL CHINA (IRE)**, 6, b g Aristocracy—Luan Causca **Mr David Zeffman**
67 **SIR CUMFERENCE**, 8, b g Sir Harry Lewis (USA)—Puki Puki **Mrs Nicola Moores**
68 **SMART MOVER**, 5, b g Supreme Leader—Rachel C (IRE) **Rendezvous Racing**
69 **SOUTHERN STAR (IRE)**, 9, ch g Montelimar (USA)—Flying Pegus **Mr Trevor Hemmings**
70 **STARS OUT TONIGHT (IRE)**, 7, b g Insan (USA)—Go And Tell **Mr Jim Lewis**
71 **SUPREME CATCH (IRE)**, 7, b g Supreme Leader—Lucky Trout **Bucknall Street Partnership**
72 4, B f Sir Harry Lewis (USA)—Tamergale (IRE) **Mrs Rita Vaughan**
73 **THE REBEL LADY (IRE)**, 7, br m Mister Lord (USA)—Arborfield Brook **The Rebel Partnership**
74 **THREAD OF HONOUR (IRE)**, 7, gr g Roselier (FR)—Sharkezan (IRE) **Sir Stephen Hastings and Partners**
75 **TOPOL (IRE)**, 6, br g Topanoora—Kislev (IRE) **Top Brass Partnership**
76 **TOY BOY (IRE)**, 6, b g Un Desperado (FR)—Too Sharp **Sir Anthony Scott**
77 4, B g Luso—Trembling Lass (IRE) **Mrs Nicola Moores**
78 **TUESDAY'S CHILD**, 5, b g Un Desperado (FR)—Amazing Silks **Mr Jim Lewis**

The power to perform, the stamina to succeed

Reproduced by Mark Johnston

The Gold Cup in the safe hands of trainer Henrietta Knight, owner Jim Lewis and jockey Jim Culloty, won in awesome style by Best Mate

The Cheltenham Gold Cup Winning Team

Henrietta Knight: "We have all of our horses on Blue Chip. We find Blue Chip Pro helps them to maintain condition, especially the more sensitive ones, whilst Blue Chip Dynamic is wonderful for their joints. Both products are very palatable and easy to feed. We are delighted with the results, the horses look so well and recover quickly after a race."

Best Mate - Powered by *Blue Chip*

MISS H. C. KNIGHT—continued

79 **TUSK**, 4, ch g Fleetwood (IRE)—Farmer's Pet **Hogarth Racing**
80 **UMBRELLA MAN (IRE)**, 8, ch g Insan (USA)—Askasilla (IRE) **Mrs J. Dollar & Mrs M. Hall**
81 **VALUSO (IRE)**, 4, b g Luso—Regal Grove (IRE) **Mrs V. Griffiths**
82 **WATER JUMP (IRE)**, 7, b g Suave Dancer (USA)—Jolies Eaux **The Earl Cadogan**
83 **WENCESLAS (IRE)**, 4, b g Un Desperado (FR)—Lady of The West (IRE) **Mr Jim Lewis**
84 **WEST COASTER (IRE)**, 6, gr g Be My Native (USA)—Donegal Grey (IRE) **White Rabbit Partnership**
85 **YARDBIRD (IRE)**, 5, b g Moonax (IRE)—Princess Lizzie (IRE) **Gilco**
86 **ZAFFAMORE (IRE)**, 8, ch g Zaffaran (USA)—Furmore **Mr Martin Broughton**
87 **ZAFFINELLO (IRE)**, 5, ch g Zaffaran (USA)—Satin Sheen **Mrs P. Jamieson**

THREE-YEAR-OLDS

88 **MIXIT (FR)**, b g Exit To Nowhere (USA)—Miss Naelle (FR) **Mr T. M. Curtis**
89 **RINGAROSES**, b g Karinga Bay—Rose Ravine **Mrs Nicholas Jones/Martin Broughton**

Other Owners: Mr Derek M. Anderson, Mr B. M. Barrett, Mrs V. J. Baxter, Mr Ronnie Beevor, Mr T. W. Biddlecombe, A. G. & S. M. Carter Bloodstock, Mrs C. H. Bothway, Mr S. G. Boyle, Mrs J. A. Brandon, Mr S. W. Broughton, Mrs A. G. Burnaby-Atkins, Mr A. Buxton, Mrs S. L. Carne, Mr G. M. Carty, Mr M. Channon, Mr N. C. Clark, Mrs Irene Clifford, Mr T. Collins, Mr J. Cooper, Mr Peter Curling, Mrs A. A. Dore, Mrs S. A. Dore, Mr B. Fitzpatrick, Mr N. Fitzpatrick, Mr N. A. Gill, Mr A. B. Greenfield, Mr H. C. Hardy, Mr L. Hare, Mr Brian M. Hartigan, Sir Stephen Hastings, Mr D. F. Hill, Mr H. P. Hogarth, Mr J. Hogarth, Mr J. L. Hogarth, Mr P. H. Hogarth, Mr P. N. Hogarth, Mr John Holmes, Mr Len Jakeman, Mrs Flora Lane, Mr Richard Lissack, Mrs G. C. Maxwell, Mrs S. E. McCathie, Mrs Gwen Meacham, Mr Jeremy Mitchell, Mr Keith Monk, Mr H. C. Hardy, Mr R. C. Palliser, Mr Graham Murrell, Mr N. Mustoe, Mrs S. Pasteur, Mrs Jill Pengelly, Miss Judy Pimblett, Dr Janet Powney, Mrs M. Powney-Jones, Mr G. Rowland-Clark, Mr J. A. Salmon, Mr Roger Sayer, Mr A. Scott, Mr H. R. Siegle, Mr M. G. Smith, Mrs Gill Softley, Mr P. J. Softley, Mrs A. Upperton, Mr P. A. Upperton, Mrs Giles Weaver, Mr D. Wells, Mr Tom Wilson, Mr Harold Winton.

Jockey (NH): J Culloty (9-7).

---

332 MR R. F. KNIPE, Allensmore
Postal: Cobhall Court Stud, Millennium House, Allensmore, Herefordshire, HR2 9BG.
Contact: PHONE (01432) 277245 MOBILE (07774) 866547

1 **ARDSTOWN**, 13, b m Ardross—Booterstown **Mrs R. F. Knipe**
2 **MISTY MEMORY**, 5, b m Alderbrook—Misty Sunset **Mrs R. F. Knipe**

Assistant Trainer: Mrs S D Knipe

---

333 MR C. LAFFON-PARIAS, Chantilly
Postal: 38, Avenue du General Leclerc, 60500 Chantilly, France.
Contact: PHONE +33 (0) 3 44 57 53 75 FAX + 33 (0) 3 44 57 52 43
E-MAIL claffon@club-internet.fr

1 **BAHAMAMIA**, 4, b f Vettori (IRE)—Daleside Ladybird **Cyril Morange**
2 **GATEWICK (IRE)**, 4, b g Sunday Silence (USA)—Greek Air (IRE) **Nelson Radwan**
3 **KRATAIOS (FR)**, 4, b c Sabrehill (USA)—Loxandra **Stilvi Compania Financera**
4 **LIGHT QUEST (USA)**, 4, b f Quest For Fame—Gleam of Light (IRE) **Stilvi Compania Financera**
5 **MARSHALL (FR)**, 4, b c Anabaa (USA)—Monitrice (FR) **Alec Head**
6 **SARRASIN (FR)**, 5, b g Bering—Sevilliana **Alec Head**

THREE-YEAR-OLDS

7 **BANKSIA**, b f Marju (IRE)—Banafsajee (USA) **Gainsborough Stud**
8 **BLUSHING IRISH (FR)**, b c Rainbow Quest (USA)—Irika (USA) **Wertheimer et Frere**
9 **BOWING SHEBA (USA)**, b f Theatrical—Ganasheba (USA) **Wertheimer et Frere**
10 **BRIGHT ABUNDANCE (USA)**, b f Quiet American (USA)—Quality Gift **Gainsborough Stud**
11 **CIENA (FR)**, ch f Gold Away (IRE)—Silwana (FR) **Wertheimer et Frere**
12 B f Nashwan (USA)—Cloud Castle **Nelson Radwan**
13 **EVERLAST (FR)**, b f Anabaa (USA)—Cutlass (IRE) **Wertheimer et Frere**
14 B c Deputy Commander (USA)—Fabulist (USA) **Nelson Radwan**
15 **GRAPHIC DESIGN (USA)**, b c Swain (IRE)—Cumulate (USA) **Gainsborough Stud**
16 B f Kingmambo (USA)—Ice Gala (USA) **Nelson Radwan**
17 **IN GOOD FAITH (USA)**, b f Dynaformer (USA)—Healing Hands **Gainsborough Stud**
18 **LA LOLA**, b f Zafonic (USA)—Opari (FR) **Felipe Hinojosa**
19 **MAJOR PERFORMANCE (IRE)**, b c Celtic Swing—Desert Serenade (USA) **Gainsborough Stud**
20 **MANANOPOULOS (FR)**, b f Sadler's Wells (USA)—Greek Air (IRE) **Nelson Radwan**
21 **MOON CATCHER (IRE)**, b f Kahyasi—Moonlight Saunter (USA) **Gainsborough Stud**

MR C. LAFFON-PARIAS—continued

22 **NAPPING (FR)**, gr c Linamix (FR)—Nany's Affair (USA) **Stilvi Compania Financeria**
23 **NIGHT TYPHOON (USA)**, b c Kingmambo (USA)—Scarab Bracelet (USA) **Gainsborough Stud**
24 **PERSEA (IRE)**, b f Fasliyev (USA)—Final Farewell (USA) **Nelson Bunker**
25 **PONY GIRL (IRE)**, b f Darshaan—Mypreciousprospect (USA) **Wertheimer et Frere**
26 **PROSPECT PARK**, b c Sadler's Wells (USA)—Brooklyn's Dance (FR) **Wertheimer et Frere**
27 **REVE D'IMAN (FR)**, b f Highest Honor (FR)—Numidie (FR) **Bates Newton**
28 **SIMPLEX (FR)**, b c Rainbow Quest (USA)—Russyskia (USA) **Wertheimer et Frere**
29 **STAR EDITION (USA)**, b f Theatrical—Fit To Lead (USA) **Gainsborough Stud**
30 **SUITE ROYALE (FR)**, ch f Diesis—Lady Lodger **Stilvi Compania Financeria**
31 **YORIK**, b g Danehill (USA)—Silver Fun (FR) **Wertheimer et Frere**

TWO-YEAR-OLDS

32 **ALMAGUER**, b c 13/3 Spectrum (IRE)—Cerita (IRE) (21644) **Chevington Stud**
33 **ANTIOCHE (FR)**, b c 12/4 Gold Away (IRE)—Tamarouna (FR) (5565) **Wertheimer et Frere**
34 **ARONDIGHT (IRE)**, b c 9/3 Zafonic (USA)—Eriza **Stilvi Compania Financeria**
35 **AWAKENING**, gr c 2/5 Daylami (IRE)—Youm Jadeed (IRE) **Gainsborough Stud**
36 **BEAUTIFIX (GER)**, b f 22/2 Bering—Beautimix (FR) **Wertheimer et Frere**
37 **BILINGUE (IRE)**, b c 16/3 Poliglote—Irika (USA) **Wertheimer et Frere**
38 **BLUE SILK (FR)**, b f 24/5 Intikhab (USA)—Edessa (IRE) **Stilvi Compania Financeria**
39 **CAROLINA MOON (IRE)**, ch f 12/2 Cadeaux Genereux—Crescent Moon **Gainsborough Stud**
40 **CASTYANA (IRE)**, b f 16/3 Anabaa (USA)—Castiya (USA) **Mme De Chambure**
41 Ch f 14/5 Southern Halo (USA)—Company (USA) **R. Radwan**
42 **DWYN (IRE)**, b c 27/3 Diktat—Diotima **Stilvi Compania Financeria**
43 **ERMANOS (IRE)**, b c 31/3 Daylami (IRE)—Epagris **Stilvi Compania Financeria**
44 B f 2/2 War Chant (USA)—Fairy West (USA) **R. Radwan**
45 Ch f 1/3 Zafonic (USA)—Fast Riot (USA) (32000) **Darpat S. L.**
46 **GOLD SOUND (FR)**, ch c 21/5 Green Tune (USA)—Born Gold (USA) **Wertheimer et Frere**
47 **HIGH WIRE**, b c 2/4 Grand Lodge (USA)—Hill Silver (USA) (44526) **Mme G. Cabrero**
48 **HISTORIX (FR)**, gr f 5/5 Linamix (FR)—Sallivera (IRE) **Wertheimer et Frere**
49 **IODAMA**, ch f 30/3 Cadeaux Genereux—Carpet of Leaves (USA) (8000) **Stilvi Compania Financeria**
50 **ISHINCA (USA)**, ch f 15/5 Mt Livermore (USA)—Nazoo (USA) **Gainsborough Stud**
51 **KUGELHOF (FR)**, b c 6/3 Kahyasi—Planoise (FR) (34013) **Stilvi Compania Financeria**
52 **LASGO (IRE)**, b f 1/2 King's Best (USA)—Selfish **Stilvi Compania Financeria**
53 **LAVEROCK (IRE)**, b c 25/3 Octagonal (NZ)—Sky Song (USA) **Gainsborough Stud**
54 **MAZEA (IRE)**, b f 14/4 Montjeu (IRE)—Filly Mignonne (IRE) (35000) **Stilvi Compania Financeria**
55 **MONTECARMELO (USA)**, b c 13/5 Lear Fan (USA)—Yafill (USA) **Gainsborough Stud**
56 B c 10/4 Entrepreneur—Mydarlingdaughter **Stilvi Compania Financeria**
57 B f 31/3 Groom Dancer (USA)—On The Top (7420) **Chevington Stud**
58 **OPHTALMO (IRE)**, b c 13/2 Spectrum (IRE)—Pinkai (IRE) **Wertheimer et Frere**
59 B c 3/2 Gone West (USA)—Ronda **Darpat S. L.**
60 **SAINT HELENS (USA)**, gr f 6/4 Verglas (USA)—Oh Lucky Day (14842) **Stilvi Compania Financeria**
61 **SAN MAMES**, b c 14/4 Dyhim Diamond (IRE)—Alegacy (FR) **Hormaeche**
62 Gr f 26/3 El Prado (IRE)—Siempre Asi (USA)
63 **SPECIAL HONOR (FR)**, ch c 28/1 Highest Honor (FR)—Secret Wells (USA) **Wertheimer et Frere**
64 **STORMINA (USA)**, b f 27/3 Gulch (USA)—Brooklyn's Storm (USA) **Wertheimer et Frere**
65 B f 24/2 Bering—Summery (USA) (61842) **Stilvi Compania Financeria**
66 **SUNANA**, b f 23/3 Anabaa (USA)—Like The Sun (USA) **Gainsborough Stud**
67 **TAILWIND**, ch c 24/2 Sendawar (IRE)—Storm Card **Stilvi Compania Financeria**
68 **THEATRALE (USA)**, b f 1/3 Theatrical (IRE)—West Brooklyn (USA) **Wertheimer et Frere**
69 **UHLAN (FR)**, b c 31/3 Bering—Hiwaayati **Gainsborough Stud**
70 **VERY GREEN (FR)**, b c 9/3 Barathea (IRE)—Green Bend (USA) **Wertheimer et Frere**
71 **WELLSALO (FR)**, b c 11/4 Sadler's Wells (USA)—Ring Pink (USA) **Wertheimer et Frere**
72 **ZEPHYR SONG**, b f 2/4 Cadeaux Genereux—Silicon Girl (FR) **Stivi Compania Financeria**

Jockey (Flat): O Peslier. **Apprentice:** Miguel Blancpain (8-0).

---

334 **MRS S. LAMYMAN, Louth**
Postal: **Ruckland Manor, Louth, Lincolnshire, LN11 8RQ.**
Contact: **PHONE** (01507) 533260 **FAX** (01507) 534236 **MOBILE** (07733) 165721

1 **ALL BLEEVABLE**, 7, b g Presidium—Eve's Treasure **Mike & Tony Blee and Roy Allerston**
2 **BRIGADIER MONTY (IRE)**, 6, b g College Chapel—Miss St Cyr **Mr P. Lamyman**
3 **CALCAR (IRE)**, 4, b g Flying Spur (AUS)—Poscimur (IRE) **Mr P. Lamyman**
4 **JAMAICAN FLIGHT (USA)**, 11, b h Sunshine Forever (USA)—Kalamona (USA) **Mr P. Lamyman**

MRS S. LAMYMAN—continued

  5 **PROTOCOL (IRE)**, 10, b g Taufan (USA)—Ukraine's Affair (USA) **Mr P. Lamyman**
  6 **SINJAREE**, 6, b g Mark of Esteem (IRE)—Forthwith **Mr P. Lamyman**
  7 **TRANSCENDANTALE (FR)**, 6, b br m Apple Tree (FR)—Kataba (FR) **Mr P. Lamyman**
  8 **VICARS DESTINY**, 6, b m Sir Harry Lewis (USA)—Church Leap **Mr Terence Deal**
  9 **VICTORY QUEST (IRE)**, 4, b g Victory Note (USA)—Marade (USA) **Mr P. Lamyman**
10 **WORLABY DALE**, 8, b g Terimon—Restandbethankful **Mr P. Lamyman**

THREE-YEAR-OLDS

11 **BURKEES GRAW (IRE)**, ch g Fayruz—Dancing Willma (IRE) **The Underlaws**

Other Owners: Mr R. Allerston, Mr A. E. Blee, Mr Mike Blee, Sotby Farming Company Limited, Mr Nigel Underwood, Mrs Sarah Underwood.

Assistant Trainer: P Lamyman

---

335   **MISS E. C. LAVELLE, Andover**
Postal: **Cottage Stables, Hatherden, Andover, Hampshire, SP11 0HY.**
Contact: **PHONE (01264) 735509 OFFICE (01264) 735412 MOBILE (07774) 993998**
E-MAIL emma@elavelle.freeserve.co.uk

  1 **ANOTHER MOOSE (IRE)**, 9, b g Mister Lord (USA)—Moose (IRE) **Remenham Racing**
  2 **AVANTI EXPRESS (IRE)**, 14, b g Supreme Leader—Muckride Lady **Mrs Sarah Stevens**
  3 **BANJO HILL**, 10, b g Arctic Lord—Just Hannah **Mr John B. Hobbs**
  4 **BANSHA BRU (IRE)**, 4, b g Fumo di Londra (IRE)—Pride of Duneane (IRE) **The Bawz Partnership**
  5 **BARFLEUR (IRE)**, 4, b f Anshan—Lulu Buck
  6 **BOARDROOM FIDDLE (IRE)**, 5, ch g Executive Perk—Opera Time (IRE) **Mr Paul Stamp**
  7 **CLOUDY GREY (IRE)**, 7, gr g Roselier (FR)—Dear Limousin **Mrs J. R. Lavelle & Mrs A. Hepworth**
  8 **COOLE SPIRIT (IRE)**, 11, b g All Haste (USA)—Chocolate Biscuit **Coole And The Gang**
  9 **FRENTZEN**, 7, b g Golden Heights—Milly Black (IRE) **Mr J. Spence**
10 **GIG HARBOR**, 5, b g Efisio—Petonica (IRE) **Fraser Miller Racing**
11 **HARRY THE HORSE**, 6, b g Sir Harry Lewis (USA)—Miss Optimist **Club Ten**
12 **HERNANDITA**, 6, b m Hernando (FR)—Dara Dee **Mr P. Clarke**
13 **IMMOLA (IRE)**, 8, b br g Quart de Vin (FR)—Jessica (FR) **Mrs Sarah Stevens**
14 **LIGHTIN' JACK (IRE)**, 6, ch g Beneficial—Cillrossanta (IRE) **Exors of the Late H. A. Watton**
15 **LION HUNTER (USA)**, 5, b h Quest For Fame—Prodigious (FR) **Fraser Miller Racing**
16 **MARJINA**, 5, b m Classic Cliche (IRE)—Cavina **Mr Paul G. Jacobs**
17 **ODAGH ODYSSEY (IRE)**, 10, ch g Ikdam—Riverside Willow **Mr R. J. Lavelle**
18 **PALUA**, 7, b g Sri Pekan (USA)—Reticent Bride (IRE) **Mark Barrett And Partners**
19 **PHAR OUT PHAVORITE (IRE)**, 5, b g Beneficial—Phar From Men (IRE) **Favourites Racing**
20 **PRESENCE OF MIND (IRE)**, 6, ch g Presenting—Blue Rose (IRE) **Mrs A. J. Davies**
21 **QUILLS (IRE)**, 5, b g Scribano—The Potwalluper **Favourites Racing**
22 **SELF DEFENSE**, 7, b h Warning—Dansara **Fraser Miller Racing**
23 **SIR LAUGHALOT**, 4, b g Alzao (USA)—Funny Hilarious (USA) **Fraser Miller Racing**
24 **STARLIGHT EXPRESS (FR)**, 4, b f Air Express (IRE)—Muramixa (FR) **Mr D. M. Bell**
25 **SUPREME ARROW (IRE)**, 9, b m Supreme Leader—Clover Run (IRE) **Mrs Jill Twomey**
26 **TANA RIVER (IRE)**, 8, b g Over The River (FR)—Home In The Glen **The Frisky Fillies**
27 **THE BANDIT (IRE)**, 7, b g Un Desperado (FR)—Sweet Friendship **Mr R. J. Lavelle**
28 **THE BAY BRIDGE (IRE)**, 5, b br g Over The River (FR)—Alamo Bay **Frisky Fillies 2**
29 **UNCLE TEDDY (IRE)**, 11, b g Arctic Cider (USA)—Ishtar **Miss N. Henton**
30 **VALERUN (IRE)**, 8, b g Commanche Run—Glenreigh Moss **Investment AB Rustningen**
31 **VICTORY ROLL**, 8, b g In The Wings—Persian Victory (IRE) **Sir Gordon Brunton**
32 **WAKEUP SMILING (IRE)**, 6, b g Norwich—Blackmiller Lady **The Wakeup Partnership**
33 **YESYES (IRE)**, 9, b g Supreme Leader—Barton Bay (IRE) **The Yomali Partnership**

MISS E. C. LAVELLE—continued
THREE-YEAR-OLDS

34 BLINDED BY LOVE (IRE), br g Imperial Ballet (IRE)—Mystic Shadow (IRE) **Lots of Luck Gentlemen Syndicate**
35 FREAK OCCURENCE (IRE), b g Stravinsky (USA)—Date Mate (USA) **Lots of Luck Gentlemen Syndicate**
36 GRACE DARLING, b f Botanic (USA)—Light On The Waves **Mr A. H. E. Birks**
37 KILINDINI, gr g Silver Patriarch (IRE)—Newlands Corner **Mr Nigel Foster**
38 YOUNG LOVE, ch f Pursuit of Love—Polar Fair **Sir Gordon Brunton**

Other Owners: Mr Mark Barrett, Mr Michael Coghlan, Mr M. Davies, Mrs P. A. Deal, Mrs J. R. Foster, Mr P. N. Gray, Mr Allan Hepworth, Mrs A. M. Hepworth, Mr Matthew Imi, Mrs Richard Jenks, Mr R. J. Jenks, Mr J. R. Lavelle, Mrs J. R. Lavelle, Mrs R. J. Lavelle, Mr J. M. Layton, Mr Steven T. Marsh, Mr B. McCormick, Peader McCoy, Mr P. B. Mitford-Slade, Mr B. G. Slade, Mrs A. Timpson, Mr A. W. Turland, Mr Michael J. Yeomans.

Jockey (Flat): S Drowne. **Jockey (NH):** B Fenton.

---

336 MR B. L. LAY, Chipping Norton
Postal: **Rest Hill Farm, Over Worton, Chipping Norton, Oxfordshire, OX7 7EW.**
Contact: **PHONE (01608) 683608 E-MAIL lawrence.lay@zoom.co.uk**

1 GWEN, 5, ch m Beveled (USA)—Taffidale **Mr B. L. Lay**
2 4, B g Manhal—Secret Stolen (USA) **Mr B. L. Lay**

Assistant Trainer: L Lay

Amateur: Mr A L Lay (10-8).

---

337 MRS J. L. LE BROCQ, Jersey
Postal: **St Etienne, Rue D'Elysee, St Peters, Jersey, JE3 7DT.**
Contact: **PHONE/FAX (01534) 481461 MOBILE (07797) 750823**

1 ARRY MARTIN, 9, b g Aragon—Bells of St Martin **Mrs J. Le Brocq**
2 CAROUSE, 9, b g Petong—Merry Rous **Lavender Racing**
3 CHEEKY GIRL, 4, b f College Chapel—Merry Rous **Miss J. V. May & Mrs A. Richardson**
4 DARMONT (FR), 13, b g Carmont (FR)—Tirole d'Or (FR) **Mrs J. Le Brocq**
5 DOBERMAN (IRE), 8, br g Dilum (USA)—Switch Blade (IRE) **Mrs J. Le Brocq**
6 HAKAM (USA), 5, ch g Woodman (USA)—Haniya (IRE) **Miss J. V. May**
7 JOHAYRO, 11, ch g Clantime—Arroganza **Mr Frank Brady**
8 MARTIN'S SUNSET, 6, ch g Royal Academy (USA)—Mainly Sunset **Miss J. V. May**
9 OUT ON A PROMISE (IRE), 12, b g Night Shift (USA)—Lover's Parlour **Promise Racing**
10 PIPS MAGIC (IRE), 8, b g Pips Pride—Kentucky Starlet (USA) **Mr Frank Brady**
11 PRINCESS DANIELLE, 12, b m Prince Daniel (USA)—Bells of St Martin **Miss J. V. May, Mrs J. Le Brocq**
12 SATINEYEVA (FR), 5, b m Goldneyev (USA)—Sataga (FR) **Mrs J. Le Brocq**
13 SKY OF HOPE (FR), 8, b g Zieten (USA)—Rain Or Shine (FR) **Bonne Nuit Racing**
14 TWIST, 7, b g Suave Dancer (USA)—Reason To Dance **Miss J. V. May**
15 WILDMOOR, 10, ch g Common Grounds—Impropriety **Miss J. V. May**

THREE-YEAR-OLDS

16 Ch f Desert Story (IRE)—Dutosky **Miss J. V. May**

Other Owners: D. Barrons, Mr & Mrs D Bates, C. Benest, Mrs J. Bentley, Sally Bethell, N. Blake, Mr Allan Butler, Mr & Mrs Colin Casey, Mr & Mrs R Champion, J. Davies, Mick Druce, Zoe Jones, A. Langois, G. Lennox, Joe Quinn.

Assistant Trainer: Martin Edwards

Jockeys (Flat): Jo Badger (7-12), M Edwards (9-5), A Proctor (9-5), V Slattery (8-9). **Jockeys (NH):** M Edwards (9-5), A Proctor (9-5), V Slattery (8-9). **Amateurs:** Mr M Brint (9-10), Mr M Burrows (9-13), Miss E Folkes (9-0), Mrs J Le Brocq (8-7).

338   MR AUGUSTINE LEAHY, Kilmallock
Postal: "Lorien", Clogher, Kilmallock, Co. Limerick, Ireland.
Contact: PHONE +353 (0) 63 90676/(087) 2580296 FAX +353 (0) 63 90676

1 4, B f Definite Article—Astronomer Lady (IRE)
2 **CELTICE WAVE (IRE)**, 6, gr m Spanish Place (USA)—Mexican Wave **R. Quinns**
3 **CLASS REUNION (IRE)**, 5, b g Spanish Place (USA)—Crazy Lady **J. I. Madden**
4 **DUSSELDORF (IRE)**, 6, b m Germany (USA)—Zoe Baird **Tom's Top Ten Racing Syndicate**
5 **FLYING BOAT**, 7, b m Desert Style—Keep Bobbin Up (IRE) **J. B. Fitzgerald**
6 **GERARD'S GIRL (IRE)**, 5, b m High Roller (IRE)—Hotel du Lac **Martin Gaughan**
7 **GET WITH IT (IRE)**, 6, b g Presenting—Strong Gara (IRE) **J. P. McManus**
8 **I'M HOME (IRE)**, 8, b g Good Thyne (USA)—Chatty Actress
9 **IRVINE (IRE)**, 12, b g Rising—Garryfine Cross **Mrs E. Leahy**
10 **KOMPRESSOR (IRE)**, 4, b g Petorius—Danny's Joy (IRE)
11 **LAKE MILLSTATT (IRE)**, 9, b m Magical Strike (USA)—Repeat Addition (IRE) **Miss M. McGrath**
12 **MUNROC DANCER (USA)**, 9, br g Show Dancer (USA)—Jessica's Spring (USA) **Kory Cornum**
13 **TOP LASSIE (IRE)**, 5, ch m Topanoora—She's Tough **J. P. McManus**

THREE-YEAR-OLDS

14 Ch f Lil's Boy (USA)—Avril Blake
15 B f Danehill Dancer (IRE)—Beech Bramble (IRE)
16 **CABRIOLET (IRE)**, b c Sesaro (USA)—Inesse
17 Ch f Goldmark (USA)—Great Land (USA)
18 **HELPLINE (IRE)**, b f Daggers Drawn (USA)—Ron's Secret
19 **KEOHANE (IRE)**, ch f Tagula (IRE)—Tismima (FR)
20 **LADY SARELLE (IRE)**, b f Tagula (IRE)—Lady Loire **Ballinilea Syndicate**
21 **LIFE CLASS (IRE)**, b f Orpen (USA)—Beguiled (IRE) **R. M. Lewis**
22 **NURBERG RING (IRE)**, b c Fumo di Londra (IRE)—Elton Mist (IRE)
23 **PAIDIR NA HOICHE (IRE)**, b f General Monash (USA)—Allamanda (IRE) **R. Quinn**
24 **TULLYBRACKEY (IRE)**, br f Daggers Drawn (USA)—Ballyewry
25 **WALK IN MY SHADOW (IRE)**, b f Orpen (USA)—Be My Folly (IRE) **M. & M. G. T. McGrath**
26 B g Danetime (IRE)—Whispering Dawn

Other Owners: T. G. Curtin, S. J. Leahy, R. M. Lewis, Alan Lillingston, Lady Virginia Petersham, Hugh Williams, Ian Williams, Winners Circle Racing Club.

Assistant Trainer: Susan Leahy

Amateur: Miss S J Leahy (8-8).

---

339   MR B. D. LEAVY, Stoke-on-Trent
Postal: Cash Heath Farm, Cash Heath, Forsbrook, Stoke on Trent, ST11 9DE.
Contact: HOME (01782) 398591 MOBILE (07855) 401154

1 **DEBBIE**, 5, b m Deploy—Elita **Bevan, Holmes & Underwood**
2 **GRIZZLY ACTIVEWEAR (IRE)**, 10, ch g Camden Town—Boro Cent **Mrs Alurie O'Sullivan**
3 **ICE AND FIRE**, 5, b g Cadeaux Genereux—Tanz (IRE) **J. T. Stimpson & B. Trubshaw**
4 **LADY OF THE ISLE (IRE)**, 6, b m Aristocracy—Smurfette **Mrs Alurie O'Sullivan**
5 **MANOR STAR**, 5, b m Weld—Call Coup (IRE) **Manor Racing Club**
6 **STEWART'S LAD**, 7, b g Well Beloved—Moneyacre **Mr S. H. Riley**
7 **TOTLAND BAY (IRE)**, 8, br g Phardante (FR)—Seanaphobal Lady **Mr J. A. Provan**
8 **TSUNAMI**, 8, b m Beveled (USA)—Alvecote Lady **Mr S. H. Riley**
9 **WHATASUCKER (IRE)**, 10, ch g Meneval—Tuney Blade **Mr B. D. Leavy**

Other Owners: Mr H. Kirkham, Mr R. Mitchell, Mr D. E. Simpson, Mr L. Yewdell.

Assistant Trainer: Miss L Cottam

Conditional: R Hobson (10-0), W Worthington (10-0).

340 MR RICHARD LEE, Presteigne
Postal: The Bell House, Byton, Presteigne, LD8 2HS.
Contact: PHONE (01544) 267672 FAX 260247 MOBILE (07836) 537145
E-MAIL rleeracing@hotmail.com WEBSITE www.rleeracing.com

1 **ALMAYDAN**, 6, b g Marju (IRE)—Cunning **George Brookes & Family**
2 **BLACK LEGEND (IRE)**, 5, b g Marju (IRE)—Lamping **Jon Waldman and Partners**
3 **BLAKESHALL BOY**, 6, b g Piccolo—Giggleswick Girl **Mr M. Bishop**
4 **BORORA**, 5, gr g Shareef Dancer (USA)—Bustling Nelly **Mrs E. M. Clarke**
5 **BRIGHT EAGLE (IRE)**, 4, ch g Eagle Eyed (USA)—Lumiere (USA) **Mr Rex Norton**
6 **BUNKUM**, 6, b g Robellino (USA)—Spinning Mouse **John Jackson and Maggie Pope**
7 **EL BANDITO (IRE)**, 10, ch g Un Desperado (FR)—Red Marble **The Another Comedy Partnership**
8 **GENEROUS WAYS**, 9, ch g Generous (IRE)—Clara Bow (USA) **George Brookes & Family**
9 **GLANMERIN (IRE)**, 13, b g Lomond (USA)—Abalvina (FR) **Mr Rex Norton**
10 **GOLA SUPREME (IRE)**, 9, gr g Supreme Leader—Coal Burn **Mr James P. Smith**
11 **HARRY BRIDGES**, 5, ch g Weld—Northern Quay **Mrs Ruth McFarlane**
12 **KAID (IRE)**, 9, b g Alzao (USA)—Very Charming **Mr Richard Lee**
13 **MACGEORGE (IRE)**, 14, b g Mandalus—Colleen Donn **Mr & Mrs J. H. Watson**
14 **MACNANCE (IRE)**, 8, b m Mandalus—Colleen Donn **Mrs Keith Lowry**
15 **MARKED MAN (IRE)**, 8, b g Grand Plaisir (IRE)—Teazle **Mr & Mrs C. R. Elliott**
16 **MASTER OF ILLUSION (IRE)**, 11, ch g Castle Keep—
Galloping Gold VII **Mrs G.Goddard,Ben Hinchliff & Des Murray**
17 **MYTHICAL KING (IRE)**, 7, b g Fairy King (USA)—Whatcombe (USA) **Mr Richard Edwards**
18 **POTTS OF MAGIC**, 5, b g Classic Cliche (IRE)—Potter's Gale (IRE) **Mr J. E. Potter**
19 **RED CHIEF (IRE)**, 4, b g Lahib (USA)—Karayb (IRE) **Mr Gareth Samuel**
20 **RUNNER BEAN**, 10, b br g Henbit (USA)—Bean Alainn **H F P Foods Limited**
21 **SAMUEL WILDERSPIN**, 12, b g Henbit (USA)—Littoral **Mr Steve Smith**
22 **SHADY EXCHANGE (IRE)**, 9, b g Le Bavard (FR)—Torus Light **The Three Tees**
23 **SOUTHERNDOWN (IRE)**, 11, ch g Montelimar (USA)—Country Melody (IRE) **Mrs Bill Neale and John Jackson**
24 **STORMHILL STAG**, 12, b g Buckley—Sweet Sirenia **Mr R. Taylor**
25 **SUSPENDID (IRE)**, 11, b g Yashgan—Spendapromise **Stockton Heath Racing**
26 **THE GLEN**, 6, gr g Mtoto—Silver Singer **Will Roseff & Partners**
27 **WASSL STREET (IRE)**, 12, b g Dancing Brave (USA)—One Way Street **Mr Rex Norton**

341 MR S. T. LEWIS, Upton-on-Severn
Postal: Whitefields Court, Longdon Heath, Upton-on-Severn, Worcestershire, WR8 0RJ.
Contact: PHONE (01684) 594650 MOBILE (07976) 556503

1 **ALEXANDER MUSICAL (IRE)**, 6, b br g Accordion—Love For Lydia (IRE) **Mr Simon T. Lewis**
2 **ATALYA**, 7, ch g Afzal—Sandy Looks **Mr Simon T. Lewis**
3 **AUDITOR**, 5, b g Polish Precedent (USA)—Annaba (IRE) **Mr Simon T. Lewis**
4 **BADEN VUGIE (IRE)**, 7, bl g Hamas (IRE)—Bag Lady **Mr Simon T. Lewis**
5 **CANON MCCARTHY (IRE)**, 8, ch g Be My Native (USA)—Archetype **Mr Simon T. Lewis**
6 **CROKER (IRE)**, 9, ch g Rainbows For Life (CAN)—Almagest **Mr Simon T. Lewis**
7 **EXECUTIVE OFFICE (IRE)**, 11, bl g Executive Perk—Lilly's Pride (IRE) **Mr Simon T. Lewis**
8 **FINAL LAP**, 8, b g Batshoof—Lap of Honour **Mr Simon T. Lewis**
9 **FIONNULA'S RAINBOW (IRE)**, 9, ch m Rainbows For Life (CAN)—Bon Retour **Mr Simon T. Lewis**
10 **GLASS NOTE (IRE)**, 6, b m Spectrum (IRE)—Alice En Ballade **Mr D. Thompson**
11 **JASEUR (IRE)**, 11, b g Lear Fan (USA)—Spur Wing (USA) **Mr J. C. Bradbury**
12 **JOLLY JOE (IRE)**, 7, b g Jolly Jake (NZ)—The Bread Robber **Mr Simon T. Lewis**
13 **JUG OF PUNCH (IRE)**, 5, ch g In The Wings—Mysistra (FR) **Mr Simon T. Lewis**
14 **LURISTAN (IRE)**, 4, b g Pennekamp (USA)—Linnga (IRE) **Mr Simon T. Lewis**
15 **MESSAGE RECU (FR)**, 8, b g Luth Dancer (USA)—High Steppe **Mr Simon T. Lewis**
16 **PAARL ROCK**, 9, ch g Common Grounds—Markievicz (IRE) **Mr J. C. Bradbury**
17 **RIVAL (IRE)**, 5, b g Desert Style (IRE)—Arab Scimatar (IRE) **Mr Simon T. Lewis**
18 **ROSSCARBERY GREY (IRE)**, 6, gr g Gothland (FR)—Millroad **Mr Simon T. Lewis**
19 **SIMIOLA**, 5, b m Shaamit (IRE)—Brave Vanessa (USA) **Mr Simon T. Lewis**

MR S. T. LEWIS—continued

20 THE GRANDSON (IRE), 9, b g Husyan (USA)—Tarary **Mr Simon T. Lewis**
21 WELSH GOLD, 5, ch g Zafonic (USA)—Trying For Gold (USA) **Mr D. Thompson**

Assistant Trainer: Mr D. Lewis

---

342 MR A. J. D. LIDDERDALE, Near Hungerford
Postal: **Eastbury Cottage Stables, Eastbury, Nr Hungerford,Berkshire RG17 7JJ.**
Contact: **PHONE (01488) 73694 MOBILE (07785) 785375**

1 BRUZELLA, 5, b m Hernando (FR)—Hills' Presidium **Mrs Sally Doyle**

TWO-YEAR-OLDS

2 B f 23/4 Zaha (CAN)—Appelania (Star Appeal) (12000)
3 B c 14/2 Erhaab (USA)—Basmaat (USA) (Cadeaux Genereux)

---

343 MRS STEF LIDDIARD, Hungerford
Postal: **Shefford Valley Stud, Great Shefford, Hungerford, Berkshire, RG17 7EF.**
Contact: **MOBILE (07887) 991292 FAX (01488) 648939 E-MAIL stef@svstud.co.uk**

1 ARC EL CIEL (ARG), 6, b g Fitzcarraldo (ARG)—Ardoise (USA) **Shefford Valley Stud**
2 EVANGELIST (IRE), 4, b f Namaqualand (USA)—Errazuriz (IRE) **Valley Fencing**
3 GIVEMETHEMOONLIGHT, 5, ch m Woodborough (USA)—Rockin' Rosie **Valley Fencing**
4 LAKOTA BRAVE, 10, ch g Anshan—Pushkinia (FR) **Valley Fencing**
5 LEWIS MEAD, 5, b g Sir Harry Lewis (USA)—Normead Lass **Mrs F. Ashfield**
6 MISTRAL SKY, 5, b g Hurricane Sky (AUS)—Dusk In Daytona **Shefford Valley Stud**
7 NEW FOUNDATION (IRE), 4, b f College Chapel—Island Desert (IRE) **Shefford Valley Stud**
8 PACIFIC OCEAN (ARG), 5, b h Fitzcarraldo (ARG)—
Play Hard (ARG) **Mr P. M. James Man & Ms W. S. Alice Woo**
9 PARADISE VALLEY, 4, b g Groom Dancer (USA)—Rose de Reve (IRE) **Valley Fencing**
10 PETROLERO (ARG), 5, gr g Perfect Parade (USA)—Louise (ARG) **Mr P. M. James Man & Ms W. S. Alice Woo**
11 TRIGGER MEAD, 4, b f Double Trigger (IRE)—Normead Lass **Mrs F. Ashfield**

THREE-YEAR-OLDS

12 INTIKRAFT (IRE), ch g Intikhab (USA)—Mysistra (FR) **Intikraft Racing**
13 SELF RAZIN (IRE), b f Inzar (USA)—Abbessingh **Mrs S. Liddiard**
14 SONNE DE LOUP, ch f Wolfhound (USA)—Son Et Lumiere **The Cross Keys Racing Club**
15 WEBBSWOOD LAD (IRE), b c Robellino (USA)—Poleaxe **H. J. Webb & Son**

TWO-YEAR-OLDS

16 DOUBLE MEAD, b f 12/4 Double Trigger (IRE)—Normead Lass (Norwick (USA)) **Mrs F. Ashfield**

Other Owners: Mr R. Eagle, Mr A. Liddiard, Mr M. McAuley, Mr A. Slattery, Mr H. Webb, Mr J. Webb.

Amateur: Mrs Stefanie A Liddiard (8-7).

---

344 MR N. P. LITTMODEN, Newmarket
Postal: **Southgate, Hamilton Road, Newmarket, Suffolk, CB8 0WY.**
Contact: **PHONE (01638) 663375 FAX (01638) 661948 MOBILE (07770) 964865**
E-MAIL nicklittmoden@btinternet.com

1 BLONDE EN BLONDE (IRE), 4, ch f Hamas (IRE)—Hulm (IRE) **Elliott and Brown Racing**
2 FAILED TO HIT, 11, b g Warrshan (USA)—Missed Again **M. C. S. D. Racing Ltd**
3 FOUR JAYS (IRE), 4, b g Alzao (USA)—Paparazzi (IRE) **V and J Properties**
4 HUGH THE MAN (IRE), 5, b g Hamas (IRE)—Run To Jenny **Silver Knight Exhibitions Ltd**
5 IKAN (IRE), 4, br f Sri Pekan (USA)—Iktidar **Mrs Linda Francis**
6 JOELY GREEN, 7, b g Binary Star (USA)—Comedy Lady **Mr Paul J. Dixon**
7 JUST WIZ, 8, b g Efisio—Jade Pet **Racing Legacy**
8 KINGSTON TOWN (USA), 4, ch g King of Kings (IRE)—Lady Ferial (FR) **Friends of the Turf Racing Limited**
9 MOAYED, 5, b g Selkirk (USA)—Song of Years (IRE) **Mr Nigel Shields**
10 MYSTERIUM, 10, gr g Mystiko (USA)—Way To Go **Alcester Associates**
11 MYSTERLOVER (IRE), 4, b g Night Shift (USA)—Jacaranda City (IRE) **The Headquarters Partnership Ltd**

MR N. P. LITTMODEN—continued

12 **NICHOLAS NICKELBY**, 4, gr g Fayruz—Alasib **Mr Paul J. Dixon**
13 **ORINOCOVSKY (IRE)**, 5, ch g Grand Lodge (USA)—Brillantina (FR) **Mr Nigel Shields**
14 **SMOKIN BEAU**, 7, b g Cigar—Beau Dada (IRE) **Turf 2000 Limited**
15 **SOUNDS LUCKY**, 8, b g Savahra Sound—Sweet And Lucky **Mr Paul J. Dixon**
16 **TIBER TIGER (IRE)**, 4, b g Titus Livius (FR)—Genetta **Mr Mark Harniman**
17 **TRINCULO (IRE)**, 7, b g Anita's Prince—Fandangerina (USA) **Miss Vanessa Church**
18 **TROUBLE NEXT DOOR (IRE)**, 6, b g Persian Bold—Adjacent (IRE) **Mrs Linda Francis**
19 **TRUE COMPANION**, 5, b g Brief Truce (USA)—Comanche Companion **Novowel Racing**

THREE-YEAR-OLDS

20 **ANOTHER CHOICE (IRE)**, ch c Be My Guest (USA)—Gipsy Rose Lee (IRE) **Mr A. A. Goodman**
21 **ASCERTAIN (IRE)**, ch g Intikhab (USA)—Self Assured (IRE) **Mr Paul J. Dixon**
22 **BENNY THE BALL (USA)**, b br c Benny The Dip (USA)—Heloise (USA) **Miss Vanessa Church**
23 **CELADON (IRE)**, b c Fasliyev (USA)—Dancing Drop **Ivan Allan & Jonathon Caplan**
24 **CRACKLEANDO**, ch g Forzando—Crackling **The Headquarters Partnership Ltd**
25 **DOCKLANDS BLUE (IRE)**, ch f Cadeaux Genereux—Copious (IRE) **Franconson Partners**
26 **DR FOX (IRE)**, b g Foxhound (USA)—Eleonora d'Arborea **TSL Racing Ltd**
27 **GARRIGON**, b c Hector Protector (USA)—Queen of The Keys **Mrs A. M. Upsdell**
28 **ILE FACILE (IRE)**, b c Turtle Island (IRE)—Easy Pop (IRE) **Mr Paul J. Dixon**
29 **MULTIPLE CHOICE (IRE)**, ch c Woodborough (USA)—Cosmona **Mr A. A. Goodman**
30 **OH GOLLY GOSH**, ch g Exit To Nowhere (USA)—Guerre de Troie **Mrs Gillian Curley**
31 **PARK AVE PRINCESS (IRE)**, b f Titus Livius (FR)—Satinette **Mr Paul J. Dixon**
32 **PERUVIAN BREEZE (IRE)**, b g Foxhound (USA)—Quietly Impressive (IRE) **M. C. S. D. Racing Ltd**
33 **PERUVIAN STYLE (IRE)**, b g Desert Style (IRE)—Lady's Vision (IRE) **M. C. S. D. Racing Ltd**
34 **SACCHARINE**, b f Whittingham (IRE)—Sweet And Lucky **Mr Paul J. Dixon**
35 **STANHOPE FORBES (IRE)**, b c Danehill Dancer (IRE)—Hinari Disk Deck **Richard Green (Fine Paintings)**
36 **VALJARV**, b f Bluebird (USA)—Iktidar **V and J Properties**
37 **VANTAGE (IRE)**, b g Marju—Anna Comnena **Mr Mark Harniman**
38 **WAVERTREE GIRL (IRE)**, b f Marju—Lust **Wavertree Racing Club (2002) Ltd Syn B**
39 **ZAFFEU**, ch g Zafonic (USA)—Leaping Flame (USA) **The Headquarters Partnership Ltd**
40 **ZAKFREE (IRE)**, b g Danetime (IRE)—Clipper Queen **Mrs Emma Littmoden**

TWO-YEAR-OLDS

41 B f 28/2 Wolfhound (USA)—Bring On The Choir (Chief Singer) **Mr Paul J. Dixon**
42 **CRY OF THE WOLF**, ch c 4/4 Loup Sauvage (USA)—
          Hopesay (Warning) (10500) **The Headquarters Partnership Ltd**
43 **FLOOSIE (IRE)**, b f 29/4 Night Shift (USA)—German Lady (Mon Tresor) (15000) **Mrs Linda Francis**
44 **ITSA MONKEY (IRE)**, b g 5/4 Merdon Melody—
          Gracious Imp (USA) (Imp Society (USA)) (6000) **Mr G. M. Kinnersley**
45 Ch c 26/4 Grand Lodge (USA)—Miss Queen (USA) (Miswaki (USA)) (52565) **Mr Ivan Allan**
46 B f 28/2 Desert Sun—Moonlight Path (IRE) (Fairy King (USA)) (15000) **Miss Vanessa Church**
47 **OUR CHOICE (IRE)**, b c 15/3 Indian Danehill (IRE—Spring Daffodil (Pharly (FR)) (28000) **Mr A. A. Goodman**
48 B c 9/4 Unfuwain (USA)—Pick of The Pops (High Top) (20000) **V and J Properties**
49 B c 21/3 Benny The Dip (USA)—Sundae Girl (USA) (Green Dancer (USA)) (19000) **Mrs Emma Littmoden**

Other Owners: Mr Toby Brereton, Mr M. Connelly, Ms Anne Dawson, Mr P. Jeffries, Mrs Emma Littmoden.

Assistant Trainer: Matt Salaman

Jockeys (Flat): T G McLaughlin (8-6), I Mongan (8-4). **Apprentice:** J P Guillembert (8-5). **Amateurs:** Mrs E Littmoden, Mr S McGeorge, Mr N Walker.

---

345 MR B. J. LLEWELLYN, Bargoed
Postal: **Ffynonau Duon Farm, Pentwyn, Fochriw, Bargoed, Mid-Glamorgan, CF81 9NR.**
Contact: **PHONE (01685) 841259 FAX (01685) 843838 MOBILE (07971) 233473/(07971) 283262**

1 **CARIBBEAN MAN**, 4, b g Hector Protector (USA)—Caribbean Star **Maenllwyd Racing Club**
2 **FRAMLINGHAM**, 9, gr g Out of Hand—Sugar Hall **Crouch Morgan Partnership**
3 **FRONTIER**, 7, b g Indian Ridge—Adatiya (IRE) **Mr B. J. Llewellyn**
4 **GLORY STOREY (IRE)**, 10, b g Tremblant—Boule de Soie **Richards & Thomas**
5 **IVY MOON**, 4, b f Emperor Jones (USA)—Bajan Rose **Mr R. L. Cox**
6 **LUDERE (IRE)**, 9, ch g Desse Zenny (USA)—White Jasmin **Mr B. W. Parren**
7 **MONKSFORD**, 5, b g Minster Son—Mortify **Mr B. W. Parren**
8 **MONSAL DALE (IRE)**, 5, ch g Desert King (IRE)—Zanella (IRE) **Mr Terry Reffell**

MR B. J. LLEWELLYN—continued

9 **PEGGY LOU**, 4, b f Washington State (USA)—Rosemary Nalden **T. G. B. Racing Club**
10 **RILEYS DREAM**, 5, b m Rudimentary (USA)—Dorazine **Mr Greg Robinson and Mr A. N. Jay**
11 **SKYE BLUE (IRE)**, 7, b g Blues Traveller (IRE)—Hitopah **Glyn Tarrel Stud**
12 **SOU'WESTER**, 4, b g Fleetwood (IRE)—Mayfair **Mr E. R. Griffiths**
13 **TOBEROE COMMOTION (IRE)**, 6, b g Great Commotion (USA)—Fionn Varragh (IRE) **Mr B. J. Llewellyn**
14 **ULSHAW**, 7, ch g Salse (USA)—Kintail **Mrs Vicki Guy**
15 **WESTERN RIDGE (FR)**, 7, b g Darshaan—Helvellyn (USA) **Mr D. H. Driscoll**
16 **WRANGEL (FR)**, 10, ch g Tropular—Swedish Princess **Miss Emily Jane Jones**

Other Owners: Mr M. B. Catris, Miss B. J. Crouch, Mr M. Frieze, Mr M. E. Frieze, Mr W. R. Jones, Mrs P. J. Lee, Mrs Audrey Morgan, Mrs B. C. Richards, Mr Craig S. Thomas.

Assistant Trainer: J L Llewellyn

Jockey (Flat): R Havlin. **Jockey (NH):** O McPhail. **Conditional:** Christian Williams.

---

346 | ## MR D. M. LLOYD, Bridgend
Postal: Avalon, Brynmenyn, Bridgend, Mid-Glamorgan, CF32 9LL.
Contact: **PHONE (01656) 724654**

1 **PETITE RISK**, 10, ch m Risk Me (FR)—Technology (FR) **Mr D. M. Lloyd**

Assistant Trainer: C Lewis

---

347 | ## MR F. LLOYD, Bangor-on-Dee
Postal: Bryn Hovah, Bangor-On-Dee, Wrexham, Clwyd, LL13 0DA.
Contact: **PHONE (01978) 780356 FAX (01978) 660152**

1 **ALTHREY RULER (IRE)**, 11, b g Phardante (FR)—Keego's Aunt **Mr F. Lloyd**
2 **PHAR RIVER (IRE)**, 5, ch g Scriband—Down By The River **Mr F. Lloyd**
3 **SECRET'S OUT**, 8, b g Polish Precedent (USA)—Secret Obsession (USA) **Mr F. Lloyd**

THREE-YEAR-OLDS

4 **OVER THE CLOUDS**, gr f Cloudings (IRE)—Althrey Flame (IRE) **Mr F. Lloyd**
5 **POSH KING**, b g Rakaposhi King—Althrey Princess (IRE) **Mr F. Lloyd**

---

348 | ## MR A. J. LOCKWOOD, Malton
Postal: Fleet Cross Farm, Brawby, Malton, North Yorkshire, YO17 6QA.
Contact: **PHONE (01751) 431796 MOBILE (07747) 002535**

1 **AQRIBAA (IRE)**, 6, b g Pennekamp (USA)—Karayb (IRE) **Mr A. J. Lockwood**
2 **COACHMAN (IRE)**, 6, b g King's Ride—Royal Shares (IRE) **Mrs Lynne Lumley**
3 **FRANKINCENSE (IRE)**, 8, gr g Paris House—Mistral Wood (USA) **Mr Chester Bosomworth**
4 **FUSILLADE (IRE)**, 4, ch g Grand Lodge—Lili Cup (FR) **Highgreen Partnership**
5 **MARTON MERE**, 8, ch g Cadeaux Genereux—Hyatti **Mr A. J. Lockwood**
6 **MILAN KING (IRE)**, 11, b g King's Ride—Milan Moss **Mr Chester Bosomworth**
7 **ONLY WORDS (USA)**, 7, ch g Shuailaan—Conversation Piece (USA) **Mrs Lynne Lumley**
8 **POMPEII (IRE)**, 7, b g Salse (USA)—Before Dawn (USA) **Mr J. B. Slatcher**
9 **WHITLEY GRANGE BOY**, 11, b g Hubbly Bubbly (USA)—Choir **Mrs Carole Sykes**

Other Owners: Mr J. L. Holdroyd, Mr D. Kilburn, Mr J. Richardson, Mr D. Wilson.

---

349 | ## MR D. R. LODER, Newmarket
Postal: Egerton House Stables, Cambridge Road, Newmarket, Suffolk, CB8 0TH.
Contact: **PHONE (01638) 665511 FAX (01638) 665310**

1 **ALEUTIAN**, 4, gr g Zafonic (USA)—Baked Alaska
2 **AMANDUS (USA)**, 4, b g Danehill (USA)—Affection Affirmed (USA)
3 **ANGLO SAXON (USA)**, 4, b c Seeking The Gold (USA)—Anna Palariva (IRE)
4 **ANNAMBO**, 4, ch c In The Wings—Anna Matrushka
5 **BALKAN KNIGHT (USA)**, 4, b c Selkirk (USA)—Crown of Light

MR D. R. LODER—continued

6 **BONECRUSHER**, 5, b g Revoque (IRE)—Eurolink Mischief
7 **DAWN PIPER (USA)**, 4, b g Desert Prince (IRE)—June Moon (IRE)
8 **GIVE THE SLIP**, 7, b g Slip Anchor—Falafil (FR)
9 **HEISSE**, 4, b c Darshaan—Hedera (USA)
10 **KHANJAR (USA)**, 4, ch g Kris S (USA)—Alyssum (USA)
11 **LOVE YOU ALWAYS (USA)**, 4, ch g Woodman (USA)—Encorenous (USA)
12 **OLD LATIN**, 4, b c Zafonic (USA)—Classic Form (IRE)
13 **PARASOL (IRE)**, 5, br h Halling (USA)—Bunting
14 **PERFECT PORTRAIT**, 4, ch g Selkirk (USA)—Flawless Image (USA)
15 **PUGIN (IRE)**, 6, b h Darshaan—Gothic Dream (IRE)
16 **RAZKALLA (USA)**, 6, b g Caerleon (USA)—Larrocha (IRE)
17 **ROYAL DIGNITARY (USA)**, 4, br g Saint Ballado (CAN)—Star Actress (USA)
18 **SCOTTY'S FUTURE (IRE)**, 6, b g Namaqualand (USA)—Persian Express (IRE)
19 **SHAMI**, 5, ch h Rainbow Quest (USA)—Bosra Sham (USA)
20 **STAKHANOVITE (IRE)**, 4, b c Darshaan—Homage

THREE-YEAR-OLDS

21 **ANDEAN**, b c Singspiel (IRE)—Anna Matrushka
22 **BACKGAMMON**, b c Sadler's Wells (USA)—Game Plan
23 **BAY TREE (IRE)**, b f Daylami (IRE)—My Branch
24 **BOSTON IVY (USA)**, b f Mark of Esteem (IRE)—Hedera (USA)
25 **BULL RUN (IRE)**, ro c Daylami (IRE)—Bulaxie
26 **CARA BELLA**, ch f Seeking The Gold (USA)—Cherokee Rose (IRE)
27 **CHERUBIM (JPN)**, ch f Sunday Silence (USA)—Curly Angel (JPN)
28 **DAVORIN (JPN)**, br c Warning—Arvola
29 **DIAMOND WAY (USA)**, ch c Boundary (USA)—Discover Silver (USA)
30 **DUBAI SUNDAY (JPN)**, b c Sunday Silence (USA)—Lotta Lace (USA)
31 **GLEN INNES (IRE)**, b f Selkirk (USA)—Shinko Hermes (IRE)
32 **HIGH SCHOOL**, b f Sadler's Wells (USA)—High Hawk
33 **HUNTING LODGE (IRE)**, ch c Grand Lodge (USA)—Vijaya (USA)
34 **ILLUSTRIOUS MISS (USA)**, b f Kingmambo (USA)—Our Wildirish Rose (USA)
35 **LAKE CHARLOTTE (USA)**, b f Danzig (USA)—Quinpool (USA)
36 **LOMMEL (UAE)**, b c Lomitas—Idrica
37 **MANNTAB (USA)**, b c Kingmambo (USA)—Saafeya (IRE)
38 **MENELAUS**, b c Machiavellian (USA)—Mezzogiorno
39 **NIGHT AIR (IRE)**, b g Night Shift (USA)—Pippas Song
40 **NORWEGIAN**, b c Halling (USA)—Chicarica (USA)
41 **ORANGE FREE STATE**, b f Danzig (USA)—Cox Orange (USA)
42 **OUTER HEBRIDES**, b g Efisio—Reuval
43 **PARLIAMENT SQUARE (IRE)**, b c Sadler's Wells (USA)—Groom Order
44 **PEARL ISLAND (USA)**, b c Kingmambo (USA)—Mother of Pearl (IRE)
45 **PHILOSOPHY**, b c Machiavellian (USA)—Twitcher's Delight
46 **SABBAAG (USA)**, ch f Mark of Esteem (IRE)—Saabga (USA)
47 **SALISBURY PLAIN**, b c Mark of Esteem (IRE)—Wild Pavane
48 **SCIENCE FICTION**, b f Starborough—Scarlet Lake
49 **SERENGETI SKY (USA)**, br c Southern Halo (USA)—Genovefa (USA)
50 **SNOW KITTEN (USA)**, b f Storm Cat (USA)—Embassy
51 **SUNDAY CITY (JPN)**, ch c Sunday Silence (USA)—Diamond City (USA)
52 **SURREPTITIOUS**, ch f Machiavellian (USA)—Nadma (USA)
53 **THREE COUNTIES (IRE)**, b c Danehill (USA)—Royal Show (USA)
54 **TRIBUTE (IRE)**, b g Green Desert (USA)—Zooming (IRE)
55 **UNITED NATIONS**, ch c Halling (USA)—Congress (USA)
56 **VARNAY**, b f Machiavellian (USA)—Valleria
57 **VAS Y CARLA (USA)**, ch f Gone West (USA)—Lady Carla
58 **WHITE HAWK**, b c Silver Hawk (USA)—Polska (USA)
59 **WISTMAN (UAE)**, br c Woodman (USA)—Saik (USA)
60 **YAAHOMM**, ch c Unfuwain (USA)—Walesiana (GER)

TWO-YEAR-OLDS

61 **ANNE OF CLEVES**, b f 13/4 Diktat—Anna Matrushka (Mill Reef (USA))
62 B c 16/4 Danetime (IRE)—Art Duo (Artaius (USA)) (17000)
63 B c 20/1 Zafonic (USA)—Bedazzling (IRE) (Darshaan) (90000)
64 Ch f 17/4 Sinndar (IRE)—Bella Lambada (Lammtarra (USA)) (100000)
65 **BEST ABOUT**, ch f 23/2 King's Best (USA)—Up And About (Barathea (IRE)) (54000)
66 **BIG BAND MUSIC (USA)**, b br c 4/3 Dixieland Band (USA)—Bashful Charmer (USA) (Capote (USA))

MR D. R. LODER—continued

67 **BIJOU A MOI,** b f 8/5 Rainbow Quest (USA)—Bianca Nera (Salse (USA))
68 **CAVORTING,** ch c 30/3 Polar Falcon (USA)—Prancing (Prince Sabo)
69 Br c 4/4 Red Ransom (USA)—Chine (Inchinor) (89285)
70 B c 1/2 Valid Expectations—Chris's Commitment (USA) (Black Tie Affair) (53571)
71 B c 28/3 Danehill Dancer (IRE)—Come Together (Mtoto) (68000)
72 **CONJECTURE,** b c 5/5 Danzig (USA)—Golden Opinion (USA) (Slew O'Gold (USA))
73 **CREME DE LA CREME,** b f 9/2 Montjeu (IRE)—Pride of Place (IRE) (Caerleon (USA))
74 **CRYSTALLINE,** b f 28/4 Green Desert (USA)—Crown of Light (Mtoto)
75 **DANCINGINTHEDARK (IRE),** b f 7/4 Fasliyev (USA)—Moviegoer (Pharly (FR)) (67000)
76 **DRAMATICUS,** b c 17/2 Indian Ridge—Corinium (IRE) (Turtle Island (IRE)) (60000)
77 **DRUMROLL (IRE),** b c 16/3 Diktat—Mystic Tempo (USA) (El Gran Senor (USA))
78 **DUBAI SURPRISE (IRE),** b f 21/3 King's Best—Toujours Irish (Irish River (FR)) (220000)
79 B c 23/1 Cadeaux Genereux—Elfin Laughter (Alzao (USA)) (120000)
80 **EVASIVE QUALITY (FR),** b f 18/4 Highest Honor (FR)—Exocet (USA) (Deposit Ticket (USA)) (160791)
81 **FASLIOVNA,** b f 18/2 Fasliyev (USA)—High Savannah (Rousillon (USA))
82 Br f 14/3 Mister Baileys—Final Shot (Dalsaan)
83 **FRAMBROISE,** ch f 16/3 Diesis—Applaud (USA) (Rahy (USA))
84 **FRANCIS CADELL,** b c 11/3 Cadeaux Genereux—Ruby Affair (IRE) (Night Shift (USA)) (55000)
85 **FREEMASON,** b c 25/2 Grand Lodge (USA)—Applecross (Glint of Gold)
86 B c 19/4 Monashee Mountain—Goldenfort Queen (IRE) (Distinctly North (USA)) (68026)
87 **GRAND SEIGNEUR (IRE),** b c 8/2 Grand Lodge (USA)—Commanche Belle (Shirley Heights) (222634)
88 **HER GRACE (IRE),** b f 2/4 Spectrum (IRE)—Overruled (IRE) (Last Tycoon)
89 **HONEY GOLD (IRE),** ch f 6/2 Indian Ridge—Half-Hitch (USA) (Diesis) (235002)
90 Br c 6/5 Celtic Swing—Implicit View (Persian Bold) (24737)
91 **KAHRAMANA,** b f 8/3 Hernando (FR)—Come On Rosi (Valiyar) (95000)
92 B c 7/3 King's Best (USA)—Liaison (USA) (Blushing Groom (FR)) (140000)
93 Ch f 5/3 Cadeaux Genereux—Lighthouse (Warning)
94 **LUBECK,** b c 16/1 Lujain (USA)—Milling (IRE) (In The Wings) (68026)
95 **MAID TO MATTER,** b f 4 Pivotal—Scarlet Lake (Reprimand)
96 **MILL END (IRE),** br c 14/3 Trans Island—Tumble (Mtoto) (75000)
97 Br f 21/2 Grand Lodge (USA)—Millitrix (Doyoun) (60000)
98 B c 16/5 Mark Of Esteem (IRE)—Morina (USA) (Lyphard (USA)) (80000)
99 B c 31/1 Red Ransom (USA)—Musical Treat (IRE) (Royal Academy (USA)) (74211)
100 B f 9/5 Sunday Silence (USA)—Oenothera (IRE) (Night Shift (USA))
101 **OPTIMUM (IRE),** b c 30/4 King's Best (USA)—Colour Dance (Rainbow Quest (USA)) (123685)
102 B c 14/3 Royal Applause—Out Like Magic (Magic Ring (IRE)) (65000)
103 **PADRAO (IRE),** b c 21/3 Cape Cross—Dazilyn Lady (Zilzal (USA)) (130000)
104 B f 15/5 Cadeaux Genereux—Papaha (FR) (Green Desert (USA)) (35000)
105 **PIANOFORTE (USA),** b c 24/2 Grand Slam (USA)—Far Too Loud (CAN) (No Louder (CAN)) (113095)
106 B f 28/2 Halling (USA)—Polska (Danzig (USA))
107 B c 2/4 Red Ransom (USA)—Printing Press (USA) (In Reality) (113095)
108 **REDEYE SPECIAL,** b f 28/3 Efisio—Red May (IRE) (Persian Bold) (85000)
109 **RED HEAVEN,** b f 28/1 Benny The Dip (USA)—Heavenly Ray (USA) (Rahy (USA))
110 B c 16/1 Alhaarth (IRE)—Ring of Kerry (IRE) (Kenmare (FR)) (148422)
111 B c 13/2 Desert Style (IRE)—Robsart (IRE) (Robellino (USA)) (75000)
112 **ROCK MUSIC,** ch c 14/3 Singspiel (IRE)—Stack Rock (Ballad Rock) (90000)
113 **ROYAL GAME,** b c 2/5 Vettori (IRE)—Ground Game (Gildoran) (16000)
114 B c 23/3 Josr Algarhoud (IRE)—Russell Creek (Sandy Creek) (26000)
115 B c 5/4 Groom Dancer (USA)—Russian Rose (IRE) (Soviet Lad (USA)) (85000)
116 **SAMUEL JOHN PEPLOE (IRE),** b c 3/3 Intikhab—Sadalsud (IRE) (Shaadi (USA)) (40197)
117 **SATCHEM (IRE),** br c 11/2 Inchinor—Mohican Princess (Shirley Heights) (100000)
118 **SHANEHILL (IRE),** b c 13/2 Danehill—Shunaire (USA) (Woodman (USA)) (80395)
119 Ch f 2/1 In The Wings—Sheer Harmony (USA) (Woodman (USA))
120 B c 25/3 Danehill Dancer (IRE)—Siana Springs (IRE) (Emarati (USA)) (68026)
121 **SILVER PHANTOM (IRE),** b c 14/2 Spectrum (IRE)—Beat It (USA) (Diesis) (19789)
122 **SIMPLIFY,** b c 2/2 Fasliyev (USA)—Simplicity (Polish Precedent (USA)) (280000)
123 B c 8/3 Desert Style (IRE)—Slipper (Suave Dancer (USA)) (50000)
124 Br c 1/3 Lujain (USA)—Slow Jazz (USA) (Chief's Crown (USA))
125 **SOVEREIGNTY (JPN),** b c 10/4 King's Best (USA)—Calando (USA) (Storm Cat (USA))
126 **SPEAR (IRE),** b c 22/1 Almutawakel—Les Hurlants (IRE) (Barathea (IRE)) (70000)
127 B c 12/4 Bahamian Bounty—Star (Most Welcome) (110000)
128 **SWORD OF DAMASCUS (IRE),** b c 7/5 Darshaan—Damascene (IRE) (Scenic) (180000)
129 B c 8/2 Mark Of Esteem (IRE)—Tanasie (Cadeaux Genereux) (35000)
130 Ch f 28/4 Inchinor—Thamud (IRE) (Lahib (USA)) (14000)
131 **THEAS DANCE,** b f 6/4 Danzig (USA)—Teggiano (IRE) (Mujtahid (USA))
132 Ch c 31/1 Foxhound (USA)—Thermopylae (Tenby)

MR D. R. LODER—continued

133 B c 3/2 Tagula (IRE)—Thornby Park (Unfuwain (USA)) (20000)
134 **TILLANDS (USA),** b c 26/2 Bahri (USA)—Tillandsia (IRE) (Unfuwain (USA))
135 B f 28/2 Orpen (USA)—Timiya (High Top) (21000)
136 **TITO GOFIRST,** b c 12/2 Gone West (USA)—Torgau (IRE) (Zieten (USA)) (32000)
137 Gr f 20/2 Desert Prince (IRE)—True Love (Robellino (USA)) (75000)
138 **TURNSTONE,** b c 12/4 Pivotal—Adeptation (USA) (Exceller (USA))
139 B c 26/2 Royal Applause—Upend (Main Reef) (160000)
140 B f 5/2 Compton Place—Urania (Most Welcome) (42000)
141 **VANISH (IRE),** b f 16/4 Barathea (IRE)—Silver Hut (USA) (Silver Hawk (USA)) (43289)
142 B c 16/4 Bahamian Bounty—Verdura (Green Desert (USA)) (26000)
143 B c 23/2 Distant View (USA)—Virgin Stanza (USA) (Opening Verse (USA)) (95000)
144 B c 28/1 Giant's Causeway—Wannabe Grand (IRE) (Danehill (USA)) (160000)

Other Owners: Sheikh Ahmed Al Maktoum, Cheveley Park Stud, Mr Marc Citron, Derek & Jean Clee, Crescent Stables Bloodstock, De La Warr Racing, Egerton House Racing, Mrs P. T. Fenwick, Sir Alex Ferguson, Mr W. E. A. Fox, Mr S. R. Frisby, Mr W. J. Gredley, Mr C. J. Harper, Highclere Thoroughbred Racing, Jumeirah Racing, Sir Edmund Loder, Lord Lloyd-Webber, Lordship Stud, Lucayan Stud, Sheikh Mohammed, Mr Kevin Murphy, Mohammed Al Nabouda, Newsells Park Stud, Normandie Stud, Octagon Partnership, Pat Eddery Racing, Pegasus Racing Ltd, Mr P. D. Player, Mr Mohammed Rashid, Richard Green (Fine Paintings), Dr Ali Ridha, Mr Rupert Rittson-Thomas, James Rowsell & Partners, Faisal Salman, Mohammed Al Shafar, Sumaya Uk Stable, Mr Michael Tabor, The Lamprell Partnership, The Royal Ascot Racing Club, Mr Michael Watt.

Assistant Trainer: R. Bowman

Apprentice: A Beech.

<table><tr><td>**350**</td><td>**MR L. LUNGO, Carrutherstown**
Postal: Hetland Hill Farm, Carrutherstown, Dumfriesshire, DG1 4JX.
Contact: **PHONE** (01387) 840691 **FAX** (01387) 840323 **MOBILE** (07850) 711438
E-MAIL office@lenlungo.com</td></tr></table>

1 **ALBERTINO LAD,** 7, ch g Mystiko (USA)—Siokra **Mr R. J. Gilbert**
2 **ARMAGUEDON (IRE),** 6, b g Garde Royale—Miss Dundee (FR) **Ashleybank Investments Limited**
3 **ASHLEYBANK HOUSE (IRE),** 7, b g Lord Americo—Deep Perk (IRE) **Ashleybank Investments Limited**
4 **BAFFLING SECRET (FR),** 4, gr g Kizitca (FR)—Kadroulienne (FR) **Mrs Barbara Lungo**
5 **BALLYSTONE (IRE),** 11, ch g Roselier (FR)—Gusserane Princess **Mr Andrew W.B.Duncan & Mr S.E.Constable**
6 **BOGUS DREAMS (IRE),** 7, ch g Lahib (USA)—Dreams Are Free (IRE) **Mrs Barbara Lungo**
7 **BRANDY WINE (IRE),** 6, b g Roselier (FR)—Sakonnet (USA) **Ashleybank Investments Limited**
8 **BRAVE LORD (IRE),** 7, ch g Mister Lord (USA)—Artic Squaw (IRE) **Solway Stayers**
9 **CAPTAIN'S LEAP (IRE),** 8, ch g Grand Plaisir (IRE)—Ballingowan Star **Mr J. Regan**
10 **CARAPUCE (FR),** 5, ch g Bigstone (IRE)—Treasure City (FR) **Mr & Mrs Raymond Anderson Green**
11 **CONTRACT SCOTLAND (IRE),** 9, br g Religiously (USA)—Stroked Again **Contract Scotland Limited**
12 **COOK O'HAWICK (IRE),** 7, b g King's Ride—Miners Yank **Ashleybank Investments Limited**
13 **CRAZY HORSE (IRE),** 11, b g Little Bighorn—Our Dorcet **Ashleybank Investments Limited**
14 **DATBANDITO (IRE),** 5, gr g Un Desperado (FR)—Most of All **Mr P. E. Truscott**
15 **DIRECT ACCESS (IRE),** 9, ch g Roselier (FR)—Spanish Flame (IRE) **Ashleybank Investments Limited**
16 **EARL SIGURD (IRE),** 6, ch g High Kicker (USA)—My Kind **Queens House**
17 **EBINZAYD (IRE),** 8, b g Tenby—Sharakawa (IRE) **Mr R. J. Gilbert**
18 **ERISKAY (IRE),** 8, b g Montelimar (USA)—Little Peach **Colonel D. C. Greig**
19 **FOUR MELONS (IRE),** 5, b g Anshan—Four Shares **Ashleybank Investments Limited**
20 **FREETOWN (IRE),** 8, b g Shirley Heights—Pageantry **Miss S. Blumberg & Mr R. Nairn**
21 **FULL IRISH (IRE),** 8, ch g Rashar (USA)—Ross Gale **Mr D. Stronach**
22 **GHOST RIDER (IRE),** 7, br g Good Thyne (USA)—Pit Runner **The Border Reivers**
23 **HALLYARDS GAEL (IRE),** 10, br g Strong Gale—Secret Ocean **Mr G. M. Mair**
24 **HELP YOURSELF (IRE),** 8, gr m Roselier (FR)—Sweet Run **Mr Alistair Duncan**
25 **HETLAND HILL,** 8, ch g Secret Appeal—Mohibbah (USA) **Mrs Barbara Lungo**
26 **HUKA LODGE (IRE),** 7, gr g Roselier (FR)—Derrella **Mrs J. M. Jones**
27 **INN FROM THE COLD (IRE),** 8, ch g Glacial Storm (USA)—Silver Apollo **Mrs Barbara Lungo**
28 **JACK POT II (IRE),** 7, ch g Luchiroverte (IRE)—Roxane II (FR) **Ashleybank Investments Limited**
29 **JOE BLAKE (IRE),** 9, b g Jurado (USA)—I've No Idea **Mr R. A. Bartlett**
30 **JOINT AUTHORITY (IRE),** 9, b g Religiously (USA)—Highway's Last **Mrs Barbara Lungo**
31 **JOLIKA (FR),** 7, b m Grand Tresor (FR)—Unika II (FR) **Dr Kenneth S. Fraser**
32 **JUPITER DE BUSSY (FR),** 7, b br g Silver Rainbow—Tosca de Bussy (FR) **Ashleybank Investments Limited**
33 5, ch g Shernazar—Kabarda **Mrs Barbara Lungo**
34 **KARATCHI (FR),** 6, b br g Iris Noir (FR)—Eclipse Royale II (FR) **Mr R. A. Bartlett**
35 **KIDITHOU (FR),** 6, b g Royal Charter (FR)—De Thou (FR) **Roman Wall Racing**

MR L. LUNGO—continued

36 **LASCAR DE FERBET (FR)**, 5, br g Sleeping Car (FR)—Belle de Ferbet (FR) **Ashleybank Investments Limited**
37 **LE BIASSAIS (FR)**, 5, b g Passing Sale (FR)—Petite Fanfan (FR) **Ashleybank Investments Limited**
38 **L'OISEAU (FR)**, 5, br g Video Rock (FR)—Roseraie (FR) **Ashleybank Investments Limited**
39 **LORD OF THE SKY**, 11, b g Lord Bud—Fardella (ITY) **Mrs Barbara Lungo**
40 **LOSCAR (FR)**, 5, b g General Holme (USA)—Unika II (FR)
41 **LOUGHCREW (IRE)**, 8, ch g Good Thyne (USA)—Marys Course **Mrs Barbara Lungo**
42 **MAGIC COMBINATION (IRE)**, 11, b g Scenic—Etage **SW Transport (Swindon) Ltd & R J Gilbert**
43 **MAUNSELL'S ROAD (IRE)**, 5, b g Desert Style (IRE)—Zara's Birthday (IRE) **Mr Clarke Boon**
44 **MER BIHAN (FR)**, 4, b f Port Lyautey (FR)—Unika II (FR) **The Hookers**
45 **MINDANAO**, 8, b m Most Welcome—Salala **Bob Slee Toby Noble & J B**
46 **MIRJAN (IRE)**, 8, b g Tenby—Mirana (IRE) **Mrs Barbara Lungo**
47 **MONOLITH**, 6, b g Bigstone (IRE)—Ancara **Elite Racing Club**
48 **MR AUCHTERLONIE (IRE)**, 7, b g Mister Lord (USA)—Cahernane Girl **Ashleybank Investments Limited**
49 **MR HORNBLOWER (IRE)**, 10, ch g Orchestra—Garland **Ashleybank Investments Limited**
50 **MR TIM (IRE)**, 6, br g Naheez (USA)—Ari's Fashion **Ashleybank Investments Limited**
51 **MR WOODENTOP (IRE)**, 8, b g Roselier (FR)—Una's Polly **Ashleybank Investments Limited**
52 **MY BEST SECRET**, 5, ch g Secret Appeal—Mohibbah (USA) **Mr C. Anderson**
53 **NOBLEFIR (IRE)**, 6, b g Shernazar—Chrisali (IRE) **P. Gaffney & J. N. Stevenson**
54 **ONLY ONCE**, 9, b g King's Ride—Rambling Gold **Ashleybank Investments Limited**
55 **PADDY THE PIPER (IRE)**, 7, b g Witness Box (USA)—Divine Dibs **Mr & Mrs Raymond Anderson Green**
56 **PLUTOCRAT**, 8, b g Polar Falcon (USA)—Choire Mhor **Mr A. W. Jack**
57 **QUEEN OF THE SOUTH**, 7, b m Cut The Mustard (IRE)—Kawarau Queen **Mr G. G. Fraser**
58 **ROSE D'APRIL (FR)**, 7, gr g April Night (FR)—Rose de Hoc (FR) **Ashleybank Investments Limited**
59 **ROYAL VARIETY (IRE)**, 6, gr g Roselier (FR)—Private Dancer **Elite Racing Club**
60 **SAGARDIAN (FR)**, 5, b g Mister Mat (FR)—Tipnik (FR) **Mrs S. J. Matthews**
61 **SARA MONICA (IRE)**, 7, ch m Moscow Society (USA)—Swift Trip (IRE) **Mr R. J. Gilbert**
62 **SCHUH SHINE (FR)**, 7, gr g Roselier (FR)—Naar Chamali **Ashleybank Investments Limited**
63 5, B g Namaqualand (USA)—Secret Ocean **Mrs Barbara Lungo**
64 **SILKEN PEARLS**, 8, b m Leading Counsel (USA)—River Pearl **Mr P. E. Truscott**
65 **SILVERTOWN**, 9, b g Danehill (USA)—Docklands (USA) **R J Gilbert & SW Transport (Swindon) Ltd**
66 **SKIPPERS CLEUCH (IRE)**, 10, b g Be My Native (USA)—Cloughoola Lady **Ashleybank Investments Limited**
67 **SUMTHYNE SPECIAL (IRE)**, 12, b g Good Thyne (USA)—Condonstown Rose **Mr J. M. Crichton**
68 **THE BAJAN BANDIT (IRE)**, 9, b g Commanche Run—Sunrise Highway VII **Ashleybank Investments Limited**
69 **THE GREY DYER (IRE)**, 10, gr g Roselier (FR)—Tawny Kate (IRE) **Ashleybank Investments Limited**
70 **THE LAIRD'S ENTRY (IRE)**, 9, b g King's Ride—Balancing Act **Ashleybank Investments Limited**
71 **THE PHAIR CRIER (IRE)**, 9, ch g Phardante (FR)—Maul-More **Ashleybank Investments Limited**
72 **THE RILE (IRE)**, 10, ch g Alphabatim (USA)—Donna Chimene **Mr & Mrs Raymond Anderson Green**
73 **THE WEAVER (FR)**, 5, ch g Villez (USA)—Miss Planette (FR) **P. Gaffney & J. N. Stevenson**
74 **THOUTMOSIS (USA)**, 5, ch g Woodman (USA)—Toujours Elle (USA) **The Border Reivers**
75 **VILLON (IRE)**, 5, b g Topanoora—Deep Adventure **Mr R. A. Bartlett**
76 **WALTZING ALONG (IRE)**, 6, b g Presenting—Clyduffe Fairy **Andrew Duncan,Vicky Royds & James Barber**
77 **WILD CANE RIDGE (IRE)**, 5, gr g Roselier (FR)—Shuil Na Lee (IRE) **Ashleybank Investments Limited**
78 **WINGED ANGEL**, 7, ch g Prince Sabo—Silky Heights (IRE) **Four Up One Down Partnership**
79 **WORD GETS AROUND (IRE)**, 6, b g King's Ride—Kate Fisher (IRE) **Mr & Mrs Raymond Anderson Green**
80 **YANKEE JAMIE (IRE)**, 10, b g Strong Gale—Sparkling Opera **Mr R. J. Gilbert**

Other Owners: Mrs Philip Arkwright, Mr James Barber, Mrs J. Bell, Miss E. Birkbeck, Miss S. Blumberg, Mr J. Conroy, Mr S. E. Constable, Mrs T. Cunningham-Jardine, Mr Andrew W. B. Duncan, Lady Eileen Duncan, Mr John J. Elliot, Mr P. Gaffney, Mr J. Good, Mrs Anita Green, Mr Raymond Anderson Green, Mr Tony Hill, Mr Malcolm Hind, Mr J. C. Hope, Mr R. Hyndman, Mr K. G. Knox, Mr P. Maddison, Mr R. Merhi, Mr R. Nairn, Mr Toby Noble, Miss M. Noden, Mr J. A. Ogle, Mr R. Paisley, Dr Roy Palmer, Mr C. Paterson, Mr Stuart Postill, Mrs Michael Royds, Mr Bob Slee, Mr J. N. Stevenson, S. W. Transport (Swindon) Ltd, Mr M. R. Wainwright, Mr A. C. Walsh.

Jockey (NH): A Dobbin (10-0). **Conditional:** G Berridge (10-0), L Berridge (9-7). **Amateur:** M J McAllister (9-7).

351 MR G. MACAIRE, Les Mathes

Postal: **Hippodrome de la Palmyre, 17570 Les Mathes, France**
Contact: **PHONE +33 (0) 546 236254/225855 FAX +33 (0) 546 225438**
MOBILE +33 (0) 607 654992 E-MAIL entrainement-g.macaire@wanadoo.fr

1 **APPLES JUICE (FR)**, 4, ch g Saint Cyrien (FR)—Une Joy (FR) **Mr R. Laffitte**
2 **ARISTOXENE (FR)**, 4, b g Star Fast (FR)—Petite Folie **Mr Roger Hoad**
3 **ARTIGAS (FR)**, 5, b g Arctic Tern (USA)—Marie de Rocroi (FR) **Mr D. Poweel**
4 **AUBANE (FR)**, 4, b f Cadoudal (FR)—Miss Dundee (FR) **Mrs F. Legriffon**
5 **BICA (FR)**, 4, b g Cadoudal (FR)—Libertina (FR) **Mr Waley-Cohen**
6 **BIELO VIESA (FR)**, 4, b g Mansonnien (FR)—Gold Or Silver (FR) **Mr F. Lazar**
7 **BRIDGE OF STARS (FR)**, 4, b g Roakarad—Hersilia (FR) **Mr M. Bessis**
8 **CARLYPHARD'S (FR)**, 4, ch g Lyphard's Wish (FR)—Carlynie (FR) **Mrs A. M. Roux**
9 **CHANTEGRIL (FR)**, 4, b c Hasa (FR)—Mazzina (FR) **Mr J. M. Reillier**
10 **CHARTERADE (FR)**, 5, b m Garde Royale—Alberade (FR) **Haras de la Faisanderie**
11 **CHOUM (FR)**, 9, b g Faucon Noir (FR)—Clementine Fleurie (FR) **Mr O. Delegue**
12 **CRIN ARGENTE (FR)**, 7, b g Nikos—Tip Smistress (FR) **Mr Hanin**
13 **CYRIEN DEUX MILLE (FR)**, 4, b g Saint Cyrien (FR)—Top Chiz (FR) **Ecurie Guillaume Macaire**
14 **DOMIROME (FR)**, 6, b g Roi de Rome (USA)—Bold Senorita (IRE) **Mrs Y. Shen**
15 **DOUZE DOUZE (FR)**, 8, ch g Saint Cyrien (FR)—Kitkelly (FR) **Mr F. Videaud**
16 **EPI DE LUNE (FR)**, 4, gr g Cadoudal (FR)—Chakini (FR) **Mr R. W. Denechere**
17 **FAUCON DU CERCLE (FR)**, 5, b h Faucon Noir (FR)—Corthalia (FR) **Mr R. Fougedoire**
18 **GAMNOR (FR)**, 4, ch g Baby Turk—Tip Smistress (FR) **Mr C. Aubree**
19 **GOLDEN FLIGHT (FR)**, 5, b g Saint Cyrien (FR)—Sunday Flight (FR) **Mr J. Cotton**
20 **GRIVERY (FR)**, 8, b g Nikos—Lady Segrave **Mr J. C. Audry**
21 **IMLIGHT (FR)**, 8, b g Lights Out (FR)—Star Dancer (FR) **Mrs Y. Shen**
22 **JAIR DU COCHET (FR)**, 7, b g Rahotep (FR)—Dilaure (FR) **Mrs F. Montauban**
23 **JAPHET (FR)**, 7, b g Perrault—Una Volta (FR) **Mr J. C. Audry**
24 **KALIMIE (FR)**, 6, b m Iris Noir (FR)—Asterie L'Ermitage (FR) **Mr J. M. Robin**
25 **KAMI DES OBEAUX (FR)**, 6, b g Saint Preuil (FR)—Ulisa II (FR) **Mrs P. Papot**
26 **KARIO KA (FR)**, 6, b g Murmure (FR)—Orphica (FR) **Mr M. Morossini**
27 **KAYSERI (FR)**, 6, b m Desert Parade—Olchany (FR) **Mrs P. Papot**
28 **LADY DANCER (FR)**, 5, b m Lesotho (USA)—Lady Thatch (FR) **Mr G. Morosini**
29 **LANCIER DU BOST (FR)**, 5, b g Mont Basile (FR)—Baby Doll (FR) **Mrs F. Montauban**
30 **LANCOME DE SOLZEN (FR)**, 5, b g Passing Sale (FR)—Tipperary II (FR) **Mr P. de Maleissye**
31 **LAURIER DE COTTE (FR)**, 5, b g Kadalko (FR)—Rafale de Cotte (FR) **Mr R. Fougedoire**
32 **LEADER DU COCHET (FR)**, 5, b g Bizantium (FR)—Voiture du Cochet (FR) **Mrs F. Montauban**
33 **LE GRAND JEU (FR)**, 5, gr g Video Rock (FR)—Almeida (FR) **Mr J. P. Moutafian**
34 **LEON DES OBEAUX (FR)**, 5, gr g Panoramic—Diese d'Estruval (FR) **Mrs N. Devilder**
35 **LE PERO (FR)**, 6, b g Perrault—Nuit d'Ecajeul (FR) **Ecurie Guillaume Macaire**
36 **LE PETIT SAINT (FR)**, 5, gr g Saint Preuil (FR)—Tourbrune (FR) **Mr R. Fougedoire**
37 **LE THEIL (FR)**, 5, b g Bayolidaan (FR)—Mazzina (FR) **Mr J. M. Reillier**
38 **LEVI DES OBEAUX (FR)**, 5, b g Royal Charter (FR)—Valse des Obeaux (FR) **Mrs N. Devilder**
39 **LIBERDAL (FR)**, 6, b g Cadoudal (FR)—Libertina (FR) **Mrs B. Gabeur**
40 **LIMBO (FR)**, 5, b g Video Rock (FR)—Urtica (IRE) **Mr R. Fougedoire**
41 **LINGOT DE L'ISLE (FR)**, 5, b g Ragmar (FR)—Ceres de L'Isle (FR) **Mr M. Froissard**
42 **LITTLE BRUERE (FR)**, 5, b g Villez (USA)—Divine Bruere (FR) **Mr R. Fougedoire**
43 **LOOK BRUERE (FR)**, 5, b g Celtic Arms (FR)—Altesse Bruere (FR) **Mr R. Fougedoire**
44 **LOOK COLLONGES (FR)**, 5, gr g Dom Alco (FR)—Tessy Collonges (FR) **Mr C. Cohen**
45 **LOR WEEN (FR)**, 5, b g Beyssac (FR)—Asterie L'Ermitage (FR) **Mrs P. Papot**
46 **LOUGAROO (FR)**, 5, ch h Snurge—Titian Queen **Mr F. Chaussonniere**
47 **LUCKI LUKE (FR)**, 5, b g Luchiroverte (IRE)—Birgonde (FR) **Mr X. Papot**
48 **MAGE D'ESTRUVAL (FR)**, 4, b g Sheyrann—Ivresse d'Estruval (FR) **Mr B. Le Gentil**
49 **MALANDRIN (FR)**, 9, ch g Albert du Berlais (FR)—Maieta (FR) **Mr J. M. Reillier**
50 **MAMIE BLEUE (FR)**, 4, b f Air du Nord (USA)—Dear Blue (FR) **Mr D. Besnouin**
51 **MARIUS DES OBEAUX (FR)**, 4, b g Grand Tresor (FR)—Diese d'Estruval (FR) **Mrs N. Devilder**
52 **MARQUIS COLLONGES (FR)**, 4, gr g Ragmar (FR)—Tessy Collonges (FR) **Mr C. Cohen**
53 **MARS DES OBEAUX (FR)**, 4, b g Panoramic—Ceres des Obeaux (FR) **Mrs N. Devilder**
54 **MASSAC (FR)**, 5, b g Garde Royale—Mirande (FR) **Mr R. Fougedoire**
55 **MASSENA (FR)**, 4, gr g April Night (FR)—Belle de Loir (FR) **Mrs M. Bryant**
56 **MECHERIA (FR)**, 4, ch g Nikos—Petite Majeste (FR) **Mr A. Chiche**
57 **MEISIR DU LUC (FR)**, 4, b c Chamberlin (FR)—Acca du Luc (FR) **Mr C. Dumeau**
58 **MERYL (FR)**, 4, ch g Garde Royale—Vindhy (FR) **Mr C. Cohen**
59 **MICADOU (FR)**, 4, b g Cadoudal (FR)—Minouche (FR) **Mr F. Videaud**
60 **MINOS DES OBEAUX (FR)**, 4, gr g Saint Preuil (FR)—Alpaga (FR) **Mrs N. Devilder**
61 **MINUIT DE COTTE (FR)**, 4, b g Kadalko (FR)—Rafale de Cotte (FR) **Mr R. Fougedoire**
62 **MISTI DU LUC (FR)**, 4, b c Passing Sale (FR)—Utiga du Luc (FR) **Mr C. Dumeau**

MR G. MACAIRE—continued

63 **MITHRIDATE DELAB (FR)**, 4, b g Chamberlin (FR)—Berenice de Frosse (FR) **Mr de la Bassetiere**
64 **MOKA DE L'ISLE (FR)**, 4, ch g Video Rock (FR)—Ceres de L'Isle (FR) **Mrs S. A. Bramall**
65 **MONDESIR DU COCHET (FR)**, 4, b g Rochesson (FR)—Epice du Cochet (FR) **Mrs F. Montauban**
66 **MONT MISERE (FR)**, 8, b g Mont Basile (FR)—Pique Flamme (FR) **Mr A. Chiche**
67 **MORGANE DU BOST (FR)**, 4, gr f Saint Preuil (FR)—Idole du Bost (FR) **Mr H. Morgat**
68 **MUST ORIGNY (FR)**, 4, b br g Sleeping Car (FR)—Coralline (FR) **Mr R. Fougedoire**
69 **MUTIN DE COTTE (FR)**, 4, ch g Iris Noir (FR)—Kariantique (FR) **Mr R. Fougedoire**
70 **MYCENE DE GOLAINE (FR)**, 4, b g Sassannian (USA)—Creole de Cotte (FR) **Mr D. Brooks**
71 **NAGGING (FR)**, 4, b g Nikos—Fassonwest (FR) **Mr D. Massias**
72 **NUIT DES CHARTREUX (FR)**, 4, b f Villez (USA)—Nuit d'Ecajeul (FR) **Mr F. Picoulet**
73 **POSITIVE THINKING (FR)**, 4, b g Nikos—Haute Tension (FR) **Mr J. C. Audry**
74 **PRINCE DES IFS (FR)**, 5, b g Sleeping Car (FR)—Miss Brodie (FR) **Mr R. Fougedoire**
75 **PRINCE TATANE (FR)**, 5, b g Agent Bleu (FR)—Sainte Astrid (FR) **Mrs P. Papot**
76 **RIB PILE (FR)**, 7, b g Garde Royale—Doll Poppy (FR) **Ecurie Rib**
77 **RIGOUREUX (FR)**, 4, b g Villez (USA)—Rouge Folie (FR) **Mr R. Fougedoire**
78 **ROBIN DE NONANT (FR)**, 4, ch c Garde Royale—Relayeuse (FR) **Mr R. Fougedoire**
79 **ROYAL ORIGNY (FR)**, 7, b g Royal Charter (FR)—Force Nine (FR) **Mr R. Fougedoire**
80 **SEPT ET NEUF (FR)**, 4, b g Esprit du Nord (USA)—Peau d'Or (FR) **Mrs F. Montauban**
81 **SHABBY BLUFF (FR)**, 4, b f Poplar Bluff—Shabby Royale (FR) **Mr G. Muller**
82 **SIKI (FR)**, 7, b g Chamberlin (FR)—Cerianthe (FR) **Mr J. Belzung**
83 **SUBEHARGUES (FR)**, 9, b g Mansonnien (FR)—Grande Yepa (FR) **Mr X. Papot**
84 **TEMPO D'OR (FR)**, 6, b g Esprit du Nord (USA)—Peau d'Or (FR) **Mrs F. Montauban**
85 **TILAOS (FR)**, 6, ch g Mansonnien (FR)—Vimosa (FR) **Mr P. de Maleissye**
86 **TORY (FR)**, 4, b g Turgeon (USA)—Fiddlesticks (FR) **Mrs H. Devin**
87 **VAL DU DON (FR)**, 4, b g Garde Royale—Vallee Normanade (FR) **Mr J. Detre**
88 **VESUVE (FR)**, 5, b g Villez (USA)—Razzamatazz (FR) **Mrs H. Devin**
89 **VILA REAL (FR)**, 4, ch f Riverquest (FR)—Mahobette (FR) **Mrs I. Campos**
90 **VINDESROIS (FR)**, 5, b g Saint Cyrien (FR)—Orlight (FR) **Ecurie Guillaume Macaire**
91 **WISCONCIEN (GER)**, 6, b g Colon (GER)—Weinblute (GER) **Mr D. Grimm**

THREE-YEAR-OLDS

92 **AMAZONE DU BERLAIS (FR)**, b f Indian River (FR)—Phedre du Berlais (FR) **Mr C. Cohen**
93 **BANDIT MANCHOT (FR)**, b g Saint Cyrien (FR)—Murakala (FR) **Mr G. Baratoux**
94 **BEN VETO (FR)**, ch g Perrault—Sainte Lea (FR) **Mrs M. Bryant**
95 **CALISSON (FR)**, ro c Mansonnien (FR)—Dona Cali (FR) **Mr O. Delegue**
96 **CARIGNAN (FR)**, b g Garde Royale—Cardoudalle (FR) **Mr R. Fougedoire**
97 **CHEPSTOW (FR)**, b g Marathon (USA)—Sterling Love (FR) **Mr J. C. Audry**
98 **DOLCE DU BERLAIS (FR)**, b f Saint Preuil (FR)—Cadouly (FR) **Mr C. Cohen**
99 **ESPRIT SAINT (FR)**, b g Mansonnien (FR)—Escopette (FR) **Mr R. Fougedoire**
100 **FIRST DE LA BRUNIE (FR)**, ch c Mansonnien (FR)—Samisti (BEL) **Mr D. Chabassier**
101 **HARTANY (GER)**, b c Lavirco (GER)—Harasava (FR) **Mrs F. Montauban**
102 B g Sassanian (USA)—Inherited Lute (IRE) **Palmyr Racing**
103 **KADISCOT (FR)**, b g Perrault—Katicala (FR) **Mrs Vanden Broele**
104 **KAUTO RAY (FR)**, b g Saint Cyrien (FR)—Kautorette (FR) **Mr J. C. Audry**
105 **MADISON DU BERLAIS (FR)**, b g Indian River (FR)—Anais du Berlais (FR) **Mr C. Cohen**
106 **MAPONA (FR)**, ro f Mansonnien (FR)—Epona du Berlais (FR) **Mr G. Ben Lassin**
107 **MEUTAC (FR)**, b c Mansonnien (FR)—La Musardiere (FR) **Haras Du Reuilly**
108 **MOUILLEURDEPONGES (FR)**, b g Saumarez—Royale Flamby (FR) **Mr R. Fougedoire**
109 **MOUSSU LESCRIBAA (FR)**, b g Panoramic—Mona Lisaa (FR) **Mrs F. Montauban**
110 **MY ASADOR (FR)**, ch f Kadounor (FR)—Apos (FR) **Mr J. Detre**
111 **NACHO DES UNCHERES (FR)**, b g Bulington (FR)—Radieuse Gamine (FR) **PB Bloodstock Services**
112 **NARVAL D'AVELOT (FR)**, b g Video Rock (FR)—Reine des Planches (FR) **Mr J. M. Robin**
113 **NECESSAIRE (FR)**, ch f Garde Royale—Nazia (FR) **Mr D. Massias**
114 **NECTAR DES BROSSES (FR)**, b g Epervier Bleu—Suzana des Brosses (FR) **Mrs P. Papot**
115 **NEMOSSUS (FR)**, b g Mont Basile (FR)—Ephyra (FR) **Mr J. M. Robin**
116 **NEOPOLIS (FR)**, ch g Ragmar (FR)—Apside (FR) **Mr R. Fougedoire**
117 **NEWHORSE (FR)**, b g Village Star (FR)—Canonniere (FR) **Mr R. Fougedoire**
118 **NEW ILLUSION (FR)**, b f Solid Illusion (USA)—Madame Nathalie (FR) **Mr Waley-Cohen**
119 **NEWTON D'AVELOT (FR)**, b g Epervier Bleu—Unaria (FR) **Mr J. M. Robin**
120 **NICKEL DU COCHET (FR)**, b g Ambroise (FR)—Diva du Cochet (FR) **Mrs M. Bryant**
121 **NIGHT RIVER (FR)**, b f Garde Royale—Urtica (FR) **Mr R. Y. Simon**
122 **NIKAIDO (FR)**, b g Nikos—Zamsara (FR) **Palmyr Racing**
123 **NIKOSTRATOS (FR)**, b g Nikos—La Voix de La Lune (FR) **Mr O. Delegue**
124 **NINOUCHKA (FR)**, b f Epervier Bleu—Grace de Vonnas (FR) **Mrs M. Bryant**
125 **NOEUD PAPILLON (FR)**, b g Video Rock (FR)—Samara IV (FR) **Mr R. Fougedoire**

MR G. MACAIRE—continued

126 **NOIR SUR BLANC,** ch f Mansonnien (FR)—Echarpe Noir (BRZ) **Mr R. Fougedoire**
127 **NOMINALE (FR),** b f Perrault—Caline de Sienne (FR) **Mrs Vanden Broele**
128 **NOTEZ LE (FR),** gr g Saint Preuil (FR)—Gibelotte (FR) **Mr R. Fougedoire**
129 **NOUVEA (FR),** ch c Perrault—Umea IV (FR) **Mrs S. Bramall**
130 **NOUVELLE DONNE (FR),** b f Sleeping Car (FR)—Nocha (FR) **Mr R. Fougedoire**
131 **NUAGE DE COTTE (FR),** b g Sleeping Car (FR)—Kariantique (FR) **Mr R. Fougedoire**
132 **NUMERO SPECIAL (FR),** b g Nikos—Ribalina (FR) **Mr R. Fougedoire**
133 **PEINTRE CELESTE (FR),** b g Cricket Ball (USA)—Harmonie Celeste (FR) **Mr R. Fougedoire**
134 **REXLOR (FR),** b g Port Lyautey (FR)—Isle du Tresor (FR) **Mr R. Fougedoire**
135 **SAMANSONNIENNE (FR),** ch f Mansonnien (FR)—Sanhia (FR) **Mr O. Delegue**
136 **TALYSKER,** b g Cadoudal (FR)—Miss Amande (FR) **Mr J. Cotton**
137 **TIKI DE LUNE (FR),** gr g Cadoudal (FR)—Tikidoune (FR) **Mr R. W. Denechere**
138 **TYSSAC (FR),** ch g Beyssac (FR)—Aktia (FR) **Mr A. M. Chiche**
139 **VOY POR USTEDES (FR),** b g Villez (USA)—Nuit d'Ecajeul (FR) **Mr F. Picoulet**
140 **WESTOS (FR),** b g Nikos—Fassonwest (FR) **Mr J. C. Audry**

TWO-YEAR-OLDS

141 **BAODAI (FR),** b c 13/5 Cadoudal (FR)—Royale Aube (FR) (Garde Royale) (10513) **Mr J. C. Audry**
142 **CRIDAC (FR),** b f 8/5 Cadoudal (FR)—Criade (FR) (Maiymad) **Mrs B. Gabeur**
143 **CROISETTE (FR),** ch f 26/3 Mansonnien (FR)—Fouinette (FR) (Azimut (FR)) **Mrs B. Gabeur**
144 **DAVENTRY,** b c 26/3 Kahyasi—Perfect Sister (USA) (Perrault) **Mr J. Detre**
145 **GOOD SPIRIT (FR),** b c 25/3 Smadoum (FR)—Haute Tension (FR) (Garde Royale) **Mr J. C. Audry**
146 **MOON SIR (GER),** b c 21/2 Surako (GER)—Moonlit Water (Rainbow Quest (USA)) (12368) **Mr R. Fougedoire**
147 **OBLAT PIERJI (FR),** b c 18/3 Epervier Bleu—Fanfare (FR) (Turgeon (USA)) (8039) **Mrs P. Papot**
148 **OCEANY (FR),** b c 18/2 Mansonnien (FR)—Infancy (FR) (Highlanders (FR)) **Mrs M. Bryant**
149 **OISEAU BAI (FR),** b c 31/3 Cadoudal (FR)—Biolaine (FR) (Iron Duke (FR)) (11750) **Mrs P. Papot**
150 **OLD WHISKY (FR),** b c 15/5 Epervier Bleu—Vodka Tonique (FR) (Quart de Vin (FR)) **Mr M. Froissard**
151 **ONIX (FR),** ch c 3/4 Ragmar (FR)—Hase (FR) (Video Rock (FR)) **Mr M. Bessis**
152 **ORGUEUIL DES DIMES (FR),** b c 30/3 Rahotep (FR)—Fiduciaire (FR) (Pamponi (FR)) (2350) **Mrs F. Montauban**
153 **OVOMALTHINE (FR),** b f 30/4 Saint Preuil (FR)—Friandise II (FR) (Mistigri (IRE)) **Mr J. C. Audry**
154 **OWARD (FR),** b c 3/4 Mansonnien (FR)—Violette d'Avril (FR) (Olmeto (IRE)) **Mr J. C. Audry**
155 **PRIMEIRA (GER),** ch f 10/4 Acatenango (GER)—Pretty Blue (GER) (Bluebird (USA)) (12368) **Mrs F. Montauban**
156 **RICH ROMEO (GER),** b c 30/3 Greinton—Richgorl (GER) (Neshad (USA)) (6184) **Mr J. Detre**
157 **SENSUALITE (FR),** ch f 14/4 Mansonnien (FR)—Creme Pralinee (FR) (Kashtan (FR)) **Mr R. Y. Simon**
158 **STOWAY (FR),** b c 16/3 Broadway Flyer (USA)—Stowe (FR) (Garde Royale) (9276) **Mr J. Detre**
159 **TITITONI (FR),** b c 23/3 Nikos—Fassonwest (FR) (Dom Pasquini (FR)) **Mr J. C. Audry**
160 **TWIST MAGIC (FR),** b c 20/4 Winged Love (IRE)—Twist Scarlett (GER) (Lagunas) (5875) **Mrs F. Montauban**
161 **VILLENTIN (FR),** b c 14/2 Villez (USA)—Cadence Vite (FR) (Cadoudal (FR)) (2473) **Mr J. Detre**
162 **VINTOX (GER),** b c 8/2 Oxalagu (GER)—Vinca (GER) (King of Macedon) **Mrs F. Montauban**

Jockeys (NH): Benoit Gicquel (9-0), Jacques Ricou (9-0). **Amateur:** Mr Adam Jones (9-0).

---

352 MRS N. J. MACAULEY, Melton Mowbray

Postal: **The Sidings, Saltby Road, Sproxton, Melton Mowbray, Leicestershire, LE14 4RA.**
Contact: **HOME (01476) 860578 OFFICE 860090 FAX 860611 MOBILE (07741) 004444**

1 **AIR MAIL,** 7, b g Night Shift (USA)—Wizardry **West Indies Capital Company Limited**
2 **BETTER OFF,** 6, ch g Bettergeton—Miami Pride **Classic Glass and Dishwashing Systems Lt**
3 **COMETE DU LAC (FR),** 7, ch m Comte du Bourg (FR)—Line du Nord (FR) **Mr Andy Peake**
4 **DIL,** 9, b g Primo Dominie—Swellegant **Mrs N. Macauley**
5 **FIENNES (USA),** 6, b br g Dayjur—Artic Strech (USA) **Mrs N. Macauley**
6 **FIRST EAGLE,** 5, b g Hector Protector (USA)—Merlin's Fancy **Mrs N. Macauley**
7 **ILLUSIONIST,** 6, b g Mujtahid (USA)—Merlin's Fancy **The Whiskey Macs**
8 **MAWHOOB (USA),** 6, gr g Dayjur (USA)—Asl (USA) **Mrs N. Macauley**
9 **MI ODDS,** 8, b g Sure Blade (USA)—Vado Via **Tic-Tac.com**
10 **MOON ROYALE,** 6, ch m Royal Abjar (USA)—Ragged Moon **Mr B. Batey**
11 **OCKER (IRE),** 10, br g Astronef—Violet Somers **Mrs N. Macauley**
12 **ON THE LEVEL,** 5, ch m Beveled (USA)—Join The Clan **Mr J. Redden**
13 **PUP'S PRIDE,** 7, b g Efisio—Moogie **West Indies Capital Company Limited**
14 **ROPPONGI DANCER,** 5, b m Mtoto—Ice Chocolate (USA) **Mr Andy Peake**
15 **SILVER CRYSTAL (IRE),** 4, b f Among Men (USA)—Silver Moon **Mrs Liz Nelson**
16 **SORBIESHARRY (IRE),** 5, gr g Sorbie Tower (FR)—Silver Moon **Mrs Liz Nelson**
17 **SPANISH STAR,** 7, b g Hernando—Desert Girl **Mrs N. Macauley**
18 **ST IVIAN,** 4, b g Inchinor—Lamarita **Mr Godfrey Horsford**

MRS N. J. MACAULEY—continued

19 **STORM SHOWER (IRE)**, 6, b g Catrail (USA)—Crimson Shower **Mrs J. Batey**
20 **SWEET AROMA**, 5, b m Bedford (USA)—Tango Country **Mrs N. Macauley**
21 **TAPAGE (IRE)**, 8, b g Great Commotion (USA)—Irena **Mrs N. Macauley**
22 **TEYAAR**, 8, b g Polar Falcon (USA)—Music In My Life (IRE) **Mr Justin R. Aaron**
23 **WESTERN COMMAND (GER)**, 8, b g Saddlers' Hall (IRE)—Western Friend (USA) **Mr Andy Peake**

THREE-YEAR-OLDS

24 **ATLANTIC BREEZE**, br f Deploy—Atlantic Air **Mr Richard Underwood**
25 **GOLNESSA**, b f Pyramus (USA)—My Pretty Niece **Mr Richard Underwood**
26 **MARIA MARIA (IRE)**, ch f Among Men (USA)—Yiayia's Girl **Mrs Liz Nelson**
27 **MYSTIC PROMISE (IRE)**, gr g Among Men (USA)—Ivory's Promise **Mrs Liz Nelson**

Other Owners: Mrs N. M. Cooper.

Jockey (Flat): A Culhane (w.a.). **Apprentices:** S Harrison (8-0), L Jones (w.a.). **Amateur:** Mrs M Morris (9-8).

---

353   MR W. J. W. MACKIE, Church Broughton
Postal: **The Bungalow, Barton Blount, Church Broughton, Derby, DE65 5AN.**
Contact: PHONE (01283) 585604/585603 FAX (01283) 585603 MOBIE (07799) 145283
E-MAIL jmackie@bartonblount.freeserve.co.uk

1 **ACCEPTING**, 7, b g Mtoto—d'Azy **Mr M. T. Bloore & Mrs J. E. Lockwood**
2 **AMY LEWIS**, 6, b m Sir Harry Lewis (USA)—Trecento **Mr F. A. Dickinson**
3 **BOLSHOI BALLET**, 6, b g Dancing Spree (USA)—Broom Isle **The M. A. S. Partnership**
4 **BRAVO**, 6, b br g Efisio—Apache Squaw **Mr Paul D. Leech**
5 **CELEBRE BLU**, 7, b g Suave Dancer (USA)—Taufan Blu (IRE) **Mr Tim Kelly**
6 **DANEBANK (IRE)**, 4, b g Danehill (USA)—Snow Bank (IRE)
7 **GUARDED SECRET**, 7, gr g Mystiko (USA)—Fen Dance (IRE) **Mr Peter McMahon**
8 **HADITOVSKI**, 8, b g Hatim (USA)—Grand Occasion **Mrs Sue Adams**
9 **HAVING A PARTY**, 6, b m Dancing High—Lady Manello **Mrs Linda Court**
10 **HIGH RANK**, 5, b g Emperor Jones (USA)—Hotel Street (USA) **Trying to Buy Fun Partnership**
11 **HOT PRODUXION (USA)**, 5, ch g Tabasco Cat (USA)—Princess Harriet (USA) **Mr A. J. Winterton**
12 **IMPISH JUDE**, 6, b m Imp Society (USA)—Miss Nanna **Mr J. W. H. Fryer**
13 **JEROPINO (IRE)**, 6, b g Norwich—Guillig Lady (IRE) **Mr J. White**
14 **KATIE SAVAGE**, 4, b f Emperor Jones (USA)—Coax Me Molly (USA) **A League of 4 English Gentlemen**
15 **KING JAMES**, 7, b g Homo Sapien—Bowling Fort **Mr A. J. Wall**
16 **KNOCK LORD (IRE)**, 7, b g Mister Lord (USA)—Sister Duke **Mr M. J. Parr**
17 **MAMBOESQUE (USA)**, 6, b g Miesque's Son (USA)—Brawl (USA) **Mr F. E. and Mrs J. J. Brindley**
18 **MEAD (IRE)**, 7, b g Mujadil (USA)—Sweetest Thing (IRE) **Lyonshall Racing**
19 **MERCURIOUS (IRE)**, 4, ch f Grand Lodge (USA)—Rousinette **Gwen K. Dot.Com**
20 **PARK LANE BILLIE**, 4, b f Double Eclipse (IRE)—Kathy's Role **Mrs Nigel Batho**
21 **REACHFORTHESTARS**, 8, b m Royal Fountain—China's Way (USA) **Fools Who Dream**
22 **RED SUN**, 7, b g Foxhound (USA)—Superetta **Bulls Head Racing Club**
23 **RIO REAL (IRE)**, 8, b g Case Law—Fine Flame
24 **SILK TRADER**, 9, b g Nomadic Way (USA)—Money Run **The Festival Dream Partnership**
25 **SIPOWITZ**, 10, b g Warrshan (USA)—Springs Welcome **Mrs J. Mackie**
26 **SPEED VENTURE**, 7, b g Owington—Jade Venture **Wall Racing Partners**
27 **STATION ISLAND (IRE)**, 7, ch g Roselier (FR)—Sweet Tulip **Mr J. S. Harlow**

Other Owners: Mr S. P. Adams, Mr R. O. Addis, Mr M. A. Bates, Mr M. T. Bloore, Mr F. E. Brindley, Mrs J. J. Brindley, Mr Ron Coleman, Mr John Dickson, Mr D. J. Emsley, Mr J. J. Finnegan, Mr Arnie Flower, Mr W. J. Furmage, Mr N. R. Jennings, Mr Robin Jones, Mr P. Joynson, Mr T. P. Keville, Mrs Jill Lockwood, Mr Andy Miller, Mr Matthew Morgan, Mr R. E. Savage, Mr S. Wade, Mr C. J. Wall, Mr R. T. Wall, Mrs S. J. Woolley, Mr R. J. Wright.

Conditional: Richard Gordon (9-4). **Amateur:** Mr Nick Pettit (10-0).

---

354   MR A. B. MACTAGGART, Hawick
Postal: **Greendale, Hawick, Roxburghshire, TD9 7LH.**
Contact: PHONE (01450) 372086 FAX (01450) 372086 MOBILE (077764) 159852/(07718) 920072
E-MAIL brucemct@btinternet.co.uk

1 **CISCO**, 6, b g Shambo—School Run **Mr Graeme Renton**
2 **CONOR'S PRIDE (IRE)**, 7, ch g Phardante (FR)—Surely Madam **HARLEQUIN RACING**

MR A. B. MACTAGGART—continued

3 **CORBIE ABBEY (IRE)**, 9, b g Glacial Storm—Dromoland Lady **Mrs Hilary Mactaggart**
4 **CRUMBS**, 4, b f Puissance—Norska **In The Pink Syndicate**
5 **DANTE'S BROOK (IRE)**, 10, ch g Phardante (FR)—Arborfield Brook **B. & J. Jeffrey**
6 **DEVINE LIGHT (IRE)**, 4, b f Spectrum (IRE)—Siskin (IRE) **Mr Graeme Renton**
7 **EYZE (IRE)**, 8, b g Lord Americo—Another Raheen (IRE) **Stoneage Paving**
8 **FRANCIS FLUTE**, 6, b g Polar Falcon (USA)—Darshay (FR) **Boots & Saddles Partnership**
9 **KING OF THE CASTLE (IRE)**, 9, b g Cataldi—Monashuna **The Potassium Partnership**
10 **LADY GODSON**, 5, ch m Bold Arrangement—Dreamy Desire **Mr B. Mactaggart**
11 **MOUNTHOOLEY**, 8, ch g Karinga Bay—Gladys Emmanuel **Ashleybank Investments Limited**
12 **OLD NOSEY (IRE)**, 8, b g Muharib (USA)—Regent Star **Potassium Partnership**
13 **OPAL'S HELMSMAN (USA)**, 5, b g Helmsman (USA)—Opal's Notebook (USA) **Mrs I. A. Forrest**
14 **THE BISCUIT**, 10, ch m Nomadic Way (USA)—Not To Worry (USA) **K. Bruce**

THREE-YEAR-OLDS

15 **CORRYONG**, ch f Wolfhound (USA)—Easy Risk **Mrs S. R. Kennedy**
16 B f Mister Lord (USA)—Craic Go Leor **B. MacTaggart**
17 **OSCAR MADISON (IRE)**, b g Petorius—She's Our Lady (IRE) **Stirling Racing Scotland**
18 **THE FOX'S HEAD (IRE)**, b f Imperial Ballet (IRE)—Lovely Leitrim (IRE) **Miss E. Johnston**

TWO-YEAR-OLDS

19 Ch g 31/3 Double Trigger (IRE)—Setter Country (Town And Country) **Mr W. B. MacTaggart**

Other Owners: Mr H. G. Beeby, Mr D. Lamb.

Assistant Trainer: Mrs H Mactaggart

Jockeys (NH): A Dempsey (10-0, w.a.), G Lee (10-0, w.a.).

---

355 MR A. H. MACTAGGART, Hawick
Postal: **Wells, Denholm, Hawick, Roxburghshire, TD9 8TD.**
Contact: **PHONE (01450) 870060 MOBILE (07711) 200445**

1 **CRANBORNE (IRE)**, 7, b m King's Ride—Random Wind **Mr A. H. Mactaggart**
2 5, B m Primitive Rising (USA)—Olive Branch **Mr A. H. Mactaggart**
3 **RUNNING MOSS**, 12, ch g Le Moss—Run'n Fly **Mrs A. H. Mactaggart**
4 **THE BYEDEIN (IRE)**, 7, b m Alflora (IRE)—Southern Squaw **Mr A. H. Mactaggart**

Assistant Trainer: Mrs M A Mactaggart

Amateurs: Mr J Mactaggart (11-7), Mr C Storey (10-3).

---

356 MR M. J. MADGWICK, Denmead
Postal: **Forest Farm, Forest Road, Denmead, Waterlooville, Hampshire, PO7 6UA.**
Contact: **PHONE (02392) 258313 FAX (02392) 258313 MOBILE (07790) 960406**

1 **CAPTAIN CLOUDY**, 4, b g Whittingham (IRE)—Money Supply **The Portsmouth Syndicate**
2 **ELLE ROSEADOR**, 5, b m El Conquistador—The Hon Rose **Mrs Monica Yates**
3 **I WISH**, 6, ch m Beveled (USA)—Ballystate **Mrs Gail Gaisford**
4 **KARIBEE**, 4, b f Karinga Bay—Jaydeebee **Mr J. D. Brownrigg**
5 **LOCH LAIRD**, 9, b g Beveled (USA)—Daisy Loch **Miss E. M. L. Coller**
6 **MAXIMINUS**, 4, b g The West (USA)—Candarela **Mr M. Madgwick**
7 **MOMENTOUS JONES**, 7, b g Emperor Jones (USA)—Ivory Moment (USA) **Mr W. V. Roker**
8 **SHARP SEAL**, 10, b g Broadsword (USA)—Little Beaver **Mr M. Madgwick**
9 **SWEET MINUET**, 7, b m Minshaanshu Amad (USA)—Sweet N' Twenty **Mr W. E. Baird**
10 **SWEET SHOOTER**, 4, ch f Double Trigger (IRE)—Sweet N' Twenty **Mr W. E. Baird**
11 **WAVERLEY ROAD**, 7, ch g Pelder (IRE)—Lillicara (FR) **All Four Corners**

THREE-YEAR-OLDS

12 **OAKLEY PRINCE**, ch g Bluegrass Prince (IRE)—Susie Oakley VII **Mr John Gregory**

MR M. J. MADGWICK—continued

TWO-YEAR-OLDS

13 Ch c 18/3 Fumo Di Londra (IRE)—Ballystate (Ballacashtal (CAN)) **Mrs Gail Gaisford**
14 **BLUE LINE**, gr f 5/4 Bluegrass Prince—Out Line (Beveled (USA)) **Miss E. M. L. Coller**

Other Owners: Mr F. W. J. Buckett, Mr R. C. Denton, Mrs E. J. Harton-Carter, Mr G. E. Heard.

Assistant Trainer: David Madgwick

Jockeys (Flat): M Fenton (8-0), T Quinn (8-0). **Jockey (NH):** J Goldstein.

---

357 MR M. A. MAGNUSSON, Upper Lambourn
Postal: **The Old Manor, Upper Lambourn, Hungerford, Berkshire, RG17 8RG.**
Contact: **OFFICE (01488) 73966 MOBILE (07775) 556306 E-MAIL mikael.magnusson@virgin.net**

1 **BACK IN ACTION**, 4, b c Hector Protector (USA)—Lucca **East Wind Racing Ltd**
2 **MANORSON (IRE)**, 5, ch h Desert King (USA)—Familiar (USA) **East Wind Racing Ltd**
3 **MUTAWAQED (IRE)**, 6, ch g Zafonic (USA)—Waqood (USA) **East Wind Racing Ltd**
4 **SIERRA NEVADA (IRE)**, 4, ch f Lake Coniston (IRE)—Spirit Lake (GER) **East Wind Racing Ltd**

THREE-YEAR-OLDS

5 **IN EVERY STREET (USA)**, br f Favorite Trick (USA)—Hit The Bid (USA) **Mr Alain Falourd**
6 **KEHAAR**, ch c Cadeaux Genereux—Lighthouse **East Wind Racing Ltd**
7 **KHALIDIA (USA)**, b c Boundary (USA)—Maniches Slew (USA) **East Wind Racing Ltd**
8 **RUSSIAN CAFE (IRE)**, b f Stravinsky (USA)—Bistro (USA) **East Wind Racing Ltd**
9 **UNAVAILABLE (IRE)**, b f Alzao (USA)—Maid of Killeen (IRE) **East Wind Racing Ltd**
10 **UNITED SPIRIT (IRE)**, b f Fasliyev (USA)—Atlantic Desire (IRE) **East Wind Racing Ltd**

TWO-YEAR-OLDS

11 Ch f 26/3 Silver Hawk (USA)—Copper Cachet (USA) (Sheikh Albadou) (170000) **East Wind Racing Ltd**
12 Ch c 12/3 Sinndar (IRE)—Demure (Machiavellian (USA)) (61842) **East Wind Racing Ltd**
13 B f 23/4 Sadler's Wells (USA)—Filia Ardross (Ardross) (330000) **East Wind Racing Ltd**
14 Ch c 10/2 Bluebird (USA)—Highly Respected (IRE) (High Estate) (49474) **East Wind Racing Ltd**
15 B c 17/3 Entrepreneur—Hilbys Brite Flite (USA) (Cormorant (USA)) (16697) **East Wind Racing Ltd**

Other Owners: Mrs Mette Campbell-Andenaes, Mr Robert Trussell.

---

358 MR P. J. MAKIN, Marlborough
Postal: **Bonita Racing Stables, Ogbourne Maisey, Marlborough, Wiltshire, SN8 1RY.**
Contact: **PHONE (01672) 512973 FAX (01672) 514166 E-MAIL hq@petermakin-racing.com**

1 **BLUEBERRY RHYME**, 5, b g Alhijaz—Irenic **Mrs P. J. Makin**
2 **CALENDAR GIRL (IRE)**, 4, b f Revoque (IRE)—March Fourteenth (USA) **Mr D. A. Poole**
3 **CANTERLOUPE (IRE)**, 6, b m Wolfhound (USA)—Missed Again **R. A. Ballin & The Billinomas**
4 **GEMMA**, 4, b f Petong—Gem **Mr T. G. Warner**
5 **GREENSLADES**, 5, ch h Perugino (USA)—Woodfield Rose **Four Seasons Racing Ltd**
6 **GUNNHILDR (IRE)**, 4, ch f In Command (IRE)—Queen Canute (IRE) **Lady Davis**
7 **INCH BY INCH**, 5, b m Inchinor—Maid Welcome **Mrs Anna L. Sanders**
8 **LIBERTY ROYAL**, 5, b g Ali-Royal (IRE)—Hope Chest **T. W. Wellard & Partners**
9 **NATHAN DETROIT**, 4, b c Entrepreneur—Mainly Sunset **Mrs J. Carrington**
10 **NOT SO DUSTY**, 4, b g Primo Dominie—Ann's Pearl (IRE) **Mrs Paul Levinson**
11 **OVAMBO (IRE)**, 6, b g Namaqualand (USA)—Razana (IRE) **Mr R. A. Henley**
12 **PERFECT SETTING**, 4, b g Polish Precedent (USA)—Diamond Park (IRE) **Mrs P. J. Makin**
13 **PIVOTAL POINT**, 4, b g Pivotal—True Precision **Mr R. A. Bernard**
14 **POINT OF DISPUTE**, 9, b g Cyrano de Bergerac—Opuntia **Mrs B. J. Carrington**
15 **STRIKE LUCKY**, 4, ch g Millkom—Lucky Flinders **Mrs P. J. Makin**
16 **TICKLE**, 6, b m Primo Dominie—Funny Choice (IRE) **Mrs Derek Strauss**

THREE-YEAR-OLDS

17 **BLACK SABBETH**, br c Desert Story (IRE)—Black Orchid (IRE) **Mr M. H. Holland**
18 **EMPIRE OF THE SUN**, b f Second Empire (IRE)—Splicing **The Highly Sociable Syndicate**
19 **HEAVENS WALK**, ch c Compton Place—Ghost Dancing **Mrs P. J. Makin**

MR P. J. MAKIN—continued

20 **MAXI'S PRINCESS (IRE),** b f Revouge (IRE)—Harmer (IRE) **Weldspec Glasgow Limited**
21 B f Norton Challenger—Minya Konka **Mrs V. Stockdale**
22 **ROCKLEY BAY (IRE),** b c Mujadil (USA)—Kilkee Bay (IRE) **John Gale & George Darling**
23 **SOUL DANCE,** b f Imperial Ballet (IRE)—Piccante **Mrs P. J. Makin**
24 **WATAMU (IRE),** b c Groom Dancer (USA)—Miss Golden Sands **Mr R. A. Henley**
25 **WOLFF TRACK,** b g Imperial Ballet (IRE)—She-Wolff (IRE) **Mr P. J. Makin**

TWO-YEAR-OLDS

26 Ch c 15/3 Dr Fong (USA)—Azola (IRE) (Alzao (USA)) (18000) **D. M. Ahier, R.P. Marchant**
27 **CASEMATE,** b c 30/3 Efisio—Flying Carpet (Barathea (IRE)) (30000) **Four Seasons Racing**
28 B c 3/1 In The Wings—Comprehension (USA) (Diesis) (8000) **Weldspec Glasgow Ltd**
29 **FONG SHUI,** ch c 13/3 Dr Fong (USA)—
               Manila Selection (USA) (Manila (USA)) (8000) **Camermile Hessert Scott Partnership**
30 B c 13/5 Kayf Tara—Ghost Dancing (Lion Cavern (USA))
31 Ch c 4/4 Loup Sauvage (USA)—Goodwood Lass (IRE) (Alzao (USA)) (2500) **Ten Of Hearts**
32 **JOHN BRATBY,** b c 1/3 Royal Academy (USA)—Side Saddle (IRE) (Saddler's Hall (IRE)) (23000) **Julian Hartnoll**
33 **KINRANDE (IRE),** b c 23/1 Sri Pekan (USA)—
               Pipers Pool (IRE) (Mtoto) (27210) **R.P.Marchant, D.M.Ahler & J.P.Carrington**
34 B c 23/3 Halling (USA)—Mavura (Bering)
35 Ch f 25/3 Bold Edge—Piccante (Wolfhound (USA))
36 B c 17/3 Pennekamp (USA)—Poker Chip (Bluebird (USA)) (20000) **J.P.Carrington, D.M.Ahier, R.P.Marchant**
37 Ch c 13/2 Bold Fact (USA)—Voodoo Rocket (Lycius (USA)) (7420) **Julian Hartnoll**
38 **ZIPADEEDOODAH,** b c 15/3 Bluebird (USA)—
               River Divine (USA) (Irish River (FR)) (8000) **Lady David, Beryl Lake,Richard Simmonds**

Other Owners: Gordon Bear, Mrs P. Blackmore, Mr James Blackshaw, Mrs Belinda Boyd, Mr Brian Brackpool, Mr David Brocklehurst, Mr J. Burke, Mr R. Byron-Scott, Mr J. R. Cleeve, Mr George Darling, Mr H. R. Dobinson, Mr J. K. Gale, Mr D. J. Holding, Mr A. C. D. Hollingworth, Mr G. F. Johnstone, Mr K. Kent, Mrs B. Kingham, Mr Peter Lycett, Mr Peter Melotti, Mr S. J. Messer, Mr Nick Pearce, Mr R. G. Percival, Mr E. John Perry, Mr Leigh Rosen, Mr Ian T. Smethurst, Mrs M. Townsend, Mr T. W. Wellard.

Jockeys (Flat): A Clark, S Sanders, D Sweeney. **Apprentice:** L McVicar. **Amateur:** Mr S Walker.

---

359 **MRS ALYSON MALZARD, Jersey**
Postal: **Mon Repos, Grosnez, St Ouen, Jersey, JE3 2AD.**
Contact: **PHONE (01534) 483773 MOBILE (07797) 738128 E-MAIL themalzards@localdial.com**

1 **CROSSWAYS,** 6, b g Mister Baileys—Miami Dancer (USA) **Mr & Mrs T. Gallienne**
2 **NOBLE REEF,** 7, b g Deploy—Penny Mint **Mrs A. Malzard**
3 **PALALA RIVER,** 11, ch m Colmore Row—Express Edition **Miss J. Edgar & Mr J. Mercier**
4 **REGAL ALI (IRE),** 5, ch g Ali-Royal—Depeche (FR) **Mr N. G. Ahier**
5 **TIME TO WYN,** 8, b g Timeless Times (USA)—Wyn-Bank **Westward Racing**
6 **UNVEIL,** 6, ch m Rudimentary (USA)—Magical Veil **Mr R. Theaker**
7 **WARRIORS PATH (IRE),** 5, b g Namaqualand (USA)—Azinter (USA) **Mr B. Le Prevost & Ms O. Liepina**

Jockeys (Flat): Simon Elliot (9-5), Ross Studholme (8-12). **Jockeys (NH):** Simon Elliot (9-7), Ross Studholme (9-7).
Amateurs: Mr D Cuthbert (10-0), Mrs G Poingdestre (8-0).

---

360 **MR JAMES J. MANGAN, Mallow**
Postal: **Curraheen, Conna, Mallow, Co. Cork, Ireland.**
Contact: **PHONE + 353 (0) 058 59116 MOBILE + 353 (0) 087 2684611**

1 **ASTOUGHASOLDBOOTS (IRE),** 5, b g m Oscar (IRE)—Island Champion (IRE) **Kirbys Olde Brogue Syndicate**
2 **CARMELS COTTAGE (IRE),** 6, b m Riberetto—Shoubad Melody **Mary Mangan**
3 **DEPUTY FAIRFAX,** 6, b g Posen (USA)—Rainbow Gurriers (IRE) **Mr Daniel Lynch**
4 **MILL BANK,** 9, b g Millfontaine—Mossy Bank (IRE) **The Maddock Syndicate**
5 **MONTY'S PASS (IRE),** 11, b g Montalimere—Friars Pass **Dee Racing Syndicate**
6 **SEE MORE BILLS,** 9, b g Seymour Hicks (FR)—Squawbil **Mary Mangan**
7 **SIGMA DOTCOMM (IRE),** 8, b g Safety Catch (USA)—Dream Academy **Sigma Communications**
8 **SINK IT (IRE),** 6, b m Executive Perk—Left Hand Woman **Mr Ian Hannon**
9 **SUBERLETTE (IRE),** 6, b m Supreme Leader—Helenium Gale **Mr Patrick Fitzgerald**
10 **TOMMY'S TOY,** 6, b m Norwich—Righthand Lady **Mac's For The Craie Syndicate**

Assistant Trainer: Mary Mangan

361 **MR C. J. MANN, Upper Lambourn**

Postal: **Whitcoombe House Stables, Maddle Road, Upper Lambourn, Hungerford, Berkshire, RG17 8RA.**
Contact: **PHONE (01488) 71717/73118 FAX (01488) 73223 MOBILE (07721) 888333**
E-MAIL charlie.mann@virgin.net

1 ABBOT, 6, b g Bishop of Cashel—Gifted **Abbott Racing Limited**
2 AFRO MAN, 6, b g Commanche Run—Lady Elle (IRE) **J. E. Brown, E. Good & R. Lucas**
3 ALLUDE (IRE), 5, b g Darshaan—Ahliyat (USA) **Abbott Racing Limited**
4 ALVAREZ, 7, b g Gran Alba (USA)—Glorious Jane **Mr Maxwell Morrison**
5 AMICELLI (GER), 5, br g Goofalik (USA)—Arratonia (GER) **Mr Jack Joseph**
6 AMMONIAS (GER), 5, b h Monsun (GER)—Augreta (GER) **Mr J. E. Brown & Mr P. Randall**
7 ANALOGY (IRE), 4, ch g Bahhare (USA)—Anna Comnena (USA) **Mr Hugh Villiers**
8 ANTONINE, 4, ch g Selkirk (USA)—Evrsince (USA) **Mr John Hersey-Walker**
9 BELCARO (GER), 5, br g Dashing Blade—Bella Carolina (USA) **Lee Bolingbroke & Partners III**
10 CELIBATE (IRE), 13, ch g Shy Groom (USA)—Dance Alone (USA) **Stamford Bridge Partnership**
11 CYRIUM (IRE), 5, b g Woodborough (USA)—Jarmar Moon **Colin and Pauline Sturgeon**
12 DAD'S ELECT (GER), 5, b g Lomitas—Diamond Lake (USA) **Mr A. L. R. Morton**
13 DARDANUS, 6, ch g Komaite (USA)—Dance On A Cloud (USA) **M. J. & C. G. Cruddace**
14 DEMI BEAU, 6, b g Dr Devious (IRE)—Charming Life (NZ) **Mr Hugh Villiers**
15 DEVIL'S TEARDROP, 4, ch g Hernando (FR)—River Divine (USA)
16 DOUBLE ACCOUNT (FR), 9, b g Sillery (USA)—Fabulous Account (USA) **M. J. & C. G. Cruddace**
17 DUNSTON BILL, 10, b g Sizzling Melody—Fardella (ITY) **All For One and One For All Partnership**
18 ETERNAL NIGHT (FR), 8, b g Night Shift (USA)—Echoes of Eternity (USA) **Mr Martin Myers**
19 FAMOUS GROUSE, 4, b g Selkirk (USA)—Shoot Clear **Mr Martin Myers**
20 FERZAO (IRE), 7, b g Alzao (USA)—Fer de Lance (IRE) **Mr Derek Crowson**
21 FLINDERS CHASE, 9, gr g Terimon—Proverbial Rose **Mr P. M. Warren**
22 GAORA BRIDGE (IRE), 6, b g Warcraft (USA)—Miss Good Night **Mr Robert Tompkins & Mrs Lynda Lovell**
23 GOLDSEAM (GER), 5, gr g Neshad (USA)—Goldkatze (GER) **M. Rowland & B. Beacham**
24 GOLD SUMMERLAND (HOL), 6, b m Learn By Heart (USA)—Sabara Raaphorst (HOL) **The Dunnkirk Partnership**
25 GOOD SHUIL (IRE), 9, b g Good Thyne (USA)—Shuil Run **R.Newsholme D.Gorton F.Wilson & B.Walsh**
26 HANDA ISLAND (USA), 5, br g Pleasant Colony (USA)—Remote (USA) **Lee Bolingbroke & Partners I**
27 HEY BOY (IRE), 5, b g Courtship—Make Me An Island
28 HOH VISS, 4, b g Rudimentary (USA)—Now And Forever (IRE) **Mr D. F. Allport**
29 ILIOS, 5, b g Grand Lodge (USA)—Ilanga (IRE)
30 INFIDEL (IRE), 4, b g Spectrum (IRE)—Implicit View
31 INVESTMENT FORCE (IRE), 6, b g Imperial Frontier (USA)—
Superb Investment (IRE) **The Whitcoombe Partnership**
32 ISTANBUL (IRE), 5, b g Revoque (IRE)—Song of The Glens **The Second Scrubbers Partnership**
33 JOLLY JOHN (IRE), 13, b g Jolly Jake (NZ)—Golden Seekers **Mrs C. J. Mann**
34 KELTIC BARD, 7, b g Emperor Jones (USA)—Broughton Singer (IRE) **M. Rowland, M. Collins & P. Cox**
35 KING SUMMERLAND, 7, b h Minshaanshu Amad (USA)—Alaskan Princess (IRE) **The Safest Syndicate**
36 LADY LOLA (IRE), 6, b m Supreme Leader—Regents Prancer **Simon Moyes & Charlie Mann**
37 LAWZ (IRE), 10, br g Lahib (USA)—Sea Port **Mr A. L. R. Morton**
38 MERCHANTS FRIEND (IRE), 9, b g Lord Americo—Buck Maid **Magic Moments**
39 MOTCOMB JAM (IRE), 7, b g Frimaire—Flying Flo Jo (USA) **Bix Racers**
40 MR FERNET, 7, b g Mtoto—Francfurter
41 MYSTIC FOREST, 5, b g Charnwood Forest (IRE)—Mystic Beauty (IRE) **Lee Bolingbroke & Partners II**
42 NATHOS (GER), 7, b g Zaizoom (USA)—Nathania (GER) **John Davies & John Trickett**
43 NATIVETRIAL (IRE), 9, ch g Be My Native (USA)—Protrial **Mrs P. Dodd, Mr & Mrs Mark Hunter**
44 POLAR SCOUT (IRE), 7, b g Arctic Lord—Baden (IRE) **Mrs L. G. Turner**
45 PROPER SQUIRE (USA), 7, b g Bien Bien (USA)—La Cumbre **The Icy Fire Partnership**
46 REGAL ACT (IRE), 8, ch g Montelimar (USA)—Portal Lady **M. Rowland & B. Beacham**
47 REGAL HOLLY, 9, b m Gildoran—Pusey Street **Dr David Harris & Mr Peter Simpson**
48 REGAL VISION (IRE), 7, b g Emperor Jones (USA)—Shining Eyes (USA) **The Whitcoombe Partnership**
49 RIVER PILOT, 10, b g Unfuwain (USA)—Cut Ahead **Mr Terry Grove**
50 ROTHERAM (USA), 4, b g Dynaformer (USA)—Out of Taxes (USA)
51 SCULPTOR, 5, b g Salse (USA)—Classic Colleen (IRE) **Magic Moments**
52 SHOWPIECE, 6, b g Selkirk (USA)—Hawayah (IRE) **C. S. G. Limited**
53 SIR LUPIN, 9, gr g Scallywag—Sentimental Me **The Whitcoombe Partnership 2**
54 SLYBOOTS (GER), 5, gr g Neshad (USA)—Shanice (USA)
55 SOUL, 7, b g Jurado (USA)—Pachamama **E. Quinn, J. Riordan & M. Lynn**
56 SPECIAL AGENDA (IRE), 10, b g Torus—Easter Blade (IRE) **The Safest Syndicate**
57 SUPREME HILL (IRE), 7, br g Supreme Leader—Regents Prancer **Mr J. E. Brown**
58 TIM'S THE MAN (IRE), 8, gr g Roselier (FR)—Pindas **The Life Of Riley Partnership**
59 URBAN FREEWAY (IRE), 5, b g Dr Devious (IRE)—Coupe d'Hebe **Mr J, E. Brown**
60 VERSUS (GER), 4, gr c Highest Honor (FR)—Very Mighty (FR) **The Safest Syndicate**

MR C. J. MANN—continued

61 **VILLAIR (IRE)**, 9, b g Valville (FR)—Brackenair **The Safest Syndicate**
62 **WINTERTIDE**, 8, b g Mtoto—Winter Queen **Mr J. E. Brown**
63 **ZADOK THE PRIEST (IRE)**, 4, br g Zafonic (USA)—Valencay (IRE)
64 **ZIGGY ZEN**, 5, b g Muhtarram (USA)—Springs Welcome **All For One And One For All Partnership**

Other Owners: Amity Finance Ltd, Mr Tony Bolingbroke, Mr D. Burgess, Mr B. R. H. Burrough, Mr Ian Coles, Mr R. Condon, Mrs Zoe Condon, Mr Lee Constable, Mr P. Cook, Mr John Cosgrove, Mr Tom Creighton, Mr Colin Day, Mr Roger Day, Mr Roy Dunnett, Mr Tony Evdemon, Mr J. Fordham, Mr David Graham, Mr Nigel Gravett, Mrs S. Van Heynengen, Mr Darren Hillier, Mr Graham Howard, Lady Helen Inchiquin, Mr Nick Irens, Mrs Rosalind Kempner, Mr Paul Kinane, Mr Ian Kirkham, Mrs Jane Lawless, Mr John Leigh, Viviann Linden, Mr Louis Martin, Mr Alan Merritt, Mr R. P. B. Michaelson, Mr Peter Morris, Mrs Dorothy Mosley, Mr C. Nugent, Mr Graham Price, Mr Mike Price, Mr Xavier Pullen, Mr Geoff See, Mr Tim Smartt, Mr Andy Smith, Mr Tony Stapleton, Mr John Taylor, Mr A. M. Tolhurst, Mr Mike Villis, Mr John Walker, Mr Neil Whitfield, Mr David Wright.

Assistant Trainer: Eamonn Fehily

Jockey (NH): Noel Fehily (10-0). **Conditional:** Stephen Craine (9-7), David Crosse (10-0).
Amateur: Mr Shane Walsh (9-7).

362
MRS J. M. E. MANN, Leamington Spa
Postal: **Hill Farm, Ufton, Leamington Spa, Warwickshire, CV33 9PP.**

1 **KILLARNEY PRINCE (IRE)**, 5, b g Lord Americo—Henry Woman (IRE) **Mrs J. M. Mann**

Amateur: Mr James Owen.

363
MR H. J. MANNERS, Swindon
Postal: **Common Farm, Highworth, Swindon, Wilts, SN6 7PP.**
Contact: PHONE (01793) 762232

1 **BLACK KITE (IRE)**, 5, br g Desert King (IRE)—Snoozeandyoulose (IRE)
2 **FOX JOHN**, 4, b g Ballet Royal (USA)—Muskerry Miss (IRE)
3 **HI RUDOLF**, 9, b g Ballet Royal (USA)—Hi Darlin'
4 **JONANAUD**, 5, b g Ballet Royal (USA)—Margaret Modes **Mr H. J. Manners**
5 **KERRY DANCER**, 8, ch m Ballet Royal (USA)—Muskerry Miss (IRE)
6 **KINDA CRAZY**, 4, b g Petoski—Margaret Modes
7 **MAN FROM HIGHWORTH**, 5, b g Ballet Royal (USA)—Cavisoir **Mr H. J. Manners**
8 **RAKASSA**, 6, ch m Ballet Royal (USA)—Shafayif **Mr H. J. Manners**
9 **RUNNING TIMES (USA)**, 7, b g Brocco (USA)—Concert Peace (USA) **Mr H. J. Manners**
10 **SYLPHIDE**, 9, b m Ballet Royal (USA)—Shafayif **Mr H. J. Manners**

Assistant Trainer: Mrs H J Manners

364
MR G. G. MARGARSON, Newmarket
Postal: **Graham Lodge, Birdcage Walk, Newmarket, Suffolk, CB8 ONE.**
Contact: HOME/FAX (01638) 668043 MOBILE (07860) 198303
E-MAIL george.margarson@virgin.net

1 **ALBURACK**, 6, b g Rock City—Suzannah's Song **Mr G. G. Margarson**
2 **ATAVUS**, 7, b h Distant Relative—Elysian **Stableside Racing Partnership II**
3 **DREAMS FORGOTTEN (IRE)**, 4, b f Victory Note (USA)—Sevens Are Wild **Mrs Julia Tanswell**
4 **ENCHANTED**, 5, b m Magic Ring (IRE)—Snugfit Annie **Norcroft Park Stud**
5 **GINGER ICE**, 4, ch g Bahamian Bounty—Sharp Top **Khan And Partners**
6 **HONEY'S GIFT**, 5, b m Terimon—Honeycroft **Mr Russell Evans**
7 **INTERNATIONALGUEST (IRE)**, 5, b g Petardia—Banco Solo **Mr John Guest**
8 **JOEY THE SCHNOZE**, 6, ch g Zilzal (USA)—Linda's Design **Oaks Racing**
9 **KYLE OF LOCHALSH**, 4, gr g Vettori (IRE)—Shaieef (IRE) **Stableside Racing Partnership 7**
10 **LITTLE CRACKER**, 8, b g Petoski—Little Serenity **Mr C. H. Feloy**
11 **MISS PEACHES**, 6, b m Emperor Jones (USA)—Dear Person **Mr G. G. Margarson**
12 **NEARLY A FOOL**, 6, b g Komaite (USA)—Greenway Lady **Jim Burns**
13 **POLAR JEM**, 4, b f Polar Falcon (USA)—Top Jem **Norcroft Park Stud**

MR G. G. MARGARSON—continued

14 **PRIDE OF THE OAKS**, 4, b f Faustus (USA)—Annabel's Baby (IRE) **Oaks Racing**
15 **SEA HOLLY (IRE)**, 4, b g Barathea (IRE)—Mountain Holly **Mr P. E. Axon**
16 **STAR OF NORMANDIE (USA)**, 5, b m Gulch (USA)—Depaze (USA) **Norcroft Park Stud**
17 **TAMARELLA (IRE)**, 4, b f Tamarisk (IRE)—Miss Siham (IRE) **The Tamarisk Partnership**

THREE-YEAR-OLDS

18 **BERTOCELLI**, ch c Vettori (IRE)—Dame Jude **Stableside Racing Partnership 8**
19 **COBALT RUNNER (IRE)**, b g Fayruz—Bui-Doi (IRE) **Oaks Racing**
20 **DELCIENNE**, b f Golden Heights—Delciana (IRE) **The Del Boys**
21 **FITTING GUEST (IRE)**, ch c Grand Lodge (USA)—Sarah-Clare **Mr John Guest**
22 **FRESH CONNECTION**, b f Danzig Connection—Naturally Fresh **The Canaries Partnership**
23 **GENUINE JAY GEE (IRE)**, b c Fasliyev (USA)—Jay Gee (IRE) **Mr John Guest**
24 **JOANS JEWEL**, ch f Wolfhound (USA)—Chatter's Princess **Mr J. Burns**
25 **KALAMANSI (IRE)**, b f Sadler's Wells (USA)—Musk Lime (USA) **Norcroft Park Stud**
26 **LEAH'S PRIDE**, b f Atraf—First Play **Oaks Racing**
27 **LENWADE**, gr f Environment Friend—Branitska **The Lenwade Partnership**
28 **LITTLE MISS LILI**, b f Danzig Connection (USA)—Little Miss Rocket **Cyril and Paul Rogers**
29 **MAURICE'S LAD (IRE)**, b g Efisio—Salsola **Oaks Racing**
30 **TARANDOT (IRE)**, b f Singspiel (IRE)—Rifada **Norcroft Park Stud**
31 **THREE SECRETS (IRE)**, b f Danehill (USA)—Castillian Queen (USA) **Norcroft Park Stud**

TWO-YEAR-OLDS

32 **HIGH CHART**, b f 9/4 Robellino (USA)—Bright Spells (Salse (USA)) (10000) **Mr Dennis Russell**
33 **KRUMPET**, b f 13/3 Mujahid (USA)—Dame Jude (Dilum (USA)) **Stableside Racing Partnership 8**

Other Owners: Mr J. D. Clements, Mr P. J. Collier, Mr C. J. S. Goodman, Mr A. J. Hollis, Mr M. D. Hollis, Mr Philip A. Jarvis, Mr Peter Johnson, Mr A. Khan, Mr Alyas Khan, Mr D. Lancaster-Smith, Dr M. J. Lancaster-Smith, Mr Stanley Merchack, Mr C. W. Rogers, Mr Paul Rogers, Mr W. Shanks, H. W. Thommes.

Assistant Trainer: Mr J. Higgins

Jockeys (Flat): G Carter (w.a.), J Mackay, P Robinson (w.a.). **Apprentice:** Kristin Stubbs.

---

365   MISS K. MARKS, Tenbury Wells
Postal: Woodstock Bower Farm, Stoke Bliss, Tenbury Wells, Worcestershire, WR15 8QN.
Contact: HOME (01885) 410309 STABLES (01885) 410317 MOBILE (07779) 504580

1 **COQ DE MIRANDE (FR)**, 10, gr g Gairloch—Carmonera (FR) **Mr Nick Shutts**
2 **DANTE'S BATTLE (IRE)**, 12, b br g Phardante (FR)—No Battle **Mr Nick Shutts**
3 **EFRHINA (IRE)**, 4, ch f Woodman (USA)—Eshq Albahr (USA) **Mr Nick Shutts**
4 **ELA D'ARGENT (IRE)**, 5, b m Ela-Mana-Mou—Petite-D-Argent **Mr Nick Shutts**
5 **GOLFAGENT**, 6, b g Kris—Alusha **Mr Nick Shutts**
6 **IT'S A WRAP (IRE)**, 6, b m Carroll House—Wraparound Sue **Mr Nick Shutts**
7 **MAJOR BENEFIT (IRE)**, 7, b g Executive Perk—Merendas Sister **Mr Nick Shutts**
8 **MILLE ET UNE NUITS (FR)**, 5, b m Ecologist—Migre (FR) **Mr Nick Shutts**
9 **POP GUN**, 5, ch g Pharly (FR)—Angel Fire **Mr Nick Shutts**

THREE-YEAR-OLDS

10 B c Deploy—Garota de Ipanema (FR) **Mr Nick Shutts**

Conditional: A Tinkler.

---

366   MR R. F. MARVIN, Rolleston
Postal: The Hunter Yard, Southwell Racecourse, Southwell, Nottinghamshire, NG25 0TS.
Contact: PHONE (01636) 814481 EX 41 (01636) 686150 MOBILE (07903) 314614

1 **ABOVE BOARD**, 9, b g Night Shift (USA)—Bundled Up (USA) **Mr W. I. Bloomfield**
2 **AFAAN (IRE)**, 11, ch h Cadeaux Genereux—Rawaabe (USA) **Mr R. F. Marvin**
3 **EAGER ANGEL (IRE)**, 6, b m Up And At 'em—Seanee Squaw
4 **MATHMAGICIAN**, 5, ch g Hector Protector (USA)—Inherent Magic (IRE) **Mrs M. A. Marvin**
5 **MELFORD RED (IRE)**, 4, b g Sri Pekan (USA)—Sunflower (IRE) **Red Lion Orby**
6 **MUCHO GUSTO**, 6, b g Casteddu—Heather Honey

MR R. F. MARVIN—continued

   7 SAMBA BEAT, 5, ch m Efisio—Special Beat **Mr M. R. A. Lancaster**
   8 TORZAL, 4, br g Hector Protector (USA)—Alathezal (USA) **Mr S. M. Deeman**

THREE-YEAR-OLDS

   9 DEMOLITION MOLLY, b f Rudimentary (USA)—Persian Fortune **Mr D. Blott**
 10 B g King Among Kings—Heavenly Pet **Mrs M. A. Marvin**
 11 JUDDA, b c Makbul—Pepeke **Mr D. Blott,Mr E Atkinson,Mr R.F.Marvin**
 12 LOUTASHA, gr f Atraf—Petinata **Mr D. G. Woods, Mr R. F. Marvin**

TWO-YEAR-OLDS

 13 B c 16/2 Danzig Connection—Funny Choice (IRE) (Commanche Run) (1000) **Mr I. Bloomfield**
 14 Ch c 2/5 Bluegrass Prince—Persian Fortune (Forzando) (2200) **Mr D. Blott**

Other Owners: Mr Colin Alton.

Assistant Trainer: M A Marvin

Jockey (Flat): T G McLaughlin (8-4). **Apprentice:** J Stevenson (8-3). **Amateurs:** Miss E Graham (8-5), Mrs M Morris (9-0).

---

367 **MR N. P. MCCORMACK, Rowlands Gill**
Postal: **The Cottage, Southfield Farm, Hamsterley Mill, Rowlands Gill, Tyne and Wear, NE39 1NQ.**
Contact: **HOME (01207) 563169 MOBILE (07961) 540173**

   1 ANSIAS (USA), 11, ch g Diesis—Alia **Mrs D. McCormack**
   2 DIDIFON, 9, b g Zafonic (USA)—Didicoy (USA) **Mrs D. McCormack**
   3 KARAHISAR (IRE), 5, b g Common Grounds—Karamiyna (IRE) **Mrs D. McCormack**
   4 THE COLLECTOR (IRE), 5, ch g Forest Wind (USA)—Glowing Reeds **Mrs D. McCormack**

Assistant Trainer: Mrs D McCormack

---

368 **MR T. P. MCGOVERN, Lewes**
Postal: **Grandstand Stables, Old Lewes Racecourse, Lewes, East Sussex, BN7 1UR.**
Contact: **PHONE (01273) 487813 MOBILE (07710) 123145 E-MAIL monicamcgovern@tiscal.co.uk**

   1 ALMONTASIR (IRE), 6, b g Distinctly North (USA)—My Blue **Mr Ahmed Abdel-Khaleq**
   2 BALLYGRIFFIN KID, 4, gr g Komaite (USA)—Ballygriffin Belle **Mr Tommy Breen**
   3 DARK THUNDER (IRE), 7, br g Religiously (USA)—Culkeern **Mr Anthony O'Gorman**
   4 ELLE ROYAL (IRE), 5, br m Ali-Royal (IRE)—Silvretta (IRE) **Mr Steve Major**
   5 INJUNEAR (IRE), 6, ch g Executive Perk—Chancy Gale (IRE)
   6 5, B m Topanoora—Katie Daly (IRE)
   7 MONTEL GIRL (IRE), 8, ch m Montelimar (USA)—Grassed **The Walking Tall Partnership**
   8 PRINCE SLAYER, 8, b g Batshoof—Top Sovereign **Mr Ahmed Abdel-Khaleq**
   9 THE DREAM LIVES ON (IRE), 8, ch g Phardante (FR)—Rare Dream **B. & M. McHugh Ltd Civil Engineering**
 10 WEST ASIDE (IRE), 10, br g Brush Aside (USA)—Chancy Belle **B. C. J. Enterprise**
 11 ZEN (IRE), 9, b g Shernazar—Mary Mary **Mr Ahmed Abdel-Khaleq**

Other Owners: Mr N. Abbott, Mr N. Boyle, Mrs B. L. Hillary, Mr C. G. Hosmer, Mrs J. L. Hosmer, Mr Richard Matthews.

---

369 **MISS D. A. MCHALE, Newmarket**
Postal: **Harratton Stables, Chapel Street, Exning, Newmarket, Suffolk, CB8 7HN.**
Contact: **OFFICE/FAX (01638) 577000 MOBILE (07748) 226823**

   1 DEN'S-JOY, 8, b m Archway (IRE)—Bonvin **Mr M. R. Watmore**
   2 GWAZI, 4, b g Pennekamp (USA)—Made of Pearl (USA) **Mr Paul Day**
   3 JADEERON, 5, b g Green Desert (USA)—Rain And Shine (FR) **K & D Racing/ Miss D. A. McHale**
   4 LOVELY YOU (IRE), 4, b g Fayruz—Lovely Me (IRE) **Mr P. Burban**
   5 MARGHUB (IRE), 5, b g Darshaan—Arctique Royale **David Andrews Construction**

MISS D. A. MCHALE—continued

6 **VANBRUGH (FR)**, 4, ch g Starborough—Renovate **Mr N. Bashir**
7 **ZAK FACTA (IRE)**, 4, b g Danetime (IRE)—Alexander Goddess (IRE) **David Andrews Construction**

Other Owners: Mr R. L. Amon, Mr P. S. Carter, Mr A. Jackson, Mr J. Pollock, Mr D. P. Walsh, Mr Keith White.

Assistant Trainer: P Burban

Jockeys (Flat): D McGaffin (w.a.), D Williams (w.a.).

---

370 MR I. W. MCINNES, Catwick
Postal: **Ivy House Farm, Main Street, Catwick, Beverley, East Yorkshire, HU17 5PJ.**
Contact: HOME **(01964) 542115** FAX **(01964) 542115** MOBILE **(07720) 451233**

1 **ALL ON MY OWN (USA)**, 9, ch g Unbridled (USA)—Some For All (USA) **Mr Ian McInnes**
2 **H HARRISON (IRE)**, 4, b g Eagle Eyed (USA)—Penrose (IRE) **Ivy House Racing**
3 **LAUREL DAWN**, 6, gr g Paris House—Madrina **Ivy House Racing**
4 **MOLOTOV**, 4, b g Efisio—Mindomica **Ivy House Racing**
5 4, B g Presidium—Nice Spice (IRE) **Mr I. W. McInnes**
6 **ROCK CONCERT**, 6, b m Bishop of Cashel—Summer Pageant **Ivy House Racing**
7 **SHAMWARI FIRE (IRE)**, 4, ch g Idris (IRE)—Bobby's Dream **Ivy House Racing**
8 **SKIBEREEN (IRE)**, 4, b g Ashkalani (IRE)—Your Village (IRE) **Ivy House Racing**
9 **ZAWRAK (IRE)**, 5, ch g Zafonic (USA)—Gharam (USA) **New Century Windows Ltd**

THREE-YEAR-OLDS

10 **BROOKLANDS TIME (IRE)**, b f Danetime (IRE)—Lute And Lyre (IRE) **Brooklands Racing**

TWO-YEAR-OLDS

11 Ch g 30/3 Piccolo—Versami (USA) (Riverman (USA)) (5000) **Rhubarb Racing**

Assistant Trainer: Mr M. Crossland

Jockey (NH): L Vickers. **Apprentice:** P Mathers.

---

371 MRS C. A. P. MCINNES SKINNER, Melton Mowbray
Postal: **John O'Gaunt House, Melton Mowbray, Leicestershire, LE14 2RE.**
Contact: PHONE **(01664) 454327** MOBILE **(07885) 215956**

1 **NIEMBRO**, 4, b g Victory Note (USA)—Diabaig **Mrs T. J. McInnes Skinner**
2 **TIP THE SCALES**, 6, b g Dancing Spree (USA)—Keen Melody (USA) **Mrs T. J. McInnes Skinner**

---

372 MR W. J. MCKEOWN, Newcastle
Postal: **East Wideopen Farm, Wideopen, Newcastle Upon Tyne, NE13 6DW.**
Contact: PHONE **(0191) 236 7545** FAX **(0191) 236 2959** MOBILE **(07931) 505593**

1 **ACES FOUR (IRE)**, 5, ch g Fourstars Allstar (USA)—Special Trix (IRE) **Mr J. Molloy**
2 **ACES ROYALE (IRE)**, 5, ch m Accordion—Miss Daisy Dee **Mr J. Molloy**
3 **CAMAIR CRUSADER (IRE)**, 10, br g Jolly Jake (NZ)—Sigrid's Dream (USA) **Mrs L. E. McKeown**
4 **CAPRICORN**, 6, b g Minster Son—Loch Scavaig (IRE) **Mr Ian Ives**
5 **HANDSHAKE**, 4, ch g Most Welcome—Lady Day (FR) **Christy Partnership**
6 **LOFTY LEADER (IRE)**, 5, b g Norwich—Slaney Jazz **Mr L. H. Gilmurray**
7 **LONGSTONE LASS**, 4, b f Wizard King—Kamaress **The Northumberland Group Racing Club**
8 **MAGIC HOUR (IRE)**, 5, b g Weldnaas (USA)—Montohouse (IRE) **Mr Matheson Green**
9 **MAN MURPHY (IRE)**, 8, b g Euphemism—Been About (IRE) **Mr W. Manners**

TWO-YEAR-OLDS

10 **MR VIAILLIE (IRE)**, b g 15/4 Kayf Tara—Formidable Task (Formidable (USA)) **Mr T. Payne**

Other Owners: Mr N. Cranston, Mr R. G. Green, Mr A. Hynd, Mr Peter G. Johnson.

373 MR B. J. MEEHAN, Upper Lambourn

Postal: **Newlands Stables, Upper Lambourn, Hungerford, Berkshire, RG17 8QX.**
Contact: **OFFICE (01488) 73656/73636 FAX (01488) 73633 MOBILE (07836) 754254**
E-MAIL brian@brianmeehan.com WEBSITE www.brianmeehan.com

1 **ARTISTRY,** 4, b f Night Shift (USA)—Arriving **Wyck Hall Stud**
2 **CHINKARA,** 4, ch g Desert Prince (IRE)—You Make Me Real (USA) **Mrs Susan Roy**
3 **DUSK DANCER (FR),** 4, b g Groom Dancer (USA)—Nightitude **Miss Gloria Abbey**
4 **HILBRE ISLAND,** 4, b c Halling (USA)—Faribole (IRE) **E. H. Jones (Paints) Ltd**
5 **INDIAN COUNTRY,** 5, ch g Indian Ridge—Arethusa **Mr Harvey Rosenblatt**
6 **KAIETEUR (USA),** 5, b h Marlin (USA)—Strong Embrace (USA) **Mrs Susan McCarthy**
7 **LUCKY ROMANCE,** 5, b m Key of Luck (USA)—In Love Again (IRE) **Mr B. J. Meehan**
8 **MAKULU (IRE),** 4, b g Alzao (USA)—Karinski (USA) **Matham Investments**
9 **PEDRO JACK (IRE),** 7, b g Mujadil (USA)—Festival of Light **Mr M.Peart**
10 **SAVANNAH BAY,** 5, ch g In The Wings—High Savannah **Mr Joe L. Allbritton**
11 **SILENCE IS GOLDEN,** 5, ch m Danehill Dancer (IRE)—Silent Girl **Miss J. Semple**
12 **SUN ON THE SEA (IRE),** 4, ch f Bering—Shimmer (FR)
13 **TAMIAMI TRAIL (IRE),** 6, ch g Indian Ridge—Eurobird **Mrs Susan Roy**
14 **TETOU (IRE),** 4, ch f Peintre Celebre (USA)—Place of Honour **Mrs Susan Roy**
15 **THURLESTONE ROCK,** 4, ch g Sheikh Albadou—Don't Smile **Mr N. Attenborough & Mrs L. Mann**
16 **TWILIGHT BLUES (IRE),** 5, ch h Bluebird (USA)—Pretty Sharp **Mrs Susan Roy**
17 **WAKE (USA),** 4, b c Storm Cat (USA)—Ladies Cruise (USA) **Mr Joe L. Allbritton**

THREE-YEAR-OLDS

18 **ABINGTON ANGEL,** ch f Machiavellian (USA)—Band (USA) **Mr F. C. T. Wilson**
19 **AMERICAN DUKE (USA),** b g Cryptoclearance (USA)—Prologue (USA) **Grays, Jaye & Connolly**
20 **APOLLO GEE (IRE),** b g Spectrum (IRE)—Suspiria (IRE) **Matham Investments**
21 **ATTUNE,** br f Singspiel (IRE)—Arriving **Wyck Hall Stud**
22 **BONUS POINTS (IRE),** b c Ali-Royal (IRE)—Asta Madera (IRE) **Mr Jim McCarthy**
23 **CAPE FEAR,** b c Cape Cross (IRE)—Only In Dreams **Kennett Valley Thoroughbreds II**
24 **CARRIZO CREEK (IRE),** b c Charnwood Forest (IRE)—Violet Spring (IRE) **Mr J. S. Threadwell**
25 **CHICA ROCA (USA),** ch f Woodman (USA)—Amenixa (FR) **Mr F. C. T. Wilson**
26 **CINNAMON RIDGE (IRE),** b g Indian Ridge—Savoury **Mr Harvey Rosenblatt**
27 **COOL CLEAR WATER (USA),** b f Seeking The Gold (USA)—Miznah (IRE) **Mr Joe L. Allbritton**
28 **CREPE DE CHINE,** b f Zafonic (USA)—Princess Zepoli **Mr J. Good**
29 **CRYSTAL (IRE),** b f Danehill (USA)—Solar Crystal (IRE) **Mr F. C. T. Wilson**
30 **DENVER (IRE),** b c Danehill (USA)—Born Beautiful (USA) **Mrs John Magnier & Mr M. Tabor**
31 **DOLCE PICCATA,** ch f Piccolo—Highland Rhapsody (IRE) **Mr H. Ponsonby**
32 **FANCY FOXTROT,** b c Danehill Dancer (IRE)—Smooth Princess (IRE) **Mr Joe L. Allbritton**
33 **FAST HEART,** b c Fasliyev (USA)—Heart of India (IRE) **Mr S. Dartnell**
34 **FAVOURABLE,** b f Mark of Esteem (IRE)—Top Society **Wyck Hall Stud**
35 **GJOVIC,** br c Singspiel (IRE)—Photo Call **Mr J. Good**
36 **GO BANANAS,** b g Primo Dominie—Amsicora **Mackey Family Ltd**
37 **GRAVARDLAX,** ch c Salse (USA)—Rubbiyati **Gravity Group**
38 **GROUVILLE,** b g Groom Dancer (USA)—Dance Land (IRE) **Mr F. C. T. Wilson**
39 **HERMITAGE COURT (USA),** ch g Out of Place (USA)—Russian Act (USA) **Gallagher Equine Ltd**
40 **IMPERIUM,** b g Imperial Ballet (IRE)—Partenza (USA) **Mrs H. Raw**
41 **INCISE,** ch f Dr Fong (USA)—Pretty Sharp **Mr & Mrs D, Brown**
42 **INNCLASSIC (IRE),** b f Stravinsky (USA)—Kyka (USA) **The Inn Partnership**
43 **INNSTYLE,** b f Daggers Drawn (USA)—Tarneem (USA) **The Inn Partnership**
44 **INSTANT RECALL (IRE),** ch c Indian Ridge—Happy Memories (IRE) **Mrs Susan Roy**
45 **JASMINE PEARL (IRE),** b f King of Kings (IRE)—Tumbleweed Pearl **O'Reilly Hyland & Pidgley Partnership**
46 **LEITRIM HOUSE,** ch c Cadeaux Genereux—Lonely Heart **Gallagher Equine Ltd**
47 **ONLY IF I LAUGH,** ch g Piccolo—Agony Aunt **Mrs B. Funnell**
48 **PIZAZZ,** ch c Pivotal—Clare Celeste **Mrs Susan Roy**
49 **QUEENSTOWN (IRE),** b g Desert Style (IRE)—Fanciful (IRE) **Matham Investments**
50 **REIGN OF FIRE (IRE),** b f Perugino (USA)—White Heat **Team Valor**
51 **ROMANTIC DRAMA (IRE),** b f Primo Dominie—Antonia's Choice **Mr F. C. T. Wilson**
52 **SAINT ZITA (IRE),** b f Desert Sun—Chatelsong (USA) **Miss J. Semple & Lee Warren**
53 **SAUCY,** ch f Muhtarram (USA)—So Saucy **Wyck Hall Stud**
54 **SCRUNCH,** b f Royal Applause—Antonia's Folly **Mr R. Tooth**
55 **SPECTESTED (IRE),** ch g Spectrum (IRE)—Nisibis **Bezwell Fixings Ltd**
56 **STAR OF LIGHT,** b g Mtoto—Star Entry **Mr J. H. Widdows**
57 **STEVEDORE,** ch c Docksider (USA)—La Belle Katherine (USA) **Mr M. A. Clark**
58 **TILL THERE WAS YOU,** b f Vettori (IRE)—Fleur Rouge **Mrs Susan Hearn**
59 **TREASURE HOUSE (IRE),** b c Grand Lodge (USA)—Royal Wolff **Mrs Susan Roy**

MR B. J. MEEHAN—continued

60 **VIOLET PARK**, b f Pivotal—Petnellajill **Mr & Mrs D. Cash**
61 **WINDSURFER (IRE)**, b c Desert Sun—Bianca Cappello (IRE) **Team Havana**
62 **YOUNG PATRIARCH**, b c Silver Patriarch (IRE)—Mortify **Mr S. Dartnell**
63 **ZOUAVE (IRE)**, b c Spectrum (IRE)—Lady Windley **E. H. Jones (Paints) Ltd**

TWO-YEAR-OLDS

64 **ABIENTOT (IRE)**, b c 28/2 Danetime (IRE)—Clandolly (IRE) (Burslem) (50000) **Clipper Group Holdings Ltd**
65 Ch f 14/1 Indian Ridge—Aliena (IRE) (Grand Lodge (USA)) (75000)
66 **ALPAGA LE JOMAGE (IRE)**, b c 12/2 Orpen (USA)—
Miss Bagatelle (Mummy's Pet) (24000) **The Top Banana Partnership**
67 **AL QUDRA (IRE)**, b c 8/3 Cape Cross (IRE)—Alvilda (IRE) (Caerleon (USA)) (16000) **Abbot Racing**
68 Gr c 15/2 Desert Style (IRE)—Aneydia (IRE) (Kenmare (FR)) (19789) **The Comic Strip Heros**
69 B c 28/1 Foxhound (USA)—Another Shadow (IRE) (Topanoora) (30000)
70 Ch c 21/4 Polar Falcon (USA)—Antonia's Double (Primo Dominie) **Chris & Antonia Deuters**
71 B c 17/4 Dansili—Aunt Jemima (Busted) (17000)
72 B c 1/2 Daylami (IRE)—Ballet Society (FR) (Sadler's Wells (USA)) (220000) **Mr Joe L. Allbritton**
73 **BENTICK (IRE)**, b c 7/3 In The Wings—Bareilly (USA) (Lyphard (USA)) (100000) **Mr F. C. T. Wilson**
74 **BRAVEMORE (USA)**, b br c 24/3 Diesis—Private Indy (USA) (A P indy (USA)) **Mrs Susan Roy**
75 **CAVARADOSSI**, gr c 18/3 Lake Coniston (IRE)—Floria Tosca (Petong) (22000) **Mrs Y. Allan**
76 Ch c 23/4 Tomba—Cherish Me (Polar Falcon (USA)) **Mr J. Good**
77 **CHIRACAHUA (IRE)**, ch c 7/3 Desert Prince (IRE)—Irish Celebrity (USA) (Irish River (FR)) (21000) **Mr D. Allan**
78 Ch c 22/3 Raise A Grand (IRE)—
Christmas Carol (IRE) (Common Grounds) **Mr N, Attenborough & Mrs G. Tucker**
79 B c 1/2 Aljabr (USA)—Dafnah (USA) (Housebuster (USA)) (15476) **E. H. Jones (Paints) Ltd**
80 B c 29/4 Titus Livius (FR)—Daisy Dobson (Gorytus (USA)) (5000)
81 B c 13/4 Orpen (USA)—Dancing At Lunasa (IRE) (Dancing Dissident (USA)) (10512) **Mr J. McCarthy**
82 Ch c 21/2 Tomba—Dancing Diana (Raga Navarro (ITY)) (16000) **Mr J. Good**
83 B c 23/2 Polar Falcon (USA)—Dark Eyed Lady (IRE) (Exhibitioner) (27000) **Gallagher Equine Ltd**
84 **DIVANI (IRE)**, b f 14/3 Shinko Forest (IRE)—
Supreme Crown (USA) (Chief's Crown (USA)) (20000) **Mrs Susan Roy**
85 Ch c 17/3 Prince Sabo—Don't Jump (IRE) (Entitled) (18500)
86 **EUPHORIA**, b f 21/4 Unfuwain (USA)—Maria Isabella (FR) (Young Generation) **Miss G. Abbey**
87 B c 3/5 Orpen (USA)—Fakhira (IRE) (Jareer (USA)) (12368) **Mr J. S. Threadwell**
88 B c 16/3 Danetime (IRE)—Faypool (IRE) (Fayruz) (8500)
89 B c 4/3 Cape Cross (IRE)—Foresta Verde (IRE) (Green Forest (USA)) (25000) **Mr J. S. Threadwell**
90 B c 14/5 Mark Of Esteem (IRE)—Forever Shineing (Glint of Gold) (30000) **Jumeirah Racing**
91 B c 5/4 Singspiel (IRE)—For More (FR) (Sanglamore (USA)) **Paul & Jenny Green**
92 Br f 17/2 Dansili—Hajat (Mujtahid (USA)) (12000) **Mr & Mrs David Brown**
93 B f 23/1 Dansili—Hard Task (Fromidable (USA)) (14000) **Mr H. Ponsonby**
94 Br c 27/4 Diktat—Heart of India (IRE) (Try My Best (USA)) (310000) **Mr Joe L. Allbritton**
95 Ch c 24/4 Dr Fong (USA)—Kelso Magic (USA) (Distant View (USA)) (30000)
96 B c 18/2 Mujadil (USA)—La Caprice (USA) (Housebuster (USA)) (25000)
97 Ch c 27/4 A P Indy (USA)—Ladies Cruise (USA) (Fappiano (USA)) **Mr Joe L. Allbritton**
98 Ch c 16/3 Raise A Grand (IRE)—Look Nonchalant (IRE) (Fayruz) (8000)
99 Ch c 29/4 Zafonic (USA)—Lovely Lyca (Night Shift (USA)) (61842) **Mr S. Dartnell**
100 **MANGO GROOVE (IRE)**, b f 28/4 Unfuwain (USA)—Solar Crystal (IRE) (Alzao (USA)) (45000) **Mr F. C. T. Wilson**
101 B c 27/2 Bluebird (USA)—Mary Hinge (Dowsing (USA)) (30000) **Tumbleweed Partnership**
102 **MASTMAN (IRE)**, ch c 8/4 Intikhab (USA)—
Spanker (Suave Dancer (USA)) (35000) **Kennet Valley Thoroughbreds III**
103 Ch c 21/3 Bluebird (USA)—Meandering Rose (USA) (Irish River (FR)) (22000) **Pat Eddery RAcing**
104 **MUSICAL DAY**, ch f 3/3 Singspiel (IRE)—Dayville (USA) (Dayjur (USA)) (20000) **Mr T. Holdcroft**
105 B f 1/2 Dr Fong (USA)—Park Charger (Tirol) (200000) **Mr F. C. T. Wilson**
106 **PAVILION**, b f 20/2 Robellino (USA)—Chiltern Court (USA) (Topsider (USA)) (3500) **Wyck Hall Stud**
107 **PERFECT CHOICE (IRE)**, gr c 1/5 Daylami (IRE)—
Fairy Contessa (IRE) (Fairy King (USA)) (155000) **Mrs Susan Roy**
108 B f 13/3 Fusaichi Pegasus—Pharapache (USA) (Lyphard (USA)) (71429)
109 B f 21/4 Indian Ridge—Please Believe Me (Try My Best (USA)) **Paul & Jenny Green**
110 **POLLITO (IRE)**, b c 15/3 Rossini (USA)—Bezee (Belmez (USA)) (25000) **Mackey Family Ltd**
111 Br c 15/3 Tomba—Princess Zara (Reprimand) **Mr J. Good**
112 Ch c 15/3 Danehill Dancer (IRE)—Richly Deserved (IRE) (Kings Lake (USA)) (40000) **Gravity Group**
113 Ch f 15/2 Pivotal—See You Later (Emerati (USA)) (30920) **Mrs S. Tucker & Mr P. Burrell**
114 **SHAHEER (IRE)**, b c 2/2 Shahrastani (USA)—
Atmospheric Blues (IRE) (Double Schwartz) (14000) **Mr D. Crichton-Watt**
115 B f 23/2 Cape Cross (IRE)—Shannon Dore (IRE) (Turtle Island (IRE)) (35000) **Mrs Wendy English**
116 **SHARP AS A TACK (IRE)**, b f 29/1 Zafonic (USA)—Pretty Sharp (Interrex (CAN)) (35000) **Mr P. Minikes**

MR B. J. MEEHAN—continued

117 B f 5/2 Barathea (IRE)—Shouk (Shirley Heights) (125000) **Mr F. C. T. Wilson**
118 SIENA GOLD, b br f 21/2 Key of Luck (USA)—
Corn Futures (Nomination) (12000) **Mr N. Attenborough & Mrs L. Mann**
119 TAKE A MILE (IRE), ch c 16/3 Inchinor—
Bu Hagab (IRE) (Royal Academy (USA)) (32000) **Kennet Valley Thoroughbreds VII**
120 B f 16/2 Bluebird (USA)—Tart (FR) (Warning) (16000) **S. McCready, T. Clinton & D. Hicks**
121 Ch f 24/2 Dr Fong (USA)—Torrid Tango (USA) (Green Dancer (USA)) **Mr S. Ryan**

Other Owners: Mr G. D. Anderson, Mr C. Bowen, C. S. G. Limited, Mrs Anna Doyle, Mr Peter Doyle, Mrs M. Gutkin, Mr J. Harvey, Mr E. B. O'Reilly Hyland, Family Amusements Ltd, Mr N. Mandell, Mr D. Margolis, Mr M. C. Moutray-Read, Mr W. T. O'Donnell, Mrs C. F. Van Straubenzee, Mr J. Newsome, Mr D. Peltz, Mr T. K. Pidgley, Mr N. J. F. Robinson, Mr Andy J Smith, Mr Barry Townsley.

Assistant Trainer: Jane Allison

Amateur: Miss Jane Allison.

374

MRS. MARY MEEK, Eastbury
Postal: Castle Piece Racing Stables, Grange Road, Eastbury, Hungerford, Berkshire, RG17 7JR.
Contact: PHONE (01488) 670100 MOBILE (07810) 866992

1 BEZWELL PRINCE, 5, ch g Bluegrass Prince (IRE)—Money Supply **Mrs Mary Meek**
2 DARK ISLAND, 9, b g Silver Season—Isle Maree **Mrs Mary Meek**
3 HIGH RESOLVE, 4, ch c Unfuwain (USA)—Asteroid Field (USA) **Mrs Mary Meek**
4 TIOMAN (IRE), 5, b br g Dr Devious (IRE)—Tochar Ban (USA) **Mrs Mary Meek**

THREE-YEAR-OLDS

5 BALLOCH, ch f Wootton Rivers (USA)—Balayer **Mrs Mary Meek**
6 CASISLE, ch f Wootton Rivers (USA)—Isle Maree **Mrs Mary Meek**

375

MR P. T. MIDGLEY, Westow
Postal: Sandfield Farm, Westow, York, YO60 7LS.
Contact: PHONE (01653) 658309 MOBILE (07976) 965220

1 FAIRY MONARCH (IRE), 5, b g Ali-Royal (IRE)—Cookawara (IRE) **Mr M. E. Elsworthy**
2 GREY COSSACK, 7, gr g Kasakov—Royal Rebeka **Mr Robert E. Cook**
3 GREY SAMURAI, 4, gr g Gothenberg (IRE)—Royal Rebeka **Mr Robert E. Cook**
4 GRUFF, 5, ch g Presidium—Kagram Queen **Mr Robert E. Cook**
5 JEY JEY KEEN, 5, ch g Keen—Jay-Dee-Jay **Mr S. W. Knowles**
6 LADY ALRUNA (IRE), 5, ch m Alhaarth (IRE)—In Tranquility (IRE) **Mr Peter Mee**
7 MAGIC EAGLE, 7, b g Magic Ring (IRE)—Shadow Bird **Mr P. T. Midgley**
8 SEDGE (USA), 4, b g Lure (USA)—First Flyer (USA) **Mr Peter Mee**
9 WILLYWONT HE, 5, b g Bollin William—Scalby Clipper **Mr A. R. Dimmock**

THREE-YEAR-OLDS

11 GREY GURKHA, gr c Kasakov—Royal Rebeka **Mr Robert E. Cook**
12 HORTON MINX, b f Timeless Times (USA)—Horton Lady **Mr Robert E. Cook**
13 MONKEY OR ME (IRE), b g Sri Pekan (USA)—Ecco Mi (IRE) **Mrs K. L. Midgley**
14 B g Petardia—Muckross Park **Mrs K. L. Midgley**

TWO-YEAR-OLDS

15 CONCERT TIME, ch f 3/3 Timeless Times (USA)—Thalya (Crofthall) (1700) **Mr Peter Mee**
16 FANTASY FEELING, b c 14/4 Easycall—Priceless Fantasy (Dunbeath (USA)) (1800) **Mr M. E. Elsworthy**
17 GREY CAVALIER, gr g 7/4 Presidium—Royal Rebeka (Grey Desire) **Mr Robert E. Cook**
18 B c 24/2 Cloudings (IRE)—Heart Broken (Bustino) (500) **Mr Michael NG**
19 Ch f 9/3 Defacto (USA)—Lonely Lass (Headin' Up) (500) **Mr Michael NG**
20 RUBY REBEL, ch f 14/4 Tomba—Miss Chiquita (IRE) (Waajib) (800) **Mr M. E. Elsworthy**
21 B g 19/3 Prince Sabo—Sorrowful (Moorestyle) (500) **Mr P. T. Midgley**

Jockeys (Flat): D Mernagh (7-12), G Parkin (8-4). **Jockey (NH):** V T Keane. **Amateur:** Mr S Walker.

376 MISS M. K. MILLIGAN, Middleham
Postal: **Castle Stables, Middleham, Leyburn, North Yorkshire, DL8 4QQ.**
Contact: **OFFICE (01969) 23221 HOME (01969) 24105 FAX (01969) 623221**
MOBILE (07721) 529857 E-MAIL kate@mkmracing.fsnet.co.uk

1 **AMJAD,** 7, ch g Cadeaux Genereux—Babita **Miss Kate Milligan**
2 **ARTHURS KINGDOM (IRE),** 8, b g Roi Danzig (USA)—Merrie Moment (IRE) **Dr Roy Palmer**
3 **CAMERON JACK,** 9, b g Elmaamul (USA)—Ile de Reine **The Aunts**
4 **DANTECO,** 9, gr g Phardante (FR)—Up Cooke **Mrs J. M. L. Milligan**
5 **DAZZLING RIO (IRE),** 5, b g Ashkalani (IRE)—Dazzling Fire (IRE) **Mrs A. Roddis**
6 **KARYON (IRE),** 4, b f Presidium—Stealthy **Mr S. Ward**
7 **LORD PAT (IRE),** 13, ch g Mister Lord (USA)—Arianrhod **The L. P. Club**
8 **MAGIC BOX,** 6, b g Magic Ring (IRE)—Princess Poquito **Raw Racing**
9 **MIDDLEWAY,** 8, b g Milieu—Galway Gal **Mrs J. M. L. Milligan**
10 **MR LAGGAN,** 9, b g Tina's Pet—Galway Gal **Mrs J. M. L. Milligan**
11 **SLEEPY RIVER (IRE),** 13, ch g Over The River (FR)—Shreelane **The Aunts**
12 **TAIPO PRINCE (IRE),** 4, b g Entrepreneur—Dedicated Lady (IRE) **Mr E. Whalley**
13 **TENDER TOUCH (IRE),** 9, gr m Weldnaas (USA)—Moments Peace **J. D. Gordon**
14 **TINA COOKE,** 8, gr m Tina's Pet—Up Cooke **R. Berry & Mrs J. M. L. Milligan**
15 **WAS A DRIVE (IRE),** 10, b g Yashgan—Alan's Rosalinda **E. C. Gordon**
16 **WESTERN BLUEBIRD (IRE),** 6, b g Bluebird (USA)—Arrastra **The W Bees**

Other Owners: Mrs D. L. Barrett, Dr B. I. McLain, Mr A. F. Monk, Mrs S. Murray-Usher, Mrs Judith Robson.

Amateur: Miss Tina Jackson.

377 MR B. R. MILLMAN, Cullompton
Postal: **The Paddocks, Kentisbeare, Cullompton, Devon, EX15 2DX.**
Contact: **PHONE (01884) 266620 FAX (01884) 266620 MOBILE (07885) 168447**
E-MAIL brmillman@tinyworld.co.uk

1 **ADANTINO,** 5, b g Glory of Dancer—Sweet Whisper **Tarka Two Racing**
2 **BATHWICK BRUCE (IRE),** 6, b g College Chapel—Naivity (IRE) **Mr W. Clifford**
3 **BATHWICK DREAM,** 7, b m Tragic Role (USA)—Trina **Mr W. Clifford**
4 **BRUNSTON CASTLE,** 4, b g Hector Protector (USA)—Villella **Seasons Holidays**
5 **CHORUS,** 7, b m Bandmaster (USA)—Name That Tune **Mrs L. S. Millman**
6 **COCONUT PENANG (IRE),** 4, b c Night Shift (USA)—Play With Fire (FR) **Mrs A. K. H. Ooi**
7 **COOL BATHWICK (IRE),** 5, b g Entrepreneur—Tarafa **Mr W. Clifford**
8 **FACTUAL LAD,** 6, b g So Factual (USA)—Surprise Surprise **Tarka Racing**
9 **FLEETWOOD BAY,** 4, b g Fleetwood (IRE)—Caviar And Candy **Mrs Julie Gavin**
10 **FROMSONG (IRE),** 6, b g Fayruz—Lindas Delight **Mrs E. Nelson, Mr Gary Dormer**
11 **HILARIOUS (IRE),** 4, b f Petorius—Heronwater (IRE) **Miles Electronics Ltd**
12 **JAZZY MILLENNIUM,** 7, ch g Lion Cavern (USA)—Woodcrest **Millennium Millionaires Partnership**
13 **OPTIMAITE,** 7, b g Komaite (USA)—Leprechaun Lady **Always Hopeful Partnership**
14 **PASO DOBLE,** 6, b g Dancing Spree (USA)—Delta Tempo (IRE) **Mr J. R. Millman**
15 **POLISH LEGEND,** 5, b g Polish Precedent (USA)—Chita Rivera **M.A.Swift, A.J.Chapman and T.Warden**
16 **POLISH SPIRIT,** 9, b g Emarati (USA)—Gentle Star **Mrs Izabel Palmer**
17 **PRINCE NUREYEV (IRE),** 4, b c Desert King (IRE)—Annaletta **Mr H. Gooding**
18 **ROYAL BATHWICK (IRE),** 4, b f King's Theatre (IRE)—Ring of Light **Mr W. Clifford**
19 **ROYAL MEASURE,** 8, b g Inchinor—Sveltissima **The Royal Partnership**
20 **SERGEANT CECIL,** 5, ch g King's Signet (USA)—Jadidh **Mr Terry Cooper**
21 **SPARKLING SABRINA,** 4, b f Classic Cliche (IRE)—Sparkling Yasmin **Mr Victor Palmer**
22 **TREMEZZO,** 6, b g Mind Games—Rosa Van Fleet **Mr G. Battocchi**

THREE-YEAR-OLDS

23 **BALEARIC STAR (IRE),** b g Night Shift (USA)—La Menorquina (USA) **Mr G. W. Dormer**
24 **BATHWICK BILL (USA),** ch g Stravinsky (USA)—Special Park (USA) **Mrs S. Clifford**
25 **BENNY BATHWICK (IRE),** b g Midyan (USA)—Sweet Pavlova **Mrs S. Clifford**
26 **CHANFRON,** ch g Double Trigger (IRE)—Mhargaidh Nua **East Burrow Racing**
27 **FIVE GOLD (IRE),** b g Desert Prince (IRE)—Ceide Dancer (IRE) **Sir Steve Redgrave and Partners**
28 **LA VIE EST BELLE,** b f Makbul—La Belle Vie **Mr Robin Lawson**
29 **LEAPING BRAVE (IRE),** b g Indian Rocket—Island Heather (IRE)
30 **LONG ROADS (IRE),** ch g Fayruz—Mystique Air (IRE) **David Lyons Racing Syndicate 3**
31 **PENEL (IRE),** b g Orpen (USA)—Jayess Elle **The Fourmidable Partnership**
32 **SHALAMAK,** b f Makbul—Shalateeno **G. J. & Mrs M. Palmer**

MR B. R. MILLMAN—continued

33 SPEARIOUS (IRE), b g Tagula (IRE)—Gloria Crown (IRE) **Miles Electronics Ltd**
34 THREE WELSHMEN, b g Muhtarram (USA)—Merch Rhyd-Y-Grug **Mouse Racing**

TWO-YEAR-OLDS

35 B f 4/2 Paris House—Arbor Ealis (IRE) (Woods of Windsor (USA)) (1000) **Mrs M. Shenkin**
36 B c 10/2 Indian Lodge (IRE)—Bolero (Rainbow Quest (USA)) (11000) **Avalon Surfacing & Partners**
37 COLONEL BILKO, b c 11/2 General Monash (USA)—
   Mari-Ela (IRE) (River Falls) (19000) **Colin Lewis, Malcolm Calvert & Ray Gudge**
38 DAVENPORT (IRE), b g 7/4 Bold Fact (USA)—Semence d'Or (FR) (Kaldoun (FR)) (3500) **Mr B. R. Millman**
39 DREEMON, ch c 3/5 Tipsy Creek (USA)—Prudence (Grundy) **Paradise Racing**
40 EMERALD PENANG (IRE), b c 15/2 Alzao (USA)—Run To Jane (IRE) (Doyoun) (38000) **Mrs A. K. H. Ooi**
41 B f 27/3 Desert Prince—Fantazia (Zafonic (USA)) (30000) **Seasons Holidays**
42 B c 1/3 Fraam—Forest Fantasy (Rambo Dancer (CAN)) (26000) **David Lyons Racing Syndicate**
43 HAPPY EVENT, b c 5/2 Makbul—La Belle Vie (Indian King (USA)) (15000) **Mr Robin Lawson**
44 B f 3/4 Namid—Lace Flower (Old Vic) (12000) **Mrs S. Clifford**
45 LADY CHEF, ch f 24/4 Double Trigger (IRE)—
   Dundeelin (Dunbeath (USA)) (2285) **Percys Country Hotel & Restaurant**
46 B f 26/4 Mark of Esteem—La Fazenda (Warning) (20000) **Seasons Holidays**
47 B f 24/4 Josr Algarhoud (IRE)—Miss Kirsty (USA) (Miswaki (USA)) **Mr D. Windebank**
48 MUSICO (IRE), ch c 13/2 Bold Fact (USA)—Scherzo Impromptu (Music Boy) (28000) **Mr E. M. Thornton**
49 POLAR DAWN, b f 23/4 Polar Falcon (USA)—Leave At Dawn (Slip Anchor) (2500) **Mr T. Pocock**
50 Ch f 29/4 Inchinor—Red Hot Dancer (USA) (Seattle Dancer (USA)) (2380) **Mr I. Macready**
51 Ch f 23/2 Stephen Got Even—Silver Trainor (USA) (Silver Hawk (USA)) (9000) **Mrs M. O'Sullivan**
52 Gr f 2/5 Paris House—To The Stars (IRE) (Zieten (USA)) (4000) **Mrs M. Shenkin**
53 B c 3/4 Bold Edge—Truly Madly Deeply (Most Welcome) (32000) **C. Lewis, M. Calvert & G. Austen-Smith**
54 B f 23/3 Brave Act—Wee Merkin (IRE) (Thatching) **Mrs S. Thornton**
55 WINTER MOON, b f 19/3 Mujadil (USA)—
   Crofters Ceilidh (Scottish Reel) (29000) **Inter Property Consultancy Ltd**

Other Owners: Mr P. Bartlam, Mr T. L. D. Blake, Mr A. J. Conway, Mrs Tina Ann Dormer, Mr A. Ferguson, Mrs A. A. Gooding, Mr E. J. Grigg, Mr C. E. Grover, Mr J. W. Haydon, Mr R. W. Huggins, Mr A. R. Jordan, D. P. J. Lyons, Mrs D. McCabe, Miss P. D. O'Sullivan, Mr N. E. Poole, Mr V. Ruia, Mr M. G. Sly, Mr R. S. Solomon, Mr G. Spilsbury, Mr Athole Still, Mr C. Tayler, Mr G. M. Thornton, Mr David Whitefield, Mrs Paula Williams, Mr Karl Zanft.

Assistant Trainer: Louise Millman

Jockey (Flat): Steve Drowne (w.a.). **Apprentice:** Michael Saunders. **Amateur:** Mr James Millman (8-10).

---

378 MR T. G. MILLS, Epsom
Postal: **Loretta Lodge, Tilley Lane, Headley, Epsom, Surrey, KT18 6EP.**
Contact: **PHONE (01372) 377209 FAX (01372) 386578**

1 AMMENAYR (IRE), 4, b g Entrepreneur—Katiyfa **Mrs L. M. Askew**
2 BOLEYN CASTLE (USA), 7, ch g River Special (USA)—Dance Skirt (CAN) **Mr M. A. Shipman**
3 DONT WORRY BOUT ME (IRE), 7, b g Brief Truce (USA)—Coggle **Mr T. G. Mills**
4 FLORIAN, 6, b g Young Ern—Murmuring **Thorpe Vernon**
5 HIGH REACH, 4, b g Royal Applause—Lady of Limerick (IRE) **Four M's**
6 INCLINE (IRE), 5, b g Danehill (USA)—Shalwar Kameez (IRE) **Mrs Pauline Merrick**
7 LET ME TRY AGAIN (IRE), 4, b g Sadler's Wells (USA)—Dathiyna (IRE) **Mr T. G. Mills**
8 NORTON (IRE), 7, ch g Barathea—Primrose Valley **Mr T. G. Mills**
9 OK PAL, 4, b g Primo Dominie—Sheila's Secret (IRE) **Sherwoods Transport Ltd**
10 OUR FRED, 7, ch g Prince Sabo—Sheila's Secret (IRE) **Sherwoods Transport Ltd**

THREE-YEAR-OLDS

11 CAMBERWELL, b g Royal Applause—Into Orbit **Welcocks Skips Ltd Waste Management**
12 COMERAINCOMESHINE (IRE), ch f Night Shift (USA)—
   Future Past (USA) **John Humphreys (Turf Accountants) Ltd**
13 DESERT TOMMY, b g Desert King (IRE)—Flambera (FR) **Mr J. J. Devaney**
14 EVALUATOR (IRE), b c Ela-Mana-Mou—Summerhill **Mrs L. M. Askew**
15 FRANKIES WINGS (IRE), b c In The Wings—River Fantasy (USA) **Mr J. J. Devaney**
16 HERE TO ETERNITY (IRE), b c In The Wings—Amnesty Bay **Mrs L. M. Askew**
17 JACKIE KIELY, ch g Vettori (IRE)—Fudge **Mrs C. Stephens**
18 KEEP ON MOVIN' (IRE), b f Danehill Dancer (IRE)—Tormented (USA) **Mr J. E. Harley**
19 ONCE AROUND (IRE), b br c Grand Lodge (USA)—Lady Lucre (IRE) **Mr T. G. Mills**

MR T. G. MILLS—continued

20 **RESPLENDENT KING (USA)**, b g King of Kings (IRE)—Sister Fromseattle (USA) **Resplendent Racing Limited**
21 **RESPLENDENT ONE (IRE)**, b c Marju (IRE)—Licentious **Resplendent Racing Limited**
22 **ROYAL STARDUST**, b g Cloudings (IRE)—Ivy Edith **Mr Glen Antill**
23 **SAVIOURS SPIRIT**, ch g Komaite (USA)—Greenway Lady **Mr J. E. Harley**
24 **SETTLEMENT CRAIC (IRE)**, b c Ela-Mana-Mou—Medway (IRE) **Buxted Partnership**
25 **SOFISTICATION (IRE)**, b f Dayjur (USA)—Cieladeed (USA) **Mrs L. M. Askew**
26 **SOMEWHERE MY LOVE**, br f Pursuit of Love—Grand Coronet **Miss J. A. Leighs**
27 **THE WAY WE WERE**, ch c Vettori (IRE)—Pandrop **Mrs C. Stephens**
28 **UNDER MY SKIN (IRE)**, ch f Mark of Esteem (IRE)—Convenience (IRE) **Mr T. G. Mills**

TWO-YEAR-OLDS

29 B c 17/4 Namid—Arab Scimetar (IRE) (Sure Blade (USA)) (9894) **Albert Suden Ltd**
30 **ENGLISH VICTORY**, ch c 29/4 Grand Lodge (USA)—Amandine (IRE) (Darshaan) (40000) **Mr J. E. Harley**
31 Ch f 2/3 Mister Baileys—Grand Coronet (Grand Lodge (USA)) (5000) **Tracey Fox**
32 **ICENI WARRIOR**, b g 22/3 Lake Coniston (IRE)—Swing Job (Ezzoud (IRE)) (6000) **Mr M. A. Shipman**
33 **I HAVE DREAMED (IRE)**, b c 7/5 Montjeu (IRE)—
                          Diamond Field (USA) (Mr Prospector (USA)) (61842) **Mr T. G. Mills**
34 **MACALAUREM**, br c 25/1 Robellino (USA)—Sheila's Secret (USA) (Bluebird (USA)) **Mr Ian West**
35 **RESH UP (IRE)**, b c 9/2 Cape Cross (IRE)—Uhud (IRE) (Mujtahid (USA)) (40000) **Mr B. Chamley**
36 **RESPLENDENT GLORY (IRE)**, ch c 16/4 Namid—Aoife (IRE) (Thatching) (120000) **Resplendent Racing Limited**
37 **SOMETHING (IRE)**, b c 13/3 Trans Island—
                          Persian Polly (Persian Bold) (61842) **John Humphreys (Turf Accountants) Ltd**
38 **SOUTH O'THE BORDER**, b c 3/4 Wolfhound (USA)—Abbey's Gal (Efisio) (32000) **Mr T. G. Mills**
39 **SWEET LORRAINE**, b f 31/3 Dashing Blade—Royal Future (IRE) (Royal Academy (USA)) (3000) **Mr P. C. Ryan**
40 **THEBESTISYETTOCOME**, b c 28/4 Montjeu (IRE)—
                          French Quartet (IRE) (Lycius (USA)) (78000) **John Humphreys (Turf Accountants) Ltd**
41 **TREMAR**, b c 14/3 Royal Applause—Sabina (Prince Sabo) (26000) **Trevor Jacobs**

Other Owners: Mr N. Boyce, Mr T. Crawley, Mr M. R. Evans, Mr Jim Hanifin, Mr G. F. Meek, Mr R. A. Mills, Mr T. F. Moxon, Mrs J. Ruthven, Mr G. W. Thorpe.

Assistant Trainer: R A Mills

Apprentice: Robert Miles (8-0).

---

379   **MR C. W. MITCHELL, Dorchester**
Postal: White House, Buckland Newton, Dorchester, Dorset, DT2 7DE.
Contact: PHONE (01300) 345276

1 5, B h Riverwise (USA)—Miss Secret **Mr C. W. Mitchell**
2 **RIVER OF WISHES**, 6, b m Riverwise (USA)—Wishful Dream **Mr C. W. Mitchell**
3 **SPIRIT OF DESTINY**, 7, ch m Riverwise (USA)—Tearful Sarah **Mr C. W. Mitchell**
4 **WALTER'S DESTINY**, 12, ch g White Prince (USA)—Tearful Sarah **Mr C. W. Mitchell**
5 **WISHFUL VALENTINE**, 8, ch g Riverwise (USA)—Wishful Dream **Mr C. W. Mitchell**

---

380   **MR D. J. MOFFATT, Cartmel**
Postal: Pit Farm Racing Stables, Cartmel, Grange Over Sands, Cumbria, LA11 6PJ.
Contact: PHONE (01539) 536689 MOBILE (07767) 367282

1 **AMBER GO GO**, 7, ch m Rudimentary (USA)—Plaything
2 **BALL GAMES**, 6, b g Mind Games—Deb's Ball **Jennie Moffatt, Evan Munro**
3 **CAYMAN MISCHIEF**, 4, b f Cayman Kai (IRE)—Tribal Mischief **Greengate Lease Syndicate**
4 **CLASSIC JAZZ (NZ)**, 9, br g Paris Opera (AUS)—Johnny Loves Jazz (NZ) **Mr R. Naylor**
5 **DANCING PHANTOM**, 9, b g Darshaan—Dancing Prize (IRE) **Bernard Bargh, Jeff Hamer, Steve Henshaw**
6 **DEB'S SON**, 7, b g Minster Son—Deb's Ball **Mr F. A. Wilson**
7 **HAYSTACKS (IRE)**, 8, b g Contract Law (USA)—Florissa (FR) **Mr & Mrs A. G. Milligan**
8 **HEATHYARDS SWING**, 6, b g Celtic Swing—Butsova **W. R. R. Syndicate**
9 **LAGO**, 6, b g Maelstrom Lake—Jugendliebe (IRE) **Bernard Bargh, Jeff Hamer, Steve Henshaw**
10 **LANZLO (FR)**, 7, b br g Le Balafre (FR)—L'Eternite (FR) **The Sheroot Partnership**
11 **LOCH TORRIDON**, 5, b g Syrtos—Loch Scavaig (IRE) **Mrs G. A. Turnball**
12 **MAJOR DRIVE (IRE)**, 6, b g Sadler's Wells (USA)—Puck's Castle **Woodburn, Gallagher & Friends**
13 **PAVEY ARK (IRE)**, 6, b g King's Ride—Splendid Run **Mr & Mrs A. G. Milligan**

MR D. J. MOFFATT—continued

14 **PHARAOH HATSHEPSUT (IRE)**, 6, b m Definite Article—Maid of Mourne
15 **STAPLE SOUND**, 7, b g Alflora (IRE)—Loch Scavaig (IRE) **Mrs G. A. Turnbull**
16 **WESSEX (USA)**, 4, ch c Gone West (USA)—Satin Velvet (USA) **The Vilprano Partnership**

THREE-YEAR-OLDS

17 **ONLY MILLIE**, b f Prince Daniel (USA)—Deb's Ball **Mr & Mrs A. G. Milligan**
18 **SMEORACH**, ch f My Generation—Mohican **Mr Ian Macleod**

TWO-YEAR-OLDS

19 **HIGHFELL**, br g 16/4 Rock City—Bold Feliciter (Bold Arrangement) (2800) **Jennie Moffatt & Brian T. Clark**
20 Gr g 18/3 Paris House—Ladycake (IRE) (Perugino (USA)) **Mike Flyne**
21 **MITCHELLAND**, b f 7/5 Namaqualand—Precious Girl (Precious Metal) **R. R. Whitton**
22 **XAAR'S STAR**, b f 26/3 Xaar—Alustar (Emarati (USA)) **Bernard Bargh**

Other Owners: Mr K. Bowron, Mrs S. A. Clyde, Ms G. K. Humpage, Mr A. R. Mills, Mr Ian Munro, Mr George K. Parrington, Mr L. Simpson.

Jockeys (Flat): J Fanning (w.a.). A Nicolls (w.a.). **Jockeys (NH):** J Crowley (10-0), A Ross (10-0). **Conditional:** P Aspell (9-11), D Elsworth (10-0). **Amateur:** Mr S Gagan (9-7).

---

381 MR PETER MONTEITH, Rosewell
Postal: Whitebog Farm, Rosewell, Midlothian, EH24 9AY.
Contact: PHONE (0131 440) 2309 MOBILE (07885) 060296 FAX (0131 440) 2226
E-MAIL pmonteith945@aol.com

1 **ALAM (USA)**, 5, b g Silver Hawk (USA)—Ghashtah (USA) **Mr G. M. Cowan**
2 **AMBUSHED (IRE)**, 8, b g Indian Ridge—Surprise Move (IRE) **Melville/Stewart**
3 **BRAVE THOUGHT (IRE)**, 9, b g Commanche Run—Bristol Fairy **Hamilton House Limited**
4 **CAITRIONA'S CHOICE (IRE)**, 13, b g Carmelite House (USA)—Muligatawny **The Dregs Of Humanity**
5 **CITA VERDA (FR)**, 6, b m Take Risks (FR)—Mossita (FR) **Mr & Mrs Raymond Anderson Green**
6 **COLORADO FALLS (USA)**, 6, b g Nashwan (USA)—Ballet Shoes (IRE) **Mr J. W. D. Campbell**
7 **CORE OF SILVER (IRE)**, 5, b g Nucleon (USA)—My Silversmith (IRE) **Mrs G. Smyth**
8 **CULCABOCK (IRE)**, 4, b g Unfuwain (USA)—Evidently (IRE) **Mrs Elizabeth Ferguson**
9 **DUNSEMORE**, 4, b f Prince Daniel (USA)—Admire-A-More **Mrs A. F. Tullie**
10 **ENCORE CADOUDAL (FR)**, 6, b g Cadoudal (FR)—Maousse (FR) **Mr P. Monteith**
11 **HUGO DE PERRO (FR)**, 9, b g Perrault—Fontaine Aux Faons (FR) **Mr J. W. D. Campbell**
12 **IDEAL DU BOIS BEURY (FR)**, 8, b br g Useful (FR)—Pampa Star (FR) **Mr G. M. Cowan**
13 **IMPINDA (IRE)**, 5, b m Idris (IRE)—Last Finale (USA) **Mrs A. F. Tullie**
14 **IRISH PLEASURE (IRE)**, 8, b br g Grand Plaisir (IRE)—Killegney **Mr J. Stephenson**
15 **JORDAN'S RIDGE (IRE)**, 8, b br g Indian Ridge—Sadie Jordan (IRE) **Melville/Stewart**
16 **LYNCHAHAUN (IRE)**, 8, b br g Good Thyne (USA)—Smart Decision (IRE) **Mr P. Monteith**
17 **MILLENNIUM HALL**, 5, b g Saddlers' Hall (IRE)—Millazure (USA) **Mrs Elizabeth Ferguson**
18 **MINSTREL HALL**, 5, b m Saddlers' Hall (IRE)—Mindomica **Melville/Stewart**
19 **MOSCOW DANCER (IRE)**, 7, ch g Moscow Society (USA)—Cromhill Lady **Mr J. Stephenson**
20 **POLYPHON (FR)**, 6, b g Murmure (FR)—Petite Folie **Mr Raymond Anderson Green**
21 **SHARES (IRE)**, 4, b g Turtle Island (IRE)—Glendora **The Dregs Of Humanity**
22 **SPREE VISION**, 8, b g Suave Dancer (USA)—Regent's Folly (IRE) **Mr I. Bell**
23 **SRI (IRE)**, 5, b m Sri Pekan (USA)—Verify (IRE) **Melville/Stewart**
24 **TAHRIMA**, 5, b m Slip Anchor—Khandjar **Mr I. Bell**
25 **THE MIGHTY FLYNN**, 5, ch g Botanic (USA)—Owdbetts (IRE) **Mr J. W. D. Campbell**
26 **ZAMAT**, 8, b g Slip Anchor—Khandjar **Mr I. Bell**

THREE-YEAR-OLDS

27 **CHISTU**, b f Piccolo—Sun Dancing (IRE) **Melville/Stewart**
28 **TORGIANO (IRE)**, b g Cadeaux General—Decimara (IRE) **Mr P. Monteith**

TWO-YEAR-OLDS

29 **VIRAGO**, b f 19/3 Mtoto—Sun Dancing (IRE) (Magical Wonder (USA)) (2000) **Melville/Stewart**

Other Owners: Mr R. M. S. Allison, Mrs Anita Green, Mr Alan Guthrie.

Assistant Trainer: Doreen Monteith

Jockey (Flat): P Fessey. **Conditional:** K Renwick. **Amateur:** Mr S Waley Cohen (11-0).

382 MR A. L. MOORE, Naas

Postal: Dereens, Naas, Co. Kildare, Ireland.
Contact: HOME +353 (0) 45 876292 FAX +353 (0) 45 899247 MOBILE (0872) 552535

1 **BACK NINE (IRE)**, 7, b g Bob Back (USA)—Sylvia Fox **Old Moss Farm Syndicate**
2 **BALLYNATIN BUCK (IRE)**, 8, b g Buckskin (FR)—Dikler Gale (IRE) **M. O'Connor**
3 **BE MY BETTER HALF (IRE)**, 9, b g Be My Native (USA)—The Mrs **J. P. McManus**
4 **BLANC C'ESS BLANC (FR)**, 7, ch g Royal Charter (FR)—Tamilda (FR) **F. Conroy**
5 **BON TEMPS ROULER (FR)**, 5, b g Hero's Honor (USA)—Top Nue (FR) **F. Clarke**
6 **CADOU ROYAL (FR)**, 8, b g Cadoudal (FR)—Leonie des Champs (FR) **Sir A. J. O'Reilly**
7 **CAPTAIN GUCCI (FR)**, 6, ch g Flying Spur (AUS)—Fado's Delight **Kiljoy Estates**
8 **CYBORSUN (FR)**, 7, ch g Cyborg (FR)—Kaprika (FR) **J. P. McManus**
9 **DERAWAR (IRE)**, 5, b g Kahyasi—Denizliya (IRE) **Mrs J. J. McGettigan**
10 **ESKIMO JACK (IRE)**, 8, ch g Glacial Storm (USA)—Covette **J McKinney**
11 **FADOUDAL DU COCHET (FR)**, 11, b g Cadoudal (FR)—Eau de Vie (FR) **Sir A. J. O'Reilly**
12 **FARINEL**, 8, b g In The Wings—Dame de L'Oise (USA) **J. P. McManus**
13 **FATHOM IT OUT**, 5, b g Karinga Bay—Atlantic View
14 **FEICHEAD GHRA (IRE)**, 5, b g Goldmark (USA)—Semiramide (IRE) **Valentines Day Syndicate**
15 **FRIENDLY CONFLICT (IRE)**, 8, b g Jolly Jake (NZ)—Deep Rival **Mrs A. L. T. Moore**
16 **GALWAY BREEZE (IRE)**, 9, b g Broussard (USA)—Furena **F. Cruess-Callaghan**
17 **GLENELLY GALE (IRE)**, 10, b g Strong Gale—Smart Fashion **F. Bradley**
18 **GO MALL (IRE)**, 5, b g Lord Americo—Cool Glen **Mrs B. M. McKinney**
19 **GREEN FINGER (IRE)**, 6, b g Environment Friend—Hunt The Thimble **Mrs M. Donnelly**
20 **I GOT IT FIVE (IRE)**, 8, gr g Agent Bleu (FR)—Una Rosa (FR) **D. Cox**
21 **INCAS (FR)**, 8, b g Video Rock (FR)—Amarante II (FR) **Incas Syndicate**
22 **IN TEHCNICOLOUR (IRE)**, 5, b g Germany (USA)—Light Argument (IRE) **Dominic J. Jones**
23 **ITSALLGREEKTOME (IRE)**, 7, b g Alphabatim (USA)—Quincy Bay **S. Dunne**
24 **JANIDOU (FR)**, 8, b g Cadoudal (FR)—Majathen (FR) **J. P. McManus**
25 **JAQUOUILLE (FR)**, 7, b g Agent Bleu (FR)—Topeka (FR) **F. Clarke**
26 **JIRLAN (FR)**, 7, b g Fill My Hopes (FR)—Belle Brune (FR) **J. P. McManus**
27 **JULIUS (FR)**, 7, b g Kadalko (FR)—Toskaninie (FR) **J. P. McManus**
28 **JUNIOR FONTAINE (FR)**, 7, b g Silver Rainbow—Blanche Fontaine (FR) **W. W. Dennison**
29 **JURADO EXPRESS (FR)**, 8, b g Jurado (FR)—Express Film **Mrs Susan Traynor**
30 **KAOUTCHOU (FR)**, 6, b g Video Rock (FR)—Capitale (FR) **C. Jones**
31 **KILT D'ESTRUVAL (FR)**, 6, b g Cyborg (FR)—Vapeur (FR) **Mrs A. L. T. Moore**
32 **LOUGH ENNEL (IRE)**, 8, b g Peacock (FR)—Lynn Princess **N. McLancy**
33 **LOUVICE (FR)**, 5, b g Mansonnien (FR)—Caline de Mars (FR) **D. Cox**
34 **LUCKY STAR (FR)**, 5, b g Luchiroverte—Lady Pat Pong (FR) **T. Bailey**
35 **MADALKO (FR)**, 6, b g Cadoudal (FR)—Mabui Princess **Mrs M. Bryant**
36 **MADONNA FAN (IRE)**, 6, b g Lear Fan (USA)—Madonna Sprite **Speculation Syndicate**
37 **MANSONY (FR)**, 5, b g Mansonnien (FR)—Hairly (FR) **M. Mulholland**
38 **MARACANA (IRE)**, 5, b m Glacial Storm (USA)—Droichidin **Mrs C. Neilson**
39 **MARCUS DU BERLAIS (FR)**, 7, gr g Saint Preuil (FR)—Rosacotte (FR) **M. Beresford**
40 **MINOR RUMPUS**, 5, b g Roselier—Avena **Mrs A. L. J. Moore**
41 **MORE THAN A STROLL (IRE)**, 12, ch g Pennine Walk—Jenny's Child **Mrs D. Greman**
42 **MOUNT KIMBLE**, 8, b g Montelimar (USA)—Sweet Thunder **P & P Racing Synidcate**
43 **MUNSTER (IRE)**, 7, b g Zaffaran (USA)—Delway **C. Ryan**
44 **NATIVE UPMANSHIP (IRE)**, 11, ch g Be My Native (USA)—Hi' Upham **Mrs J. Magnier**
45 **NORVADANO (FR)**, 7, b g Turgeon (USA)—Esposente (FR) **Mrs A. L. T. Moore**
46 **PHARIWARMER (IRE)**, 10, b g Phardante (FR)—Arabian Sands **J. P. McManus**
47 **POLLY ANTHUS**, 5, b m Kahyasi—Bayariyka (IRE) **T. Ryan**
48 **RHEINDROSS (IRE)**, 9, gr g Ala Hounak—Ardcarn Girl **C. Jones**
49 **ROB THE FIVE (IRE)**, 8, b g Supreme Leader—Derravaragh Lady (IRE) **J. P. McManus**
50 **ROYAL PLAISIR (IRE)**, 9, b g Grand Plaisir (IRE)—Royal Well **Glenavet Racing Syndicate**
51 **SWINGS 'N STRINGS (IRE)**, 6, b g Accordion—Midsummer Blends (IRE) **Mrs A. L. T. Moore**
52 **SYROCO (FR)**, 5, b g Homme de Loi (IRE)—La Pommeraie (FR) **V. Kennedy**
53 **THE GATHERER (IRE)**, 10, b g Be My Native (USA)—Reaper's Run **J. P. McManus**
54 **THE RAILWAY MAN (IRE)**, 5, b g Shernazar—Sparky Sue (IRE) **S. Dunne**
55 **TIGER CRY**, 6, b g Germany—Dream Academy **C. Jones**
56 **TOU CHARMING**, 6, b g Toulon—Lucky Charm (IRE) **Tom Charming Syndicate**
57 **VALSKI (FR)**, 6, b g Ski Chief (USA)—Valmante (FR) **P. M. Law**
58 **WESTERN ROAD (GER)**, 4, b f King's Theatre (IRE)—Walkona **Western Road Syndicate**
59 **WHAT PERK (IRE)**, 5, b g Executive Perk—Milford Run **Lyreen Syndicate**

Jockeys (NH): B Cash (10-6), C O'Dwyer (10-4). **Conditional:** D Howard (9-4). **Amateurs:** Mr R. T. Dunne (9-7), Mr J D Moore (10-0).

383 MR G. L. MOORE, Brighton

Postal: **4 Downland Close, Woodingdean, Brighton, Sussex, BN2 6DN.**
Contact: **YARD (01273) 620405 HOME/FAX (01273) 620106 MOBILE (07753) 863123**

1 **ACORAZADO (IRE)**, 5, b g Petorius—Jaldi (IRE) **D T L Limited**
2 **ADECCO (IRE)**, 5, b g Eagle Eyed (USA)—Kharaliya (FR)
3 **ADOPTED HERO (IRE)**, 4, b g Sadler's Wells (USA)—Lady Liberty (NZ) **Mr N. J. Jones**
4 **ALCHEMYSTIC (IRE)**, 4, b g In The Wings—Kama Tashoof **Mr N. J. Jones**
5 **ALRAFID (IRE)**, 5, ch h Halling (USA)—Ginger Tree (USA) **Gillespie Brothers**
6 **AMNESTY**, 5, ch g Salse (USA)—Amaranthus **G. Jackman, J. Jackman**
7 **ANOTHER SECRET**, 6, b m Efisio—Secrets of Honour **Pleasure Palace Racing**
8 **ARC EN CIEL**, 6, b g Rainbow Quest (USA)—Nadia Nerina (CAN) **Mrs M. J. George**
9 **ASSOON**, 5, b g Ezzoud (IRE)—Handy Dancer
10 **BARCELONA**, 7, b h Barathea (IRE)—Pipitina
11 **BHUTAN (IRE)**, 9, b g Polish Patriot (USA)—Bustinetta
12 **BLUE STREAK (IRE)**, 7, ch g Bluebird (USA)—Fleet Amour (USA) **Mr D. R. Hunnisett**
13 **BRAVE CARADOC (IRE)**, 6, b g Un Desperado (FR)—Drivers Bureau **Mr M. K. George**
14 **BRAVURA**, 6, ch g Never So Bold—Sylvan Song **Mr R. Kiernan**
15 **CAPE CANAVERAL (IRE)**, 5, b g Sadler's Wells (USA)—Emmaline (USA) **Gillespie Brothers**
16 **CHARLIEMOORE**, 8, ch g Karinga Bay—Your Care (FR)
17 **CHEESE 'N BISCUITS**, 4, b f Spectrum (IRE)—Bint Shihama (USA) **D T L Limited**
18 **CHEROKEE BAY**, 4, b f Primo Dominie—Me Cherokee
19 **CHOCOLATE BOY (IRE)**, 5, b g Dolphin Street (FR)—Kawther **Sigma Estates**
20 **COLD TURKEY**, 4, b br g Polar Falcon (USA)—South Rock **Mr A. Grinter**
21 **COLNE VALLEY AMY**, 7, b m Mizoram (USA)—Panchellita (USA)
22 **CONSTANTINE**, 4, gr g Linamix (FR)—Speremm (IRE)
23 **CRAFTY POLITICIAN (USA)**, 7, ch h Supremo (USA)—
                                       Sauve Qui Peut (CAN) **Mr Raymond Gross, Ms Adrienne Gross**
24 **DANGEROUSLY GOOD**, 6, b g Shareef Dancer (USA)—Ecologically Kind
25 **DOLZAGO**, 4, b g Pursuit of Love—Doctor's Glory (USA)
26 **DUE TO ME**, 4, gr f Compton Place—Always Lucky **Mrs Sheila Clarke**
27 **EARLSFIELD RAIDER**, 4, ch g Double Trigger (IRE)—Harlequin Walk (IRE) **Mrs R. J. Doorgachurn**
28 **EHAB (IRE)**, 5, b g Cadeaux Genereux—Dernier Cri **The Go For Brokers Partnership**
29 **ESTRELLA LEVANTE**, 4, ch g Abou Zouz (USA)—Star of Modena (IRE) **Mr W. P. Flynn**
30 **FLYING SPIRIT (IRE)**, 5, b g Flying Spur (AUS)—All Laughter
31 **FORT SAUMAREZ**, 5, b g Magic Ring (IRE)—Rocquaine Bay
32 **FOSFORITO (IRE)**, 6, b g Zieten (USA)—Bardouine (USA)
33 **GABOR**, 5, b g Danzig Connection (USA)—Kiomi **Leydens Farm Stud**
34 **GEMI BED (FR)**, 4, b g Double Bed (FR)—Gemia (FR) **Mr B. Lennard**
35 **GIN PALACE (IRE)**, 6, gr g King's Theatre (IRE)—Ikala
36 **GOING GLOBAL (IRE)**, 7, ch g Bob Back (USA)—Ukraine Girl **Allen House Partnership**
37 **GRAND PRAIRIE (SWE)**, 8, br g Prairie—Platonica (ITY)
38 **GUN SALUTE**, 4, b g Mark of Esteem (IRE)—Affair of State (IRE) **Mr R. Henderson**
39 **GURU**, 6, b g Slip Anchor—Ower (IRE) **Mr Will Bennett**
40 **HAAFEL (USA)**, 7, ch g Diesis—Dish Dash
41 **HARIK**, 10, ch g Persian Bold—Yaqut (USA) **The Best Beech Partnership**
42 **HIGH HOPE (FR)**, 6, ch h Lomitas—Highness Lady (GER) **RDM Racing**
43 **HUCKLEBERRY FINN**, 4, b g Sadler's Wells (USA)—Cruising Height
44 **I D TECHNOLOGY (IRE)**, 8, ch g Commanche Run—Lady Geeno (IRE)
45 **KIRAT**, 6, b h Darshaan—Kafsa (IRE)
46 **LAFFAH (USA)**, 9, b g Silver Hawk (USA)—Sakiyah (USA)
47 **LIGHTNING STAR (USA)**, 9, b g El Gran Senor (USA)—Cuz's Star (USA)
48 **LOGSDAIL**, 4, b g Polish Precedent (USA)—Logic **D T L Limited**
49 **LORD HECCLES (IRE)**, 5, b g Supreme Leader—Parsons Law
50 **LUCKY VALENTINE**, 4, b f My Best Valentine—Vera's First (IRE)
51 **MAD CAREW (USA)**, 5, ch g Rahy (USA)—Poppy Carew (IRE) **Mr David Allen**
52 **MAJHOOL**, 5, b g Mark of Esteem (USA)—Be Peace (USA) **Lancing Racing Syndicate**
53 **MASTER T (USA)**, 5, b g Trempolino (USA)—Our Little C (USA) **Lancing Racing Syndicate**
54 **MID SUSSEX SPIRIT**, 5, b g Environment Friend—Ranyah (USA) **Saloop**
55 **MISTER PICKWICK (IRE)**, 9, ch g Commanche Run—Buckfast Lass **Barry Prichard & Wayne Russell**
56 **MONDURU**, 7, b g Lion Cavern (USA)—Bint Albadou (IRE) **Pleasure Palace Racing**
57 **MOSTARSIL (USA)**, 6, ch g Kingmambo (USA)—Naazeq
58 **MOWBRAY (USA)**, 9, b br g Opening Verse (USA)—Peppy Raja (USA)
59 **NAWAMEES (IRE)**, 6, b h Darshaan—Truly Generous (IRE) **Mr Paul Stamp**
60 **OPERASHAAN (IRE)**, 4, b g Darshaan—Comic Opera (IRE)
61 **ORTHODOX**, 5, gr g Baryshnikov (AUS)—Sancta **Mrs Elizabeth Kiernan**
62 **PAIRING (IRE)**, 6, ch g Rudimentary (USA)—Splicing

MR G. L. MOORE—continued

63 PARDISHAR (IRE), 6, b g Kahyasi—Parapa (IRE) **Mr D. R. Hunnisett**
64 PEQUENITA, 4, b f Rudimentary (USA)—Sierra Madrona (USA) **Mr N. J. Jones**
65 PORAK (IRE), 7, ch g Perugino (USA)—Gayla Orchestra
66 PRINCE DOMINO, 5, b g Primo Dominie—Danzig Harbour (USA) **Mr D. R. Hunnisett**
67 RESSOURCE (FR), 5, b h Broadway Flyer (USA)—Rayonne **The Straight Forward Partnership II**
68 ROB LEACH, 7, b g Robellino (USA)—Arc Empress Jane (IRE)
69 SADLER'S ROCK, 6, b g Sadler's Wells—Triple Couronne (USA) **Regal Racing**
70 SHAMAN, 7, b g Fraam—Magic Maggie **Mr Paul Chapman**
71 SNUKI, 5, b h Pivotal—Kennedys Prima **The Hove Racing Club**
72 SPACE COWBOY (IRE), 4, b c Anabaa (USA)—Lady Moranbon **Platt Sanderson Partnership**
73 STARS DELIGHT (IRE), 7, ch g Fourstars Allstar (USA)—Celtic Cygnet
74 STORMY SKYE (IRE), 8, b g Bluebird (USA)—Canna
75 TIKRAM, 7, ch g Lycius (USA)—Black Fighter (USA) **Mike Charlton And Rodger Sargent**
76 TWENTY DEGREES, 6, ch g Beveled (USA)—Sweet N' Twenty **Mr W. E. Baird**
77 VERY EXCLUSIVE (USA), 5, b g Royal Academy (USA)—Exclusive Davis (USA) **Mr Danny Bloor**
78 WAIT FOR THE WILL (USA), 8, ch g Seeking The Gold (USA)—You'd Be Surprised (USA)
79 WATCHFUL WITNESS, 4, ch c In The Wings—Eternal **Mr J. F. Reeves**
80 WE'LL MAKE IT (IRE), 6, b g Spectrum (IRE)—Walliser **Wayne Barr,John Ripley,D.Goff,S.Moss**
81 ZIMBABWE, 4, b g Kahyasi—Zeferina (IRE) **Sargent Gillespie**

THREE-YEAR-OLDS

82 AT THE READY (IRE), b c Daggers Drawn (USA)—Highly Motivated
83 CHAMPAGNE SHADOW (IRE), b g Kahyasi—Moet (USA)
84 CZARS PRINCESS (IRE), b f Soviet Star (USA)—Pearl Shell (USA) **Mr E. Farncombe**
85 EVEN EASIER, gr f Petong—Comme Ca
86 FIRST TARF, ch f Primo Dominie—Tarf (USA)
87 FLYING PATRIARCH, gr c Silver Patriarch (IRE)—Flying Wind **Heart of the South Racing**
88 JOINT DESTINY (IRE), b f Desert Prince (IRE)—Brogan's Well (IRE) **Mrs J. Moore**
89 JOY AND PAIN, b g Pursuit of Love—Ice Chocolate (USA) **E. Farncombe T/A EWS Shavings**
90 PANGLOSS (IRE), ch c Croco Rouge (IRE)—Kafayef (USA)
91 PRIME POWERED, b c Barathea (IRE)—Caribbean Quest
92 SONDEBORG, b f Great Dane (IRE)—Nordico Princess
93 STAGECOACH RUBY, b f Bijou d'Inde—Forum Girl (USA)

TWO-YEAR-OLDS

94 Ch c 30/3 Double Trigger (IRE)—Harlequin Walk (IRE) (Pennine Walk) **Mrs R. J. Doorgachurn & Mr C.Stedman**
95 PRIMED UP (IRE), b c 25/2 Rainbow Quest (USA)—Cape Mist (USA) (Lure (USA)) (18000) **Prime Power Ltd**
96 B c 20/4 Trans Island—Seattle Siren (USA) (Seattle Slew (USA)) **Messrs Brian & Jock Crainey**

Other Owners: Mrs J. L. Agnew, Mr M. Avery, Mr Wayne Barr, Mr C. Bevis, Mr C. Bond, Mrs C. S. Braga, Mr S. J. Brant, Mr J. M. Bush, Mrs S. K. Bush, Mr T. Carter, Mr N. Cash, Mr M. R. Charlton, Mr Dean Clark, Mr M. L. Dalton, Mr S. Danahar, Mr Paul Deakin, Mrs B. Farncombe, Mr Robin Fuller, Mr J. A. Gent, Mr S. G. Gillespie, Mr T. G. Gillespie, Mr R. De Giovanni, Mrs D. Goff, Mr I. Goldsmith, Mrs Maria Goldsmith, Ms Adrienne Gross, Mr Raymond Gross, Mr J. S. G. Haslem, Mr Darrell Hinds, Mr J. Hinds, Mr C. J. Hodges, Mr G. D. Jones, Mr H. Nicholas Lund, Mrs Nicola McGreavy, Mrs S. Moss, Mrs J. Peel, Mrs K. E. Thorbes, Mr R. A. Muddle, Mr S. Packham, Mrs Caroline Penny, Mr John Penny, Mr M. E. Platt, Mr A. Pook, Mr N. S. L. Price, Mr Barry Prichard, Mr John Ripley, Mr Wayne Russell, Prof A. R. Sanderson, Mr Rodger Sargent, Mr R. E. Thorbes, Vogue Development Company (Kent) Ltd.

Assistant Trainer: David Wilson

Jockeys (Flat): I Mongan, L Moore. **Jockeys (NH):** M Batchelor (w.a.), P Hide (w.a.), A P McCoy (w.a.). **Apprentices:** J Marshall, H Poulton. **Conditional:** J E Moore. **Amateurs:** Mr E Demdishdi, q W Demdishdi.

384
MR G. M. MOORE, Middleham
Postal: **Warwick Lodge Stables, Middleham, Leyburn, North Yorkshire, DL8 4PB.**
Contact: PHONE (01969) 623823 FAX (01969) 623823
E-MAIL carolmoore@tinyworld.co.uk WEBSITE www.george-moore-racing.co.uk

1 ACTIVIST, 4, ch g Diesis—Shicklah (USA) **Mr John Robson**
2 AGNESE, 4, ch f Abou Zouz (USA)—Efizia **Mrs H. I. S. Calzini**
3 ALICE BRAND (IRE), 6, b m Nucleon (USA)—Tormented **Mr L. Tucker**
4 ALMENARA, 5, ch m Weld—Dishcloth **The Three Socks Partnership**
5 ARGENTO, 7, b g Weldnaas (USA)—Four M's **Mr J. B. Wallwin**
6 ASHNAYA (FR), 6, b m Ashkalani (IRE)—Upend (IRE) **Mr B. Bradshaw**

MR G. M. MOORE—continued

7 **AVEBURY**, 8, b g Fairy King (USA)—Circle of Chalk (FR) **The Tupgill Partnership**
8 **BATTO**, 4, b g Slip Anchor—Frog **Mrs I. I. Plumb**
9 **BEAMISH PRINCE**, 5, ch g Bijou d'Inde—Unconditional Love (IRE) **Mrs S. E. Turnbull**
10 **CASTLE RICHARD (IRE)**, 7, gr g Sexton Blake—Miss McCormick (IRE) **Mrs Mary and Miss Susan Hatfield**
11 **CIARA'S RUN (IRE)**, 4, ch f Topanoora—Rugged Run **Mr David Bushell**
12 **DAILY RUN (IRE)**, 6, b g Supreme Leader—Rugged Run **Mr A. J. Coupland**
13 **EMERGING STAR (IRE)**, 4, b g Desert Style (IRE)—Feather Star **Arthur, Chris and Geoff Peacock**
14 **FORTUNES FAVOURITE**, 4, ch f Barathea (IRE)—Golden Fortune **Lucayan Stud**
15 **GLENDEVON GREY**, 5, gr g Karinga Bay—Sandy Etna (IRE) **Mrs J. M. Gray**
16 **IRON EXPRESS**, 8, b g Teenoso (USA)—Sylvia Beach **Mr David Parker**
17 **IRON WARRIOR (IRE)**, 4, b g Lear Fan (USA)—Robalana (USA) **Mr David Parker**
18 **JUNGLE JINKS (IRE)**, 9, b g Proud Panther (FR)—Three Ladies **Mrs Mary and Miss Susan Hatfield**
19 **KARAJAN (IRE)**, 7, b g Fairy King (USA)—Dernier Cri **J. R. F. (Management Consultants) Ltd**
20 **LAGOSTA (SAF)**, 4, ch g Fort Wood (USA)—Rose Wine **Mrs A. Roddis**
21 **LA SYLPHIDE**, 7, ch m Rudimentary (USA)—Primitive Gift **Mr Geoff & Mrs Sandra Turnbull**
22 **MICHAELS JOY (IRE)**, 5, br g Presenting—Scarteen Lower (IRE) **Mr John Robson**
23 **NUCLEAR PROSPECT (IRE)**, 4, ch g Nucleon (USA)—Carraigbyrne (IRE) **Mrs Mary and Miss Susan Hatfield**
24 **ONEFORBERTANDHENRY (IRE)**, 6, b g Rashar (USA)—Roi Vision **J. B. Partnership**
25 **PAVONE QUEST**, 7, ch g Jumbo Hirt (USA)—Gilsan Grey **Inter Enterprise IES Ltd**
26 **PREMIER DRIVE**, 11, ch g Black Minstrel—Ballyanihan **Mr A. W. Sergeant**
27 **PRINCE ADJAL (IRE)**, 4, b g Desert Prince (IRE)—Adjalisa (IRE) **J & M Leisure / Unos Restaurant**
28 **PRIZE RING**, 5, ch g Bering—Spot Prize (USA) **Gordon Brown/Bert Watson**
29 **QUARTER MASTERS (IRE)**, 5, b g Mujadil (USA)—Kentucky Wildcat **The Dowdstown Boy's**
30 **ROMAN RODNEY**, 7, b g Feelings (FR)—Pohet **Mr W. J. Laws**
31 **ROMIL STAR (GER)**, 7, b g Chief's Crown (USA)—Romelia (USA) **Mr M. R. Johnson**
32 **SCOTMAIL LAD (IRE)**, 10, b g Ilium—Nicholas Ferry **Gordon Brown/Bert Watson**
33 **SIR STORM (IRE)**, 8, b g Ore—Yonder Bay (IRE) **J. R. F. (Management Consultants) Ltd**
34 **SPRING GAMBLE (IRE)**, 5, b g Norwich—Aurora Run (IRE) **Mr J. B. Wallwin**
35 **SUPREME LASS**, 8, b m Supreme Leader—Falas Lass **A. J. Racehorses**
36 **SYLVIESBUCK (IRE)**, 7, b g Kasmayo—Sylvies Missiles (IRE) **Mrs I. I. Plumb**

THREE-YEAR-OLDS

37 **BEAMSLEY BEACON**, ch g Wolfhound (USA)—Petindia **J. Lishman & K. Kirkup & D. Neale**
38 **FIRST ACORN**, b f Petong—Mimining **The Little Acorn Partnership**
39 **FUTOO (IRE)**, b g Foxhound (USA)—Nicola Wynn **Mr M. K. Roddis**
40 **IRON TEMPTRESS (IRE)**, ch f Piccolo—River Divine **Mr David Parker**
41 **JALOUSIE DREAM**, b f Easycall—Forest Maid **Mrs Susan Moore**
42 B c Petong—Miss Tri Colour **Mrs D. N. B. Pearson**
43 **PAGAN RIVER**, b c River Falls—Pagan Star **Mr R. Phizacklea**

TWO-YEAR-OLDS

44 **FROG'S GIFT (IRE)**, gr f 30/4 Danehill Dancer (IRE)—Warthill Whispers (Grey Desire) **Mrs I. I. Plumb**
45 B c 13/3 Sinndar (IRE)—Kindle (Selkirk (USA)) (10000) **Valueplace Ltd**
46 **MERCARI**, ch f 5/3 Bahamian Bounty—Aonach Mor (Anabaa (USA)) **Mr Peter Player**
47 Ch c 4/4 Weldnaas—Riverain (Bustino) **Mr J. Pickavance**
48 **SERENE PEARL (IRE)**, b f 20/4 Night Shift (USA)—
Shanjah (Darshaan) (16000) **Mrs Mary & Miss Susan Hatfield**

Other Owners: Mr A. C. Birkle, Mr D. J. Bushell, Mr B. Collier, Mr T. J. Crehan, Mr Graham Frankland, Mr J. Heald, Mr A. Peacock, Mr Chris Peacock, Mr Geoff Peacock, Mr S. Smith (Bradford), Mr M. A. Tebbutt, Mr Robert Watson, Mr A. S. Whitwham, Mrs J. A. Whitwham.

Jockeys (NH): Russ Garritty, A Ross. **Apprentice:** T Eaves (8-3). **Conditional:** B Orde-Powlett (10-0). **Amateur:** Mr G Hardisty (10-0).

---

385 MR K. A. MORGAN, Melton Mowbray

Postal: **Hall Farm Stables, Waltham On The Wolds, Melton Mowbray, Leicestershire, LE14 4AJ.**
Contact: **PHONE** (01664) 464711/464488 **FAX** (01664) 464492 **MOBILE** (07768) 996103

1 **AQUIFORM**, 4, ch f Cadeaux Genereux—Aquarelle **Mr D. S. Cooper**
2 **ARADNAK (IRE)**, 4, b f Son of Sharp Shot (IRE)—Kandara (FR) **Mr K. A. Morgan**
3 **BLAU GRAU (GER)**, 7, gr g Neshad (USA)—Belle Orfana (GER) **Mr D. S. Cooper**
4 **BYLAND**, 4, b g Danzig (USA)—Coxwold (USA) **Mrs G. Bradley**
5 **COLOPHONY (USA)**, 4, ch g Distant View (USA)—Private Line (USA) **Mr H. A. Blenkhorn & Partners**

MR K. A. MORGAN—continued

6 COURT OF JUSTICE (USA), 8, b g Alleged (USA)—Captive Island **Roemex Ltd**
7 CRAZY MAZIE, 7, b m Risk Me (FR)—Post Impressionist (IRE) **The Tricoloure Partnership**
8 DANZIG PRINCE, 5, b g Danzig Connection (USA)—Lovely Greek Lady **Wentdale Limited**
9 DIRECTION, 6, b m Lahib (USA)—Theme (IRE) **J.Sheridan,G.S.Alcock,Miss S.M.Cosgrove**
10 ELSUNDUS (USA), 6, b g Gone West (USA)—Aljawza (USA) **Roemex Ltd & G. S. Alcock**
11 FASIH (USA), 4, b g Bahri (USA)—Minifah (USA) **Mrs G. Bradley**
12 FLUFFY, 6, b m Perpendicular—Hinton Bairn **Mrs P. Goodman**
13 FLYOFF (IRE), 7, b g Mtoto—Flyleaf (FR) **Harmer Personal Care Ltd**
14 JAZIL, 9, b g Nashwan (USA)—Gracious Beauty (USA) **Mrs Jo Champion**
15 KINGKOHLER (IRE), 5, b g King's Theatre (IRE)—Legit (IRE) **Mrs Jo Champion, H. Morgan, E. Barlow**
16 MACREATER, 6, b m Mazaad—Gold Caste (USA) **Mr Nigel Stokes**
17 MARIGLIANO (USA), 11, b g Riverman (USA)—Mount Holyoke **G. S. Alcock & B. R. Jones**
18 MAUNBY ROLLER (IRE), 5, b g Flying Spur (AUS)—Brown Foam **Mr D. S. Cooper**
19 MY WILD ROVER, 4, b g Puissance—June Fayre **Mr D. S. Cooper**
20 PENALTY CLAUSE (IRE), 4, b g Namaqualand (USA)—Lady Be Lucky (IRE) **Hall Farm Racing**
21 ROYAL DRAGON, 4, b g Octagonal (NZ)—Belladera (IRE) **Mrs G. Bradley**
22 SEA DRIFTING, 7, b g Slip Anchor—Theme (IRE) **Mr S. & Mrs M. Giles & Mr & Mrs J. Taqvi**
23 SEE MY GIRL, 6, gr m Terimon—Nessfield **Mr J. Duckworth**
24 SELKIRK GRACE, 4, b g Selkirk (USA)—Polina **Mr D. S. Cooper**
25 TAKE HEED, 8, b g Warning—Tunaria (USA) **Roemex Ltd**
26 TOJONESKI, 5, b g Emperor Jones (USA)—Sampower Lady **Mr M. Shirley**
27 TORQUE, 4, b g Pennekamp (USA)—Tunaria (USA) **Hall Farm Racing**
28 WALTHAM DOVE, 9, br g Gypsy Castle—Dovetail **Mr K. A. Morgan**
29 WATERCRESS, 4, b f Slip Anchor—Theme (USA) **Mr S. & Mrs M. Giles**
30 YALLAMBIE, 5, b m Revoque (IRE)—Tahnee **Mr D. S. Cooper**

THREE-YEAR-OLDS

31 EMKANAT (IRE), ch f Unfuwain (USA)—Raaqiyya (USA) **Mr K. A. Morgan**
32 GREEK STAR, b g Soviet Star (USA)—Graecia Magna (USA) **Mr D. S. Cooper**

TWO-YEAR-OLDS

33 LITTLE WALTHAM, ch f 28/5 Tomba—Post Impressionist (IRE) (Ahonoora) **Mr T. A. Robinson**

Other Owners: Mrs P. A. L. Butler, Mr D. A. Charlesworth, Mr M. Ogburn.

---

386 MR C. P. H. MORLOCK, Wantage
Postal: Raceyard Cottage Stables, Kingston Lisle, Wantage, Oxfordshire, OX12 9QH.
Contact: HOME/FAX (01367) 820510 MOBILE (07768) 923444
E-MAIL morlock@raceyard.freeserve.co.uk

1 BOBALONG (IRE), 7, b g Bob's Return (IRE)—Northern Wind **Pell-mell Partners**
2 GIFTNEYEV (FR), 5, b br g Goldneyev (USA)—Girl's Gift (FR) **Pell-mell Partners**
3 GRACEFUL DANCER, 7, b m Old Vic—Its My Turn **The Fairway Connection**
4 HENRY'S HAPPINESS, 5, b m Bob's Return (IRE)—Irish Mint **Mr & Mrs W. R. Morlock**
5 KAOLIN DE PERCHE (FR), 6, b g Luchiroverte (IRE)—Craven II (FR) **Pell-mell Partners**
6 KYNANCE COVE, 5, b g Karinga Bay—Excelled (IRE) **Mrs Jenny Melbourne**
7 LAND ROVER LAD, 6, ch g Alflora—Filliode **Mc Coy's Neighbours**
8 LE DIAMONT (FR), 5, ch g Broadway Flyer (USA)—Lady Diamond (FR) **Pell-mell Partners**
9 LIN D'ESTRUVAL (FR), 5, b g Cadoudal (FR)—Recolte d'Estruval (FR) **Pell-mell Partners**
10 MAXIMUS (IRE), 9, br g Un Desperado (FR)—Fais Vite (USA) **Cockerell Cowing Racing**
11 OXIDOR (IRE), 9, br g Be My Native (USA)—Euroblend (IRE) **Mr D. and Mrs H. Woodhall**
12 5, B g Executive Perk—Rare Picture **Temple Dean**
13 RARE PRESENCE (IRE), 5, b g Sadler's Wells (USA)—Celebrity Style (USA) **The Shouting Men**
14 SUNDAWN LADY, 6, b m Faustus—Game Domino **Mr Michael Padfield & Mr Philip Dean**
15 4, B g Afzal—Threads **Mr C. Morlock & Mr B. McNamee**

THREE-YEAR-OLDS

16 LORD GREYSTOKE (IRE), b c Petardia—Jungle Story (IRE) **The Greystoke Partnership**

Other Owners: Mr R. J. Atkinson, Mr J. C. Berry, Mr J. Chromiak, Mr Barry J. Cockerell, Mr Alan Cowing, Mr Philip Dean, Mr P. R. Fisher, Mr Richard Gilder, Mr G. Hodgson, Mr Michael Padfield, Mrs Diana Patterson, Mr S. R. C. Philip, Mr S. M. Polley, Mr P. Webb, Mr D. Woodhall, Mrs H. Woodhall.

Jockeys (NH): T Doyle (10-0), J A McCarthy (10-0).

387 MR M. MORRIS, Fethard

Postal: Everardsgrange, Fethard, Co. Tipperary, Ireland.
Contact: PHONE +353 (0) 52 31474 FAX +353 (0) 52 31654
E-MAIL mouse@eircom.net WEBSITE www.mousemorris.com

1 ALCAPONE (IRE), 10, b g Roselier (FR)—Ann's Cap (IRE) Mrs Ann Daly
2 BAILY BREEZE (IRE), 5, b g Zaffaran (USA)—Mixed Blends Mr A. Scott
3 BAILY MIST (IRE), 7, b g Zaffaran (USA)—Mixed Blends Mr A. Scott
4 BROWNIE RETURNS (IRE), 11, b g Dry Dock—What A Brownie Mrs Ann Daly
5 BUACHAILL HAZE (IRE), 5, b g Great Marquess—Claudette M. F. Morris
6 DONT MAKE ME CHOSE (IRE), 7, b g Insan (USA)—Stream Flyer David O'Loughlin
7 FOTA ISLAND (IRE), 8, b g Supreme Leader—Mary Kate Finn J. P. McManus
8 FRESHWATER (IRE), 6, b m Commanche Run—Prolific Scot Mr Stephen Daly
9 HURTON (IRE), 10, b g Glacial Storm (USA)—Shuil Ub Mrs Ann Daly
10 HYDERABAD, 6, ch h Deploy—Ajuga (USA) Sir A. J. O'Reilly
11 KEEPATEM (IRE), 8, ch g Be My Native (USA)—Ariannrun J. P. McManus
12 KING'S EQUERRY (IRE), 8, b g King's Ride—Tiny Tina Sir A. J. O'Reilly
13 LORD RED, 5, ch g Presenting—My Adventure (IRE) M. A. Kilduff & Partners
14 MICK DIVINE (IRE), 6, b g Roselier (FR)—Brown Forest M. O'Flynn
15 MONIFETH MAN (IRE), 9, b g Be My Native (USA)—Outdoor Ivy M. F. Morris
16 NORTH GOLD (IRE), 6, b g Distinctly North (USA)—Miss Goldie Locks Mr P. Nelson
17 ROSTROPOVICH (IRE), 7, gr h Sadler's Wells (USA)—Infamy Mr M. A. Kilduff & Partners
18 SEAFORDE (IRE), 4, ch g Titus Livius (FR)—Rosy Affair (IRE) Sir A. J. O'Reilly
19 SHANNAHYDE (IRE), 6, ch g Shernazar—Fernhill (IRE) M. F. Morris
20 SHE'S GOT TO GO (IRE), 7, ch m Glacial Storm (USA)—Chalk It Down McCarthy Syndicate
21 SKIBB (IRE), 7, b g Be My Native (USA)—Inch Lady Mrs Ann Daly
22 THE GALLANTJOHNJOE (IRE), 6, ch m Beneficial—Better Thana Brief (IRE) Ms Catherine White
23 TOM SAYERS (IRE), 6, b g Toulon—Jillie James M. F. Morris
24 VELVET HUXLEY (IRE), 6, b g Fourstars Allstar (USA)—Gentle Leader (IRE) M. F. Morris
25 WAR OF ATTRITIAN (IRE), 5, br g Presenting—Una Juna (IRE) M. O'Leary
26 WING BACK (IRE), 6, b g Be My Native (USA)—Decent Skin (IRE) Sir A. J. O'Reilly
27 ZERO TO HERO (IRE), 6, b g Lord Americo—Sea Island D. Desmond

Jockey (NH): D Casey.

388 MR H. MORRISON, East Ilsley

Postal: Summerdown, East Ilsley, Newbury, Berkshire, RG20 7LB.
Contact: PHONE (01635) 281678 FAX (01635) 281746 MOBILE (07836) 687799
E-MAIL hughie@hughiemorrison.co.uk

1 ALCAZAR (IRE), 9, b g Alzao (USA)—Sahara Breeze J. Repard & Partners
2 BALTIC KING, 4, b c Danetime (IRE)—Lindfield Belle (IRE) Thurloe Thoroughbreds VIII
3 BOX BUILDER, 7, ch g Fraam—Ena Olley Mr M. Hutchinson
4 CAPE ST VINCENT, 4, gr g Paris House—Cape Merino Barbara Janet & Templeton Stud
5 ELA JAY, 5, b m Double Eclipse (IRE)—Papirusa (IRE) J & L Wetherald - M & M Glover
6 FLETCHER, 10, b g Salse (USA)—Ballet Classique (USA) Lady Margadale
7 FLINT RIVER, 6, b g Red Ransom (USA)—She's All Class (USA) The Firm
8 HARELDA, 4, ch f Hector Protector (USA)—Hen Harrier Sir Thomas Pilkington
9 INDIAN WELCOME, 5, ch g Most Welcome—Qualitair Ridge The Most Welcome Partnership
10 JASMICK (IRE), 6, ch m Definite Article—Glass Minnow (IRE) The Melksham Craic
11 KINGS BAY, 5, ch m Beveled (USA)—Storm of Plenty Mr P. J. Doherty
12 KYLKENNY, 9, b g Kylian (USA)—Fashion Flow Mr H. Morrison
13 PADDINGTON GREEN, 6, b g Primitive Rising (USA)—Mayfair Minx R.Sweet,Mrs M. Wilson,F.Flynn,R.Madden
14 PANGO, 5, ch g Bluegrass Prince (IRE)—Riverine Pangfield Partners
15 PASCALI, 4, b f Compton Place—Pass The Rose (IRE) Mrs Eleanor Kent
16 PESSIMISTIC DICK, 11, b g Derrylin—Tycoon Moon Frank Flynn and Richard Madden
17 PURDEY, 4, ch f Double Trigger (USA)—Euphorie (GER) Mrs Lee Ann Day & Mr Brian Hammond
18 SANGIOVESE, 5, b g Piccolo—Kaprisky (IRE) Kentisbeare Quartet
19 SECRET PLOY, 4, b g Deploy—By Line Mr A. M. Carding
20 SPLASH OUT AGAIN, 6, gr g River Falls—Kajetana (FR) Mr M. Bevan
21 STARZAAN (IRE), 5, b g Darshaan—Stellina (IRE) Mr Ben Arbib
22 TAFFY DANCER, 6, b g Emperor Jones (USA)—Ballerina Bay Rosemary Jenks & Partners
23 THE LAST CAST, 5, ch g Prince of Birds (USA)—Atan's Gem (USA) Mr D. P. Barrie
24 THIEVES'GLEN, 6, b g Teenoso (USA)—Hollow Creek Panda Christie & Rory Sweet
25 TILLA, 4, b f Bin Ajwaad (IRE)—Tosca Mr M. E. Wates

MR H. MORRISON—continued

26 **TOM PADDINGTON**, 9, b g Rock Hopper—Mayfair Minx **M.S.Wilson Mrs Wilson (Camp Farm Racing)**
27 **ZEIS (IRE)**, 4, ch c Bahhare (USA)—Zoom Lens (IRE) **Mr D. J. Donner**

THREE-YEAR-OLDS

28 **BARBILYRIFLE (IRE)**, b c Indian Rocket—Age of Elegance **B. Arbib and G. Fillery**
29 **BLUE JAVA**, ch c Bluegrass Prince (IRE)—Java Bay **Pangfield Partners**
30 **BROUGH SUPREME**, b g Sayaarr (USA)—Loriner's Lady **Mrs Jenny Willment**
31 **ELSINORA**, b f Great Dane (IRE)—Deanta In Eirinn **Mr John R. Goddard and Mr John Steel**
32 **EVA JEAN**, b f Singspiel (IRE)—Go For Red (IRE) **Dr & Mrs J. Wilson**
33 **FIDDLE ME BLUE**, ch f Bluebird (USA)—Fiddle-Dee-Dee (IRE) **Mr David Dobson**
34 **GREAT GIDDING**, b g Classic Cliche (IRE)—Arcady **Mr James Henderson**
35 **GWEN JOHN (USA)**, ch f Peintre Celebre (USA)—River Jig (USA) **Lord Margadale**
36 **HIHO SILVER LINING**, gr f Silver Patriarch (IRE)—By Line **Lady Blyth**
37 **HOH NELSON**, b c Halling (USA)—Birsay **Mr D. Allport & Mr Michael T. Lynch**
38 **HUNTING PINK**, b f Foxhound (USA)—Dancing Bluebell (IRE) **Mr & Mrs W. G. B. Hungerford**
39 **KILLINALLAN**, b f Vettori (IRE)—Babycham Sparkle **Lord Margadale & Partners**
40 **KYTHIA (IRE)**, b f Kahyasi—Another Rainbow (IRE) **Mr L. A. Garfield**
41 **LIQUIDATE**, b g Hector Protector (USA)—Cut And Run **The Phantom Partnership**
42 **LITTLE RIDGE (IRE)**, b g Charnwood Forest (IRE)—Princess Natalie **Lady Margadale**
43 **MEDICA BOBA**, b f Dr Fong (USA)—Silly View (IRE) **Mr M. E. Wates**
44 **ODIHAM**, b g Deploy—Hug Me **Odiham Partnership**
45 **OLYMPIAS (IRE)**, b f Kahyasi—Premier Amour **Mr L. A. Garfield**
46 **OPEN BOOK**, b f Mark of Esteem (IRE)—Sweetness Herself **The Phantom Partnership**
47 **PASTORAL PURSUITS**, b c Bahamian Bounty—Star **The Pursuits Partnership**
48 **PETROLINA (IRE)**, b f Petardia—Arbitration (IRE) **Wilson, Carding, Morrison & Trenchard**
49 Ch f Bien Bien (USA)—Riverine **Mr T. J. Billington**
50 **RUBY ROCKET (IRE)**, b f Indian Rocket—Geht Schnell **Thurloe Thoroughbreds IX**
51 **SHIBUMI**, ch f Cigar—Hurricane Rose **Get Ahead Racing**
52 **WAZIRI (IRE)**, b c Mtoto—Euphorie (GER) **Ashley House Racing**

TWO-YEAR-OLDS

53 Ch f 18/5 Inchinor—All The Time (Dancing Brave (USA) **A. R. Macdonald-Buchanan & Partners**
54 B c 1/3 Forzando—Barsham (Be My Guest (USA)) (22000) **H. Scott-Barrett, S. Dibb, M.Kerr-Dineen**
55 B c 5/5 Dr Fong (USA)—Bustling Nelly (Bustino) (10000) **A Partnership**
56 **CASTANZA**, b f 8/2 Bachir (IRE)—Sylhall (Sharpo) (40000) **Mr D. P. Barrie & Mr M. J. Rees**
57 B f 24/2 Dansili—Catriona (Bustino) **Ashley House Stud Racing**
58 Ch f 17/1 Piccolo—Duena (Grand Lodge (USA)) (40000) **Thurloe Thoroughbreds X**
59 **EMERALD DANCER**, b f 31/1 Groom Dancer (USA)—
Green Bonnet (IRE) (Green Desert (USA)) (70000) **The Taheh Partnership**
60 **ESTANCIA**, b f 25/1 Grand Lodge (USA)—Donostia (Unfuwain (USA)) (44000) **Karen Scott-Barrett & Partners**
61 B f 29/1 Atraf—Gerundive (USA) (Twilight Agenda (USA)) (2200) **Mrs Mary Wilson**
62 **GROOMSMAN**, b c 29/3 Groom Dancer (USA)—
Trois Heures Apres (Soviet Star (USA)) (40000) **Wood Street Syndicate**
63 **HAWK ARROW (IRE)**, ch c 13/1 In The Wings—Barbizou (FR) (Selkirk (USA)) (27000) **Noodles Racing**
64 B c 11/4 Almutawakel—Institutrice (IRE) (College Chapel) (30920) **Thurloe Thoroughbreds XII**
65 **INTREPID JACK**, b c 27/2 Compton Place—Maria Theresa (Primo Dominie) (20000) **Mr Michael T. Lynch**
66 **KEY OF SOLOMON**, b c 25/1 Machiavellian (USA)—
Minerva (IRE) (Caerleon (USA)) (50000) **Mrs Belinda Strudwick**
67 **LUJAIN ROSE**, b f 9/3 Lujain—Rose Chime (IRE) (Tirol) (9276) **M. T. & A. Bevan & Partners**
68 B c 8/4 Danetime (IRE)—
Lyphard Abu (IRE) (Lyphard's Special (USA)) (13000) **Scott-Barrett,Tufnel,Kerr-Dineen,Burley**
69 **PINAFORE**, ch f 11/1 Fleetwood (IRE)—Shi Shi (Alnasr Alwasheek) (800) **Mrs J. Willment**
70 **PRINCE OF THE MAY**, ch c 16/5 Bluegrass Prince—Maytime (Pivotal) **Mr Ian Cameron**
71 **TOQUE**, ch f 5/3 King's Best (USA)—Barboukh (Night Shift (USA)) **WRB Racing**

MR H. MORRISON—continued

72 **VANDERVELT (USA)**, b c 3/5 Spinning World (USA)—Rich And Famous (FR) (Deep Roots) **De La Warr Racing**
73 B gr f 14/3 Zilzal (USA)—Wakeful Night (FR) (Linamix (FR)) **Ashley House Stud Racing**

Other Owners: Mr A. H. Bartlett, Mr Alan Bavin, Mr J. Bernstein, Mrs Gemma Billington, Mr R. J. Bolam, Mr D. L. Brooks, Mrs R. Buck, Ms P. J. Carter, Mr J. Clitheroe, Mr William Eason, Mr James Flower, Mr C. Foley, Mr K. Freeman, Miss C. A. Green, Mrs F. M. Hallett, Mr David Harrison, Mr R. Head, Mrs Nicholas Jones, Mr J. A. Knight, Mr D. Lawson, Mr S. Little, Mr K. A. Mullin, Mr Geoff Nicholas, Mrs D. O'Dell, Mr R. X. O'Rahilly, Mr M. J. Pallett, Mr I. Pering, Mr J. Ratcliffe, Hon Philip Remnant, Mrs G. E. Renwick, Mr Nigel Rich, Mr G. C. Rothwell, Mrs Angela Scott, Mrs Julia Scott, Mr P. E. Selway Smith, Mr M. A. Styles, Mr J. P. M. Sullivan, Mr R. W. Swallow, Mr G. D. W. Swire, Mr K. Taylor, Mr M. Taylor, Mrs S. M. Tourres, Mr R. P. Tullett, Mrs S. L. Tupman, Mr I. J. Wassell, Mr A. W. Wood.

Assistant Trainer: Gerry Gracey

Apprentice: Luke Fletcher. **Amateur:** Mr James Rees (10-0).

389 MR M. P. MUGGERIDGE, Crawley Down

Postal: **Oakfield Stables, Hophurst Lane, Crawley Down, Crawley, West Sussex, RH10 4LN.**
Contact: PHONE (01342) 717825 MOBILE (07850) 203881/(07712) 897613
E-MAIL mpmuggeridge@hotmail.com

1 **ELA APHRODITE**, 6, b m Halling (USA)—Darcey Bussell **Mr Andreas Michael**
2 **HARLYN DEED**, 17, b g Henricus (ATA)—Dunedin Lass **Mr R. W. Vincent**

THREE-YEAR-OLDS

3 **INDIAN OAK (IRE)**, b f Indian Rocket—Marathon Maid **Mr R. W. Vincent**
4 **PENNY CHASE**, b f Bien Bien (USA)—Fullfilling (IRE) **Mr R. W. Vincent**

Assistant Trainer: Miss S M Vincent

Jockey (NH): Sean Curran (10-0). **Amateur:** Mr William Rich (10-0).

390 MR WILLIAM R. MUIR, Lambourn

Postal: **Linkslade, Wantage Road, Lambourn, Hungerford, Berkshire, RG17 8UG.**
Contact: OFFICE (01488) 73098 HOME 73748 FAX 73490 MOBILE (07831) 457074
E-MAIL williamr.muir@virgin.net

1 **CASTAWAY QUEEN (IRE)**, 5, ch m Selkirk (USA)—Surfing **Mr M. J. Caddy**
2 **CHEM'S LEGACY (IRE)**, 4, b g Victory Note (USA)—Merlannah (IRE) **Mrs C. Wheatley**
3 **GILDED DANCER**, 6, b g Bishop of Cashel—La Piaf (FR) **Perspicacious Punters Racing Club**
4 **IMPELLER (IRE)**, 5, ch g Polish Precedent (USA)—Almaaseh (IRE) **Mr D. G. Clarke**
5 **MATERIAL WITNESS (IRE)**, 7, br g Barathea (IRE)—Dial Dream **Mr M. J. Caddy**
6 **POPPYLINE**, 4, b f Averti (IRE)—Shalverton (IRE) **Dulverton Equine**
7 **SAMBAMAN**, 4, b g Groom Dancer (USA)—Guest of Anchor **Song and Dance Partnership - 2**
8 **SNOW'S RIDE**, 4, gr c Hernando (FR)—Crodelle (IRE) **The Parkside Partnership**
9 **TEXAS GOLD**, 6, ch g Cadeaux Genereux—Star Tulip **Mr C. L. A. Edginton**
10 **ZARGUS**, 5, b g Zamindar (USA)—My First Romance **Mrs M. Bruce-Copp**

THREE-YEAR-OLDS

11 **BUY ON THE RED**, b c Komaite (USA)—Red Rosein **Mr R. Haim**
12 **CHANCE FOR ROMANCE**, ch f Entrepreneur—My First Romance **Mr M. J. Caddy**
13 **CHORISTAR**, ch g Inchinor—Star Tulip **Mike Caddy & Brian Moss**
14 **FAR FOR LULU**, ch f Farfelu—Shady Habitat **Mr F. Rupe**
15 **HIGH FREQUENCY (IRE)**, ch c Grand Lodge (USA)—Freak Out (FR) **Mr M. J. Caddy**
16 **ILLEANA (GER)**, ch f Lomitas—Illyria (IRE) **Foursome Thoroughbreds**
17 **INESCAPABLE (USA)**, b c Cape Town (USA)—Danyros (IRE) **Mr M. J. Caddy**
18 **IVORY COAST (IRE)**, b f Cape Cross (IRE)—Ivory League **Mrs J. M. Muir**
19 **KILMINCHY LADY (IRE)**, b f Cape Cross (IRE)—Lace Flower **Mr M. McGinn**
20 **MEMORY MAN**, b c Primo Dominie—Surrealist (ITY) **Mr C. L. A. Edginton**
21 **MISS JUDGEMENT (IRE)**, b f Revoque (IRE)—Mugello **Double D Partnership**
22 **MR JACK DANIELLS (IRE)**, b g Mujadil (USA)—Neat Shilling (IRE) **Mr M. P. Graham**
23 **ONIZ TIPTOES (IRE)**, ch g Russian Revival (USA)—Edionda (IRE) **Drawn2win.co.uk partnership**
24 **PRINCIPAL WITNESS (IRE)**, b c Definite Article—Double Eight (IRE) **Mr M. J. Caddy**
25 **PURE EMOTION**, b f Primo Dominie—Yasalam (IRE) **Mr Saleh Al Homeizi**
26 **REBEL ROUSER**, b g Kris—Nanouche **Mr D. G. Clarke**

MR WILLIAM R. MUIR—continued

27 **TOTALLY YOURS (IRE)**, b f Desert Sun—Total Aloof **Foursome Thoroughbreds**
28 **WHAT A SPREE**, ch f Dancing Spree (USA)—Saint Navarro **North Farm Stud**

TWO-YEAR-OLDS

29 **BOLD DIKTATOR**, b c 18/3 Diktat—Madam Bold (Never So Bold) **Kilmuir Partnership**
30 **CREE**, b c 12/3 Indian Ridge—Nightitude (Night Shift (USA)) (10000) **Inflite Partners**
31 B f 15/3 In The Wings—Freak Out (FR) (Bering) (19789) **Mr M. J. Caddy**
32 B c 12/5 Averti (IRE)—Green Run (USA) (Green Dancer (USA)) (5000)
33 B c 7/4 Fayruz—Haraabah (USA) (Topsider (USA)) (30000) **Mr M. J. Caddy**
34 B c 9/5 Groom Dancer (USA)—Jezyah (USA) (Chief's Crown (USA)) (4200) **Mr S. Lamb**
35 B c 15/2 Handsome Ridge—Justfortherecord (Forzando) (5000)
36 B br c 12/2 Aljabr (USA)—Matinee Mimic (USA) (Silent Screen (USA)) (34013) **Mr M. J. Caddy**
37 Gr c 6/4 Averti (IRE)—Miss Mirror (Magic Mirror) (25000)
38 **PIPPA'S DANCER (IRE)**, b f 4/4 Desert Style (IRE)—
  Soreze (IRE) (Gallic League) (27828) **Perspicacious Punters Racing Club**
39 B f 16/2 Spectrum (IRE)—Prosaic Star (IRE) (Common Grounds) (25973) **Mrs D. L. Edginton**
40 B c 23/3 Mister Baileys—Ring Queen (USA) (Fairy King (USA)) (40000) **Mike Caddy & Brian Moss**
41 B c 13/2 Dr Fong (USA)—Silver Sun (Green Desert (USA)) (25000)
42 B c 22/1 Tagula (IRE)—Simply Sooty (Absalom) (28000) **Mr Brian Moss**
43 B f 23/4 Trans Island—Singled Out (IRE) (Fairy King (USA)) (1236)
44 B c 28/1 Entrepreneur—Taisho (IRE) (Namaqualand (USA)) (10000)
45 B c 6/4 Efisio—Tarneem (USA) (Zilzal (USA)) (12000)
46 **TRAPPETO (IRE)**, b c 9/2 Barathea (IRE)—Campiglia (IRE) (Fairy King (USA)) (16079) **Mr R. Haim & Partners**
47 B c 14/4 Anabaa (USA)—Viking's Cove (USA) (Miswaki (USA)) **Mr M. J. Caddy**

Other Owners: Dr W. Bogie, Mr J. D. Clements, Mr P. J. H. Dalton, Ms J. N. Duke, Mr David Fleet, Mr D. P. Knox, Mrs Celia Maile, Mrs A. Muir, Mr David J. Muir, Mr A. J. De V. Patrick, Mr Bryan Ryan, Mr Mikir Shah, Mr P. J. Wheatley, Mr David F. White.

Jockeys (Flat): Martin Dwyer (7-12), Richard Mullen (8-2). **Apprentice:** J Tucker (8-7).

---

391 ## MR J. W. MULLINS, Amesbury
Postal: **Wilsford Stables, Wilsford-Cum-Lake, Amesbury, Salisbury, Wiltshire, SP4 7BL.**
Contact: **PHONE (01980) 626344 FAX (01980) 626344 MOBILE (07702) 559634**
E-MAIL mullinsjwm@aol.com WEBSITE www.zyworld.com/jwmullins/jwm.htm

1 **AMBIENCE LADY**, 8, b m Batshoof—Upper Caen **First Impressions Racing Group 2**
2 **ANOTHER CONQUEST**, 5, b m El Conquistador—Kellys Special **Mr F. G. Matthews**
3 **AU LAC**, 10, b g North Col—Janlarmar **Mr Don Hazzard**
4 **BILLYWILL (IRE)**, 10, b br g Topanoora—Sandy Maid **Mr P. F. Kehoe**
5 **BOB'S FINESSE**, 4, ch f Gran Alba (USA)—High Finesse **Miss C. A. James**
6 **BONNIE FLORA**, 8, b m Then Again—My Minnie **The Late Mrs W.J.B. Protheroe-Bey**
7 **BROOKLANDS LAD**, 7, b g North Col—Sancal **Mr B. R. Edgeley**
8 **CANSALRUN (IRE)**, 5, b m Anshan—Monamandy (IRE) **Mrs Josephine S. Blackwell**
9 **CLASSIC CHINA**, 7, ch m Karinga Bay—Chanelle **Amesbury China**
10 **COMPTON CHICK (IRE)**, 6, b m Dolphin Street (FR)—Cecina **New Forest Racing Partnership**
11 **CON TRICKS**, 11, b g El Conquistador—Dame Nellie **Shildon Racing**
12 **CORRECT AND RIGHT (IRE)**, 5, b m Great Commotion (USA)—Miss Hawkins **Mr Seamus Mullins**
13 **DENNY ISLAND**, 8, b g Rock Hopper—Bara Peg **Mr D. H. Smith**
14 **EARLY START**, 6, ch m Husyan (USA)—Gipsy Dawn **Mr Adam Day**
15 **EL PENYON**, 7, b g Rock Hopper—Capel Lass **Mr Patrick Everard**
16 **GOLDEN CRUSADER**, 7, b g Gildoran—Pusey Street **First Impressions Racing Group**
17 **HILL FORTS HENRY**, 6, ch g Karinga Bay—Maggie Tee **Mrs J. C. Scorgie**
18 **INDEED TO GOODNESS (IRE)**, 9, b m Welsh Term—Clare's Sheen **Mr Ian M. McGready**
19 **ITSASURETHING**, 4, b c Sure Blade (USA)—Ginka **Mr M. Jenkins**
20 **IT'S GOT BUCKLEYS**, 5, b g El Conquistador—Saucey Pup
21 **JIMAL**, 7, b g Reprimand—Into The Fire **Sally Mullins**
22 **KENTFORD GREBE**, 5, b m Teenoso (USA)—Notinhand **Mr D. I. Bare**
23 **KILLY BEACH**, 6, b g Kuwait Beach (USA)—Spiritual Lily **Mr J. A. G. Meaden**
24 **KIMMERIDGE BAY**, 6, b m Karinga Bay—Chanelle **Mrs J. M. Bailey**
25 **MCSNAPPY**, 7, ch g Risk Me (FR)—Nannie Annie **Cum-Lake Racing**
26 **MIDDLEMISS (IRE)**, 4, b f Midhish—Teresa Deevey **Mr Don Hazzard**
27 **MISTER PEARLY**, 7, ch g Alflora (IRE)—Pearly Dream **Mrs Hilary Pike**
28 **MUTADARRA (IRE)**, 11, ch g Mujtahid (USA)—Silver Echo **Mr M. S. Green**

MR J. W. MULLINS—continued

29 NOTWHATSHEWANTED (IRE), 7, b g Supreme Leader—Wise Nellie (IRE) **M. Rayner**
30 OUR JOLLY SWAGMAN, 9, b g Thowra (FR)—Queens Dowry **Mr F. G. Matthews**
31 RUBY TOO, 5, b m El Conquistador—Ruby Flame **Dr R. Jowett**
32 SATIVA BAY, 5, ch g Karinga Bay—Busy Mittens **Mr D. I. Bare**
33 SEEADOR, 5, b g El Conquistador—Shepani **Mr J. A. G. Meaden**
34 SEE ME THERE, 4, b g Busy Flight—See-A-Rose **Mr J. A. G. Meaden**
35 SEE YOU AROUND, 9, b g Sharp Deal—Seeborg **The Infamous Five**
36 SEE YOU SOMETIME, 9, b g Sharp Deal—Shepani **Mr J. A. G. Meaden**
37 SPECIAL CONQUEST, 6, b g El Conquistador—Kellys Special **Mr F. G. Matthews**
38 SPECTACULAR HOPE, 4, b f Marju (IRE)—Distant Music **Woodford Valley Racing Partnership**
39 TAILS I WIN, 5, b g Petoski—Spinayab **John Mead**
40 TERRIBLE TENANT, 5, gr g Terimon—Rent Day **Mr D. I. Bare**
41 THE BEANFIELD (IRE), 5, b g Good Thyne (USA)—Carry Me (IRE) **Miss S. A. Ryder**
42 THE LAND AGENT, 13, b g Town And Country—Notinhand **D. I. Bare**
43 TRUE LOVER (GER), 7, b g Winged Love (IRE)—Truneba (GER)

Other Owners: Mr P. R. Attwater, Mr P. J. Bealing, Mr W. Brockway, Mr P. C. Fry, Mrs S. I. Fry, Mr Richard E. Gray, Mr R. Hatchard, Mrs M. J. Henry, Mrs Audrey Kley, Mr T. K. Pearce, Mr J. H. Young.

Assistant Trainer: Miss S Young

Jockeys (NH): S Curran (w.a.), M Fitzgerald (w.a.), A Thornton (w.a.), J Tizzard (w.a.), R Young (9-7). **Amateur:** Mr Tim Hampton (9-7).

---

392 MR WILLIAM P. MULLINS, Carlow
Postal: Closutton, Bagenalstown, Co. Carlow, Ireland.
Contact: **PHONE** 059 97 21786 **FAX** 059 97 21786 **MOBILE** (087) 2564940
E-MAIL wpmullins@eircom.net **WEBSITE** www.wpmullins.com

1 ADAMANT APPROACH (IRE), 10, b g Mandalus—Crash Approach **The Green Star Syndicate**
2 ALEXANDER ACCORDION (IRE), 5, b g Accordion—Breaking Cover **Mrs N. O. Callaghan**
3 ALEXANDER BANQUET (IRE), 11, b g Glacial Storm—Black Nancy **Mrs N. O'Callaghan**
4 ARCH STANTON, 6, b h Lahib (USA)—Sweet Repose **J. Brennan**
5 ASSESSED (IRE), 10, b g Montelimar (USA)—Tax Code **Festival Syndicate**
6 BALLYAMBER (IRE), 9, b g Glacial Storm (USA)—El Scarsdale **Sean Mulyran**
7 BASSETT TIGER (IRE), 8, b g Shardari—Bassett Girl **Mr Tom Gilligan**
8 BELINKIN, 4, b c Robellino (USA)—Kintail **D. Flynn**
9 BONEYARROW (IRE), 8, ch g Over The River (FR)—Apicat **J. Comerford**
10 BOTTOM DOLLAR (IRE), 5, b g Pierre—Felicitas **Paul Hennessey**
11 BUNKERS HILL (IRE), 4, b c Lahib (USA)—Ela's Gold (IRE) **Mr David Flynn**
12 CAROLINA (FR), 7, b m Baby Turk—Record High (FR) **Railbus Racing Club**
13 CASTLE WEIR (IRE), 7, b g Lord Americo—Alchymia **Castle Racing Club**
14 CLOUNTIES HILL (IRE), 7, b g Simply Great (FR)—Pass Thurn **IIEN Syndicate**
15 CRAANFORD MILL, 5, b g Vettori (IRE)—Northern Bird **Oilean Ciarrai Syndicate**
16 CZAR OF PEACE (IRE), 6, ch g Brief Truce (USA)—Metroella (IRE) **M. Hanrahan**
17 DAVENPORT DEMOCRAT (IRE), 6, ch g Fourstars Allstar (USA)—Storm Court (IRE)
18 DAVENPORT MILENIUM (IRE), 8, b g Insan (USA)—Society Belle **Mrs N. O'Callaghan**
19 DETONANTE (FR), 4, ch f Cardoun (FR)—Cardwell (FR) **The Red Roosters Syndicate**
20 DIEGO GARCIA (IRE), 4, b c Sri Pekan (USA)—Chapel Lawn **J. Brennan**
21 DONNA LORNA (IRE), 6, b m Be My Native (USA)—Ah Donna **T. Gilligan**
22 EURO LEADER (IRE), 6, b g Supreme Leader—Noreaster (IRE) **J. Cox**
23 FLORIDA BELLE (IRE), 5, b m Florida Son—Life of A Lady (IRE) **Holy Racing Syndicate**
24 FLORIDA PEARL (IRE), 12, b g Florida Son—Ice Pearl **Mrs V. O'Leary**
25 GAYLE ABATED (IRE), 5, b g Moscow Society (USA)—Hurricane Girl (IRE) **Jean Dunne**
26 GLACIAL MOSS (IRE), 6, ch g Glacial Storm (USA)—Garrenroe **D. O'Connor**
27 GRANNY KELLYS TART (IRE), 6, ch g Old Vic—Le Idol **P. J. Fahy**
28 HEDGEHUNTER (IRE), 8, b g Montelimar (USA)—Aberedw (IRE) **Trevor Hemmings**
29 HEEZAPISTOL (FR), 6, b g Pistolet Bleu (IRE)—Strictly Cool (USA) **Amber Syndicate**
30 HOLY ORDERS (IRE), 7, b h Unblest—Shadowglow **A. McLuckie**
31 HOMER WELLS, 6, b g Arctic Cider (USA)—Run And Shine **Mrs M. McMahon**
32 JASMIN D'OUDAIRIES (FR), 7, b g Apeldoorn (FR)—Vellea (FR) **The Deise and Dubs Syndicate**
33 JOUEUR D'ESTRUVAL (FR), 7, gr g Perrault—Alrose (FR) **Mrs V. O'Leary**
34 KAMPALA II (FR), 6, b m Cyborg (FR)—Badj II (FR) **Mrs J. M. Mullins**
35 KEAVENEY, 6, ch g Gunner B—Kentucky Calling **Sunny House Syndicate**
36 KELLY'S CRAFT, 7, b g Warcraft (USA)—Kelly's Bridge **PM Racing Syndicate**

MR WILLIAM P. MULLINS—continued

37 **KILLULTAGH STORM (IRE)**, 10, b g Mandalus—Rostrevor Lady **Mrs Rose Boyd**
38 **KILLULTAGH THUNDER (IRE)**, 8, b g Bravefoot—Rostrevor Lady **Mrs Rose Boyd**
39 **KIM FONTAINE (FR)**, 6, b g Silver Rainbow—Blanche Fontaine (FR) **B. Doyle**
40 **KNOCKABOOLY (IRE)**, 5, ch g John French—Valiyist (IRE) **Margaret O'Rourke**
41 **KOME BACK (FR)**, 6, b g Trebrook (FR)—Vaderetro II (FR) **Mrs J. M. Mullins**
42 **KRONOS DES OBEAUX (FR)**, 6, b g Grand Tresor (FR)—Brune de Cotte (FR) **Kevin Cronin**
43 **LA FISARMONICA (IRE)**, 4, b f Accordion—Moycullen **Mrs J. Mullins**
44 **LANJOU ROUGE (FR)**, 5, b g Start Fast (FR)—Raika (FR) **Road Runner Syndicate**
45 **LASQUINI DU MOULIN (FR)**, 5, gr g Saint Preuil (FR)—Api (FR) **Sunny Bank Syndicate**
46 **LIVINGSTONEBRAMBLE (IRE)**, 8, b g Supreme Leader—Killney Side **Favorites Racing Syndicate**
47 **LOVE DITTY (FR)**, 6, ch g Green Tune (USA)—Rolloverdarling **Sean O'Driscoll**
48 **MACS GILDORAN (IRE)**, 10, b g Gildoran—Shamrock Bridge **Mrs M. McManus**
49 **MACS VALLEY (IRE)**, 7, b g Hubbly Bubbly (USA)—Black Valley (IRE) **Mrs M. McManus**
50 **MAJOR BURNS (IRE)**, 6, b g Aahsaylad—Night Matron (IRE) **Festival Syndicate**
51 **MAJOR VERNON**, 5, b g Flemensfirth (USA)—Rainys Run **Brendan Doyle**
52 **MALAHIDE MARINA**, 5, b g Teenoso (USA)—Marina Bird **Tom Gilligan**
53 **MAN ON THE NILE (IRE)**, 4, b c Snurge—Spirt of The Nile (FR) **Mr David Flynn**
54 **MARKS MEDICO (IRE)**, 7, gr g Roselier (FR)—Born Lucky (FR) **Sport Racing Club**
55 **MARTATOMIC (IRE)**, 6, b g Vestris Abu—Oonagh's Teddy **The Greenstar Syndicate**
56 **MASRIYNA'S ARTICLE (IRE)**, 5, ch m Definite Article—Masriyna (IRE) **Sport Racing Club**
57 **MILKAT (IRE)**, 6, b g Machiavellian (USA)—Desert Victory **J. Comerford**
58 **MONTEEPA (IRE)**, 7, b g Montelimar (USA)—Arakeepa **Mrs J. M. Mullins**
59 **MOSSY GREEN (IRE)**, 10, b g Moscow Society (USA)—Green Ajo **Greenstar Syndicate**
60 **MR BABBAGE (IRE)**, 6, ch g Carroll House—Winsome Doe **George Creighton**
61 **MRS WALLENSKY (IRE)**, 6, gr m Roselier (FR)—Shannon Dee (IRE) **Mrs M. T. Quinn**
62 **NAZARI (IRE)**, 4, b g Alzao (USA)—Naziriya (FR) **The Motto Syndicate**
63 **OF COURSE (IRE)**, 6, ch g Montelimar (USA)—Linda's Course (IRE) **Mrs J. M. Mullins**
64 **ONE NIGHT OUT (IRE)**, 8, b g Jamesmead—Deladeuce **R. Ryan**
65 **PORT SALON (IRE)**, 6, b g Commanche Run—Brave Vixen (IRE) **Louise O'Keeffe Murphy**
66 **QUEL DOUN (FR)**, 4, b g Tel Quel (FR)—Dounasa (FR) **Roo Syndicate**
67 **RAIKKONEN (IRE)**, 4, b g Lake Coniston (IRE)—Jour Ferie (IRE) **A. Fanning**
68 **RED OR WHITE (IRE)**, 5, ch g Semillon—Sweet Chimes **Threetops Syndicate**
69 **REVE DE ROSE**, 5, b m Emperor Jones (USA)—Rose de Reve (IRE) **Mrs M. McMahon**
70 **ROUNDSTONE LADY**, 4, b br f Anshan—Young Preacher **MMD Syndicate**
71 **ROYAL ALPHABET (IRE)**, 6, b g King's Theatre (IRE)—A-To-Z (IRE) **Ballyinch Stud**
72 **RULE SUPREME (IRE)**, 8, b g Supreme Leader—Book of Rules (IRE) **J. Lynch**
73 **SADLERS WINGS (IRE)**, 6, b h In The Wings—Anna Comnena (IRE) **J. Brennan**
74 **SHANDON STAR (IRE)**, 5, b m Priolo (USA)—Noble Choice **W. P. Roche**
75 **SHERBERRY (IRE)**, 5, b m Shernazar—Bilberry **Does Size Matter Syndicate**
76 **SILK SCREEN (IRE)**, 4, b c Barathea (IRE)—Sun Screen **J. Brennan**
77 **SUNAMI STORM (IRE)**, 6, b m Glacial Storm—Live It Up **W. P. Roche**
78 **TEMPLELUSK (IRE)**, 6, ch g Over The River (FR)—Leafy Moss **J. Comerford**
79 **TUESDAY (IRE)**, 9, b g Satco (FR)—Beech Glen **Mrs V. O'Leary**
80 **ULTIMATE ACCOLADE (IRE)**, 8, b g Insan (USA)—Echo Creek (IRE) **Mrs J. Mullins**
81 **VERROCCHIO (IRE)**, 4, b c Entrepreneeur—Our Hope **J. Brennan**
82 **WARRENS CASTLE (IRE)**, 7, b g Fourstars Allstar (USA)—Jerusalem Cruiser (IRE) **J. J. Brennan**
83 **WATER STORM (IRE)**, 6, ch g Glacial Storm (USA)—Water Sprite **Mrs J. M. Mullins**

THREE-YEAR-OLDS

84 **DIACONATE (IRE)**, b f Cape Cross (IRE)—Shadowglow **J. Brennan**
85 **FIRE OF KEN (FR)**, b c Kendor (FR)—Terre de Feu (FR) **D. Flynn**
86 **FRANKLINS TRAIL (IRE)**, b c Imperial Ballet (IRE)—Nettle **J. Brennan**
87 **PHANTASOS (USA)**, ch c Kris—Acquiesce **D. Flynn**
88 **RIVER ROUGE (IRE)**, b f Croco Rouge (IRE)—Moy Water (IRE) **J. Brennan**

TWO-YEAR-OLDS

89 Ch f 19/4 Guy Butters (GR)—Alika's Dance (USA) (Green Dancer (USA)) (11428) **Mrs Alexandra J. Chandris**
90 Ch c 9/3 Military Fashion—Analampi (GR) (Flash N Thunder (USA)) (6666) **Mrs Alexandra J. Chandris**
91 B c 10/3 Denebola Way (GR)—Dada (GR) (Ice Reef) (8571) **Mrs Alexandra J. Chandris**
92 Br c 17/2 Tony Galvin (GR)—Fortunate Way (GR) (Wadood (USA)) (14285) **Mrs Alexandra J. Chandris**
93 B c 15/2 Spectrum (IRE)—Gipsy Anna (IRE) (Marju (IRE)) (12000) **Mrs J. M. Mullins**
94 B f 8/2 Fascinating Way (GR)—Light Wind (GR) (Lai Lai (GR)) (7142) **Mrs Alexandra J. Chandris**

MR WILLIAM P. MULLINS—continued

95 B f 16/3 King's Theatre (IRE)—Niamh Cinn Oir (IRE) (King of Clubs) (14841) **Mrs J. M. Mullins**
96 B f 13/2 Wadood (USA)—Northern Moon (Ile de Bourbon (USA)) (11428) **Mrs Alexandra J. Chandris**

Jockey (NH): Ruby Walsh (10-4). **Apprentice:** David Condon (7-3). **Amateurs:** Mr J Codd (10-5), Mr James Nash (10-7).

---

393 **MR F. MURPHY, Leyburn**
Postal: **Wynbury Stables, West Witton, Leyburn, North Yorkshire, DL8 4LR.**
Contact: PHONE **(01969) 622289 & (01969) 624200 FAX (01969) 625278 MOBILE (07703) 444398**
E-MAIL **ferdy@ferdymurphyracing.com & office@wynburystables.fsnet.co.uk**

1 **AD GLORIA (IRE)**, 4, b f Shernazar—Knockarctic **Racegoers Club Owners Group**
2 **ALFIE TWOFOURTWO (IRE)**, 8, b g Jolly Jake (NZ)—Spin N'Win **Mrs G. P. Seymour**
3 **ALGENON**, 4, br g Asaasy (USA)—La Tante (FR) **Mr Paul Murphy**
4 **ARTEMESIA**, 9, b m Teenoso (USA)—Annicombe Run **Beautifully Bred Partnership**
5 **ATLANTIC HAWK**, 6, b g Daar Alzaman (IRE)—Pyewacket **Mr Richard Sunter**
6 **BALLINCLAY KING (IRE)**, 10, b g Asir—Clonroche Artic **I. Guise, B. Leatherday & N. L. Spence**
7 **BARROW (SWI)**, 7, br g Caerleon (USA)—Bestow **Miss J. V. Morgan**
8 **BEACON OF LIGHT (IRE)**, 6, b m Lake Coniston (IRE)—Deydarika (IRE) **Mr Paul T. Murphy**
9 **BE UPSTANDING**, 9, ch g Hubbly Bubbly—Two Travellers **Mr M. Holmes**
10 **BIRKDALE (IRE)**, 13, gr g Roselier (FR)—Clonroche Lady **Miss J. V. Morgan**
11 **BLUE LIZARD (IRE)**, 7, b g Roselier (FR)—Rathsallagh Tartan **Mr A. Bloom**
12 **BONNIE PARKER (IRE)**, 5, b m Un Desperado (IRE)—Strong Gara (IRE) **Racegoers Club Owners Group**
13 **CANAVAN (IRE)**, 5, gr g Bob Back (USA)—Silver Glen (IRE) **Mr John Duddy**
14 **CARLYS QUEST**, 10, ch g Primo Dominie—Tuppy (USA) **Yorkeys Knob Racing Club**
15 **CHANCERS DANTE (IRE)**, 8, b g Phardante (FR)—Own Acre **Mrs P. B. Symes**
16 **CHARLY JACK**, 5, b g Alderbrook—Reperage (USA) **Mr L. M. Symes**
17 **CHICAGO BREEZE (IRE)**, 7, b m Lord Americo—Anguillita (IRE) **Mr W. H. Winlow**
18 **CLONROCHE VINYLS (IRE)**, 9, ch m Rashar (USA)—Clonroche Beggar **Mr Nicholas Butterly**
19 **COOL DEGREE (IRE)**, 6, br g Arctic Lord—Ballyfin Maid (IRE) **Mr Trevor Hemmings**
20 **DAGUYDA (FR)**, 5, b g Northern Crystal—La Domizia (FR) **D. Williams, D. Awty & G.Petit**
21 **DIGGING DEEP**, 8, ch m Scorpio (FR)—Two Travellers **Mrs Elaine Holmes**
22 **DOMINIKUS**, 7, br g Second Set (IRE)—Dolce Vita (GER) **The Aarons Archer Partnership**
23 **EWE BEAUTY (FR)**, 4, b f Phantom Breeze—Baie de Chalamont (FR) **Mr & Mrs Neil Iveson**
24 **FAMILY VENTURE (IRE)**, 7, br g Montelimar (USA)—Well Honey **The Family Venture Partnership**
25 **FASHIONS MONTY (IRE)**, 8, ch m Montelimar (USA)—Fashions Side **Mr Brian Mulholland**
26 **FASHIONS MYSTIQUE (IRE)**, 6, b m Religiously (USA)—
                                                   Fashions Side **Miss J. V. Morgan & Mr Brian Mulholland**
27 5, B m Flemensfirth (USA)—Finnuala Supreme (IRE) **Mr Michael Conlon**
28 **FROM LITTLE ACORNS (IRE)**, 8, b g Denel (FR)—Mount Gawn **Mrs N. L. Spence**
29 **GARDE BIEN**, 7, br g Afzal—May Lady **Mrs M. B. Scholey**
30 **GORTMORE MEWS (IRE)**, 10, b g Persian Mews—Flat Out **John McMullen W F-Clennell Susan Sample**
31 **GRANIT D'ESTRUVAL (FR)**, 10, b g Quart de Vin (FR)—Jalousie (FR) **Mr W. J. Gott**
32 **GREEN IDEAL**, 6, b g Mark of Esteem (IRE)—Emerald (USA) **Mrs J. Morgan**
33 **GROUNDSWELL (IRE)**, 8, b g Common Grounds—Fuchsia Belle **Miss J. V. Morgan**
34 **HAS SCORED (IRE)**, 6, b g Sadler's Wells (USA)—City Ex **The Has Scored Partnership**
35 **HIGH CHEVIOT**, 7, b g Shirley Heights—Cutleaf
36 **HISTORG (FR)**, 9, b g Cyborg (FR)—Kalliste (FR) **Mr Jim McCarthy**
37 **HOT WELD**, 5, b g Weld—Deb's Ball **Mr S. Hubbard Rodwell**
38 **HOWABOYS QUEST (USA)**, 7, b g Quest For Fame—Doctor Black (USA) **Winlow Brothers**
39 **ICHI BEAU (IRE)**, 10, b g Convinced—May As Well **Mrs Fiona Butterly**
40 **INN ANTIQUE (FR)**, 8, b g Lute Antique (FR)—Taghera (FR) **Mr W. J. Gott**
41 **ISLAND FAITH (IRE)**, 7, b g Turtle Island (IRE)—Keep The Faith **Mr K. Lee**
42 **JACK LYNCH**, 8, ch g Lancastrian—Troublewithjack **Mrs Helen Lynch**
43 **JOE PUBLIC (IRE)**, 6, b g Actinium (IRE)—Cool Boreen **Mr Anthony O'Gorman**
44 **JUST FOR FUN (IRE)**, 6, br g Kahyasi—Copper Breeze (IRE) **Northumberland Jumpers**
45 **KA ROSE (FR)**, 6, b g Missolonghi (USA)—Quelle Etoile V (FR) **Mr Ferdy Murphy**
46 **KING OF CONFUSION (IRE)**, 5, br g Topanoora—Rich Desire **Mr J. Taqvi**
47 **LANICENE (FR)**, 5, b g Moon Madness—Ocylla (FR) **Network Training**
48 **LEADING MAN (IRE)**, 4, br g Old Vic—Cudder Or Shudder (IRE) **Mrs C. McKeane**
49 **LE MINO (FR)**, 5, b g Noblequest (FR)—Minouche (FR) **Mr G. R. Orchard**
50 **LEN ROSS**, 5, b g Bob's Return (IRE)—Instabene **Mr Patrick Atkinson**
51 **LEYLAND COMET (IRE)**, 6, b br g Roselier (FR)—Firey Comet (IRE) **Mr Trevor Hemmings**
52 4, Br f Heron Island (IRE)—Likeness **Ferdy Murphy**
53 **LOOKING FORWARD**, 8, br g Primitive Rising (USA)—Gilzie Bank **Mrs G. Handley**

MR F. MURPHY—continued

54 **LORIO DU MISSELOT (FR)**, 5, gr g Dom Alco (FR)—Byrsa (FR) **R. J. V. Partnership**
55 **LUZCADOU (FR)**, 11, b g Cadoudal (FR)—Luzenia (FR) **Mr A. G. Chappell**
56 **MAC'S SUPREME (IRE)**, 12, b g Supreme Leader—Merry Breeze **Mr B. McEntaggart**
57 **MAN ON THE HILL (IRE)**, 10, b g Mandalus—Gipsey Jo **Mr D. A. Johnson**
58 **MIJICO (IRE)**, 8, b g Lord Americo—Mijette **Mrs R. D. Cairns**
59 **MONKEY ISLAND**, 9, b g Jupiter Island—Mikey's Monkey **The Monkey Island Partnership**
60 **MONTY FLOOD (IRE)**, 7, b g Camden Town—Clonroche Artic **Mr J. Taqvi**
61 **NATIVE LEGEND (IRE)**, 9, b g Be My Native (USA)—Tickhill **Mr J. D. Gordon**
62 5, Br g Presenting—Nish Bar **Mr Walter Gott**
63 **ONE A DACKIE**, 5, br m Lord Americo—Oriel Dream **Mr Jack Lodon**
64 **OUTSIDE INVESTOR (IRE)**, 4, br g Cadeaux Genereux—Desert Ease (IRE) **Mr Anthony O'Gorman**
65 **PAPHIAN BAY**, 6, b g Karinga Bay—Bichette **Mr S. Hubbard Rodwell**
66 **PROFILER (USA)**, 9, b g Capote (USA)—Magnificent Star (USA) **Miss J. V. Morgan**
67 **RAGU**, 6, b m Contract Law (USA)—Marnworth **Mr Raj Patel**
68 **RARCHNAMARA (IRE)**, 9, b g Commanche Run—Knollwood Court **Mr John Duddy**
69 **RED SOCIETY (IRE)**, 6, ch g Moscow Society (USA)—Allendara (IRE) **Mr Eamon Kelly**
70 **RELIX (FR)**, 4, gr c Linamix (FR)—Resleona
71 **RIOTHAMUS (IRE)**, 6, b g Supreme Leader—Kemchee **RP Racing**
72 **ROSSLARE (FR)**, 5, b g Lute Antique (FR)—Baie de Chalamont (FR) **Mr K. Lee**
73 **SEASQUILL (AUS)**, 9, br g Squill (USA)—Sea Surge (AUS) **Mr G.V. Wilson,Tom Murphy & Janet Morgan**
74 **SERPENTINE ROCK**, 4, ch g Hernando (FR)—Serpentara **Burns Farm Racing**
75 **SHAYS LANE (IRE)**, 10, b g The Bart (USA)—Continuity Lass **Mrs C. McKeane**
76 **SHELU**, 6, b g Good Thyne (USA)—Nearly Married **Mr Raj Patel**
77 **SIR ROWLAND HILL (IRE)**, 5, b g Kahyasi—Zaila (IRE) **Mr A. G. Chappell**
78 **STAR OF GERMANY (IRE)**, 4, b g Germany (USA)—Twinkle Bright (USA) **Mr Brendan J. O'Rourke**
79 5, B m Teenoso (USA)—State Lady (IRE) **Mr C. W. Cooper**
80 **STREAMSTOWN (IRE)**, 10, br g Rashar (USA)—Lady Torsil **Haydock Park National Hunt Partnership**
81 **SUPREME BREEZE (IRE)**, 9, b g Supreme Leader—Merry Breeze **The Supreme Three**
82 **THE QUADS**, 12, b g Tinoco—Queen's Royale **Mr John Duddy**
83 **TOULON ROUGE (FR)**, 7, b m Toulon—Master Nidee **Racegoers Club Owners Group**
84 **TRIBAL VENTURE (FR)**, 6, gr g Dom Alco (FR)—Babacha (FR) **Network Training**
85 **TRUCKERS TAVERN (IRE)**, 9, ch g Phardante (FR)—Sweet Tulip **Mrs M. B. Scholey**
86 **TUFTY HOPPER**, 7, b g Rock Hopper—Melancolia **Mr Michael Tufts**
87 **ULUSABA**, 8, b g Alflora (IRE)—Mighty Fly **Dorothy Clinton, Chris McHugh, Jon King**
88 **UNION DEUX (FR)**, 5, ch g Nikos—Sanhia (FR) **Mrs M. B. Scholey**
89 **URBAN HYMN (IRE)**, 8, ch g College Chapel—Soltura (IRE) **Mr D. A. Johnson**
90 **WHAT A WONDER (IRE)**, 9, gr g Roselier (FR)—Lady Abednego VII **The Sheepscar Syndicate**
91 **WORLD VISION (IRE)**, 7, ch g Denel (FR)—Dusty Lane (IRE) **R. & M. J. Partnership**
92 **WYNBURY FLYER**, 9, ch g Risk Me (FR)—Woolcana **Mrs G. P. Seymour**
93 **YOUR A GASSMAN (IRE)**, 6, b g King's Ride—Nish Bar **Mr W. J. Gott**
94 **YOUR MY ANGEL (FR)**, 8, b m Commanche Run—Marshtown Fair (IRE) **Mr S. Hubbard Rodwell**

THREE-YEAR-OLDS

95 **BLUE RISING**, gr g Primitive Rising (USA)—Pollytickle **Mrs G. P. Seymour**
96 **NAIAD DU MISSELOT (FR)**, b g Dom Alco (FR)—Une Nuit (FR)
97 **NIARCO MALTA (FR)**, gr g Dom Alco (FR)—Dame Au Diamant **Mr R. Joseph, Mr D. Abrey & Mr F. Murphy**

Other Owners: Mr David Abrey, Miss Kate Abrey, Mr W. M. Aitchinson, Mr P. Asquith, Mr Wayne Asquith, Mr Patrick Atkinson, Mr K. M. Cartner, Ms Rebecca Chapman, Mr A. Coldron, Mr M. C. Coldron, Mr Cedric Croston, Mr Guy Faber, Mr R. A. Fisher, Mr E. C. Gordon, Mr M. Hill (Taunton), Mr D. N. Iveson, Mrs J. E. Iveson, Mr R. Joseph, Ms M. J. Kitson, Mr S. P. Marsh, Miss J. M. Murray, Mr D. Neale, Mr Tony Outhart, Mr David Parry, Mr J. R. Rowbottom, Ms L. Schofield, Mr R. H. Scholey, Mrs C. Seymour, Mr P. J. Shaw, Mrs J. Storrow, Mrs M. H. Sutcliffe, Mr Richard Taylor (Sheffield), Mr C. R. Trembath, Mr D. Winlow.

Assistant Trainer: Janet Morgan

Jockey (NH): D N Russell (10-0). **Apprentice:** D Stamp (7-13). **Conditional:** N Mulholland (9-11), C Sharkey (9-7), R Utley (9-7). **Amateurs:** S Graham (10-0), Mr K Mercer (9-9), Miss Z Morgan-Murphy (9-0), Miss K S Naylor (8-12), Miss M Sowerby (9-0).

394 MR P. G. MURPHY, Hungerford
Postal: **Mabberleys, Front Street, East Garston, Hungerford, Berkshire, RG17 7EU.**
Contact: **OFFICE (01488) 648473 FAX (01488) 649775 MOBILE (07831) 410409**
E-MAIL pat@mabberleys.freeserve.co.uk

1 BOWING, 4, b g Desert Prince (IRE)—Introducing **The Golden Anorak Partnership**
2 CAPRIOLO (IRE), 8, ch g Priolo (USA)—Carroll's Canyon (IRE) **Mr S. J. Kingshott**
3 CROGHAN LOCH (IRE), 7, b g Mister Lord (USA)—Croghan Katie **Mrs Dianne Murphy**
4 GREENWOOD, 6, ch g Emarati (USA)—Charnwood Queen **The Golden Anorak Partnership**
5 LOCH NA BPEISC (IRE), 7, b g Over The River (FR)—Ballyhire Lady (IRE) **Mrs John Spielman**
6 MUNFARID (IRE), 4, ch g Alhaarth (IRE)—Meursault (IRE) **The Golden Anorak Partnership**
7 MUNTASIR, 4, b g Rainbow Quest (USA)—Licorne **Mr J. Cooper**
8 ON GUARD, 6, b g Sabrehill (USA)—With Care **The Paddysaurus Coming Partnership**
9 TRAVELLER'S TALE, 5, b g Selkirk (USA)—Chere Amie (USA) **Mrs Dianne Murphy**

Other Owners: Mr Robert Day, Mrs K. M. Graham, Mr R. Hart, Mr T. Hart, Mr A. D. Potts, Mr S. Theaker.

Assistant Trainer: Mrs Dianne Murphy

Jockeys (Flat): S Drowne (8-2), D Kinsella (7-12). **Jockey (NH):** L Aspell (10-0). **Conditional:** J Quintin (10-0).

395 MR F. P. MURTAGH, Carlisle
Postal: **Hurst Farm, Ivegill, Carlisle, Cumbria, CA4 0NL.**
Contact: **PHONE (017684) 84649 MOBILE (0771) 4026741 E-MAIL finbar@murtaghs.fsnet.co.uk**

1 BARRELBIO (IRE), 9, b g Elbio—Esther **Mrs M. E. James**
2 CREED (IRE), 4, ch g Entrepreneur—Ardent Range (IRE) **Hurst Farm Racing**
3 DOOLEY GATE, 7, b g Petoski—High 'b' **F. P. Murtagh**
4 DUNDROD, 7, ch g Riverwise (USA)—Pallanda **Mr Sam Hamilton**
5 GLOBE STAR (IRE), 5, b m Germany (USA)—Chaparelle **G. & P. Barker Ltd/Globe Engineering**
6 HAMBLETON JO, 4, ch g Bijou d'Inde—Elegant Rose **3 J's Partnership**
7 HIGH CLASS PET, 4, b f Petong—What A Pet **Mr R. Millican**
8 HOLLOWS MILL, 8, b g Rudimentary (USA)—Strawberry Song **The Great Expectations Sporting Club**
9 HOLLOWS MIST, 6, b g Missed Flight—Joyfulness (FR) **The Great Expectations Sporting Club 2**
10 LA MAGO, 4, b f Wizard King—Dancing Dancer **Petroman Partnership**
11 MAGENKO (IRE), 7, ch g Forest Wind—Bebe Auction (IRE) **R & J Wharton**
12 MATTHEW MY SON (IRE), 4, ch g Lake Coniston (IRE)—Mary Hinge **Mr R. Millican**
13 MINSTER BLUE, 6, b m Minster Son—Elitist **Mr M. Elliott**
14 NAP HAND, 4, ch c Jumbo Hirt (USA)—Hand On Heart (IRE)
15 NATURAL (IRE), 7, b g Bigstone (IRE)—You Make Me Real (USA) **G. & P. Barker Ltd/Globe Engineering**
16 NORTHERN MINSTER, 5, b g Minster Son—Hand On Heart (IRE) **Mr L. Irving & Mr T. Littleton**
17 SHALFORETTE (IRE), 6, br m Shalford (IRE)—Chaparelle **Hurst Farm Racing**
18 SPECTACULAR (IRE), 5, b g Spectrum (IRE)—Azra (IRE) **Mr F. P. Murtagh**
19 SPECTRUM STAR, 4, b g Spectrum (IRE)—Persia (IRE) **Mr D. O'Connor**
20 THE COUNT (FR), 5, b g Sillery (USA)—Dear Countess (FR) **Jack The Lads**

THREE-YEAR-OLDS

21 MINSTREL'S DOUBLE, ch c Jumbo Hirt (USA)—Hand On Heart (IRE)

Other Owners: Mr C. Davidson, Mr G. J. Dowds, Mr B. M. Johnson, Mr T. D. Watson, Mrs J. Wharton, Mr T. Wharton, Mr Derek Wilson, Mr T. W. Wilson, Mr N. M. Wright.

Assistant Trainer: S A Murtagh

Jockeys (NH): A Dobbin, B Harding, C McCormack.

396 MR W. J. MUSSON, Newmarket
Postal: **Saville House, St Mary's Square, Newmarket, Suffolk, CB8 0HZ.**
Contact: **PHONE (01638) 663371 FAX (01638) 667979 E-MAIL wjm@williemusson.co.uk**

1 ANNAKITA, 4, b f Unfuwain (USA)—Cuban Reef **Mr K. L. West & Mr Neil Rooney**
2 BARRISSIMO (IRE), 4, b g Night Shift (USA)—Belle de Cadix (IRE) **Maurice Charge & Barry Fulton**
3 BLAKESEVEN, 4, b g Forzando—Up And Going (FR) **Mr Michael Liddy**
4 BROUGHTON KNOWS, 7, b g Most Welcome—Broughtons Pet (IRE) **Broughton Thermal Insulation**

MR W. J. MUSSON—continued

5 BROUGHTON MELODY, 5, ch m Alhijaz—Broughton Singer (IRE) **Broughton Thermal Insulation**
6 BROUGHTONS FLUSH, 6, b g First Trump—Glowing Reference **Broughton Thermal Insulation**
7 , B g Weldnaas (USA)—Broughton's Gold (IRE) **Broughton Thermal Insulation**
8 CLASSIC MILLENNIUM, 6, b m Midyan (USA)—Classic Colleen (IRE) **Broughton Thermal Insulation**
9 COMPTON DYNAMO, 5, b g Wolfhound (USA)—Asteroid Field (USA) **Broughton Thermal Insulation**
10 CRUISE DIRECTOR, 4, b g Zilzal (USA)—Briggsmaid **Mr K. A. Cosby**
11 DORCHESTER, 7, b g Primo Dominie—Penthouse Lady **The Square Table**
12 DUMARAN, 6, b g Be My Chief—Pine Needle **Propak Sheet Metal Ltd**
13 ELLENS LAD (IRE), 10, b g Polish Patriot (USA)—Lady Ellen **Mrs Rita Brown**
14 FEARBY CROSS (IRE), 8, b g Unblest—Two Magpies **Mrs Rita Brown**
15 FOLIO (IRE), 4, b g Perugino (USA)—Bayleaf **Broughton Thermal Insulation & Partner**
16 FREE OPTION (IRE), 9, ch g Indian Ridge—Saneena **Mrs Valerie Bennett**
17 JAIR OHMSFORD (IRE), 5, b g Hamas (IRE)—Harry's Irish Rose (USA) **Mr K. A. Cosby**
18 KAREEB (FR), 7, b g Green Desert (USA)—Braari (USA) **The Finos Partnership**
19 KRUGERRAND (USA), 5, ch g Gulch (USA)—Nasers Pride (USA) **The Square Table II**
20 LEGAL SET (IRE), 8, gr g Second Set (USA)—Tiffany's Case (IRE) **Mr K. King**
21 LONGHOPE BOY, 5, b g Rock Hopper—Always A Pleasure **Mr R. D. Musson**
22 MOLLY BE, 4, ch f First Trump—Broughton Singer (IRE) **Broughton Thermal Insulation & J. Taylor**
23 NEW OPTIONS, 7, b g Formidable (USA)—No Comebacks **Broughton Thermal Insulation**
24 PRINCE CYRANO, 5, b g Cyrano de Bergerac—Odilese **Mrs Rita Brown & Partner**
25 SISTER SOPHIA (USA), 4, br f Deputy Commander (USA)—Sophia's Choice (USA) **Suffolk RAcing**
26 STREET LIFE (IRE), 6, ch g Dolphin Street (FR)—Wolf Cleugh (IRE) **Howard Spooner & Partners (I)**
27 SWEET REFLECTION (IRE), 4, b f Victory Note (USA)—Shining Creek (CAN) **Saville House Racing**
28 TE ANAU, 7, b m Reprimand—Neenah **Mr W. J. Musson**
29 TRACE CLIP, 6, b g Zafonic (USA)—Illusory **Goodey & Broughton Thermal Insulation**
30 WOODYATES, 7, b m Naheez (USA)—Night Mission (IRE) **Mr & Mrs C.Cooper & Mr & Mrs J. Richards**

THREE-YEAR-OLDS

31 BIENHEUREUX, b g Bien Bien (USA)—Rochea **Mr K. L. West**
32 BREATHING SUN (IRE), b g Bahhare (USA)—Zapata (IRE) **Mr Howard Spooner**
33 BRIGHT FIRE (IRE), b f Daggers Drawn (USA)—Jarmar Moon **Mr Howard Spooner**
34 BROUGHTON BOUNTY, b f Rudimentary (USA)—Broughtons Lure (IRE) **Broughton Thermal Insulation**
35 BROUGHTON SUNNY, b f Bahamian Bounty—Sleave Silk (IRE) **Broughton Thermal Insulation**
36 GENUINELY (IRE), b f Entrepreneur—Fearless **Mr Howard Spooner**
37 GOLDEN MAIZE, ch f Danzig Connection (USA)—Mysterious Maid (USA) **Far Afield Partnership**
38 INTRODUCTION, b g Opening Verse (USA)—Cartuccia (USA) **All For One And One For All Partnership**
39 LADY BROUGHTON (IRE), ch f Grand Lodge—Veronica **Broughton Thermal Insulation**
40 MUGEBA, b f Primo Dominie—Ella Lamees **Billings & Broughton Thermal Insulation**
41 ROYAL PAVILLION (IRE), b c Cape Cross (IRE)—Regal Scintilla **Mr Howard Spooner**
42 STAR WELCOME, ch f Most Welcome—My Greatest Star **The Runaway Partnership**
43 TIDES, b f Bahamian Bounty—Petriece **Mr Howard Spooner**

TWO-YEAR-OLDS

44 B f 28/2 Prince Sabo—Coy Debutante (IRE) (Archway (IRE)) (2000) **Broughton Thermal Insulation**
45 D'ARCY SPICE, b c 5/4 Silver Patriarch (IRE)—Pallas Athene (Jupiter Island) **Mr & Mrs Peter Trend**
46 B f 27/4 Pivotal—Ella Lamees (Statoblest) (15000) **Broughton Thermal Insulation**
47 B c 16/1 Bahhare (USA)—Goldfill (Marju (IRE))
48 B f 5/3 Groom Dancer (USA)—Hetra Heights (USA) (Cox's Ridge (USA)) (3000) **Mr K. L. West**
49 Ch c 17/2 Definite Article—Itkan (IRE) (Marju (IRE)) (20000)
50 Ch c 10/3 Raise A Grand (IRE)—Lindas Delight (Batshoof) (12500) **Mrs Melba Bryce & Mr Robin Clark**
51 B c 21/3 Soviet Star (USA)—My-Lorraine (IRE) (Mac's Imp (USA)) (21644) **Spoons, Weaves, Jamie & Dukey**
52 B c 20/4 Pivotal—Pearl Venture (Salse (USA)) (50000) **Mr Howard Spooner**
53 B c 8/3 Desert Style (IRE)—Petite Maxine (Sharpo) (46000) **Mrs Rita Brown**
54 B c 1/2 Desert Story (IRE)—Sesame Heights (IRE) (High Estate) (11000) **Mr Howard Spooner & Mr Ian Weaver**
55 B c 31/1 Desert Style (URE)—Song of The Glens (Horage) (28000)

MR W. J. MUSSON—continued

56 B g 2/3 Deploy—Vic Melody (FR) (Old Vic) (3500) **Runaway Partnership**
57 B c 28/2 Desert King (IRE)—White Paper (IRE) (Marignan (USA)) (12000)

Other Owners: Mr Roger Aylett, Mr K. Balfour, Mr Richard Beare, Mr Michael Billings, Mr Paul Bowler, Mrs C. J. Broughton, Mr M. E. Broughton, Mr David Burgess, Mr Peter Burke, Mr Peter Cook, Mr Peter Cornwell, Mr Con Dower, Mr Neil Dower, Mr Josef Elliott, Mr T. Gilbert, Mr M. W. Goodey, Mr John Gunnell, Mrs Ruth Hatley, Mr T. Horsley, Mr Philip Hylander, Mrs Alison Jackson, Mr I. Johnson, Mr David Lobban, Mr D. Macgregor, Mr P. J. Mohan, Mr Colin Bryce, Mr A. Nicholls, Mr Bryan Peirson, Mrs Marcella Porcas, Mr P. Price, Mr Brendan Rooney, Mr Howard Scott, Mr Robert Tappin, Mr Bryan Taylor, Mr A. J. Thomson, Mrs N. A. Ward, Mr Laurence Weir.

Assistant Trainer: Mr Gordon Storrie

Jockeys (Flat): Paul Eddery (8-2), R Mullen. **Apprentices:** Lisa Jones (7-9), Laura Pike (7-12), A Rutter (8-0). **Amateur:** Miss J Pledge (8-7).

397 MRS A. M. NAUGHTON, Richmond
Postal: **High Gingerfield, Hurgill Road, Richmond, North Yorkshire, DL10 4TD.**
Contact: **PHONE (01748) 822803 MOBILE (07977) 576712**

1 CAMADERRY (IRE), 6, ch g Dr Devious (IRE)—Rathvindon **Mrs A. M. Naughton**
2 4, Ch f General Monash (USA)—Goold's Opal (IRE)
3 LOCH RED, 5, ch g Primitive Rising (USA)—Lochcross **Mrs Jillian Murphy**
4 LOCH SOUND, 8, b g Primitive Rising (USA)—Lochcross **Mrs Jillian Murphy**
5 NEEDWOOD SPIRIT, 9, b g Rolfe (USA)—Needwood Nymph **Famous Five Racing**

Other Owners: Mr R. Allen, Mr C. N. Harrison, Mr A. J. Markley, Mr D. H. Montgomerie, Mr F. Previtali.

Conditional: Gerard Supple. **Amateur:** Mr David McCubbin (10-0).

398 DR J. R. J. NAYLOR, Shrewton
Postal: **The Cleeve, Elston Lane, Shrewton, Wiltshire, SP3 4HL.**
Contact: **PHONE (01980) 620804 FAX (01980) 621999 MOBILE (07771) 740126**

1 BELLAPORT GIRL, 6, b m Supreme Leader—Derry Nell **Gallery Racing**
2 CHRISTON CANE, 6, b g El Conquistador—Dancing Barefoot **Mrs Mary Heritage**
3 DALLINGTON BROOK, 5, b g Bluegrass Prince (IRE)—Valetta **Dr J. R. J. Naylor**
4 DAPHNE'S DOLL (IRE), 9, b m Polish Patriot (USA)—Helietta **Mrs S. P. Elphick**
5 GALANDORA, 4, b f Bijou d'Inde—Jelabna **Dr John Pattillo**
6 INDIAN CHANCE, 10, b g Teenoso (USA)—Icy Miss **Chris and Stella Watson and Jock Cullen**
7 INDIAN CHASE, 7, b g Terimon—Icy Gunner **The Indian Chase Partnership**
8 INDIAN GUNNER, 11, b g Gunner B—Icy Miss **Mrs S. P. Elphick**
9 JIM LAD, 4, b g Young Ern—Anne's Bank (IRE) **Chris and Stella Watson**
10 LADYALDER, 6, br m Alderbrook—Ina's Farewell **Magor Golden Boys**
11 LADY WEST, 4, b f The West (USA)—Just Run (IRE) **Dr J. R. J. Naylor**
12 LYNPHORD GIRL, 13, ch m Lyphento (USA)—Woodlands Angel **The Cayford Partnership**
13 MISTER WEBB, 7, b g Whittingham (IRE)—Ruda (FR) **Mr Norman E. Webb**
14 MORLESS, 5, b m Morpeth—Bush Radio **Mr P. Tosh**
15 MY BROTHER, 10, b g Lugana Beach—Lucky Love **Dr J. R. J. Naylor**
16 RURAL REPRIMAND, 5, br g Reprimand—Lady Gwenmore **Mr Howard Smith**
17 SEE MORE JOCK, 6, b g Seymour Hicks (FR)—Metafan **Mrs B. Bishop**

THREE-YEAR-OLDS

18 WEBBINGTON LASS (IRE), b f Petardia—Richardstown Lass (IRE) **Mr Norman E. Webb**

TWO-YEAR-OLDS

19 B f 7/3 Victory Note (USA)—Paddys Cocktail (IRE) (Tremblant) (1809) **Dr J. R. J. Naylor**

Other Owners: Mr D. F. Barnett, Mr N. Boyd, Mr P. R. Burch, Mr A. Cayford, Mrs J. A. Cayford, Mr R. M. Donald, Mrs S. Shepherd, Ms A. J. B. Smalldon, Mr P. Williams.

Assistant Trainer: Lucy Russell

399 MR J. L. NEEDHAM, Ludlow
Postal: **Gorsty Farm, Mary Knoll, Ludlow, Shropshire, SY8 2HD.**
Contact: **PHONE (01584) 872112/874826 FAX (01584) 873256 MOBILE (07811) 451137**

1 **ANOTHER JOKER,** 9, b g Commanche Run—Just For A Laugh **Miss Joanna Needham**
2 5, Ch m Fourstars Allstar (USA)—Carlingford Belle **Mr J. L. Needham**
3 **FLASH HENRY,** 7, b g Executive Perk—Running Valley **Mr J. L. Needham**
4 5, B m Supreme Leader—Just For A Laugh **Miss Joanna Needham**
5 **KIRKFIELD (IRE),** 9, b m Commanche Run—Another Grange **Mr J. L. Needham**
6 5, B m Roselier (FR)—Leinthall Fox **Miss Joanna Needham**
7 6, B g Supreme Leader—Leinthall Fox **Miss Joanna Needham**
8 **ONE MORE NATIVE (IRE),** 7, ch g Be My Native (USA)—Romany Fortune **Miss Joanna Needham**

Assistant Trainer: P Hanly

Jockeys (NH): T Doyle, J M Maguire. **Conditional:** T P Phelan. **Amateur:** Mr A Hanly (10-10).

400 MR P. NEEDHAM, Barnard Castle
Postal: **Woolhouse Farm, Marwood, Barnard Castle, Co. Durham, DL12 8RG.**
Contact: **PHONE (01833) 690155**

1 **CLASSIC LASH (IRE),** 8, b g Classic Cheer (IRE)—Khaiylasha (IRE) **Mr P. Needham**
2 6, B m Perpendicular—Kate O'Kirkham **Mr P. Needham**
3 **PERCY BECK,** 8, ch g Minster Son—Kate O'Kirkham **Mr P. Needham**
4 **RUSHEN RAIDER,** 12, br g Reprimand—Travel Storm **Mr P. Needham**

Assistant Trainer: Sally Richardson

Jockey (NH): Calvin McCormack (10-0).

401 MR A. G. NEWCOMBE, Barnstaple
Postal: **Lower Delworthy, Yarnscombe, Barnstaple, Devon, EX31 3LT.**
Contact: **PHONE (01271) 858554 FAX (01271) 858554 MOBILE (07785) 297210**

1 **GAELIC PRINCESS,** 4, b f Cois Na Tine (IRE)—Berenice (ITY) **Mr M. K. F. Seymour**
2 **INTERSTICE,** 7, b h Never So Bold—Mainmast **Alex Gorrie Combi (UK)**
3 **KAKI CRAZY (FR),** 9, b g Passing Sale (FR)—Radiante Rose (FR) **Mr M. Patel**
4 **KENTUCKY BULLET (USA),** 8, b g Housebuster—Exactly So **Mrs B. J. Sherwin**
5 **LEVANTINE (IRE),** 7, b g Sadler's Wells (USA)—Spain Lane (USA) **Good Company Partnership**
6 **MAGIC CHARM,** 6, b m Magic Ring (IRE)—Loch Clair (IRE) **Wetherby Racing Bureau**
7 **MANDY'S COLLECTION,** 5, ch m Forzando—Instinction **Mr A. Newby**
8 **MEELUP (IRE),** 4, ch g Night Shift (USA)—Centella (IRE) **Mr M. K. F. Seymour**
9 **MIDDLETON GREY,** 6, gr g Ashkalani (IRE)—Petula **Mr Andy Beard**
10 **MUFREH (USA),** 6, br g Dayjur (USA)—Mathkurh (USA) **Mr M. K. F. Seymour**
11 **NIMELLO (USA),** 8, b g Kingmambo—Zakota (IRE) **Ms Gerardine P. O'Reilly**
12 **RELAX,** 4, ch g Dancing Spree (USA)—Fortuitious (IRE) **Mr A. G. Newcombe**
13 **RESONATE (IRE),** 6, b h Erins Isle—Petronelli (USA) **Mr S. Langridge**
14 **STARLADY,** 4, b f Mind Games—Ma Rivale **Ms Gerardine P. O'Reilly**
15 **THE BEST YET,** 6, ch h King's Signet (USA)—Miss Klew **Mr Ronnie de Beau-Lox**
16 **WIND CHIME (IRE),** 7, ch h Arazi (USA)—Shamisen **Advanced Marketing Services Ltd**

THREE-YEAR-OLDS

17 **CREWES MISS ISLE,** b f Makbul—Riviere Rouge **Mr A. McRoberts**
18 **DREAMS UNITED,** br f Dancing Spree (USA)—Kaliala (FR) **Mr A. G. Newcombe**
19 **FLEETING MAGIC,** b f Silver Wizard (USA)—Quick As A Wink **Ms Rose Jones**
20 **FORTUNATELY MINE,** b f Dancing Spree (USA)—Fortuitious (IRE) **Dreams United**
21 **MOSCOW MARY,** b f Imperial Ballet (IRE)—Baileys Firecat **Mr Andy Beard**
22 **SAMARA SOUND,** b c Savahra Sound—Hosting **Mr S. F. Turton**

MR A. G. NEWCOMBE—continued

23 **THE KING OF ROCK**, b c Nicolotte—Lv Girl (IRE) **Ms Gerardine P. O'Reilly**
24 B c Danzig Connection (USA)—Trina's Pet **Mr A. G. Newcombe**

Other Owners: Mr Andrew Bates, Mr Alex Gorrie, Mr Chris Page, Mr B. P. Ryan, Mr Nigel S. Scandrett, Mr Michael Stead, Mr H. Wetter.

Jockeys (Flat): J Quinn, S Whitworth. **Jockeys (NH):** B J Crowley, A Thornton. **Amateur:** Miss C Hannaford (8-8).

402

MR. M B. NICHOLLS, Somerton
Postal: **Victory House Stables, West Charlton, Charlton Mackrell, Somerton, Somerset, TA11 7AL.**
Contact: **PHONE (01458) 224589 FAX (01458) 224580 MOBILE (07734) 436610**

1 **BLUE SHANNON (IRE)**, 6, b m Be My Native (USA)—Shannon Foam **Mrs Angela Tincknell**
2 6, B m Sir Harry Lewis (USA)—Cream By Post **Mr T. C. Frost**
3 **CYINDIEN (FR)**, 7, b br g Cyborg (FR)—Indiana Rose (FR) **Sir Robert Ogden**
4 **DAVOSKI**, 10, b g Niniski (USA)—Pamela Peach **Sir Robert Ogden**
5 **DERREEN BOY (IRE)**, 7, ch g Tanaos—Lancana (IRE) **The Boyz R Uz Partnership**
6 **FLORIDA DREAM (IRE)**, 5, b g Florida Son—Ice Pearl **D. J. & S. A. Goodman & T.Puffett**
7 **LORD NOELIE (IRE)**, 11, b g Lord Americo—Leallen **Executive Racing**
8 **LUCKY BAY (IRE)**, 8, b g Convinced—Current Liability **Executive Racing II**
9 **MINORA BLUE**, b m Bob Back (USA)—Minora (IRE) **Mrs Angela Tincknell**
10 4, B g Anshan—Miss Fern **Mr & Mrs P. Andrews**
11 **MURT'S MAN (IRE)**, 10, b g Be My Native (USA)—Autumn Queen **Mr Derek Millard**
12 **PLUMIER (FR)**, 6, b g Beyssac (FR)—Plume Rose (FR) **Sir Robert Ogden**
13 **PRINCE HIGHWAY (IRE)**, 9, b g Lord Americo—Madamme Highlights **The Summer Solstice Partnership**
14 **SILENT APPEAL**, 7, b m Afflora (IRE)—Silent Surrender **Mrs E. R. Smith**
15 **SUPREME NATIVE (IRE)**, 8, b g Be My Native (USA)—Ballough Bui (IRE) **Mrs A. Tincknell**
16 **TRIBAL KING (IRE)**, 9, b br g Be My Native (USA)—Island Bridge **Mrs Peter Andrews**
17 **UNMISTAKABLY (IRE)**, 7, br g Roselier (FR)—Decent Debbie **Sir Robert Ogden**
18 **WHISPERING JOHN (IRE)**, 8, b g Grand Plaisir (IRE)—London Anne **Premiership Racing**

Other Owners: Mr Anthony B. Buckwell, Mr Brian M. Hartigan, Mr R. W. Humphreys, Mrs J. P. Jackson, Mr P. Lazenby, Mrs Wendy Lomas, Mrs Rosemary Paterson, Mr Ian Rees, Mrs Carole Solman, Mr W. Tincknell, Mr G. T. Watson.

403

MR D. NICHOLLS, Thirsk
Postal: **Tall Trees Racing Ltd, Tall Trees, Sessay, Thirsk, North Yorkshire, YO7 3ND.**
Contact: **PHONE (01845) 501470 FAX (01845) 501666 MOBILE (07971) 555105**
E-MAIL david.nicholls@btconnect.com

1 **ALBASHOOSH**, 6, b g Cadeaux Genereux—Annong (USA) **A A Bloodstock**
2 **AMERICAN COUSIN**, 9, b g Distant Relative—Zelda (USA) **Middleham Park Racing XIV**
3 **ATLANTIC VIKING (IRE)**, 9, b g Danehill (USA)—Hi Bettina **Mr David Faulkner**
4 **AWAKE**, 7, ch g First Trump—Pluvial **Lucayan Stud & D. Nicholls**
5 **BAHAMIAN PIRATE (USA)**, 9, ch g Housebuster (USA)—Shining Through (USA) **Lucayan Stud**
6 **BAILIEBOROUGH (IRE)**, 5, b g Charnwood Forest (IRE)—Sherannda (USA) **Middleham Park Racing XVIII**
7 **BALLYBUNION (IRE)**, 5, ch g Entrepreneur—Clarentia **Mr I Blakey, Mr M Gosse, Mr D Nicholls**
8 **BANJO BAY (IRE)**, 6, b g Common Grounds—Thirlmere **Middleham Park Racing XXIII**
9 **BANNISTER**, 6, ch g Inchinor—Shall We Run **Montague Racing**
10 **BATOOL (USA)**, 5, b m Bahri (USA)—Mrs Paddy (USA) **Mr Ian W. Glenton**
11 **BLACKHEATH (IRE)**, 8, ch g Common Grounds—
　　　　　　　　　　　　　　　　　　　Queen Caroline (USA) **Middleham Park Racing XX & Streamhill**
12 **BOISDALE (IRE)**, 6, b g Common Grounds—Alstomeria **Mrs S Tang,Mr J Nicholls,Mrs S Thomson**
13 **BORDER ARTIST**, 5, ch g Selkirk (USA)—Aunt Tate **F. F. Racing Services Partnership V**
14 **BRAVE BURT (IRE)**, 7, ch g Pips Pride—Friendly Song **Lucayan Stud & D. Nicholls**
15 **BRECONGILL LAD**, 12, b g Clantime—Chikala **Mr P. Davidson-Brown**
16 **CANDLERIGGS (IRE)**, 8, ch g Indian Ridge—Ridge Pool (IRE) **Mr D. Nicholls**
17 **CAPTAIN CLIPPER**, 4, ch g Royal Applause—Collide **Clipper Group Holdings**
18 **COMPTON ARROW (IRE)**, 8, b g Petardia—Impressive Lady **Mr A. Bloom**
19 **COMPTON DRAGON (USA)**, 5, ch g Woodman (USA)—Vilikaia (USA) **Mr John Connor**
20 **CONTINENT**, 7, ch g Lake Coniston (IRE)—Krisia **Lucayan Stud**
21 **ETON (GER)**, 8, ch g Suave Dancer (USA)—Ermione **Mr D. Nicholls**
22 **EXTINGUISHER**, 5, ch g Zamindar (USA)—Xaymara (USA) **Mr Mike Browne**
23 **FIRE UP THE BAND**, 5, b h Prince Sabo—Green Supreme **Mr P. Crane, Mr A. Barker & Mr S. Short**
24 **FOURTH DIMENSION (IRE)**, 5, b g Entrepreneur—Isle of Spice (USA) **Mr V. Greaves**

MR D. NICHOLLS—continued

25 **FUNFAIR WANE**, 5, b g Unfuwain (USA)—Ivory Bride **Mrs Jean Keegan & Mr D. Nicholls**
26 **GOLDEN SPECTRUM (IRE)**, 5, ch g Spectrum (USA)—Plessaya (USA) **Mr T. G. Meynell**
27 **HAIL THE CHIEF**, 7, b h Be My Chief (USA)—Jade Pet **Mr Peter M. Crane**
28 **IZMAIL (IRE)**, 5, b g Bluebird (USA)—My-Lorraine (IRE) **Mr G. M. McGuinness**
29 **JABAAR (USA)**, 6, gr g Silver Hawk (USA)—Sierra Madre (FR) **Mr P. Lake & Mr S. Hull**
30 **JUBILEE STREET (IRE)**, 5, b g Dr Devious (IRE)—My Firebird **Mr D. W. Holdsworth & Mr J. A. McMahon**
31 **LINCOLN DANCER (IRE)**, 7, b g Turtle Island (IRE)—Double Grange (IRE) **The Gardening Partnership**
32 **LOCOMBE HILL (IRE)**, 8, b g Barathea (IRE)—Roberts Pride **Mr Ian W. Glenton**
33 **LORD MERLIN (IRE)**, 5, b g Turtle Island (IRE)—My-O-My (IRE) **Mr Neil Smith**
34 **LORD OF THE EAST**, 5, b g Emarati (USA)—Fairy Free **The Wayward Lads**
35 **LOW CLOUD**, 4, b g Danehill (USA)—Raincloud **Maxilead Ltd**
36 **LOYAL TYCOON (IRE)**, 6, br g Royal Abjar (USA)—Rosy Lydgate **Michael A. J. Hall & Mrs Mandy Hall**
37 **LUCAYAN DANCER**, 4, b g Zieten (USA)—Tittle Tattle (IRE) **Lucayan Stud**
38 **MACHINIST (IRE)**, 4, b g Machiavellian (USA)—Athene (IRE) **Mr V. Greaves**
39 **MERLIN'S DANCER**, 4, b g Magic Ring (IRE)—La Piaf (FR) **Chalfont Food Halls**
40 **NATIVE TITLE**, 6, b g Pivotal—Bermuda Lily **Mr C. McKenna**
41 **NEMO FUGAT (IRE)**, 5, b g Danehill Dancer (IRE)—Do The Right Thing **Mr John Hair**
42 **ONLINE INVESTOR**, 5, b g Puissance—Anytime Baby **Mr R. G. Leatham**
43 **ONLYTIME WILL TELL**, 6, ch g Efisio—Prejudice **Mr J. Hair & Mr D. Faulkner**
44 **PALANZO (IRE)**, 4, b g Green Desert (USA)—Karpacka (IRE) **Fayzad Thoroughbred Limited**
45 **PAX**, 7, ch g Brief Truce (USA)—Child's Play (USA) **Mr D. Nicholls**
46 **PAYS D'AMOUR (IRE)**, 7, b g Pursuit of Love—Lady of The Land **The Inglenookers**
47 **PIETER BRUEGHEL (USA)**, 5, b g Citidancer (USA)—Smart Tally (USA) **Mr David Faulkner**
48 **PLATEAU**, 5, b g Zamindar (USA)—Painted Desert **A A Bloodstock**
49 **POMFRET LAD**, 6, b g Cyrano de Bergerac—Lucky Flinders **Maxilead Ltd**
50 **PROUD NATIVE (IRE)**, 10, b g Imp Society (USA)—Karamana **Mr P. D. Savill**
51 **RECTANGLE (IRE)**, 4, ch g Fayruz—Moona (USA) **Mr Paul Sellars and Mr Nik Ingham**
52 **SAWWAAH (IRE)**, 7, b g Marju (IRE)—Just A Mirage **Fayzad Thoroughbred Limited**
53 **SHIFTY**, 5, b g Night Shift (USA)—Crodelle (IRE) **Wetherby Racing Bureau 39**
54 **SHIRLEY NOT**, 8, gr g Paris House—Hollia **Peter Whinham & Jeff Stelling**
55 **SIR DON (IRE)**, 5, b g Lake Coniston (IRE)—New Sensitive **Mrs Dian Plant**
56 **SMIRFYS PARTY**, 6, ch g Clantime—Party Scenes **Mrs Dian Plant**
57 **SPEEDY JAMES (IRE)**, 8, ch g Fayruz—Haraabah (USA) **Fiona Scott**
58 **STERLING GUARANTEE (USA)**, 6, b g Silver Hawk (USA)—
Sterling Pound (USA) **Mr D. Nicholls, I. Glenton & P. Whinham**
59 **TIME TO REMEMBER (IRE)**, 6, b g Pennekamp (USA)—Bequeath (USA) **The Knavesmire Alliance**
60 **T K O GYM**, 5, b g Atraf—Pearl Pet **Mr Mark F. Sheasby**
61 **TRUE NIGHT**, 7, b g Night Shift (USA)—Dead Certain **Benton and Partners**
62 **VIGOROUS (IRE)**, 4, b f Danetime (IRE)—Merrily **F. F. Racing Services Partnership V**
63 **WATCHING**, 7, ch g Indian Ridge—Sweeping **M.A.Leatham, G.H.Leatham & R.G.Leatham**
64 **WINNING VENTURE**, 7, b g Owington—Push A Button **Mr A. Bloom**
65 **ZANJEER (IRE)**, 8, ch g Averti (IRE)—Cloudslea (USA) **Mr Mark F. Sheasby**
66 **ZUHAIR**, 11, ch g Mujtahid (USA)—Ghzaalh (USA) **The Gardening Partnership**

THREE-YEAR-OLDS

67 **ARTIE'S LAD (IRE)**, ch g Danehill Dancer (IRE)—Bold Avril (IRE) **Mr D. Metcalf**
68 **BIEN GOOD**, b f Bien Bien (USA)—Southern Sky **Mr Bill Brown**
69 **BURKEES GRAW (IRE)**, ch g Fayruz—Dancing Willma (IRE) **Mr D. Nicholls**
70 **DORISIMA (FR)**, ch f Mark of Esteem (IRE)—Suhaad **Mr Steve Hull**
71 **FANLING LADY**, gr f Highest Honor (FR)—Pain Perdu (IRE) **Mr Ambrose Turnbull**
72 **FULL AS A ROCKET (IRE)**, b g Foxhound (USA)—Taysala (IRE) **H W Racing**
73 **HAMAASY**, b g Machiavellian (USA)—Sakha **Mr J. Honeyman**
74 **ICE PLANET**, b c Polar Falcon (USA)—Preference **Mr David Faulkner**
75 **JIMMY GEE (IRE)**, b g Efisio—Stica (IRE) **Mr D. Nicholls**
76 **SESSAY**, b g Cyrano de Bergerac—Green Supreme **Mr P. Crane, Mr A. Barker & Mr S. Short**
77 **SKYHARBOR**, b g Cyrano de Bergerac—Pea Green **Sussex Syndicate**
78 **VOLATICUS (IRE)**, b c Desert Story—Haysel (IRE) **Ms J Davies Mr S Parkin & Mr G McGuiness**
79 **WANCHAI LAD**, b c Danzero (AUS)—Frisson **Mr Ambrose Turnbull**
80 **YOUNG WARRIOR (IRE)**, b g Desert Style (IRE)—Arctic Splendour (USA) **Paul & Anne Sellars**

MR D. NICHOLLS—continued

TWO-YEAR-OLDS

81 B f 27/2 Cape Cross (IRE)—Night Spirit (IRE) (Night Shift (USA)) (20000) **Mr Ambrose Turnbull**
82 **ON THE BRIGHT SIDE,** b f 14/3 Cyrano de Bergerac—Jade Pet (Petong) (13000) **The Oak Tree Syndicate**

Assistant Trainer: Ben Beasley, Ernie Greaves

Jockey (Flat): Alex Greaves (8-8). **Apprentice:** L Treadwell. **Amateurs:** Mr J Gee (10-0), Miss K Harrison (9-0), Mrs N Wilson (9-7).

---

404 **MR P. F. NICHOLLS, Shepton Mallet**
Postal: **Manor Farm Stables, Ditcheat, Shepton Mallet, Somerset, BA4 6RD.**
Contact: PHONE **(01749) 860656 FAX (01749) 860523**

1 **AIDE DE CAMP (FR),** 5, b g Saint Preuil (FR)—Baraka de Thaix II (FR) **Sir Robert Ogden**
2 **AIN'T THAT A SHAME (IRE),** 4, ch g Broken Hearted—Alvinru **Ashleybank Investments Limited**
3 **ALBUHERA (IRE),** 6, b g Desert Style (IRE)—Morning Welcome (IRE) **D. J. & F. A. Jackson**
4 **ALEXANDERTHEGREAT (IRE),** 6, b g Supreme Leader—Sandy Jayne (IRE) **The Irish Connection**
5 **ALFORMASI,** 5, b g Alflora (IRE)—Anamasi **Mr J. Hales**
6 **ANDREAS (FR),** 4, b g Marchand de Sable (USA)—Muscova Dancer (FR) **Mr Mark Tincknell**
7 **ARMARIVER (FR),** 4, ch g River Mist (USA)—Armalita (FR) **Mrs Bunty Millard**
8 **ARMATURK (FR),** 7, ch g Baby Turk—Armalita (FR) **Mr B. C. Marshall**
9 **ASK THE GATHERER (IRE),** 6, b g Be My Native (USA)—Shean Bracken (IRE) **Mrs Toni S. Tipper**
10 **ASPIRING ACTOR (IRE),** 4, b g Old Vic—Stasias Dream (IRE) **Mrs J. Stewart**
11 **AZERTYUIOP (IRE),** 7, b g Baby Turk—Temara (FR) **Mr J. Hales**
12 **AZZEMOUR (FR),** 5, ch g Morespeed—Tarde (FR)
13 **BAL DE NUIT (FR),** 5, gr g Balleroy (USA)—Eoline (FR) **Mrs Monica Hackett**
14 **BANCHORY TWO (IRE),** 4, b g Un Desperado—Theyllallwin (IRE) **Mr B. C. Marshall**
15 **BLUE AMERICO (IRE),** 6, br g Lord Americo—Princess Menelek **Mrs Angela Tincknell**
16 **BLUE BUSINESS,** 6, br g Roselier (FR)—Miss Redlands **Mrs Angela Tincknell**
17 **BLUE ENDEAVOUR (IRE),** 6, b g Endeavour (USA)—Jingle Bells (FR) **Mrs Angela Tincknell**
18 **BLUSHING BULL,** 5, b g Makbul—Blush **Mr Richard Barber**
19 **CENKOS (FR),** 10, ch g Nikos—Vincenza **Mrs J. Stewart**
20 **CHOCKDEE (FR),** 4, b g King's Theatre (IRE)—Chagrin d'Amour (USA) **Mr and Mrs J. D. Cotton**
21 **CLASSIFY,** 5, b g Classic Cliche (IRE)—Slmaat **Mrs P Pullin, Mr A Banks, Mr J G Olds**
22 **COBRECES,** 6, b g Environment Friend—Oleada (IRE) **Gerry Mizel & Terry Warner**
23 **COMANCHE WAR PAINT (IRE),** 7, b g Commanche Run—Galeshula **Tony Fear & Tim Hawkins**
24 **CORNISH GALE (IRE),** 10, br g Strong Gale—Seanaphobal Lady **Mr C. G. Roach**
25 **CORNISH REBEL (IRE),** 7, br g Un Desperado—Katday (FR) **Mr C. G. Roach**
26 **DEVON VIEW (IRE),** 10, b g Jolly Jake (NZ)—Skipaside **Mr Jeffrey Hordle**
27 **DRAGON'S DREAM,** 6, b g Afzal—Another Relation **Mr Richard Barber**
28 **DUSTY BANDIT (IRE),** 6, ch g Un Desperado (FR)—Marble Miller (IRE) **Mrs J. Stewart**
29 **EARTHMOVER (IRE),** 13, ch g Mister Lord (USA)—Clare's Crystal **Mr R. M. Penny**
30 **EAST LAWYER (FR),** 5, b g Homme de Loi (IRE)—East Riding (FR) **Champneys Partnership**
31 **ELJAY'S BOY,** 6, b g Sir Harry Lewis (USA)—Woodland Flower **Stephen Purdew and Des Nichols**
32 **EMANATE,** 6, ch g Nicholas Bill—Sleepline Princess **Mr G. Z. Mizel**
33 **EXISTENTIAL (FR),** 9, b g Exit To Nowhere (USA)—Lyceana (USA) **Mr H. B. Geddes**
34 **EXIT SWINGER (FR),** 9, b g Exit To Nowhere (USA)—Morganella (USA) **Sandicroft Stud I**
35 **EXIT TO WAVE (FR),** 8, ch g Exit To Nowhere (USA)—Hereke **Mr Malcolm Pearce & Mr Gerry Mizel II**
36 **FASGO (FR),** 9, b g Montelimar (USA)—Action Plan **F. A. Smith**
37 **FLYING WANDA,** 4, b f Alzao (USA)—Royal York **Sir Robert Ogden**
38 **FRENCH EXECUTIVE (IRE),** 9, br g Beau Sher—
                    Executive Move (IRE) **T.Chappell,R.Eddy,Mrs Jackson,Mrs Solman**
39 **FROM THIS MOMENT (IRE),** 6, b g Parthian Springs—Swatter (IRE) **Mr Mick Coburn**
40 **FRUIT DEFENDU (FR),** 7, b g Exit To Nowhere (USA)—Pauvresse (FR) **Mrs Monica Hackett**
41 **GARDE CHAMPETRE (FR),** 5, b g Garde Royale—Clementine Fleurie (FR) **Million in Mind Partnership**
42 **GENERAL CLAREMONT (IRE),** 11, gr g Strong Gale—Kasam **Mr K. G. Manley**
43 **GOBLET OF FIRE (USA),** 5, b g Green Desert (USA)—Laurentine (USA) **Mrs Susan Roy**
44 **GRANDE CREOLE (IRE),** 5, b g Byzantium (USA)—Sclos (FR) **Sir Robert Ogden**
45 **GREAT TRAVEL (FR),** 5, b g Great Palm (USA)—Travel Free **Mrs J. Stewart**
46 **HARAPOUR (FR),** 6, b g Valanour (IRE)—Haratiyna **Mrs Jan Smith**
47 **HATTERAS (FR),** 5, b g Octagonal (NZ)—Hylandra (USA) **Mr Neil Smith**
48 **IRBEE,** 12, b g Gunner B—Cupids Bower **Mrs Bunty Millard**
49 **IT'S BEYOND BELIEF (IRE),** 10, b g Supreme Leader—Rossacurra **Mr J. G. Crumpler**
50 **IVANOPH (FR),** 8, b g Roi de Rome (USA)—Veronique IV (FR) **Mr Neil Smith**

MR P. F. NICHOLLS—continued

51 **JANITURE (FR)**, 7, gr m Turgeon (USA)—Majaway (FR) **Mr Malcolm Pearce & Mr Gerry Mizel**
52 **JOLI SADDLERS**, 8, b m Saddlers' Hall (IRE)—Vitality **Joli Racing**
53 **JOLLY GIANT (IRE)**, 8, b g Jolly Jake (NZ)—Reve Clair **Mr Derek Millard**
54 **JOYEUX ROYAL (FR)**, 7, b g Cyborg (FR)—Samba du Cochet (FR) **Barry Fulton, Liam Brady, Tony Hayward**
55 **JULIE'S LEADER (IRE)**, 10, b g Supreme Leader—Parkavoureen **Mr T. Curry**
56 **KADAM (IRE)**, 4, b g Night Shift (USA)—Kadassa (IRE) **Notalotterry**
57 **KADARANN (IRE)**, 7, b g Bigstone (IRE)—Kadassa (IRE) **Notalotterry**
58 **KHALADJISTAN (IRE)**, 6, gr g Tirol—Khaladja (IRE) **Notalotterry**
59 **KIWI BABE**, 5, b m Karinga Bay—Sunshine Gal **Mr David Chown**
60 **KJETIL (USA)**, 4, b g King of Kings (IRE)—I Wich (FR) **Mr Clive D. Smith**
61 **LADALKO (FR)**, 5, b g Kadalko (FR)—Debandade (FR) **Mr Paul K Barber & Mrs M Findlay**
62 **L'AVENTURE (FR)**, 5, b m Cyborg (FR)—Amphitrite (FR) **Mr C. J. Harriman**
63 **LE DUC (FR)**, 5, b g Villez (USA)—Beberova (FR) **Mrs J. Stewart**
64 **LE PASSING (FR)**, 5, b g Passing Sale (FR)—
                                  Petite Serenade (FR) **The Hon Mrs Townshend & Mr J.R.Townshend**
65 **LE ROI MIGUEL (FR)**, 6, b g Point of No Return (FR)—Loumir (USA) **Mrs J. Stewart**
66 **LEROY'S SISTER (FR)**, 4, b f Phantom Breeze—Loumir (USA) **Mrs J. Stewart**
67 **LORD EARTH (IRE)**, 6, b g Mister Lord (USA)—Mizuna **Mr R. M. Penny**
68 **LORD LINGTON (FR)**, 5, b g Bulington (FR)—Tosca de Bussy (FR) **Mr Paul K Barber & Mrs M Findlay**
69 **LOU DU MOULIN MAS (FR)**, 5, b g Sassanian (USA)—Houf (FR) **The Eight Amigos Racing Syndicate**
70 **LUNCH WAS MY IDEA (IRE)**, 4, b br g Tawrrific (NZ)—Equity Law (IRE) **Mr D. J. Nichols**
71 **LUNERAY (FR)**, 5, b m Poplar Bluff—Casandre (FR) **Sandicroft Stud I**
72 **MAIFUL (FR)**, 4, b g Useful (FR)—Shailann (FR) **Hill Fuels Limited**
73 **MAJED (FR)**, 8, b g Fijar Tango (FR)—Full of Passion (USA) **Sandicroft Stud I**
74 **MANLY MONEY**, 6, b g Homo Sapien—Susie's Money **Mrs Susie Chown**
75 **MASTER FLORIAN (IRE)**, 7, gr g Roselier (FR)—Paddy's Well **Mr K. G. Manley**
76 **MISTER BANJO (FR)**, 8, b g Mister Mat (FR)—Migre (FR) **Mr J. Hales**
77 **MONTIFAULT (FR)**, 9, ch g Morespeed—Tarde (FR) **Mrs A. E. Fulton**
78 **MONTI FLYER**, 6, b g Terimon—Coole Pilate **Mr B. C. Marshall**
79 **MOUNT KARINGA**, 6, b g Karinga Bay—Candarela **Mr Derek Millard**
80 **MY WILL (FR)**, 4, b g Saint Preuil (FR)—Gleep Will (FR) **Mrs J. Stewart**
81 **NORTHERN EDITION (IRE)**, 7, br g Good Thyne (USA)—Early Pace **You Boyz Is Lost**
82 **ONWARDSANDUPWARDS (IRE)**, 5, b br g Un Desperado (FR)—
                                  Kalifornia Katie (IRE) **Paul K Barber & Barry Marshall**
83 **PARSON PLOUGHMAN**, 9, br g Riverwise (USA)—Pretty Pantoes **Mr Andrew Wadsworth**
84 **PATCHES (FR)**, 5, b br g Presenting—Ballykilleen **Mrs Marianne G. Barber**
85 **PERANGE (FR)**, 8, ch g Perrault—La Mesange (FR) **Mrs Kathy Stuart**
86 **PEROUSE**, 6, ch g Alderbrook—Track Angel **J. Dickson & S. McVie**
87 **PHAR FROM A FIDDLE (IRE)**, 8, b b br g Phardante (FR)—Lucycello **Mrs J. Stewart**
88 **PITMINSTER**, 6, b g Karinga Bay—Eleanora Muse **Mr R. H. Dunn**
89 **QUID PRO QUO (FR)**, 5, b g Cadoudal (FR)—Luzenia (USA) **Sir Robert Ogden**
90 **RED DEVIL ROBERT (IRE)**, 6, ch g Carroll House—Well Over **Barry Marshall & Paul K Barber**
91 **RIGMAROLE**, 6, b g Fairy King (USA)—Cattermole (USA) **Mr & Mrs Mark Woodhouse**
92 **ROYAL AUCLAIR (FR)**, 7, ch g Garde Royale—Carmonera (FR) **Mr Clive D. Smith**
93 **RUBY GALE (IRE)**, 8, b g Lord Americo—Well Over **Mrs Angela Tincknell**
94 **RYE BROOK**, 7, b g Romany Rye—Nearly A Brook **Mrs S. J. Maltby**
95 **SAINT ESTEBEN (FR)**, 5, b g Poliglote—Highest Tulip (FR) **Formpave Ltd**
96 **SANTENAY (FR)**, 6, b g Mister Mat (FR)—Guigone (FR) **The Hon Mrs Townshend**
97 **SATSHOON (IRE)**, 11, b g Satco (FR)—Tudor Lady **Mr Mick Coburn**
98 **SILENCE REIGNS**, 10, b g Saddlers' Hall (IRE)—Rensaler (USA) **Mr K. W. Biggins**
99 **SILVER BIRCH (IRE)**, 7, b g Clearly Bust—All Gone **Mr D. J. Nichols**
100 4, B g Luso—Simple Mind **Mr Paul K Barber & Mrs M Findlay**
101 **SLEEPING NIGHT (FR)**, 8, b g Sleeping Car (FR)—Doll Night (FR) **D. J. & F. A. Jackson**
102 **SPORAZENE (IRE)**, 5, gr g Cozzene (USA)—Sporades (USA) **Ged Mason & David Jackson**
103 **SPORTING MAN (IRE)**, 7, ch g Insan (USA)—Gleann Oge **Mr Paul K Barber & Mrs M Findlay**
104 **STAVORDALE LAD (IRE)**, 6, b g Mister Lord (USA)—Ath Trasna **Mr T. G. A. Chappell & Mr Paul K. Barber**
105 **STORM DAMAGE**, 12, b g Waajib—Connaught Lace **Mrs Penny Mitchell**
106 **ST PIRRAN (IRE)**, 9, b br g Be My Native (USA)—Guess Twice **Mr C. G. Roach**
107 **SUD BLEU (FR)**, 6, b g Pistolet Bleu (IRE)—Sudaka (FR) **Barry Marshall & Terry Warner**
108 **SWEET DIVERSION (IRE)**, 5, b g Carroll House—Serocco Wind **Mr & Mrs Ian Marshall**
109 **THE BAG MAN**, 5, b g Alflora (IRE)—Lady Claudia (IRE) **J. Dickson & S. McVie**
110 **THISTHATANDTOTHER (IRE)**, 8, b g Bob Back (USA)—Baden (IRE) **Mr C. G. Roach**
111 **THORNTOUN HOLM**, 6, ch g Dancing Spree (USA)—Furry Friend **Mr Richard Barber**
112 **TINOVERITAS (FR)**, 6, b g Saint Estephe (FR)—Tinorosa (FR) **Mr C. G. Roach**
113 **TORDUFF EXPRESS (IRE)**, 13, b g Kambalda—Marhabtain **Two Plus Two**
114 **TRAGIC OHIO**, 5, b g Tragic Role (USA)—Kiniohio (FR) **Sandicroft Stud I**

MR P. F. NICHOLLS—continued

115 **UN JOUR A VASSY (FR)**, 9, b g Video Rock (FR)—Bayalika (FR) **Mrs Bunty Millard**
116 **VENN OTTERY**, 9, b g Access Ski—Tom's Comedy **Mr O. J. Carter**
117 **WERE IN TOUCH (IRE)**, 6, b g Old Vic—Winterland Gale (IRE) **Paul Barber,Malcolm Calvert,Colin Lewis**
118 **WHITFORD DON (IRE)**, 6, b g Accordion—Whitford Breeze **Mr J. Hales**
119 **WHITTON PARK**, 4, b g Sillery (USA)—Lady Golconda (FR) **The Eight Amigos Racing Syndicate**
120 **WILD KNIGHT (IRE)**, 7, b g Jurado (USA)—Knight's Maid **Hunt & Co (Bournemouth) Ltd**
121 **YOUNG DEVEREAUX (IRE)**, 11, b br g Lord Americo—Miss Iverk **Paul K.Barber,Mick Coburn,Colin Lewis 2**

Other Owners: Mr Arron F. A. Banks, Mr Paul K. Barber, Mr I. Bewley, Mr A. R. Bromley, Mr Chris J. Buckerfield, Miss K. S. Buckley, Mr M. Calvert, Mr T. G. A. Chappell, Mrs B. Cotton, Mr J. D. Cotton, Mr Graham Craig, Mrs J. A. Curry, Mr J. Dickson, Mr M. Dragisic, Mr R. G. Eddy, Mr A. G. Fear, Mrs M. Findlay, Mr Steve Fisher, Mr J. M. French, Mr B. N. Fulton, Mr Graham Goode, Miss L. Hales, Mr T. J. Hawkins, Mr Tony A. Hayward, Mr T. Hubbard, Mr David J. Jackson, Mrs John Jackson, Mr F. A. Jackson (Beds), Mr Colin Lewis, Mrs Elizabeth Marshall, Mr Ian Marshall, Mr Ged Mason, Mr S. McVie, Mr R. J. Metherell, Mr J. S. Middleton, Mr D. Minton, Mr M. Morgan, Mr David Nicholson, Mr T. H. Northwood, Exors Of The Late J. G. Olds, Mr Malcolm Pearce, Mrs Pauline Pullin, Mr S. J. Purdew, Mrs Carole Solman, Mr W. Tincknell, Mr J. R. Townshend, Mr Terry Warner, Mr Mark Woodhouse, Mrs Mark Woodhouse.

Assistant Trainer: Jeremy Young

Jockeys (NH): Sam Stronge (10-0), Joe Tizzard (10-0), Ruby Walsh (10-1). **Conditional:** Anthony Honeyball (10-0), Bobby McNally (9-11), Christian Williams (9-11). **Amateurs:** Miss Rilly Goschen (10-7), Mr Liam Heard (9-11), Mr James Jenkins (10-0), Miss Chloe Roddick (9-7), Miss Charlotte Tizzard (10-0), Mr Nick Williams (9-9).

---

405 MR P. D. NIVEN, Malton
Postal: **Clovafield, Barton-Le-Street, Malton, North Yorkshire, YO17 6PN.**
Contact: **(01653) 628176 MOBILE (07860) 260999 E-MAIL willmary@onetel.net.uk**

1 **ADIOS (GER)**, 5, b g Lagunas—Aerope **Mr Ian G. M. Dalgleish**
2 5, B m Grand Plaisir (IRE)—Bolaney Girl (IRE) **Mr P. D. Niven**
3 **CLASSIC CALVADOS (FR)**, 5, b br g Thatching—Mountain Stage (IRE) **Mr David H. Cox**
4 **DARK SLANEY (IRE)**, 9, b g Meneval (USA)—Black Valley (IRE) **Mr David Bamber**
5 **FATHER BOB**, 7, gr g Bold Fox—Annie Bee **Mr R. N. Forman**
6 **HURRICANE BAY**, 8, ch g Karinga Bay—Clodaigh Gale **Mr Ian G. M. Dalgleish**
7 **KIORA BAY**, 7, b g Karinga Bay—Equasion (IRE) **Mr C. D. Carr**
8 **MISTER FRIDAY (IRE)**, 7, b br g Mister Lord (USA)—Rebecca's Storm (IRE) **Mr R. A. Bartlett**
9 **MYSTIC GLEN**, 5, b m Vettori (IRE)—Mystic Memory **Mrs J. A. Niven**
10 **NO GLOATING (IRE)**, 5, b g King's Ride—Arctic Gale (IRE) **IBT Racing**
11 **OPTIMUM NIGHT**, 5, b g Superlative—Black Bess **Mrs H. M. Lipscomb**
12 **PANMURE (IRE)**, 8, b g Alphabatim (USA)—Serjitak **The Poppet Partnership**
13 **RED BRAE**, 7, b g Rakaposhi King—Sayshar **Mr C. D. Carr**
14 **ROTHKO (IRE)**, 6, b g Naheez (USA)—Dizzy Lady (IRE) **Mr R. A. Bartlett**
15 **SIMPLY MYSTIC**, 4, ch f Simply Great (FR)—Mystic Memory **Mrs J. A. Niven**
16 **SONO**, 7, b g Robellino (USA)—Sweet Holland (USA) **Kinloch Arms (Carnoustie) Ltd**
17 **SUPERPRIDETWO**, 4, b g Superpower—Lindrake's Pride **Mrs Muriel Ward**
18 **TALARIVE (USA)**, 8, ch g Riverman (USA)—Estala **Mr Ian G. M. Dalgleish**

Other Owners: Mr J. J. Fildes, Mr C. Lishman, Miss V. Medwell, Mr L. M. Rutherford.

Jockeys (NH): A Ross, P Whelan.

---

406 MR G. R. S. NIXON, Selkirk
Postal: **Oakwood Farm, Ettrickbridge, Selkirk, Selkirkshire, TD7 5HJ.**
Contact: **PHONE (01750) 52245**

1 **ALLEZ SCOTIA**, 5, ch m Minster Son—Allez **Mr G. R. S. Nixon**
2 **JUST SAL**, 8, b m Silly Prices—Hanim (IRE) **Mr G. R. S. Nixon**
3 **KEMPSKI**, 4, b g Petoski—Little Katrina
4 **MELITMA**, 9, gr g Gods Solution—Melsil **Mr G. R. S. Nixon**
5 **MILL TOWER**, 7, b g Milieu—Tringa (GER) **Mr G. R. S. Nixon**
6 **POLITICAL CRUISE**, 6, b g Royal Fountain—Political Mill **Mr G. R. S. Nixon**
7 **POLITICAL SOX**, 10, br g Mirror Boy—Political Mill **Mr G. R. S. Nixon**
8 **SULAGH RUN**, 10, b g Sula Bula—Brackagh Run **Mr G. R. S. Nixon**

Other Owners: Mrs S. Nixon.

Assistant Trainer: Mrs S Nixon

407 **MRS S. NOCK, Stow-on-the-Wold**
Postal: **Smenham Farm, Icomb, Stow On The Wold, Cheltenham, Gloucestershire, GL54 1JQ.**
Contact: **PHONE (01451) 831688 FAX (01451) 831404**

1 4, Ch g Zaffaran (USA)—Alavie (FR) **Mr Gerard Nock**
2 **BALLYALBANY (IRE)**, 6, b g Lord Americo—Raisin Turf (IRE) **Mr Gerard Nock**
3 **DICTUM (GER)**, 6, ch g Secret 'n Classy (CAN)—Doretta (GER) **Mr Gerard Nock**
4 **LISA DU CHENET (FR)**, 5, b m Garde Royale—Tchela (FR) **The Siblings**
5 **MISTER FELIX (IRE)**, 8, b g Ore—Pixies Glen **Mr Gerard Nock**
6 **ROSS LEADER (IRE)**, 8, b g Supreme Leader—Emmagreen **Mr Gerard Nock**
7 **TOM COSTALOT (IRE)**, 9, gr g Black Minstrel—Hop Picker (USA) **Mr Gerard Nock**
8 **TSAR PARTY (IRE)**, 7, b g Moscow Society (USA)—Full Choke **Mr Gerard Nock**

Other Owners: A. C. M. Duncanson, Miss C. D. Nock, Miss R. Nock, Mrs A. Olivier.

408 **MR D. A. NOLAN, Wishaw**
Postal: **Riverside Racing Stables, 227a Bonkle Road, Newmains, Wishaw, Lanarkshire, ML2 9QQ.**
Contact: **PHONE (01698) 383850 FAX (01698) 383850**

1 **ALFIE LEE (IRE)**, 7, ch g Case Law—Nordic Living (IRE) **Miss McFadyen-Murray**
2 **AVESA**, 4, br f Averti (IRE)—Andalish **Miss McFadyen-Murray**
3 **EYES DONT LIE (IRE)**, 6, b g Namaqualand (USA)—Avidal Park **Miss McFadyen-Murray**
4 **GO THUNDER (IRE)**, 10, b g Nordico (USA)—Moving Off **Miss McFadyen-Murray**
5 **HOWARDS DREAM (IRE)**, 6, b g King's Theatre (IRE)—Keiko **Miss McFadyen-Murray**
6 **LAS RAMBLAS (IRE)**, 7, b g Thatching—Raise A Warning **Miss McFadyen-Murray**
7 **LORD ADVOCATE**, 16, br g Law Society—Kereolle **Mrs J. McFadyen-Murray**
8 **MUTAYAM**, 4, b g Compton Place—Final Shot **Miss McFadyen-Murray**
9 **NAUGHTYNELLY'S PET**, 5, b g Balnibarbi—Naughty Nessie **Mr William Prentice**
10 **NORTHERN SVENGALI (IRE)**, 8, b g Distinctly North (USA)—Trilby's Dream (IRE) **Miss McFadyen-Murray**
11 **REEDS RAINS**, 6, b m Mind Games—Me Spede **Miss McFadyen-Murray**
12 **SECOND WIND**, 9, ch g Kris—Rimosa's Pet **Miss McFadyen-Murray**
13 **SQUARE DANCER**, 8, b g Then Again—Cubist (IRE) **Miss McFadyen-Murray**
14 **THE ANGEL GABRIEL**, 9, ch g My Generation—Minsk **Miss McFadyen-Murray**
15 **WOOLFE**, 7, ch m Wolfhound (USA)—Brosna (USA) **Miss McFadyen-Murray**

THREE-YEAR-OLDS

16 **ANNETTES STAR**, b f Captain Maverick (USA)—Miss Hostess **Miss McFadyen-Murray**
17 **TAILI**, b f Taipan (IRE)—Doubtfire **Mr J. A. Davidson**
18 B g Beauchamp King—Valley of Time (FR) **Mr F. Jestin**

Assistant Trainer: Miss McFadyen-Murray

Jockey (Flat): Paul Fessey.

409 **MRS L. B. NORMILE, Glenfarg**
Postal: **Duncrievie, Glenfarg, Perthshire, PH2 9PD.**
Contact: **PHONE (01577) 830330 FAX (01577) 830658 MOBILES (07721) 454818 (07968) 585395**
E-MAIL lucy@normileracing.co.uk

1 **ALFIE BRIGHT**, 6, ch g Alflora (IRE)—Candlebright **Mr J. M. Crichton & Mrs D. A. Whitaker**
2 **ARIJAZ**, 7, b g Teenoso (USA)—Zajira (IRE) **L B N Racing Club**
3 **ARROW**, 5, b g Pivotal—Cremets **Laurence Flynn**
4 **ASTRO GLIDE**, 8, ch m Star Quest—Polly-Glide **L B N Racing Club**
5 **BALINAHINCH CASTLE (IRE)**, 7, b g Good Thyne (USA)—Emerald Flair **Mr K. J. Fehilly**
6 5, B g Bob's Return (IRE)—Candlebright
7 **CELTA VIGO (IRE)**, 6, b m Executive Perk—Alice Freyne (IRE) **Mrs Janice M. Fraser**
8 **CLAN LAW (IRE)**, 6, b g Danehill (USA)—My-O-My (IRE)
9 **COLONIAL RULE (USA)**, 7, b g Pleasant Colony (USA)—Musicale (USA) **A. K. Collins and D. J. Hindmarsh**
10 **DALKEYS LAD**, 4, b g Supreme Leader—Dalkey Sound **Mr G. S. Brown**
11 **DUSHAAN**, 9, ch g Anshan—Soon To Be **Out The Box Racing**
12 **FATHOM**, 6, ch g Zafonic—River Lullaby (USA) **Mr K. J. Fehilly**
13 **FLAMENCA (USA)**, 5, b m Diesis—Highland Ceilidh (IRE) **Mr Allan A. Grant**
14 **FLAMING HECK**, 7, b g Dancing High—Heckley Spark **Mr D. A. Whitaker**
15 **GOODBYE MRS CHIPS**, 5, ch m Zilzal (USA)—Happydrome **Mr Robert Gibbons**

MRS L. B. NORMILE—continued

16 **LOCHIEDUBS,** 9, br g Cragador—Linn Falls **Mr B. Thomson**
17 **MACHRIHANISH,** 4, b g Groom Dancer (USA)—Goodwood Lass (IRE) **Mr John Findlay**
18 **MOFFIED (IRE),** 4, b g Nashwan (USA)—Del Deya (IRE) **Fyffees & Mr A. K. Collins**
19 **PACIFIC HIGHWAY (IRE),** 5, b g Sadler's Wells (USA)—Obeah **Red Rock Racing**
20 **RATTY'S BAND,** 10, ch g Gunner B—Arctic Ander **Mrs D. A. Whitaker**
21 **RODDER (USA),** 8, ch g Rodrigo de Triano (USA)—Berceau (USA) **Mr K. J. Fehilly and Mr A. K. Collins**
22 **SAYOUN (IRE),** 5, gr g Primo Dominie—Sarafia **Red Rock Racing**
23 **SHARABAD (FR),** 6, b g Ela-Mana-Mou—Sharbada (FR) **A. K. Collins and D. J. Hindmarsh**
24 **SINALCO (USA),** 6, b g Quest For Fame—Sin Lucha (USA) **A. K. Collins and D. J. Hindmarsh**
25 **TANDAWIZI,** 7, b m Relief Pitcher—Arctic Ander **Perth Racers**
26 **THE HONEY GUIDE,** 8, gr g Homo Sapien—The Whirlie Weevil **Mrs J. Olivier**
27 6, Ro gr g Alflora (IRE)—The Whirlie Weevil
28 **TOAD HALL,** 10, b g Henbit (USA)—Candlebright **Mr John Findlay**
29 **VANDAS CHOICE (IRE),** 6, b g Sadler's Wells (USA)—Morning Devotion (USA) **Mr J. Petterson**
30 **YOUNG OWEN,** 6, b g Balnibarbi—Polly Potter **Mr Alf Chadwick**

TWO-YEAR-OLDS

31 B g 11/3 Silver Patriarch—Dalkey Sound (Crash Course) **Mr G. S. Brown**
32 Br g 8/3 Silver Patriarch—Gale (Dalkey Sound) **Mr G. S. Brown**

Other Owners: Mrs Linda Dyer, Mr D. Futong, Mr L. H. Gilmurray, Mr E. Murray.

Assistant Trainer: Alan Normile

Jockeys (NH): Mark Bradburne (10-0), C McCormack, M H Naughton.

---

410 MR J. R. NORTON, Barnsley
Postal: **Globe Farm, High Hoyland, Barnsley, South Yorkshire, S75 4BE.**
Contact: **PHONE (01226) 387633 FAX (01226) 387633 MOBILE (07970) 212707**
E-MAIL johnrnorton@hotmail.com

1 **ABZUSON,** 7, b g Abzu—Mellouise **Abzuson Syndicate**
2 **AMANDA KASAKOVA,** 8, ch m Kasakov—Manna Green **Mrs Hazel Tattersall**
3 **IRELAND'S EYE (IRE),** 9, b g Shareef Dancer (USA)—So Romantic (IRE) **Ejam Connection**
4 5, Ch m Abzu—Iron Lass **Mr C. R. Green**
5 **KAGOSHIMA (IRE),** 9, b g Shirley Heights—Kashteh (IRE) **Keep On Running**
6 5, Ch g Abzu—Mellouise **Mr C. R. Green**
7 **PRINTSMITH (IRE),** 7, br m Petardia—Black And Blaze **Mrs Hazel Tattersall**
8 **RED RIVER REBEL,** 6, b g Inchinor—Bidweaya (USA) **Mr Jeff Slaney**
9 **RIVER RAMBLER,** 5, ch m River Falls—Horsepower **Mr J. Norton**
10 **SQUANDAMANIA,** 11, b g Ela-Mana-Mou—Garden Pink (FR) **Jaffa Racing Syndicate**
11 **TEENO ROSSI (IRE),** 6, b m Teenoso (USA)—Mistress Ross **Miss A. J. Hurst**
12 **VICTORIA RYAN (IRE),** 6, b m Good Thyne (USA)—No Not **Mr G. A. Hancock & Mr A. Parsonage**

THREE-YEAR-OLDS

13 **AIREDALE LAD (IRE),** b g Charnwood Forest (IRE)—Tamarsiya (USA) **In Memory of Mary Syndicate**
14 **FISHER'S DREAM,** b g Groom Dancer (USA)—Cremets **Mrs Jean Ennis**
15 **NORTHERN SUMMIT (IRE),** b g Danehill Dancer (IRE)—Book Choice **Mr Chris Howitt**
16 **PATTERN MAN,** b c Wizard King—Quick Profit **David Scott and Co (Pattern Makers) Ltd**
17 B g Vettori (IRE)—Pussy Foot **Mr J. Norton**
18 **QUAY WALLOPER,** b g In Command (IRE)—Myrrh **Jaffa Racing Syndicate**
19 **SAM THE SORCERER,** b c Wizard King—Awham (USA) **Mr Tim Simcox and Mrs Pamela Farrow**
20 **SAVANNAH SUE,** b f Emarati (USA)—Bidweaya (USA) **Mr Jeff Slaney**
21 **SECRET BLOOM,** b g My Best Valentine—Rose Elegance **Reddal Racing**
22 **WEAVER SPELL,** b g Wizard King—Impy Fox (IRE) **Mr J. Wightman and Mr K. Swift**

TWO-YEAR-OLDS

23 B g 26/1 Fraam—Heavenly Abstone (Interrex (CAN)) (1000) **J. R. Norton Ltd**
24 B g 23/3 Lake Coniston (IRE)—Lycius Touch (Lycius (USA)) (800) **J. R. Norton Ltd**
25 Ch g 19/4 Abou Zouz (USA)—Meadmore Magic (Mansingh (USA)) (2400) **J. R. Norton Ltd**

Other Owners: Mr M. Charles, Mr John Devine, Mr R. M. Firth, Mr P. J. Marshall, Mr I. D. McEwen, Mr K. McEwen, P. Scholefield.

Jockey (NH): C Rafter (10-0). **Conditional:** N Hannity (10-0).

411

MR J. J. NOSEDA, Newmarket
Postal: Shalfleet, 17 Bury Road, Newmarket, Suffolk, CB8 7BX.
Contact: **PHONE (01638) 664010 MOBILE (07710) 294093 FAX (01638) 664100**
E-MAIL jeremy.noseda@virgin.net WEBSITE www.jeremynoseda.com

1 **ADIEMUS**, 6, b g Green Desert (USA)—Anodyne
2 **ALMAVIVA (IRE)**, 4, b f Grand Lodge (USA)—Kafayef (USA)
3 **COURAGEOUS DUKE (USA)**, 5, b g Spinning World (USA)—Araadh (USA)
4 **JUST JAMES**, 5, b g Spectrum (IRE)—Fairy Flight (IRE)
5 **LODGER (FR)**, 4, ch c Grand Lodge (USA)—Light River (USA)
6 **MANAAR (IRE)**, 4, b g Titus Livius (FR)—Zurarah
7 **PROMOTER**, 4, ch g Selkirk (USA)—Poplina (USA)
8 **WIZARD OF NOZ**, 4, b g Inchinor—Winning Girl

THREE-YEAR-OLDS

9 **AIR OF SUPREMACY (IRE)**, gr c Royal Applause—Lap of Luxury
10 **BAHAMIAN BREEZE**, b g Piccolo—Norgabie
11 **BALIMAYA (IRE)**, b f Barathea (IRE)—Banque Privee (USA)
12 **BALMONT**, b c Stravinsky (USA)—Aldebaran Light (USA)
13 **BURNING MOON**, b c Bering—Triple Green
14 **CHIMALI (IRE)**, b c Foxhound (USA)—Mari-Ela (IRE)
15 **DIAMOND LODGE**, ch f Grand Lodge (USA)—Movieland (USA)
16 **DOUBLE DAGGER LADY (USA)**, b f Diesis—Darby Jane (CAN)
17 **ECOMIUM (IRE)**, b c Sadler's Wells (USA)—Encens
18 **GLENCALVIE (IRE)**, ch c Grand Lodge (USA)—Top of The Form (IRE)
19 **JOJEEMA**, b f Barathea (IRE)—Knight's Baroness
20 **KATAVI (USA)**, b f Stravinsky (USA)—Halholah (USA)
21 **LONG ROAD (USA)**, b c Diesis—Tuviah (USA)
22 **MAJORS CAST (IRE)**, b c Victory Note (USA)—Ziffany
23 **NIETZSCHE (IRE)**, b c Sadler's Wells (USA)—Wannabe
24 **PEAK TO CREEK**, b c Royal Applause—Rivers Rhapsody
25 **SILVER CACHE (USA)**, b f Silver Hawk (USA)—Nina Ashley (USA)
26 **SOLDIER'S TALE (USA)**, ch c Stravinsky (USA)—Myrtle
27 **SON OF SAMSON (IRE)**, ch c Diesis—Delilah (IRE)
28 **ST FRANCIS WOOD (USA)**, ch f Irish River (FR)—Francisco Road (USA)
29 **STRAW HAT**, b c Cape Cross (IRE)—Shamrock Fair (IRE)
30 **TROPICAL STORM (IRE)**, ch g Alhaarth (IRE)—Rainstone
31 **TWO STEP KID**, ch c Gone West (USA)—Marsha's Dancer (USA)

TWO-YEAR-OLDS

32 B f 10/3 Night Shift (USA)—Alonsa (IRE) (Trempolino (USA)) (30920)
33 B c 23/2 Zafonic (USA)—Amellnaa (IRE) (Sadler's Wells (USA))
34 **AUSONE**, b f 20/3 Singspiel (IRE)—Aristocratique (Cadeaux Genereux) (35000)
35 **BALDASSARE**, ch c 8/3 Grand Lodge (USA)—Royal York (Bustino)
36 Br c 24/4 Zafonic (USA)—Blasted Heath (Thatching) (58000)
37 **BRIDGE LOAN**, ch c 14/4 Giant's Causeway—Credit A Plenty (Generous (IRE))
38 B f 6/4 Royal Applause—Briggsmaid (Elegant Air) (24000)
39 B c 24/1 Lear Fan (USA)—Cap of Dignity (Shirley Heights) (50595)
40 B f 6/2 Green Desert (USA)—Comme d'Habitude (USA) (Caro) (160000)
41 Gr c 18/4 Machiavellian (USA)—Crodelle (IRE) (Formidable (USA)) (220000)
42 B c 6/3 Desert Prince (IRE)—Crystal Flute (Lycius (USA)) (180000)
43 **DOMINATING VISTA**, b f 29/4 Diktat—Colorvista (Shirley Heights)
44 B c 3/2 King's Best (USA)—Elude (Slip Anchor) (65000)
45 **EMERALD LODGE**, b c 12/2 Grand Lodge (USA)—Emerald Peace (IRE) (Green Desert (USA)) (90000)
46 **FIRST SHOW**, b c 2/5 Cape Cross (IRE)—Rose Show (Belmez (USA))
47 **FOR SCARLETT (USA)**, b f 1/2 Red Ransom (USA)—Lady Dixie (USA) (Dixieland Band (USA)) (119048)
48 B c 12/4 Zafonic (USA)—Hasta (Theatrical) (260000)
49 B f 6/3 Miswaki (USA)—Hawzah (Green Desert (USA)) (170000)
50 Ch f 27/2 King's Best (USA)—Kansa (FR) (Linamix (FR)) (49474)
51 Ch c 10/2 Giant's Causeway—Karen S (USA) (Kris S (USA)) (89285)
52 B f 1/3 Bluebird (USA)—Kathleen's Dream (Last Tycoon) (34013)
53 **LEGEND OF SILLA (FR)**, b f 23/3 Spectrum (IRE)—Royal Hostess (IRE) (Be My Guest) (49474)
54 **MACHISMO**, b c 11/4 Machiavellian (USA)—Dance By Night (Northfields (USA))
55 B c 6/3 Danzig (USA)—Maidee (USA) (Roberto (USA))
56 B c 14/3 Quiet American (USA)—Mata Cara (Storm Bird (CAN))
57 B c 18/4 Stravinsky (USA)—May Wedding (USA) (French Deputy (USA)) (110000)

MR J. J. NOSEDA—continued

58 Ch f 4/5 Machiavellian (USA)—Melanzane (Arazi) (USA) (50000)
59 B c 1/3 Sadler's Wells (USA)—Minne Habit (Habitat)
60 B c 20/3 Desert Prince (IRE)—Moy Water (IRE) (Tirol) (185528)
61 B c 19/2 Fusaichi Pegasus—Name of Love (IRE) (Petardia) (59524)
62 Ch c 13/1 Awesome Again (CAN)—Native Roots (IRE) (Indian Ridge) (44643)
63 B f 29/1 King's Best (USA)—Nimble Lady (AUS) (Fairy King (USA)) (92764)
64 **ORNAMENTATION (USA),** b c 15/3 Honour And Glory—Aldebaran Light (USA) (Seattle Slew (USA))
65 **PARK APPROACH (IRE),** gr f 23/2 Indian Ridge—Abyat (USA) (Shadeed (USA)) (86580)
66 B c 16/4 Danehill Dancer (IRE)—Persian Empress (IRE) (Persian Bold) (95000)
67 **PESQUERA,** b f 12/4 Green Desert (USA)—Rose des Andes (IRE) (Royal Academy (USA)) (60000)
68 B f 24/4 Danehill (USA)—Prends Ca (IRE) (Reprimand) (90000)
69 B c 10/4 Red Ransom (USA)—Prospectora (USA) (Mr Prospector (USA)) (208333)
70 **PURITANICAL (IRE),** ch f 3/2 Desert King (IRE)—Zariysha (IRE) (Darshaan) (50000)
71 B f 17/2 Cape Cross (IRE)—Safe Exit (FR) (Exit To Nowhere (USA)) (27828)
72 Ch c 8/3 Desert Prince (IRE)—Saibhreas (IRE) (Lasy Tycoon) (120000)
73 **SCARP (USA),** b c 29/3 Gulch—Rhetorical Lass (USA) (Capote (USA))
74 B f 9/2 Desert Prince (IRE)—Sevi's Choice (USA) (Sir Ivor) (260000)
75 Gr c 1/5 King's Best (USA)—Shamarra (FR) (Zayyani) (84000)
76 B c 7/4 Rossini (USA)—Sliding (Formidable (USA)) (55000)
77 **STRAVINSKAYA (USA),** ch f 9/5 Stravinsky (USA)—Lady Fairfax (Sharrood (USA))
78 B c 10/4 Danehill (USA)—Sun Silk (USA) (Gone West (USA)) (250000)
79 B f 8/3 King's Best (USA)—Tanzilla (Warning)
80 B f 6/5 King's Best (USA)—Tegwen (USA) (Nijinsky (CAN))
81 B c 23/2 Dansili—Witch of Fife (USA) (Lear Fan (USA)) (120000)

Other Owners: Mr Arashaan Ali, Mr Saif Ali, Mohammed Al Shafar, Saeed H Altayer, Abdullah Saeed Belhab, Mr Syd Belzberg, Sir Gordon Brunton, Mrs Seamus Burns, Mrs C Burns-Sharma, Mr P. Byrne, Mr L. Calvente, Mrs A. Doyle, Mr P. Doyle, Mrs P Duffin, Fieldspring Racing, Mr C. Fox, Mr P. G. Goulandris, Mrs J. Harris, Mr A. M. Hayes, Hesmonds Stud, Mr C. Holt, Mr Al Homeizi, Mr M. Ings, Jayeff S Stables, Jeremy Noseda Racing Ltd, Jumeirah Racing, Mr S. Kuqi, Mr G. Lansbury, Mr R. Levin, Mr R. Levitt, Lucayan Stud, Meon Valley Stud, H. E. Sheikh Rashid Bin Mohammed, Newgate Stud, Mr J. Newsome, Miss K. Nikkel, Mr A. Nolan, Sir R. Ogden, Pad Eddery Racing, Mr O. Pawle, Mr A. Purvis, Sheikh Rashid, Razza Pallorsi Snc, Mr Sanford Robertson, Mr P. Roy, Mrs S. Roy, Mrs J. M. Ryan, Mrs K. Sellars, Mrs P. Shanahan, Mr M. Tabor, Thoroughbred Farms Ltd, Thurloe Thoroughbreds XII, Mr B. Wong, Woodcote Stud, Wood Hall Stud, Mr D. Woods, Mr J. Wright.

Assistant Trainer: Dave Bradley

---

412 MR D. C. O'BRIEN, Tonbridge
Postal: **Knowles Bank, Capel, Tonbridge, Kent, TN11 0PU.**
Contact: **PHONE (01892) 824072**

1 DARCY, 10, ch g Miswaki (USA)—Princess Accord (USA)
2 **FADDAD (USA),** 8, b g Irish River (FR)—Miss Mistletoes (IRE) **Mr D. C. O'Brien**
3 POLYPHONY (USA), 10, b g Cox's Ridge—Populi (USA) **Mr D. C. O'Brien**

Jockey (Flat): G Bardwell. Jockeys (NH): M Batchelor, Jim Culloty, Warren Marston.

---

413 MR J. O'KEEFFE, Leyburn
Postal: **Highbeck, Brecongill, Coverham, Leyburn, North Yorkshire, DL8 4TJ.**
Contact: **PHONE (01969) 640330 FAX (01969) 640397 MOBILE (07710) 476705**
E-MAIL jeddokeeffe@compuserve.com

1 BEAT THE HEAT (IRE), 6, b g Salse (USA)—Summer Trysting (USA) **Mr Richard Berry**
2 DARK CHAMPION, 4, b g Abou Zouz (USA)—Hazy Kay (IRE) **Mr J. Potts**
3 FACE THE LIMELIGHT (IRE), 5, b g Quest For Fame—Miss Boniface **Highbeck Racing**
4 FIZZY LIZZY, 4, b f Cool Jazz—Formidable Liz **The Only For Fun Partnership**
5 JIMMY BOND, 5, b g Primitive Rising (USA)—Miss Moneypenny **The Odd Jobs**
6 MISSION TO BE, 5, ch g Elmaamul (USA)—All The Girls (IRE) **Mr John E. Lund**
7 MYSTERINCH, 4, b g Inchinor—Hakone (IRE) **Colin & Melanie Moore**
8 NOBLE CYRANO, 9, ch g Generous (IRE)—Miss Bergerac **Wetherby Racing Bureau 38**
9 4, Br g Catrail (USA)—Ostrusa (AUT) **Jedd O'Keeffe Racing**
10 PARISIAN PLAYBOY, 4, gr g Paris House—Exordium **Playboy Partnership**
11 RESCIND (IRE), 4, b f Revoque (IRE)—Sunlit Ride **Wetherby Racing Bureau 58**
12 ROUTE SIXTY SIX (IRE), 8, b m Brief Truce (USA)—Lyphards Goddess (IRE) **Wetherby Racing Bureau 47**

MR J. O'KEEFFE—continued

13 **SIR NIGHT (IRE)**, 4, b g Night Shift (USA)—Highly Respected (IRE) **Highbeck Racing**
14 **SNOW BUNTING**, 6, ch g Polar Falcon (USA)—Marl **Wetherby Racing Bureau 49**
15 **SPECIAL BRANCH**, 4, ch g Woodborough (USA)—Sixslip (USA) **Wetherby Racing Bureau 56**
16 **STRAIT TALKING (FR)**, 6, b g Bering—Servia **Mr E. Rider**
17 **TIYOUN (IRE)**, 6, b g Kahyasi—Taysala **Miss Sharon Long**

THREE-YEAR-OLDS

18 **GRANDISSIMO (IRE)**, b g Grand Lodge (USA)—Tuscaloosa **Colin & Melanie Moore**
19 **HABITUAL DANCER**, b g Groom Dancer (USA)—Pomorie (IRE) **The Country Stayers**
20 **IMPULSIVE BID (IRE)**, b f Orpen (USA)—Tamburello (IRE) **Mr A. Walker**
21 **MAGICAL MIMI**, b f Magic Ring (IRE)—Naval Dispatch **Derek & Brenda Allen**
22 **SARATOGA SPLENDOUR (USA)**, b f Diesis—Saratoga One (USA) **Mr J. Potts**
23 **TYTHEKNOT**, b g Pursuit of Love—Bundled Up (USA) **Arthur Walker & Paul Chapman**
24 **ZAMEEL (IRE)**, b g Marju (IRE)—Impatiente (USA) **The Noble Flames**

TWO-YEAR-OLDS

25 **ALANI (IRE)**, b f 5/3 Benny The Dip (USA)—Toi Toi (IRE) (In The Wings) (7500) **Miss Sharon Long**
26 Ch c 12/5 My Best Valentine—Bramble Bear (Beveled (USA)) (2000) **Wetherby Racing Bureau**
27 **LADY MISHA**, b f 26/1 Mister Baileys—Hakone (IRE) (Alzao (USA)) (6000) **Allen, Kelly & Moore**
28 B f 12/4 High Estate—Movieland (USA) (Nureyev (USA)) (800) **Chippenham Lodge Stud Ltd**
29 Br f 15/2 Daggers Drawn (USA)—Taajreh (IRE) (Mtoto) (1000) **Mr A. Walker**

Other Owners: Mr Andrew Bates, Mr Clive Beetlestone, Mr Mike Chapman, Mr Peter Charter, Mr Harry English, Mr Alan Henderson, Miss C. L. Hewson, Mr Barry Hickson, Mr Trevor Hodges, Mr Richard Johnson, Mr Chris Lloyd, Mr Chris Machin, Mr Bruce McAllister, Mrs Jane Moule, Mr R. W. Tunstall, Mr Harry Roberts, Mr Roland Roper, Mr Michael Sadler, Mr & Mrs Paul Sellars, Mr Mark Soloman, Mr Colin Wardman, Mr Gary A. Wedgner, Mr Peter Wilkinson.

Assistant Trainer: Andrea O'Keeffe

Jockey (NH): Brian Harding (10-0, w.a.).   **Apprentice:** Leanne Kershaw (7-5).   **Amateur:** Miss Jenna Waring (8-9).

---

414   MR J. J. O'NEILL, Cheltenham
Postal: **Jackdaws Castle, Temple Guiting, Cheltenham, Gloucestershire, GL54 5XU.**
Contact: PHONE (01386) 584209 FAX (01386) 584219
E-MAIL enquiries@jonjooneillracing.com WEBSITE www.jonjooneillracing.com

1 **ALCRIS**, 5, b br g Alderbrook—One of Those Days **Home Run Syndicate Ltd**
2 **AR MUIN NA MUICE (IRE)**, 8, ch m Executive Perk—Raashideah **Mrs G. Smith**
3 **BALLYLUSKY (IRE)**, 7, b g Lord Americo—Blackbushe Place (IRE) **Black Sheep Racing**
4 **BARON BLITZBERG**, 6, b g Sir Harry Lewis—Steel Typhoon **Mrs Ann Bish**
5 **BOLD BISHOP (IRE)**, 7, b g Religiously (USA)—Ladybojangles (IRE) **Mrs G. Smith**
6 **BRANDESTON RON (IRE)**, 6, b g Presenting—Boolavogue (IRE) **Mr Ron George**
7 **CAMPAIGN TRAIL (IRE)**, 6, b g Sadler's Wells (USA)—Campestral (USA) **Mr M. Tabor**
8 **CANON BARNEY (IRE)**, 9, b br g Salluceva—Debbies Candy **Mr J. P. McManus**
9 **CELTIC MAJOR (IRE)**, 6, br g Roselier (FR)—Dun Oengus (USA) **Walters Plant Hire Ltd**
10 **CHARLIE MOON (IRE)**, 5, gr g Moonax (IRE)—Charlottes Lot **Trevor Hemmings**
11 **CHERUB (GER)**, 4, b c Winged Love (IRE)—Chalkidiki (GER) **Atlantic Joinery**
12 **CLAN ROYAL (FR)**, 9, b g Chef de Clan II (FR)—Allee du Roy (FR) **Mr J. P. McManus**
13 **CLASSIC NATIVE (IRE)**, 6, b br g Be My Native (USA)—Thats Irish **Ray & Sue Dodd Partnership**
14 **CLAUDE GREENGRASS**, 8, ch g Shalford (IRE)—Rainbow Brite (BEL) **Mr J. P. McManus**
15 **CREON**, 9, b g Saddlers' Hall (IRE)—Creake **Mr J. P. McManus**
16 **DANCER LIFE (POL)**, 5, b h Professional (IRE)—Dyktptorka (POL) **J. P. McManus**
17 **DARK ROOM (IRE)**, 7, b g Toulon—Maudlin Bridge (IRE) **Mr J. P. McManus**
18 **DAY DU ROY (FR)**, 6, b g Ajdayt (USA)—Rose Pomme (FR) **Mrs Mo Done**
19 **DIAMANT NOIR**, 6, b m Sir Harry Lewis (USA)—Free Travel **Mr D. J. Burke**
20 **DROMBEAG (IRE)**, 6, b g Presenting—Bula Beag (IRE) **Mr J. P. McManus**
21 **EXOTIC DANCER (FR)**, 4, b g Turgeon (USA)—Northine (FR) **Sir Robert Ogden**
22 **FEEL THE PRIDE (IRE)**, 6, b m Persian Bold—Nordic Pride **Mrs M. Liston**
23 **FERN LORD (IRE)**, 7, ch h Mister Lord—Deep Fern **Mrs L. Busteed**
24 **FUNDAMENTAL**, 5, ch g Rudimentary—I'll Try **David Green**
25 **GIMMICK (FR)**, 10, b g Chamberlin (FR)—Jaida (FR) **The Risky Partnership**
26 **GLOBAL CHALLENGE (IRE)**, 5, b g Sadler's Wells (USA)—
                                   Middle Prospect (USA) **Mrs John Magnier & Mr M. Tabor**
27 **GOLDEN RAMBLER (IRE)**, 8, br g Roselier (FR)—Goldiyana (FR) **J. C., J. R. & S. R. Hitchins**

MR J. J. O'NEILL—continued

28 **HASTY PRINCE**, 6, ch g Halling (USA)—Sister Sophie (USA) **F. F. Racing Services Partnership III**
29 **HAUTCLAN (FR)**, 5, b g Chef de Clan II (FR)—Haute Tension (FR) **Trevor Hemmings**
30 **HERE WE GO (IRE)**, 5, b g Bob Back (USA)—Bold Lyndsey **Mr D. N. Green**
31 **HEY REF (IRE)**, 7, b g King's Ride—Jeanarie **Mr J. P. McManus**
32 **INTERSKY FALCON**, 7, gr g Polar Falcon (USA)—I'll Try **Interskyracing.com & Mrs Jonjo O'Neill**
33 **IRIS'S GIFT**, 7, gr g Gunner B—Shirley's Gift **Mr Robert Lester**
34 **JOSS NAYLOR (IRE)**, 9, b g Be My Native (USA)—Sister Ida **Mr Darren C. Mercer**
35 **KEEN LEADER (IRE)**, 8, b g Supreme Leader—Keen Gale (IRE) **Mrs Stewart Catherwood**
36 **LINGO (IRE)**, 5, b g Poliglote—Sea Ring (FR) **Mr J. P. McManus**
37 **LORENZINO (IRE)**, 7, ch g Thunder Gulch (USA)—Russian Ballet (USA) **Mr P. Piller**
38 **MAJESTIC MOONBEAM (IRE)**, 6, b g Supreme Leader—Magic Moonbeam (IRE) **Mr J. P. McManus**
39 **MANNERS (IRE)**, 6, b g Topanoora—Maneree **Mr M. Tabor**
40 **MANOUBI**, 5, b g Doyoun—Manuetti (IRE) **F. F. Racing Services Partnership III**
41 **MASTER TERN (USA)**, 9, ch g Generous (IRE)—Young Hostess (FR) **Mr J. P. McManus**
42 **MEDICI (FR)**, 6, b br g Cadoudal (FR)—Marie de Valois (FR) **Sir Robert Ogden**
43 **MIGHTY KILCASH (IRE)**, 11, ch g Black Minstrel—Any Wonder **Monica Sweeney**
44 **MILLENAIRE (FR)**, 5, b br g Mister Mat (FR)—Mille Perles (FR) **The Risky Partnership**
45 **MINI SENSATION (IRE)**, 11, b g Be My Native (USA)—Minorettes Girl **Mr J. P. McManus**
46 **MONBONAMI (IRE)**, 7, b g Beau Sher—Hard Riche **Mrs Katrina Berry**
47 **MONTEVIDEO**, 4, b g Sadler's Wells (USA)—Montessori **Mr J. P. McManus**
48 **MULTEEN RIVER (IRE)**, 8, b g Supreme Leader—Blackwater Mist (IRE) **Mr J. P. McManus**
49 **NATIVE EMPEROR**, 8, br g Be My Native (USA)—Fiona's Blue **J. R., J. C. & S. R. Hitchins**
50 **NEVER (FR)**, 7, b g Vettori (IRE)—Neraida (USA) **Sir Peter O'Sullevan**
52 **PERSONAL ASSURANCE**, 7, b br g Un Desperado (FR)—Steel Typhoon **Mr Christopher W. T. Johnston**
53 **PREDICAMENT**, 5, br g Machiavellian (USA)—Quandary (USA) **Sir Robert Ogden**
54 **PROGRESSIVE (IRE)**, 6, ch g Be My Native (USA)—Move Forward **Mr J. P. McManus**
55 **PROKOFIEV (USA)**, 8, br g Nureyev (USA)—Aviara (USA) **Mrs Sylvia Darlington**
56 **PURE PLATINUM (IRE)**, 6, gr g Roselier (FR)—Waterloo Ball (IRE) **Mrs G. Smith**
57 **PURRFECT PRINCE (IRE)**, 6, b g Commanche Run—Castle Leney **Home Run Syndicate Ltd**
58 **QUAZAR (IRE)**, 6, b g Inzar (USA)—Evictress (IRE) **Mr C. D. Carr**
59 **REFINEMENT (IRE)**, 5, b m Oscar (IRE)—Maneree **Mr M. Tabor**
60 **RENVYLE (IRE)**, 6, b br g Satco (FR)—Kara's Dream (IRE) **The Four Exiles**
61 **RHINESTONE COWBOY (IRE)**, 8, b g Be My Native (USA)—Monumental Gesture **Mrs John Magnier**
62 **SARATOV (GER)**, 5, b g Acatenango (GER)—Sovereign Touch (IRE) **Mr P. Piller**
63 **SEEYAAJ**, 4, b g Darshaan—Subya **Weller Racing Partnership,Mrs J. O'Neill**
64 **SELVAS (GER)**, 4, ch c Lomitas—Subia (GER) **Getjar Ltd**
65 **SHAMAWAN (IRE)**, 9, b g Kris—Shamawna (IRE) **Mr J. P. McManus**
66 **SH BOOM**, 6, b g Alderbrook—Muznah **T. G. K. Construction Ltd**
67 **SHE'S NO MUPPET**, 4, b f Teenoso (USA)—Persian Dream (IRE) **Andrew & Sue May**
68 **SHERKIN ISLAND (IRE)**, 6, b g Shernazar—Tullerolli (IRE) **Mr J. P. McManus**
69 **SIMPLY GIFTED**, 9, b g Simply Great (FR)—Souveniers **Mr Steve Hammond**
70 **SOCIETY AFFAIR (IRE)**, 5, b g Moscow Society (USA)—Society News **Mr John Power**
71 **SOME JUDGE**, 7, ch g Rakaposhi King—Si-Gaoith **Mr John Power**
72 **SPECTROSCOPE (IRE)**, 5, b g Spectrum (IRE)—Paloma Bay (IRE) **Mrs G. Smith**
73 **SPECULAR (AUS)**, 8, b g Danehill (USA)—Spyglass (NZ) **Mr J. P. McManus**
74 **SPIKE AND DIVEL (IRE)**, 6, b g Zaffaran (USA)—Lady Go Marching (USA) **Mr J. P. McManus**
75 **SPIKE JONES (NZ)**, 6, b g Colonel Collins (USA)—Gloss (NZ) **Mrs Sarah Granger**
76 **STARBLAZER**, 6, b g Supreme Leader—Romany Fortune **Home Run Syndicate Ltd**
77 **TARDAR (NZ)**, 8, br g Prince Ferdinand—La Magnifique (NZ) **Ray & Sue Dodd Partnership**
78 **TEN PRESSED MEN (FR)**, 4, b g Video Rock (FR)—Recolte d'Estruval (FR) **Mrs Valda Burke**
79 **THENAMEESCAPESME**, 4, b g Alderbrook—Gaygo Lady **Mrs Sharon Neilson**
80 **THE PENNYS DROPPED (IRE)**, 7, ch g Bob's Return—Shuil Alainn **Mr J. P. McManus**
81 **THE SISTER**, 7, b m Alflora (IRE)—Donna Farina **Mrs R. H. Thompson**
82 **THUMPER (IRE)**, 6, b g Grand Lodge (USA)—Parkeen Princess **Mrs Susan Granger**
83 **THYNE FOR INTERSKY (IRE)**, 5, ch g Good Thyne (USA)—One Last Chance **Interskyracing.com**
84 **TIDJANI (IRE)**, 12, b g Alleged (USA)—Tikarna (FR) **Mr J. P. McManus**
85 **TIGERS LAIR (IRE)**, 5, br g Accordion—Eadie (IRE) **Home Run Syndicate Ltd**
86 **TOON TROOPER (IRE)**, 7, ch g Bob Back (USA)—Salmoncita **Mr Mike Browne**
87 **VERY OPTIMISTIC (IRE)**, 6, b g Un Desperado (FR)—Bright Future (IRE) **Mrs G. Smith**
88 **WAGNER (IRE)**, 7, b br g Lure (USA)—Tapaculo **Ossian Construction Ltd**
89 **WINAPENNY (IRE)**, 5, b g Right Win—Penny Pauper **Mr Trevor Hemmings**
90 **WORLD WIDE WEB (IRE)**, 8, b g Be My Native (USA)—Meldrum Lass **Mr J. P. McManus**
91 **WOULDN'T YOU AGREE (IRE)**, 8, ch g Toulon—Mention of Money **Mr J. P. McManus**
92 **YOULBESOLUCKY (IRE)**, 5, b g Accordion—Gaye Humour **Home Run Syndicate Ltd**
93 **YOUR ADVANTAGE (IRE)**, 4, b g Septieme Ciel (USA)—Freedom Flame **Mrs G. Smith**

MR J. J. O'NEILL—continued

94 ZAWOYSKI (IRE), 7, b g Posen (USA)—Cri Basque **Mrs J. Mason**

THREE-YEAR-OLDS

95 WILFRED (IRE), gr g Desert King (IRE)—Kharaliya (FR) **Christopher Johnston**

Other Owners: Mrs Ann Bish, Patsy Byrne, Mr John Connor, Mr B. T. Forrest, Mr Michael Masterton, Mr Jim McGrath, Tom Mohan, Sir Peter O'Sullivan, Mr Albert Reynolds, Mrs April Thompson, Mrs J. T. Thompson, Mr Peter S. Thompson.

---

415 **MR O. O'NEILL, Cheltenham**
Postal: **Cleeve Lodge, Cleeve Hill, Cheltenham, Gloucestershire, GL52 3PW.**
Contact: **PHONE (01242) 673275 FAX (01242) 673275 MOBILE (07733) 210177**

1 DARING NEWS, 9, b g Risk Me (FR)—Hot Sunday Sport **Mr Michael J. Brown**
2 FOREST GREEN FLYER, 8, b m Syrtos—Bolton Flyer **Mr T. Horsley**
3 LADY LILBOURNE, 4, b f Alflora (IRE)—Jims Sister **Mr James A. Atkin**
4 MAZAMET (USA), 11, b g Elmaamul (USA)—Miss Mazepah (USA) **Mr O. O'Neill**
5 OLD IRISH, 11, gr g Old Vic—Dunoof **Mr R. Fletcher**
6 RICARDO'S CHANCE, 5, b g Alflora (IRE)—Jims Sister **Mr James A. Atkin**
7 RUSHMORE (USA), 7, ch g Mt Livermore (USA)—Crafty Nan (USA) **Mr O. O'Neill**

Other Owners: Mr K. G. Boulton.

Assistant Trainer: John C Gilbert

Jockey (NH): J V Slattery (10-0).

---

416 **MR J. G. M. O'SHEA, Westbury on Severn**
Postal: **Tudor Racing Stables, Elton, Westbury on Severn, Gloucestershire, GL14 1JN.**
Contact: **OFFICE (01452) 760835 FAX (01452) 760903 MOBILE (07789) 496402**

1 ALIABAD (IRE), 9, b br g Doyoun—Alannya (FR) **Mr N. G. H. Ayliffe**
2 BEAULY (IRE), 9, b g Beau Sher—Woodland Theory **Mr K. A. Wells**
3 BRADY BOYS (USA), 7, b g Cozzene (USA)—Elvia (USA) **Mr D. Cound and Mr R. Davies**
4 CUSH JEWEL (IRE), 8, b m Executive Perk—Shannon Jewel (IRE) **The Cross Racing Club**
5 FARAWAY LOOK (USA), 7, b g Distant View (USA)—Summer Trip (USA) **The Binocular Partnership**
6 FATTAAN (IRE), 4, b c Danehill (USA)—Bintalshaati **Mr Gary Roberts**
7 GREGORIAN (IRE), 7, b g Foxhound (USA)—East River (FR) **Mrs Ruth Nelmes**
8 JIM BELL (IRE), 9, br g Supreme Leader—Mightyatom **Mr K. W. Bell**
9 KIMBERLEY, 9, b g Shareef Dancer (USA)—Willowbank **K. W. Bell & Son Ltd**
10 MAJOR BLUE, 9, ch g Scallywag—Town Blues **Mrs Ruth Nelmes, C L Dubois, P Smith**
11 NORDIC PRINCE (IRE), 13, b g Nordance (USA)—Royal Desire **Blue Shirts**
12 PORT MORENO (IRE), 4, b c Turtle Island (IRE)—Infra Blue (IRE) **Mr C. B. Beck**
13 RAVENGLASS (USA), 5, b h Miswaki (USA)—Urus (USA) **Mr K. W. Bell**
14 SO SURE (IRE), 4, b g Definite Article—Zorilla **Mr Bill Tyler**
15 STAFFORD KING (IRE), 7, b h Nicolotte—Opening Day **Mr N. G. H. Ayliffe**
16 STYLISH PRINCE, 4, b g Polar Prince (IRE)—Simply Style **Mr Gary Roberts**
17 THE RECRUITER, 4, gr g Danzig Connection (USA)—Tabeeba **Premier-Racing.Net**
18 TOM BELL (IRE), 4, b g King's Theatre (IRE)—Nordic Display (IRE) **Mr K. W. Bell**
19 VAL DE FLEURIE (GER), 9, b m Mondrian (GER)—Valbonne **Mrs Mary Konig**

THREE-YEAR-OLDS

20 FINIANS GOLD, b c Fasliyev (USA)—Belle Esprit **Mr Gary Roberts**
21 RABITATIT (IRE), b f Robellino (USA)—Coupled **Mr Gary Roberts**
22 TUDOR BELL (IRE), b c Definite Article—Late Night Lady (IRE) **K. W. Bell & Son Ltd**

Other Owners: Mr K. Batchelor, Mr J. P. Dickinson, Mrs M. J. Whitehead.

Jockeys (Flat): R Havlin, D Sweeney. **Conditional:** Greg Richards (10-0).

417 MR EUGENE M. O'SULLIVAN, Mallow

Postal: "Millwood", Currabower, Lombardstown, Mallow, Co. Cork, Ireland.
Contact: PHONE +353 (0) 22 47304/47116 FAX +353 (0) 22 47588 MOBILE +353 (0) 86 2541398
E-MAIL eugenemosullivan@eircom.net

1 ARCTIC TIMES (IRE), 8, ch g Montelimar (USA)—Miss Penguin **Trevor Hemmings**
2 ARISTOCRATIC YANK (IRE), 5, b g Lord Americo—Dixons Dutchess (IRE) **Anne O'Sullivan**
3 BE TELLING (IRE), 5, b g Oscar (IRE)—Manhattan King (IRE) **P. Byrne**
4 BLACK LORD (IRE), 6, b g Mister Lord (USA)—Deruma Lady (IRE) **J. Fitzpatrick**
5 BRIAR'S MIST (IRE), 7, gr g Roselier (FR)—Clay Castle (IRE) **Trevor Hemmings**
6 CHAPEL CROSS (IRE), 6, b g Old Vic—Desert Flight (IRE) **E. M. O'Sullivan**
7 COME HEER TO ME (IRE), 6, b m Supreme Leader—Easy Run (IRE) **E. J. O'sullivan**
8 COPPERPOT (IRE), 7, ch g Treasure Hunter—Merillion **Trevor Hemmings**
9 5, b g Octagonal (AUS)—Coral Sound (IRE) **Gerard O'Sullivan**
10 DR JAZZ (IRE), 8, b m Mister Lord (USA)—Nautilus **Victor Bowling**
11 FOUR EAGLES (USA), 6, b g Lear Fan (USA)—Bloomingly (ARG) **Oliver McDowell**
12 HANG SONG (IRE), 6, b g Phardante (FR)—Portia's Delight (IRE) **John White & Dermot Grumley**
13 HERALDRY (IRE), 4, b g Mark of Esteem (IRE)—Sorb Apple (IRE) **Gerard O'Sullivan**
14 IAMHERE (IRE), 6, b g Mister Lord (USA)—Angie's Delight **J. Fitzpatrick**
15 JOHN STORM (IRE), 5, b g Glacial Storm (USA)—Johns Rose (IRE) **E. M. O'Sulivan & M. Foley**
16 LORD ON THE RUN (IRE), 6, b g Lord Americo—Polar Crash **Gerard O'Sullivan**
17 LOUGHLIN (IRE), 5, b g Norwich—Deep Green **Anne O'Sullivan**
18 LUBY (IRE), 6, b g Be My Native (USA)—Foxed (IRE) **E. M. O'Sullivan**
19 NIGHT BILLIARDS (IRE), 6, b g Distinctly North (USA)—Harp Song **Kate Jarvey**
20 5, B m Classic Cliche (IRE)—Olnistar (FR) **E. M. O'Sullivan**
21 PASERELLA (IRE), 6, b g Persian Mews—Knockaville **Eamon Murray & Maura Moylan**
22 PEACH OF A CITIZEN (IRE), 5, b m Anshan—Sweet Peach (IRE) **E. J. O'Sullivan**
23 5, Br g Anshan—Sassy Sally (IRE) **Trevor Hemmings**
24 SWEET CITIZEN (IRE), 7, b g Supreme Leader—Sweet Peach (IRE) **E. J. O'Sullivan & Denis O'Driscoll**
25 TEO PERUGO (IRE), 5, b g Perugino (USA)—Teodosia **Camden Racing Syndicate**
26 THE ALTER BOY (IRE), 6, b g Executive Perk—Beyond It **T.Cremin, J. Quaid, C. O. Crualaoi**
27 THE BEEKER (IRE), 6, b g Mister Lord (USA)—Statoil (USA) **E. M. O'Sullivan**
28 TUBA (IRE), 9, b g Orchestra—Princess Paula **Kilshannig Racing Syndicate**
29 TWO EXCUSES (IRE), 6, ch g Germany (USA)—Argideen Diver (IRE) **Kilshannig Racing Syndicate**

Other Owners: A. Ahern, Kevin Dennehy, Aidan Foley, John Hickey, Mr Denis A. Linehan, John G. Linehan, Paul McDowell, Sean O'Donovan, Mrs M. C. O'Sullivan, Ger Stack.

Apprentice: D G O'Shea (7-0). Amateurs: Mr Martin Ferris (10-0), Mr Barry J Foley (9-7), Mr William O'Sullivan (11-0), Mr Justin Rea (9-7).

418 MR J. A. B. OLD, Wroughton

Postal: Upper Herdswick Farm, Hackpen, Burderop, Wroughton, Wiltshire, SN4 0QH.
Contact: OFFICE (01793) 845200 CAR (0836) 721459 FAX (01793) 845201

1 ANGELLO (IRE), 7, ch g Selkirk (USA)—Pomorie (IRE) **Mrs Anne Yearley**
2 ARKLEY REGAL (IRE), 9, b g Orchestra—Lady Geneva **Mr Nigel Dempster**
3 ATTORNEY GENERAL (IRE), 5, b g Sadler's Wells (USA)—Her Ladyship **Mr W. E. Sturt**
4 BOUNDARY HOUSE (IRE), 6, ch g Afflora (IRE)—Preacher's Gem **Mr Nick Viney**
5 BRIGHT GREEN (IRE), 5, b g Green Desert (USA)—Shining High **Mr W. E. Sturt**
6 CAPTAIN AUBREY (IRE), 5, b g Supreme Leader—Hamers Girl (IRE) **Mr W. E. Sturt**
7 5, B g Bob's Return (IRE)—Celtic Tore (IRE) **Mr W. E. Sturt**
8 DAME MARGARET, 4, ch f Elmaamul (USA)—Her Ladyship **Mrs Anne Yearley**
9 DON IDO (ARG), 8, b g Lazy Boy (ARG)—She's Got You (ARG) **Old Fools Partnership**
10 DOUBLEWOOD (IRE), 6, b m Charnwood Forest (IRE)—Double On (IRE) **Mr W. E. Sturt**
11 DUNSHAUGHLIN (IRE), 7, b g Supreme Leader—Russian Gale (IRE) **Mr W. E. Sturt**
12 DURANTE (IRE), 6, ch g Shernazar—Sweet Tune **Mr W. E. Sturt**
13 EXODOUS (ARG), 8, ch g Equalize (USA)—Empire Glory (ARG) **Mr W. E. Sturt**
14 FLEXIBLE CONCIENCE (IRE), 9, br g Glacial Storm (USA)—Philly Athletic **Old Fools Partnership**
15 HOUSEPARTY (IRE), 6, b br g Grand Lodge (USA)—Special Display **Mr W. E. Sturt**
16 KATOOF (USA), 6, b g Silver Hawk (USA)—The Caretaker **Mr W. E. Sturt**
17 KINGTOBEE (IRE), 6, b g King's Ride—Zephyrelle (IRE) **Mr W. E. Sturt**
18 LITTLE HERMAN (IRE), 8, b g Mandalus—Kilbricken Bay **Mr W. E. Sturt**
19 LITTLE MICK (IRE), 7, br g Mister Lord (USA)—Strong Trump (IRE) **Mrs J. Fowler**
20 MAISEY DOWN, 7, b m Rakaposhi King—Win Green Hill **Mr J. A. B. Old**
21 MAJESTIC BAY (IRE), 8, b g Unfuwain (USA)—That'll Be The Day (IRE) **W. J. Smith and M. D. Dudley**

MR J. A. B. OLD—continued

22 **MASTER JED (IRE)**, 7, br g Bob's Return (IRE)—Evan's Love **Mr W. E. Sturt**
23 **MISS MAILMIT**, 7, b m Rakaposhi King—Flora Louisa **Mr Peter Guntrip**
24 5, B g Shernazar—Miss Nancy **Mr W. E. Sturt**
25 **MONEY MOUNTAIN**, 7, ch g Rakaposhi King—Black H'Penny **Mr A. J. Britten**
26 **MONTEFORTE**, 6, b g Alflora (IRE)—Double Dutch **Mr W. E. Sturt**
27 **NATIVE PEACH**, 9, ch g Be My Native (USA)—Larry's Peach **Mr W. E. Sturt**
28 **PARACHUTE**, 5, ch g Hector Protector (USA)—Shortfall **W E Sturt - Osborne House VI**
29 **PERSIAN KING (IRE)**, 7, ch g Persian Bold—Queen's Share **Mr W. E. Sturt**
30 **PHYSICAL GRAFFITI (USA)**, 7, b g Mister Baileys—Gleaming Water (USA) **Old Fools Partnership**
31 **PIP MOSS**, 9, ch g Le Moss—My Aisling **Mrs Jim Old**
32 **ROMAN HIDEAWAY (IRE)**, 6, b g Hernando (FR)—Vaison La Romaine **Mr W. E. Sturt**
33 **SARGASSO SEA**, 7, gr g Greensmith—Sea Spice **Miss S. Blumberg**
34 4, Ch g Anshan—Shuil Na Mhuire (IRE) **Mr W. E. Sturt**
35 **SIR TALBOT**, 10, b g Ardross—Bermuda Lily **Mr W. E. Sturt**
36 **SMEATHE'S RIDGE**, 6, b g Rakaposhi King—Mrs Barty (IRE) **Mr Peter Guntrip**
37 **SMOKESTACK (IRE)**, 8, b g Lord Americo—Chiminee Fly **M. Lovatt/C. Jenkins**
38 **SOMETHING DANDY (IRE)**, 11, b g Brush Aside (USA)—Hawthorn Dandy **Blomeley/Lovatt Partnership**
39 **STEVE THE FISH (IRE)**, 8, ch g Dry Dock—Country Clothing **The Old Boys Partnership**
40 **THEATRE CALL (IRE)**, 6, b g Old Vic—Jennycomequick **Mr W. E. Sturt**
41 **THE DUCKPOND (IRE)**, 7, ch g Bob's Return (IRE)—Miss Gosling **Mr W. E. Sturt**
42 **TOMFOOLARY (IRE)**, 7, ch g Erins Isle—Liberty Bird (USA) **Mrs C. H. Antrobus**
43 **WAIN MOUNTAIN**, 8, b g Unfuwain (USA)—Mountain Memory **W. J. Smith and M. D. Dudley**
44 **WISE KING**, 14, b g Rakaposhi King—Sunwise
45 **YOUNG COLLIER**, 5, b g Vettori (IRE)—Cockatoo Island **Mr W. E. Sturt**

Other Owners: Mr D. W. Blomeley, Mr M. D. Dudley, Eclipse Thoroughbreds, Mr Neil Greig, Mr Anthony D. Hopkins, Mr Arthur D. Hopkins, Mr M. F. Hopkins, Mr Chris Jenkins, Mr Martin Lovatt, Mr William J. Smith.

Jockeys (NH): Leighton Aspell (w.a.), M Bradburne.

---

419 | **MRS J. K. M. OLIVER, Hawick**
Postal: **The Stables Cottage, Hassendean Bank, Hawick, Roxburghshire, TD9 8RX.**
Contact: **PHONE (01450) 870216 MOBILE (07774) 426017 FAX (01450) 870216**

1 **EVENING SPLASH (IRE)**, 8, b m Royal Fountain—Red Dusk **Mrs J. K. M. Oliver**
2 5, B g Keen—Gilston Lass **Mrs J. K. M. Oliver**
3 **HE'S MY UNCLE**, 9, ch g Phardante (FR)—Red Dusk **Mrs J. K. M. Oliver**
4 **LOUDY ROWDY (IRE)**, 13, br g Strong Gale—Express Film **The British Beef Partnership**
5 **MINSGILL GLEN**, 8, b m Minster Son—Gilmanscleuch (IRE) **Miss J. S. Peat**
6 **OLIBERI**, 8, b g First Trump—Rhiannon **Miss J. S. Peat**
7 **PRINCESS GILLIE**, 5, b m Prince Daniel (USA)—Gilmanscleuch (IRE) **Miss J. S. Peat**
8 **ROYAL GILLIE**, 7, br m Royal Fountain—Gilmanscleuch (IRE) **Miss J. S. Peat**

Other Owners: Mrs R. Davidson, Mr W. Stuart Wilson.

---

420 | **MR J. A. OSBORNE, Upper Lambourn**
Postal: **Kingsdown, Upper Lambourn, Hungerford, Berkshire, RG17 8QX.**
Contact: **PHONE (01488) 73139 FAX (01488) 73084 MOBILE (07860) 533422**
E-MAIL jamieosborne@dial.pipex.com

1 **BILLY BIRD**, 4, b g Bluebird—Classic Dilemma **Sarah Gallagher**
2 **DANGER OVER**, 7, b h Warning—Danilova (USA) **Paul J. Dixon and Mountgrange Stud**
3 **ELECTRIQUE (IRE)**, 4, b g Elmaamul (USA)—Majmu (USA) **Mr Paul J. Dixon**
4 **ESPADA (IRE)**, 8, b g Mukaddamah (USA)—Folk Song (CAN) **John Livock and Partners**
5 **HELLBENT**, 5, b g Selkirk (USA)—Loure (USA) **Mr J. A. Osborne**
6 **LORD MELBOURNE (IRE)**, 5, b g Lycius (USA)—Adana (IRE) **Mr Paul J. Dixon**
7 **MOROCCO (IRE)**, 15, b g Cyrano de Bergerac—Lightning Laser **Mr Martin Myers**
8 **ONCE (FR)**, 4, gr g Hector Protector (USA)—Moon Magic **Lord Blyth**
9 **PAPILLON DE BRONZE (IRE)**, 4, b f Marju (USA)—Soviet Maid (IRE) **Lord Blyth**
10 **SAHAAT**, 6, b brg Machiavellian (USA)—Tawaaded (IRE) **Mr Paul J. Dixon**
11 **SPINDOR (USA)**, 5, ch g Spinning World (USA)—Doree (USA) **Mr Paul J. Dixon**
12 **TODLEA (IRE)**, 4, b g Desert Prince (IRE)—Imelda (USA) **Lynn Wilson Giles Wilson Martin Landau**
13 **VANDENBERGHE**, 5, b g Millkom—Child Star (FR) **Mr D. Marks**

MR J. A. OSBORNE—continued

THREE-YEAR-OLDS

14 AMONG DREAMS, ch f Among Men (USA)—Russell Creek **Dreams United**
15 ANGELO'S PRIDE, ch c Young Ern—Considerable Charm **Mr J. A. Osborne**
16 CARTRONAGEERAGHLAD (IRE), b c Mujadil (USA)—
  Night Scent (IRE) **Mr David N.Reynolds and Mr Chris Watkins**
17 CHARLIEISMYDARLING, b g Mind Games—Blessed Lass (HOL) **Mrs Patricia Hughes**
18 DESPERATE DAN, b c Danzero (AUS)—Alzianah **Mountgrange Stud**
19 FISSION, ch f Efisio—Area Girl **Mr Paul J. Dixon**
20 FU FIGHTER, b g Unfuwain (USA)—Runelia **Mrs Nicole Myers**
21 GENEROUS SPIRIT (IRE), ch c Cadeaux Genereux—Miss Rossi **Mr J. Palmer-Brown**
22 HAWKIT (IRE), b g Silver Hawk (USA)—Hey Ghaz (USA) **Mr Paul J. Dixon**
23 HOUSE OF BLUES, b c Grand Lodge (USA)—Sartigila **Mr Michael Buckley**
24 LAAWARIS (USA), b c Souvenir Copy (USA)—Seattle Kat (USA) **Mr J. A. Osborne**
25 B f Kahyasi—Lautrea (IRE) **Mr J. A. Osborne**
26 MILK IT MICK, b c Millkom—Lunar Music **Mr Paul J. Dixon**
27 MOORLAW (IRE), b c Mtoto—Belle Etoile (FR) **L. Wilson, M. St Quinton, M. Landau**
28 MORSE (IRE), b c Shinko Forest (IRE)—Auriga **Turf 2000 Limited**
29 NAFFERTON GIRL (IRE), b f Orpen—Petomi **Paul J. Dixon and R. C. Bond**
30 OKTIS MORILIOUS (IRE), b g Octagonal (NZ)—Nottash (IRE) **Mr A. Irvine**
31 OVERDRAWN (IRE), b g Daggers Drawn (USA)—In Denial (IRE) **Mr Paul J. Dixon**
32 PLACE COWBOY (IRE), b c Compton Place—Paris Joelle (IRE) **Mountgrange Stud**
33 REGULATED (IRE), b g Alzao (USA)—Royal Hostess (IRE) **Mr Richard Leslie**
34 RULES FOR JOKERS (IRE), b g Mujadil (USA)—Exciting **Jim McGrath and Reg Griffin**
35 RYE (IRE), b f Charnwood Forest (IRE)—Silver Hut (USA) **Mr Danny Durkan**
36 SIMONOVSKI (USA), b c Miswaki (USA)—Earthra (USA) **Mr Richard Leslie**
37 SOLINIKI, b g Danzero (AUS)—Pride of My Heart **Mr Richard Leslie**

TWO-YEAR-OLDS

38 B c 30/3 Desert Sun—Accounting (Sillery (USA)) (30920) **Mr Richard Leslie**
39 B f 27/2 Revoque (IRE)—Adjriyna (Top Ville) (21644) **P. Shanahan**
40 B c 1/4 Josr Algarhoud (IRE)—Adrianna Aldini (Habitat) **Mr Paul J. Dixon**
41 B f 7/5 Soviet Star (USA)—Alriyaah (Shareef Dancer (USA)) (32158) **Mr Richard Leslie**
42 Ch f 3/3 Singspiel (USA)—Baize (Efisio) (37105) **Mr Paul J. Dixon**
43 Ch f 8/4 Daggers Drawn (USA)—Be Prepared (IRE) (Be My Guest (USA)) (11000)
44 B f 29/1 Averti (IRE)—Bint Albadou (IRE) (Green Desert (USA)) (33000) **Mr & Mrs C. Deuters**
45 Ch f 28/2 Bahamian Bounty—By Candlelight (IRE) (Roi Danzig (USA)) (32000) **M. Kerr-Dineen**
46 B c 3/4 Royal Applause—Chrysalis (Soviet Star (USA)) (110000) **Mountgrange Stud**
47 B f 16/5 Spectrum (IRE)—Creme Caramel (USA) (Septieme Ciel (USA)) (6000) **WRB**
48 Ch c 19/4 Alhaarth (IRE)—Danishkada (Thatch (USA)) (15460) **Breeze (JAO)**
49 B c 20/4 Ashkalani (IRE)—Dashing Rocksville (Rock City) (11131)
50 B f 8/3 Cape Cross (IRE)—Destinating (IRE) (Wolfhound (USA)) (21025) **Fergus Jones**
51 B f 8/2 Royal Applause—Devastating (Bluebird (USA)) (34000) **M. Kerr-Dineen**
52 Br f 27/3 Key Of Luck (USA)—Doo Han (IRE) (Doulab (USA)) (47000) **Mr Richard Leslie**
53 B c 12/3 Barathea (IRE)—Edwina (IRE) (Caerleon (USA)) (21644)
54 B f 25/3 Polish Precedent—Eldina (Distant Relative) (4000)
55 B c 15/4 Inchinor—Ellebanna (Tina's Pet) (45000)
56 B f 13/2 Alzao (USA)—Eman's Joy (Lion Cavern (USA)) (28000) **Fergus Jones**
57 GLAD BIG (GER), b c 27/2 Big Shuffle (USA)—Glady Sun (GER) (Big Shuffle (USA)) (32158)
58 B c 1/4 Xaar—Hero's Pride (FR) (Hero's Honor (USA)) (17315) **D. Reynolds & C. Watkins**
59 Ch f 29/3 Raise A Grand (IRE)—Highland Crumpet (First Trump) (4019) **Task Ltd**
60 Ch c 11/3 Inchinor—Ice House (Northfields (USA)) (100000) **Mountgrange Stud**
61 Ch f 25/1 Alhaarth (IRE)—Ide Say (IRE) (Grand Lodge (USA)) (40000) **Mrs E. Roberts**
62 B f 17/2 Primo Dominie—In Love Again (IRE) (Prince Rupert (FR)) (17000) **Goldmouse Racing**
63 B c 14/5 Mujadil (USA)—Isabella R (IRE) (Indian Ridge) (20407)
64 B f 29/3 Titus Livius (FR)—Isolette (Wassi) (6183) **Whitemouse Racing**
65 B f 10/3 Rossini (USA)—Kebabs (IRE) (Catrail (USA)) (2163)
66 KHOOSA KHANOOM (IRE), b f 4/3 Royal Applause—Kshessinskaya (Hadeer) (15000) **Karmaa Racing**
67 B c 8/3 Lujain (USA)—Kicka (Shirley Heights) (34000)
68 B c 14/4 Indian Danehill (USA)—Lady's Vision (IRE) (Vison (USA)) (26000)
69 B c 7/4 Orpen—Lady Taufan (IRE) (Taufan (USA)) (32158) **Pat Eddery Racing**
70 B c 17/3 Bluebird (USA)—Laura Margaret (Persian Bold) (28000) **Mr & Mrs I. H. Bendelow**
71 LITHOS, ch c 16/3 Inchinor—Leisure (FR) (Fast Topaze (USA)) (16697)
72 B f 13/3 Mind Games—Lunar Music (Komaite (USA)) (100000) **Mr Paul J. Dixon**
73 Ch c 14/4 Raise A Grand (IRE)—Magic Melody (Petong) (21025) **H. Rosenblatt & D. Margolis**

MR J. A. OSBORNE—continued

74 Ch c 5/3 Forzando—Mazurkanova (Song) (19000) **Cavendish Racing**
75 B f 20/4 Desert Sun—Miss Margate (IRE) (Don't Forget Me) (3710) **Mrs Patricia Hughes**
76 B f 14/2 Inchinor—Mountain Bluebird (USA) (Clever Trick (USA)) (18000) **Mr & Mrs I. H. Bendelow**
77 Ch c 28/3 Grand Lodge (USA)—Nawara (Welsh Pageant) (40000) **Mr Paul J. Dixon**
78 B c 8/4 Fasliyev (USA)—Obsessed (Storm Bird (CAN)) (36000) **Mountgrange Stud**
79 PERSIAN ROCK (IRE), b c 15/3 Namid—
                             Cairo Lady (IRE) (Persian Bold) (37000) **Waney Racing Group & Karmaa Racing**
80 B f 29/4 Royal Applause—Piney River (Pharly (FR)) (18000) **Whitemouse Racing**
81 B f 16/3 Rossini (USA)—Pipe Opener (Prince Sabo) (24737)
82 Br c 20/1 Xaar—Royal Gift (Cadeaux Genereux) (32000) **De La Warr Racing**
83 Gr f 2/2 Mind Games—Sapphire Mill (Petong) (3200)
84 SERGEANT LEWIS, gr c 12/2 Mind Games—Silver Blessings (Statoblest) (9000) **Turf 2000**
85 B c 18/2 Efisio—Shining Cloud (Indian Ridge) (12000)
86 B f 16/4 Green Desert (USA)—Soviet Maid (IRE) (Soviet Star (USA)) (100000) **Bill Durkan**
87 Ch c 10/5 Atraf—Verbena (IRE) (Don't Forget Me) (15000) **Discreet Partnership**
88 B c 6/4 Soviet Star (USA)—Welsh Mist (Damister (USA)) (47619)
89 Ch c 16/2 Zafonic (USA)—Wigging (Warning) (30000)
90 B c 25/1 Namid—Wildflower (Namaqualand (USA)) (30920) **Mr & Mrs I. H. Bendelow**
91 Ch c 20/1 In The Wings—Wishful (IRE) (Irish River (FR)) (62000) **Mountgrange Stud**

Other Owners: Nr Andy Beard, East Wind Racing Ltd, Mr G. A. Lucas, Mr R. Newark, Mrs E. J. Norwich, R R. P. Norwich, Mr S. J. Piper, Mr B. P. Ryan, Surrey Laminators Ltd.

Assistant Trainer: Roddy Griffiths

Apprentice: Steven Crawford (9-0). **Conditional:** Steven Crawford (9-0).

---

421 MR BRYN PALLING, Cowbridge
Postal: **Ty-Wyth-Newydd, Tredodridge, Cowbridge, South Glam, CF71 7UL.**
Contact: **PHONE (01446) 760122 FAX (01446) 760067**

1 **AMONG FRIENDS (IRE)**, 4, b g Among Men (USA)—Anita's Contessa (IRE) **Mr Peter Morgan**
2 **A ONE (IRE)**, 5, b g Alzao (USA)—Anita's Contessa (IRE) **Mr Albert Yemm**
3 **BRIGHT MIST**, 5, b m Anita's Prince—Out On Her Own **Mrs L. Hedlund**
4 **CONCHONITA**, 4, b f Bishop of Cashel—Cactus Road (FR) **Los Cabelleros**
5 **CORREY'S LASS**, 5, b m Almutanabbi—Jolly Girl **Mrs M. M. Palling**
6 **DANE RHAPSODY (IRE)**, 4, b f Danetime (IRE)—Hil Rhapsody **Mr B. Reynolds**
7 **DANIELLE'S LAD**, 8, b g Emarati (USA)—Cactus Road (FR) **Mrs M. M. Palling**
8 **ELIDORE**, 4, b f Danetime (IRE)—Beveled Edge **Mr Nigel Thomas**
9 **GIOCOSO (USA)**, 4, b c Bahri (USA)—Wing My Chimes (USA) **Mr W. Devine & Mr P. Morgan**
10 **LOLANITA**, 6, b m Anita's Prince—Jimlil **Mrs M. M. Palling**
11 **PARKER**, 7, b g Magic Ring (IRE)—Miss Loving **Lamb Brook Associates**
12 **TEEHEE (IRE)**, 6, b g Anita's Prince—Regal Charmer **Mrs M. M. Palling & Mr Paul Young**
13 **WELSH AND WYLDE (IRE)**, 4, b g Anita's Prince—Waikiki (GER) **Mrs Anita Quinn**

THREE-YEAR-OLDS

14 **ARIAN'S LAD**, b c Prince Sabo—Arian Da **Mr Christopher J. Mason**
15 **CYFRWYS (IRE)**, b f Foxhound (USA)—Divine Elegance (IRE) **Derek and Jean Clee**
16 **FRED'S FIRST**, b g Nomination—Perecapa (Cactus Road (FR)) **Mr Fred Lalies**
17 **GOJO (IRE)**, b f Danetime (IRE)—Pretonic **Mr Albert Yemm**
18 **INDIAN EDGE**, ch g Indian Rocket—Beveled Edge **Nigel Thomas and Christopher Mason**
19 **JAKARMI**, b g Merdon Melody—Lady Ploy **Mrs M. M. Palling**
20 **KINISKA**, b f Merdon Melody—Young Whip **Mrs M. M. Palling**
21 **MY MICHELLE**, b f Ali-Royal (IRE)—April Magic **Mr Peter Morgan**
22 **PRINCIPESSA**, b f Machiavellian (USA)—Party Doll **Derek and Jean Clee**
23 **SINGITTA**, b f Singspiel (IRE)—Ferber's Follies (USA) **Mr W. Devine & Mr P. Morgan**
24 **SWOON**, b f Night Shift (USA)—Rock The Boat **Mr W. Devine & Mr P. Morgan**
25 **YNYS**, b c Turtle Island (IRE)—Kiss Me Goodnight **Derek and Jean Clee**

TWO-YEAR-OLDS

26 B f 17/4 Lend A Hand—Anita's Love (IRE) (Anita's Prince)
27 Ch c 12/4 Magic Ring (IRE)—Arian Da (Superlative) **Mr Christopher J. Mason**
28 Br f 19/4 Chickawicka (IRE)—Ballasilla (IRE) (Puissance) **Mrs M. M. Palling**
29 B f 24/4 Barathea (IRE)—Carranita (IRE) (Anita's Prince) **Mrs A. Quinn**

MR BRYN PALLING—continued

- 30 B c 17/3 Petorius—Creggan Vale Lass (Simply Great (FR)) (4946)
- 31 Ch c 22/2 Bahhare (USA)—Ericeira (IRE) (Anita's Prince) (1855)
- 32 **GRANARY GIRL**, b f 8/2 Kingsinger (IRE)—Highland Blue (Never So Bold) (952) **Mr Barry Minty**
- 33 Ch f 31/3 Intikhab (USA)—Grannys Reluctance (IRE) (Anita's Prince) **Mrs A. Quinn**
- 34 B c 14/3 Revoque (IRE)—Mystic Thoughts (IRE) (Shernazar) (1236)
- 35 B c 17/4 Anita's Prince—Out On Her Own (Superlative)
- 36 B f 3/2 Kingsinger (IRE)—Paula's Joy (Danehill (USA)) (666) **Mrs M. M. Palling**
- 37 Ch f 19/4 Chickawicka (IRE)—Princess Kelly (Prince Daniel (USA)) **Mrs M. M. Palling**

Other Owners: Mr D. Baker, Mr T. Clarke, Mr Derek D. Clee, Mrs Jean P. Clee, Mr D. E. Crompton, Mrs N. J. Funnell, Mr P. R. John, Mr Keith Lloyd, Mr Martin Lloyd, Mr K. A. Morris, Mr K. M. Rideout, Mr P. A. Rowley, Mr M. Sims.

---

422 | **MR ANDREW PARKER, Lockerbie**
Postal: Parker Racing, Douglas Hall Farm, Lockerbie, Dumfriesshire, DG11 1AD.
Contact: PHONE (01576) 510232 FAX (01576) 510232 MOBILE (07968) 325650

- 1 **BEHAVINGBADLY (IRE)**, 9, b g Lord Americo—Audrey's Turn **Mr R. A. Bartlett**
- 2 **BRIGHT STEEL (IRE)**, 7, gr g Roselier (FR)—Ikeathy **Mr & Mrs Raymond Anderson Green**
- 3 **BUSTAMANTE**, 8, ch g Sir Harry Lewis (USA)—Carribean Sound **Hamilton House Limited**
- 4 **CHAMPAGNE LOU LOU**, 6, b m Supreme Leader—Highfrith **Mr Derrick Mossop**
- 5 **CRAMOND (IRE)**, 6, b g Lord Americo—Rullahola **Mr R. A. Bartlett**
- 6 **CURLY SPENCER (IRE)**, 10, br g Yashgan—Tim's Brief **Mr & Mrs Raymond Anderson Green**
- 7 **D J FLIPPANCE (IRE)**, 9, b g Orchestra—Jane Bond **Mr & Mrs Raymond Anderson Green**
- 8 **EM'S GUY**, 6, b g Royal Fountain—Gaelic Empress **Mr J. John Paterson**
- 9 **EM'S ROYALTY**, 7, b g Royal Fountain—Gaelic Empress **Mr J. John Paterson**
- 10 **FOR YOUR EARS ONLY (IRE)**, 8, b g Be My Native (USA)—Sister Ida **Mr & Mrs Raymond Anderson Green**
- 11 **GANGSTERS R US (IRE)**, 8, br g Treasure Hunter—Our Mare Mick **Mr J. B. Purefoy**
- 12 **HADES DE SIENNE (FR)**, 9, b g Concorde Jr (USA)—Aube de Sienne (FR) **Mr & Mrs Raymond Anderson Green**
- 13 **HARLOV (FR)**, 9, ch g Garde Royale—Paulownia (FR) **Mr & Mrs Raymond Anderson Green**
- 14 **HUGO DE GRÉZ (FR)**, 9, b g Useful (FR)—Piqua des Gres (FR) **Mr & Mrs Raymond Anderson Green**
- 15 **JACKSONVILLE (FR)**, 7, b g Petit Montmorency (USA)—
  Quinine des Aulnes (FR) **Mr & Mrs Raymond Anderson Green**
- 16 **LAMPION DU BOST (FR)**, 5, b g Mont Basile—Ballerine du Bost (FR) **The Dodoz Partnership**
- 17 **LEADAWAY**, 5, b g Supreme Leader—Annicombe Run **Mr & Mrs Raymond Anderson Green**
- 18 **OVERSERVED**, 5, b g Supreme Leader—Divine Comedy (IRE) **Mr & Mrs Raymond Anderson Green**
- 19 **SECRET PEARL (IRE)**, 5, b m Alphabatim (USA)—Petite Deb **Mr Derrick Mossop**
- 20 **TO THE FUTURE (IRE)**, 8, ch g Bob Back (USA)—Lady Graduate (IRE) **Mr & Mrs Raymond Anderson Green**
- 21 **TUDOR NATIVE (IRE)**, 8, b m Distinct Native—Tudorfield Girl **Mrs Cathrine Matthews**
- 22 **TULACH ARD (IRE)**, 9, b g Erdelistan (FR)—Noon Hunting **Mr M. C. Mackenzie & Mrs S. B. Mackenzie**
- 23 **WORKAWAY**, 8, b g Afflora (IRE)—Annicombe Run **Mr & Mrs Raymond Anderson Green**

Other Owners: Mr Billy Dodds, Mrs Anita Green, Mr Craig Moore, Mrs Janet Parker, Mrs S. E. B. Purefoy.

Assistant Trainer: Mrs J Parker & G. Kerrr

Conditional: P Robson.

---

423 | **MR J. E. PARKES, Malton**
Postal: Garth Cottage, Upper Helmsley, North Yorkshire, YO41 1JY.
Contact: PHONE (01759) 372258 MOBILE (0771) 8217769 E-MAIL lynjon@afsmail.net

- 1 **ALL BUT (IRE)**, 12, b g Roselier (FR)—Cloncunny **Mr D. Mossop**
- 2 **BELLA LIANA (IRE)**, 4, b f Sesaro (USA)—Bella Galiana (ITY) **Mr D. Mossop**
- 3 **BEST PORT (IRE)**, 8, b g Be My Guest (USA)—Portree **Mr M. Wormald**
- 4 **BOLESLAV (USA)**, 4, br g Polish Precedent (USA)—True Glory (IRE) **J. Parkes**
- 5 **DIWAN (IRE)**, 6, b g Be My Guest (USA)—Nectarine (IRE) **Mr M. Wormald**
- 6 **GRUB STREET**, 8, b g Barathea (IRE)—Broadmara (IRE) **Mrs B. J. Sands**
- 7 **KING NICHOLAS (USA)**, 5, b g Nicholas (USA)—Lifetime Honour (USA) **Mr M. Wormald**
- 8 **MR COONEY (IRE)**, 10, b g Van Der Linden (FR)—Green Orchid **Mr D. Mossop**
- 9 **NEWTONIAN (USA)**, 5, ch g Distant View (USA)—Polly Adler (USA) **Mr Ray Flegg**
- 10 4, b g General Monash—Not Too Near (IRE) **J. Parkes**
- 11 **PHANTOM HAZE**, 11, gr g Absalom—Caroline Lamb **Mr F. Mossop**
- 12 **SPY MASTER**, 6, b g Green Desert (USA)—Obsessive (USA) **Mr G. Parkinson**

MR J. E. PARKES—continued

13 **ZAP ATTACK**, 4, b g Zafonic (USA)—Rappa Tap Tap (FR) **Mr J. Bousfield**
14 **ZELEA (IRE)**, 5, br m Be My Guest (USA)—Ebony And Ivory (IRE) **Mr W. A. Sellers**

TWO-YEAR-OLDS

15 B f 10/4 Darnay—Adjamiya (USA) (Shahrastani (USA)) **Mr Jim Kelly**
16 B f 30/4 Monashee Mountain—Tender Time (Tender King) (6000) **Mr D. Mossop**

Other Owners: Nr D. E. Furman, Mr G. Parkinson.

Assistant Trainer: Mrs L Parkes

---

424 **MR J. R. PAYNE, Dulverton**
Postal: **Lower Holworthy Farm, Brompton Regis, Dulverton, Somerset, TA22 9NY.**
Contact: **HOME/FAX (01398) 371244**

1 **ATHNOWEN (IRE)**, 12, b g Lord Americo—Lady Bluebird **Mr R. J. Payne**
2 **COUNT TIROL (IRE)**, 7, b g Tirol—Bid High (IRE) **Mr J. R. Payne**
3 **DASHING DOLLAR (IRE)**, 13, b g Lord Americo—Cora Swan **Mr R. J. Payne**
4 5, B g Puissance—Jennies' Gem **Mr J. R. Payne**

---

425 **MR J. W. PAYNE, Newmarket**
Postal: **Frankland Lodge, Hamilton Road, Newmarket, Suffolk, CB8 7JQ.**
Contact: **PHONE (01638) 668675 FAX (01638) 668675 MOBILE (07850) 133116**
E-MAIL **pip.payne@virgin.net**

1 **ANA WINTA (FR)**, 4, b g Anabaa (USA)—Steeple **Mr C. Cotran**
2 **CHELSEA BLUE (ITY)**, 6, ch m Barathea (IRE)—Indigo Blue (IRE) **Mrs J. W. Payne**
3 **EZZ ELKHEIL**, 5, b g Bering—Numidie (FR) **Mr C. Cotran**
4 **HONORINE (IRE)**, 4, b f Mark of Esteem (IRE)—Blue Water (USA) **Mrs R. A. C. Vigors**
5 **KOMENA**, 6, b m Komaite (USA)—Mena **The Frankland Lodgers**
6 **NIGHT PROSPECTOR**, 4, b c Night Shift (USA)—Pride of My Heart **Mr C. Cotran**
7 **NORTH BY NORTHEAST (IRE)**, 6, ch g Polish Precedent (USA)—Catalonda **Mrs J. W. Payne**
8 **POINT MAN (IRE)**, 4, b g Pivotal—Pursuit of Truth (USA) **Mr C. Cotran**
9 **ROZANEE**, 4, ch f Nashwan (USA)—Belle Genius (USA) **Mrs R. A. C. Vigors**
10 **SEA JADE (IRE)**, 5, b m Mujadil (USA)—Mirabiliary (USA) **Mr T. H. Barma**
11 **TABOOR (IRE)**, 6, b g Mujadil (USA)—Christoph's Girl **Mr T. W. Morley**
12 **TAIYO**, 4, b f Tagula (IRE)—Tharwa (USA) **Mrs J. Morley**
13 **TERIVIC**, 4, br g Terimon—Ludoviciana **Mr G. W. Paul**
14 **VICIANA**, 5, b m Sir Harry Lewis (USA)—Ludoviciana **Mr G. W. Paul**

THREE-YEAR-OLDS

15 **DARLA (IRE)**, b f Night Shift (USA)—Darbela (IRE) **Mrs R. A. C. Vigors**

TWO-YEAR-OLDS

16 Ch c 25/4 Grand Lodge (USA)—Broken Romance (IRE) (Ela-Mana-Mou) (44000)
17 B f 24/4 Raise A Grand (IRE)—Dragon Star (Rudimentary (USA)) (3200) **Mr T. H. Barma**
18 **LADRO VOLANTE (IRE)**, b c 20/2 Benny The Dip (USA)—Genoa (Zafonic (USA)) **Mr M. H. Dixon**
19 B f 4/3 Raise A Grand (IRE)—Non Dimenticar Me (IRE) (Don't Forget Me) (16000)

Apprentice: Brian Reilly (8-0).

---

426 **MR R. E. PEACOCK, Malmesbury**
Postal: **Oliver House Stud, Chedglow, Malmesbury, Wiltshire, SN16 9EZ.**
Contact: **PHONE (01666) 577238 MOBILE (07748) 565574**

1 **CALL MY GUEST (IRE)**, 14, b g Be My Guest (USA)—Overall **Derek and Jean Clee**
2 **CANDY ANCHOR (FR)**, 5, b m Slip Anchor—Kandavu **Mr R. E. Peacock**

MR R. E. PEACOCK—continued

THREE-YEAR-OLD

3 **KNIGHT OF HEARTS (IRE)**, gr g Idris (IRE)—Heart To Heart (IRE) **Mrs Alurie O'Sullivan**

Other Owners: Mr Derek D. Clee, Mrs Jean P. Clee.

Assistant Trainer: Mrs C Peacock

Jockeys (Flat): Seb Sanders (8-0, w.a.), V Slattery. **Jockey (NH):** V Slattery (10-0).

---

427 **MR B. A. PEARCE, Lingfield**
Postal: **Sheridan Farm, West Park Road, Newchapel, Lingfield, Surrey, RH7 6HT.**
Contact: **PHONE (01342) 713437 MOBILE (07710) 513913**

1 **ASIAN PERSUASION (IRE)**, 5, gr g Danehill Dancer (IRE)—Kaitlin (IRE) **Mr Martin J. Gibbs**
2 **EAU PURE (FR)**, 7, b m Epervier Bleu—Eau de Nuit **Mr Trevor Painting**
3 **FATALISTE (FR)**, 10, b g Nikos—Faracha (FR) **Mr Dennis Cook**
4 **FRAAMTASTIC**, 7, b m Fraam—Fading **Mr Richard J. Gray**
5 **J'UBIO**, 5, b m Bijou d'Inde—Eternal Triangle (USA) **Mr Patrick Barter**
6 **KICKBACK**, 4, b g High Kicker (USA)—Moniques Venture **Mr Martin J. Gibbs**
7 **LEYAALY**, 5, ch m Night Shift (USA)—Lower The Tone (IRE) **Mr Mervyn Merwood**
8 **MANTEL MINI**, 5, b m Reprimand—Foretell **Miss J. Webster**
9 **NO MERCY**, 8, ch g Faustus (USA)—Nashville Blues (IRE) **Mr Patrick Barter**
10 **SHAAMIT'S ALL OVER**, 5, br m Shaamit (IRE)—First Time Over **Mr Richard J. Gray**

Other Owners: Mr R. D. John, Mr T. M. J. Keep, Mrs Christine Painting, Mr T. David Reed, Mr J. Salter.

Assistant Trainer: Leila White

Jockey (NH): Chris Murray. **Conditional:** Chris Murray.

---

428 **MR K. R. PEARCE, Carmarthen**
Postal: **The Brambles, Laugharne, Carmarthen, Carmarthenshire, SA33 4QP.**
Contact: **HOME (01994) 427486 WORK (01994) 427868 FAX (01994) 427967**
MOBILE (07884) 184417 E-MAIL sandra.pearce@tiscali.co.uk

1 **AIR ATTACHE (USA)**, 9, b g Sky Classic (CAN)—Diplomatic Cover **Mr Keith R. Pearce**
2 **ILE DISTINCT (IRE)**, 10, b g Dancing Dissident (USA)—Golden Sunlight **Mr Keith R. Pearce**
3 **NEWMARKET MAGIC (IRE)**, 8, b g Vasco (USA)—Prodical Daughter **Mr Keith R. Pearce**
4 **PEACEFUL BOW (IRE)**, 7, b g Beau Sher—Peaceful Kyle (IRE) **Mr Keith R. Pearce**

Amateurs: Mr David S Jones (11-0), Mrs Lucy A Rowsell (10-5).

---

429 **MR J. E. PEASE, Chantilly**
Postal: **Villa Primerose, Chemin des Aigles, 60500 Chantilly, France.**
Contact: **PHONE +33 (0) 44 58 19 96/+33 (0) 44 57 23 09 FAX +33 (0) 44 57 59 90**
E-MAIL jpease8639@aol.com

1 **AEGLE**, 4, b f Night Shift (USA)—Aka Lady (FR) **John Goelet**
2 **AFFIRMATIVE ACTION (IRE)**, 4, b c Rainbow Quest (USA)—Bombazine (IRE) **G. W. Leigh**
3 **AGOG (IRE)**, 5, ch h Singspiel (IRE)—Shining Eyes (USA) **George Strawbridge**
4 **COREMIS**, 4, ch f Bering—Silicon Lady (USA) **John Goelet**
5 **IMAGO MUNDI**, 4, b c Spinning World (USA)—Turning Wheel (USA) **The Niarchos Family**
6 **INDIAN DANCER**, 4, ch f Indian Ridge (IRE)—Bluebell Dancer (USA) **Peter Pritchard**
7 **LILLA CREEK**, 4, b f Quest For Fame—Alice Springs (USA) **George Strawbridge**
8 **SALUTARE (IRE)**, 4, b f Sadler's Wells (USA)—Contare **George Strawbridge**
9 **SECRET SLOPE (USA)**, 4, b c Quest For Fame—Kerulen **George Strawbridge**
10 **TOTALLY MAJESTIC (FR)**, 6, b g Mtoto—Majestic Image **L. Roy, J. Pease**

THREE-YEAR-OLDS

11 **ALNITAK (USA)**, b c Nureyev (USA)—Very True (USA) **The Niarchos Family**
12 **APIA (FR)**, b f Lord of Men—Krislody (FR) **Ecurie Defer**

MR J. E. PEASE—continued

13 BAGO, b c Nashwan (USA)—Moonlight's Box (USA) **The Niarchos Family**
14 BONNIE MEMORIES (FR), ch f Alhaarth (USA)—Diese Memory (USA) **L. Roy/J. E. Pease**
15 BRAVADO, b c Priolo (USA)—Briesta (USA) **George Strawbridge**
16 COOL BRITANNIA (IRE), b c Rainbow Quest (USA)—Anka Britannia (USA) **The Leigh Family**
17 DAY OR NIGHT, gr c Daylami (IRE)—Amaryllis (IRE) **George Strawbridge**
18 DEDALE (FR), gr f Turgeon (USA)—Labyrinth (USA) **John Goelet/ J. E. Pease**
19 DYNAMIC CAT (USA), b f Dynaformer (USA)—Silent Cat (USA) **George Strawbridge**
20 EIGHT DELIGHTS (JPN), ch f Spinning World (USA)—Metaphor (USA) **The Niarchos Family**
21 FIN, b f Groom Dancer (USA)—Bonne Ile **A. M. Budgett**
22 GREENY (FR), b c Green Tune (USA)—La Bijou (FR) **W. Wolf**
23 HIGHLAND DANCER (FR), ch c Kendor (FR)—Zarzaya (USA) **L. Roy/ D. How**
24 HOUSTON CALLING (USA), b c Rahy (USA)—Eath To Jackie (USA) **George Strawbridge**
25 LADY ROSETTA (USA), b f Bering (USA)—Bluebell Dancer (USA) **Peter Pritchard**
26 NORTHERN CROWN (IRE), b f Soviet Star (USA)—Gazar **Mrs W. Tuttle**
27 SCARCITY (USA), b f Polish Numbers—Tarika (USA) **George Strawbridge**
28 SHADOW MOUNTAIN, ch f Selkirk (USA)—Petronilla (USA) **George Strawbridge**
29 STARNEVEES (FR), b c Kaldounevees (FR)—Stadia (FR) **Ecurie Defer**
30 TARENTUM (IRE), b c Grand Lodge (USA)—Contare **George Strawbridg**

TWO-YEAR-OLDS

31 B c 12/2 Selkirk (USA)—Amaryllis (IRE) (Sadler's Wells (USA)) **George Strawbridge**
32 BASEMAH (FR), b f 23/2 Lemon Drop Kid (USA)—
            Attractive Crown (USA) (Chief's Crown (USA)) (117501) **Baron F. C. Von Oppenheim**
33 BAVARIA STREET (FR), b f 24/3 Dolphin Street (FR)—Silicon Bavaria (FR) (Procida (USA)) **W. Wolf**
34 B f 10/2 Darshaan—Cape Grace (IRE) (Priolo (USA)) **George Strawbridge**
35 CELTIC SEA (IRE), b f 7/2 Celtic Swing—Sismi Que (Warning) **N. J. Forman Hardy**
36 B f 14/5 Montjeu (IRE)—Contare (Shirley Heights) **George Strawbridge**
37 B f 8/2 Selkirk (USA)—Dazzling Heights (Shirley Heights) **Peter Pritchard**
38 DREAM QUEEN (FR), ch c 29/4 Green Tune (USA)—
            Ella Nico (IRE) (Archway (IRE)) (64935) **L. Roy, P. Tham, D. How & J. E. Pease**
39 Gr c 3/4 Highest Honor (FR)—Ekaterina (USA) (Danzig (USA)) **George Strawbridge**
40 FLIGHT PATH (FR), ch f 14/1 Forzando—Uplifting (Magic Ring (IRE)) **H. Seymour**
41 B f Polish Precedent (USA)—Kimba (USA) (Kris S (USA)) **George Strawbridge**
42 B f 15/2 Red Ransom (USA)—Last Approach (USA) (Far Out East (USA)) **George Strawbridge**
43 B c 7/2 Sendawar (IRE)—Marsakara (IRE) (Turtle Island) (37105) **George Strawbridge**
44 B f 4/3 Darshaan—Moonlight's Box (Nureyev (USA)) **The Niarchos Family**
45 B c 9/2 Hernando (FR)—Obscura (USA) (Mr Prospector (USA)) **The Niarchos Family**
46 Ch f 6/4 Nashwan (USA)—Petronilla (USA) (Lyphard (USA)) **George Strawbridge**
47 RIDDLE, gr c 11/5 Turgeon (USA)—Labyrinth (Exit To Nowhere (USA)) **J. E. Pease**
48 SAPAS (USA), ch f King Mambo (USA)—Very True (USA) (Proud Truth (USA)) **The Niarchos Family**
49 SECOND HAPPINESS (USA), b f 7/5 Storm Cat (USA)—Miesque (USA) (Nureyev (USA)) **The Niarchos Family**
50 Gr f 18/3 Kendor (FR)—Silicon Lady (USA) (Mille Balles (FR)) **J. Goelet**
51 TOP SPINNER (FR), b c 8/2 Spinning World (USA)—Flurry (FR) (Groom Dancer (USA)) **J. E. Pease**
52 B c 26/2 Selkirk (USA)—With Fascination (USA) (Dayjur (USA)) **George Stawbridge**

Jockey (Flat): T Gillet (8-7). **Apprentice:** C Stefan (8-5).

---

430 MISS L. A. PERRATT, Ayr
Postal: Cree Lodge, 47 Craigie Road, Ayr, KA8 0HD.
Contact: PHONE/FAX (01292) 266232 MOBILE (07931) 306147
E-MAIL linda.perratt@ntlworld.com

1 FOREST AIR (IRE), 4, br f Charnwood Forest (IRE)—Auriga **Mrs Kathleen Anne Cullen**
2 FRIAR TUCK, 9, ch g Inchinor—Jay Gee Ell **Cree Lodge Racing Club**
3 GETATEM, 5, b g Up And At 'em—Fiaba
4 GET STUCK IN (IRE), 8, b g Up And At 'em—Shoka (FR) **Mr David R. Sutherland**
5 HO LENG (IRE), 9, ch g Statoblest—Indigo Blue (IRE) **Mr Alan Guthrie**
6 HO PANG YAU, 6, b gr g Pivotal—La Cabrilla **Mr Alan Guthrie**
7 I T CONSULTANT, 6, b g Rock City—Game Germaine **Mr M. G. Michaels**
8 PIRLIE HILL, 4, b f Sea Raven (IRE)—Panayr **The Hon Miss Heather Galbraith**
9 PTARMIGAN RIDGE, 8, b h Sea Raven (IRE)—Panayr **The Hon Miss Heather Galbraith**
10 SEAFIELD TOWERS, 4, ch g Compton Place—Midnight Spell **Mr N. J. Angus**
11 SHERWOOD FOREST, 4, ch g Fleetwood (IRE)—Jay Gee Ell **Miss L. McFadzean**
12 SKIDDAW JONES, 4, b g Emperor Jones (USA)—Woodrising **Mr John Wills**

MISS L. A. PERRATT—continued

13 4, B g King's Theatre (IRE)—Sorara **Mr John Wills**
14 **STRAWBERRY PATCH (IRE)**, 5, b g Woodborough (USA)—Okino (USA) **Mrs Lucille Bone**
15 **XANADU**, 8, ch g Casteddu—Bellatrix **Mr David R. Sutherland**

THREE-YEAR-OLDS

16 **BALWEARIE (IRE)**, b g Sesaro (USA)—Eight Mile Rock **Mr N. J. Angus**
17 **CHAMPAGNE CRACKER**, ch f Up And At 'em—Kiveton Komet **Mr Jim McLaren**
18 **GETATIT**, gr f Up And At 'em—Leading Princess (IRE) **Mr David R. Sutherland**
19 **LAPDANCING**, ch f Pursuit of Love—Petrikov (IRE) **Mr T. P. Finch**
20 **LOUIS PRIMA**, gr c Paris House—Chanson d'Amour (IRE) **Mr R. Stewart**
21 **ONE 'N' ONLY (IRE)**, b f Desert Story (IRE)—Alpina (USA) **Miss L. A. Perratt**
22 **SWEET CANDO (IRE)**, b br f Royal Applause—Fizzygig **Mrs Lucille Bone**
23 **THEGAYBISHOP**, b c Bishop of Cashel—Very Bold **Mr T. P. Finch**

TWO-YEAR-OLDS

24 **CASTLECLARY LASS (IRE)**, ch f 2/3 Namid—
       Limerick Princess (IRE) (Polish Patriot (USA)) (7500) **Mrs Kathleen Anne Cullen**
25 B c 23/1 Soviet Star (USA)—
       Cheese Soup (USA) (Spectacular Bid (USA)) (32000) **Mr N. J. Angus & Mr Gordon Cowan**
26 B c 6/3 Josr Algarhoud (IRE)—Merry Mary (Magic Ring (IRE)) (6000) **Mr Gordon Cowan & Mr N. J. Angus**
27 Br f 28/2 Namid—Scanno's Choice (IRE) (Pennine Walk) (12000)
28 B f 27/1 Atraf—Star Dancer (Groom Dancer (USA)) (1000) **Mr Peter Tsim**
29 **SWEET ROYALE**, b f 29/1 Royal Applause—Sorara (Aragon) (15000) **Mrs Lucille Bone**

Other Owners: Mr T. Hughes, Mr John C. Mariett, Mr R. M. Mitchell, Mrs Christine Richard.

Assistant Trainer: Mr George Perratt

Jockeys (Flat): K Dalgleish, K Darley, G Duffield (w.a.), M Kinane, F Lynch, R Winston. **Jockeys (NH):** A Dobbin, G Lee. **Apprentice:** T Eaves. **Amateur:** Mr J J McLaren.

---

431   MRS A. J. PERRETT, Pulborough

Postal: **Coombelands Racing Stables, Pulborough, West Sussex, RH20 1BP.**
Contact: **OFFICE (01798) 873011 HOME 874894 FAX 875163 MOBILE (07803) 088713**
E-MAIL aperrett@coombelands-stables.com

1 **BIG MOMENT**, 6, ch g Be My Guest (USA)—Petralona (USA) **R.Doel,A.Black,Dr J.Howells & D.Broad**
2 **BOBSLEIGH**, 5, b g Robellino (USA)—Do Run Run **Mr A. Ogilvy and Mrs F. Ogilvy**
3 **DANCE IN THE SUN**, 4, ch f Halling (USA)—Sunny Davis **Hesmonds Stud**
4 **DUSTY TOO**, 6, gr m Terimon—Princess Florine (USA) **Mr S. P. Tindall**
5 **IT'S THE LIMIT (USA)**, 5, b g Boundary (USA)—Beside (USA)
6 **KAPAROLO (USA)**, 5, ch g El Prado (IRE)—Parliament House (USA) **Mr John Connolly**
7 **LATEST MOMENT (USA)**, 5, br g Quest For Fame—Estala **Mr K. Abdulla**
8 **MAGICAL QUEST**, 4, b c Rainbow Quest (USA)—Apogee **Mr K. Abdulla**
9 **MARY'S BABY**, 4, b f Magic Ring (IRE)—Everdene **Mr S. P. Tindall**
10 **NEEDWOOD MYSTIC**, 9, b m Rolfe (USA)—Enchanting Kate **Mrs G. Harwood**
11 **ORANGE TOUCH (GER)**, 4, b c Lando (GER)—Orange Bowl **Cheveley Park Stud**
12 **PAGAN DANCE (IRE)**, 5, b g Revoque (IRE)—Ballade d'Ainhoa (FR) **The Gap Partnership**
13 **POLAR WAY**, 5, ch g Polar Falcon (USA)—Fetish **Mr K. Abdulla**
14 **REJUVENATE (IRE)**, 4, ch c Grand Lodge (USA)—Nawara **Mr Mark Tracey**
15 **ROYAL STORM (IRE)**, 5, b h Royal Applause—Wakayi **The Cloran Family**
16 **SERIEUX**, 5, b h Cadeaux Genereux—Seranda (IRE) **Mrs S. L. Whitehead**
17 **SILVER CITY**, 4, ro g Unfuwain (USA)—Madiyla **Mr Ken Buchanan and Mr Bernard Keay**
18 **STRAW BOSS (IRE)**, 4, b g Darshaan—Ezana
19 **SUSSEX LAD**, 7, b g Prince Sabo—Pea Green **Mrs Amanda Perrett**
20 **TEN CARAT**, 4, ch c Grand Lodge (USA)—Emerald (USA) **Mr K. Abdulla**
21 **TILLERMAN**, 8, b h In The Wings—Autumn Tint (USA) **Mr K. Abdulla**
22 **VENGEANCE**, 4, b c Fleetwood (IRE)—Lady Isabell **Mr T. Staplehurst**
23 **WESTMORELAND ROAD (USA)**, 4, b c Diesis—Tia Gigi (USA) **Miss Belinda Bauer**

THREE-YEAR-OLDS

24 **AETHELING (USA)**, b f Swain (IRE)—Etheldreda (USA) **Dr J. A. Chandler**
25 **AFRICAN STAR**, b c Mtoto—Pass The Rose (IRE) **The Ascot Heathens**

MRS A. J. PERRETT—continued

26 **ART TRADER (USA)**, b c Arch (USA)—Math (USA) **Matthew Green & Oliver Simmons**
27 **AUTUMN WEALTH (IRE)**, ch f Cadeaux Genereux—Prickwillow (USA) **Mr D. J. Burke**
28 **BELISCO (USA)**, b c Royal Academy (USA)—A Mean Fit (USA) **Mr Michael H. Watt**
29 **BREAD OF HEAVEN**, b f Machiavellian (USA)—Khubza **Usk Valley Stud**
30 **CHARMED BY FIRE (USA)**, b c Silver Charm (USA)—Mama Dean (USA) **Hesmonds Stud**
31 **CONCERT HALL (USA)**, b f Stravinsky (USA)—Proflare (USA) **Mr K. Abdulla**
32 **CORSICAN NATIVE (USA)**, b c Lear Fan (USA)—Corsini **Mr K. Abdulla**
33 **DAY VIEW**, gr c Daylami (IRE)—Ancara
34 **DUKE'S VIEW (IRE)**, b g Sadler's Wells—Igreja (ARG) **Mr J. H. Richmond-Watson**
35 **DU PRE**, b f Singspiel (IRE)—Child Prodigy (IRE)
36 **ENRAPTURE (USA)**, b f Lear Fan (USA)—Cheviot Hills (USA) **Cheveley Park Stud**
37 **EXTERIOR (USA)**, ch c Distant View (USA)—Alvernia (USA) **Mr K. Abdulla**
38 **GIVE CHASE**, b f In The Wings—Silver Pursuit **Mr K. Abdulla**
39 **HELIBEL (IRE)**, gr f Pivotal—Boughtbyphone **Mr D. J. Burke**
40 **KHABFAIR**, b c Intikhab (USA)—Ruby Affair (IRE) **Star Pointe Ltd & Arlington Bloodstock**
41 **LIGHT WIND**, ch f Unfuwain (USA)—River Spey **Hesmonds Stud**
42 **LOMAPAMAR**, b f Nashwan (USA)—Morina (USA)
43 **LOOK AGAIN**, ch g Zilzal (USA)—Last Look **Mr J. H. Richmond-Watson**
44 **MARKET LEADER**, b f Marju (IRE)—I Will Lead (USA) **Mr K. Abdulla**
45 **MISS STONY (USA)**, b f Slew City Slew (USA)—Artful Pleasure (USA) **Mr D. J. Burke**
46 **MOUNTAIN MEADOW**, ch g Deploy—Woodwardia (USA) **Mr K. Abdulla**
47 **NEATH**, b f Rainbow Quest (USA)—Welsh Autumn **Mr K. Abdulla**
48 **PAGAN CEREMONY (USA)**, ch g Rahy (USA)—Delightful Linda (USA) **The Gap Partnership**
49 **PAINTBOX**, b f Peintre Celebre (USA)—Photogenic
50 **PAOLA MARIA**, b f Daylami (IRE)—Napoleon's Sister (IRE)
51 **POLAR DANCER**, b f Polar Falcon (USA)—Petonica (USA) **R.Doel, T.Harvey, J.Cleeve, T.Wellard**
52 **RANGOON (USA)**, b c Distant View (USA)—Rustic (IRE) **Mr K. Abdulla**
53 **REAL PZAZZ**, b f Green Desert (USA)—Panache Arabelle **Helena Springfield Ltd**
54 **RED SILK**, b f Polish Precedent (USA)—Red Tulle (USA) **Cheveley Park Stud**
55 **RESIDENTIAL**, ch c Zilzal (USA)—House Hunting **Mr K. Abdulla**
56 **ROYAL STARLET**, b f Royal Applause—Legend **The Cloran Family**
57 **SEARCH MISSION (USA)**, b f Red Ransom (USA)—Skimble (USA) **Mr K. Abdulla**
58 **SECRET VISION (USA)**, ch f Distant View (USA)—Secret Angel **Mr K. Abdulla**
59 **SHALL WE TELL**, b f Intikhab (USA)—Confidante **Cheveley Park Stud**
60 **SIMONDA**, ch f Singspiel (IRE)—Jetbeeah (IRE) **Mr S. P. Tindall**
61 **SNOW PATROL**, gr g Linamix (FR)—Overcast (IRE) **Mr Michael H. Watt**
62 **SOULACROIX**, b c Kylian (USA)—California Dreamin **Mr G. C. Stevens**
63 **SPORTULA**, b f Silver Patriarch (IRE)—Portent **Hesmonds Stud**
64 **SPRING ADIEU**, b f Green Desert (USA)—Nanda **Mr D. J. Burke**
65 **STAGE SECRET (IRE)**, ch c Zilzal (USA)—Tuxford Hideaway **Cheveley Park Stud**
66 **TAMINOULA (IRE)**, b f Tagula (IRE)—Taormina **Tandridge Racing (jdrp)**
67 **THIRTEEN TRICKS (USA)**, b f Grand Slam (USA)—Talltalelady (USA) **Cheveley Park Stud**
68 **TORINMOOR (USA)**, ch c Intikhab (USA)—Tochar Ban (USA) **Mr & Mrs R. Scott**
69 **TUNGSTEN STRIKE (USA)**, ch g Smart Strike (CAN)—Bathilde (IRE) **Mr John Connolly**
70 **TURTLE PATRIARCH (IRE)**, b c Turtle Island (IRE)—La Doyenne (IRE) **Mr D. Angell**
71 **VAUGHAN**, b c Machiavellian (USA)—Labibeh (USA) **Mr J. E. Bodie and Mr R. Wells**
72 **ZEN GARDEN**, b f Alzao (USA)—Maze Garden (USA) **Mr K. Abdulla**

TWO-YEAR-OLDS

73 **ALFIE NOAKES**, b c 24/4 Groom Dancer (USA)—
Crimson Rosella (Polar Falcon (USA)) (36000) **Mr G. C. Stevens**
74 **ALL HAIL**, b c 18/2 Royal Applause—Heavenly Waters (Celestial Storm (USA)) (27828) **The Trinity Partnership**
75 B c 19/2 Bluebird (USA)—Aneeda (Rainbow Quest (USA)) **Pat Eddery Racing**
76 **ART ROYAL (USA)**, b c 19/4 Royal Academy (USA)—
Chelsea Green (USA) (Key To The Mint (USA)) (39579) **Mr Matthew Green**
77 **BAYEUX DE MOI (IRE)**, b c 19/2 Barathea (IRE)—Rivana (Green Desert (USA)) **Lady Clague**
78 **BELITA**, b f 16/3 Hernando (FR)—Anchorage (IRE) (Slip Anchor) (13000) **Mr Paul Hancock**
79 **BLING BLING (IRE)**, b f 18/4 Indian Ridge—Sweeping (Indian King (USA)) **Normandie Stud**
80 Ch f 25/4 Zafonic (USA)—Bloudan (USA) (Damacus (USA)) **Mr K. Abdulla**
81 B c 30/3 Montjeu (IRE)—Bulaxie (Bustino) **Hesmonds Stud**
82 **CORCORAN (USA)**, b f 28/3 Lear Fan (USA)—Corsini (Machiavellian (USA)) **Mr K. Abdulla**
83 **CROIX ROUGE (USA)**, b c 8/3 Chester House (USA)—Rougeur (Blushing Groom (FR)) **Mr K. Abdulla**
84 **DANCE NATION**, b f 24/4 Groom Dancer (USA)—
Star And Garter (Soviet Star (USA)) (9000) **Star Pointe Ltd & Arlington Bloodstock**
85 **DANGER ZONE**, b c 21/4 Danzero (AUS)—Red Tulle (USA) (A P Indy (USA)) (5000) **Alleynian Racing (Jdrp)**

MRS A. J. PERRETT—continued

86 **DANIEL THOMAS (IRE)**, b c 29/1 Danehill—Last Look (Rainbow Quest (USA)) **Mr J. H. Richmond-Watson**
87 **DREAM ALONG**, b c 6/5 Sinndar (IRE)—Dream Quest (Rainbow Quest (USA)) **Hesmonds Stud**
88 **ENAMOURED**, b f 27/4 Groom Dancer (USA)—Ascendancy (Sadler's Wells (USA)) **Cheveley Park Stud**
89 B c 24/3 Fasliyev (USA)—Fleet River (USA) (Riverman (USA)) **Mr K. Abdulla**
90 **FLEUR A LAY (USA)**, br f 12/5 Mr Greeley (USA)—
              Toor A Lay (USA) (The Minstrel (CAN)) (65476) **Mr M. Flitton**
91 **KADDASAN**, b c 28/2 Indian Lodge (IRE)—Kadassa (IRE) (Shardari) (65000) **Hesmonds Stud**
92 B c 6/3 Boundary (USA)—Lasha (USA) (Rahy (USA)) (53571) **Priscilla Graham**
93 **LUCEO (GER)**, b c 3/2 Royal Academy (USA)—
              Lady Member (FR) (Saint Estephe (FR)) (58000) **Mr Mark Tracey**
94 B c 1/4 Dansili—Maze Garden (USA) (Riverman (USA)) **Mr K. Abdulla**
95 B c 30/3 Zafonic (USA)—Moss (Alzao (USA)) **Mr K. Abdulla**
96 **OFF COLOUR**, b c 15/4 Rainbow Quest (USA)—
              Air of Distinction (IRE) (Distinctly North (USA)) **Mr Nicholas Cooper**
97 B c 17/4 Storm Creek (USA)—One Moment In Time (USA) (Magesterial (USA)) (23810) **Priscilla Graham**
98 **PAGAN SWORD**, ch c 3/4 Selkirk (USA)—Vanessa Bell (IRE) (Lahib (USA)) (52565) **The Gap Partnership**
99 **POTION (GER)**, b f 14/4 Dr Fong (USA)—
              Lauderdale (GER) (Nebos (GER)) (61842) **Highclere Thoroughbred Racing**
100 B f 28/4 Diktat—Premiere Cuvee (Formidable (USA)) **Mr & Mrs D. Hicks**
101 **REGISTRAR**, ch c 16/4 Machiavellian (USA)—Confidante (Dayjur (USA)) **Cheveley Park Stud**
102 B c 28/3 Storm Creek (USA)—Sandhill (BRZ) (Baynoun (IRE)) (50595) **Priscilla Graham**
103 Gr c 23/10 Desert King (IRE)—Silver Pursuit (Rainbow Quest (USA)) **Mr K. Abdulla**
104 Ch c 13/4 Rahy (USA)—Societe Royale (Milford) (29762) **A. D. Spence**
105 **STAGE MANAGER (IRE)**, ch c 9/4 In The Wings—Evangola (Persian Bold) **Cheveley Park Stud**
106 B f 18/1 Dansili—Stardom (Known Fact (USA)) **Mr K. Abdulla**
107 B c 2/4 Efisio—St Clair (Distant Relative) (37105) **Mr & Mrs Fred Cotton**
108 Ch c 18/4 Giant's Causeway—Taibhseach (USA) (Secreto (USA)) (89285) **A. D. Spence**
109 B f 6/4 Celtic Swing—Tainted Halo (USA) (Halo (USA)) (7420) **Mr M. Flitton**
110 Ch f 21/4 Pivotal—Tangerine (Primo Dominie) (40000) **Hesmonds Stud**
111 **THIS IS MY SONG**, b f 20/3 Polish Precedent—Narva (Nashwan (USA)) **Woodcote Stud**
112 **TURNER'S TOUCH**, ch c 5/3 Compton Place—
              Chairmans Daughter (Unfuwain (USA)) (30000) **Mr Matthew Green**
113 **WATER PISTOL**, b c 22/2 Double Trigger (IRE)—
              Water Flower (Environment Friend) (24000) **Fred & Sacha Cotton & Partners**
114 **WEDDING PARTY**, ch f 18/3 Groom Dancer (USA)—Ceanothus (IRE) (Bluebird (USA)) **Cheveley Park Stud**
115 B c 17/4 Halling (USA)—West Dakota (USA) (Gone West (USA)) **Mr K. Abdulla**
116 **WESTLAND (USA)**, gr c 3/2 Cozzene (USA)—
              Cherie Yvonne (USA) (Vice Regent (CAN)) (107143) **Mr & Mrs R. Scott**
117 B f 18/3 Danehill (USA)—Windmill (Ezzoud (IRE)) (350000) **Mr & Mrs R. Scott**
118 B f 12/3 Royal Academy (USA)—Woodland Orchid (IRE) (Woodman (USA)) **Mr & Mrs R. Scott**
119 **WOODWARD (USA)**, b c 1/2 Diesis—
              Dance Gaily (USA) (Nureyev (USA)) (49474) **Mr J. E. Bodie & Tessona Racing**
120 B f 9/4 Diesis—Zante (Zafonic (USA)) **Mr K. Abdulla**

Other Owners: Mr P. R. Anders, Mr B. J. Cloran, Mrs G. V. Cloran, Mr S. Cloran, Mrs Z. F. Cloran, Mr John Dunbar, Mr Peter Hodgson, Mr G. D. P. Materna, Mr K. J. Mercer, Mrs S. Mercer, Mr O. R. Schick, Star Pointe Ltd, Mr P. Steger, Miss Helena Weinfeld, Mr M. Weinfeld.

Apprentice: Liam Treadwell. **Amateur:** Miss Lucinda Harwood (8-0).

432	**MR R. T. PHILLIPS, Moreton-in-Marsh**

Postal: **Adlestrop Stables, Adlestrop, Moreton-in-Marsh, Gloucestershire, GL56 0YN.**
Contact: **PHONE (01608) 658710 FAX (01608) 658713 MOBILE (07774) 832715**
E-MAIL info@richardphillipsracing.com WEBSITE www.richardphillipsracing.com

1 **ADLESTROP**, 4, ch f Alderbrook—Lady Buck **The Listeners**
2 **AFEEF (USA)**, 5, b br g Dayjur (USA)—Jah (USA) **Ellangowan Racing Partners II**
3 **ALDERMAN ROSE**, 4, b g Alderbrook—Rose Ravine **Mrs Nicholas Jones/Martin Broughton**
4 **ANOTHER GENERAL (IRE)**, 9, b g Glacial Storm (USA)—
              Whats In A Name (IRE) **Paul Duffy, Alan Beard, Brian Beard**
5 6, ba m Karinga Bay—Arctic Advert **Mrs R. E. Hambro**
6 5, Br m Presenting—Arumah **Mrs J. K. Powell**
7 **ASSUMPTALINA**, 4, b f Primitive Rising (USA)—New Broom (IRE) **Mr Mick Barnes**
8 **BAKIRI (IRE)**, 6, b g Doyoun—Bakiya (USA) **Ford Associated Racing Team**
9 **BALLYBOLEY (IRE)**, 6, b g Roselier (FR)—Benbradagh Vard (IRE) **Mrs N. L. Spence**

MR R. T. PHILLIPS—continued

10 **BARNEY MCALL (IRE)**, 4, b g Grand Lodge (USA)—Persian Song **Mr & Mrs R. Scott**
11 **BEST ACTRESS (IRE)**, 4, ch f Shahrastani (USA)—Casting Vote (USA) **Hintlesham AB Partners**
12 **BRAEBURN**, 9, b g Petoski—Great Granny Smith **Mrs T. Stopford-Sackville**
13 **BROOKING (IRE)**, 6, b g Roselier (FR)—Kilkil Pin **Annapurna Partnership**
14 **CAESAREAN HUNTER (USA)**, 5, ch g Jade Hunter (USA)—Grey Fay (USA) **Mr A. A. Wickham**
15 **CARNOUSTIE (USA)**, 6, gr m Ezzoud (IRE)—Sarba (USA) **Dozen Dreamers Partnership**
16 **CASH AND NEW (IRE)**, 5, b m Supreme Leader—Shannon Lough (IRE) **The 23rd Floor**
17 **CASH CONVERTER (IRE)**, 6, ch g Houmayoun (FR)—Golden Symphony **Thurloe Thoroughbreds XI**
18 **CENTRAL COMMITTEE (IRE)**, 9, ch g Royal Academy (USA)—Idle Chat (USA) **The Escape Committee**
19 **CHANGE AGENT**, 8, br g Royal Fountain—Flashy Looks **Mr M. W. Harris**
20 **CHASTLETON BOY (IRE)**, 5, b g Muroto—Noon Hunting **Garry and Catriona Braybrooke Jones**
21 **CHOPNEYEV (IRE)**, 6, b g Goldneyev (USA)—Pierre de Soleil (FR) **Mrs Claire Smith**
22 **CORALS LAUREL (IRE)**, 5, b g Accordion—Bold Tipperary (IRE)
23 **CORRAGE (IRE)**, 7, b g Corrouge (USA)—Cora Gold **Mr Michael Gates**
24 5, Br g Roselier (FR)—Cotton Gale **Mr & Mrs R. Scott**
25 **DARK'N SHARP (GER)**, 9, b g Sharpo—Daytona Beach (GER) **Ascot Five Plus One**
26 **DATITO (IRE)**, 9, b g Over The River (FR)—Crash Call **Mr G. Lansbury**
27 **DEFINITE APPROACH (IRE)**, 6, b g Presenting—Crash Approach **Ascot Five Plus One**
28 **DIAMANIKOS (FR)**, 8, b g Nikos—Diamarella (FR) **Mrs B. J. Lockhart**
29 **EASTWELL VIOLET**, 4, b f Danzig Connection (USA)—Kinchenjunga **Eastwell Manor Racing Ltd**
30 **FIVE PENCE**, 8, b g Henbit (USA)—Le Saule d'Or **Mr Bill Naylor**
31 **FOREST MILLER**, 5, b g Classic Cliche (IRE)—Its My Turn **The Old Foresters Partnership**
32 **FOREST SPRITE**, 4, b f Sir Harry Lewis (USA)—Formal Affair **The Old Foresters Partnership**
33 **GALAPIAT DU MESNIL (FR)**, 10, b g Sarpedon (FR)—Polka de Montrin (FR) **Mr Mel Fordham**
34 **GEE AKER MALAYO (IRE)**, 8, b g Phardante (FR)—Flying Silver **Mr Darren Bloom & Mr Matthew Miller**
35 **GENERAL DUROC (IRE)**, 8, ch g Un Desperado (FR)—Satula **Mr Graeme Love**
36 **GENERAL GOSSIP (IRE)**, 8, b br g Supreme Leader—Sno-Sleigh **The Early Birds**
37 **GEORGIAN HARRY (IRE)**, 7, b g Warcraft (USA)—Solo Player **Dennis, Gale, Golden and Martin**
38 **GINGERBREAD HOUSE (IRE)**, 6, b g Old Vic—Furun (IRE) **Mrs J. Stewart**
39 **GLASSON HOUSE (IRE)**, 5, b m Supreme Leader—Nasowas (IRE) **Supreme Corner Gang**
40 **GREAT OVATION (IRE)**, 5, ch m Boston Two Step (USA)—Baldiloa **Ladbrokes Staff Racing Partnership**
41 **GREENFIELD (IRE)**, 6, ch g Pleasant Tap (USA)—No Review (USA) **Mrs S. J. Harvey**
42 **HIM OF DISTINCTION**, 5, br g Rainbow Quest (USA)—Air of Distinction (IRE) **Mr Nicholas Cooper**
43 **INLAND RUN (IRE)**, 8, b g Insan (USA)—Anns Run **A Beard, B Beard, P Doble, T Pearce**
44 **ITS A MYSTERY (IRE)**, 5, b m Idris (IRE)—Blue Infanta **Mr Richard Phillips**
45 **JESPER (FR)**, 7, b g Video Rock (FR)—Belle des Airs (FR) **Mrs R. J. Skan**
46 **KAFRI D'AIRY (FR)**, 6, b m Sheyrann—Afrika d'Airy (FR) **Mrs Claire Smith**
47 **KAISER (IRE)**, 4, b g Barathea (IRE)—Emerald Waters **Mr Paul Green**
48 **KALIN DE THAIX (FR)**, 6, ch g Agent Bleu (FR)—Une Amie (FR) **Million in Mind Partnership**
49 **KICKING BEAR (IRE)**, 6, b g Little Bighorn—Rongo (IRE) **The Brightling Club 1998**
50 **LAAZIM AFOOZ**, 11, b g Mtoto—Balwa (USA) **Mr Richard Phillips**
51 **LA LANDIERE (IRE)**, 9, b br m Synefos (USA)—As You Are (FR) **Mrs R. J. Skan**
52 **LAST REBEL (IRE)**, 5, b g Danehill (USA)—La Curamalal (IRE) **Coral & Graham Russell**
53 **LONESOME MAN (IRE)**, 8, ch g Broken Hearted—Carn-Na-Ros **Mr P. Docherty**
54 **MANDINGO CHIEF (IRE)**, 5, b g Flying Spur (AUS)—Elizabethan Air **Mr R. S. Williams**
55 **MASTERPOINT**, 4, ch g Mark of Esteem (IRE)—Baize **Mr Michael Gates**
56 **MINIBALLIST (IRE)**, 6, b m Tragic Role (USA)—Herballistic **Mrs B. J. Lockhart**
57 **MITHAK (USA)**, 10, b g Silver Hawk (USA)—Kapalua Butterfly (USA) **T. Milson C. Merson P. Nichols R. Stokes**
58 **MR PHIPPS**, 8, b g Shareef Dancer (USA)—Frost In Summer **Mr Bill Naylor**
59 **MR RHUBARB (IRE)**, 6, ch g Shardari—Gale Griffin (FR) **Mr & Mrs C. Schwick**
60 **MRS FIZZIWIG**, 5, b m Petoski—Dans Le Vent **Mrs Peter Prowting**
61 **NO RETREAT (NZ)**, 11, b g Exattic (USA)—Lerwick (NZ) **M. W. & A. N. Harris**
62 **ON Y VA (FR)**, 6, b g Goldneyev (USA)—Shakna (FR) **ROA Red Alligator Partnership**
63 **PEACHY (IRE)**, 9, b g Un Desperado (FR)—Little Peach **Mr Colin Pocock**
64 **PERTEMPS TIMMY**, 6, b g Petoski—Brilliant Future **Pertemps Group Limited**
65 **RAVEN'S LAST**, 5, b g Sea Raven (IRE)—Lavenham's Last **Mrs Stewart Catherwood**
66 **RESEDA (IRE)**, 7, b g Rock Hopper—Sweet Mignonette **Mr R. S. Williams**
67 **RETURN TICKET**, 5, br g Bob's Return (IRE)—Mrs Jennifer **Mr & Mrs F. C. Welch**
68 **ROARINGWATER (IRE)**, 5, b g Roselier (FR)—Supreme Cherry **Rip-Roarers**
69 **ROYAL CLICHE (IRE)**, 5, b g Classic Cliche (IRE)—Princess Hotpot (IRE) **The New Club Partnership**
70 **SENOR SOL (USA)**, 4, b g El Prado (IRE)—One Moment In Time (USA) **Thurloe Thoroughbreds X**
71 **SHARP JACK (IRE)**, 6, b g Be My Native (USA)—Polly Sharp **Mrs Claire Smith**
72 **SILK ROPE (IRE)**, 4, br f Presenting—Osiery Girl (IRE) **Mr & Mrs R. Scott**
73 **SILVER PRAYER (IRE)**, 5, gr m Roselier (FR)—Decent Preacher **Mr Nicholas Cooper**
74 **STICKY WICKET**, 5, b m Petoski—Avec Le Vent (IRE) **Mrs Peter Prowting**
75 **SUPREME TOSS (IRE)**, 8, b g Supreme Leader—Sleemana **The Coin Tossers**

MR R. T. PHILLIPS—continued

76 **TAWEELL (IRE)**, 5, b g Mtoto—Kronengold (USA) **Mrs J. Stewart**
77 **TEREK (GER)**, 8, ch g Irish River (FR)—Turbaine (USA) **Ford Associated Racing Team II**
78 **THRILLING PROSPECT (IRE)**, 7, b m King's Ride—Bail Out **Mr H. Fowler**
79 **TOG GO BOGE (IRE)**, 6, b br g Erins Isle—Vision of Spring **Redmade**
80 **TUBBER STREAMS (IRE)**, 7, b g Great Marquess—Much Obliged **The Donnington Drinkers**
81 **VALERIO**, 8, b g Be My Native (USA)—Laurello **Mr Nicholas Cooper**
82 **VA VAVOOM (IRE)**, 6, b g Supreme Leader—Shalom Joy **Mr H. R. Mould**
83 **WARJAN (FR)**, 7, b g Beaudelaire (USA)—Twilight Mood (USA) **Mr Graeme Love**
84 **WIMBLEDONIAN**, 5, b m Sir Harry Lewis (USA)—Ardent Love (IRE) **OWRC Partnership No 1**
85 **YANN'S (FR)**, 8, b g Hellios (USA)—Listen Gyp (USA) **Mr Darren Bloom & Mr Matthew Miller**
86 5, B g North Col—Zalina

THREE-YEAR-OLDS

87 **BONSAI (IRE)**, b f Woodman (USA)—Karakia (IRE) **Flying Tiger Partnership**
88 B f Orpen (USA)—Red Leggings **Mr Richard Phillips**

Other Owners: Mrs S. E. Acland, Mr David Allan, Mr F. J. Allen, Mr Hugh Arthur, Mrs Pam Bates, Mr Alan Beard, Mr B. Beard, Mr S. F. Benton, Mr Alan Bird, Mrs Linda Bird, Mr A. R. Blackman, Mr Darrell Blake, Mr Mark Blake, Mr D. J. Bloom, Mr Martin Bourke, Mrs Catriona Braybrooke Jones, Mr A. R. Bromley, Mr Martin Broughton, Mr S. W. Broughton, Mr Ian Brown, Mr P. W. Brown, Mr John Cantrill, Mr M. T. Cleary, Mr Alan Cowing, Mr Kevin Cullen, Mr Nigel Dempster, Mr M. N. Dennis, Mr P. G. J. Devlin, Mr P. R. Doble, Mr Paul Duffy, Mr Ian Dunbar, Mr D. Gale, Mr A. Golden, Mr Graham Goode, Mrs A. N. Harris, Mrs Alan Heber-Percy, Mr Jeremy Hulme, Mr Garry Jones, Mrs Nicholas Jones, Mr G. J. King, Mr J. J. Kunicki, Mr John Martin, Mrs C. A. Maryan Green, Mr David M. Mason, Miss S. McHale, Mr R. J. Meaney, Mr C. Merson, Mr M. M. Miller, Mr Terry Milson, Mr D. Minton, Mr Terry Neill, Mr Charles F. Newman, Mr Christopher Newport, Mr Peter Nichols, Mr David Nicholson, Mr Julian Palfreyman, Mr Oliver Pawle, Mr Tim Pearce, Mr M. T. Phillips, Mr S. J. Popple, Mr Paul Porter, Mr D. Poulton, Mr John H. Rosbotham, Mrs Coral Russell, Mr Graham Russell, Mr C. Schwick, Mrs C. Schwick, Mrs P. M. Scott, Mr Robert Scott, Mr M. A. F. Shenfield, Mr C. B. Smith, Mr Simon C. Smith, Mr M. S. Smith, Mr W. L. Smith, Mr R. D. W. Stokes, Mr N. Tafuro, Mrs S. M. Tourres, Mrs Giles Weaver, Mr F. Welch, Mrs S. C. Welch, Mr Nev Whitfield, Mr Tom Wilson, Mr Adrian Wright, Mr Andrew P. Wyer.

Jockeys (NH): R Johnson (10-0), W Marston (10-0), J Mogford (10-0).

---

433 MR S. L. PIKE, Sidmouth
Postal: **Synderborough Farm, Sidbury, Sidmouth, Devon, EX10 0QJ.**
Contact: **PHONE & FAX (01395) 597485**
E-MAIL synderborough@barclays.net pikes@btconnect.com

1 **FASHION HOUSE**, 8, b m Homo Sapien—High Heels (IRE) **Mr Stewart Pike**
2 4, B c Accordion—Lady Geneva **Mr Stewart Pike**
3 5, B g Belfort (FR)—Loch Tain **Mr Stewart Pike**
4 **LOUP DU SUD (FR)**, 5, b g Loup Solitaire (USA)—Jetty (FR) **Mr Stewart Pike**

Assistant Trainer: Mrs M P Pike

Jockey (NH): R Thornton. **Conditional:** Ben Hitchcott. **Amateur:** Miss P Gundry.

---

434 MR ANTHONY D. PINDER, Wantage
Postal: **Little Farm, Fawler Road, Kingston Lisle, Wantage,** Oxfordshire, OX12 9QH.
Contact: **PHONE (01367) 820280 MOBILE (07711) 396191**
E-MAIL davidpinderracing@ukonline.co.uk

1 **DEXILEOS (IRE)**, 5, b g Danehill (USA)—Theano (IRE) **Mrs Angela Pinder**
2 **GLOBE BEAUTY (IRE)**, 6, b m Shalford (IRE)—Pen Bal Duchess **G. & P. Barker Ltd/Globe Engineering**
3 **KINDNESS**, 4, ch f Indian Ridge—Kissing Gate (USA) **Ms R. V. Richards**
4 **LOGISTICAL**, 4, b c Grand Lodge (USA)—Magic Milly **The Little Farm Partnership**

THREE-YEAR-OLDS

5 **DANISH MONARCH**, b g Great Dane (IRE)—Molt **The Little Farm Partnership II**

Other Owners: Ms L. Barber, Mr P. J. Barnes, Ms L. Burns, Mr C. Cavanagh, Mr T. Eales, Mr R. Furniss, Mr & Mrs N. Morgan, Mr M. Pinder.

435 **MR M. C. PIPE, Wellington**
Postal: Pond House, Nicholashayne, Wellington, Somerset, TA21 9QY.
Contact: OFFICE (01884) 840715 FAX (01884) 841343
E-MAIL martin@martinpipe.co.uk WEBSITE www.martinpipe.co.uk

1 **AKARUS (FR)**, 9, b g Labus (FR)—Meris (FR) **Mr A. J. White**
2 **ANATAR (IRE)**, 6, b g Caerleon (USA)—Anaza **Eminence Grise Partnership**
3 **ARABIAN MOON (IRE)**, 8, ch b Barathea (IRE)—Excellent Alibi (USA) **No Dramas Partnership**
4 **ARLAS (FR)**, 9, b g Northern Fashion (USA)—
          Ribbon In Her Hair (USA) **Mr Matt Archer & Miss Jean Broadhurst**
5 **ARMEN (FR)**, 7, b g Kaldoun (FR)—Anna Edes (FR) **Mr T. M. Hely-Hutchinson & Partner**
6 **AULD NICK (IRE)**, 6, b g Old Vic—Grey Tor **Mr S. Lucey**
7 **BAJAN GIRL (FR)**, 4, b f Emperor Jones—Lovely Noor (USA) **Mr M. C. Pipe**
8 **BARTON SANDS (IRE)**, 7, b g Tenby—Hetty Green **Mr Stuart M. Mercer**
9 **BELLA BAMBINA**, 4, b f Turtle Island (IRE)—Lady Eurolink **Eurolink Group Plc**
10 **BLOWING WIND (IRE)**, 11, b br g Fabulous Dancer (USA)—Bassita **Mr P. A. Deal**
11 **BONGO FURY**, 5, b m Sillery (USA)—Nativelee (FR) **Lord Donoughmore & Countess Donoughmore**
12 **BOUNCE BACK (USA)**, 8, ch g Trempolino (USA)—Lattaquie (FR) **Mrs Belinda Harvey**
13 **CALAMINTHA**, 4, b f Mtoto—Calendula (USA) **Axom**
14 **CANADA**, 6, b g Ezzoud (IRE)—Chancel (USA) **Mr W. J. Gredley**
15 **CANADIANE (FR)**, 9, ch m Nikos—Carmonera (FR) **Mr D. A. Johnson**
16 **CARLOVENT (FR)**, 9, b g Cadoudal (FR)—Carlaya (FR) **C. M., B. J. & R. F. Batterham**
17 **CARRYONHARRY (IRE)**, 10, gr g Roselier (FR)—Bluebell Avenue **Drs' D Silk,J Castro,M Gillard,P Walker**
18 **CELESTIAL GOLD (IRE)**, 6, b g Persian Mews—What A Queen **Mr D. A. Johnson**
19 **CELTIC SON (FR)**, 5, b g Celtic Arms (FR)—For Kicks (FR) **Mr D. A. Johnson**
20 **CHICUELO (FR)**, 8, b g Mansonnien (FR)—Dovapas (FR) **Mrs Belinda Harvey**
21 **COMMERCIAL FLYER (IRE)**, 5, ch g Carroll House—Shabra Princess **Mr D. A. Johnson**
22 **COMPLY OR DIE (IRE)**, 5, b g Old Vic—Madam Madcap **Mr D. A. Johnson**
23 **CONTRABAND**, 6, b g Red Ransom (USA)—Shortfall **Mr D. A. Johnson**
24 **CONTROL MAN (IRE)**, 6, ch g Glacial Storm (USA)—Got To Fly (IRE) **Mr D. A. Johnson**
25 **COPELAND**, 9, b g Generous (IRE)—Whitehaven **Prof. D. B. A. Silk and Mrs Heather Silk**
26 **CYFOR MALTA (FR)**, 11, b g Cyborg (FR)—Force Nine (FR) **Mr D. A. Johnson**
27 **DARK STRANGER (FR)**, 13, b g Iveday (FR)—Abeille Royale (USA) **Mr Terry Neill**
28 **DEANO'S BEENO**, 12, b g Far North (CAN)—Sans Dot **Axom**
29 **DESERT AIR (JPN)**, 5, ch g Desert King (IRE)—Greek Air (IRE) **Mrs Belinda Harvey**
30 **DINARELLI (FR)**, 5, gr g Linamix (FR)—Dixiella (FR) **Lord Donoughmore & Countess Donoughmore**
31 **DON FERNANDO**, 5, b h Zilzal (USA)—Teulada (USA) **Lucayan Stud**
32 **DOWNTHEREFORDANCIN (IRE)**, 4, b g Groom Dancer (USA)—Merlin's Fancy **The Reims Partnership**
33 **DUBAI SEVEN STARS**, 6, ch m Suave Dancer (USA)—Her Honour **Mr M. C. Pipe**
34 **FAST MIX (FR)**, 5, gr g Linamix (FR)—Fascinating Hill (FR) **Mr Jim Weeden**
35 **FIGARO DU ROCHER (FR)**, 4, ch g Beyssac (FR)—Fabinou (FR) **Mr Simon Roberts**
36 **FONTANESI (FR)**, 4, b g Sadler's Wells (USA)—Northern Script (USA) **Mr D. A. Johnson**
37 **FORBEARING (IRE)**, 7, b g Bering—For Example (USA) **Mr A. J. Lomas**
38 **FORTUNE ISLAND (IRE)**, 5, b g Turtle Island (IRE)—Blue Kestrel (IRE) **J. M. Brown & M. J. Blackburn**
39 **FREE WILLIE (IRE)**, 4, b g Ridgewood Ben—Dance In The Wings **Mr D. A. Johnson**
40 **FRIENDLY FELLOW**, 5, gr g Environment Friend—Good Fetch **Mr D. A. Johnson**
41 **GEBORA (FR)**, 5, ch g Villez (USA)—Sitapanoki (FR) **Mr Neil J. Edwards**
42 **GOLDEN ALPHA (IRE)**, 10, b g Alphabatim (USA)—Gina's Love **Mr D. A. Johnson**
43 **GONE FAR (USA)**, 7, b g Gone West (USA)—Vallee Dansante (USA) **Mr Matt Archer & Miss Jean Broadhurst**
44 **GONE TOO FAR**, 6, b g Reprimand—Blue Nile (USA) **Mr D. A. Johnson**
45 **GOOD OUTLOOK (IRE)**, 5, b g Lord America—I'll Say She Is **Mr D. A. Johnson**
46 **GUARD DUTY**, 7, b g Deploy—Hymne d'Amour (USA) **Neil Edwards and Malcolm Jones**
47 **HENRIETTA (IRE)**, 6, b m Hushang (IRE)—Jennie's First **Mr B. A. Kilpatrick**
48 **HE'S A LEADER (IRE)**, 5, b g Supreme Leader—Raise The Bells **Mr Matt Archer & Miss Jean Broadhurst**
49 **HORUS (IRE)**, 9, b g Teenoso (USA)—Jennie's First **Mr B. A. Kilpatrick**
50 **HURRICANE FLOYD (IRE)**, 6, ch g Pennekamp (USA)—Mood Swings (USA) **Lucayan Stud**
51 **IDAHO D'OX (FR)**, 8, b br g Bad Conduct (USA)—Queseda (FR) **The Dionysius Partnership**
52 **ILABON (FR)**, 8, ch g Secret Haunt (USA)—Ahuille (FR) **Beau Girls**
53 **ILE MICHEL (FR)**, 7, b g Machiavellian (USA)—Circe's Isle **Mr P. J. Finn**
54 **IMPERIAL DE THAIX (FR)**, 8, b g Roi de Rome (USA)—Soiree d'Ete (FR) **Mr J. S. Lammiman**
55 **ISARD III (FR)**, 8, gr g Royal Charter (FR)—Aurore d'Ex (FR) **C. M., B. J. & R. F. Batterham II**
56 **IT'S MUSIC (IRE)**, 5, b g Accordion—Leadon Lady **Mr D. A. Johnson**
57 **IT TAKES TIME (IRE)**, 10, b g Montelimar (USA)—Dysart Lady **Mr D. A. Johnson**
58 **IZNOGOUD (FR)**, 8, b br g Shafoun (FR)—Vancia (FR) **County Stores-Avalon Surfacing**
59 **JANUS DU COCHET (FR)**, 7, b g Rahotep (FR)—Qualite du Cochet (FR) **Mr Terry Neill**
60 **JARDIN FLEURI (FR)**, 7, ch g Cyborg (FR)—Merry Durgan (FR) **Mr M. C. Pipe**
61 **JAYBEJAY (NZ)**, 9, b g High Ice (USA)—Galaxy Light (NZ) **Lady Clarke**

MR M. C. PIPE—continued

62 **JURANCON II (FR)**, 7, b g Scooter Bleu (IRE)—Volniste (FR) **Mr D. A. Johnson**
63 **KILLERS FURY (IRE)**, 5, br g Topanoora—Ellen Gail (IRE) **Mr D. A. Johnson**
64 **KOCEANE (FR)**, 6, gr m Royal Charter (FR)—Amanda de La Motte (FR) **Mr M. C. Pipe**
65 **KORELO (FR)**, 6, b g Cadoudal (FR)—Lora du Charmil (FR) **Mr D. A. Johnson**
66 **KOUROS DES OBEAUX (FR)**, 6, b g Grand Tresor (FR)—Valse des Obeaux (FR) **Mr D. J. Ayres**
67 **LAGO NAM (FR)**, 5, gr g Cardoun (FR)—Rivalago (FR) **Mr D. A. Johnson**
68 **LATALOMNE (USA)**, 10, ch g Zilzal (USA)—Sanctuary **Alderclad Roofing/Mr K. M. Everitt**
69 **LATITUDE (FR)**, 5, b m Kadalko (FR)—Diyala III (FR) **Mr Neil J. Edwards**
70 **LECHE BOTTES (FR)**, 5, b g Sleeping Car (FR)—Gibelotte (FR) **Mr M. C. Pipe**
71 **LEGATUS (FR)**, 7, ch g Alphabatim (USA)—Take A Guess (IRE) **Mr B. A. Kilpatrick**
72 **LIBERMAN (IRE)**, 6, br g Standiford (USA)—Hail To You (USA) **Mr D. A. Johnson**
73 **LOCKSMITH**, 4, b br g Linamix (FR)—Zenith **Mr D. A. Johnson**
74 **LOTUS DES PICTONS (FR)**, 5, b g Grand Tresor (FR)—
                                      Ballaway (FR) **Lord Donoughmore & Countess Donoughmore**
75 **LOUGH DERG (FR)**, 4, b g Apple Tree (FR)—Asturias (FR) **Mr W. Frewen**
76 **LUCIFER BLEU (FR)**, 5, b g Kadalko (FR)—Figa Dancer (FR) **Mr A. J. White**
77 **MAGICAL BAILIWICK (IRE)**, 8, ch g Magical Wonder (USA)—Alpine Dance (USA) **Islands Racing Connection**
78 **MAIDSTONE MISTRAL**, 4, b g Slip Anchor—Cayla **Mrs Judith E. Wilson**
79 **MAITRE LEVY (GER)**, 6, b g Monsun (GER)—Meerdunung (EG) **Favourites Racing**
80 **MAJOR SPECULATION (IRE)**, 4, b g Spectrum (IRE)—Pacific Grove **Latona Leisure Limited**
81 **MALDOUN (IRE)**, 5, b g Kaldoun (FR)—Marzipan (IRE) **The Dionysius Partnership**
82 **MANX ROYAL (FR)**, 5, b g Cyborg (FR)—Badj II (FR) **James and Antoinette Kennedy**
83 **MARAGUN (GER)**, 8, b g General Assembly (USA)—Marcelia (GER) **Emlyn Hughes & Stuart Mercer**
84 **MARK EQUAL**, 8, b g Nicholas Bill—Dissolution **Heeru Kirpalani Racing**
85 **MAXIMIZE (IRE)**, 10, b g Mandalus—Lone Run **Mr D. A. Johnson**
86 **MEMBERS ONLY**, 5, b g Kris—Could Have Been **Mr D. A. Johnson**
87 **MILORD LESCRIBAA (FR)**, 4, b g Cadoudal (FR)—Mona Lisaa (FR) **Jimmyz Jokers**
88 **MIOCHE D'ESTRUVAL (FR)**, 4, bl g Lute Antique (FR)—Charme d'Estruval (FR) **Mr Joe Moran**
89 **MIRANT**, 5, b h Danzig Connection (USA)—Ingerence (FR) **Lucayan Stud**
90 **MISS COOL**, 8, b m Jupiter Island—Laurel Diver **Mr N. G. Mills**
91 **MONDIAL JACK (FR)**, 5, ch g Apple Tree (FR)—Cackle (USA) **C. M., B. J. & R. F. Batterham II**
92 **MONTREAL (FR)**, 7, b g Chamberlin (FR)—Massada (FR) **Mr D. A. Johnson**
93 **MR COOL**, 10, b g Jupiter Island—Laurel Diver **Mr N. G. Mills**
94 **MUJALINA (IRE)**, 6, b g Mujadil (USA)—Talina's Law (IRE) **Mr & Mrs M. Bovingdon & Mr C. Langley**
95 **MURAT (FR)**, 4, b g Useful (FR)—La Marianne (FR) **Mr P. A. Deal**
96 **NEUTRON (IRE)**, 7, ch g Nucleon (USA)—Balistic Princess **Mr Matt Archer & Miss Jean Broadhurst**
97 **NOCKSKY (IRE)**, 11, b g Niniski (USA)—Olivana (GER) **Mr Terry Neill**
98 **OH VLO (FR)**, 5, b br g Sassanian (USA)—Lady Christine (FR) **Mrs Judith E. Wilson**
99 **OUR HOUSE (IRE)**, 5, ch g Carroll House—Farinella (IRE) **Mr D. A. Johnson**
100 **OUR VIC (IRE)**, 6, b g Old Vic—Shabra Princess **Mr D. A. Johnson**
101 **OVER THE CREEK**, 5, br g Over The River (FR)—Solo Girl (IRE) **Mr D. A. Johnson**
102 **PAPILLON DE IENA (FR)**, 4, ch g Varese (FR)—Belle du Chesne (FR) **Mr Joe Moran**
103 **PENNY PICTURES (IRE)**, 5, b h Theatrical—Copper Creek **Mr Terry Neill**
104 **PHENOMENON**, 6, b m Unfuwain (USA)—Pure **Mr W. J. Gredley**
105 **PHILIPPA YEATES (IRE)**, 5, b m Hushang (IRE)—Miss Bobby Bennett **Mr B. A. Kilpatrick**
106 **PICCINI (FR)**, 4, ch g Sillery (USA)—Emblem **Mr J. A. Head**
107 **PIERRE DU FOREZ (FR)**, 6, ch g Sicyos (USA)—Pierre du Luizet (FR) **Mr M. C. Pipe**
108 **PILCA (FR)**, 4, ch g Pistolet Bleu (IRE)—Caricoe **Eminence Grise Partnership**
109 **POITIERS (FR)**, 5, b g Bering—Prusse (USA) **David Manning Associates**
110 **POLAR RED**, 7, ch g Polar Falcon (USA)—Sharp Top **Lady Clarke**
111 **PRINCE DIMITRI**, 5, ch g Desert King (IRE)—Pinta (USA) **Lucayan Stud**
112 **PUNCHY (IRE)**, 8, b br g Freddie's Star—Baltimore Fox (IRE) **G-Force Partnership**
113 **PUNTAL (FR)**, 8, b g Bering—Saveur **Mr Terry Neill**
114 **QUICK**, 4, b g Kahyasi—Prompt **Kinsford Champagne Partnership**
115 **RAVENSWOOD (IRE)**, 7, b g Warning—Green Lucia **Mr D. A. Johnson**
116 **RED WILLIE**, 5, b g Master Willie—Ormania (IRE) **Mr Terry Neill**
117 **ROBBIE ON TOUR (IRE)**, 5, b g Oscar (IRE)—Mystery Woman **Mr D. A. Johnson**
118 **ROVERETTO**, 9, b g Robellino (USA)—Spring Flyer (IRE) **Swanvista Limited/B. E. Case**
119 **ROYAL PREDICA (FR)**, 10, ch g Tip Moss (FR)—Girl Vamp (FR) **Mr P. A. Deal, J. S. Dale & A. Stennett**
120 **RUN OF KINGS (IRE)**, 6, b g King's Ride—Arctic Tartan **Mr D. A. Johnson**
121 **SAFARI PARADISE (IRE)**, 7, ch g Red Paradise—Safari Liz (USA) **P. Deal, J. Dale, T. Neill**
122 **SAMON (GER)**, 7, ch g Monsun (GER)—Savanna (GER) **The Macca & Growler Partnership**
123 **SAMSAAM (IRE)**, 7, b g Sadler's Wells—Azyaa **Mr Matt Archer & Miss Jean Broadhurst**
124 **SEEBALD (GER)**, 9, b g Mulberry (FR)—Spartina (USA) **The Macca & Growler Partnership**
125 **SHOOTING LIGHT (IRE)**, 11, b g Shernazar—Church Light **J. M. Brown & M. J. Blackburn**
126 **SIMOUN (IRE)**, 6, b g Monsun (GER)—Suivez (FR) **The Macca & Growler Partnership**

MR M. C. PIPE—continued

127 **SINDAPOUR (IRE)**, 6, b g Priolo (USA)—Sinntara (IRE) **Mrs Mary Burke**
128 **SIXO (IRE)**, 7, gr g Roselier (FR)—Miss Mangaroo **Mr Matt Archer & Miss Jean Broadhurst**
129 **STORMEZ (IRE)**, 7, b g Ezzoud (IRE)—Stormy Scene (USA) **Mr D. A. Johnson**
130 **STRENUE (USA)**, 4, ch g Crafty Prospector (USA)—Shawgatny (USA) **Mrs Belinda Harvey**
131 **SULPHUR SPRINGS (IRE)**, 12, ch g Don't Forget Me—Short Wave (FR) **Mr P. A. D. Scouller**
132 **TAMARINBLEU (FR)**, 4, b g Epervier Bleu—Tamainia (FR) **The Arthur White Partnership**
133 **TANGO ROYAL (FR)**, 8, gr g Royal Charter (FR)—Nazia (FR) **Mr B. A. Kilpatrick**
134 **TANTERARI (IRE)**, 6, b g Safety Catch (USA)—Cobblers Crest (IRE) **Mr D. A. Johnson**
135 **TARXIEN**, 10, b g Kendor (FR)—Tanz (IRE) **Mr B. A. Kilpatrick**
136 **TEAM TASSEL (IRE)**, 6, b g Be My Native (USA)—Alcmena's Last **Mr Matt Archer & Miss Jean Broadhurst**
137 **THE BIKER (FR)**, 7, br g Arctic Lord—Glenravel **Mr D. A. Johnson**
138 **THEREALBANDIT (IRE)**, 7, b g Torus—Sunrise Highway VII **Mr D. A. Johnson**
139 **THE THREE BANDITS (IRE)**, 4, b g Accordion—Katie Baggage (IRE) **Mr D. A. Johnson**
140 **TIME TO REFLECT (IRE)**, 5, ch g Anshan—Castlemitchle (IRE) **Mr D. A. Johnson**
141 **TIUTCHEV**, 11, b g Soviet Star (USA)—Cut Ahead **The Liars Poker Partnership**
142 **TOMWONTPAYALOT**, 5, gr g Overbury (IRE)—Alice Smith **Mr D. A. Johnson**
143 **TOTO TOSCATO (FR)**, 10, br g Lesotho (USA)—Tosca de Bellouet (FR) **Lady Clarke**
144 **TRADE OFF (IRE)**, 6, b g Roselier (FR)—Lady Owenette (IRE) **Mr D. A. Johnson**
145 **TRESOR DE MAI (FR)**, 10, ch g Grand Tresor (FR)—Lady Night (FR) **Mr Joe Moran**
146 **TUCACAS (FR)**, 7, gr m Highest Honor (FR)—Three Well (FR) **Mrs Belinda Harvey**
147 **TURKESTAN (FR)**, 7, b br g Petit Loup (USA)—Turkeina (FR) **E. H. Fowler & G. Myers**
148 **UPGRADE**, 10, b g Be My Guest (USA)—Cantanta **Mr Matt Archer & Miss Jean Broadhurst**
149 **VANORMIX (FR)**, 5, gr g Linamix (FR)—Vadsa Honor (FR) **Mr Jim Weeden**
150 **VILLA**, 8, b g Jupiter Island—Spoonhill Wood **Mr Matt Archer & Miss Jean Broadhurst**
151 **VISIBILITY (FR)**, 5, gr g Linamix (FR)—Visor (USA) **Mr Jim Weeden**
152 **VODKA BLEU (FR)**, 5, b g Pistolet Bleu (IRE)—Viva Vodka (FR) **Mr D. A. Johnson**
153 **WAHIBA SANDS**, 11, b g Pharly (FR)—Lovely Noor (USA) **Mr D. A. Johnson**
154 **WATERLAW**, 10, b g Kahyasi—Shuss (USA) **Waterlaw Limited**
155 **WELCOME TO UNOS**, 7, ch g Exit To Nowhere (USA)—Royal Loft **J & M Leisure / Unos Restaurant**
156 **WELL CHIEF (GER)**, 5, ch g Night Shift (USA)—Wellesiena (GER) **Mr D. A. Johnson**
157 **WESTENDER (FR)**, 8, b g In The Wings—Trude (GER) **Mr Matt Archer & Miss Jean Broadhurst**
158 **WILL OF THE PEOPLE (IRE)**, 9, b g Supreme Leader—Another Partner **Drs' D.Silk,M.Gillard,P.Walker,R.Purkis**
159 **WYN DIXIE (IRE)**, 5, b g Great Commotion (USA)—Duchess Affair (IRE) **Mr D. A. Johnson**
160 **YOU'RE AGOODUN**, 12, ch g Derrylin—Jennie Pat **Mr J. S. Lammiman**
161 **YOURMAN (IRE)**, 4, b g Shernazar—Lantern Lover **Mr D. A. Johnson**
162 **YOUR SO COOL**, 7, ch g Karinga Bay—Laurel Diver **Mr Matt Archer & Miss Jean Broadhurst**
163 **ZETA'S RIVER (IRE)**, 6, ch g Over The River (FR)—Laurebon **Mr D. A. Johnson**

THREE-YEAR-OLDS

164 **CHUBBES**, b c Kris—St Radegund **Garden Shed Racing 1**
165 **NANTUCKET SOUND (USA)**, b c Quiet American (USA)—Anna **Mr T. M. Hely-Hutchinson**

Other Owners: Mrs L. D. Ayres, Mrs L. Barnes, Mr S. Barnes, Mr Terry Benson, Mr Philip Curry, Mr N. Ender, Mr Frank A. Farrant, Mr R. Fowler, Mr Ron George, Mr Robert B. Gray, Mrs Angie Malde, Mr S. McManaman, Mr Trevor Painting, Mr Alan Perkins, Mr Richard Pitman, Mrs Jane Reiss, Mrs Y. J. Reynolds, Mr Gerry Scanlon, Dr Ian R. Shenkin, Mrs Maureen Shenkin, Mr R. Stanley, Mr Jerry Wright.

Assistant Trainer: David E Pipe

Jockeys (NH): R Greene (10-0), A P McCoy (10-0), T Scudamore (10-0), G Supple (10-0). **Conditional:** N Kavanagh, G Supple (9-11). **Amateur:** Mr J E Moore (9-7).

436

MR M. A. PITMAN, Upper Lambourn
Postal: **Weathercock House, Upper Lambourn, Hungerford, Berkshire, RG17 8QT.**
Contact: **YARD** (01488) 73311 **FAX** (01488) 71065 **MOBILE** (07836) 792771
E-MAIL mark.pitman@markpitmanracing.com WEBSITE www.markpitmanracing.com

1 **ADVANTA GOLD (IRE)**, 8, b g Zaffaran (USA)—Greenslades Lady **Mr H. J. Jarvis**
2 **ANGLANIT (CZE)**, 5, b g Lanitos—Anglointernational **Mr Martin Butler**
3 **BAY LEGEND (IRE)**, 6, b g Toulon—Kabarda **Simpsonair Worldwide Distribution Ltd**
4 4, Gr g Taipan (IRE)—Bee In The Rose (IRE) **Mr Malcolm C. Denmark**
5 **BELUGA (IRE)**, 5, gr g John French—Mesena **Mr Malcolm C. Denmark**
6 **BE MY DESTINY (IRE)**, 7, b g Be My Native (USA)—Miss Cali **Mrs Elizabeth Pearce**
7 **BEST ACTOR (IRE)**, 5, b g Oscar (IRE)—Supreme Princess (IRE) **Mr Malcolm C. Denmark**

MR M. A. PITMAN—continued

8 **BOHEMIAN BOY (IRE)**, 6, gr g Roselier (FR)—Right Hand **Mr S. D. Hemstock**
9 **BRIAR (CZE)**, 5, b h House Rules (USA)—Bright Angel (AUT) **Mr J. F. Garrett**
10 **BUDDHI (IRE)**, 6, b g Be My Native (USA)—Paean Express (IRE) **Mrs T. Brown**
11 4, B g Carroll House—Callmartel (IRE) **Mr B. R. H. Burrough**
12 **CAPTAIN CORELLI**, 7, b g Weld—Deaconess **Mr Patrick Bancroft**
13 **CAPTAIN MADUCK (IRE)**, 6, b g Distinctly North (USA)—Avril's Choice **Mr S. D. Hemstock**
14 **COUNT CAMPIONI (IRE)**, 10, br g Brush Aside (USA)—Emerald Flair **Mr J. F. Garrett**
15 **CRAFTY MONKEY (IRE)**, 7, b g Warcraft (USA)—Mikey's Monkey **G. Pascoe & S. Brewer**
16 **DEMPSEY (IRE)**, 6, b g Lord Americo—Kyle Cailin **Mrs T. Brown**
17 **DEO GRATIAS (POL)**, 4, b c Enjoy Plan (USA)—Dea (POL) **Mr M. Pitman**
18 **DESIGNER LABEL (IRE)**, 8, ch g Insan (USA)—Belle Babillard (IRE) **Mrs Sue Venton**
19 **DOMART (POL)**, 4, b c Baby Bid (USA)—Dominet (POL) **Mr H. J. Jarvis**
20 **DONALD (POL)**, 4, b c Enjoy Plan (USA)—Dahira (POL) **Mr J. F. Garrett**
21 **DULAS BAY**, 10, b g Selkirk (USA)—Ivory Gull **Mr M. Pitman**
22 **FINELY TUNED (IRE)**, 5, b g Gusserane Princess **Mr Malcolm C. Denmark**
23 **FIREBALL MACNAMARA (IRE)**, 8, b g Lord Americo—Glint of Baron **Mr J. C. Hitchins**
24 **FLYING TRIX (IRE)**, 8, b g Lord Americo—Bannow Drive (USA) **Mr Patrick Bancroft**
25 **FROZEN ASSETS (IRE)**, 7, b g Shardari—Frost Bound **The Nicky Watts Partnership**
26 **GENUINE ARTICLE (IRE)**, 8, ch g Insan (USA)—Rosemount Rose **Mr Malcolm C. Denmark**
27 **GIGS BOUNTY**, 6, ch g Weld—City's Sister **Mr J. Barson**
28 **GIGS LETITIA (IRE)**, 7, ch g Hubbly Bubbly (USA)—Music Slipper **Mr J. Barson**
29 **GODFATHER (IRE)**, 6, ch g Insan (USA)—Lady Letitia **Mr Malcolm C. Denmark**
30 **GOOD SAMARITAN (IRE)**, 5, ch g Insan (USA)—Ballymave (IRE) **Mr Malcolm C. Denmark**
31 **GOODTIME GEORGE (IRE)**, 11, b g Strong Gale—Game Sunset **Mrs M. J. Bone**
32 **HOT SHOTS (FR)**, 9, b g Passing Sale (FR)—Uguette IV (FR) **Mrs Jill Eynon & Mr Robin Eynon**
33 **IRONMAN MULDOON (IRE)**, 7, gr g Roselier (FR)—Darjoy Miss **Mrs M. J. Bone**
34 **KNOWHOW (IRE)**, 8, b g Mister Lord—Mossy Mistress (IRE) **Mr Malcolm C. Denmark**
35 B, g Mister Lord (USA)—Lee Valley Lady (IRE) **Mr Malcolm C. Denmark**
36 **LIMITED EDITION (IRE)**, 6, b g Parthian Springs—Rosemount Rose **Mr Malcolm C. Denmark**
37 **MARMADUKE (IRE)**, 8, ch g Perugino (USA)—Sympathy **Mr Martin Butler**
38 **MASTER TRIX (IRE)**, 7, b g Lord Americo—Bannow Drive (IRE) **Mr Patrick Bancroft**
39 **MITCHELDEAN (IRE)**, 8, b g Be My Native (USA)—Pil Eagle (FR) **Mr Ray Pascoe**
40 **MONSIGNOR (IRE)**, 10, ch g Mister Lord (USA)—Dooney's Daughter **Mr Malcolm C. Denmark**
41 **MRS RITCHIE**, 7, b m Teenoso (USA)—Material Girl **Just Good Fun Club**
42 **MUKHALIF (IRE)**, 8, ch h Caerleon (USA)—Potri Pe (ARG) **Mrs T. Brown**
43 4, B g Aflora—Northwood May **Mr Malcolm C. Denmark**
44 **PATRIARCH (IRE)**, 8, b g Alphabatim (USA)—Strong Language **Mr Malcolm C. Denmark**
45 **PROUD PEER (IRE)**, 6, ch g Mister Lord—Rafeen Pride **Mr G. Stevens**
46 **RED DAHLIA**, 7, b m Aflora (IRE)—Redgrave Devil **The Barrossa Syndicate**
47 **SHEER GENIUS (IRE)**, 8, b g Insan (USA)—Mulberry (IRE) **Mr Malcolm C. Denmark**
48 **SMART (SLO)**, 5, b br g Glenstal (USA)—Satyra (POL) **Mr Malcolm C. Denmark**
49 **SMARTY (IRE)**, 11, b br g Royal Fountain—Cahernane Girl **Mrs T. Brown**
50 **SOLDIER OF ROME (IRE)**, 7, b g Satco (FR)—Queens Tricks **Mr M. Pitman**
51 **STERLING STEWART (IRE)**, 9, b g Insan (USA)—Kyle Eile (IRE) **Mr R. George**
52 **SZEROKI BOR (POL)**, 5, b h In Camera (IRE)—Szuana (POL) **G Pascoe, S Brewer, J Newton & I Mcewen**
53 **TEORBAN (POL)**, 5, b g Don Corleone—Tabaka (POL) **Something In The City Partnership**
54 **TOO FORWARD (IRE)**, 8, ch g Toulon—One Back (IRE) **T. Gibson & D. Mathias**
55 **TOP OF THE AGENDA**, 5, b g Michelozzo (USA)—Expensive Lark **The Leaflet Company Ltd**
56 **TORYT (POL)**, 5, b h Beaconsfield—Torana (POL) **Mr M. Pitman**
57 **UNUSUAL SUSPECT**, 5, b g Syrtos—Sally Maxwell **The Tsar Partnership**
58 5, Ch g Executive Perk—Will I Or Wont I (IRE) **Mr Malcolm C. Denmark**
59 **WITHOUT A DOUBT**, 5, b g Singspiel (USA)—El Rabab (USA) **Mr Malcolm C. Denmark**
60 **WORD OF HONOUR (IRE)**, 8, b g Supreme Leader—Shaping **Mr Malcolm C. Denmark**

Other Owners: Mr D. S. Arnold, Mrs S. M. Arnold, Mr Glen Paul Ash, Mrs Hester Bancroft, Dr W. Bogie, Mr Mark Crossley, Mr P.J. Dixon, Mr Brendan Donoghue, Mr D. Ellis, Mr L. G. Frankum, Mr Andrew Harding, Mr Chris Kyriacou, Mr Tele Kyriacou, Ms Jane Parker, Mrs J. Roff, Mr S. Simpson, Mr D. H. Steel, Mr Mark Tracey, Mr Daniel Watkins, Mrs G. Watts.

Assistant Trainer: Paul Price

Jockey (NH): T J Murphy (w.a.).

437 **MR C. T. POGSON, Newark**
Postal: Allamoor Farm, Mansfield Road, Farnsfield, Nottinghamshire, NG22 8HZ.
Contact: PHONE (01623) 882717 MOBILE (07966) 725102

1 BELLA MARY, 9, b m Derrylin—Pro-Token **Mr C. T. Pogson**
2 BRUSH A KING, 9, b g Derrylin—Colonial Princess **Mr C. T. Pogson**
3 DERRY DICE, 8, b g Derrylin—Paper Dice **Mr C. T. Pogson**
4 QUINCY'S PERK (IRE), 11, ch g Executive Perk—Quincy Bay **Mr C. T. Pogson**
5 REEL MISSILE, 5, b g Weld—Landsker Missile **Mr C. T. Pogson**

Assistant Trainer: Mrs K J Pogson

Conditional: A Pogson (9-12).

438 **MR M. J. POLGLASE, Newark**
Postal: The Training Centre, Southwell Racecourse, Rolleston, Nottinghamshire, NG25 0TS.
Contact: PHONE (01636) 816717 MOBILE (07813) 103490 E-MAIL polglaseracing@aol.co.uk

1 AVENTURA (IRE), 4, b c Sri Pekan (USA)—La Belle Katherine (USA) **APB Racing**
2 DUBAI DREAMS, 4, b g Marju (IRE)—Arndilly **APB Racing**
3 KING PRIAM (IRE), 9, b g Priolo (USA)—Barinia
4 MALAHIDE EXPRESS (IRE), 4, gr g Compton Place—Gracious Gretclo **Mr M. J. Polglase**
5 MON PETIT DIAMANT, 4, b f Hector Protector (USA)—Desert Girl **Mr M. J. Polglase**
6 NO TIME (IRE), 4, b c Danetime (IRE)—Muckross Park **Mr Paul J. Dixon**
7 ROAN RAIDER (USA), 4, gr ro g El Prado (USA)—Flirtacious Wonder (USA) **Tomlinson, Shelley, Dixon**
8 SOLOMON'S MINE (USA), 5, b g Rahy (USA)—Shes A Sheba (USA) **Mr Paul J. Dixon**
9 SON OF A GUN, 10, b g Gunner B—Sola Mia **Mr Ron Spore & Mr Michael Crompton**

THREE-YEAR-OLDS

10 ALIZAR (IRE), b f Rahy (USA)—Capua (USA) **Mr G. A. Lucas**
11 BISHOP TO ACTRESS, ch f Paris House—Chess Mistress (USA) **Mr Paul J. Dixon**
12 B g Danetime (IRE)—Classic Choice **Mr M. J. Polglase**
13 HELLO ROBERTO, b f Up And At 'em—Hello Hobson's (IRE) **G. A. Lucas and I. Buckley**
14 LIZHAR (IRE), b f Danetime (IRE)—Amelesa (IRE) **Mr G. A. Lucas**
15 SIR ERNEST (IRE), b g Daggers Drawn (USA)—Kyra Crown (IRE) **Mr G. A. Lucas**
16 WOLVERENE, b g Wolfhound (USA)—Blushing Victoria **Mr Paul J. Dixon**

TWO-YEAR-OLDS

17 ANN'S DELIGHT (IRE), b f 19/3 Imperial Ballet (IRE)—Najariya (Northfields (USA)) (13604) **APB Racing**
18 MISTY PRINCESS, gr f 18/2 Paris House—Miss Whittingham (IRE) (Fayruz) **Mrs M. Tanner**
19 SMALL TIME BLUES (IRE), b f 4/5 Danetime (IRE)—Barinia (Corvaro (USA)) (9800) **Mr B. Green**

Other Owners: Mr Paul Bacon, Mr Ian Buckley, Mr M. J. Crompton, General Sir Geoffrey Howlett, Mrs A. Potts, Mr Alan Potts, Mr Ron Spore.

Assistant Trainer: Jim Bird

Apprentices: Kevin Ghunowa (7-10), Sarah Mitchell (7-12), Manav Nem (7-0).

439 **MR B. N. POLLOCK, Market Harborough**
Postal: Medbourne Grange, Nevil Hoit, Market Harborough, Leicestershire, LE16 8DY.
Contact: PHONE (01858) 565225 MOBILE (07968) 032774 E-MAIL ben@nbpracing.com

1 A GLASS IN THYNE (IRE), 6, br g Glacial Storm (USA)—River Thyne (IRE) **Mr J. B. Dale**
2 BARON ARON (IRE), 9, br g Lord Americo—Eleika **Baroness Pitkeathley and Charles Wilson**
3 BEAU TORERO (FR), 6, gr g True Brave (USA)—Brave Lola (FR) **Mrs K Lloyd Mrs L Pollock Mr L Stilwell**
4 FEELING BLUE, 5, b m Missed Flight—Blues Indigo **Manor Farm Stud (Rutland)**
5 GAME ON (IRE), 8, b g Terimon—Nun So Game **Mrs S. Platt**
6 MINNIE SECRET, 5, b m Primitive Rising (USA)—Mobile Miss (IRE) **Major G. W. Thompson**
7 NADEEMA (FR), 6, gr m Linamix (FR)—Nabagha (FR) **Mr S. G. B. Morrison**

MR B. N. POLLOCK—continued

8 **PASSED OUT (IRE)**, 6, b g Shahanndeh—Ah Suzie (IRE) **Mrs Nicola Pollock**
9 **ROSE BOWL BOY (IRE)**, 6, ch g Lahib (USA)—Danita (IRE) **The All Blues**

Other Owners: Mrs Jenny Dale, Mrs K. M. Lloyd, Baroness J. E. Pitkeathley, Mrs L. Pollock, Mr L. F. Stilwell, Mrs Nicolas Townsend, Mr C. M. Wilson.

Jockey (Flat): J D Smith (8-6). **Jockey (NH):** R Greene (10-0).

440

MR N. J. POMFRET, Tilton-on-the-Hill
Postal: **Red Lodge Farm, Marefield Lane, Tilton-on-the-Hill, Leicester, LE7 9LJ.**
Contact: **PHONE (01162) 597537**

1 **BALLARDS BOY (FR)**, 5, b g Sleeping Car (FR)—Anita (FR) **Mrs Liz Deacon**
2 **COOL CHILLI**, 6, gr g Gran Alba (USA)—Miss Flossa (FR) **Mr R. P. Brett**
3 **INTREPID MOGAL**, 7, b g Terimon—Padrigal **Mr J. N. Cheatle**

441

MR C. L. POPHAM, Taunton
Postal: **Bashford Racing Stables, West Bagborough, Taunton, Somerset, TA4 3EF.**
Contact: **PHONE (01823) 432769 MOBILE (07967) 506430**

1 **CANTORIS**, 4, b g Unfuwain (USA)—Choir Mistress **Mr H. J. W. Davies, Mr Rodney Peacock**
2 **DALCASSIAN BUCK (IRE)**, 10, ch g Buckskin (FR)—Menebeans (IRE) **The Four Bucks**
3 **HUW THE NEWS**, 5, b g Primo Dominie—Martha Stevens (USA) **Mr H. J. W. Davies**
4 **INDIAN BEAT**, 7, ch g Indian Ridge—Rappa Tap Tap (FR) **Mrs C. R. Hayton**

Other Owners: Mr L. A. Heard, Mr P. Littlejohns, Mr A. S. Skidmore, Mr Richard Weeks.

Assistant Trainer: Saul McHugh

Amateur: Mr Saul McHugh (11-0).

442

MR J. G. B. PORTMAN, Compton
Postal: **Hamilton Stables, Hockham Road, Compton, Newbury, Berkshire, RG20 6QJ.**
Contact: **HOME (01635) 578031 FAX (01635) 579323 E-MAIL portman.hamiltonstables@virgin.net**

1 **ANNIE BYERS**, 8, ch m Sula Bula—Tuneful Flutter **Mr M. J. Vandenberghe**
2 **ASK FOR LUCK (IRE)**, 7, b g Camden Town—French Thistle **Mr Anthony Boswood**
3 **BLUE SAVANNA**, 4, ch g Bluegrass Prince (IRE)—Dusk In Daytona **Mr A. S. B. Portman**
4 **BODFARI CREEK**, 7, ch g In The Wings—Cormorant Creek **Pump Technology Limited**
5 **EMPHATIC (IRE)**, 9, ch g Ela-Mana-Mou—Sally Rose **Hockham Racing**
6 **HERBERT (FR)**, 4, b g Hernando (FR)—Balsamine **Mrs R. Pease**
7 **HIERS DE BROUAGE (FR)**, 9, b g Neustrien (FR)—Thalandrezienne (FR) **Seddon - Brown Partnership**
8 **HOUGHTON BAY (IRE)**, 9, b g Camden Town—Royal Bavard **Mrs William Hall**
9 **KING OF SPARTA**, 11, b g Kefaah (USA)—Khaizaraan (CAN) **Mrs S. Portman**
10 **LYNRICK LADY (IRE)**, 8, b m Un Desperado (FR)—Decent Lady **Milady Partnership**
11 **MEASURELESS**, 9, ch g Lion Cavern (USA)—Magnetic Point (USA) **Mr J. G. B. Portman**
12 **POLITELY**, 6, b m Tragic Role (USA)—Polly Worth **Dr Nigel Knott**
13 **RIDICULE**, 5, b g Piccolo—Mockingbird **Pump Technology Limited**
14 **ROSE OF YORK (IRE)**, 4, b f Emarati (USA)—True Ring **Col E. C. York**
15 **SAUCYNORWICH (IRE)**, 6, b g Norwich—Kelly Gales (IRE) **Mrs Richard Tice**
16 **SOPRANO LASS (IRE)**, 7, ch m Black Monday—Kam Country (IRE) **Mr Anthony Boswood**
17 **WASTED TALENT (IRE)**, 4, b f Sesaro (USA)—Miss Garuda **Wasted Talent Partnership**

THREE-YEAR-OLDS

18 **BULLYRAG**, b g Makbul—Dusk In Daytona **A. S. B. Portman**
19 **CARTE NOIRE**, b f Revoque (IRE)—Coffee Cream **A. H. Robinson**
20 **DEIGN TO DANCE (IRE)**, b f Danetime (IRE)—Lady Montekin **Mr Edward Benson**
21 **FRAMBO (IRE)**, b f Fraam—Wings Awarded
22 **LIVIA (IRE)**, b f Titus Livius (FR)—Passing Beauty **Pump Technology Ltd**
23 **ONE UPMANSHIP**, ch g Bahamian Bounty—Magnolia **Mr M. J. Vandenberghe**
24 **SAFFRON FOX**, ch f Saffawan—Fox Oa (FR) **Mrs R. Pease**

MR J. G. B. PORTMAN—continued

25 **SILKEN JOHN (IRE)**, ch c Grand Lodge (USA)—Lady Ela (IRE) **J. Lyons**
26 **VARUNI (IRE)**, b f Ali-Royal (IRE)—Sauvignon (IRE)

TWO-YEAR-OLDS

27 B f 18/3 Piccolo—Bella Helena (Balidar) (5500) **Mrs F. Veasey**
28 B 27/1 Lujain (USA)—Coffee Cream (Common Grounds) (6800) **Hockham Racing**
29 B f 10/3 Mujahid (USA)—Cointosser (IRE) (Nordico (USA)) (6500) **Hockham Racing**
30 B c 20/3 Piccolo—Coir 'a' Ghaill (Jalmood (USA)) (4500) **J. T. Habershon-Butcher**
31 B g 3/4 Atraf—E Sharp (USA) (Diesis) (7500)
32 B g 28/4 Silver Patriarch—Folly Fox (Alhijaz) (3000)
33 B br f 24/1 Indian Danehill (IRE)—Grade A Star (IRE) (Alzao (USA)) (14223) **City & Provincial Partnership**
34 **MISS PATRICIA,** b f 17/3 Mister Baileys—Zoena (Emarati (USA)) **Mrs R. Pease**
35 Br f 28/4 Rossini (USA)—Misty Rain (Polar Falcon (USA)) (2000)
36 Br f 4/4 Lujain (USA)—Without Warning (IRE) (Warning) (13000) **Coriocan Partnership**

Other Owners: Mr D. Barlow, Mr S. Barrow, Mr Jeremy Brownlee, Mrs T. Brudenell, Mr G. Clark, Mr K. Clark, Mr G. Clement, Mr C. Cosham, Mr Charles Curtis, Mr P.A. Deal, The Hon J. Deedes, Mrs C. Dell, Mr R. Dollar, Mr M. Edwards, Mr T. Edwards, Mr C. J. Elkins, Mr D. Erwin, Mr I. S. Flooks, Mrs E. J. Garvin, Mr R. G. Giles, Mr S. R. Hope, Miss J. Kempsey, Mrs V. R. W. Miller, Mr J. Hawkins-Byass, Mr N. S. Seddon-Brown, Mrs E. J. Edwards-Heathcote, Mrs G. Heyward-Cole, Mr D. Powell, Mr D. Prior, Mrs M. Roberts, Mr M. Shaw, Mr M. Shilling, Mr R. Simmons, Mr W. L. Simmons, Mr S. J. Skinner, Mr Howard Spooner, Mrs P. Thorman, Mrs E. Tice, Mr G. Wordsworth, Mr N. Zawoga.

Assistant Trainer: Sophie Portman

---

443   MR J. C. POULTON, Newmarket
Postal: **Meddler Racing Stables, Meddler Stud, Kentford, Newmarket, Suffolk, CB8 7PT.**
Contact: **PHONE (01638) 751504 FAX (01638) 751602 MOBILE (07779) 229827**
E-MAIL meddlerstud@aol.com

1 **AFRICAN CZAR**, 6, b g Inzar (USA)—African Grace (USA)
2 4, B g Danzig Connection (USA)—Bertie's Girl
3 6, B h Suave Dancer (USA)—Bertie's Girl
4 **BOOGARBAROO (IRE)**, 6, gr g Turtle Island (IRE)—Lingdale Lass
5 **DANCING DOLPHIN (IRE)**, 5, b m Dolphin Street (FR)—Dance Model
6 **EJAY**, 5, b br m Emperor Jones (USA)—Lough Erne
7 **EN FIN (FR)**, 5, b m Loup Solitaire (USA)—Isola d'Elba (USA)
8 **HAMMER OF THE GODS (IRE)**, 4, ch g Tagula (IRE)—Bhama (FR)
9 **INDIAN STEPPES (FR)**, 5, b m Indian Ridge—Ukraine Venture
10 **ITALIAN MIST (FR)**, 5, b g Forzando—Digamist Girl (IRE)
11 **LADY AT LEISURE (IRE)**, 4, ch f Dolphin Street (FR)—In A Hurry (FR)
12 **LEGALITY**, 4, b f Polar Falcon (USA)—Lady Barrister
13 **LEGAL VENTURE**, 8, ch g Case Law—We Two
14 **L FOR LEISURE**, 5, ch g Cosmonaut—York Street (USA)
15 **LUCKY'S SON**, 7, gr g Lucky Guest—April Wind
16 **MALAAH (IRE)**, 8, gr g Pips Pride—Lingdale Lass
17 **MISHKA**, 6, b g Mistertopogigo (IRE)—Walsham Witch
18 **MR UPPITY**, 5, b g Shareef Dancer (USA)—Queenfisher
19 **NASTY NICK**, 5, gr g Petong—Silver Spell
20 **PRIVATE SEAL**, 9, b g King's Signet (USA)—Slender
21 **RAFTERS MUSIC (IRE)**, 9, b g Thatching—Princess Dixieland (USA)
22 **REPENT AT LEISURE**, 4, b g Bishop of Cashel—Sutosky
23 **SAMAR QAND**, 5, b m Selkirk (USA)—Sit Alkul (USA)
24 **SILK ST JOHN**, 10, b g Damister (USA)—Silk St James
25 4, B g Vettori (IRE)—Skip To Somerfield
26 **TEE JAY KASSIDY**, 4, b g Petong—Priceless Fantasy
27 **TRUE THUNDER**, 7, b g Bigstone (IRE)—Puget Dancer (USA)
28 4, B c Dancing Spree (USA)—Zac's Desire

THREE-YEAR-OLDS

29 **ALI ZANDRA**, b f Prince Sabo—Priceless Fantasy
30 **ANISETTE**, b f Abou Zouz (USA)—Natural Gold (USA)
31 **DAGGERS CANYON**, ch g Daggers Drawn (USA)—Chipewyas (FR)
32 **DANCING BEAR**, b c Groom Dancer (USA)—Sickle Moon
33 **DUMNONI**, b f Titus Livius (FR)—Lamees (USA)

MR J. C. POULTON—continued

34 FUBOS, b g Atraf—Homebeforemidnight
35 JATH, b f Bishop of Cashel—Night Trader (USA)
36 RUSSALKA, b f Opening Verse (USA)—Philarmonique (FR)
37 TALE OF THE TIGER, ch c Bijou d'Inde—La Belle Dominique

TWO-YEAR-OLDS

38 B f 23/3 Easycall—As Mustard (Anna Karietta)
39 B f 26/4 Tipsy Creek (USA)—Belle de Nuit (IRE) (Statoblest) (4500)
40 B f 28/3 Mujahid (USA)—Fancier Bit (Lion Cavern (USA)) (2000)
41 B f 20/2 Silver Patriarch—Fox Star (IRE) (Foxhound (USA))
42 B f 23/4 Tipsy Creek (USA)—La Belle Mystere (Lycius (USA)) (2600)
43 B f 5/5 Vettori (USA)—Lamees (Lomond (USA))
44 B c 8/4 Mark of Esteem (IRE)—Night Over Day (Most Welcome) (1700)
45 B c 15/3 Opening Verse (USA)—Philarmonique (FR) (Trempolino (USA))
46 Ch f 5/4 Case Law—Precious Air (Precocious)

Other Owners: At Leisure Racing, Mr R. P. Beare, Mrs V. I. Beare, Mr James E. S. Colling, Mr M. Crompton, Gryfindor, Mr Stuart Kemp, Mr M. Mason, Meddler Bloodstock, Meddler Racing, Meddler Stud, Ormonde Racing, Mr J. Porteus, Mr & Mrs Alan Shaw, Mr David Shearer, Mr S Shore, Miss F. R. Smith, Mr Mike Sullivan, Sutton Oil (Bermuda) Leasing Ltd, Mr Dave Symondson, Mr T. Taylor, Tba, The Headquarters Partnership, Mr & Mrs Richard Withers.

Assistant Trainer: Mrs Elizabeth Reed & Mr John Ryan

Jockeys (Flat): N Callan, I Mongan. **Jockey (NH):** Jimmy McCarthy. **Apprentice:** John Jeffery.

---

444 **MR J. R. POULTON, Lewes**
Postal: **White Cottage, Stud Farm, Telscombe, Lewes, East Sussex, BN7 3HZ.**
Contact: **HOME (01273) 300127 YARD (01273) 302486 MOBILE (07980) 596952**
E-MAIL jamiepoulton@yahoo.co.uk

1 AGILIS (IRE), 4, b g Titus Livius (FR)—Green Life **Mr Chris Steward**
2 BISHOPS FINGER, 4, b g Bishop of Cashel—Bit of A Tart **Ormonde Racing**
3 BRIEF CONTACT (IRE), 6, b g Brief Truce (USA)—Incommunicado (IRE) **Mr George H. Gibson**
4 BRILLIANT RED, 11, b g Royal Academy (USA)—Red Comes Up (USA) **Mrs M. J. George**
5 CALIWAG (IRE), 8, b g Lahib (USA)—Mitsubishi Style **Lottie Collins Partnership**
6 CORRIB ECLIPSE, 5, b g Double Eclipse (IRE)—Last Night's Fun (IRE) **Mr M. Ioannou**
7 DANGEROUS DAVE, 5, b g Superpower—Lovely Lilly **Mr Jamie Poulton**
8 DISPOL EVITA, 5, ch m Presidium—She's A Breeze **Mr Kenneth Wilkinson**
9 DOLPHINELLE (IRE), 8, b g Dolphin Street (FR)—Mamie's Joy **Mr Chris Steward**
10 FERNWORTHY, 4, ch g Sheikh Albadou—Daring Damsel **Miss Kate Waddington**
11 FULVIO (USA), 4, b g Sword Dance—One Tuff Gal (USA) **Lancing Racing Syndicate**
12 KOYAANISQATSI, 4, ch g Selkirk (USA)—Bogus John (CAN) **Ormonde Racing**
13 LEARNED LAD (FR), 6, ch g Royal Academy (USA)—Blushing Storm (USA) **Mr J. Wotherspoon**
14 PIPSSELO (SPA), 7, b g Pips Pride—Tesalia (SPA) **Mr Chris Steward**
15 PRIVATE BENJAMIN, 4, gr g Ridgewood Ben—Jilly Woo **Mrs J. Wotherspoon**
16 RIVER BUG (IRE), 10, ch g Over The River (FR)—Fiona's Wish **Ormonde Racing**
17 SAMMY'S SHUFFLE, 9, b g Touch of Grey—Cabinet Shuffle **Mrs G. M. Temmerman**
18 THEATRE (USA), 5, b g Theatrical—Fasta (USA) **Lone Star Racing Partnership**
19 TOMMY CARSON, 9, gr g Last Tycoon—Ivory Palm (USA) **Mr J. Logan**

THREE-YEAR-OLDS

20 CROCODILE DUNDEE (IRE), b c Croco Rouge (IRE)—Miss Salsa Dancer **Mr R. W. Huggins**
21 DIEQUEST (USA), ch c Diesis—Nuance (IRE) **Rainbow Racing**
22 MYSTIC LAD, gr g Magic Ring (IRE)—Jilly Woo **Mr J. Wotherspoon**
23 TIGER TIGER (FR), b c Tiger Hill (IRE)—Adorable Emilie (FR) **Mr R. W. Huggins**

Other Owners: Mr M. Avery, Mrs H. E. Bohan, Mr C. Bond, Mr G. J. Bush, Mr J. H. Bush, Mr T. L. Gray, Mr M. G. Lawson, Mr J. McGuigan, Mr G. J. Price, Mr J. M. Rands.

Assistant Trainer: Mrs C D Poulton

Jockeys (Flat): I Mongan, S Whitworth. **Jockey (NH):** L Cummins (10-0). **Apprentices:** D Kinsella (7-3), H Poulton. **Conditional:** C Bolger (9-7). **Amateur:** Mrs C Poulton (9-7).

MR B. G. POWELL, Winchester

445 Postal: **Morestead Stables, Morestead, Twyford, Winchester, Hampshire, SO21 1JD.**
Contact: HOME (01962) 717705 FAX (01962) 717706 MOBILE (07768) 390737

1 **ANALYZE (FR)**, 6, b g Anabaa (USA)—Bramosia **The Arkle Bar Partnership**
2 **AOIFEROB (IRE)**, 6, b g Commanche Run—Lancana (IRE) **W. T. Racing Syndicate**
3 **APOLLO VICTORIA (FR)**, 7, b g Sadler's Wells (USA)—Dame Solitaire (CAN) **R. J. T. 290 Limited**
4 **AVEIRO (IRE)**, 8, b g Darshaan—Avila **The Dream Connection**
5 **BACKPACKER (IRE)**, 6, b g Petoski—Yellow Iris **C. R. H. Racing**
6 **BALLYAAHBUTT (IRE)**, 5, b g Good Thyne (USA)—Lady Henbit (IRE) **Mrs A. Ellis**
7 **BALLY GOOD**, 6, b g Alderbrook—Another Debt **Jubert Family**
8 **BEAUSEJOUR (USA)**, 6, ch m Diesis—Libeccio (NZ) **Miss K. Mundy**
9 **BIG ROB (IRE)**, 5, b g Bob Back (USA)—Native Shore (IRE) **Mr P. H. Betts**
10 **BOW SPRIT**, 4, ch g Fleetwood (IRE)—Longwood Lady **Mr Nigel Stafford**
11 **CASTLE RIVER (USA)**, 5, b g Irish River (FR)—Castellina (USA) **H C T Racing**
12 **CHATEAU NICOL**, 5, b g Distant Relative—Glensara **Basingstoke Commercials**
13 5, ch m Moscow Society (USA)—Cloona Lady (IRE) **P. H. Betts**
14 **COLNSIDE BOBBIN**, 6, b m Afzal—Khatti Hawk **Mr A. Cutler**
15 **COLNSIDE BROOK**, 5, b m Sovereign Water (FR)—Armagnac Messenger **Mr A. Cutler**
16 **COLONEL FRANK**, 7, b g Toulon—Fit For Firing (FR) **The Hambledon Hunters**
17 **CRUISE THE FAIRWAY (IRE)**, 8, b g Insan (USA)—Tickhill **R. J. T. 290 Limited**
18 **DELPHI**, 8, ch g Grand Lodge (USA)—Euridice (IRE) **P. Banfield**
19 **DOON RUN (IRE)**, 10, ch g Commanche Run—Paupers Spring **L. C. J. J. Partnership**
20 **DOUBLE SCOOP**, 5, b g Double Eclipse (IRE)—Grayrose Double **Mr P. H. Betts**
21 **DRAMATIC APPROACH (IRE)**, 10, b g Dry Dock—Gayles Approach **Mr John Plackett**
22 **EASTBOROUGH (IRE)**, 5, b g Woodborough (USA)—Easter Girl **Mr Christopher Shankland**
23 **EAU DE COLOGNE**, 12, b g Persian Bold—No More Rosies **Dr M. Evans**
24 **EL BLADE**, 7, b g Dashing Blade—Elisha (GER) **Favourites Racing**
25 **FRIAR PETER**, 7, b g Petoski—Misty Lough **Mr M. J. Howard**
26 **GLANAMANA (IRE)**, 8, b g Be My Native (USA)—Brides Choice **Mrs M. O'Kelly**
27 **HADATH (IRE)**, 7, br g Mujtahid (USA)—Al Sylah **Mr Seamus Mannion**
28 **HOULIHANS CHOICE**, 7, ch g Norton Challenger—Model Lady **Mr Paddy O'Donnell**
29 **IRISH OPTION (IRE)**, 11, ch g Executive Perk—Erins Treasure **Mrs Jean Plackett**
30 **JOYE DES ILES (FR)**, 7, b g Mont Basile (FR)—Titjana (FR) **Mr John Studd**
31 **JUBBA'S JESTER (USA)**, 5, b g St Jovite (USA)—Wisecrack (USA) **J. R. Vail & P. D. Vail**
32 **KENZO III (FR)**, 5, b g Agent Bleu (FR)—Kelinda (FR) **J. Studd**
33 **KIROV KING (IRE)**, 4, b c Desert King (IRE)—Nymphs Echo (IRE)
34 **LABULA BAY**, 10, b g Sula Bula—Lady Barunbe **Richard Cook Ltd**
35 **LINNING WINE (IRE)**, 8, b g Scenic—Zallaka (IRE) **Favourites Racing**
36 **LITTLE EDWARD**, 6, gr g King's Signet (USA)—Cedar Lady **J. Mursell**
37 **LITTLE FELLA**, 5, b g Kahyasi—Copper Breeze (IRE) **Mrs Jean R. Bishop**
38 **LUCKY SINNA (IRE)**, 8, b br g Insan (USA)—Bit of A Chance **Mr John Plackett**
39 **MAGICAL WONDERLAND**, 5, br m Thowra (FR)—Alice's Mirror **Mr R. H. Kerswell**
40 **MAJOR BLADE (GER)**, 6, b g Dashing Blade—Misniniski **G. Lloyd, G. Allmond & R. Barrs**
41 **MINERS DANCE (IRE)**, 11, b g Miner's Lamp—Prudent Birdie **Mr John Studd**
42 **MISTER BIGTIME (IRE)**, 10, br g Roselier (FR)—Cnoc An Oir **Mrs Jean R. Bishop**
43 **MUMBLING (IRE)**, 6, ch g Dr Devious—Valley Lights (IRE) **Mr Robert Gunn**
44 **MY GALLIANO (IRE)**, 8, b g Muharib (USA)—Hogan Stand **Mr L. Gilbert**
45 **NORTHERN TENNESSEE (IRE)**, 9, ch g Muharib (USA)—Corun Girl **A. Head**
46 **OFF THE SEAL (NZ)**, 8, b g Imperial Seal—Grand Countess (NZ) **Sasha Harrison**
47 **OUR KEV (IRE)**, 8, b g Be My Native (USA)—Sunbath **Mrs Jean R. Bishop**
48 **PADDY'S THYME (IRE)**, 8, gr g Good Thyne (USA)—Nanny Kehoe (IRE) **Mr Paddy O'Donnell**
49 **PARDON WHAT**, 8, b g Theatrical Charmer—Tree Poppy **Mrs A. Ellis**
50 **PIMLICO (IRE)**, 6, b g Imp Society (USA)—Willow Gale **Mr John Plackett**
51 **PRINCE AURUM**, 9, b g Mystiko (USA)—Jarin Rose (IRE) **Miss S. Smith**
52 **RANDOM PRECISION (IRE)**, 5, ch g Presenting—Rendezvous **Mr John Studd**
53 **REASONABLE RESERVE (IRE)**, 7, ch g Fourstars Allstars (USA)—Alice O'Malley **S. Mannion**
54 **ROSE TINA**, 7, b m Tina's Pet—Rosevear (IRE) **Church Racing**
55 **RUBY GLEN (IRE)**, 6, b m Insan (USA)—Le Glen **Mr John Studd**
56 **SITTING DUCK**, 5, b g Sir Harry Lewis (USA)—Fit For Firing (FR) **Mr M. Powers**
57 **SOUTHERN FRANCE (IRE)**, 7, b g Toulon—High Fi **Mr John B. Sunley**
58 **SUNGIO**, 6, b g Halling (USA)—Time Or Never (FR) **Mrs Rachel A. Powell**
59 **SUZY SPITFIRE**, 6, ch m Afzal—Oatis Rose **Mr J. Howson**
60 **TACIN (IRE)**, 7, b br g Supreme Leader—Nicat **Mrs Jean R. Bishop**
61 **THE GAY FOX**, 10, gr g Never So Bold—School Concert **Mr Jack Green**
62 **ZALKANI (IRE)**, 4, ch g Cadeaux Genereux—Zallaka (IRE) **Favourites Racing**

MR B. G. POWELL—continued

THREE-YEAR-OLDS

63 **BEBOPSKIDDLEY**, b g Robellino (USA)—Adarama (IRE) **A. Head**
64 **CAPESTAR (IRE)**, b f Capecross (IRE)—Sedulous **D. & J. Newell**
65 **KITLEY**, b g Muhtarram (USA)—Salsita **Mr & Mrs D. Gamble**
66 **SCARRABUS (IRE)**, b g Charnwood Forest (IRE)—Errazuriz (IRE) **Swan Racing**

TWO-YEAR-OLDS

67 Gr c 16/4 Monashee Mountain—Lady Celina (FR) (Crystal Palace (FR)) (19789) **Mr & Mrs D. Gamble**

Other Owners: Mr D. Bellis, Mr Gary Flood, Mrs P. Jubert, Exors Of The Late P. R. Jubert, Mr B. P. McNamee, Mrs C. M. Poland, Mr D. Teevan, Mr G. E. Tuite, Mr J. R. Vail.

Assistant Trainer: Rachel Powell

Jockey (Flat): L P Keniry. **Jockey (NH):** J P McNamarra. **Apprentices:** A Hindley, K Peppio. **Conditional:** J Davies. **Amateurs:** Mr Wayne Kavanagh, Mrs R Powell, Mr Charles Studd.

---

446 **SIR MARK PRESCOTT BT, Newmarket**
Postal: **Heath House, Newmarket, Suffolk, CB8 8DU.**
Contact: **PHONE (01638) 662117 FAX (01638) 666572**

1 **ALBANOVA**, 5, gr m Alzao (USA)—Alouette **Miss K. Rausing**
2 **ASTYANAX (IRE)**, 4, b c Hector Protector (USA)—Craigmill **Lady Katharine Watts**
3 **COAT OF HONOUR (IRE)**, 4, gr g Mark of Esteem (IRE)—Ballymac Girl **E. B. Rimmer - Osborne House**
4 **CORDIAL (IRE)**, 4, gr g Charnwood Forest (IRE)—Moon Festival **Mrs L. Burnet - Osborne House**
5 **FALL IN LINE**, 4, gr g Linamix (FR)—Shortfall **Neil Greig - Osborne House II**
6 **FOREIGN AFFAIRS**, 6, ch h Hernando (FR)—Entente Cordiale (USA) **Mr C. Walker**
7 **LAWRENCE OF ARABIA (IRE)**, 4, b g Desert King (USA)—Cumbres (FR) **L. A. Larratt - Osborne House**
8 **NADESZHDA**, 4, ch f Nashwan (USA)—Ninotchka (USA) **Miss K. Rausing**
9 **NO REFUGE (IRE)**, 4, ch g Hernando—Shamarra (FR) **W. E. Sturt - Osborne House III**
10 **ONE OFF**, 4, b g Baratthea (IRE)—On Call **Lady O'Reilly**

THREE-YEAR-OLDS

11 **AURELIA**, b f Rainbow Quest (USA)—Fern **Mr Faisal Salman**
12 **CIRCASSIAN (IRE)**, b g Groom Dancer (USA)—Daraliya (IRE) **Lady Katharine Watts**
13 **FIRST ORDER**, b g Primo Dominie—Unconditional Love (IRE) **Cheveley Park Stud**
14 **FRITILLARY**, b f Vettori (IRE)—Fetlar **Dr Catherine Wills**
15 **INCROYABLE**, gr f Linamix (FR)—Crodelle (IRE) **Lady O'Reilly**
16 **MARIA VETSERA**, ch f Selkirk (USA)—Scandalette **Miss K. Rausing**
17 **OPTIMAL (IRE)**, gr f Green Desert (USA)—On Call **Lady O'Reilly**
18 **OUR EMMY LOU**, ch f Mark of Esteem (IRE)—Regent's Folly (IRE) **Lady Roborough**
19 **PEDRILLO**, b g Singspiel (IRE)—Patria (USA) **Hesmonds Stud**
20 **PURE FOLLY (IRE)**, b f Machiavellian (USA)—Spirit Willing (IRE) **Sir Edmund Loder**
21 **QUARRYMOUNT**, b g Polar Falcon (USA)—Quilt **Lady Fairhaven**
22 **RED DAMSON (IRE)**, b g Croco Rouge (IRE)—Damascene (IRE) **W. E. Sturt - Osborne House V**
23 **REGAL SETTING (IRE)**, br g King's Theatre (IRE)—Cartier Bijoux **W. E. Sturt - Osborne House**
24 **RHETORICAL**, b g Unfuwain (USA)—Miswaki Belle (USA) **Ne'er Do Wells II**
25 **SEGURO (IRE)**, b f Indian Ridge—For Example (USA) **Mr Faisal Salman**
26 **STRAW BEAR (USA)**, ch c Diesis—Highland Ceilidh (IRE) **Mr C. Jenkins**
27 **TRILEMMA**, b f Slip Anchor—Thracian **Mrs Sonia Rogers**
28 **VEVINA (USA)**, b f Rahy (USA)—Lovely Keri (USA) **Mr Faisal Salman**

TWO-YEAR-OLDS

29 **ALDENTE**, b f 26/4 Green Desert (USA)—Alruccaba (Crystal Palace (FR)) **Mrs S. Rogers**
30 **ALVARITA**, gr f 12/2 Selkirk (USA)—Alborada (Alzao (USA)) **Miss K. Rausing**
31 **ANNIBALE CARO**, b c 22/4 Mtoto—Isabella Gonzaga (Rock Hopper) (16000) **Mr Cyril Humphris**
32 **BESPOKE**, b c 23/2 Pivotal—Immaculate (Mark of Esteem (IRE)) **Cheveley Park Stud**
33 **COMIC STRIP**, b c 7/5 Marju (IRE)—Comic (IRE) (Be My Chief (USA)) (26000) **Neil Greig - Osborne House**
34 **COUNTDOWN**, ch c 2/3 Pivotal—Quiz Time (Efisio) (170000) **Cheveley Park Stud**
35 **CUPID'S GLORY**, b c 9/4 Pursuit Of Love—
　　　　Doctor's Glory (USA) (Spectacular Bid (USA)) (48000) **Hesmonds Stud**

SIR MARK PRESCOTT BT—continued

36 **EMPIRE CITY (USA)**, b c 25/4 Carson City (USA)—
    Teeming Shore (USA) (L'Emigrant (USA)) **Mr Timothy J. Rooney**
37 **EPICES**, b c 17/4 Mtoto—French Spice (Cadeaux Genereux) **Mr C. Spence**
38 **ESPRIT DE CORPS**, b c 3/2 Hernando (FR)—
    Entente Cordiale (USA) (Affirmed (USA)) (160000) **W. E. Sturt - Osborne House II**
39 **FANTAISISTE**, b f 25/1 Nashwan (USA)—Fantastic Belle (Night Shift (USA)) **Miss K. Rausing**
40 **HEREDITARY**, ch c 30/4 Hernando (FR)—
    Eversince (USA) (Foolish Pleasure (USA)) (22000) **Eclipse Thoroughbreds - Osborne House**
41 **HYPNOTIC**, ch c 16/3 Lomitas—Hypnotize (Machiavellian (USA)) **Cheveley Park Stud**
42 **INTRIGUED**, gr f 2/2 Darshaan—Last Second (IRE) (Alzao (USA)) **Mr Faisal Salman**
43 **KANGRINA**, b f 13/1 Acatenango (GER)—Kirona (Robellino (USA)) (21026) **Mr Faisal Salman**
44 **KEY TIME (IRE)**, b g 8/4 Darshaan—Kasota (IRE) (Alzao (USA)) (37105) **G. Moore - Osborne House**
45 **KISWAHILI**, ch f 16/2 Selkirk (USA)—Kiliniski (Niniski (USA)) **Miss K. Rausing**
46 **OBLIQUE (IRE)**, b f 25/4 Giant's Causeway—On Call (Alleged (USA)) **Lady O'Reilly**
47 **PIVOTAL ROLE**, ch f 25/1 Pivotal—Heckle (In The Wings) **Cheveley Park Stud**
48 **PREDATORY (USA)**, ch b 3/2 Silver Hawk (USA)—
    La Chatte (Apalachee) (USA)) **Eclipse Thoroughbreds - Osborne House IV**
49 **RED OPERA**, ch c 10/3 Nashwan (USA)—La Papagena (Habitat) (95000) **Syndicate 2003**
50 **RED PEONY**, b f 25/3 Montjeu (IRE)—Red Azalea (Shirley Heights) **Cheveley Park Stud**
51 **ROCK DOVE (IRE)**, b f 26/3 Danehill (USA)—Littlefeather (IRE) (Indian Ridge) **Sir Edmund Loder, BT**
52 **SAFE HARBOUR**, b f 18/2 Docksider (USA)—
    Number One Spot (Reference Point) (17000) **Mrs S. Thomson Jones**
53 **SAINTPAULIA (USA)**, b f 8/2 Dynaformer (USA)—
    Saintly Manner (St Jovite (USA)) (17857) **Hesmonds Stud**
54 **SCRIPTED**, b c 8/5 Diktat—Krameria (Kris) (26000) **Lord Roborough**
55 **SONGERIE**, b f 6/3 Hernando (FR)—Summer Night (Nashwan (USA)) **Miss K. Rausing**
56 **SPECTAIL**, b c 12/3 Spectrum (IRE)—Shanghai Girl (Distant Relative) **Mr Edward S. A. Belcher**
57 **STAR APPLE**, b f 15/2 Barathea (IRE)—Apple Town (Warning) **Dr Catherine Wills**
58 **SUCCESSION**, ch f 16/3 Groom Dancer (USA)—Pitcroy (Unfuwain (USA)) **Dr Catherine Wills**
59 **SUNLIT SKIES**, b f 5/3 Selkirk (USA)—Shimmering Sea (Slip Anchor) **Miss K. Rausing**
60 **TANGIBLE**, b f 23/2 Hernando (FR)—Trinity Reef (Bustino) **Cheveley Park Stud**
61 **TERMINATE (GER)**, ch c 28/3 Acatenango (GER)—
    Taghareed (USA) (Shadeed (USA)) (55658) **Eclipse Thoroughbreds-Osborne House III**
62 **VAGARY (IRE)**, gr f 24/1 Zafonic (USA)—Vadsagreya (FR) (Linamix (FR)) (90000) **Lord Roborough**
63 **VALE DE LOBO**, b f 29/3 Loup Sauvage (USA)—Frog (Akarad (FR)) **Mr B. Haggas**
64 **VARENKA (IRE)**, b f 8/2 Fasliyev (USA)—Castara Beach (IRE) (Danehill (USA)) **Lady Roborough**

Other Owners: Mr R. Aird, Mr Keith Bowry, Mr J. M. Brown, Mr B. D. Burnet, Mr J. Carroll, Mr T. Carroll, Mr N. Cobby, Mrs M. Dennis, Mr F. Done, Mr J. Durkin, Mr Roger T. Ferris, Mr J. E. Fishpool, Mr P. G. Goulandris, The Hon Mrs G. Greenwood, Mr D. Harding, Mrs J. Lambert, The Hon Pearl Lawson Johnston, Mr D. Lowrey, Mr D. Mackenzie, Mrs Jane Rimmer, Mrs J. Rock, Skymarc Farm Inc, Mr I. Spearing, Tessona Racing Limited, Mr C. Walker, Mrs S. L. Warman, Mr K. Wilde, Mr E. J. Williams.

Assistant Trainer: William Butler

Jockeys (Flat): G Duffield (8-2), S Sanders (8-5). **Apprentice:** Simon Archer (8-5). **Amateur:** Mr Matthew Harvey (9-10).

---

447   MRS A. PRICE, Presteigne
Postal: **The Meeting House, Norton, Presteigne, Powys, LD8 2HA.**
Contact: **PHONE (01544) 267221**

1 **CLASSIC REVIVAL**, 6, ch g Elmaamul (USA)—Sweet Revival **Mrs A. Price**
2 **DRUMLIN (IRE)**, 9, b g Glacial Storm (USA)—Shannon Lough (IRE) **Mrs A. Price**
3 **FOXY ROYALE**, 8, b g Bold Fox—Celtic Royale **Mrs A. Price**
4 **GENEREUX**, 11, ch g Generous (USA)—Flo Russell (USA) **Mrs A. Price**
5 **HUNTERSWAY (IRE)**, 7, ch g Treasure Hunter—Dunmanway **Mrs A. Price**
6 **NORTON WOOD (IRE)**, 8, b g Shardari—Colligan Forest **Mrs A. Price**
7 **SAYWHEN**, 12, br g Say Primula—Practicality **Mrs A. Price**
8 **WHITE IN FRONT**, 13, ch g Tina's Pet—Lyaaric **Mrs A. Price**

Jockey (NH): J Goldstein. **Amateurs:** Mr R Hodges (9-7), Miss E James (9-0).

448 MR A. E. PRICE, Leominster
Postal: **Eaton Hall Farm, Leominster, Herefordshire, HR6 0NA.**
Contact: **PHONE (01568) 611137 MOBILE (07729) 838660 E-MAIL** price.eaton@tinyworld.co.uk

1 **BROOKSY DOVE,** 6, ch g Alderbrook—Coney Dove **M. G. Racing**
2 **CASTANET,** 5, b m Pennekamp (USA)—Addaya (IRE) **Mrs Carol Davis**
3 **CLOVER DOVE,** 5, b m Overbury (IRE)—Coney Dove **Mrs M. Price**
4 **ESHER COMMON (IRE),** 6, b g Common Grounds—Alsahah (IRE) **Lea Hall Lodge Racing I**
5 **MIDNIGHT GUNNER,** 10, b g Gunner B—Light Tonight **M. G. Racing**
6 **MOSCOW GOLD (IRE),** 7, ch g Moscow Society (USA)—Vesper Time **Mrs Carol Davis**
7 **OUR TOMMY,** 11, ch g Ardross—Ina's Farewell **Mrs H. L. Price**
8 **TERIDOVE,** 7, b g Terimon—Flakey Dove **Mrs M. Price**

Other Owners: Mr D. Bandey, Miss S. Bather, Mr A. G. Bathurst, Mr J. Bywater, Mr N. Hodge, Mr B. S. Jones, Mrs E. R. Kilt.

Assistant Trainer: Mrs H L Price

449 MR C. J. PRICE, Leominster
Postal: **Brockmanton Hall, Brockmanton, Leominster, Herefordshire, HR6 0QU.**
Contact: **PHONE (01568) 760695**

1 **DANCING PEARL,** 6, ch m Dancing Spree (USA)—Elegant Rose **Mr J. E. Heymans**
2 **DOLLY DOVE,** 9, b m Gran Alba (USA)—Celtic Dove **Mr Ryan Price**
3 **REGAL EMPRESS,** 6, b m Regal Embers (IRE)—Mis-E-Fishant **Mr H. E. Turberfield**
4 **SCRATCH THE DOVE,** 7, b m Henbit (USA)—Coney Dove **Mr Cecil J. Price**
5 **SO DAISY,** 6, b m Teenoso (USA)—La Margarite **Mr W. J. Butler**
6 **SOLAR DOVE,** 8, b g Jupiter Island—Celtic Dove **Mr M. J. Low**

THREE-YEAR-OLDS

7 B f Wizard King—Deadly Dove **Mr Cecil J. Price**

450 MR J. K. PRICE, Ebbw Vale
Postal: **41 Beaufort Terrace, Ebbw Vale, Gwent, NP23 5NW.**
Contact: **PHONE (01495) 306113 MOBILE (07870) 475156**

1 **DORSET FERN (IRE),** 8, b m Tirol—La Duse **Mr J. K. Price**
2 **HARMONY HALL,** 10, ch g Music Boy—Fleeting Affair **Mr J. K. Price**

Assistant Trainer: A J Price

451 MR RICHARD J. PRICE, Hereford
Postal: **Criftage Farm, Ullingswick, Hereford, Herefordshire, HR1 1JG.**
Contact: **PHONE (01432) 820263 MOBILE (07929) 200598**

1 **BOBSBEST (IRE),** 8, b g Lashkari—Bobs **Mr R. A. Jefferies**
2 **BUSINESS TRAVELLER (IRE),** 4, ch g Titus Livius (FR)—Dancing Venus **Karl And Patricia Reece**
3 **COMMANCHE HERO (IRE),** 11, ch g Cardinal Flower—Fair Bavard **Mr Pete Holder**
4 **COURT EMPEROR,** 4, b g Mtoto—Fairfields Cone **Derek & Cheryl Holder**
5 **COURT SHAREEF,** 9, b g Shareef Dancer (USA)—Fairfields Cone **Derek & Cheryl Holder**
6 **HARRY B,** 5, b g Midyan (USA)—Vilcabamba (USA) **Fox and Cub Partnership**
7 **LILAC,** 5, ch m Alhijaz—Fairfield's Breeze **Derek & Cheryl Holder**
8 **PRIDEWOOD DOVE,** 5, b m Alderbrook—Flighty Dove **Mrs B. Morris**
9 **REFLEX BLUE,** 7, b g Ezzoud (IRE)—Briggsmaid **Fox and Cub Partnership**
10 **SHELLIN HILL (IRE),** 10, ch g Sharp Victor (USA)—Queenspay **My Left Foot Racing Syndicate**
11 **SPRING PURSUIT,** 8, b g Rudimentary (USA)—Pursuit of Truth (USA) **Mr E. G. Bevan**
12 **ZANOORA (IRE),** 6, br m Topanoora—Zagliarelle (FR) **Mr R. J. Price**

MR RICHARD J. PRICE—continued

THREE-YEAR-OLDS

13 **RED LANCER,** ch g Deploy—Miss Bussell **Fox and Cub Partnership**

Other Owners: Mr A. J. Chance, Mr B. S. Hill, Mr S. S. Hill, Mr P. J. Hoare, Mrs Cheryl Holder, Mr Derek C. Holder, Mr K. Reece, Mrs Patricia Reece.

Assistant Trainer: Jane Price

Amateur: Miss V Price (9-7).

---

452 **MR P. A. PRITCHARD, Shipston-on-Stour**
Postal: **The Gate House, Whatcote, Shipston-On-Stour, Warwickshire, CV36 5EF.**
Contact: **PHONE (01295) 680689**

1 **ASTRAL AFFAIR (IRE),** 5, br m Norwich—Jupiters Jill **Woodland Generators**
2 **BEN GORM (IRE),** 4, ch g Tagula (IRE)—Regal Entrance **Mr P. A. Pritchard**
3 **FOLLOW THE FLOW (IRE),** 8, ch g Over The River (FR)—October Lady **Woodland Generators**
4 4, B f Mister Lord (USA)—Gayley Gale (IRE) **Mr P. A. Pritchard**
5 **JUST SUPERB,** 5, ch g Superlative—Just Greenwich **Mr D. R. Pritchard**
6 **McCRACKEN (IRE),** 8, b g Scenic—Sakanda (IRE) **Mr P. A. Pritchard**
7 4, Ch f Anshan—Play It By Ear (IRE) **Mr P. A. Pritchard**
8 5, Ch g Southern Music—Prospect of Whitby **Mr P. A. Pritchard**
9 **SAFE TO BLUSH,** 6, gr m Blushing Flame (USA)—Safe Arrival (USA) **Mr D. R. Pritchard**
10 **SCARLET FANTASY,** 4, b g Rudimentary (USA)—Katie Scarlett **Mr Thomas D. Goodman**
11 **WOODLANDS GENPOWER (IRE),** 6, gr g Roselier (FR)—Cherished Princess (IRE) **Woodland Generators**
12 **WOODLANDS LASS,** 8, ch m Nearly A Hand—Maranzi **Woodland Generators**

THREE-YEAR-OLDS

13 B g Oscar (IRE)—Gayley Gale (IRE) **Mr P. A. Pritchard**

TWO-YEAR-OLDS

14 B f 26/4 Oscar (IRE)—Play It By Ear (IRE) (Be My Native (USA)) **Mr P. A. Pritchard**

Jockey (Flat): S Righton (7-12). **Jockey (NH):** M Bradbourne. **Amateurs:** Mr T Greenway, Mr F Hutsby (10-0).

---

453 **DR P. L. J. PRITCHARD, Purton**
Postal: **Timber Pond House, Purton, Berkeley, Gloucestershire, GL13 9HY.**
Contact: **PHONE (01453) 811989 FAX (01453) 521557**
E-MAIL philip@timberpondracing.com WEBSITE www.timberpondracing.com

1 **BLAZING BATMAN,** 11, ch g Shaab—Cottage Blaze **Jumping Jokers**
2 **CYANARA,** 8, b m Jupiter Island—Shamana **Mr Steven R. Hanney**
3 **DAMIEN'S CHOICE (IRE),** 12, b g Erin's Hope—Reenoga **Norwester Racing Club**
4 **FIFTH GENERATION (IRE),** 14, b g Bulldozer—Fragrant's Last **Mrs T. Pritchard**
5 **FOREST IVORY (NZ),** 13, ch g Ivory Hunter (USA)—Fair And Square (NZ) **Lady Maria Coventry**
6 **GLOSTER GUNNER,** 5, ch g Gunner B—Blue Empress **Four For Fun**
7 **GOOD LORD MURPHY (IRE),** 12, br g Montelimar (USA)—Semiwild (USA) **The Breakfast Set**
8 **HAPPY HUSSAR (IRE),** 11, b g Balinger—Merry Mirth **Dr J. J. Kabler**
9 **HI TECH,** 5, b g Polar Falcon (USA)—Just Speculation (IRE) **Mrs T. Pritchard**
10 **KNOCKRIGG (IRE),** 10, ch g Commanche Run—Gaiety Lass **Mrs T. Pritchard**
11 **MANTLES PRIDE,** 9, br g Petong—State Romance **Mrs T. Pritchard**
12 **ONLY FOR GOLD,** 9, b g Presidium—Calvanne Miss **Juro Antiques**
13 **POETRY AND JAZZ,** 5, b g Nomadic Way (USA)—Indian Crown **Miss T. R. Johnson**
14 **PREMIER GENERATION (IRE),** 11, b g Cadeaux Genereux—Bristle **Mr Ray Edwards**

DR P. L. J. PRITCHARD—continued

15 **RED EMPEROR,** 10, b g Emperor Fountain—Golden Curd (FR) **Mrs T. Pritchard**
16 **SEATTLE ART (USA),** 10, b g Seattle Slew (USA)—Artiste **Lady Maria Coventry**

Other Owners: Mr R. H. Brookes, Mr David Byrne, Mr C. J. Dennis, Mr W. J. Eaton, Mrs J. George, Mr B. S. Hicks, Mr G. H. Hicks, Mr R. Hughes, Mr A. E. Kendell, Mrs N. P. Lloyd, Mr D. G. Long, Mr T. Mountford, Mr P. Nurcombe.

Assistant Trainer: Mrs T. Pritchard

Jockeys (NH): R Greene (w,a), Mogford, J Mogford (w,a). **Amateurs:** Mr O Dayman (9-7), Dr P L J Pritchard (9-11).

---

454 **MR G. PRODROMOU, East Harling**
Postal: **Georges Farm, Bryants Bridge, East Harling, Norfolk, NR16 2JR.**
Contact: **PHONE (01953) 717224 MOBILE (07899) 071001**

1 **ARAWAK PRINCE (IRE),** 8, ch g College Chapel—Alpine Symphony **Mr George Prodromou**
2 **BREATHTAKING VIEW (USA),** 8, b g Country Pine (USA)—Lituya Bay (USA) **Mrs B. Macalister**
3 **COURT LENEY (IRE),** 9, b g Commanche Run—Dont Call Me Lady **Mr Alan Macalister**
4 **GOODYS (IRE),** 5, ch g Good Thyne (USA)—Katie Baggage (IRE) **Mrs B. Macalister**
5 **IN ERNEST (IRE),** 6, ch m Forest Wind (USA)—Picnic Basket **Mr George Prodromou**
6 **LA PUCE VOLANTE,** 8, ch m Grand Lodge (USA)—Gold Linnet **Mr George Prodromou**
7 **MINNIE BLOO MIN (IRE),** 5, b m Blues Traveller (IRE)—White Jasmin **Mr George Prodromou**
8 **MR HICKMAN (IRE),** 7, b g Montelimar (USA)—Cabin Glory **Mr Alan Macalister**
9 **SAXON QUEEN,** 10, b m Lord Bud—Saxon Slave **Mr George Prodromou**
10 **TAKE THE ODDS (IRE),** gr g Roselier (FR)—Skinana **Mr Alan Macalister**
11 **TOULON CREST (IRE),** 7, b g Toulon—Another Contact **Mr Alan Macalister**
12 **VALS WELL (IRE),** 9, b g Be My Native (USA)—Castle-Lady **Mr George Prodromou**

THREE-YEAR-OLDS

13 **KING OF KNIGHT (IRE),** gr g Orpen (USA)—Peace Melody (IRE) **Mr M. M. Foulger**
14 **KING OF MEZE (IRE),** b g Croco Rouge (IRE)—Cossack Princess (IRE) **Mr F. & Mrs A. Butler**
15 **KING OF MUSIC (USA),** ch g Jade Hunter (USA)—Hail Roberta (USA) **Mrs B. Macalister**

TWO-YEAR-OLDS

16 **KALHMERA (IRE),** b f 16/4 Gone Fishin—Biddy Widdy (IRE) (Phardante (FR))

Other Owners: Mrs A. Butler, Mr F. Butler.

Assistant Trainer: Alan Macallister

Jockey (Flat): Oscar Urbina. **Jockey (NH):** R Thornton. **Conditional:** Mathew Smith (9-10). **Amateur:** Mr Paul Fergunson (9-10).

---

455 **MR P. D. PURDY, Bridgwater**
Postal: **Fyne Court Farm, Broomfield, Bridgwater, Somerset, TA5 2EQ.**
Contact: **PHONE (01823) 451632 MOBILE (07860) 392786 FAX (01823) 451632**

1 **COURT EMPRESS,** 7, ch m Emperor Fountain—Tudor Sunset **Mr P. D. Purdy**
2 **COURT NANNY,** 10, ch m Nicholas Bill—Tudor Sunset **Mr P. D. Purdy**
3 **COURT OLIVER,** 6, ch g One Voice (USA)—Tudor Sunset **Mr P. D. Purdy**
4 **COURT SENOR,** 8, gr g Gran Alba (USA)—Tudor Sunset **Mr P. D. Purdy**
5 **GREY COURT,** 9, ro g Gran Alba (USA)—Tudor Sunset **Mr P. D. Purdy**
6 **SUNRISE COURT,** 5, ch g One Voice (USA)—Tudor Sunset **Mr P. D. Purdy**
7 **SUTTON BALLAD,** 10, b m Emperor Fountain—Crescent Cottage **Mr P. D. Purdy**
8 **SUTTON LION,** 12, b g Lyphento (USA)—Crescent Cottage **Mr P. D. Purdy**
9 **TUDOR NICKOLA,** 12, ch m Nicholas Bill—Cottage Melody **Mr P. D. Purdy**

THREE-YEAR-OLDS

10 **COURT FINALE,** ch g One Voice (USA)—Tudor Sunset **Mr P. D. Purdy**

Assistant Trainer: Alison J Purdy

Amateur: Miss Alison Jane Purdy (9-2).

456 MR M. QUINLAN, Newmarket
Postal: **Athnid Stables, Jamesfield Place, Hamilton Road, Newmarket, Suffolk CB8 7JQ.**
Contact: **OFFICE (01638) 603530 FAX (01638) 603488 MOBILE (07815) 072946**

1 **CAZENOVE**, b c Royal Applause—Celestina (IRE) **P. Benedetti**
2 **DIVERTED**, b f Averti (IRE)—Whittle Rock **Mrs J. Quinlan**
3 **FRANK SONATA**, b c Opening Verse (USA)—Megdale (IRE) **Messrs Adams, Flynn, Arnold**
4 **JAPIGIA (IRE)**, b f Singspiel (IRE)—Japan Exile (FR) **Dr Bruno Bardi**
5 **LAURENS GIRL (IRE)**, br f Imperial Ballet (IRE)—Tresor Vert (USA) **J. Meehan**
6 **LOVE OF LIFE**, b f Spectrum (IRE)—Night Over Day **Love Of Life Partnership**
7 **MAC REGAL (IRE)**, b c King's Theatre (IRE)—Shine Silently (IRE) **Dr Angelo Macchi**
8 **SIERA SPIRIT (IRE)**, b f Desert Sun—Jay And A (IRE) **P. Ashmore & Mrs J. Quinlan**

TWO-YEAR-OLDS

9 Ch c 3/3 Piccolo—Anna Karietta (Precocious) (23000) **O'Connor Racing**
10 B f 10/3 Tagula (IRE)—Black Jack Girl (IRE) (Ridgewood Ben) (7420)
11 B c 26/3 Fasliyev (USA)—Conquete (USA) (Distant View (USA)) (20000) **Dr A. Macchi**
12 **COSTIERA**, b f 1/5 Polar Falcon (USA)—Celestina (IRE) (Priolo (USA)) **P. Benedetti**
13 B f 4/2 Revoque (IRE)—Fanciful (IRE) (Mujtahid (USA)) (4500)
14 B c 25/1 Bachir (IRE)—Glittering Image (IRE) (Sadler's Wells (USA)) (16079) **Dr A. Macchi**
15 B c 24/2 Night Shift (USA)—Glow Blue (USA) (Cure The Blues (USA)) (21025)
16 B c 2/3 Rossini (USA)—Green Wings (General Assembly) (18000) **Mrs B. Johnston**
17 Ch f 29/3 Barathea (IRE)—High Flying Adored (IRE) (In The Wings) (28000) **Mr L. Cashman**
18 B f 21/1 Mind Games—Its All Relative (Distant Relative) (800) **Mrs R. Smith**
19 B f 3/3 Night Shift (USA)—Let Alone (Warning) (6000) **Dr A. Macchi**
20 B f 17/3 Tipsy Creek (USA)—Margarets First (Puissance) (1200) **Mrs R. Smith**
21 B c 14/4 Spectrum (IRE)—Milly Ha Ha (Dancing Brave) (USA) (5500)
22 B c 21/5 Lahib (USA)—Noci (USA) (Lypheor) **A. Pettinari**
23 B c 8/5 Turtle Island (IRE)—Nonnita (Welsh Saint) (3091) **G. Manfredini**
24 Ch c 26/3 Opening Verse (USA)—Perian Fountain (IRE) (Persian Heights) **Mr W. Flynn**
25 Br f 5/3 Lend A Hand—Rapturous (Zafonic (USA)) (18000) **A. Pettinari**
26 B f 28/4 Entrepreneur—Shalwell (IRE) (Shalford (IRE)) (4638)
27 Ch c 22/2 Royal Academy (USA)—Statua (IRE) (Statoblest) (8500) **Mr J. de Selincourt**
28 B c 30/3 Sendawar (IRE)—Suhaad (Unfuwain (USA)) (2473) **Mrs N. McGreavy**
29 B c 28/3 Entrepreneur—Tammany Hall (IRE) (Petorius) (6183)
30 B c 2/4 Sagamix (FR)—Tigava (USA) (Machiavellian) (USA) (15460) **Dr A. Macchi**
31 B c 27/2 In The Wings—Tocade (IRE) (Kenmare (FR)) (15460) **Dr A. Macchi**

Other Owners: Mr A. Asquith, John O'Connor.

Assistant Trainer: N Quinlan

Jockeys (Flat): A Culhane (w.a.), S. W. Kelly. **Apprentice:** Nicol Polli.

457 MR J. J. QUINN, Malton
Postal: **Bellwood Cottage Stables, Settrington, Malton, North Yorkshire, YO17 8NR.**
Contact: **PHONE (01944) 768370 FAX (01944) 768261 MOBILE (07899) 873495**
E-MAIL jjq@quinn-settrington.freeserve.co.uk

1 **ADJAWAR**, 6, b g Ashkalani (IRE)—Adjriyna **Mrs M. Taylor**
2 **ALERON (IRE)**, 6, b h Sadler's Wells (USA)—High Hawk **Mr Grahame Liles**
3 **ANGELICA PICKLES (IRE)**, 4, b f Sesaro (USA)—Iva's Flyer (IRE) **Mrs S. Quinn**
4 **ARCHIE BABE (IRE)**, 8, ch g Archway (IRE)—Frensham Manor **Bowett Lamb & Kelly**
5 **BASINET**, 6, b g Alzao (USA)—Valiancy **Tara Leisure**
6 **BEAUVRAI**, 4, b g Bahamian Bounty—Lets Be Fair **Mr G. A. Roberts**
7 **CAPTAIN VENTI**, 5, br g Ventiquattrofogli (IRE)—Lady Liza **I Buckley L Cross P Dixon N Watts**
8 **CARIBBEAN CORAL**, 5, ch g Brief Truce (USA)—Caribbean Star **Roberts, Dawson, Green & Quinn**
9 **DIRECT DESCENDANT (IRE)**, 5, ch g Be My Guest (USA)—Prague Spring **Miss D. A. Johnson**
10 **ESTANBAN**, 4, b g Groom Dancer (USA)—Ellie Ardensky **Snailwell Stud Company**
11 **EVERY NOTE COUNTS**, 4, b g Bluegrass Prince (IRE)—Miss Mirror **Tara Leisure**
12 **FANTASY BELIEVER**, 6, b g Sure Blade (USA)—Delicious **Fantasy Fellowship B**
13 **GREEN ADMIRAL**, 5, b g Slip Anchor—Jade Mistress **Mrs C. T. Bletsoe**
14 **GREENAWAY BAY (USA)**, 10, ch g Green Dancer (USA)—
Raise 'n Dance (USA) **A.Page, L.Pickering, J.Taylor, J.Ward**

15 **HOV**, 4, gr g Petong—Harifa **Mr G. A. Lucas**

MR. J. J. QUINN—continued

16 **INCH ISLAND (IRE)**, 4, b g Turtle Island (IRE)—Persian Light (IRE) **Birdstown Syndicate**
17 **INTO BATTLE**, 10, b g Daring March—Mischievous Miss **Lady Anne Bentinck**
18 **JAKE BLACK (IRE)**, 4, b g Definite Article—Tirhala (IRE) **Mr G. A. Lucas**
19 **MASTER NIMBUS**, 4, b g Cloudings (IRE)—Miss Charlie **John Hewitt**
20 **MIZHAR (USA)**, 8, b g Dayjur (USA)—Futah (USA) **Mr A. Page**
21 **ROCINANTE (IRE)**, 4, b g Desert Story (IRE)—Antapoura (IRE) **Mrs M. Taylor**
22 **SMART HOSTESS**, 5, gr m Most Welcome—She's Smart **Mr B. Shaw**
23 **SMART MINISTER**, 4, gr g Muhtarrah (USA)—She's Smart **Mr B. Shaw**
24 **SMART PREDATOR**, 8, gr g Polar Falcon (USA)—She's Smart **Mr B. Shaw**
25 **THUNDERCLAP**, 5, b g Royal Applause—Gloriana **Mr M. Paley**
26 **WINTHORPE (IRE)**, 4, b g Tagula (IRE)—Zazu **Mr G. A. Lucas**

THREE-YEAR-OLDS

27 **A BIT OF FUN**, ch g Unfuwain (USA)—Horseshoe Reef **The Funseekers**
28 **ICENASLICE (IRE)**, b f Fayruz—Come Dancing **Miss D. A. Johnson**
29 **LETS GET IT ON (IRE)**, b f Perugino (USA)—Lets Clic Together **Usual Suspects**
30 **SMART DANNY**, gr g Danzero (AUS)—She's Smart **Mr B. Shaw**
31 **SOFT MIST (IRE)**, b g Up And At 'em—Morgiana **Marsh & waltham**
32 **SUJOISE**, b g Prince Sabo—Statliette **Mrs S. Quinn**
33 **TIME TO REGRET**, b g Presidium—Scoffera **B Selective Partnership**
34 **TIME TO RELAX (IRE)**, b f Orpen (USA)—Lassalia **Mr Grahame Liles**

TWO-YEAR-OLDS

35 **BIGALOS BANDIT**, ch c 9/3 Compton Place—Move Darling (Rock City) (13500) **Mr Ian Buckley**
36 Ch f 26/3 Defacto (USA)—Chimes of Peace (Magic Ring (IRE)) **Mrs M. Lingwood**
37 **CRAIGOWER (IRE)**, b f 28/3 Brace Act—Peplin (Coquelin) **Mr C. Marsh & Mrs S. Quinn**
38 B c 3/4 Grandlodge (USA)—Dundel (IRE) (Machiavellian (USA)) (80000) **Mr J. Henderson**
39 **ELLIS CAVE**, gr g 12/3 Diktat—Cole Slaw (Absalom) (22000) **Mr Ian Buckey & Mr G. A. Lucas**
40 **FANTASY DEFENDER (IRE)**, b g 20/4 Fayruz—Mrs Lucky (Royal Match) (3500) **Fantasy Fellowship D**
41 **HARRYS HOUSE**, gr c 25/2 Paris House—Rum Lass (Distant Relative) **Mr N. Bulmer**
42 B c 28/1 Almaty—Lawless Bridget (Alnasr Alwasheek) (4500) **Mr Timothy Woods**
43 B f 30/4 Kayf Tara—Morgannwg (Simply Great (FR)) **Mr Bletsoe**
44 B c 19/3 Factual (USA)—Queens Check (Komaite (USA)) (1200) **Mr Rowbottom**
45 **STREET DANCER**, b g 26/4 Imperial Ballet (IRE)—Life On The Street (Statoblest) (18000) **Mr Grahame Liles**
46 **TARAS KNIGHT**, b g 19/2 Indian Danehill (IRE)—
                     Queen of Art (IRE) (Royal Academy (USA)) (18552) **Tara Leisure**
47 **TARAS TREASURE**, b f 19/2 Desert King (IRE)—Oklahoma (Shareef Dancer (USA)) (29683) **Tara Leisure**
48 **TARA TARA (IRE)**, b f 2/4 Fayruz—Gobolino (Don) (12368) **Tara Leisure**
49 **WHY HARRY**, b g 5/4 Cyrano De Bergerac—Golden Ciel (USA) (Septieme Ciel (USA)) (5000) **Mr D. Bloy**

Other Owners: Mrs E. J. Bletsoe, Mr J. J. Devine, Mr M. G. Kerrigan, Mr D. P. McEvoy, Mrs E. J. Bletsoe, Mr A. P. Reed, Mr John Ward.

Jockeys (Flat): J Fortune (w.a.), D Holland (w.a.).

---

458 MRS J. R. RAMSDEN, Thirsk
Postal: J. R. Racing Ltd, Breckenbrough House, Sandhutton, Thirsk, North Yorkshire, YO7 4EL.
Contact: **PHONE** (01845) 587226 **FAX** (01845) 587443 **E-MAIL** jack.ramsden@virgin.net

1 **ARCALIS**, 4, gr g Lear Fan (USA)—Aristocratique
2 **BISHOPS COURT**, 10, ch g Clantime—Indigo
3 **BLACKTHORN**, 5, ch g Deploy—Balliasta (USA)
4 **CAPE ROYAL**, 4, b g Prince Sabo—Indigo
5 **CHANTRESS**, 4, b f Peintre Celebre (USA)—Up Anchor (IRE)
6 **DISTANT COUNTRY (USA)**, 5, b g Distant View (USA)—Memsahb (USA)
7 **FAVOUR**, 4, b f Gothenberg (IRE)—Prejudice
8 **GREENWICH MEANTIME**, 4, b g Royal Academy (USA)—Shirley Valentine
9 **HICCUPS**, 4, b g Polar Prince (IRE)—Simmie's Special
10 **KANGARILLA ROAD**, 5, b g Magic Ring (IRE)—Kangra Valley
11 **METEORITE SUN (USA)**, 6, b g Miesque's Son—Myth To Reality (FR)
12 **MYSTERY MOUNTAIN**, 4, b g Mistertopogigo (IRE)—Don't Jump (IRE)

MRS J. R. RAMSDEN—continued

THREE-YEAR-OLDS

13 **DOUBLE VODKA (IRE)**, b br c Russian Revival (USA)—Silius
14 **FAIRLIE**, b f Halling (USA)—Fairy Flax (IRE)
15 **JOHNNY PARKES**, b g Wolfhound (USA)—Lucky Parkes
16 **LEOPARD CREEK**, ch f Weldnaas (USA)—Indigo
17 **MOUNT VETTORE**, br g Vettori (IRE)—Honeyspike (IRE)
18 **NEW MEXICAN**, ch g Dr Fong (USA)—Apache Star
19 **TROJAN FLIGHT**, ch g Hector Protector (USA)—Fairywings
20 **UTAH FLATS (IRE)**, ch g Bluebird (USA)—Desert Rose

TWO-YEAR-OLDS

21 **ABLE CHARLIE (GER)**, ch g 19/2 Lomitas—Alula (GER) (Monsun (GER)) (17316)
22 **ADMITTANCE (USA)**, b br f 12/2 Red Ransom (USA)—Quittance (USA) (Riverman (USA)) (14841)
23 **ALONG THE NILE**, b c 12/2 Desert Prince (IRE)—Golden Fortune (Forzando) (40000)
24 **DAVY CROCKETT**, b g 9/2 Polar Prince (IRE)—Sing With The Band (Chief Singer) (2000)
25 B f 7/3 Fraam—Discrimination (Efisio)
26 **DR GNOME**, b c 16/1 Dr Fong (USA)—Metronome (Salse (USA)) (24000)
27 **ENTAILMENT**, b c 12/3 Kris—Entail (USA) (Riverman (USA)) (30000)
28 Ch g 13/4 Loup Sauvage (USA)—Fairy Flax (IRE) (Dancing Brave (USA))
29 **FERRANDO**, b g 15/5 Hernando (FR)—Oh So Misty (Teenoso (USA)) (8000)
30 **HALLA SAN**, b c 14/3 Halling (USA)—St Radegund (Green Desert (USA)) (37000)
31 B f 3/2 Entrepreneur—Logic (Slip Anchor)
32 **LORNA DUNE**, b f 21/2 Desert Story (IRE)—Autumn Affair (Lugana Beach) (11000)
33 **MUSARDIERE**, b f 23/4 Montjeu (IRE)—Majestic Image (Niniski (USA)) (34000)
34 **PRO TEMPORE**, b f 18/1 Fraam—Record Time (Clantime) (21000)
35 Ch c 22/2 Primo Dominie—Showcase (Shareef Dancer (USA)) (37000)
36 **TANFORAN**, b g 9/3 Mujahid (USA)—Florentynna Bay (Aragon) (8000)
37 **TURNAROUND (GER)**, gr c 2/2 Highest Honor (FR)—Tamacana (Windwurf (GER)) (24737)

Other Owners: Mr D. R. Brotherton, Mr M. Charlton, Manor Farm Stud (Rutland), Mr W. J. Gredley, Mr J. Heler, Mr D. Morrison, Mr P. R. C. Morrison, Mr N. Munton, Mr J. Musgrave, Newbyth Stud, Mr T. J. O'Gram, Swiss Partners, K. Pratt & Associates, Miss E. L. Ramsden, Mrs E. E. Ranson, Mr J. M. Ranson, Mrs A. E. Sigsworth, Mr L. C. Sigsworth, Mr R. C. Thompson.

---

459 | **MR D. REES, Haverfordwest**
Postal: **The Grove Yard, Clarbeston Road, Haverfordwest, Pembrokeshire, SA63 4SP.**
Contact: **PHONE (01437) 731308 MOBILE (07831) 800172/(07775) 662463**
E-MAIL davidreesfencing@lineone.net

1 **ADIYSHA (IRE)**, 7, b m Namaqualand (USA)—Adira (IRE) **Mr D. A. Rees & Mr P. Harris**
2 **BONNY BOY (IRE)**, 9, b g Bustino—Dingle Bay **Mr D. Rees**
3 **CRUISING HOME**, 6, b g Homo Sapien—Fast Cruise **Mr Philip Harris**
4 **RUNNING LORD (IRE)**, 6, b g Mister Lord (USA)—Craic Go Leor **Mr D. A. Rees & Mr P. Harris**
5 **SCARLET DAWN (IRE)**, 6, b m Supreme Leader—Dawn Appeal **Mr D. Rees**
6 **SUPREMELY RED (IRE)**, 7, b g Supreme Leader—Her Name Was Lola **Mr D. A. Rees & Mr P. Harris**

Assistant Trainer: Miss D J Green

---

460 | **MRS G. S. REES, Preston**
Postal: **Moor Farm, Sollom, Preston, Lancashire, PR4 6HR.**
Contact: **PHONE (01772) 812780 MOBILE (07789) 436991**

1 **BABY BARRY**, 7, b g Komaite (USA)—Malcesine (IRE) **Mr John W. Barry**
2 **GEMINI LADY**, 4, b f Emperor Fountain—Raunchy Rita **Mobberley Manor Racing**
3 **GLEN VALE WALK**, 7, ch g Balla Cove—Winter Harvest **Mr Dominic Brady**
4 **NEWCORP LAD**, 4, b g Komaite (USA)—Gleam of Gold **Red Rose Partnership**
5 **SCENT AHEAD (USA)**, 5, b g Foxhound—Sonseri **Mr J. Brough**
6 **SUBADAR MAJOR**, 7, b g Komaite—Rather Gorgeous **Major Bailey**
7 **SWEETSTOCK**, 6, b m Anshan—Stockline **Mrs Annette C. Barlow**

MRS G. S. REES—continued
THREE-YEAR-OLDS

8 **CALCULAITE,** b g Komaite (USA)—Miss Calculate **Mrs G. S. Rees**
9 **CUTE CAIT,** b f Atraf—Clunk Click **Mr E. Hemming**

TWO-YEAR-OLDS

10 B g 21/5 Komaite (USA)—Amy Leigh (IRE) (Imperial Frontier (USA)) **Mrs G. S. Rees**
11 B f 19/2 Komaite (USA)—Jamarj (Tyrnavos) **Philip Bamford**
12 **ROSEIN,** b f 22/4 Komaite (USA)—Red Rosein (Red Sunset) (20000) **Mr Tom Murray**

Other Owners: Mr Alan Sidebottom, Mr Derek R. Whitehead.

Assistant Trainer: Capt J H Wilson

Jockeys (Flat): G Duffield, A Mackay, S Sanders.

 MRS H. E. REES, Dorchester
Postal: **Distant Hills, Chalmington, Dorchester, Dorset, DT2 0HB.**
Contact: PHONE (01300) 320683 MOBILE (07715) 558289
E-MAIL rupertandhelenrees@distanthills.freeserve.co.uk

1 **SHOTACROSS THE BOW (IRE),** 7, b g Warning—Nordica **Mrs H. E. Rees**

Assistant Trainer: Mr Rupert Rees

 MR A. S. REID, Mill Hill, London
Postal: **Highwood Lodge, Highwood Hill, Mill Hill, London, NW7 4HB.**
Contact: PHONE (0208) 9061255 MOBILE (07836) 214617

1 **AL MUALLIM (USA),** 10, b g Theatrical—Gerri N Jo Go (USA) **Mr L. R. Gotch**
2 **BULAWAYO,** 7, b g Prince Sabo—Ra Ra Girl **Mr A. S. Reid**
3 **CONFUZED,** 4, b g Pivotal—Times of Times (IRE) **Mr A. S. Reid**
4 4, B f Parthian Springs—Double Dose **Ms Corrina Hirst**
5 **FIRE DOME (IRE),** 12, ch g Salt Dome—Penny Habit **Mr A. S. Reid**
6 **HARIPUR,** 5, b h Rainbow Quest (USA)—Jamrat Jumairah (IRE) **Mr A. S. Reid**
7 **INDIAN BLAZE,** 10, ch g Indian Ridge—Odile **Mrs Irene Clifford**
8 **PANTS,** 5, b m Pivotal—Queenbird **Mr A. S. Reid**
9 **RAINBOW WORLD (IRE),** 4, b c Rainbow Quest (USA)—Far Fetched (IRE) **Mr A. S. Reid**
10 **TAYIF,** 7, b g Taufan (USA)—Rich Lass **Mr A. S. Reid**
11 **TEMPER TANTRUM,** 6, b g Pursuit of Love—Queenbird **The Little House Partnership**
12 **TROUSERS,** 5, b g Pivotal—Palo Blanco **Mr A. S. Reid**
13 **WILLHECONQUERTOO,** 4, ch g Primo Dominie—Sure Care **Mr A. S. Reid**

THREE-YEAR-OLDS

14 **ECCENTRIC,** ch g Most Welcome—Sure Care **Mr A. S. Reid**
15 **LADY MO,** b f Young Ern—Just Run (IRE) **Mr A. S. Reid**
16 **LADY PREDOMINANT,** b f Primo Dominie—Enlisted (IRE) **Mr A. S. Reid**
17 **LITTLETON LIBERTY,** b f Royal Applause—Lammastide **Mr A. S. Reid**
18 **MAD,** br f Pursuit of Love—Emily-Mou (IRE) **Mr A. S. Reid**
19 **PEKA IMO (IRE),** b c Sri Pekan (USA)—Chambolle Musigny (USA) **Mr A. S. Reid**
20 **RISE,** b f Polar Falcon (USA)—Splice **Mr A. S. Reid**
21 **TROTTERS BOTTOM,** b g Mind Games—Fleeting Affair **Mr A. S. Reid**
22 **VENDORS MISTAKE (IRE),** b f Danehill (USA)—Sunspangled (IRE) **Mr A. S. Reid**

TWO-YEAR-OLDS

23 **AGGRAVATION,** b g 24/4 Sure Blade (USA)—Confection (Formidable (USA)) (5714) **Mr A. S. Reid**
24 **DEPRESSED,** ch f 20/4 Most Welcome—Sure Care (Caerleon (USA)) (2857) **Mr A. S. Reid**
25 Gr f 6/2 Soviet Star (USA)—Felicita (IRE) (Catrail (USA)) (36000) **Mr A. S. Reid**
26 **MANIC,** br f 26/4 Polar Falcon (USA)—Gentle Irony (Mazilier (USA)) (2666) **Mr A. S. Reid**

MR A. S. REID—continued

27 **QUESTION MARK**, b g 7/2 Polar Falcon (USA)—Frankie Fair (IRE) (Red Sunset) (3047) **Dr D. Myres**
28 **WRIT (IRE)**, ch g 6/4 Indian Lodge (IRE)—Carnelly (IRE) (Priolo) (USA) (5000) **Mr A. S. Reid**

Other Owners: Mr P. M. A. Gazeley, Mr D. T. Norton.

Assistant Trainer: Martin Dunne

---

463 MR E. R. RETTER, South Brent
Postal: **5a Dolbeare Road, Ashburton, Newton Abbot, TQ13 7AS.**
Contact: **MOBILE (07973) 969911**

1 **BISHOP'S BLADE**, 7, b g Sure Blade (USA)—Myrtilla **Mr Edward Retter**
2 **CRUISING CLYDE**, 5, ch g Karinga Bay—Bournel **Mr Edward Retter**
3 **GREAT GAME**, 4, b g Indian Ridge—Russian Grace (IRE) **Mr Edward Retter**
4 **KARINGA CITY**, 7, ch g Karinga Bay—Panicaly **Mr Edward Retter**
5 5, Ch b g Sylvan Express—Mermaid Bay **Mr Edward Retter**
6 **THE DOORMAN**, 8, b g Gildoran—Mandarling **Mr Edward Retter**

Assistant Trainer: Miss Sarah Gaisford

Amateur: Miss Sarah Gaisford (9-7).

---

464 MRS J. G. RETTER, Swindon
Postal: **Foxhill Farm Stables, Foxhill, Swindon, Wiltshire, SN4 0DS.**
Contact: **PHONE (01793) 791515**

1 **BICKWELL**, 6, br m Afzal—Flying Cherub **Mrs J. G. Retter**
2 **NADDERWATER**, 12, br g Arctic Lord—Flying Cherub **Mrs J. G. Retter**
3 **WHITESTONE**, 8, b m Sula Bula—Flying Cherub **Mrs J. G. Retter**

---

465 MRS G. R. REVELEY, Saltburn
Postal: **Groundhill Farm, Lingdale, Saltburn, Cleveland, TS12 3HD.**
Contact: **PHONE (01287) 650456 FAX (01287) 653095 MOBILE (07802) 449085**

1 **ALWAYS SOMETHING (IRE)**, 7, b br m Insan (USA)—Lizzie Simms (IRE) **The Mary Reveley Racing Club**
2 **A PIECE OF CAKE (IRE)**, 11, gr g Roselier (FR)—Boreen Bro **Lightbody Celebration Cakes Ltd**
3 **BIRDWATCH**, 6, b g Minshaanshu Amad (USA)—Eider **Jeremy Mitchell and Janet Powney**
4 **BOARD WALK (IRE)**, 9, b g Commanche Run—Swift Tide **Mrs M. Hoey**
5 **BROCTUNE MELODY**, 5, b br g Merdon Melody—Eider **D. Playforth + D. Young**
6 **BUSINESS CLASS (NZ)**, 12, b g Accountant (NZ)—Fury's Princess (NZ) **Mr Ernie Fenwick**
7 **BUSTED FLAT (IRE)**, 11, br g Bustino—Trailing Rose **Mr R. Burridge**
8 **CARRICK TROOP (IRE)**, 11, gr g Roselier (FR)—Over The Pond (IRE) **Major J. C. K. Young**
9 **CELTIC LEGEND (FR)**, 5, br g Celtic Swing—Another Legend **Mr P. D. Savill**
10 **CELTIC ROMANCE**, 5, b m Celtic Swing—Southern Sky **Mr H. G. W. Brown**
11 **CLOUDING OVER**, 4, gr f Cloudings (IRE)—Wellwotdouthink **Mr W. D. Hockenhull**
12 **COLOURFUL LIFE (IRE)**, 6, ch g Rainbows For Life (CAN)—Rasmara **Andy Peake & David Jackson**
13 **COMMANCHE QUEST (IRE)**, 8, b g Commanche Run—Conna Dodger (IRE) **The Eleven O'Clock Club**
14 **CROWNFIELD**, 5, b g Blushing Flame (USA)—Chief Island **Mr H. G. W. Brown**
15 **DARA CAPALL**, 4, b g Simply Great (FR)—She's Pretty **Revival Racing Ltd**
16 **DIAMOND SAL**, 6, b m Bob Back (USA)—Fortune's Girl **Mr R. Haggas**
17 **DIKLERS ROSE (IRE)**, 5, gr m Roselier (FR)—Diklers Run **The Mary Reveley Racing Club**
18 **DING DONG BELLE**, 5, ch m Minster Son—Corn Lily **Mrs Susan McDonald**
19 **DUKE OF BRITTANY (IRE)**, 5, ch g Rifapour (IRE)—Fox Trot V (FR) **Sir Robert Ogden**
20 **FLAME OF ZARA**, 5, ch m Blushing Flame (USA)—Sierra Madrona (USA) **Mr R. Meredith**
21 **FLORIDA RAIN (IRE)**, 8, b g Florida Son—Ameretto **Mr Andy Peake**
22 **GAY KINDERSLEY (IRE)**, 6, ch g Roselier (FR)—Ramble Bramble **W. J. Smith and M. D. Dudley**
23 **GOLDEN ODYSSEY (IRE)**, 4, ch f Barathea (IRE)—Opus One **Sir Robert Ogden**
24 5, B h Primitive Rising (USA)—Grand Queen
25 **GREAT ANTICIPATION (FR)**, 6, b g Useful (FR)—Casaque du Perche (FR) **Sir Robert Ogden**
26 **HENRIANJAMES**, 9, b g Tina's Pet—Real Claire **Mr K. Benson**
27 **HIDDEN BOUNTY (IRE)**, 8, b g Generous (USA)—Sought Out (IRE) **Mr M. E. Foxton**
28 **HIGH COTTON (IRE)**, 9, gr g Ala Hounak—Planalife **Mr R. Burridge**
29 **HUNTERS CREEK (IRE)**, 10, b g Persian Mews—Creek's Sister **Bewley's Hotels, Glasgow (BSH Ltd)**

MRS G. R. REVELEY—continued

30 **ICY RIVER (IRE)**, 7, ch g Over The River (FR)—Icy Lou **Mr Andy Peake**
31 **I GOT RHYTHM**, 6, gr m Lycius (USA)—Eurythmic **Mr G. Thomson**
32 **IL CAVALIERE**, 9, b g Mtoto—Kalmia **The Thoughtful Partnership**
33 **ILLICIUM**, 5, b m Fourstars Allstar (USA)—Sweet Mignonette **Mr & Mrs W. J. Williams**
34 **INTO THE SHADOWS**, 4, ch f Safawan—Shadows of Silver **Mr R. C. Mayall**
35 **ISLANDS FAREWELL**, 4, b g Emarati (USA)—Chief Island **Mr H. G. W. Brown**
36 **JUNE'S RIVER (IRE)**, 11, ch g Over The River (FR)—June Bug **Mr A. Flannigan**
37 **KINGS BLOOM (IRE)**, 6, b g Supreme Leader—Sweet Mignonette **Mr E. Fenwick & Mr R. Manners**
38 **KONKER**, 9, ch g Selkirk (USA)—Helens Dreamgirl **J & M Leisure / Unos Restaurant**
39 **LEFT BANK (IRE)**, 8, ch g Over The River (FR)—My Friend Fashion **Mr C. C. Buckley**
40 **LE ROYAL (FR)**, 5, b g Garde Royale—Caucasie (FR) **Mrs Stephanie Smith**
41 **LOOP THE LOUP**, 8, b g Petit Loup—Mithi Al Gamar (USA) **Mr and Mrs J. D. Cotton**
42 **LORD LAMB**, 12, gr g Dunbeath (USA)—Caroline Lamb **Mr J. Renton**
43 **MACEO (GER)**, 10, ch g Acatenango (GER)—Metropolitan Star (USA) **Mr Les De La Haye**
44 **MAGICAL FIELD**, 6, ch m Deploy—Ash Glade **Lightbody Celebration Cakes Ltd**
45 **MAGIC DRAGON (FR)**, 6, ch g Cyborg (FR)—Dix Huit Brumaire (FR) **Sir Robert Ogden**
46 **MALEK (IRE)**, 8, b g Tremblant—Any Offers **Mrs J. W. Furness & Lord Zetland**
47 **MARMADUKE JINKS**, 10, b g Primitive Rising (USA)—Keldholme **Minster Commercials**
48 **MINSTER MISSILE**, 6, b g Minster Son—Manettia (IRE) **Mr G. Stevenson**
49 **MISS LEHMAN**, 6, ch m Beveled (USA)—Lehmans Lot **Mr P. A. Tylor**
50 **MR LEHMAN**, 7, ch g Presidium—Lehmans Lot **Mr Renton, Mr Tylor & Mrs Reveley**
51 **MY LINE**, 7, b g Perpendicular—My Desire **Mrs M. Hoey**
52 **MYRTUS**, 5, ch g Double Eclipse (IRE)—My Desire **J. and A. Spensley**
53 **NIPPY AYR**, 8, b g Distinctly North (USA)—Tees Gazette Girl **Mrs Thwaites & Mr Stevenson**
54 **NOBRATINETTA (FR)**, 5, b m Celtic Swing—Bustinetta **Mr P. D. Savill**
55 **NORTHERN NATIVE (IRE)**, 8, br m Be My Native (USA)—Charming Mo (IRE) **Mrs Stephanie Smith**
56 **NORTHERN RAMBLER (IRE)**, 7, gr g Roselier (FR)—Ramble Bramble **W. J. Smith and M. D. Dudley**
57 **NORTHERN SHADOWS**, 5, b m Rock Hopper—Shadows of Silver **M J Hutton, Mrs M Laing, Mrs G Waters**
58 **OCTOBER MIST (IRE)**, 10, gr g Roselier (FR)—Bonny Joe **Mrs E. A. Murray**
59 **OUR DREAM (IRE)**, 5, b m Bob Back (USA)—Baybush **Scart Stud**
60 **OVERSTRAND (IRE)**, 5, b g In The Wings—Vaison La Romaine **F. F. Racing Services Partnership IV**
61 **PETERSON'S CAY (IRE)**, 6, b g Grand Lodge (USA)—Columbian Sand (USA) **Mr A. Frame**
62 **POLISH FLAME**, 6, b g Blushing Flame (USA)—Lady Emm **O'Brien Kent Racing**
63 **POWDER CREEK (IRE)**, 7, b g Little Bighorn—Our Dorcet **Mr T. M. McKain**
64 **PROTECTION MONEY**, 4, ch g Hector Protector (USA)—Three Piece **Mr P. D. Savill**
65 **RAMBLING MINSTER**, 6, b g Minster Son—Howcleuch **The Lingdale Optimists**
66 **RANDOM HARVEST (IRE)**, 15, br g Strong Gale—Bavello **Mr C. C. Buckley**
67 **RED ROVER**, 7, ch m Infantry—M I Babe **Mr J. F. Mernagh**
68 **ROBBO**, 10, b g Robellino (USA)—Basha **The Scarth Racing Partnership**
69 **ROUGE ET NOIR**, 6, b g Hernando (FR)—Bayrouge (FR) **The Mary Reveley Racing Club**
70 **RUBY LEGEND**, 6, b g Perpendicular—Singing High **Mrs J. M. Grimston**
71 **SHAFFISHAYES**, 12, ch g Clantime—Mischievous Miss **Mr P. Davidson-Brown**
72 **SOUTHERN CLASSIC**, 4, b g Classic Cliche (IRE)—Southern Sky **Mr Bill Brown**
73 **SPITTING IMAGE (IRE)**, 4, ch f Spectrum (IRE)—Decrescendo (IRE) **The Mary Reveley Racing Club**
74 **SUN KING**, 7, ch g Zilzal (USA)—Opus One **The Mary Reveley Racing Club**
75 **SUPREME FORTUNE (IRE)**, 10, b g Supreme Leader—Lucylet **The Supreme Partnership**
76 **SUPREME'S LEGACY (IRE)**, 5, b g Supreme Leader—Lucylet **The Supreme Alliance**
77 **TARA'S FLAME**, 4, ch g Blushing Flame (USA)—Lady Emm **Mr R. Wardlaw**
78 **TEES COMPONENTS**, 9, b g Risk Me (FR)—Lady Warninglid **Tees Components Ltd**
79 **THE RING (IRE)**, 4, b g Definite Article—Renata's Ring (IRE) **Mr P. D. Savill**
80 **THIS THYNE**, 8, b g Good Thyne (USA)—Dalkey Sound **Mr G. S. Brown**
81 **TIME MARCHES ON**, 6, b g Timeless Times (USA)—Tees Gazette Girl **Mrs M. B. Thwaites**
82 **TIME OF FLIGHT (IRE)**, 11, ch g Over The River (FR)—Icy Lou **Mr A. Peake**
83 **TOTALLY SCOTTISH**, 8, b g Mtoto—Glenfinlass **The Phoenix Racing C.O.**
84 **UNGARO (FR)**, 5, b g Epervier Bleu—Harpyes (FR) **Sir Robert Ogden**
85 **WELDMAN**, 5, b g Weld—Manettia (IRE) **Mr Guy Stevenson**
86 5, B m Rakaposhi King—Wellwotdouthink **Mr A. Flannigan & Mrs Reveley**
87 **ZAPATA HIGHWAY**, 7, ch g Bold Arrangement—Trailing Rose **R.& H.Burridge, M.Matheson, A.S.Wing**

THREE-YEAR-OLDS

88 **HERNANDO'S BOY**, b g Hernando (FR)—Leave At Dawn **Crack of Dawn Partnership**
89 Ch c Danzig Connection (USA)—Lady Warninglid **Mr A. Flannigan & Mrs Reveley**
90 **LET IT BE**, ch f Entrepreneur—Noble Dane (IRE) **Mrs Reveley**
91 B f Saddlers' Hall (IRE)—Shaiymara (IRE) **Tees Components Ltd**
92 B c Saddlers' Hall (IRE)—Sweet Mignonette

MRS G. R. REVELEY—continued
TWO-YEAR-OLDS

93 **AZAHARA,** b f 17/2 Vettori (IRE)—Branston Express (Bay Express) (11000) **Mr Stevenson**
94 B f 10/3 Rakaposhi King—Bayrouge (IRE) (Gorytus (USA)) **Mrs Reveley**
95 **CELTIC CARISMA,** b f 2/4 Celtic Swing—Kathryn's Pet (Blakeney) **Mr H. G. W. Brown**
96 **CELTIC LOVER,** b f 23/2 Celtic Swing—Native Thatch (IRE) (Thatching) **Mr H. G. W. Brown**
97 **JASS,** b g 28/2 Robellino (USA)—Iota (Niniski (USA)) (21000) **The Scarth Racing Partnership**
98 B c 25/3 Silver Patriarch—Smart Spirit (IRE) (Persian Bold) **Mrs S. Smith**
99 B f 16/3 Saddlers' Hall (IRE)—Windswept Lady (IRE) (Strong Gale) **Tees Components Ltd**

Other Owners: Mr R. J. Ainscough, Mr R. A. Atkinson, Mrs Joyce Bailey, Mr Malcolm Bailey, Mr G. Barnard, Mrs Marilyn Bauckham, N. R. Bendelow, Mr R. A. Black, Mr K. E. Bodenham, Mrs S. F. Bodenham, Mr N. Bradley, Mr M. J. Burns, Mr B. Callaghan, Mrs Angela Chatterton, Mr Hugh Chatterton, Mrs M. Clark-Wright, Ms J. Clarson, Mr D. C. Clewer, Mr J. W. Coates, Mr E. Coil, Mr A. E. Corbett, A. J. Cork, Mr Dan Daly, Mr Bernard Drinkall, Mr Michael Dunbar, Mr J. A. Evans, Mr Robert Fraser, Mrs A. Fulton, Mr Brian W. Goodall, Mr David A. Green, Mrs D. Greenhalgh, Mr R. M. Halliday, Mr Roger Hart, Mr S. A. Heley, Mr P Hudson, Mr H. Hurst, Ms Joy Jenkinson, Mr Ernest Johnson, Mrs David Laing, Mr S. F. Lincoln, Mr P Longstaff, Mr A. Macdonald, Mr Ron Macdonald, Mr Jamie Maclean, Ms M. H. Matheson, Mr Neil McGann, Miss J. Mitchell, Mr R. D. Morrall, Mr P Morrison, Mr Ian Nicol, Mrs Jean O'Donnell, Mrs D. A. Oliver, Mr Con O'Shea, Mr R. R. Parker, Mr Alexander J. Paterson, Mr D. M. Peel, Mrs D. L. Pink, Mrs B. Playforth, Mr A. W. Pooley, Mr S. Purcell, Mr M. G. Roberts, Mr J. Scarth, Mr Dave Scott, Mrs Carole Anne Sewell, Miss E. Shepherd, Mr R. H. Shepherd, Mr J. Sherwood, Mr Gerry Slater, Mr John Snaith, Mr K. Sobey, Mrs Ann Starkie, Mr Richard Stephens, Mr V. P. Stevens, Mr S. G. Storr, Mr Jim Struth, Mr G. P. Triefus, Mr Thomas Walsh, Mrs G. Waters, Mr Ron Whitehead, Mr David Wild, Mr John Wilson, Mr Andy Wing, Mr M. Wood.

Assistant Trainer: K Reveley

Jockey (NH): A Dempsey (10-0). **Conditional:** P Aspell (9-7), Fergus King (10-0), B Walsh (9-7). **Amateurs:** Mr T Collier, Mr O Nelmes (9-7).

MR P. M. RICH, Usk

466

Postal: **Llangowendr Stables, Llangovan, Monmouth, Gwent, NP25 4BT.**
Contact: **PHONE (01291) 690864/(01633) 262791 FAX (01633) 262791 MOBILE (07971) 218286**
E-MAIL paul@m-rich.freeserve.co.uk

1 **ALFY RICH,** 8, b g Alflora (IRE)—Weareagrandmother **Mr P. M. Rich**
2 **CALLED TO THE BAR,** 11, b g Legal Bwana—Miss Gaylord **Mr B. Meadmore**
3 **COULD IT BE LEGAL,** 7, b g Roviris—Miss Gaylord **Mr B. Meadmore**
4 **FAIRMEAD PRINCESS,** 6, b m Rudimentary (USA)—Lessons Lass (IRE) **Mr E. J. Ford**
5 **GRANRICH,** 4, ch f Alflora (IRE)—Weareagrandmother **Mr P. M. Rich**
6 **HAYDENS FIELD,** 10, b g Bedford (USA)—Releta **Miss H. Lewis**
7 **RICHWAY,** 5, ch g Nomadic Way (USA)—Weareagrandmother **Mr P. M. Rich**
8 **ROBBIE WILLIAMS,** 6, b g Missed Flight—Michelle's Ella (IRE) **Mr Robert J. Williams**
9 **ROYAL OPAL,** 9, b m Loretto Collection (USA)—Boxers Delight **Mrs M. M. Cook**
10 **THOMO (IRE),** 6, b g Faustus (USA)—Dawn O'Er Kells (IRE) **Mr A. J. Cook**
11 **WEARERICH,** 7, ch m Alflora (IRE)—Weareagrandmother **Mr P. M. Rich**

Assistant Trainer: Mr D Thomas

Amateur: Mr J Cook (10-0).

MRS LYDIA RICHARDS, Chichester

467

Postal: **Lynch Farm, Hares Lane, Funtington, Chichester, West Sussex, PO18 9LL.**
Contact: **HOME (01243) 574882 YARD (01243) 574379 MOBILE (07803) 199061**

1 **AIDEN (IRE),** 10, b g Supreme Leader—Chevaux-Vapeur **The Aiden Partnership**
2 **DOUBLE M,** 7, ch h First Trump—Girton Degree **Mr Bryan Mathieson**
3 **KAPPELHOFF (IRE),** 7, b g Mukaddamah (USA)—Miss Penguin **Mrs Lydia Richards**
4 **KINGLEY VALE,** 10, br g Neltino—Altaghaderry Run **Mr B. Seal**
5 **MANINGA,** 8, ch m Karinga Bay—Amberush **The Maninga Partnership**
6 **MANQUE NEUF,** 5, b g Cadeaux Genereux—Flying Squaw **Mr B. Seal**
7 **NEW LEADER (IRE),** 7, b g Supreme Leader—Two Spots **Mr E. T. Wright**
8 **TROOPER KIT,** 5, b g Petoski—Rolling Dice **Mr Leonard Howard**

Other Owners: Mr M. E. Thompsett.

468 MR N. G. RICHARDS, Greystoke

Postal: **The Old Rectory, Greystoke, Penrith, Cumbria, CA11 0UJ.**
Contact: **OFFICE** (017684) 83392 **HOME** 83160 **FAX** 83933 **MOBILE** (07771) 906609
E-MAIL n.g.richards@virgin.net

1 **ANOTHER BARGAIN (IRE)**, 5, b g Mister Lord (USA)—Flashy Treasure **It's A Bargain Syndicate**
2 **AVERSE (USA)**, 5, b m Lord Avie (USA)—Averti (USA) **Mr Kevin Johnston**
3 **BIG WHEEL**, 9, ch g Mujtahid (USA)—Numuthej (USA) **Hale Racing Limited**
4 **BOB THE PILER**, 8, b g Jendali (USA)—Laxay **Taranto De Pol**
5 **BRIGANTE GIRL (IRE)**, 6, b m Old Vic—Strong Winds (IRE) **Mr Kevin Johnston**
6 **BROKEN KNIGHTS (IRE)**, 7, ch g Broken Hearted—Knight's Row **The Broken Knights**
7 **BYRON LAMB**, 7, b g Rambo Dancer (CAN)—Caroline Lamb **Mr Edward Melville**
8 **CARRIAGE RIDE (IRE)**, 6, b g Tidaro (USA)—Casakurali **Mr James Callow & Mr David Wesley Yates**
9 **CORDILLA (IRE)**, 6, b g Accordion—Tumble Heather **Mr Trevor Hemmings**
10 5, B g Overbury (IRE)—Dark City **Ashleybank Investments Limited**
11 **DROUMLEIGH LAD (IRE)**, 9, b g Jurado (USA)—Myra Gaye **It's A Bargain Syndicate**
12 **EMPEROR ROSS (IRE)**, 9, b g Roselier (FR)—Gilded Empress **Mr James Callow & Mr David Wesley Yates**
13 **FERGAL THE PILER**, 5, b g Jendali (USA)—Dorado Beach **Taranto De Pol**
14 **GLENMOSS TARA (IRE)**, 6, b m Zaffaran (USA)—Majestic Run **West Coast Fiddlers**
15 **GLINGER (IRE)**, 11, b g Remainder Man—Harilla **Mr James Westoll**
16 **GRANITE STEPS**, 8, gr g Gran Alba (USA)—Pablena **Mrs T.H.Barclay/Mrs F.D.McInnes Skinner**
17 **HARMONY BRIG (IRE)**, 5, ch g Accordion—Bridges Daughter (IRE) **Mr Alistair Duff**
18 **HECKLEY CLARE GLEN (IRE)**, 8, b m Dancing High—Heckley Spark **Mr James Callow & Mr David Wesley Yates**
19 **HEYNESTOWN PRIDE (IRE)**, 7, ch m Zaffaran (USA)—Mayobridge **Mrs O. E. Matthews**
20 **JAZZ D'ESTRUVAL (FR)**, 7, gr g Bayolidaan (FR)—Caro d'Estruval (FR) **Ashleybank Investments Limited**
21 **JUST SOOTY**, 9, br g Be My Native—March Fly **Mr David Wesley Yates**
22 **KEEN AND ABLE**, 4, ch f Keen—Four Thyme **Mr E. Briggs**
23 **LETITIA'S LOSS (IRE)**, 6, ch m Zaffaran (USA)—Satin Sheen **The Saddleworth Knights**
24 **LORD JACK (IRE)**, 8, ch g Mister Lord (USA)—Gentle Gill **Mr Trevor Hemmings**
25 **MAZZAREME (IRE)**, 6, b g Supreme Leader—Mazza **Ashleybank Investments Limited**
26 **MOFIDA GOLD**, 5, ch m Elmaamul (USA)—Mellow Gold **Mr & Mrs G. Middlebrook**
27 **MONET'S GARDEN (IRE)**, 6, gr g Roselier (FR)—Royal Remainder (IRE) **Mr David Wesley Yates**
28 **MUCKLE FLUGGA (IRE)**, 5, ch m Karinga Bay—Dancing Dove (IRE) **Dr Kenneth S. Fraser**
29 **NEXT TO NOTHING (IRE)**, 7, b g Bob's Return (IRE)—Shuil Abhaile **Ashleybank Investments Limited**
30 **PAPERPROPHET**, 6, b g Glory of Dancer—Living Legend (ITY) **The Jockeys Whips**
31 **PRINCE AMONG MEN**, 7, b g Robellino—Forelino (USA) **Mr Jim Ennis**
32 **ROCKET BLEU (FR)**, 4, ch g Epervier Bleu—Egeria (FR) **Mr Jimmy Dudgeon**
33 **SEEKING SHELTER (IRE)**, 5, b m Glacial Storm (USA)—Seking Gold (IRE) **Kinneston Racing**
34 **SHANNON'S PRIDE (IRE)**, 8, gr g Roselier (FR)—Spanish Flame (IRE) **Mr J. Hales**
35 **SOBRAON (IRE)**, 5, b g Topanoora—Anniepepp (USA) **Mrs Julia Young & Mrs Sarah Walsh**
36 **SPIDER MUSIC**, 8, ch g Orchestra—Muffet's Spider **Mrs F. D. McInnes Skinner**
37 **STEPPES OF GOLD (IRE)**, 7, b g Moscow Society (USA)—
Trysting Place **Independent Twine Manufacturing Co Ltd**
38 **SUPREME OPTIMIST (IRE)**, 7, b g Supreme Leader—Armagale (IRE) **Mr H. R. C. Catherwood**
39 **TELEMOSS (IRE)**, 10, b g Montelimar (USA)—Shan's Moss **Ashleybank Investments Limited**
40 **THE FRENCH FURZE (IRE)**, 10, ch g Be My Guest (USA)—Exciting **Mr Jim Ennis**
41 **TONY THE PILER**, 8, br g Tidaro (USA)—Adabiya (IRE) **Taranto De Pol**
42 **TOPANBERRY (IRE)**, 5, ch m Topanoora—Mulberry (USA) **Mrs D. McGawn**
43 **TOROSAY (IRE)**, 6, b g Presenting—Mazuma (IRE) **Mr J. Hales**
44 **TRUE BEAUTY (FR)**, 4, ch f Shernazar—Re-Release **Mr Jim Ennis**
45 **VENTURE TO FLY (IRE)**, 10, ch g Roselier (FR)—Fly Run **Ashleybank Investments Limited**
46 **VIC THE PILER (IRE)**, 5, ch g Old Vic—Strong Gale Pigeon (IRE) **Taranto De Pol**
47 **WESTMEATH FLYER**, 9, bg Deploy—Re-Release **Mr Jim Ennis**
48 **WINDY HILLS**, 4, bl g Overbury (IRE)—Chinook's Daughter (IRE) **Lord Cavendish, Lord Reay & Mrs T Riley**
49 **ZAFFARAN EXPRESS (IRE)**, 5, b m Zaffaran (USA)—Majestic Run **Mr Jimmy Dudgeon & Partners**

THREE-YEAR-OLDS

50 **FUNNY TIMES**, b f Silver Patriarch (IRE)—Elegant City **Mr E. Briggs**

Other Owners: Mr Edward Birkbeck, Mr & Mrs J. Dodd, Mr J. M. Elliott, Mrs G. B. Fairbairn, Miss L. Hales, Mrs J. Heburn, Mr S. Leece, Mr I. Lightfoot, Col & Mrs R. Martin, Mr P. McMahon, Mr C. P. Norbury, Mr B. Robb, Mr S. J. Simpson, Mr A. D. Stewart.

Jockeys (NH): A Dobbin (10-0), B Harding (10-0). **Conditional:** P Robson (10-1), G Thomas (10-0).

469 **MR M. G. RIMELL, Witney**
Postal: Fairspear Racing Stables, Fairspear Road, Leafield, Witney, Oxfordshire, OX29 9NT.
Contact: PHONE (01993) 878551 MOBILE (07778) 648303 (07973)627054

1 ARCEYE, 7, b g Weld—Flower of Tintern **Mr Mark Rimell**
2 CROSSBOW CREEK, 7, b g Lugana Beach—Roxy River **Mrs M. R. T. Rimell**
3 GOLDERS GREEN, 7, b g Gildoran—Mayfair Minx **Mrs M. D. W. Wilson**
4 GREY FANDANGO (IRE), 7, gr g Roselier (FR)—Fancy Step **Mr Mark Rimell**
5 HORCOTT BAY, 4, b f Thowra (FR)—Armagnac Messenger
6 HOTPOT, 11, br g Hotfoot—Miss Polly Peck **Mr W. E. Dudley**
7 ICE GREEN PEARL, 6, b m Green Ruby (USA)—Ice Moon **Mrs M. R. T. Rimell**
8 6, B m Karinga Bay—Marina Bird **Mr Mark Rimell**
9 MONTEMOSS (IRE), 7, ch g Montelimar (USA)—Gaye Le Moss **Wychwood Racing Partnership**
10 ONEWAY (IRE), 7, b g Bob's Return (IRE)—Rendezvous **Mrs Charlotte Oram**
11 ROLLO (IRE), 6, gr g Roselier (FR)—Comeragh Queen **Mr Mark Rimell**
12 SILVER DANCER (IRE), 8, gr g Roselier (FR)—Fancy Step **Mr Mark Rimell**

Other Owners: Mr A. J. Collins, Mr W. E. Dudley, Mr R. A. Kidner, Mr R. F. Shepherd.

Assistant Trainer: Miss Anne Dudley

Amateur: Mr M Rimell (10-5).

470 **MISS V. C. ROBERTS, Upper Lambourn**
Postal: Frenchmans Stables, Upper Lambourn, Hungerford, Berkshire, RG17 8QT.
Contact: PHONE (01488) 72132 MOBILE (07768) 366935 E-MAIL frenchmans.stables@virgin.net

1 CHAMPETRE (FR), 6, ch g Pursuit of Love—Fermiere (FR) **The Champetre Partnership**
2 DANGEROUS DEPLOY, 7, b g Deploy—Emily-Mou (IRE) **Mrs P. Roberts**
3 DASHING SPUR (IRE), 4, b g Flying Spur (AUS)—Glamour Stock (USA) **Mr D. C. Roberts**
4 DEALER'S CHOICE (IRE), 10, gr g Roselier (FR)—Cam Flower VII **P. Duffy, G. King, D. Roberts, B. Savage**
5 DIAMOND DARREN (IRE), 5, ch g Dolphin Street (FR)—Deerussa (IRE) **Mr A. Smith**
6 FINCHES LANE (IRE), 10, b g Le Bavard (FR)—Alice Mann **Miss Victoria Roberts**
7 FOUR OF DIAMONDS (IRE), 5, b g Fourstars Allstar (USA)—
Wine Rock Diamond (IRE) **Paul Duffy Diamond Partnership**
8 MIXED MARRIAGE, 6, ch g Indian Ridge—Marie de Flandre (FR) **Miss Victoria Roberts**
9 ONE MORE STRIDE, 8, gr g Beveled (USA)—Gem of Gold **Mr C. F. Stratford**
10 PERIWINKLE LAD (IRE), 7, b g Perugino (USA)—Bold Kate **Mr D. C. Roberts**
11 5, B g Master Willie—Singing Hills **Miss Victoria Roberts**
12 TELL HER OFF, 4, b f Reprimand—My Valentina **Mr Andy Middleton**
13 6, B m Commanche Run—The Last Mackay (IRE) **Mr T. Webb**

THREE-YEAR-OLDS

14 B f Gildoran—Lazybird Blue (IRE) **Mr J. Bradley**

Other Owners: Mrs S. Bagg, Mr K. Bennett, Mr R. H. Brookes, Mr J. Cotterell, Mr M. Graves, Mr C. Hardy, Mr N. A. Harris, Mrs S. Hayhow, Mr C. Heard, Mr W. Lamb, Mr C. Lowe, Mr N. Pollard.

Jockey (NH): T J Murphy (10-0). Conditional: C J Rafter (9-11).

471 **MRS P. ROBESON, Newport Pagnell**
Postal: Fences Farm, Tyringham, Newport Pagnell, Buckinghamshire, MK16 9EN.
Contact: PHONE (01908) 611255 FAX (01908) 611255 MOBILE (07831) 579898
E-MAIL robesons@attglobal.net

1 CETTI'S WARBLER, 6, gr m Sir Harry Lewis (USA)—Sedge Warbler **Mrs P. Robeson**
2 CORALBROOK, 4, b g Alderbrook—Coral Delight **Mrs P. Robeson**
3 GORDON HIGHLANDER, 5, ch m Master Willie—No Chili **Mr T. E. Short**
4 HORNBILL, 6, b g Sir Harry Lewis (USA)—Tangara **Mrs P. Robeson**
5 HYLIA, 5, ch m Sir Harry Lewis (USA)—Lady Stock **Mrs P. Robeson**
6 MISS PROSS, 4, b f Bob's Return (IRE)—Lucy Manette **Mrs F. Kehoe**
7 OLNEY LAD, 5, b g Democratic (USA)—Alipampa (IRE) **The Tyringham Partnership**

MRS P. ROBESON—continued

8 **PINTAIL**, 4, b g Petoski—Tangara **Mrs P. Robeson**
9 **STOCK DOVE**, 6, ch m Deploy—Lady Stock **Mrs P. Robeson**

Other Owners: Mr Nicholas Brown, Mr Ron Cossins, Mrs Ann Garratt.

---

472 | **MR A. ROBSON, Hawick**
Postal: **Windyknowes, 7 Burnflat Brae, Hawick, Roxburghshire, TD9 0DJ.**
Contact: **PHONE (01450) 376886 FAX (01450) 376886 MOBILE (07721) 605131**

1 **FAYS TWO (IRE)**, 6, b m Binary Star (USA)—Claudette **Mr A. Robson**
2 **GILFOOT BREEZE (IRE)**, 7, b g Forest Wind (USA)—Ma Bella Luna **Mr A. Robson**

Conditional: Paul D Robson (10-0).

---

473 | **MISS P. ROBSON, Capheaton**
Postal: **Kidlaw Farm, Capheaton, Newcastle Upon Tyne, NE19 2AW.**
Contact: **PHONE (01830) 530241 MOBILE (07721) 887489 E-MAIL pauline.robson@virgin.net**

1 **HARROVIAN**, 7, b g Deploy—Homeoftheclassics **Major I. Straker & Mrs I. Straker**
2 **ON THE LUCE**, 7, b g Karinga Bay—Lirchur **Mrs P. R. Crawfurd**
3 **THOSEWERETHEDAYS**, 11, b g Past Glories—Charlotte's Festival **Mrs J. D. Goodfellow**

Assistant Trainer: David Parker

Jockey (NH): Richard McGrath (10-0). **Amateurs:** Mr Luke Morgan, Miss Pauline Robson (9-3).

---

474 | **MR W. M. ROPER, Curragh**
Postal: **French Furze, Maddenstown, The Curragh, Co. Kildare, Ireland.**
Contact: **HOUSE & YARD +353 (0) 45 441821 MOBILE (086) 8234279**

1 **ABOVE (NZ)**, 6, b g Yamanin Vital (NZ)—Arena (NZ) **Bellevue Ltd**
2 **ACHATES (IRE)**, 5, br m Charnwood Forest—Trojan Relation **Mr J. Lynch**
3 **ARBORETA (IRE)**, 6, b m Charnwood Forest (IRE)—Blazing Glory (IRE) **Mr J. Kindregan**
4 **BELLEVUE HERO (NZ)**, 7, b g Heroicity (AUS)—Rummage (NZ) **Bellevue Ltd**
5 **BOOK BINDER (IRE)**, 4, b g Perugino (USA)—Dulceata (IRE) **Mr M. Roper**
6 **EDIRNELI (IRE)**, 7, b g Ela-Mana-Mou—Evivrna (USA)
7 **FLYING KNIGHT (IRE)**, 6, b h Flying Spur (AUS)—Clarification (IRE) **Mr R. Demuyser**
8 **GAMBLELANDED (NZ)**, 7, ch g Beau Zephyr (AUS)—Dubra Crown (NZ) **Bellevue Ltd**
9 **HAWKFIELD LAD (IRE)**, 6, b g Shernazar—Auction Piece (IRE) **Mr G. Connors**
10 **HONOR'S STAG (USA)**, 10, ch g Blushing John (USA)—Bobbinette (USA) **Mr M. Wyley**
11 **JIRAN (IRE)**, 7, b m Jurado (USA)—Melika Iran **Mr E. Newell**
12 **KITCHENCOOK**, 8, b m Domitor (USA)—Dawn O'Er Kells (IRE) **Mr A. Cook**
13 **LUAS LASAIR (IRE)**, 4, gr f College Chapel—Moonlight Truce (IRE) **Ms A. Doran**
14 **PROUD MYTH (IRE)**, 4, b f Mark of Esteem (IRE)—Folklore **Ms A. Doran**

Other Owners: J. Lynch, P. Quigley, M. Wyley.

---

475 | **MR B. S. ROTHWELL, Nawton**
Postal: **Arthington Barn, Little Manor Farm Stables, Highfield Lane, Nawton, York, YO62 7TU.**
Contact: **OFFICE (01439) 770437 HOME (01439) 770168 MOBILE (07968) 848724**
E-MAIL rothwellb@freeuk.com

1 **ALMOST FREE**, 7, b g Darshaan—Light Fresh Air (USA) **Mr Ron MacDonald**
2 **ALWAYS RAINBOWS (IRE)**, 6, b g Rainbows For Life (CAN)—Maura's Guest (IRE) **Mr J. Eddings**
3 **CELTIC BLAZE (IRE)**, 5, b m Charente River (IRE)—Firdaunt **Cleaning And Paper Disposables Ltd**
4 **CEOL NA SRAIDE (IRE)**, 5, b m King's Theatre (IRE)—My Lady's Key (USA) **Mr J. Eddings**
5 **HELDERBERG (USA)**, 4, b f Diesis—Banissa (USA) **D. J. Coles**
6 5, Br g Norwich—Katie Dick (IRE)
7 **LADY NETBETSPORTS (IRE)**, 5, b m In The Wings—Auntie Maureen (IRE) **Paul Moorhouse**
8 **LITTLE ALFIE (IRE)**, 7, b g Shahanndeh—Debbies Scud (IRE) **Mr John H. Price**
9 **MANY THANKS**, 4, b f Octagonal (NZ)—Answered Prayer **D. J. Coles**
10 **MISS JOJO (IRE)**, 4, b f Darnay—Rose Tint (IRE) **Brian Rothwell**

MR B. S. ROTHWELL—continued

11 **RISKY WAY**, 8, b g Risk Me (FR)—Hot Sunday Sport **Mr Mike Gosse**
12 **SMUDGER SMITH**, 7, ch g Deploy—Parfait Amour **Mr S. P. Hudson**
13 **STAR COUNCEL (IRE)**, 8, b m Leading Counsel (USA)—Black Avenue (IRE) **Mrs Liz Hunt**
14 5, Br m Needle Gun (IRE)—The Foalicule
15 5, Ch m Roselier (FR)—Vulcan Belle
16 **ZAN LO (IRE)**, 4, ch f Grand Lodge (USA)—Zanella (IRE) **D. J. Coles**

THREE-YEAR-OLDS

17 Ch f Defacto (USA)—Lindrick Lady (IRE) **S. P. Hudson**
18 **SHELIAK**, b f Binary Star (USA)—Flo's Choice (IRE) **Mrs Helen Godfrey**
19 **SPRING DEW (FR)**, b f Starborough—Penniless (IRE) **J. T. Brown**

TWO-YEAR-OLDS

20 Ch c 4/5 Keen—Auntie Fay (IRE) (Fayruz) **S. P. Hudson**
21 B f 4/5 Kayf Tara—Lindrick Lady (IRE) (Broken Hearted) **S. P. Hudson**
22 B c 18/3 Forzando—Triple Concerto (Grand Lodge (USA)) **Brian Rothwell**

Other Owners: Mr J. K. Carson, Ms D. Doyle.

Jockey (Flat): M Fenton (w.a.). **Jockey (NH):** A Ross.

---

476 MR R. ROWE, Pulborough
Postal: **Ashleigh House Stables, Sullington Lane, Storrington, Pulborough, West Sussex, RH20 4AE.**
Contact: **PHONE (01903) 742871 MOBILE (07831) 345636 FAX (01903) 740110**
E-MAIL r.rowe.racing@virgin.net

1 **ACERTACK (IRE)**, 7, b g Supreme Leader—Ask The Madam **Mr Keith Hunter**
2 **ALBERT SQUARE (IRE)**, 7, b g Alflora (IRE)—Place Stephanie (IRE) **Mr J. C. H. Berry**
3 **AMBER STARLIGHT**, 6, b m Binary Star (USA)—Stupid Cupid **The Exclusive Partnership**
4 **APOLLO THEATRE**, 6, b g Sadler's Wells (USA)—Threatening **The Encore Partnership II**
5 **CELTIC RUFFIAN (IRE)**, 6, b g Celio Rufo—Candid Lady **Mrs P. V. Crocker**
6 **CITIUS (IRE)**, 8, b g Supreme Leader—Fancy Me Not (IRE) **Mr Tom Perkins**
7 **COUGAR (IRE)**, 4, b g Sadler's Wells (USA)—Pieds de Plume (FR) **Capt A. Pratt**
8 **CROWN INN (IRE)**, 8, b g Glacial Storm (USA)—Manna Rose **Mr Tim Clowes**
9 **DIRK COVE (IRE)**, 10, ch g Montelimar (USA)—Another Miller **Dr B. Alexander**
10 **FAIR ENOUGH (IRE)**, 9, b m Phardante (IRE)—Woodford Princess **Mr & Mrs Robin Lamb**
11 **FLINDERS**, 9, b m Henbit (USA)—Stupid Cupid **Leith Hill Chasers**
12 **FRENCH DIRECTION (IRE)**, 5, ch g John French—Shelikesitstraight (IRE) **Mrs R. A. Proctor**
13 **GLADTOKNOWYOU (IRE)**, 11, b g Over The River (FR)—Jonsemma (IRE) **Mr W. Packham**
14 **ICE COOL LAD (IRE)**, 10, b g Glacial Storm (USA)—My Serena **The Reality Partnership**
15 **I'LLEVEIT TOU (IRE)**, 8, b g King Luthier—Shady Jumbo **Mr Thomas Thompson**
16 **JOAN OF ARC**, 6, b m Supreme Leader—Place Stephanie (IRE) **Mrs A. Pratt**
17 **KING COAL (IRE)**, 5, b br g Anshan—Lucky Trout **Mr Anthony D. Kerman**
18 **LEITH HILL STAR**, 8, ch m Comme L'Etoile—Sunnyday **Mrs N. F. Maltby**
19 **LORD 'N' MASTER (IRE)**, 8, b g Lord Americo—Miss Good Night **Dr B. Alexander**
20 **MAGIC OF SYDNEY (IRE)**, 8, b g Broken Hearted—Chat Her Up **Ann & John Symes**
21 **MARRON PRINCE (FR)**, 4, ch g Cyborg (FR)—Colombine (USA) **Mrs Celia Rayner**
22 **MAZZINI (IRE)**, 13, b g Celio Rufo—Dontellvi **Mr Richard Rowe**
23 **NATIVE NEW YORKER (IRE)**, 9, b g Be My Native (USA)—Sunbath **Ann & John Symes**
24 4, Ch c Accordion—Place Stephanie (IRE) **Capt A. Pratt**
25 **PREMIER CHEVAL (USA)**, 5, ch g Irish River (FR)—Restikarada (FR) **Mr R. C. Stillwell**
26 **PREMIER ESTATE (IRE)**, 7, b g Satco (FR)—Kettleby (IRE) **Mrs Jacky Field**
27 **RENALOO (IRE)**, 9, gr g Tremblant—Rare Flower **Mr Tim Clowes**
28 **SECURON DANCER**, 6, b m Emperor Jones (USA)—Gena Ivor (USA) **Mrs R. A. Proctor**
29 **SIR TOBY (IRE)**, 11, br g Strong Gale—Petite Deb **Capt A. Pratt**
30 **SIX OF ONE**, 6, b g Kahyasi—Ten To Six **Mrs R. A. Proctor**
31 **SOUTHDOWN HOUSE**, 8, b m Husyan (USA)—Inger-Lea **Southdown Holdings Limited**
32 **STATLEY RAJ (IND)**, 5, b g Mtoto—Donna Star **The Colonial Partnership**
33 **TANSHAN**, 9, ch g Anshan—Nafla (FR) **Mr Richard Rowe**

MR R. ROWE—continued

34 **UP AT MIDNIGHT**, 4, b f Midnight Legend—Uplift **Mr D. R. L. Evans**
35 **WINDSOR BEAUTY (IRE)**, 6, b br g Woods of Windsor (USA)—Tumble Dale **Capt A. Pratt**

Other Owners: Mr A. L. Abrahams, Miss Clare Berry, Mr Alastair Blades, Lady Blaker, Mr D. Bradshaw, Mrs H. C. G. Butcher, Mrs J. Case, Mr David Coe, Mrs A. E. Dawes, Mrs J. E. Debenham, Mr F. C. Eliet, Mr D. T. Ellingham, Mrs P. E. Finn, Mr Martin Fletcher, Mr Gary Flood, Mr D. D. Janes, Mrs G. S. Knight, Mrs R. J. Lamb, Mr Robin A. Lamb, Mr A. R. Lewers, Mr M. I. Lewis, Mr N. J. McKibbin, Exors Of The Late Mr R. C. Murdoch, Mrs Robert Murdoch, Lady Neville, Mr P. E. Paulson, Mr N. M. Prest, Mr B. J. Reid, Mr B. Richardson, Mr J. M. J. Smee, Mrs Ann Symes, Mr J. Symes, Mr A. Taylor, Mr Clive Turner, Mrs J. C. Ware.

Jockey (NH): Barry Fenton (10-0).

477 MISS M. E. ROWLAND, Lower Blidworth
Postal: **Kirkfields, Calverton Road, Lower Blidworth, Nottingham, Nottinghamshire, NG21 0NW.**
Contact: **PHONE (01623) 794831 MOBILE (07768) 224666**

1 **DIMINUTIVE (USA)**, 11, b g Diesis—Graceful Darby (USA) **Goldliner Racing Club**
2 **HIGHLAND TRACKER (IRE)**, 9, ch g Indian Ridge—Track Twenty Nine (IRE) **Mr J. Taqvi**
3 **HUMMING**, 7, b g Bluebird (USA)—Risanda **Miss M. E. Rowland**
4 **IRISHTOWN LEADER (IRE)**, 6, b g Supreme Leader—Glamorous Gale **The Christie Partnership**
5 **MASOURI SANA (IRE)**, 7, br m Broken Hearted—Say Thanks **Mr Paul Mayo**
6 **MISS JESSICA (IRE)**, 4, b br f Woodborough (USA)—Sarah Blue (IRE) **Mr K. Hopkin, Mr S. Deeman**
7 **NINE BARROW DOWN (IRE)**, 12, b g Danehill (USA)—Rising Spirits **Goldliner Racing Club**
8 **PETROS CHIEF**, 7, b g Factual (USA)—Dancing Ballerina **Mrs R. A. Murrell**
9 **REAL CHIEF (IRE)**, 5, b g Caerleon (USA)—Greek Air (IRE) **Miss M. E. Rowland**
10 5, B m Ridgewood Ben—Say Thanks **Miss M. E. Rowland**
11 5, B m Executive Perk—Spring Trix (IRE) **Miss M. E. Rowland**
12 5, Gr m Broken Hearted—Tender Guest (IRE) **Miss M. E. Rowland**

Other Owners: Mr C. Hollins, Mr Ian Allan Todd.

Jockey (Flat): A Culhane. **Jockey (NH):** R Hobson (10-2). **Conditional:** R Hobson (10-2).

478 MR A. DE ROYER-DUPRE, Chantilly
Postal: **3 Chemin des Aigles, 60500 Chantilly, France.**
Contact: **PHONE + 33 (0) 4 4580303 FAX + 33 (0) 4 4573938 MOBILE + 33 (0) 613 011009**

1 **ADJIROUN (IRE)**, 4, b f Unfuwain (USA)—Adjriyna **H. H. Aga Khan**
2 **ANADIYLA (IRE)**, 4, b f Barathea (IRE)—Anaza **H. H. Aga Khan**
3 **ASHALA (FR)**, 4, b f Starborough—Ashkara (USA) **Mrs M. O. Bryant**
4 **BEHKARA (IRE)**, 4, b f Kris—Behera **H. H. Aga Khan**
5 **DARASA (IRE)**, 4, b f Barathea (IRE)—Darashandeh (IRE) **H. H. Aga Khan**
6 **DEBONNAIRE (FR)**, 4, ch c Highest Honor (FR)—Dear Marianne (FR) **Marquise de Moratalla**
7 **EUBEA (FR)**, 5, b m Anabaa (USA)—Enodia (GER) **Succession Egon Wanke**
8 **GREEN MAJOR (IRE)**, 5, gr g Kendor (FR)—Green Rosy (USA) **Mme Renee Geffroy**
9 **HAMIRPOUR (IRE)**, 11, b h Shahrastani—Hamaliya **H. H. Aga Khan**
10 **KALAJORANN (FR)**, 6, b g Salse (USA)—Kalajana (USA) **Mr Antoine Fontaine**
11 **KARANI (FR)**, 5, b g Distinctly North—Karikata (IRE) **H. H. Aga Khan**
12 **KASAKIYA (IRE)**, 4, b f Zafonic (USA)—Kassiyda **H. H. Aga Khan**
13 **KHALASHA (IRE)**, 4, b f Linamix (FR)—Khalisa (IRE) **H. H. Aga Khan**
14 **KIERAMON (IRE)**, 4, b c Kendor (IRE)—Kiera Marie (IRE) **6 C Racing Ltd**
15 **LE CARRE (USA)**, 6, gr g Miswaki (USA)—Dibs (USA) **Mr J. R. Aragao Bozano**
16 **NABIR (FR)**, 4, b c Linamix (FR)—Nabagha (FR) **H. H. Aga Khan**
17 **PUPPETEER**, 4, b c Singspiel (IRE)—Pidona (FR) **6 C Racing Ltd**
18 **QUISISANA (IRE)**, 4, b f Rainbow Quest (USA)—Wellspring (IRE) **6 C Racing Ltd**
19 **QUIT RENT (IRE)**, 6, gr g Fairy King (USA)—Kembla **Marquise de Moratalla**
20 **RIDAAR (FR)**, 4, b c Starborough—Ridiyara (USA) **H. H. Aga Khan**
21 **RIDAFA (IRE)**, 4, b f Darshaan—Ridaiyma (IRE) **H. H. Aga Khan**
22 **ROYSTONEA**, 4, b f Polish Precedent (USA)—Alleluia Tree (IRE) **Marquise de Moratalla**
23 **SASANUMA (USA)**, 4, b f Kingmambo (USA)—Sassy Bird (USA) **6 C Racing Ltd**
24 **SHAIYBA (IRE)**, 4, b f Singspiel (IRE)—Shaiybara (IRE) **H. H. Aga Khan**
25 **SHAKANNDI (FR)**, 4, b c Marju (IRE)—Sharakanda (USA) **H. H. Aga Khan**
26 **SILLERY RIVER (FR)**, 4, b g Sillery (USA)—Rixe River (USA) **Mr Henri Philippart**
27 **SILPHARD (FR)**, 6, ch g Funambule (USA)—Siljohnia (FR) **Mr Roger Cluzel**

MR A. DE ROYER-DUPRE—continued

28 **TASTE THE STARS (USA)**, 5, b br h Benny The Dip (USA)—Sassy Bird (USA) **6 C Racing Ltd**
29 **VALIANT WINGS (FR)**, 4, ch c Valanour (IRE)—Lacewings (USA) **Mr Eduardo Fierro**
30 **VANGELIS (USA)**, 5, gr h Highest Honor (FR)—Capades Dancer (USA) **6 C Racing Ltd**
31 **ZIYAR (FR)**, 4, b c Valanour (IRE)—Zariya (USA) **H. H. Aga Khan**

THREE-YEAR-OLDS

32 **ADJAMI (IRE)**, b c Entrepreneur—Adjriyna **H. H. Aga Khan**
33 **AFRAD (FR)**, b c Linamix (FR)—Afragha (IRE) **H. H. Aga Khan**
34 **ALMANSA (IRE)**, b f Dr Devious (IRE)—Alasana (IRE) **H. H. Aga Khan**
35 **BANDIRMA (IRE)**, b c Dr Devious (IRE)—Banaja (IRE) **H. H. Aga Khan**
36 **BEHLAYA (IRE)**, b f Kahyasi—Behera **H. H. Aga Khan**
37 **COSER Y CANTAR (IRE)**, gr f Grand Lodge (USA)—Amiarma (IRE) **Marquise de Moratalla**
38 **DALATAYA (IRE)**, b c Sadler's Wells (USA)—Daltawa (IRE) **H. H. Aga Khan**
39 **DALAYAN (IRE)**, b c Nashwan (USA)—Dalara (IRE) **H. H. Aga Khan**
40 **DARAYKA (FR)**, b f Dr Fong (USA)—Daraydala (IRE) **H. H. Aga Khan**
41 **DARKARA (FR)**, b f Halling (USA)—Daralbayda (IRE) **Princesse Zahra**
42 **DARYAL (IRE)**, b c Night Shift (USA)—Darata (IRE) **H. H. Aga Khan**
43 **DARYAMAR (FR)**, b c Machiavellian (USA)—Daryaba (IRE) **H. H. Aga Khan**
44 **DELICIAS BLUES (USA)**, b f Grindstone (USA)—Magic Blue (USA) **Mr J. W. Preston**
45 **DEYNIZI (IRE)**, b c Kris—Denizliya (IRE) **H. H. Aga Khan**
46 **DYARCHY (IRE)**, b c Fasliyev (USA)—Anazara (USA) **Marquise de Moratalla**
47 **EJINA (FR)**, gr f Highest Honor (FR)—Enodia (GER) **Famile Wanke**
48 **ERZEL (FR)**, b c Zieten (USA)—Erduiya (IRE) **H. H. Aga Khan**
49 **HALEEMA (IRE)**, b f College Chapel—Haladiya (IRE) **H. H. Aga Khan**
50 **HAWAZI (IRE)**, b c Ashkalani (IRE)—Hawala (IRE) **H. H. Aga Khan**
51 **JOURSANVAULT (FR)**, gr c Verglas—Jane Brust (FR) **Mr Beniamino Arbib**
52 **KALIYOUN (IRE)**, b c Grand Lodge (USA)—Kaliana (IRE) **H. H. Aga Khan**
53 **KASALI (IRE)**, b c Green Desert (USA)—Kassiyda **H. H. Aga Khan**
54 **KHALILIA (FR)**, b f Polish Precedent (USA)—Khalisa (IRE) **H. H. Aga Khan**
55 **LE HAUT BOIS (FR)**, ch c Take Risks (FR)—Bahia Mar (USA) **Mr Beniamino Arbib**
56 **MAN RAY (USA)**, ch c Theatrical (IRE)—Irtifa **6 C Racing Ltd**
57 **MANRENT**, b c Highest Honor (FR)—Ring Queen (USA) **Marquise de Moratalla**
58 **MIDSOU (FR)**, b c Midyan (USA)—Queensouth (USA) **Mr Henri Philippart**
59 **MOORE'S MELODY (IRE)**, b f Marju (IRE)—Liege (IRE) **6 C Racing Ltd**
60 **ODARSHAAN (FR)**, b c Darshaan—Odalisque (IRE) **Marquise de Moratalla**
61 **SANADA (IRE)**, b f Priolo (USA)—Sanariya (IRE) **H. H. Aga Khan**
62 **SARABA (IRE)**, b f Soviet Star (USA)—Sarliya (IRE) **H. H. Aga Khan**
63 **SENDAR (FR)**, b c Priolo—Sendana (FR) **H. H. Aga Khan**
64 **SHAIYBANIA (IRE)**, b f Priolo (USA)—Shaiybara (IRE) **H. H. Aga Khan**
65 **SHAMDIYNA (IRE)**, b f Machiavellian (USA)—Shamadara (IRE) **H. H. Aga Khan**
66 **SHANAJITA (FR)**, b f Dr Devious (IRE)—Shamanara (IRE) **H. H. Aga Khan**
67 **SHEMRANA (IRE)**, b f Woodman (USA)—Shemaya (IRE) **H. H. Aga Khan**
68 **SWING VOTER**, b c Machiavellian (USA)—Joyeuse Entree **Marquise de Moratalla**
69 **TASHKIYR (IRE)**, b c Desert Prince (IRE)—Tashiriya (IRE) **H. H. Aga Khan**
70 **TASHTIKAR (FR)**, b c Hernando (FR)—Tashtiyana (IRE) **H. H. Aga Khan**
71 **TCHIKALA**, b f Inchinor—Tajrebah (USA) **6 C Racing Ltd**
72 **TORICELLA (USA)**, gr f Tactical Cat (USA)—Harlan Honey (USA) **Mrs Ornella Cozzi Carlini**
73 **VERMENTINA (IRE)**, b c Darshaan—Vereva (IRE) **H. H. Aga Khan**
74 **ZAILAWAR (FR)**, b c Daylami (IRE)—Zalaiyka (FR) **H. H. Aga Khan**
75 **ZAIYAD (FR)**, b c Sadler's Wells—Zaila (IRE) **H. H. Aga Khan**
76 **ZANDAK (FR)**, b c Spectrum (IRE)—Zankara (FR) **H. H. Aga Khan**
77 **ZANJAN (FR)**, b c Indian Ridge—Zainta (IRE) **H. H. Aga Khan**
78 **ZANNA (FR)**, b f Soviet Star (USA)—Zanata **H. H. Aga Khan**
79 **ZARKALI (FR)**, b c Starborough—Zarkana (IRE) **H. H. Aga Khan**

TWO-YEAR-OLDS

80 B c 13/3 Kahyasi (IRE)—Afragha (IRE) (Darshaan) **H. H. Aga Khan**
81 B c 26/2 Dr Fong (USA)—Ashara (IRE) (Kahyasi (IRE)) **H. H. Aga Khan**
82 B f 18/5 Sendawar—Ashkara (IRE) (Chief Singer) **H. H. Aga Khan**
83 B c 9/2 Soviet Star (USA)—Ashtarka (Dalsaan) **H. H. Aga Khan**
84 B c 24/3 Grand Lodge (USA)—Bayrika (IRE) (Kahyasi (IRE)) **H. H. Aga Khan**
85 B c 28/4 Darshaan—Behariya (IRE) (Sadler's Wells) **H. H. Aga Khan**
86 **CATALAN HILL (IRE)**, b f 31/3 Danehill (USA)—Catalonia Express (USA) (Diesis) **Mr Edoardo Balbo di Vinadio**
87 Ch f 6/2 Machiavellian (USA)—Classic Reign (CAN) (Vice Regent (CAN)) **6 C Racing Ltd**
88 B f 26/2 King's Best (USA)—Darariyna (IRE) (Shirley Heights) **H. H. Aga Khan**

MR A. DE ROYER-DUPRE—continued

89 **DARAYBAD (FR)**, b c 24/5 Octagonal (NZ)—Daraydala (IRE) (Royal Academy (USA)) **H. H. Aga Khan**
90 **DARGASH (IRE)**, b c 15/4 Darshaan—Darata (IRE) (Vayrann) **H. H. Aga Khan**
91 **DASHTAKI (FR)**, b c 23/2 Night Shift (USA)—Darashandeh (IRE) (Darshaan) **H. H. Aga Khan**
92 **HAMALI (IRE)**, b c 28/4 Muhtarram (USA)—Haladiya (IRE) (Darshaan) **H. H. Aga Khan**
93 B c 18/4 Highest Honor (FR)—Kalajana (IRE) (Green Dancer (USA)) **H. H. Aga Khan**
94 B f 12/2 Sendawar (IRE)—Khalisa (IRE) (Persian Bold) **H. H. Aga Khan**
95 B c 10/4 Dr Devious (IRE)—Khaytada (IRE) (Doyoun) **H. H. Aga Khan**
96 **KLUTE (FR)**, b c 27/4 Zafonic (USA)—Alleluia Tree (IRE) (Royal Academy (USA)) **Marquise de Moratalla**
97 **LAY DAYS (FR)**, bl f 12/4 Daylami (IRE)—
                Just For Fun (FR) (Lead On Time (USA)) (24737) **Marquise de Moratalla**
98 B f 27/2 Ashkalani (IRE)—Mandalara (IRE) (Lahib (USA)) **Princesse Zahra**
99 B c 17/4 Sendawar (IRE)—Mannsara (IRE) (Royal Academy (USA)) **H. H. Aga Khan**
100 B c 16/2 Night Shift (USA)—More Magic (GER) (Dashing Blade) (46382) **6 C Racing Ltd**
101 B f 24/3 Kendor (FR)—Nadira (FR) (Green Desert (USA)) **H. H. Aga Khan**
102 **ON THE WIND (IRE)**, ch f 2/3 Machiavellian (USA)—
                Lettre de Cachet (USA) (Secreto (USA)) **Marquise de Moratalla**
103 **SANAGORA (IRE)**, b f 6/3 Mujadil (USA)—Sanariya (IRE) (Darshaan) **H. H. Aga Khan**
104 B f 31/3 Rainbow Quest (USA)—Sarliya (IRE) (Doyoun) **H. H. Aga Khan**
105 **SERAYA (FR)**, b f 28/1 Danehill (USA)—Sendana (FR) (Darshaan) **H. H. Aga Khan**
106 B c 20/2 Kahyasi—Shamanara (IRE) (Danehill (USA)) **H. H. Aga Khan**
107 B f 3/3 Sinndar (IRE)—Shamawna (IRE) (Darshaan) **H. H. Aga Khan**
108 **SHAMDALA (IRE)**, b f 15/2 Grand Lodge (USA)—Shamadara (IRE) (Darshaan) **H. H. Aga Khan**
109 B f 8/4 Sendawar (IRE)—Sharakanda (USA) (Alleged (USA)) **H. H. Aga Khan**
110 **SHARDAKHAN (IRE)**, b c 26/3 Dr Devious (IRE)—Sharamana (IRE) (Darshaan) **H. H. Aga Khan**
111 B c 10/2 Darshaan—Shemaka (IRE) (Nishapour (FR)) **H. H. Aga Khan**
112 **SHEMRIYNA (IRE)**, b f 15/4 King of Kings (IRE)—Shemaya (IRE) (Darshaan) **H. H. Aga Khan**
113 B f 25/2 Daylami (IRE)—Sherana (IRE) (Alleged (USA)) **H. H. Aga Khan**
114 B f 31/3 Docksider (USA)—Shesawa (IRE) (Doyoun) **H. H. Aga Khan**
115 B c 30/3 Grand Lodge (USA)—Shezerma (IRE) (Kahyasi) **H. H. Aga Khan**
116 **SHIRLEY MOON (IRE)**, b f 21/4 Montjeu (IRE)—Greek Moon (IRE) (Shirley Heights) (40197) **6 C Racing Ltd**
117 **STASH THE ICE (IRE)**, ch f 11/2 Daylami (IRE)—
                Valley Quest (IRE) (Rainbow Quest (USA)) (92764) **Marquise de Moratalla**
118 B c 8/5 Green Tune (USA)—Super Vite (USA) (Septieme Ciel (USA)) (21645) **6 C Racing Ltd**
119 B f 22/2 Cape Cross (IRE)—Tabariya (IRE) (Doyoun) **H. H. Aga Khan**
120 B c 14/2 Kahyasi—Tarabaya (IRE) (Warning) **H. H. Aga Khan**
121 B c 18/2 Darshaan—Tashiriya (IRE) (Kenmare (FR)) **H. H. Aga Khan**
122 B f 6/4 Rainbow Quest (USA)—Zalaiyka (FR) (Royal Academy (USA)) **H. H. Aga Khan**
123 B f 26/2 Octagonal (NZ)—Zankara (FR) (Linamix (FR)) **H. H. Aga Khan**
124 B f 18/4 Red Ransom (USA)—Zarkiya (IRE) (Catrail (USA)) **H. H. Aga Khan**

Jockey (Flat): Christophe Soumillon.

---

479 MRS L. V. RUSSELL, Kinross

Postal: **Arlary House Stables, Milnathort, Kinross, Tayside, KY13 9SJ.**
Contact: **OFFICE (01577) 862482 YARD 865512 FAX 861171 MOBILE (07970) 645261**
E-MAIL lucinda@arlary.fsnet.co.uk

1 **BAY MAGIC (IRE)**, 11, b g Ela-Mana-Mou—Come In **Mr A. R. Trotter**
2 **BROADGATE FLYER (IRE)**, 10, b g Silver Kite (USA)—Fabulous Pet **D. G. Pryde**
3 **BRORA SUTHERLAND (IRE)**, 5, b g Synefos (USA)—Downtotheswallows (IRE) **Mr William A. Powrie**
4 **CAESAR'S PALACE (GER)**, 7, ch g Lomitas—Caravene (FR) **Mr Peter J. S. Russell**
5 **CATCH THE PERK (IRE)**, 7, b g Executive Perk—Kilbally Quilty (IRE) **Mr A. A. Bissett**
6 **DARK CRUSADER (IRE)**, 9, br g Cajetano—Glissade **Brahms & Liszt**
7 **DOTTIE DIGGER (IRE)**, 5, b m Catrail (USA)—Hint-of-Romance (IRE) **Dig In Racing**
8 **DUKE ORSINO (IRE)**, 4, b g Old Vic—Deselby's Choice **Mr Peter K. Dale**
9 **FIRST ADARE (IRE)**, 4, ch g Un Desperado (FR)—First Mistake **Mrs C. G. Greig**
10 **FLORA BUNDY**, 4, ch f Genuine Gift (CAN)—Pharly Rose **Alight Bloodstock**
11 **GLENBURN (IRE)**, 6, br g Dr Devious (IRE)—Edwina (IRE) **Mrs Ann Rutherford**
12 **GLENFARCLAS BOY (IRE)**, 8, b g Montelimar (USA)—Fairy Blaze (IRE) **Mrs Ishbel Grant**
13 **JOCKIE WELLS (IRE)**, 6, b g Primitive Rising (USA)—Princess Maxine (IRE) **Miss G. Joughin**
14 **JOFI (IRE)**, 5, b g Shernazar—Giolla Donn **Mr J. R. Adam**
15 **KERRY LADS (IRE)**, 9, ch g Mister Lord (USA)—Minstrel Top **Mrs C. G. Greig**
16 **LANTERN LEADER (IRE)**, 9, b g Supreme Leader—Lantern Line **Mr Peter J. S. Russell**
17 **LAUDERDALE**, 8, b g Sula Bula—Miss Tullulah **Kelso Members Lowflyers Club**
18 **MASTER SEBASTIAN**, 5, ch g Kasakov—Anchor Inn **Mrs J. M. Grimston**

MRS L. V. RUSSELL—continued

19 **MISTER SMITH (IRE)**, 5, b g Mister Lord (USA)—Just A Swop (IRE) **Mrs L. R. Joughin**
20 **MUMARIS (USA)**, 10, b br g Capote (USA)—Barakat **Mr Peter J. S. Russell**
21 **NOLIFE (IRE)**, 8, b g Religiously (USA)—Garnerstown Lady **Peter J. S. Russell**
22 **NORAS LEGACY (IRE)**, 6, b m Old Vic—Balda Girl (IRE) **Mr Harry Gettings**
23 **SALTRIO**, 6, b g Slip Anchor—Hills' Presidium **Mr R. McNeil**
24 **SANTA LUCIA**, 8, b m Namaqualand (USA)—Villasanta **Mr H. Gettings**
25 **SCALLYWAGS RETURN**, 5, b m Bob's Return (IRE)—Bee-A-Scally **Roberts Racing**
26 **SCRAPPIE (IRE)**, 4, b g Fourstars Allstar (USA)—Clonyn **John R. Adam & Sons**
27 **SPORTS EXPRESS**, 6, ch m Then Again—Lady St Lawrence (USA) **Powrie, Valentine, Hawkins & McManus**
28 **STRONG RESOLVE (IRE)**, 8, gr g Roselier (FR)—Farmerette **Fair City Flyers**
29 **SUNDAY RAIN (USA)**, 7, b g Summer Squall (USA)—Oxava (FR) **Peter K. Dale Ltd**
30 **TETRAGON (IRE)**, 4, b g Octagonal (NZ)—Viva Verdi (IRE) **Mr William A. Powrie**
31 **WAINAK (USA)**, 6, b g Silver Hawk (USA)—Cask **W. A. Powrie**
32 **WINTER GARDEN**, 10, ch g Old Vic—Winter Queen **Mr A. A. Bissett**

Other Owners: Mr W. Agnew, Mr A. Bayvel, Mr J. D. I. Bell, Mr A. Black, Mr G. Bollan, Mr A. Brierley, Mr P. Brierley, Mr I. Crole, Mr Bill Everett, Mr T. Hawkins, Mr T. Hutton, Mr S. Keily, Mr Lamb, Mr B. Lamming, The Countess Of Lanesborough, Mr R. S. Macdonald, Mr K. N. R. Macnicol, Mr David McIntosh, Mr A. McManus, Mr D. McManus, Mr K. Milne, Mrs Margaret Rees, Mr M. Roberts, Mr G. Ruddock, Miss E. Sawyer, Mrs E. Sawyer, Mr C. Selby, Mr A. D. Stewart, Mrs Karen Thomson, Mr B. Valentine, Mrs C. Whiteway, Mr Barry Wilson, Major R. B. H. Young.

Assistant Trainer: Magnus Nicholson & Jaimie Duff

Jockeys (NH): R Johnson (10-0), M H Naughton (10-0), T Scudamore. **Amateur:** Mr R Trotter (10-0).

480 MR K. A. RYAN, Hambleton
Postal: Hambleton Lodge, Hambleton, Thirsk, North Yorkshire, YO7 2HA.
Contact: YARD (01845) 597622 HOME (01845) 597010 MOBILE (07768) 016930
FAX (01845) 597622 E-MAIL kevin.hambleton@virgin.net

1 **ALLEGRINA (IRE)**, 4, b f Barathea (IRE)—Pianola (USA) **Mr I. Bray**
2 **ARTE ET LABORE (IRE)**, 4, b f Raphane (USA)—Bouffant **Mr John W. Howarth**
3 **BELLS BOY'S**, 5, b g Mind Games—Millie's Lady (IRE) **Wooster Partnership**
4 **CARDINAL VENTURE (IRE)**, 6, b g Bishop of Cashel—Phoenix Venture (IRE) **Mr Tony Fawcett**
5 **CD EUROPE (IRE)**, 6, ch g Royal Academy (USA)—Woodland Orchid (IRE) **Mr L. Neill and Mr G. Flitcroft**
6 **CLOUD DANCER**, 5, b m Bishop of Cashel—Summer Pageant **Mr G. Frankland**
7 **DILSAA**, 7, ch g Night Shift (USA)—Llia **Yorkshire Racing Club V**
8 **ENDLESS SUMMER**, 6, b g Zafonic (USA)—Well Away (IRE) **Platinum Racing Club Limited**
9 **GRALMANO (IRE)**, 9, b g Scenic—Llangollen (IRE) **Coleorton Moor Racing**
10 **HALMAHERA (IRE)**, 9, b g Petardia—Champagne Girl **Mr J. Duddy and Mrs G. Quinn**
11 **JOSHUAS BOY**, 4, ch c Bahhare (USA)—Broadway Rosie **Mrs C. Reilly & Mr J. Moulden**
12 **LAWOOD (IRE)**, 4, gr g Charnwood Forest (IRE)—La Susiane **Mrs Kennedy**
13 **LEGALIS (USA)**, 6, ch g Gone West (USA)—Loyalize (USA) **Sunpak Potatoes**
14 **MILLKOM ELEGANCE**, 5, b m Millkom—Premier Princess **Yorkshire Racing Club IV**
15 **MYSTIC MAN (FR)**, 6, b g Cadeaux Genereux—Shawanni **R J H Limited**
16 **NORTHERN GAMES**, 5, b g Mind Games—Northern Sal **Mr & Mrs R. Robinson**
17 **NOUL (USA)**, 5, ch g Miswaki (USA)—Water Course (USA) **Mr John Duddy**
18 **ONLY ONE LEGEND (IRE)**, 6, b g Eagle Eyed (USA)—Afifah **Sunpak Potatoes**
19 **OVER RATING**, 4, ch f Desert King (IRE)—Well Beyond (IRE) **Whitestonecliffe Racing Syndicate**
20 **PETRULA**, 5, ch g Tagula (IRE)—Bouffant **Mr & Mrs Peter Foden**
21 **PLATINUM CHARMER (IRE)**, 4, b g Kahyasi—Mystic Charm **Platinum Racing Club Limited**
22 **QUIET TIMES (IRE)**, 5, ch g Dolphin Street (FR)—Super Times **Yorkshire Racing Club and Francis Moll**
23 **RAYMOND'S PRIDE**, 4, b g Mind Games—Northern Sal **Mr & Mrs R. E. Robinson**
24 **ST JUDE**, 4, b c Deploy—Little Nutmeg **Ms Kim Jansen**
25 **UHOOMAGOO**, 9, ch g Namaqualand (CAN)—Point of View **Platinum Racing Club**
26 **WINCHESTER**, 9, ch g Gunner B—Tracy Jack **Mr & Mrs K. Hughes**
27 **YENALED**, 7, gr g Rambo Dancer (CAN)—Fancy Flight (FR) **The Fishermen**
28 **YOUNG SCOTTON**, 4, b g Cadeaux Genereux—Broken Wave **The I.B. & B.D.F. Partnership**

THREE-YEAR-OLDS

29 **BLADE'S DAUGHTER**, gr f Paris House—Banningham Blade **Crown Select**
30 **BRIDGEWATER BOYS**, b g Atraf—Dunloe (IRE) **Bishopthorpe Racing**
31 **COLEORTON PRINCE (IRE)**, b g Paris House—Tayovullin (IRE) **Coleorton Moor Racing**
32 **ISKANDER**, b g Danzero (AUS)—Amber Mill **Mrs Margaret Forsyth**

MR K. A. RYAN—continued

33 **JOE CHARLIE,** ch g Daggers Drawn (USA)—La Ballerine **Mr John Duddy**
34 **KINGS ROCK,** ch g Kris—Both Sides Now (USA) **Miss Claire King and Mr Peter McBride**
35 **KNIGHT TO REMEMBER (IRE),** ch g Fayruz—Cheerful Knight (IRE) **Platinum Racing Club Limited**
36 **LADY SUNSET (IRE),** b f Entrepreneur—Sunset Reigns (IRE) **Mr G. Frankland**
37 **LUKE SHARP,** gr g Muhtarram (USA)—Heaven-Liegh-Grey **Mr P. Dodd**
38 **MILLIETOM (IRE),** b g General Monash (USA)—June Lady **Mr Gary Flitcroft**
39 **MISTER REGENT,** b c Mind Games—River of Fortune (IRE) **Mr Roger Hammond**
40 **MOLLYS RAINBOW (IRE),** b f Desert Style (IRE)—Rainbow Reliance **Mr J. Stephenson**
41 **MY PARIS,** b g Paris House—My Desire **J. & A. Spensley**
42 **NORTHERN SPIRIT,** b g Kadeed (IRE)—Elegant Spirit **Mr R. Murray**
43 **PLATINUM MICHELLE,** b f Pivotal—Berenice (ITY) **Platinum Racing Club**
44 **POPPYS FOOTPRINT (IRE),** ch f Titus Livius (FR)—Mica Male (ITY) **Kimian Barfly**
45 B g Alzao (USA)—Romoosh **Mr R. Millican**
46 **TRYSTING GROVE (IRE),** b f Cape Cross (IRE)—Elton Grove (IRE) **Mr B. Hayes & Mrs J. Ryan**

TWO-YEAR-OLDS

47 Ch c 13/3 Paris House—Banningham Blade (Sure Blade (USA)) (4200) **Crown Select**
48 B c 6/2 Cois Na Tine (IRE)—Berenice (ITY) (Litigant (USA)) (17000) **Mrs G. Quinn**
49 B f 6/2 Desert Style (IRE)—Chummy's Friend (IRE) (Be My Guest (IRE)) (5565) **Mrs J. Ryan**
50 **COLEORTON DANCER,** ch c 2/4 Danehill (USA)—
Tayovullin (IRE) (Shalford (IRE)) (6000) **Coleorton Moor Racing**
51 **COLEORTON DANE,** gr c 24/5 Danehill Dancer (USA)—
Cloudy Nine (Norton Challenger) (6200) **Coleorton Moor Racing**
52 B c 5/4 Mind Games—Crystal Sand (GER) (Forzando) (34000) **Mr B. MacDonald**
53 **DARIO GEE GEE,** ch c 28/3 Bold Fact (USA)—
Magical Peace (IRE) (Magical Wonder (USA)) (12000) **Crewe & Nantwich R Club**
54 **DISTINCTIVE MIND,** b c 3/2 Mind Games—Primus Tempus (Primo Dominie) **Mr Julian & Mrs Rosie Richer**
55 **GIFTED GAMBLE,** b c 28/1 Mind Games—Its Another Gift (Primo Dominie) (8000) **Margarets Partnership**
56 B c 11/3 Nicolette—It's All Academic (IRE) (Mazaad) (21000) **Mr R. Peel**
57 **LINZIS LAD,** ch c 24/2 Magic Ring (IRE)—Come On Katie (Cadeaux Genereux) (7000) **Mr Lucas Neill**
58 B f 21/3 Zaha (USA)—Little Miss Rocker (Rock Hopper) (8000) **Zaha Racing Syndicate**
59 B f 15/2 Cape Cross—Machudi (Bluebird (USA)) (8000) **Rightprice Racing**
60 **MISSED TURN,** b f 9/2 Mind Games—Miss Beverley (Beveled (USA)) (14000) **Mr T. G. & Mrs M. E. Holdcroft**
61 B c 18/3 Mind Games—Nom Francais (First Trump) (21000) **Mrs M. Forsyth**
62 B f 21/2 Orpen (USA)—Secret Hideaway (USA) (Key To The Mint (USA)) (18000) **Mrs Angie Bailey**
63 **THROW THE DICE,** b c 26/3 Lujain (USA)—Euridice (IRE) (Woodman (USA)) (13000) **Pendle Inn Partnership**
64 Gr f 26/2 Paris House—Time of Night (USA) (Night Shift (USA)) (1300) **Mr W. Calvert**
65 B f 29/4 Cois Na Tine (IRE)—Water Pixie (IRE) (Dance of Life (USA)) (1200) **Mrs G. Quinn**

Assistant Trainer: M Birch

Jockeys (Flat): N Callan, P Fessey, F Lynch, R Winston. **Jockey (NH):** G Lee. **Apprentices:** J Maher, C Williams. **Amateur:** Mr Miles Seston.

---

481 | MR A. M. SADIK, Kidderminster

Postal: **Wolverley Court Coach House, Wolverley, Kidderminster, Worcestershire, DY10 3RP.**
Contact: **PHONE (01562) 852362 MOBILE (0780) 3040344**

1 **CAROLS CHOICE,** 7, ch m Emarati (USA)—Lucky Song **Mr A. Sadik**
2 **CRUSOE (IRE),** 7, b g Turtle Island (IRE)—Self Reliance **Mr A. Sadik**
3 **DANCER POLISH (POL),** 6, b g Professional (IRE)—Doloreska (POL) **Mr A. Sadik**
4 **GREEN GO (GER),** 6, ch g Secret 'n Classy (CAN)—Green Fee (GER) **Mr A. Sadik**

Assistant Trainer: Cengiz Sadik

---

482 | MISS B. SANDERS, Epsom

Postal: **Chalk Pit Stables, Headley Road, Epsom, Surrey, KT18 6BW.**
Contact: **PHONE (01372) 278453 FAX (01372) 276137**

1 **ANOTHER GLIMPSE,** 6, gr g Rudimentary (USA)—Running Glimpse (IRE) **Mr Edward Hyde**
2 **A WOMAN IN LOVE,** 5, gr m Muhtarram (USA)—Ma Lumiere (FR) **High & Dry Racing**
3 **CANTRIP,** 4, b f Celtic Swing—Circe **Mr A. C. Verdie**
4 **FIREWIRE,** 6, b g Blushing Flame (USA)—Bay Risk **Miss Jennie Wisher**

MISS B. SANDERS—continued

5 **FRANKSALOT (IRE)**, 4, ch g Desert Story (IRE)—Rosie's Guest (IRE) **Peter Crate, Jane Byers, Roger Knight**
6 **FRANKSKIPS**, 5, b g Bishop of Cashel—Kevins Lady **Mr Peter Crate**
7 **JAYANJAY**, 5, b g Piccolo—Morica **Mr Peter Crate**
8 **KATIYPOUR (IRE)**, 7, ch g Be My Guest (USA)—Katiyfa **Mr Peter Crate**
9 **LARA FALANA**, 6, b m Tagula (IRE)—Victoria Mill **Mr R. Lamb**
10 **MELODY MASTER (IRE)**, 4, b c Woodborough (USA)—Tabasco Jazz **Mr J. M. Quinn**
11 **MUYASSIR (IRE)**, 9, b g Brief Truce (USA)—Twine **Mr J. M. Quinn**
12 **SUPERCHIEF**, 9, b g Precocious—Rome Express **Mr Edward Hyde**
13 **VIVA ATLAS ESPANA**, 4, b f Piccolo—Bay Risk **Atlas International**

THREE-YEAR-OLDS

14 **INTRIGUING GLIMPSE**, b br f Piccolo—Running Glimpse (IRE) **Mr Edward Hyde**

TWO-YEAR-OLDS

15 **KING OF FIRE**, b g Magic Ring (IRE)—Alaskan Princess (IRE) (Prince Rupert (FR)) (5000) **Mrs C. D. Jefferiss**

Other Owners: Mr Mark L. Champion, Mr Jason Matthias.

483
MR M. S. SAUNDERS, Wells
Postal: **Blue Mountain Farm, Wells Hill Bottom, Haydon, Wells, Somerset, BA5 3EZ.**
Contact: **OFFICE (01749) 841011 MOBILE (07771) 601035 FAX (01749) 841011**
E-MAIL malcolm@malcolmsaunders.co.uk WEBSITE www.malcolmsaunders.co.uk

1 **BALI ROYAL**, 6, b m King's Signet (USA)—Baligay **Mrs R. J. Manning**
2 **CAUSTIC WIT (IRE)**, 6, b g Cadeaux Genereux—Baldemosa (FR) **Mrs Sandra Jones**
3 **CHANDELIER**, 4, ch g Sabrehill (USA)—La Noisette **Chris Scott & Peter Hall**
4 **CRAIC SA CEILI (IRE)**, 4, b f Danehill Dancer (IRE)—Fay's Song (IRE) **Charles Saunders Ltd**
5 **DEVISE (IRE)**, 5, b g Hamas (IRE)—Soreze (IRE) **Mr D. Naylor**
6 **FIAMMA ROYALE (IRE)**, 6, b m Fumo di Londra (IRE)—Ariadne **Mr Chris Scott**
7 **INDIAN MAIDEN (IRE)**, 4, br f Indian Ridge—Jinsiyah (USA) **Chris Scott & Peter Hall**
8 **LOCKSTOCK (IRE)**, 6, b g Inchinor—Risalah **Mr Chris Scott**
9 **MY GIRL PEARL (IRE)**, 4, b f Sri Pekan (USA)—Desert Bloom (FR) **Mr T. A. Godbert**
10 **REPERTORY**, 11, b g Anshan—Susie's Baby **Mr M. S. Saunders**

THREE-YEAR-OLDS

11 **MELAINA**, b f Whittingham (IRE)—Oh I Say **Bali Royal Racing**

TWO-YEAR-OLDS

12 Br c Millkom—Double Fault (IRE) (Zieten (USA)) (12000)

Other Owners: Mr K Everall, Mrs M. M. Godbert, Mr Peter Hall, Mr R. J. Manning, Mr C. D. Pritchard.

Amateur: Miss K Jones.

484
MRS H. D. SAYER, Penrith
Postal: **Town End Farm, Hackthorpe, Penrith, Cumbria, CA10 2HX.**
Contact: **PHONE (01931) 712245 MOBILE (07980) 295316**

1 **COOL MATE (IRE)**, 6, br g Montelimar (USA)—Another Advantage (IRE) **Mr A. Slack**
2 **GETINBYBUTONLYJUST**, 5, b g King's Ride—Madame President (IRE) **Mr Andrew Sayer**
3 **GREENFIRE (FR)**, 6, ch g Ashkalani (IRE)—Greenvera (USA) **Mr Andrew Sayer**
4 **I'M YOUR MAN**, 5, gr g Bigstone (IRE)—Snowgirl (IRE) **Mr A. Slack**
5 **STONERAVINMAD**, 6, ch g Never So Bold—Premier Princess **Mrs Evelyn Slack**
6 **TRAVELLER'S FAYRE (IRE)**, 5, b g Fayruz—The Way She Moves **Mr A. Slack**
7 **VERY TASTY (IRE)**, 7, ch g Be My Native (USA)—Jasmine Melody **Mrs Dianne Sayer**
8 **YOU'RE THE MAN (IRE)**, 7, b g Lapierre (IRE)—Another Advantage (IRE) **Mr A. Slack**

Assistant Trainer: Mr Andrew Sayer

485 DR J. D. SCARGILL, Newmarket
Postal: **Red House Stables, Hamilton Road, Newmarket, Suffolk, CB8 0TE.**
Contact: **PHONE (01638) 663254 MOBILE (07785) 350705**

1 **ASBO,** 4, b f Abou Zouz (USA)—Star **J P T Partnership**
2 **BRONX BOMBER,** 6, ch g Prince Sabo—Super Yankee (IRE) **Mr R. A. Dalton**
3 **MR FLEMING,** 5, b br g Bin Ajwaad (IRE)—Fabulous Night (FR) **Mrs Susan Scargill**
4 **RANNY,** 4, b f Emperor Jones (USA)—Defined Feature (IRE) **Mr Derek W. Johnson**
5 **XIXITA,** 4, ch f Fleetwood (IRE)—Conquista **J P T Partnership**

THREE-YEAR-OLDS

6 **ABSOLUTELY SOAKED (IRE),** b f Alhaarth (IRE)—Vasilopoula (IRE) **The Four April Fools**
7 **BOBBY CHARLES,** ch c Polish Precedent (USA)—Dina Line (USA) **Ms Bobby Cohen**
8 **SCARLETT ROSE,** b f Royal Applause—Billie Blue **Mr R. A. Dalton**
9 **STONEBRIDGE ROSE,** ch f Fleetwood (IRE)—Periwinkle (FR) **The Hon Mrs R. Pease**
10 **SWEET INDULGENCE (IRE),** ch c Inchinor—Silent Indulgence (USA) **Ms Bobby Cohen**

TWO-YEAR-OLDS

11 Ch c 13/4 Cadeaux Generoux—Billie Blue (Ballad Rock) **R. A. Dalton**
12 B f 23/1 Diktat—Defined Feature (IRE) (Nabeel Dancer) **Derek W. Johnson**
13 Br c 16/4 Tipsy Creek (USA)—Fabulous Night (FR) (Fabulous Dancer (USA)) (800) **Mrs Susan Scargill**

Other Owners: Mr Michael Bacon, G. A. Brigford, Mrs M. Coppitters, Mrs E. Goudge, Mr A. Holness, Mr D. Meilton, Mr A. Millar, Ms A. Prior, Mr G. F. L. Robinson, Mr K. Ruttle, Mr N. Ruttle, Mrs M. Stanton, Mr P. Stanton, Mr I. Wagstaff, Mr B. Watson, Mrs R. Watson, Mr C. A. Wotton, Mr S. Wrightson.

486 MR D. D. SCOTT, Minehead
Postal: **East Lynch, Minehead, Somerset, TA24 8SS.**
Contact: **PHONE (01643) 702430**

1 **BESUTO (IRE),** 7, br g Fourstars Allstar (USA)—Mabbots Own **D. D. Scott**
2 **IMPORTANT BOY (ARG),** 7, ch g Equalize (USA)—Important Girl (ARG) **Mrs D. D. Scott**

487 MRS E. B. SCOTT, Axbridge
Postal: **Moorland Farm, Axbridge, Somerset, BS26 2BA.**
Contact: **PHONE (01934) 733341 MOBILE (07773) 343282 E-MAIL moorlandfarm@btinternet.com**

1 **CHARLIE COLLIS,** 9, b g Deltic (USA)—Oneninefive **Mrs E. B. Scott**
2 **DANCING HILL,** 5, b m Piccolo—Ryewater Dream **Mrs E. B. Scott**
3 **HALLEM HALL,** 7, ch g Little Wolf—Oneninefive **Mrs E. B. Scott**
4 **WILL'SILLYSHANKERS,** 9, b g Silly Prices—Hannah's Song **Mrs E. B. Scott**

Amateur: Mr David Luff (11-0).

488 MRS J. SCRASE, Pulborough
Postal: **Scrase Farms, Pulborough, West Sussex, RH20 1DF.**
Contact: **PHONE (01403) 700525 MOBILE (07970) 888013**

1 **NELTINA,** 8, gr m Neltino—Mimizan (IRE) **Mrs J. E. Scrase**
2 **TINARANA GALE (IRE),** 6, b m Mister Lord (USA)—Dozing Gal (IRE) **Mrs J. E. Scrase**

489 MR M. J. SCUDAMORE, Hoarwithy
Postal: **Eccleswall Court, Bromsash, Ross-On-Wye, Herefordshire, HR9 7PP.**
Contact: **PHONE (01989) 750844 FAX (01989) 750281 E-MAIL peter.scu@ic24.net**

1 **AFZAL ROSE,** 4, b f Afzal—Fortria Rosie Dawn **M. J. & W. J. Fenn**
2 **ANACLONE (IRE),** 6, b g Zaffaran (USA)—Monteith (IRE) **The Meld Partnership**
3 **BONNY GLEN (IRE),** 6, b m Zaffaran (USA)—Bramble Hatch **The "Yes" - "No" - "Wait" ....Sorries**
4 **BORO SOVEREIGN (IRE),** 11, b g King's Ride—Boro Penny **Mrs P. de W. Johnson**
5 **COLESHILL LAD,** 4, br g Wizard King—Hallowed Ground (IRE) **Mr Jack Joseph**
6 **ELGAR,** 7, ch g Alflora (IRE)—School Run **Mrs S. Tainton**

MR M. J. SCUDAMORE—continued

7 FINZI (IRE), 6, b g Zaffaran (USA)—Sporting Talent (IRE) **The Meld Partnership**
8 FRIXOS (IRE), 4, ch g Barathea (IRE)—Local Lass **The "Yes" - "No" - "Wait"....Sorries**
9 GALLIUM, 7, gr m Terimon—Genie Spirit **Mrs J. D. Kington**
10 GAYE DREAM, 6, b g Gildoran—Gaye Fame **Mrs S. Tainton**
11 GOLDAMIE (IRE), 5, ch m Zaffaran (USA)—Keeping Company **Mrs S. Tainton**
12 GREENWICH, 10, br g Handsome Sailor—Praise The Lord **Mrs Marilyn Scudamore**
13 ITS GOTTA BE ALFIE (IRE), 9, ch g Zaffaran (USA)—Nimbi **Mrs S. Tainton**
14 JANBRE (IRE), 5, br g Zaffaran (USA)—Black Gayle (IRE) **Granite By Design Ltd**
15 JASPER, 5, gr g Environment Friend—Fisima **Mr J. Huckle & Miss E. Saunders**
16 JIVER (IRE), 5, b g Flemensfirth (USA)—Choice Brush (IRE) **Mrs S. Tainton**
17 JOURNAL PRINCESS (IRE), 5, b m Zaffaran (USA)—Bramble Hatch **Hereford Journal Racing Club**
18 LOCH SIDE, 6, gr m Tina's Pet—Sparkling Time (USA) **Mrs S. Tainton**
19 NOTANOTHERDONKEY (IRE), 4, b g Zaffaran (USA)—Sporting Talent (IRE) **Mr Nick Ponting**
20 RIVER TRIX (IRE), 10, b g Riverhead (USA)—Game Trix **The Viva Vialli Partnership**
21 SELASSIE, 5, ch g Alflora (IRE)—Zanditu **Mrs V. Stockdale**
22 SHAAMIT THE VAAMIT (IRE), 4, b c Shaamit (IRE)—Shocker (IRE) **Mrs S. Tainton**
23 SPEEDY RICHARD (IRE), 4, ch g Zaffaran (USA)—Chadandy (USA) **Mr Stephen W. Molloy**
24 STAR TIME (IRE), 5, b g Fourstars Allstar (USA)—Punctual **Successracing.com**
25 THE VILLAGER (IRE), 8, br g Zaffaran (USA)—Kitty Wren **Mrs S. Tainton**
26 THREE EAGLES (USA), 7, ch g Eagle Eyed (USA)—Tertiary (USA) **Granite By Design Ltd**
27 TIANYI (IRE), 8, b g Mujadil (USA)—Skinity **Mr Eddie Moss**
28 TORCHE (IRE), 6, b g Taos (IRE)—Orchette (IRE) **Mrs S. Tainton**
29 TOWNS ENDER (IRE), 6, b g Zaffaran (USA)—Delway **Mrs S. Tainton**
30 UNCLE SAM, 5, ch g Superpower—Treasure Time (IRE) **Mr J. Huckle & Miss E. Saunders**
31 WAYNESWORLD (IRE), 6, b g Petoski—Mariners Mirror **Mr F. J. Mills & Mr W. Mills**
32 ZANTANA BOY (IRE), 6, ch g Zaffaran (USA)—Ardtana (IRE) **The Carried Away Syndicate**

Other Owners: Mr Andrew Brush, Mr Chris Coley, Mr Martyn Court, Mr David Hussey, Mr R. F. Kelly, Mr N. Sharrocks.

Assistant Trainer: Peter Scudamore

Jockey (NH): Tom Scudamore (10-0). **Amateur:** Mr John Kington (9-0).

---

490 **MR I. SEMPLE, Carluke**
Postal: **Belstane Racing Stables, Belstane Road, Carluke, Strathclyde, ML8 5HN.**
Contact: **PHONE (01555) 773335 MOBILE (07788) 150969 FAX (01555) 772243**

1 AROGANT PRINCE, 7, ch g Aragon—Versaillesprincess **Tic-Tac.com**
2 BANDOS, 4, ch g Cayman Kai (IRE)—Lekuti **J. O. Hall, Ken Topham, Linda Straker**
3 CHERISHED NUMBER, 5, b g King's Signet—Pretty Average **Joseph Leckie & Sons Ltd**
4 CHOOKIE HEITON (IRE), 6, br g Fumo di Londra (IRE)—Royal Wolff **Hamilton Park Members Syndicate**
5 DESERT HEAT, 6, b h Green Desert (USA)—Lypharitissima (FR) **Mr Gordon McDowall**
6 EASIBET DOT NET, 4, gr g Atraf—Silvery **WWW.EASIBET DOT NET**
7 FLIGHT COMMANDER (IRE), 4, b g In The Wings—Lucrezia (IRE) **Woodspeen Sport & Leisure**
8 GIFTED FLAME, 5, b g Revoque (IRE)—Little Lady Leah (USA) **Mr Raymond Miquel**
9 JORDANS ELECT, 4, ch g Fleetwood (USA)—Cal Norma's Lady (IRE) **Mr Ian Crawford**
10 KILLALA (IRE), 4, b g Among Men (USA)—Hat And Gloves
11 MAKTAVISH, 5, b h Makbul—La Belle Vie **Mr D. G. Savala**
12 MILLAGROS (IRE), 4, b f Pennekamp (USA)—Grey Galava **Mr James A. Cringan**
13 RIDGEBACK, 4, ch c Indian Ridge—Valbra **Mr Ian Anderson**
14 SANDGATE CYGNET, 4, ch f Fleetwood (USA)—Dance of the Swans (IRE) **Mrs A. M. Young**
15 SARRAAF (IRE), 8, ch g Perugino (USA)—Blue Vista (IRE) **Mr Gordon McDowall**
16 SCARLETTI (GER), 7, ch g Master Willie—Solidago (USA) **Strathayr Publishing Ltd**
17 SILVER SEEKER (USA), 4, gr c Seeking The Gold (USA)—Zelanda (IRE) **Ecosse Racing**
18 SPEEDFIT FREE (IRE), 7, b g Night Shift (USA)—Dedicated Lady (IRE) **Mr A. R. M. Galbraith**
19 TANDAVA (IRE), 6, ch g Indian Ridge—Kashka (USA) **Woodspeen Sport & Leisure**
20 TEMPLET (USA), 4, b c Souvenir Copy (USA)—Two Step Trudy (USA)
21 ULYSEES (IRE), 5, b g Turtle Island (IRE)—Tamasriya (IRE) **Mr John F. Allan**
22 VIEWFORTH, 6, b g Emarati (USA)—Miriam **Mr Gordon McDowall**
23 VIJAY (IRE), 5, ch h Eagle Eyed (USA)—Foolish Fun **Tough Construction Ltd**

THREE-YEAR-OLDS

24 APPALACHIAN TRAIL (IRE), b c Indian Ridge—Karinski (USA)
25 HOWARD'S LASS, ch f Compton Place—Al Guswa **Mr Gordon McDowall**

MR I. SEMPLE—continued

26 **HOWARDS ROCKET**, ch c Opening Verse (USA)—Houston Heiress (USA)
27 **JORDANS SPARK**, ch c Opening Verse (USA)—Ribot's Pearl **Mr Ian Crawford**
28 **LI'L LEES (IRE)**, ch g Lake Coniston (IRE)—Kayrava **Mr Raymond Miquel**
29 **LYFORD LASS**, b f Bahamian Bounty—Ladykirk **Evelyn Duchess of Sutherland**
30 **PAR INDIANA (IRE)**, b f Indian Rocket—Paryiana (IRE) **The Greens Committee**
31 **PETERS CHOICE**, ch g Wolfhound (USA)—Dance of The Swans (IRE) **Mr Peter Tsim**
32 **PLAYFUL LADY**, ch f Theatrical Charmer—Lady Day (FR) **Evelyn Duchess of Sutherland**
33 **SAAMEQ (IRE)**, b c Bahhare (USA)—Tajawuz **Raeburn Brick Ltd**
34 **THE NUMBER**, gr g Silver Wizard (USA)—Elite Number (USA) **The Northreg Racing Partnership**
35 **TRIBALINNA (IRE)**, b f Indian Rocket—Cappuchino (IRE) **Belstane Racing Partnership (One)**
36 **WEST HIGHLAND WAY (IRE)**, b g Foxhound (USA)—Gilding The Lily (IRE) **Laumar Racing**

TWO-YEAR-OLDS

37 **HOWARDS PRINCESS**, gr f 28/2 Lujain (USA)—Grey Princess (IRE) (Common Grounds) **Mr Gordon McDowall**
38 Ch f 27/2 Handsome Ridge—Il Dorja (IRE) (Mac's Imp (USA)) **Mr David & Rachel Platt**

Other Owners: Mr W. Brand, Mr Robert Brown, Mr I. M. Buchan, Mr P. J. Burns, Mr William Docherty, Mr L. H. Gilmurray, Mr J. O. Hall, Mr B. Jordan, Mr Jonathan R. Kennerley, Mr R. M. J. Macnair, Mr Patrick H. Marron, Mr A. C. Mathieson, Mrs H. G. Peplinsky, Mr John H. Price, Mr J. M. Raeburn, Raeburn Brick Limited, Mr James Smith, Mrs L. M. Straker, Mr George D. Taylor, M Kenny Topham, Mr Martin Tucker.

Assistant Trainer: Martin McGoldrick

Jockeys (Flat): George Duffield (w.a.), Paul Hanagan, Robert Winston (8-6, w.a.). **Amateur:** Mr John McShane.

---

491 **MR A. SENIOR, Macclesfield**
Postal: **The Stables, Oak Lane, Kerridge, Macclesfield, Cheshire, SK10 5AP.**
Contact: **PHONE (01625) 575735 MOBILE (07796) 121334 E-MAIL asenior99@tesco.net**

1 **DANCING RIDGE (IRE)**, 7, b g Ridgewood Ben—May We Dance (IRE) **Mr A. Senior**
2 **MISTBLACK**, 4, b f Wizard King—Dear Heart **Mr Chris Etridge**
3 **SHEARWATER**, 7, b m Shareef Dancer (USA)—Sea Ballad (USA) **Mr A. Senior**

THREE-YEAR-OLDS

4 **RAETIHI**, b f Wizard King—Foreno **Miss S. L. Fagg**
5 **SPARTAN ODYSSEY**, b g Overbury (IRE)—Spartan Native **Mr G. B. Maher**

---

492 **MRS N. S. SHARPE, Abergavenny**
Postal: **Penbiddle Farm, Penbidwal, Pandy, Abergavenny, Gwent, NP7 8EA.**
Contact: **PHONE/FAX (01873) 890957 MOBILE (07977) 753437**
E-MAIL nikki@penbiddle.fsnet.co.uk

1 **ARNBI DANCER**, 5, b g Presidium—Travel Myth **Mr P. T. Evans**
2 **ATLANTIC LADY (GER)**, 6, br m Dashing Blade—Atlantic City (GER) **Mr J. Pritchard**
3 **BLUE YONDER**, 4, b f Terimon—Areal (IRE) **The Blue Yonder Partnership**
4 **BUCKSKIN LAD (IRE)**, 9, b br g Buckskin (FR)—Loverush **The Blue Yonder Partnership**
5 **CHAPEL ROYALE (IRE)**, 7, gr g College Chapel—Merci Royale **The Blue Yonder Partnership**
6 **HELL OF A TIME (IRE)**, 7, b g Phardante (FR)—Ticking Over (IRE) **Mr Islwyn Thomas**
7 **ILLINEYLAD (IRE)**, 10, b g Whitehall Bridge—Illiney Girl **The Illiney Group**
8 **LILY SAUNDERS**, 4, b f Piccolo—Saunders Lass **Mrs M. Gitting-Watts**
9 **MCMAHON'S BROOK**, 5, br g Alderbrook—McMahon's River **Mr J. V. C. Davenport**
10 **STAR SEVENTEEN**, 6, ch m Rock City—Westminster Waltz **Mr Islwyn Thomas**
11 **THE CROPPY BOY**, 5, b g Arctic Lord—Deep Cut **Mrs N. S. Sharpe**
12 **THE PECKER DUNN (IRE)**, 10, b g Be My Native (USA)—Riversdale Shadow **The Illiney Group**

Other Owners: Mr Michael Jenkins, Mr David P. Stanton, Mr D. J. Wallis.

Jockeys (NH): B J Crowley (w.a.), J Mogford (w.a.).

493 MR D. SHAW, Newark

Postal: **Danethorpe Racing, Danethorpe Lane, Danethorpe, Newark, Notts NG24 2PD.**
Contact: **MOBILE (07721) 039645 E-MAIL** derek.shaw@tiscali.co.uk

1 **ARCTIC BURST (USA)**, 4, b br g Royal Academy (USA)—Polar Bird **Swann Racing Ltd**
2 **ATTORNEY**, 6, ch g Wolfhound (USA)—Princess Sadie **Mr K. Nicholls**
3 **CHAMPAGNE RIDER**, 8, b g Presidium—Petitesse **The Whiteman Partnership**
4 **CHARNWOOD STREET (IRE)**, 5, b g Charnwood Forest (IRE)—La Vigie **Swann Racing Ltd**
5 **HAITHEM (IRE)**, 7, b g Mtoto—Wukk (IRE) **Century Racing**
6 **HUMDINGER (IRE)**, 4, b f Charnwood Forest (IRE)—High Finish **Mr K. Nicholls**
7 **LADIES KNIGHT**, 4, b g Among Men (USA)—Lady Silk **Swann Racing Ltd**
8 **LONG WEEKEND (IRE)**, 6, b h Flying Spur (AUS)—Friday Night (USA) **The Marlow Lewin Partnership**
9 **LUCIUS VERRUS (USA)**, 4, b c Danzig (USA)—Magic of Life (USA) **Swann Racing Ltd**
10 **MODEM (IRE)**, 7, b g Midhish—Holy Water **Dr J. Charlesworth**
11 **MUTARAFAA (USA)**, 5, b g Red Ransom (USA)—Mashaarif (USA) **Swann Racing Ltd**
12 **OASES**, 5, ch g Zilzal (USA)—Markievicz (IRE) **The Whiteman Partnership**
13 **PARK STAR**, 4, b f Gothenberg (IRE)—Miriam **Steve Wood**
14 **PHAROAH'S GOLD (IRE)**, 6, b g Namaqualand (USA)—Queen Nefertiti (IRE) **The Whiteman Partnership**
15 **PROMISES**, 4, b br f Nashwan (USA)—Balliasta (USA) **Mrs Jackie Cornwell**
16 **PROUD VICTOR (IRE)**, 4, b g Victory Note (USA)—Alberjas (IRE) **Swann Racing Ltd**
17 **RAYWARE BOY**, 8, b g Scenic—Amata (USA) **Rayton Racing**
18 **SAWAH**, 4, gr g Linamix (FR)—Tarhhib **Swann Racing Ltd**
19 **SEA THE WORLD (IRE)**, 4, b g Inzar (USA)—Annie's Travels (IRE) **Swann Racing Ltd**
20 **SO SOBER (IRE)**, 6, b g Common Grounds—Femme Savante **Swann Racing Ltd**
21 **STATOYORK**, 11, b g Statoblest—Ultimate Dream **Derek Shaw**
22 **SURE SIGN**, 4, ch g Selkirk (USA)—Beyond Doubt **Swann Racing Ltd**
23 **TATWEER (IRE)**, 4, b g Among Men (USA)—Sandystones **Swann Racing Ltd**
24 **TROPICAL SON**, 5, b g Distant Relative—Douce Maison (IRE) **Swann Racing Ltd**

THREE-YEAR-OLDS

25 **A BID IN TIME (IRE)**, b f Danetime (IRE)—Bidni (IRE) **Swann Racing Ltd**
26 **DESERT LIGHT**, b c Desert Sun—Nacote (IRE) **Swann Racing Ltd**
27 **FLY SO HIGH**, br f Danzero (AUS)—Fly The Flag (AUS) **Mrs S. Cornwall**
28 **SAHARA SILK (IRE)**, b f Desert Style (IRE)—Buddy And Soda (IRE) **Swann Racing Ltd**
29 **SWEET MILITARY MAN (USA)**, b c Allied Forces (USA)—Brown Sugar (VEN) **Swann Racing Ltd**

TWO-YEAR-OLDS

30 **BAZELLE**, ch f 29/3 Ashkalani (IRE)—Dona Royale (IRE) (Darshaan) (21644) **Mrs J. Cornwall**
31 B f 30/3 Monashee Mountain—Breezy Louise (Dilum (USA)) (3500) **Swann Racing Ltd**
32 B f 16/2 Tagula (IRE)—Cafe Solo (Nomination) (3500) **Swann Racing Ltd**
33 B f 28/2 Polish Precedent—Chelsea (USA) (Miswaki (USA)) (3200) **D. R. Tucker**
34 B f 9/2 Desert Style (IRE)—Ervedya (IRE) (Doyoun) (8500) **Swann Racing Ltd**
35 B c 24/4 Josr Algarhoud (IRE)—Feather-In-Her-Cap (Primo Dominie) (4000) **Swann Racing Ltd**
36 B f 31/3 Emarati (USA)—Floral Spark (Forzando) (3200) **Swann Racing Ltd**
37 B f 2/5 Tagula (IRE)—It's So Easy (Shaadi (USA)) (11000) **Swann Racing Ltd**
38 B f 22/4 Atraf—Madame Sisu (Emarati (USA)) (6000) **Derek Shaw**
39 **MYTORI**, ch f 26/4 Vettori (IRE)—Markievicz (IRE) (Doyoun) **Whiteman Partnership**
40 B c 24/4 Atraf—Prim Lass (Reprimand) (3000) **Swann Racing Ltd**
41 B f 20/2 Polar Prince—Simply Style (Bairn (USA)) (1500) **Swann Racing Ltd**
42 B f 16/4 Desert Style (IRE)—Tereed Elhawa (Cadeaux Genereux) (8000) **Swann Racing Ltd**
43 B c 29/4 Merdon Melody—Woodland Steps (Bold Owl) (4600) **Swann Racing Ltd**

Other Owners: Mr N. Cornwall, Mr A. B. Endfield, Mr R. H. Endfield, Mr Richard Hill, Mr Andy Lees, Mr R. Lewin, Mrs D. A. Marlow, Mrs Karin Swann, Mr Peter Swann, Mr P. A. Whiteman, Mr S. A. Whiteman, Mrs Barbara Wilkinson.

Jockeys (Flat): N Callan (8-5, w.a.), J K Fanning (8-2, w.a.), Darran Williams (8-5, w.a.). **Apprentice:** Dawn Watson (8-0). **Conditional:** A Podgson (10-0).

494 MR J. J. SHEEHAN, Findon

Postal: **Woodmans Stables, London Road, Ashington, West Sussex, RH20 3AU.**
Contact: **YARD (01903) 893031 MOBILE (07710) 495951**

1 **ATLANTIC WALTZ**, 4, b g Singspiel (IRE)—Fascination Waltz **Mrs Christina Dowling**
2 **CLASSICAL WALTZ (IRE)**, 6, ch m In The Wings—Fascination Waltz **Mrs Christina Dowling**
3 **GALEY RIVER (USA)**, 5, ch g Irish River (FR)—Carefree Kate (USA) **Mr D. J. Dowling**

MR J. J. SHEEHAN—continued

4 **GRAND MUSIC (IRE)**, 4, b c Grand Lodge (USA)—Abury (IRE) **Mrs Eileen Sheehan**
5 **IMPERIAL ISLAND (FR)**, 5, b g Exit To Nowhere (USA)—Imperial Prospect (USA) **Mrs Eileen Sheehan**
6 **MISS GRACE**, 4, ch f Atticus (USA)—Jetbeeah (IRE) **Mrs Eileen Sheehan**
7 **PALACE PRINCE (IRE)**, 4, b g Desert Prince (IRE)—Rainbow Reliance **Mr P. J. Sheehan**
8 **SADLERS SWING (USA)**, 8, b g Red Ransom (USA)—Noblissima (IRE) **Mrs Eileen Sheehan**
9 **SPECTOR (IRE)**, 4, gr c Spectrum (IRE)—Safkana (IRE) **Mrs Eileen Sheehan**

Assistant Trainer: P Sheehan

Jockey (Flat): A Clark. **Jockey (NH):** J Culloty.

---

495 **MR M. I. SHEPPARD, Ledbury**
Postal: **Home Farm Cottage, Eastnor, Ledbury, Herefordshire, HR8 1RD.**
Contact: **FAX (01531) 634846 MOBILE (07770) 625061**
E-MAIL matthew.sheppard1@btopenworld.com

1 **ASPARAGUS (IRE)**, 10, b g Roselier (FR)—Arctic Bead (IRE) **Mr Simon Gegg**
2 **BURNING TRUTH (USA)**, 10, ch g Known Fact (USA)—Galega **G. Jones**
3 **COME THE DAWN**, 8, b m Gunner B—Herald The Dawn **The Dawn Raiders**
4 **DELICEO (IRE)**, 11, br g Roselier (FR)—Grey's Delight **The Blues Partnership**
5 **DISTINCTLY WELL (IRE)**, 7, b g Distinctly North (USA)—Brandywell **Miss A. Bevan**
6 **MOOR HALL HOPPER**, 8, gr g Rock Hopper—Forgiving **Mrs Rosie Newman**
7 **ORIENT BAY (IRE)**, 9, b g Commanche Run—East Link (IRE) **Mr R. W. Guilding**
8 **PRIORY WOOD**, 8, ch m Gunner B—Penlea Lady **Mrs S. G. Addinsell**
9 **RUDETSKI**, 7, b g Rudimentary (USA)—Butosky **Mr M J Jordan and Mr J N Jordan**

Other Owners: Mr M. R. Bown, Mr J. N. Jordan, Mr M. J. Jordan, Mr A. M. Morley.

Amateur: Miss A Bevan (9-7).

---

496 **MR O. M. C. SHERWOOD, Upper Lambourn**
Postal: **Rhonehurst House, Upper Lambourn, Hungerford, Berkshire, RG17 8RG.**
Contact: **PHONE (01488) 71411 OFFICE 71411 FAX 72786 MOBILE (07979) 591867**
E-MAIL oliver.sherwood@virgin.net WEBSITE www.oliversherwood.com

1 **ALFLORIANO**, 5, b g Alflora (IRE)—Swallowfield **The Chamberlain Addiscott Partnership**
2 **BEAT THE BANK (IRE)**, 9, br g Good Thyne (USA)—Must Clear **Mr Chris Munro**
3 **BEL OMBRE (FR)**, 4, b g Nikos—Danse du Soleil (FR) **P. Deal, J. Tyndall, M St Quinton**
4 **CABER (IRE)**, 4, b g Celtic Swing—Arusha (IRE) **Mr Raymond Tooth**
5 **CELESTIAL HEIGHTS (IRE)**, 5, b g Fourstars Allstar (USA)—Aon Dochas (IRE) **Ledwidge Best Fforde**
6 **CHALOM (IRE)**, 6, b g Mujadil (USA)—The Poachers Lady (IRE) **Maagar UK Ltd**
7 **CLAYMORE (IRE)**, 8, b g Broadsword (USA)—Mazza **Mr B. T. Stewart-Brown**
8 **CLIQUEY**, 5, b g Muhtarram (USA)—Meet Again **Mr Colin G. B. Booth**
9 **DANDY LAD (IRE)**, 7, b g Zaffaran (USA)—Gerdando Lady (IRE) **Mr O. M. C. Sherwood**
10 **ERIC'S CHARM (FR)**, 4, b g Nikos—Ladoun (FR) **M. St Quinton & P. Deal**
11 **FAIR MAJORITY (IRE)**, 7, b g Simply Great (FR)—Bonne Fair **Mr R. Waters**
12 **FARNAHEEZVIEW (IRE)**, 6, b g Naheez (USA)—Sweet View **Mr O. M. C. Sherwood & Mr J. McCarthy**
13 **HARPASGON DE L'OMBRE (FR)**, 9, b g Mbaiki (FR)—Undress (FR) **It Wasn't Us**
14 **HULYSSE ROYAL (FR)**, 9, ch g Garde Royale—Ulysse Moriniere (FR) **Mr R. K. Carvill**
15 **HUSSARD (FR)**, 9, b g Concorde Jr (USA)—Cerise de Totes (FR) **Mr H. M. Heyman**
16 **KOHINOR**, 5, b m Supreme Leader—Always Shining **Mr R. J. Bassett**
17 **LIGHT DES MULOTTES (FR)**, 5, gr g Solidoun (FR)—Tango Girl (FR) **Mr R. K. Carvill**
18 **LYON**, 4, gr g Pivotal—French Gift **Mr Raymond Tooth**
19 **MARCHENSIS (IRE)**, 6, ch g Great Marquess—Trelissick **Mr O. M. C. Sherwood**
20 **MARK OF ZORRO (IRE)**, 4, br g Mark of Esteem (IRE)—Sifaara (IRE) **The Waney Racing Group Inc.**
21 **MINI DARE**, 7, b g Derrylin—Minim **Furrows Ltd**
22 **MUSIMARO (FR)**, 6, b g Solid Illusion (USA)—Musimara (FR) **Mr P. Joe Davis**
23 **ONASSIS**, 7, b g Roselier (FR)—Jack's The Girl (IRE) **P. Joe Davis & Peter McNeil**
24 **RODALKO (FR)**, 6, b g Kadalko (FR)—Darling Rose (FR) **Mr J. Palmer-Brown**
25 **RODOLFO**, 6, b g Tragic Role (USA)—Be Discreet **Mr P. Joe Davis**
26 **ROYAL MAID (FR)**, 6, b g Bakharoff (USA)—Swimming Maid (FR) **Mr O. M. C. Sherwood**
27 **SALOUP**, 6, b m Wolfhound (USA)—Sarcita **Mr Raymond Tooth**
28 **SAMBY**, 6, ch g Anshan—Mossy Fern **Mr R. Waters**
29 **SCURRY DANCER (FR)**, 8, b g Snurge—Fijar Dance (FR) **The St Joseph Partnership**

MR O. M. C. SHERWOOD—continued

30 **SECRET DRINKER (IRE)**, 8, b g Husyan (USA)—Try Le Reste (IRE) **Mr S. Channing-Williams**
31 **SHANNON QUEST (IRE)**, 8, b br g Zaffaran (USA)—Carrick Shannon **Ledwidge Best Fforde**
32 **SPUD ONE**, 7, b g Lord Americo—Red Dusk **Mr R. K. Carvill**
33 **STRONGTROOPER (IRE)**, 9, b g Doubletour (USA)—Moss Gale **Munro, Milne, Hoddell, Robertson**
34 **SURPRISING**, 9, b g Primitive Rising (USA)—Ascot Lass **Mr M. G. St Quinton**
35 **THE LYME VOLUNTEER (IRE)**, 7, b m Zaffaran (USA)—Dooley O'Brien **The Chamberlain Addiscott Partnership**
36 **TIK-A-TAI (IRE)**, 9, b g Alphabatim (USA)—Carrig Ross **The Chamberlain Addiscott Partnership**
37 **TWENTYTWOSILVER (IRE)**, 4, gr ro g Emarati (USA)—St Louis Lady **Ruelles Partners**
38 **WINSLEY**, 6, gr g Sula Bula—Dissolve **Absolute Solvents Ltd**

Other Owners: Mrs D. L. Addiscott, Mr G. Addiscott, Mr R. F. Bailey, Mr J. C. Best, Mr W. J. Bridge, Mr J. P. Cavanagh, Mr Nigel Chamberlain, Mrs P. C. Chamberlain, Mr Mike Donnelly, Mrs R. J. Feilden, Mr Rob E. L. Frost, Dr M. A. Herbich, Mrs A. Lambert, Mr J. P. Ledwidge, Mr K. D. Mellor, Mr Michael J. O'Leary, Mr J. A. Osborne, Mr Julian Palfreyman, Mr S. J. Piper, Mr H. M. J. Pope, Mr L. Setna, Mr B. P. Traynor, Mr D. P. Walsh, Mr V. J. Walsh.

Jockey (NH): J McCarthy (10-0). **Conditional:** O Kozak (9-7).

---

497 **MR S. E. H. SHERWOOD, Bromyard**
Postal: **The Day House, Bredenbury, Bromyard, Herefordshire, HR7 4TL.**
Contact: **OFFICE (01885) 488567 FAX (01885) 488677 MOBILE (07836) 215639**
E-MAIL seh.sherwood@virgin.net

1 **ACCADEMIC (IRE)**, 7, ch g Accordion—Giolla's Bone **Lady Thompson**
2 **ALL THINGS EQUAL (IRE)**, 5, b g Supreme Leader—Angel's Dream **Mr J. Hales**
3 **BALLYBROPHY (IRE)**, 9, gr g Roselier (FR)—Bavardmore **Mr Keith Berry**
4 **COME ON GEORGE (IRE)**, 8, b g Barathea (IRE)—Lacovia (USA) **Mr Brian Gray**
5 **DERRINTOGHER YANK (IRE)**, 10, b g Lord Americo—Glenmalur **Mr Con O'Connor**
6 **FINBAR'S REVENGE**, 9, b g Gildoran—Grotto Princess **Mr K. A. Price**
7 **IL'ATHOU (FR)**, 8, b g Lute Antique (FR)—Va Thou Line (FR) **Lady Thompson**
8 **LAURIER D'ESTRUVAL (FR)**, 5, ch g Ragmar (FR)—Grive d'Estruval (FR) **Mr T. N. Siviter**
9 **LUMYNO (IRE)**, 5, b g Lute Antique (FR)—Framboline (FR) **Mrs Yvonne S. Kennedy**
10 **MOUNTAIN MAN (FR)**, 6, b g Cadoudal (FR)—Montagne Bleue **The Hon Mrs S. Sherwood**
11 **OAKLEY GOLD**, 6, ch m Afzal—Romany Gold **Mrs J. Tarran**
12 **ON THE OUTSIDE (IRE)**, 5, ch m Anshan—Kate Fisher (IRE) **Mr Geoffrey Vos**
13 **REAL SHARP (IRE)**, 6, br g Son of Sharp Shot (IRE)—Lady By Chance (IRE) **The Perseverance Mob**
14 **ROBBIE'S RETURN**, 5, b g Bob's Return (IRE)—Si-Gaoith **Mr J. Hales**
15 **RUSSIAN COURT**, 8, b g Soviet Lad (USA)—Court Town **Rosemary Viscountess Boyne**
16 **SCRUMPY**, 5, b g Sir Harry Lewis (USA)—Superfina (USA) **Mrs Strachan,Graham,Boyne,Lywood,Parkes**
17 **WAGGY (IRE)**, 8, b g Cataldi—Energance (IRE) **Mrs A. Gordon**

Other Owners: Mrs Douglas Graham, Mr John Rhys Harris, Mr J. Lywood, Mrs P. I. May, Mr D. Parkes, Mrs Richard Strachan, Sir Peter Thompson.

Assistant Trainer: Anita Gibbons

Jockey (NH): H Oliver.

---

498 **MR R. SHIELS, Jedburgh**
Postal: **Thickside Farm, Jedburgh, Roxburghshire, TD8 6QY.**
Contact: **PHONE (01835) 864060 MOBILE (07790) 295645**

1 **BIT OF A BROAD**, 7, b m Tudor Diver—Broad Appeal **Mr R. Shiels**
2 **CARRADIUM**, 8, b g Presidium—Carrapateira **Mr R. Shiels**
3 **JUST JED**, 5, b g Presidium—Carrapateira **Mr R. Shiels**
4 **NEEDWOOD BUCOLIC (IRE)**, 6, br g Charnwood Forest (IRE)—Greek Icon **Mr R. Shiels**
5 **SMITHS WYND**, 12, gr g Alias Smith (USA)—Carrapateira **Mr R. Shiels**

THREE-YEAR-OLDS

6 **KITUHWA (USA)**, br g Cherokee Run (USA)—Ruhnke (USA) **Mr R. Shiels**

499 **MR S. H. SHIRLEY-BEAVAN, Hawick**
Postal: **Gatehousecote, Bonchester Bridge, Hawick, Roxburghshire, TD9 8JD.**
Contact: **(01450) 860210**

1 **BRUSH AND GO (IRE)**, 10, b g Brush Aside (USA)—Knockacool Breeze **Mrs S. H. Shirley-Beavan**
2 **MINOUCHKA (FR)**, 4, br f Bulington (FR)—Elbury (FR) **Mrs S. H. Shirley-Beavan**
3 **RUNNING MUTE**, 10, b g Roscoe Blake—Rose Albertine **Mr J. E. M. Vestey**
4 **THEMANFROMCARLISLE**, 8, br g Jupiter Island—Country Mistress **Mrs S. H. Shirley-Beavan**

500 **MISS L. C. SIDDALL, Tadcaster**
Postal: **Stonebridge Farm, Colton, Tadcaster, North Yorkshire, LS24 8EP.**
Contact: **PHONE (01904) 744291 FAX (01904) 744291 MOBILE (07778) 216692/4**

1 **BENEFIT**, 10, b g Primitive Rising (USA)—Sobriquet **Mrs D. Ibbotson**
2 **CANTYS BRIG (IRE)**, 7, gr g Roselier (FR)—Call Catherine (IRE) **Mrs D. Ibbotson**
3 **DAN DE MAN (IRE)**, 13, b g Phardante (FR)—Slave De **Miss L. C. Siddall**
4 **EXPLODE**, 7, b g Zafonic (USA)—Didicoy (USA) **Lynn Siddall Racing II**
5 **FORMERIC**, 8, ch g Formidable (USA)—Irish Limerick **Podso Racing**
6 **LAYAN**, 7, b m Puissance—Most Uppitty **Lynn Siddall Racing**
7 **LEAHSTAR**, 5, ch m In The Wings—Moondance **Mrs D. J. Morris**
8 **MICHAEL FINNEGAN (IRE)**, 11, b br g Phardante (FR)—Decent Slave **Mrs D. J. Morris**
9 **MONTE ROUGE (IRE)**, 7, ch g Montelimar (USA)—Drumdeels Star (IRE) **The Full Monte**
10 **MR CHRISTIE**, 12, b g Doulab (USA)—Hi There **Lynn Siddall Racing**
11 4, B f Merdon Melody—Sharp Ego (USA)
12 **SILENT SNIPE**, 11, ch g Jendali—Sasol **Mrs D. Ibbotson**
13 4, B f Merdon Melody—Woodland Steps

Other Owners: Mr A. P. Buxton, Mrs P. J. Clark, Mrs E. W. Cooper, Mr A. Emmerson, Mr I. Grice, Mrs P. K. Hornby, Miss L. Ibbotson, Mr G. Kennington, Mrs K. M. Kennington, Miss S. Lythe, Mr D. Mann, Mr D. McGhee, Miss Sue Vinden.

Assistant Trainer: Stephen Hackney

Jockey (NH): T Siddall (10-0).

501 **MR D. M. L. SIMCOCK, Newmarket**
Postal: **Trillium Place Stables, Birdcage Walk, Newmarket, Suffolk CB8 ONE.**
Contact: **PHONE/FAX (01638) 662968 MOBILE (07808) 954109**
E-MAIL davidsimcock@ukonline.co.uk

1 **DARK SHAH (IRE)**, 4, b g Night Shift (USA)—Shanjah
2 **KAWADER (USA)**, 4, ch g Kingmambo (USA)—Tajannub (USA)
3 **SILVER CHIME**, 4, gr f Robellino (USA)—Silver Charm

THREE-YEAR-OLDS

4 **CUT AND DRIED**, ch g Daggers Drawn (USA)—Apple Sauce

TWO-YEAR-OLDS

5 **CAUSEWAY GIRL (IRE)**, br f 22/2 Giant's Causeway—Darbela (IRE) (Doyoun) (34000)
6 **CAYENNE (GER)**, ch f 7/3 Efisio—Carola Rouge (Arazi (USA)) (18000)
7 B c 29/1 Nashwan (USA)—Cream Jug (IRE) (Spectrum (IRE)) (5000)
8 **ELISHA (IRE)**, ch f 4/4 Raise A Grand (IRE)—Social Butterfly (Sir Ivor)
9 B f 2/3 Brave Act—Jungle Story (IRE) (Alzao (USA)) (11131)
10 B f 8/2 Lujain (USA)—Masrora (USA) (Woodman (USA)) (2000)
11 B c 18/4 Entrepreneur—Prima Silk (Primo Dominie)
12 B c 10/5 Pyramus—Princess Aurora (Prince Sabo)
13 **ROBESON**, br c 2/2 Primo Dominie—Montserrat (Aragon)
14 B f 26/3 Night Shift (USA)—Top Jem (Damister (USA))
15 B c 9/3 Josr Algarhoud (IRE)—Upping The Tempo (Dunbeath (USA)) (20000)

Other Owners: Mr J. Cook, Mr L. Cox, Mr D. R. Driver, Easton Park Stud, Mr D. Fountain, Mr C. Hancock, Dr S. Kold, Mr C. Lysaght, Mrs S. Matthews, Norcroft Park Stud, Mr J. Payne, Mr & Mrs M. Sincock, Mr R. Trotter, Mr C. Vines, Mr R. Ward, Mrs S. Yearley.

Jockey (Flat): M J Dwyer (w.a.).

502 MRS P. M. SLY, Peterborough
Postal: **Singlecote, Thorney, Peterborough, Cambridgeshire, PE6 0PB.**
Contact: **PHONE (01733) 270212 MOBILE (07850) 511267**

1 **BONNET'S PIECES**, 5, b m Alderbrook—Chichell's Hurst **The Stablemates II**
2 **COLLINE DE FEU**, 7, b m Sabrehill (USA)—Band of Fire (USA) **Mr David L. Bayliss**
3 **COULTHARD (IRE)**, 11, ch g Glenstal (USA)—Royal Aunt **Mr R. Brazier**
4 **CRINAN (IRE)**, 6, ch g Carroll House—Esther **Mrs V. M. Edmonson**
5 **FILLE DETENTE**, 4, ch f Double Trigger (IRE)—Matoaka **Mr David L. Bayliss**
6 **FULLARDS**, 6, b g Alderbrook—Milly Kelly **Mrs M. S. Smith**
7 **HARLEY**, 6, ch g Alderbrook—Chichell's Hurst **Mr P. J. Turner**
8 **HARRYCONE LEWIS**, 6, b g Sir Harry Lewis (USA)—Rosie Cone **The Craftsmen**
9 **HAWTHORN PRINCE (IRE)**, 9, ch g Black Monday—Goose Loose **Messrs G.A.Libson,D.L.Bayliss & G.Taylor**
10 4, B g Alderbrook—Ima Delight **Mrs P. M. Sly**
11 **LONGSHORE**, 11, ch g Lord Bud—Milly Kelly **Mr M. S. Smith**
12 **ROSECHARMER**, 7, ch m Charmer—Rosie Cone **Thorney Racing Club**
13 **SAN MARCO (IRE)**, 6, b g Brief Truce (USA)—Nuit des Temps **Mr R. Brazier**
14 **SENOR HURST**, 9, b g Young Senor (USA)—Broadhurst **Thorney Racing Club**
15 **STANDING BLOOM**, 8, ch m Presidium—Rosie Cone **The Stablemates**
16 **TOMTHEVIC**, 6, ch g Emarati (USA)—Madame Bovary **Thorney Racing Club**
17 **UPRIGHT IMA**, 5, b m Perpendicular—Ima Delight **RBK Partnership**

THREE-YEAR-OLDS

18 **SAIDA LENASERA (FR)**, b f Fasliyev (USA)—Lenasara **David L. Bayliss & Mrs P. M. Sly**

Other Owners: Mr R. K. Blackman, Dr T. J. W. Davies, Mrs S. E. Godfrey, Mr T. E. Kerfoot, Mr A. Robinson, Mr Derek Sly, Mr Bob W. Smith.

Assistant Trainer: Matt Mills

Jockey (Flat): A Culhane (w.a.). **Jockeys (NH):** Paul Maloney (w.a.), W Marston (w.a.). **Amateur:** Miss Louise Allan.

503 MR D. SMAGA, Lamorlaye
Postal: **17 Voie de la Grange des Pres, 60260 Lamorlaye, France.**
Contact: **PHONE +33 (0) 44 21 50 05 FAX 03 44 21 53 56**

1 **ABU'L FAZL (FR)**, 11, b h Legend of France (USA)—Mevlana (IRE) **D. Smaga**
2 **BUSINESSMAN (FR)**, 4, b c Entrepreneur—Ariel (IRE) **R. Bellaiche**
3 **FAIRY NOTE (FR)**, 4, b c Victory Note (USA)—Catherine Schratt **Ecurie Chalhoub**
4 **HONOR RIVER (FR)**, 4, b c Highest Honor (FR)—Antilles (IRE) **Ecurie Chalhoub**
5 **IN THE DARK (FR)**, 4, b c Akarad (FR)—Petard Exppress (IRE) **Baron T. Van Zuylen**
6 **JARJARBIN (FR)**, 4, b c Zafonic (USA)—Hasanati (FR) **David Smaga**
7 **LARCA (FR)**, 4, b f Sicyos (USA)—Largesse **Baron T. Van Zuylen**
8 **LIGHT SABER (FR)**, 4, b f Kendor (FR)—Leariva (USA) **Baron T. Van Zuylen**
9 **LOCKOUT (IRE)**, 4, b c Spectrum (IRE)—Luvia **Claude Darty**
10 **LOHENGREEN (IRE)**, 4, b c Grand Lodge (USA)—Liu (IRE) **Lily Ades**
11 **MARILDO (FR)**, 17, b g Romildo—Marike **David Smaga**
12 **NIGHT BOKBEL (FR)**, 5, b h Night Shift (USA)—Liu (IRE) **R. Bellaiche**
13 **PRENDS TON TEMPS (FR)**, 7, b h Exit To Nowhere (USA)—Sarooh's Love (USA) **Ecurie Chalhoub**
14 **SNOW CAP (FR)**, 5, b h Bering—Girl of France **Baron T. Van Zuylen**
15 **SPECIAL KALDOUN (IRE)**, 5, b h Alzao (USA)—Special Lady (FR) **Ecurie Chalhoub**

THREE-YEAR-OLDS

16 **AIN SAADE (IRE)**, b c Desert Style (IRE)—Victoire Classique **Ecurie Chalhoub**
17 **ALCINOS (FR)**, b c Highest Honor (FR)—Alshazam (USA) **Baron T. Van Zuylen**
18 **A LITTLE DREAM (FR)**, b c Green Tune (USA)—Estava (FR) **Baron T. Van Zuylen**
19 **BUBBLY MOLLY (FR)**, b f Wagon Master (FR)—Shining Molly (FR) **Alain Morice**
20 **COMPROMISE (FR)**, b f Fasliyev (USA)—Kate Marie (USA) **Michel Henochsbe**
21 **CONFLUENCE (IRE)**, gr c Linamix (FR)—River Swan (GB) **Succession Weinstock**
22 **ELLE S'VOYAIT DEJA (FR)**, b f Carson City (USA)—Sudden Storm Bird (USA) **Maurice Lagasse**
23 **GRANDES ILLUSIONS (FR)**, ch f Kendor (FR)—Largesse **Baron T. Van Zuylen**
24 **GRECIAN GRAIL (IRE)**, ch f Rainbow Quest (USA)—Grecian Urn **David Smaga**
25 **HIGH FRIGHT (FR)**, ch f Croco Rouge (IRE)—High Five (FR) **Baron T. Van Zuylen**
26 **IN MEDIA RES (FR)**, b c Dushyantor (USA)—Colour Scheme (FR) **Baron T. Van Zuylen**
27 **KASLIK (FR)**, b f Desert Prince (IRE)—Mrs Ting (USA) **Ecurie Chalhoub**

MR D. SMAGA—continued

28 **LE COMTE EST BON (USA)**, br c King of Kings (IRE)—Navratilovna (USA) **Mme Ades-Hazan**
29 **NORTH STRAIT (FR)**, ch c Bering—Green Rose (USA) **David Adams**
30 **REGARDEZ MOI (USA)**, ch f Diesis—Pleaselookatmenow (USA) **Nelson Radwan**
31 **SHAKIRA (FR)**, b f Fasliyev (USA)—Sao (IRE) **Mme M. de Chambure**
32 **SHINING EXIT (FR)**, b f Exit To Nowhere (USA)—Shining War (USA) **Mme G. Aoudai**
33 **SPEED ACADEMY (FR)**, b c Royal Academy (USA)—Cordon Bleu (USA) **Christian Serre**
34 **SUMMER STORM (FR)**, b c Sabrehill (USA)—Girl of France **Baron T. Van Zuylen**
35 **VOIX DU NORD (FR)**, b c Valanour (IRE)—Dame Edith (FR) **Baron T. Van Zuylen**

TWO-YEAR-OLDS

36 B c 23/1 Selkirk (USA)—Abime (USA) (Woodman (USA)) **David Adams**
37 **BONNE FOI**, ch c 12/4 Bering—Consolation (Troy) (49474) **Ecurie Chalhoub**
38 **CELERE (FR)**, ch f 16/2 Kabool—Flying Past (FR) (Kendor (FR)) (22881) **Baron T. Van Zuylen**
39 **CLOCKWORK (FR)**, b f 24/2 Octagonal (NZ)—Timely Lady (FR) (Lead On Time (USA)) **Baron T. Van Zuylen**
40 **DYONISIENNE**, b f 10/1 Groom Dancer (USA)—Direcvil (Top Ville) **Haras d'Etreham**
41 **ESTAFILADE (FR)**, b f 13/2 Gold Away (IRE)—Estava (FR) (Top Ville (FR)) **Baron T. Van Zuylen**
42 **FABULEUX DESTIN (FR)**, ch c 26/2 Baryshnikov (AUS)—Sangrilla (FR) (Sanglamore) **Baron T. Van Zuylen**
43 B c Highest Honor (FR)—Green Rose (USA) (Green Dancer (USA)) (19789) **Mme G. Aoudai**
44 **JANJAN (IRE)**, ch c 31/3 Highest Honor (FR)—Fay Wray (FR) (Primo Dominie) (80395) **Ecurie Chalhoub**
45 **LE SINDBAD (IRE)**, bl c 17/3 Xaar—Fantastic Charm (USA) (Seattle Dancer (USA)) (40197) **R. Bellaiche**
46 **MA FLECHE (FR)**, b f 26/4 Count On Me (FR)—Shinning War (FR) (Shining Steel) **Mme G. Aoudai**
47 **MIYAZAKI (IRE)**, b f 23/2 Spectrum (IRE)—Zelah (IRE) (Alzao (USA)) (12368) **Mme Dominique Smaga**
48 **NEFEROUN (FR)**, bl f 31/1 Sicyos (USA)—Largesse (FR) (Saumarez) **Baron T. Van Zuylen**
49 **NON SONO SOLO (IRE)**, b c 19/1 Montjeu (IRE)—Margi (FR) (General Holme (USA)) (49474) **Ecurie Chalhoub**
50 **ORESME (FR)**, b f 27/5 Bering—Glivana (FR) (Highest Honor (FR)) **Baron T. Van Zuylen**
51 **PERFIDIE (IRE)**, b f 7/2 Monsun (GER)—Pelagic (Rainbow Quest (USA)) **Haras d'Etreham**
52 **ROSS BURG (FR)**, b f 14/3 Bering—Dancing Rose (FR) (Dancing Spree (USA)) (21645) **Mr Thierry Roland**
53 **SATIE (IRE)**, b f 24/2 Fasliyev (USA)—Sao (IRE) (Dolphin Street (FR)) **Mr Marc de Chambure**
54 **SEA SCAN (FR)**, b c 21/4 Dr Fong (USA)—Sea Picture (IRE) (Royal Academy (USA)) **Succession Weinstock**
55 **SECOND TOUR (FR)**, b c 21/4 Highest Honor (FR)—
　　　　　Girl of France (Legend of France (USA)) **Baron T. Van Zuylen**
56 **SEVEN NO TRUMP (FR)**, ro f 1/3 Highest Honor (FR)—Colour Scheme (FR) (Perrault) **Baron T. Van Zuylen**
57 **SUR MA VIE (USA)**, b f 23/3 Fusaichi Pegasus—Boubskaia (Niniski (USA)) **Mr Maurice Lagasse**
58 **TREE OF LIFE (FR)**, ch c 20/3 Grape Tree Road—Avellaneda (FR) (Fabulous Dancer (USA)) **Ecurie Seutet**
59 **WINGS OF THE DOVE (FR)**, b f 1/3 Sabrehill (USA)—Rain Drop (FR) (Pistolet Bleu (IRE)) **Baron T. Van Zuylen**
60 **ZENON (FR)**, b c 28/1 Sendawar (IRE)—Glebe Place (FR) (Akarad (FR)) **Baron T. Van Zuylen**

Jockey (Flat): D Boeuf.

504

MR B. SMART, Thirsk
Postal: Hambleton House, Sutton Bank, Thirsk, North Yorkshire, YO7 2HA.
Contact: PHONE (01845) 597481 FAX (01845) 597480 MOBILE (07748) 634797
E-MAIL vicky.smart@virgin.net

1 **ATLANTIC ACE**, 7, b g First Trump—Risalah **Mr Richard Page**
2 **BEADY (IRE)**, 5, b g Eagle Eyed (USA)—Tales of Wisdom **Mr B. Smart**
3 **BOND BECKS (IRE)**, 4, ch g Tagula (IRE)—At Amal (IRE) **Mr R. C. Bond**
4 **BOND BOY**, 7, b g Piccolo—Arabellajill **Mr R. C. Bond**
5 **BOND DOMINGO**, 5, b g Mind Games—Antonia's Folly **Mr B. Smart**
6 **BOND MAY DAY**, 4, b f Among Men (USA)—State Romance **The Bond Girls Partnership**
7 **BOND MILLENNIUM**, 6, ch g Piccolo—Farmer's Pet **Mr R. C. Bond**
8 **BOND PLAYBOY**, 4, b g Piccolo—Highest Ever (FR) **Mr R. C. Bond**
9 **BOND ROYALE**, 4, ch f Piccolo—Passiflora **Mr R. C. Bond**
10 **BRANDY COVE**, 7, b g Lugana Beach—Tender Moment (IRE) **Miss N. Jefford**
11 **CRESKELD (IRE)**, 5, b g Sri Pekan (USA)—Pizzazz **Creskeld Racing**
12 **DIFFERENTIAL (USA)**, 7, b br g Known Fact (USA)—Talk About Home (USA) **Mr B. Smart**
13 **FANTASMIC RIVER (IRE)**, 4, ch f Magic Ring (IRE)—River Maiden (USA) **Mr B. Smart**
14 **FESTIVE AFFAIR**, 6, b g Mujadil (USA)—Christmas Kiss **Miss N. Jefford**
15 **FRIDAY'S TAKINGS**, 5, ch g Beveled (USA)—Pretty Pollyanna **Mr Paul Darling**
16 **MARSHAL BOND**, 5, b g Celtic Swing—Arminda **Mr R. C. Bond**
17 **MON SECRET (IRE)**, 6, b g General Monash—Ron's Secret **Pinnacle Monash Partnership**
18 **MONSIEUR BOND (IRE)**, 4, ch c Danehill Dancer (IRE)—Musical Essence **Mr R. C. Bond**
19 **MY LAST BEAN (IRE)**, 7, gr g Soviet Lad (USA)—Meanz Beanz **The Coopyline Racing Club Ltd**
20 **PROPRIUS**, 4, b g Perpendicular—Pretty Pollyanna **The Page Racing Partnership**

MR B. SMART—continued

21 **TWICE UPON A TIME**, 5, ch m Primo Dominie—Opuntia **Mr John W. Ford**
22 **WELL CONNECTED (IRE)**, 4, b g Among Men (USA)—Wire To Wire **Mr C. D. Carr**

THREE-YEAR-OLDS

23 **ADEES DANCER**, b f Danehill Dancer (IRE)—Note (GER) **Tap and Barrel Racing Club**
24 **ALIBA**, ch g Ali-Royal (IRE)—Kiba (IRE) **Mr C. D. Carr**
25 **ALICE BLACKTHORN**, b f Forzando—Owdbetts (IRE) **Pinnacle Forzando Partnership**
26 **ANNIE HARVEY**, ch f Fleetwood (IRE)—Resemblance **Annie Harvey Partnership**
27 **BOLD BLADE**, b g Sure Blade (USA)—Golden Ciel (USA) **Mr Paul J. Dixon**
28 **BOND BROOKLYN**, b c Mind Games—Crystal Sand (GER) **Mr R. C. Bond**
29 **BOND MOONLIGHT**, ch g Danehill Dancer (IRE)—Interregnum **Mr P. M. Rose**
30 **BOND ROMEO (IRE)**, ch g Titus Livius (FR)—At Amal (IRE) **Mr R. C. Bond**
31 **BOND SHAKIRA**, ch f Daggers Drawn (USA)—Cinnamon Lady **Mr R. C. Bond**
32 **BONJOUR BOND (IRE)**, ro g Portrait Gallery (IRE)—Musical Essence **Mr R. C. Bond**
33 **BONNE DE FLEUR**, b f Whittingham (IRE)—L'Estable Fleurie (IRE) **Miss N. Jefford**
34 **BOOK MATCHED**, b g Efisio—Princess Latifa **Mr Paul Darling**
35 **CHICAGO BOND (USA)**, b f Real Quiet (USA)—Shariyfa (FR) **Mr R. C. Bond**
36 **COMMANDER BOND**, b g Piccolo—Lonesome **Mr R. C. Bond**
37 **DALMARNOCK**, ch g Grand Lodge (USA)—Lochbelle **Mr C. D. Carr**
38 **DAWN DUEL (IRE)**, b f Daggers Drawn (USA)—Dawn's Folly (IRE) **Mr Paul J. Dixon**
39 **FAMILIAR AFFAIR**, b g Intikhab (USA)—Familiar (USA) **Pinnacle Intikhab Partnership**
40 **FIRST BOND**, b f Piccolo—Bond Girl **Mr R. C. Bond**
41 **MEGABOND**, b g Danehill Dancer (IRE)—Apple Peeler (IRE) **The Bond Girls Partnership**
42 **REDWOOD ROCKS (IRE)**, b g Blush Rambler (USA)—Crisp And Cool (USA) **Mr Dan Hall**
43 **SAROS (IRE)**, b br c Desert Sun—Fight Right (FR) **Pinnacle Desert Sun Partnership**
44 **SENOR BOND (USA)**, ch g Hennessy (USA)—Troppa Freska (USA) **Mr R. C. Bond**
45 **SIR BOND (IRE)**, ch g Desert Sun—In Tranquility (IRE) **Mr R. C. Bond**
46 **TYUP POMPEY (IRE)**, ch g Docksider (USA)—Cindy's Baby **Pompey Racing Club**
47 **VADEMECUM**, br g Shinko Forest (IRE)—Sunshine Coast **EKOS Pinnacle Partnership**

TWO-YEAR-OLDS

48 B c 11/3 Piccolo—Aegean Flame (Anshan) (17500) **Pinnacle Piccolo Partnership**
49 **BOND BABE**, b f 10/3 Forzando—Lindfield Belle (IRE) (Fairy King (USA)) (14000) **Mr R. C. Bond**
50 **BOND CAT**, ch f 9/2 Raise A Grand (IRE)—Merrily (Sharrood (USA)) (30920) **Mr R. C. Bond**
51 **BOND CITY (IRE)**, b g 10/4 Trans Island—Where's Charlotte (Sure Blade (USA)) (16000) **Mr R. C. Bond**
52 **BOND FINESSE**, b f 25/4 Danehill Dancer (IRE)—Funny Cut (IRE) (Sure Blade (USA)) (2473) **Mr R. C. Bond**
53 **BOND PUCCINI**, b c 27/2 Piccolo—Baileys By Name (Nomination) (12000) **Mr R. C. Bond**
54 **BOND ROCKERFELLA**, b c 27/2 Lend A Hand—Highest Ever (FR) (Highest Honor (FR)) (28000) **Mr R. C. Bond**
55 **CHINA BOND (IRE)**, ch c 4/5 Shahrastani (USA)—At Amal (IRE) (Astronef) (3000) **Mr R. C. Bond**
56 B f 10/3 Lujain (USA)—Christmas Kiss (Taufan (USA)) (9200) **Pinnacle Lujain Partnership**
57 Ch f 18/3 Intikhab (USA)—Esteraad (IRE) (Cadeaux Genereux) (17315) **EKOS Pinnacle Partnership**
58 **HANNAH'S TRIBE (IRE)**, b f 17/4 Daggers Drawn (USA)—
        Cala-Holme (IRE) (Fools Holme (USA)) (4000) **Harlequin Pinnacle Partnership**
59 B c 20/2 Whittingham (IRE)—Hot Ice (IRE) (Petardia) (9200) **Mr C. Prosser**
60 **JUST BOND (IRE)**, b c 10/4 Namid—Give Warning (IRE) (Warning) (23500) **Mr R. C. Bond**
61 **MARY READ**, ch f 30/3 Bahamian Bounty—Hill Welcome (Most Welcome) (10000) **Mrs F. Denniff**
62 B c 27/2 Marju (IRE)—Midnight Allure (Aragon) (7000) **Pinnacle Marju Partnership**
63 Ch f 5/5 Polar Falcon (USA)—Opuntia (Rousillon (USA)) (8000) **Mr John W. Ford**
64 Ch f 17/3 Bold Edge—Pretty Pollyanna (General Assembly (USA)) (5000) **Mrs F. Denniff**
65 B c 26/3 First Trump—Princess Latifa (Wolfhound (USA)) (4000) **Mr Paul Darling**
66 **RAINBOW IRIS**, b br f 24/2 Mister Baileys—Kastaway (Distant Relative) (14000) **Mr Paul K. Spencer**
67 B f 28/2 Josr Algarhoud (IRE)—Rania (Aragon) (17934) **Mr R. C. Bond**
68 **REAL BOND**, b c 27/1 Mind Games—Bond Girl (Magic Ring (IRE)) (500) **Mr R. C. Bond**
69 B f 23/2 Cape Cross (IRE)—Runelia (Runnett) (8500) **Mr Paul Darling**
70 **SHANKLY BOND (IRE)**, ch c 16/4 Danehill Dancer (IRE)—Fanellan (Try My Best (USA)) (28000) **Mr R. C. Bond**
71 Ch f 18/3 Wolfhound (USA)—Stealthy (Kind of Hush) (2200) **Mr John Wills**
72 B f 29/4 Orpen (USA)—The Poachers Lady (IRE) (Salmon Leap (USA)) (12368) **The Orpen Partnership**

MR B. SMART—continued

73 B f 21/2 Marju (IRE)—Tide of Fortune (Soviet Star (USA)) (18000) **Mrs Julie Martin**
74 **TIGER BOND,** br c 23/2 Diktat—Blackpool Belle (The Brianstan) (8200) **Mr R. C. Bond**

Other Owners: Mr M. H. D. Barlow, Mr T. Brady, Mr P. A. Deal, Mr D. Elders, Mr M. Ford, Mr J. G. Howse, Mrs A. C. Hudson, Mrs J. A. Hyde, Ms S. Johnson, Miss Claire King, Mrs S. M. Maine, Mr M. Mandaric, Mr David R. Martin, Mr J. Massy-Collier, Mr S. Pailor, Mr Harry Redknapp, Ms P. Roche, Mr Peter J. Skinner, Mrs V. R. Smart, Mr P. J. Storrie, Mr G. Tendrick, Mr N. H. Tritton, Mrs C. E. White, Mr N. C. White.

Assistant Trainer: Mrs V R Smart

Jockey (Flat): R Ffrench (w.a.). **Apprentice:** M Stainton (7-12). **Amateurs:** Mrs V Smart (9-0), Miss A J Smith (9-4).

---

505 | **MR A. D. SMITH, Westward Ho**
Postal: **Duckhaven Stud, Cornborough Road, Westward Ho, Bideford, Devon, EX39 1AA.**
Contact: **PHONE/FAX (01237) 478648 E-MAIL duckhavenstud@btinternet.com**

1 4, B c Double Trigger (IRE)—Kathy Fair (IRE)
2 **PERTEMPS BIANCA,** 4, b f Dancing Spree (USA)—Bay Bianca (IRE) **Duckhaven Stud**
3 **PERTEMPS WIZARD,** 4, br g Silver Wizard (USA)—Peristyle **Pertemps Group Limited**

THREE-YEAR-OLDS

4 **JOB SHOP,** b c Dancing Spree (USA)—Kathy Fair (IRE) **Pertemps Group Limited**
5 **MAID THE CUT,** ch f Silver Wizard (USA)—Third Dam **Grass Syndicate**
6 **PERTEMPS JOB,** b c First Trump—Happy And Blessed (IRE) **Pertemps Group Limited**
7 **PERTEMPS RED,** ch c Dancing Spree (USA)—Lady Lullaby (IRE) **Pertemps Group Limited**
8 **PERTEMPS STYLE,** b br f Double Trigger (IRE)—Peristyle **Pertemps Group Limited**
9 **YORK DANCER,** ch f Dancing Spree (USA)—York Street (USA) **Duckhaven Stud**

TWO-YEAR-OLDS

10 B f 18/4 Silver Wizard (USA)—Kathy Fair (IRE) (Nicholas Bill)
11 Br f 26/4 Mark of Esteem (IRE)—Lozzie (Siberian Express (USA)) (2500) **Mr David M. Williams**
12 B f 10/3 Royal Applause—Rustie Bliss (Kris) (2000) **Mr David M. Williams**
13 B f 2/3 Dancing Spree (USA)—Total Rach (IRE) (Nordico (USA)) (1000) **Miss Kerensa Pluess**
14 B c 20/4 Lake Coniston (IRE)—Velvet Heart (IRE) (Damister (USA)) (1000) **Mr David M. Williams**

Other Owners: Mr Martin Green, Mr I. S. Phipps, Mrs J. M. Smith.

Assistant Trainer: Mat Druce

Amateur: Mr Gavin Hall (9-0).

---

506 | **MR G. J. SMITH, Melton Mowbray**
Postal: **Fox Covert Farm, Narrow Lane, Wymeswold, Loughborough, Leicestershire, LE12 6SD.**
Contact: **PHONE (01509) 881250 MOBILE (07831) 531765**

1 **MOSSTOWIE,** 8, b m Le Moss—Rowan Ville **Ibra Racing Co**
2 **SADLER'S SECRET (IRE),** 9, b g Sadler's Wells (USA)—Athyka (USA) **Slow Donkey Partnership**

Other Owners: Mr B. Hall, Miss W. D. Hall, Mrs D. Key, Mrs H. Renshaw.

Assistant Trainer: R J Smith

---

507 | **MR JULIAN SIMON SMITH, Tirley**
Postal: **Tirley Court, Tirley, Gloucester, GL19 4HA.**
Contact: **PHONE (01452) 780461 FAX (01452) 780461 MOBILE (07880) 732337**

1 **BRUSH THE ARK,** 10, b m Brush Aside (USA)—Expensive Lark **Mr Donald Smith**
2 **COUNTY FLYER,** 11, b g Cruise Missile—Random Select **R. J. Heathman (County Contractors) Ltd**
3 **GLEN WARRIOR,** 8, b g Michelozzo (USA)—Mascara VII **Mr Donald Smith**
4 **STEEL WARRIOR,** 7, ch g Michelozzo (USA)—Iskra Bay (IRE) **Mr Donald Smith**

MR JULIAN SIMON SMITH—continued

5 **TIRLEY STORM**, 9, b g Tirley Gale—Random Select **Mr Donald Smith**
6 **VALLEY WARRIOR**, 7, b g Michelozzo (USA)—Mascara VII **Mrs J. A. Benson**

Other Owners: Miss S. N. Benson, Mr A. Brookes.

Assistant Trainer: Mrs Nicky Smith

Jockeys (NH): W Marston, T J Murphy. **Conditional:** Anthony Evans.

---

508 **MR N. A. SMITH, Upton Snodsbury**
Postal: **The Barn, Lower Cowsden Farm, Upton Snodsbury, Worcester, WR7 4NY.**
Contact: **OFFICE (01905) 381077 FAX (01905) 381077 MOBILE (07855) 511709**
E-MAIL nasmithracing@aol.com

1 **DEADLY DORIS**, 10, b m Ron's Victory (USA)—Camp Chair **Stan Hey and Partners**
2 **PARISIAN EIRE (IRE)**, 5, gr g Paris House—La Fille de Feu **Mr P. E. T. Chandler**
3 **PARISIAN INFERNO (IRE)**, 6, b g Paris House—La Fille de Feu **Mr P. E. T. Chandler**

TWO-YEAR-OLDS

4 Gr g 13/4 Makbul—Miss Nova (Ra Nova) **Mrs G. C. List**

Other Owners: Mr S. Hey, Mr Edwin Smith, Mr I. Wilson, Mrs J. Wilson.

Assistant Trainer: Miss E Grainger

Jockey (Flat): J Bramhill. **Jockey (NH):** O McPhail. **Amateurs:** Miss E Grainger (9-7), Mr Ben Neale (10-7).

---

509 **MRS NADINE SMITH, Pulborough**
Postal: **Hillside Cottage Stables, Bury, Pulborough, West Sussex, RH20 1NR.**
Contact: **PHONE (01798) 831206**

1 **ALASIL (USA)**, 4, b br c Swain (IRE)—Asl (USA) **Tony Hayward and Barry Fulton**
2 **CULLIAN**, 7, b m Missed Flight—Diamond Gig **The Cullian Partnership**
3 **GENERAL**, 7, b g Cadeaux Genereux—Bareilly (USA) **Mr Tony A. Hayward**
4 **IBAL (FR)**, 8, b g Balsamo (FR)—Quart d'Hekla (FR) **Tony Hayward and Barry Fulton**
5 **MARRAKECH (USA)**, 7, ch m Barathea (IRE)—Nashkara **T Hayward, B Fulton, M Charge, D Wallis**
6 **MISTER PUTT (USA)**, 6, b br g Mister Baileys—Theresita (GER) **Tony Hayward and Barry Fulton**
7 **PHOTOGRAPHER (USA)**, 6, b br g Mountain Cat (USA)—
                              Clickety Click (USA) **Tony Hayward, Barry Fulton, Jamie Bruce**
8 **WHIST DRIVE**, 4, ch g First Trump—Fine Quill **Tony Hayward and Barry Fulton**

Other Owners: Mr J. M. Bruce, Mr Maurice Charge, Mr B. N. Fulton, Mrs J. Rucklidge, Mr S. C. Rucklidge, Mr D. C. Wallis.

Assistant Trainer: A M Smith

---

510 **MR R. J. SMITH, Naunton**
Postal: **1 Sunnybank, Naunton, Gloucestershire, GL54 3AS.**
Contact: **PHONE (01451) 850180 MOBILE (07880) 742050**
E-MAIL smith720.fsbusiness.co.uk

1 **BOB'S GONE (IRE)**, 6, ch g Eurobus—Bob's Girl (IRE) **Team Cobra Racing Syndicate**
2 **BOUGHT DIRECT**, 5, b h Muhtarram (USA)—Muhybb (USA) **Mr R. Smith**
3 **CANADA ROAD (IRE)**, 6, b g Great Marquess—New Technique (FR) **Oliver Ryan, Kieran Ryan, Janet Baker**
4 6, B m Supreme Leader—Dawn Hunt (IRE) **Mr R. Smith**
5 **DICK THE TAXI**, 10, b g Karlinsky (USA)—Another Galaxy (IRE) **Dicks Backers**
6 **KIMBO LADY**, 6, ch m Husyan (USA)—Fair Cruise **A.Harris,R.Wealthy,R.Wareing,P.Turner**
7 **NAUNTON DOWNS**, 10, b g Teenoso (USA)—Kitty Come Home **Mr Dick Hibberd**
8 **REDDE (IRE)**, 9, ch g Classic Memory—Stoney Broke **D.Jackson,M.Stock,R.W.Hibberd,C.Harrison**
9 **SEAHORSE GIRL**, 7, b m Sea Raven (IRE)—Kakapo **Berry Racing**

MR R. J. SMITH—continued

THREE-YEAR-OLDS

10 BERRY RACER (IRE), ch f Titus Livius (FR)—Opening Day **Berry Racing**

Other Owners: Ms Janet Baker, Mr Brian J. Doherty, Miss Georgina Eager, Mr Alan Harris, Mr C. Harrison, Mr S. A. Henshaw, Mr D. M. Jackson, Mrs J. A. Jackson, Mr D. H. Morgan, Mr Kieran P. Ryan, Mr Oliver Ryan, Mr Martin Stock, Mrs P. D. Turner, Mr R. G. Wareing, Mr R. Wealthy, Mrs Ann Whitten, Mr J. L. Whitten.

Assistant Trainer: Jayne Smith

---

511 **MISS S. SMITH,** Lewes
Postal: **County Stables, The Old Racecourse, Lewes, East Sussex, BN7 1UR.**
Contact: **PHONE (01273) 477173 MOBILE (07812) 067909 E-MAIL suzy@racing951.fsnet.co.uk**

1 DADS LAD (IRE), 10, b g Supreme Leader—Furryvale **Miss Suzy Smith**
2 EMPRESS OF CHINA (IRE), 5, br m Anshan—Suggia **Mr Robin Smith**
3 FAREWELL CHILD, 7, b m Afzal—Bye Bye Baby (FR) **Mr John Young**
4 JIM JAM JOEY (IRE), 11, ch g Big Sink Hope (USA)—Ascot Princess **Miss Suzy Smith**
5 JOHNLEGOOD, 8, ch g Karinga Bay—Dancing Years (USA) **Mr S. E. Gordon-Watson**
6 KALIC D'ALM (FR), 6, b g Passing Sale (FR)—Bekaa II (FR) **Mr Robin Smith**
7 MATERIAL WORLD, 6, b m Karinga Bay—Material Girl **Southern Bloodstock**
8 PRINCE OF ARAGON, 8, b g Aragon—Queens Welcome **Miss Suzy Smith**

THREE-YEAR-OLDS

9 NIZA D'ALM (FR), b br f Passing Sale (FR)—Bekaa II (FR) **Mr Robin Smith**

Other Owners: Mr C. Derben, Mr J. Logan, Mr C. W. N. Peel, Mrs V. J. Smith, Mr M. W. Woolveridge.

Assistant Trainer: Mr S E Gordon-Watson

Amateur: Mr S E Gordon-Watson.

---

512 **MRS S. J. SMITH,** Bingley
Postal: **Craiglands Farm, High Eldwick, Bingley, West Yorkshire, BD16 3BE.**
Contact: **PHONE (01274) 564930**

1 AFTER ME BOYS, 10, b g Arzanni—Realm Wood **Mr Keith Nicholson**
2 AMBRY, 7, br g Machiavellian (USA)—Alkaffeyeh (IRE) **Mr Raymond Gross, Ms Adrienne Gross**
3 ARDENT SCOUT, 12, b g Ardross—Vidette **Mrs Alicia Skene & W. S. Skene**
4 ARTIC JACK (FR), 8, b g Cadoudal (FR)—Si Jamais (FR) **Mr Trevor Hemmings**
5 BALLYARDS (IRE), 6, gr g Roselier—Another Partner **Widdop Wanderers**
6 BALLY'S BAK, 6, ch m Bob Back (USA)—Whatagale **Formulated Polymer Products Ltd**
7 BETTER DAYS (IRE), 8, b g Supreme Leader—Kilkilrun **Mr Trevor Hemmings**
8 BLACK FROST (IRE), 8, ch g Glacial Storm (USA)—Black Tulip **Mr Trevor Hemmings**
9 BUSHIDO (IRE), 5, br g Brief Truce (USA)—Pheopostown **Mrs B. Ramsden**
10 CARDINAL MARK (IRE), 10, b g Ardross—Sister of Gold **Mr G. T. Pierse**
11 CELIOSO (IRE), 7, b g Celio Rufo—Bettons Rose **Leigh Musketeer Racing Club**
12 CILL CHURNAIN (IRE), 11, b g Arctic Cider (USA)—The Dozer (IRE) **Mr Keith Middleton**
13 DESTINO, 5, ch g Keen—Hanajir (IRE) **Mrs Enid Brindle**
14 DICEMAN (IRE), 9, b g Supreme Leader—Henry's Gamble (IRE) **John Veitch, Graham Allen, Patrick Veitch**
15 FLAKE, 4, ch g Zilzal (USA)—Impatiente (USA) **Mr Keith Nicholson**
16 FORUM CHRIS (IRE), 7, ch g Trempolino (USA)—Memory Green (USA) **Mrs Jacqueline Conroy**
17 FRANCIS BAY (USA), 9, b g Alleged (USA)—Montage (USA) **M. Magowan & T. Sinnamon**
18 FREE TO RUN (IRE), 10, b g Satco (FR)—Lady Oats **Mr Keith Nicholson**
19 FROMRAGSTORICHES (IRE), 8, b g Supreme Leader—Family Birthday **Mrs S. Smith**
20 GALEN (IRE), 13, br g Roselier (FR)—Gaye Le Moss **Mr David Campbell**
21 GEMINEYE LORD (IRE), 7, b g Mister Lord (USA)—Mum's Eyes **The Kalleys**
22 GOTTABE, 11, ch g Gunner B—Topsy Bee **Mr Keith Nicholson**
23 HAYBURN VAULTS, 6, b m Bettergeton—Agdistis **Mrs A. E. Astall**
24 HELLO MRS, 6, b m Sir Harry Lewis (USA)—Five And Four (IRE) **Mr A. P. Russell**
25 HILL CHARM, 6, ch m Minster Son—Snarry Hill **Mr Roy Robinson**
26 IT'S EJ, 6, b g Karinga Bay—Merry Marigold **Mrs S. Smith**
27 IT'S HARRY, 6, b g Aragon—Andbracket **Mr Keith Nicholson**
28 ITS SUNNY, 10, ch m Sunley Builds—Free To Go **Mrs S. Smith**

MRS S. J. SMITH—continued

29 **KEEN TO THE LAST (FR)**, 12, ch g Keen—Derniere Danse **Mr D. E. Allen & Mr S. Balmer**
30 **KELLY PRIDE**, 7, b g Alflora (IRE)—Pearly-B (IRE) **J. Townson, A. Thomason, P. Chapman**
31 **LIKE A LORD (IRE)**, 6, b br g Arctic Lord—Likashot **Mr Billy McCullough**
32 **LISDANTE (IRE)**, 11, b g Phardante (FR)—Shuil Eile **Mr Keith Nicholson**
33 **LITTLE BIG HORSE (IRE)**, 8, b g Little Bighorn—Little Gort **Mr Paul J. Dixon**
34 **LOOK TO THE FUTURE (IRE)**, 10, b g Roselier (FR)—Toevarro **M.C.V.Racing**
35 **MELDRUM STAR (IRE)**, 7, ch g Fourstars Allstar (USA)—Meldrum Lass **Mr Alan Potts**
36 **MISTER DAVE'S (IRE)**, 9, ch g Bluffer—Tacovaon **Mr David Campbell**
37 **MISTER MCGOLDRICK**, 7, b g Sabrehill (USA)—Anchor Inn **Mr Richard Longley**
38 **MISTY CLASS (IRE)**, 12, gr g Roselier (FR)—Toevarro **Widdop Wanderers**
39 **NOSHINANNIKIN**, 10, ch g Anshan—Preziosa **M.C.V.Racing**
40 **OSO MAGIC**, 6, gr g Teenoso (USA)—Scottish Clover **Mr Michael Thompson**
41 **POTTSY'S JOY**, 7, b g Syrtos—Orange Spice **Mrs Ann Potts**
42 **PRESUMPTUOUS**, 4, ch g Double Trigger (IRE)—T O O Mamma's (IRE)
43 **RECTORY (IRE)**, 5, b g Presenting—Billys Pet **Mr J. Henderson (Co Durham)**
44 **RETURNED UN PAID (IRE)**, 7, b g Actinium (FR)—Claregalway Lass **Mrs M. Ashby**
45 **RIVAL BIDDER**, 7, ch g Arzanni—Beltalong **Mr Keith Nicholson**
46 **ROSS GEE (IRE)**, 8, gr g Roselier (FR)—Miss Leader **Mrs S. Smith**
47 **ROYAL AMARETTO (IRE)**, 10, b g Fairy King (USA)—Melbourne Miss **Mr M. Keightley**
48 **ROYAL EMPEROR (IRE)**, 8, gr g Roselier (FR)—Boreen Bro **Widdop Wanderers**
49 **SHARDANTE (IRE)**, 11, ch g Phardante (FR)—Shirabas **Mr W. A. Bethell**
50 **SIMPLY SUPREME (IRE)**, 7, b g Supreme Leader—Some Gift **Mr Trevor Hemmings**
51 **SUN CAT (IRE)**, 4, br g Catrail (USA)—Susie Sunshine (IRE) **Mr Paul J. Dixon**
52 **SUPREME BREEZE (IRE)**, 9, b g Supreme Leader—Merry Breeze **The Supreme Three**
53 **THE KEW TOUR (IRE)**, 8, ch g Un Desperado (FR)—Drivers Bureau **Mr Keith Nicholson**
54 **TIPSY MOUSE (IRE)**, 8, ch g Roselier (FR)—Darjoy **Mr Trevor Hemmings**
55 **TOMENOSO**, 6, b gr g Teenoso (USA)—Guarded Expression **Mr Keith Nicholson**
56 **TONOCO**, 11, b g Teenoso (USA)—Lady Shoco **Mr Trevor Hemmings**
57 **TOWN CRIER (IRE)**, 9, br g Beau Sher—Ballymacarett **Mr Trevor Hemmings**
58 **UNDENIABLE**, 6, b g Unfuwain (USA)—Shefoog **Mr Keith Nicholson**

Other Owners: Mr G. C. W. Allan, Mrs B. Allen, Mr D. E. Allen, Mr Paul Bacon, Mr S. Balmer, Mr K. M. Cartner, Mr P. Chapman, Mr A. Coldron, Mr M. C. Coldron, Mr J. Conroy, Mr A. Donald, Mr B. J. Gallacher, Ms Adrienne Gross, Mr Raymond Gross, Mrs Sara Jane Haley, Mr A. D. Hollinrake, Mr N. R. Kelly, Mr M. Magowan, Mr Clive Saxby, Mrs Judie Short, Mr T. Sinnamon, Mrs A. Skene, Mr W. S. Skene, Mr A. A. Thomason, Mr J. Townson, Mr John Veitch, Mr Patrick Veitch, Mr T. M. Wilson.

Jockeys (NH): Seamus Durack, R Wilkinson. **Conditional:** J Crowley, D Elsworth.

---

513 MISS J. A. SOUTHCOMBE, Chard
Postal: Holemoor Farm Bungalow, Combe St Nicholas, Chard, Somerset, TA20 3AE.
Contact: PHONE (01460) 68865 MOBILE (07968) 178121
E-MAIL jane@southcomberacing.co.uk WEBSITE www.southcomberacing.co.uk

1 **BENJAMIN (IRE)**, 6, b g Night Shift (USA)—Best Academy (USA) **Mr Mark Savill**
2 **EASTER OGIL (IRE)**, 9, ch g Pips Pride—Piney Pass **Mr Mark Savill**
3 **GIKO**, 10, b g Arazi (USA)—Gayane **V. R. V. Partnership**
4 **GLORIOUS WELCOME**, 6, b g Past Glories—Rest And Welcome **Mrs V. H. Nicholas**
5 **MASTER RATTLE**, 5, b g Sabrehill (USA)—Miss Primula **The Master Rattles Partnership**
6 **SALFORD FLYER**, 8, b g Pharly (FR)—Edge of Darkness **Mr P. L. Southcombe**
7 **TINTON MILL**, 5, b m Shambo—Mill Thyme **Mr Mark Savill**
8 **TYRO'S BID**, 6, b g Greensmith—Two Hearts **Major R. P. Thorman**

TWO-YEAR-OLDS

9 Ch f 17/2 Devil's Bag (USA)—Vital Laser (USA) (Seeking The Gold (USA)) (10000)

Other Owners: Mrs Rose Vivian, Miss Vanda Vivian.

Jockey (Flat): V Slattery. **Jockey (NH):** V Slattery. **Apprentice:** N Kavanagh. **Amateur:** Miss W Southcombe (8-0).

514 MR M. E. SOWERSBY, York
Postal: **Southwold Farm, Goodmanham Wold, Market Weighton, York, East Yorkshire, YO43 3NA.**
Contact: **PHONE (01430) 810534 MOBILE (0785) 5551056**

1 CRYPTOGAM, 4, b f Zamindar (USA)—Moss **Mr R. D. Seldon**
2 DIAMOND JOSHUA (IRE), 6, b g Mujadil (USA)—Elminya (IRE) **The Prize Guys Partnership**
3 DONNY BOWLING, 4, b f Sesaro (USA)—Breakfast Creek **Racing Ladies**
4 DOUBLE HELIX, 5, b g Marju (IRE)—Totham **Mr A. Milner**
5 FRAZER'S LAD, 7, b g Whittingham (IRE)—Loch Tain **Mr A. Milner**
6 HOLLYWEST (FR), 4, ch g Sillery (USA)—Hollywood Trick (USA) **The Southwold Set**
7 JACK FLUSH (IRE), 10, gr b g Broken Hearted—Clubhouse Turn (IRE) **Mr B. Walker (Hull)**
8 JOHN RICH, 8, b g Mesleh—South Lodge **Mr C. N. Richardson**
9 MINELLY, 4, b f Defacto (USA)—Lady Liza **The Southwold Set**
10 ROSEBERRY ROSE, 5, ch m Keen—Scotch Imp **Mr James Ritchie**
11 ROSE TINTED, 5, b m Spectrum (IRE)—Marie La Rose (FR) **The Southwold Set**

THREE-YEAR-OLDS

12 BOWLING ALONG, b f The West (USA)—Bystrouska **Keith Brown Properties (Hull) Ltd**
13 CLUB OASIS, b f Forzando—Tatouma (USA) **Mr M. E. Sowersby**
14 DANCE TO MY TUNE, b f Halling (USA)—Stolen Melody **R. S. Cockerill (Farms) Ltd**
15 DONT TELL SIMON, ch g Keen—Circumnavfiate **Mr G. Scott**
16 GAME FLORA, b f Mind Games—Breakfast Creek **The Southwold Set**
17 LONE PINE, b f Sesaro (USA)—North Pine **The Hen Party**
18 MIND PLAY, b f Mind Games—Diplomatist **Mr M. E. Sowersby**
19 SHAMROCK TEA, b c Imperial Ballet (IRE)—Yellow Ribbon (IRE) **Keith Brown Properties (Hull) Ltd**

TWO-YEAR-OLDS

20 Ch f 5/4 Aragon—Acinom (Rambo Dancer (CAN)) (1100) **Mr M. E. Sowersby**
21 Gr c 26/2 Danzig Connection—Evening Falls (Bevelled (USA)) (4200) **Keith Brown Properties (Hull) Ltd**
22 Gr c 17/4 Paris House—Lady Pennington (Blue Cashmere) (1400) **Keith Brown Properties (Hull) Ltd**
23 B c 17/3 Timeless Times (USA)—Ohnonotagain (Kind of Hush) (1500) **Mr M. E. Sowersby**

Other Owners: Mr E. Bailey, Mrs J. Breen, Mr Paul Clifton, Miss S. A. Cockerill, Mr S. Cromie, Mr A. Cruikshank, Mr P. Laverack, Mrs D. McNulty, Mrs P. Cockerill, Mrs E. Mudd, Miss F. K. Mudd, Mrs Jean W. Robinson, Mr R. Standring, Mrs E. Stubbins, Mr T. J. Stubbins, Mr K. Townend, Mr J. Vincent, Mrs P. Webster, Mr A. West.

Assistant Trainer: Mary Sowersby

Jockey (Flat): P Hanagan. **Jockey (NH):** G Lee. **Apprentice:** S Hitchcott. **Amateur:** Mr Guy Brewer.

515 MR J. L. SPEARING, Kinnersley
Postal: **Kinnersley Racing Stables, Kinnersley, Severn Stoke, Worcestershire, WR8 9JR.**
Contact: **PHONE (01905) 371054 FAX (01905) 371054**
E-MAIL caroline@johnspearinghorseracing.com WEBSITE www.johnspearinghorseracing.com

1 ABSOLUTE UTOPIA (USA), 11, b g Mr Prospector (USA)—Magic Gleam (USA) **Mr M. T. Lawrance**
2 BLAKESHALL GIRL, 4, ch f Piccolo—Giggleswick Girl **Mr M. Bishop**
3 CASHEL MEAD, 4, b f Bishop of Cashel—Island Mead **Masonaires**
4 CHINA CHASE (IRE), 5, br g Anshan—Hannies Girl (IRE) **Mr T. N. Siviter**
5 EMBER DAYS, 5, gr m Reprimand—Evening Falls **Mrs Carol J. Welch**
6 GALLERY BREEZE, 5, b m Zamindar (USA)—Wantage Park **Appleby Lodge Stud**
7 HAKIM (NZ), 10, ch g Half Iced (USA)—Topitup (NZ) **Mr T. N. Siviter**
8 HOPBINE, 8, ch m Gildoran—Haraka Sasa **Miss S. Howell**
9 JACKS CRAIC (IRE), 5, b g Lord Americo—Boleree (IRE) **BBB Computer Services**
10 KITTY JOHN (IRE), 7, gr m Safety Catch (USA)—La Baladina **Masonaires**
11 KNIGHT'S EMPEROR (IRE), 7, b g Grand Lodge (USA)—So Kind **Mrs P. Joynes**
12 PAUNTLEY GOFA, 8, b g Afzal—Gotageton
13 PINTLE, 4, b f Pivotal—Boozy **Mr Robert Heathcote**
14 Ch m Gunner B—Prevada
15 SEVERN AIR, 6, b m Alderbrook—Mariner's Air **Mrs Peter Badger**
16 STOKESIES BOY, 4, gr c Key of Luck (USA)—Lesley's Fashion **Mr Byron J. Stokes**
17 STOKESIES WISH, 4, ch f Fumo di Londra (IRE)—Jess Rebec **Mr Byron J. Stokes**
18 STORM PRINCE (IRE), 7, ch g Prince of Birds (USA)—Petersford Girl (IRE) **Mr D. J. Oseman**
19 THEORIST, 4, b g Machiavellian (USA)—Clerio **Mr I. Astle**
20 THIHN (IRE), 9, ch g Machiavellian (USA)—Hasana (USA) **The Square Milers**

MR J. L. SPEARING—continued

21 **TIMELESS CHICK**, 7, ch m Timeless Times (USA)—Be My Bird **Be Luckies**
22 **TOM'S PRIZE**, 9, ch g Gunner B—Pandora's Prize **Mrs P. Joynes**
23 **WATERSPRAY (AUS)**, 6, ch g Lake Coniston (IRE)—Forain (NZ) **Bache Silk**

THREE-YEAR-OLDS

24 **ADRIATIC ADVENTURE (IRE)**, ch f Foxhound (USA)—Theda **Masonaires**
25 **ARMENTIERES**, b f Robellino (USA)—Perfect Poppy **Mr J. Spearing**
26 **BOLD WOLF**, b g Wolfhound (USA)—Rambold **Mr R. Collins**
27 **BORZOI MAESTRO**, ch g Wolfhound (USA)—Ashkernazy (IRE)
28 **CRISPIN GIRL (IRE)**, ch f General Monash (USA)—Penultimate Cress (IRE) **J. Durnin - W. Casey & M. Diggin**
29 **DORINGO**, b c Prince Sabo—Mistral's Dancer **Mr Robert Heathcote**
30 **FLYING SPUD**, ch g Fraam—Lorcanjo **Mr M. Bishop**

TWO-YEAR-OLDS

31 Ch f 19/3 Trans Island—Farmers Swing (IRE) (River Falls) (7500)
32 **IVORY WOLF**, ch g 6/3 Wolfhound (USA)—Ashkernazy (IRE) (Salt Dome (USA)) (2500) **The Square Milers**
33 B f 28/1 Pursuit of Love—Jucea (Bluebird (USA)) **Mr G. Eales**
34 **MISTER ELEGANT**, b c 25/3 Fraam—Risky Valentine (Risk Me (FR)) (2800) **Mr M. T. Lawrance**
35 Br f 14/4 Prince Sabo—Mistral's Dancer (Shareef Dancer (USA)) (8500) **Mr Robert Heathcote**
36 B f 24/3 Pursuit of Love—Salinas (Bay Express) (800)
37 B f 6/3 Second Empire (IRE)—Salva (Grand Lodge (USA)) (1600)
38 B g 26/4 Pursuit of Love—Top of The Parkes (Mistertopogigo (IRE)) (2200)

Other Owners: Mr Peter Bache, Mr B. Beale, Mrs Sarah Beale, Mr R. M. Bluck, Mr A. A. Campbell, Mr W. H. Cooper, Mr S. J. Court, Mr W. J. Goddard, Mr P. L. Jackson, Mrs F. A. Lockwood, Dr T. Megaw, Mr G. Hampson Silk, Mrs J. E. Young.

Assistant Trainer: Miss T Spearing

Jockeys (Flat): A Daly (w.a.), Steve Drowne (w.a.), Jamie Mackay (w.a.), S Sanders (w.a.). **Jockeys (NH):** Henry Oliver (10-0), Robert Thornton (w.a.).

---

516   MR P. SPOTTISWOOD, Hexham
Postal: Cleugh Head, Greenhaugh, Tarset, Hexham, Northumberland, NE48 1PT.
Contact: PHONE (01434) 240336 MOBILE (07977) 502281

1 **THE ROOKEN (IRE)**, 5, b g Fourstars Allstar (USA)—Be My Sweetheart (IRE) **Mr P. Spottiswood**
2 **WYLDE WINTER (IRE)**, 6, b g Fourstars Allstar (USA)—Wintry Shower **Mr P. Spottiswood**

Assistant Trainer: Anne Spottiswood

---

517   MR T. STACK, Golden
Postal: Thomastown Castle, Golden, Co. Tipperary, Ireland.
Contact: PHONE +353 (0) 62 54129 FAX (062) 54399 E-MAIL tommystack@eircom.net

1 **BRUEGEL (IRE)**, 4, ch c Entrepreneur—Miss Enjoleur (USA)
2 **GOLDEN BASKET (IRE)**, 4, ch f College Chapel—Touche-A-Tout (IRE)
3 **HIT THE NET (IRE)**, 7, b g Be My Native (USA)—Thetravellinglady (IRE)
4 **KERRY WAY (IRE)**, 5, b h Dolphin Street (FR)—Fairy Highlands (IRE)
5 **KINDERLAND (IRE)**, 4, b f Dr Devious (IRE)—Fairy Highlands (IRE)
6 **SEROV (IRE)**, 6, ch h Mujtahid (USA)—Title Roll (IRE)
7 **SWISS ROLL (IRE)**, 4, b f Entrepreneur—On Air (FR)
8 **TINQUEST**, 5, b m Rainbow Quest (USA)—Tizona
9 **TOLPUDDLE (IRE)**, 4, b c College Chapel—Tabdea (USA)

THREE-YEAR-OLDS

10 **CRASSUS (IRE)**, b c Spectrum (IRE)—Fairy Highlands (IRE)
11 **ENFIELD CHASE (IRE)**, b c Foxhound (USA)—Melinte
12 **ESPERENTOS (IRE)**, b f Spectrum (IRE)—Tabdea (USA)
13 **EXPLOSIVE FOX (IRE)**, ch c Foxhound (USA)—Grise Mine (FR)
14 **HOLLOW QUAILL (IRE)**, b f Entrepreneur—Deloraine
15 **KANISFLUH (IRE)**, b f Pivotal—Kahina (GER)
16 **LOVINGIT (IRE)**, b f Fasliyev (USA)—Zing Ping (IRE)

MR T. STACK—continued

17 B f Second Empire (IRE)—Lucy Limelight
18 **OTHERWISE (IRE)**, ch f Dr Devious (IRE)—Touche-A-Tout (IRE)
19 **PASSION KILLER (IRE)**, b f Orpen (USA)—Smart (IRE)

TWO-YEAR-OLDS

20 Gr c 7/3 Nashwan (USA)—Ashjaan (USA) (Silver Hawk (USA)) (7500)
21 **BERENSON (IRE)**, b c 17/3 Entrepreneur—On Air (FR) (Chief Singer)
22 B f 18/2 Brave Act—Canary Bird (IRE) (Catrail (USA)) (3091)
23 **EL PEQUENO**, ch c 28/3 Pivotal—Marbella Beach (IRE) (Bigstone (IRE)) (30920)
24 Ch c 21/3 High Yield—Fardus (IRE) (Danehill (USA)) (40197)
25 Ch c 15/4 Monashee Mountain—God Speed Her (Pas de Seul) (4328)
26 **GREAT QUEST (IRE)**, b f 20/2 Montjeu (IRE)—Paparazzi (IRE) (Shernazar)
27 **HOFFMAN (IRE)**, ch c 24/1 Dr Devious (IRE)—Morale (Bluebird (USA))
28 Ch c 15/5 Dr Fong (USA)—Itqan (Sadler's Wells (USA)) (17934)
29 **JANSKY (IRE)**, b f 8/5 Spectrum (IRE)—Time Limit (IRE) (Alzao (USA)) (988)
30 **LIVE IN FEAR (IRE)**, b c 11/4 Fasliyev (USA)—Fear And Greed (IRE) (Brief Truce (USA))
31 B c 26/5 Entrepreneur—Moonsilk (Solinus) (8657)
32 **PERCE ROCK**, b c 14/3 Dansili—Twilight Secret (Vaigly Great) (11000)
33 **QUASIMODO (IRE)**, b c 28/5 Night Shift (USA)—Daziyra (IRE) (Doyoun) (4328)
34 **RAMAYNA (IRE)**, b f 29/4 Entrepreneur—Fruition (Rheingold)
35 **RONSARD (IRE)**, b c 6/4 Spectrum (IRE)—Touche-A-Tout (IRE) (Royal Academy (USA)) (3400)
36 **SHIYAADHA (IRE)**, b f 6/2 Daylami (IRE)—Samothrace (IRE) (Arazi (USA)) (22262)
37 B f 12/2 Montjeu (IRE)—Susun Kelapa (USA) (St Jovite (USA)) (15000)
38 B f 26/4 Marju (IRE)—Tafrah (IRE) (Sadler's Wells (USA)) (27828)
39 **WOMAN'S CHAT (IRE)**, b f 17/5 Montjeu (IRE)—Shesadelight (Shirley Heights)
40 B c 7/5 Entrepreneur—Zing Ping (IRE) (Thatching)

Other Owners: Mr M. A. Begley, Mr P. A. Byrne, Mr T. Corden, Ms W. Cousins, Mrs J. Donnelly, Mr Benedikt Fassbender, Arthur Finnan, Pearse Gately, Miss C. Lynch, Mrs John Magnier, Mr J. P. McManus, Mrs Diane Nagle, Mrs Wendy O'Leary, Lady O'Reilly, Mr Peter Piller, Mr R. E. Sangster, Mrs T. Stack, Ms K. Vaughan.

Jockey (Flat): W M Lordan. **Apprentice:** W J Lee (7-10).

---

518 MR A. C. STEWART, Newmarket
Postal: **Clarehaven, Bury Road, Newmarket, Suffolk, CB8 7BY.**
Contact: **PHONE (01638) 667323 FAX (01638) 666389**
E-MAIL stewart@clarehaven.com WEBSITE www.clarehaven.com

1 **COLISAY**, 5, b g Entrepreneur—La Sorrela (IRE) **Mr M. Hawkes**
2 **FLARAN**, 4, b g Emarati (USA)—Fragrance **Ms Frances Dakers**
3 **MR VELOCITY (IRE)**, 4, b g Tagula (IRE)—Miss Rusty (IRE) **Mr A. M. Pickering CBE**
4 **PLUM**, 4, br f Pivotal—Rose Chime (IRE) **Sir Robert Stewart**
5 **SALINOR**, 4, ch g Inchinor—Salanka (IRE) **M. J. C. Hawkes & A. Goddard**
6 **SECLUDED**, 4, b g Compton Place—Secret Dance **Racing For Gold**
7 **SELECTIVE**, 5, b g Selkirk (USA)—Portelet **Mr Bruce Corman**
8 **TARJMAN**, 4, b c Cadeaux Genereux—Dodo (IRE) **Sheikh Ahmed Al Maktoum**

THREE-YEAR-OLDS

9 **ADMIRAL COMPTON**, ch c Compton Place—Sunfleet **Racing For Gold**
10 **ALFHALA (IRE)**, b f Acatenango (GER)—Maid of Kashmir (IRE) **Sheikh Ahmed Al Maktoum**
11 **ARRJOOK**, b c Intikhab (USA)—Chief Ornament (USA) **Sheikh Ahmed Al Maktoum**
12 **ASALEEB**, b f Alhaarth (IRE)—Gharam (USA) **Mr Hamdan Al Maktoum**
13 **BOLD PHOENIX (IRE)**, b c Dr Fong (USA)—Subya **Sir Stephen Hastings**
14 **CAPITOLE (IRE)**, b g Imperial Ballet (IRE)—Blue Glass **A. Goddard & M. J. C. Hawkes**
15 **CELLARMASTER (IRE)**, ch g Alhaarth (IRE)—Cheeky Weeky **Hill-Smith, Fine, Goddard, Sangster**
16 **DAY TO REMEMBER**, gr c Daylami (IRE)—Miss Universe (IRE) **Racing For Gold**
17 **EIJAAZ (IRE)**, b c Green Desert (USA)—Kismah **Mr Hamdan Al Maktoum**
18 **GRANATO (GER)**, b c Cadeaux Genereux—Genevra (IRE) **Sheikh Ahmed Al Maktoum**
19 **HABLAIN (USA)**, b br c Unbridled (USA)—Bahr Alsalaam (USA) **Sheikh Ahmed Al Maktoum**
20 **HUM (IRE)**, ch f Cadeaux Genereux—Ensorceleuse (FR) **N. Bashir**
21 **MANDOBI (IRE)**, ch c Mark of Esteem (IRE)—Miss Queen (USA) **Sheikh Ahmed Al Maktoum**
22 **MAREN (USA)**, b c Gulch (USA)—Fatina **Mr Hamdan Al Maktoum**
23 **MEADAAF (IRE)**, b c Swain (IRE)—Virgin Hawk (USA) **Sheikh Ahmed Al Maktoum**
24 **MESAYAN (IRE)**, ch c Grand Lodge (USA)—Missish **Sheikh Ahmed Al Maktoum**

MR A. C. STEWART—continued

25 **MIJDAAF (FR)**, b c Mtoto—Zobaida (IRE) **Sheikh Ahmed Al Maktoum**
26 **MURBAAT (IRE)**, b c Deploy—Ozette **Sheikh Ahmed Al Maktoum**
27 **NAMROC (IRE)**, b c Indian Ridge—Hesperia **Mr Bruce Corman**
28 **POLISH ROSE (IRE)**, ch f Polish Precedent (USA)—Messila Rose **Milton Park Stud & Mr John Beveridge**
29 **PORTMEIRION**, b f Polish Precedent (USA)—India Atlanta **Usk Valley Stud**
30 **PREMIER ROUGE**, b g Croco Rouge (IRE)—Petit Point (IRE) **M. J. C. Hawkes & P. T. Saunders**
31 **QUDRAAT (IRE)**, b c In The Wings—Urgent Liaison (IRE) **Mr Hamdan Al Maktoum**
32 **RAAKAAN**, b c Halling—Glimpse **Sheikh Ahmed Al Maktoum**
33 **RADISH (IRE)**, b f Alhaarth (IRE)—Nichodoula **De La Warr Racing**
34 **RAYSOOT (IRE)**, b c Cape Cross (IRE)—Mashkorah (USA) **Sheikh Ahmed Al Maktoum**
35 **REVENIR (IRE)**, ch g Spectrum (IRE)—Petite Liqueurelle (IRE) **Mr M. A. Whelton**
36 **TANMEYAA**, gr f Linamix (FR)—Ta Awun (USA) **Mr Hamdan Al Maktoum**
37 **TASHREEFAT (IRE)**, b f Danehill (USA)—Aigue **Mr Hamdan Al Maktoum**

TWO-YEAR-OLDS

38 **ALBAHJA**, b f 15/3 Sinndar (IRE)—Eshq Albahr (USA) (Riverman (USA)) **Sheikh Ahmed Al Maktoum**
39 **ALFAASIL**, b c 6/2 Darshaan—Bright Halo (IRE) (Bigstone (IRE)) (200000) **Mr Hamdan Al Maktoum**
40 **ANOTHER STEP (IRE)**, b c 10/5 Raise A Grand (IRE)—Moira My Girl (Henbit (USA)) (16000) **Mr Peter Webb**
41 **BALWARAH**, ch f 23/4 Soviet Star (USA)—Kismah (Machiavellian (USA)) **Mr Hamdan Al Maktoum**
42 **BASHRRI**, b f 30/1 Bachir (IRE)—Bezzaaf (Machiavellian (USA)) **Sheikh Ahmed Al Maktoum**
43 **CAMERONS FUTURE (IRE)**, b c 20/4 Indian Danehill (IRE)—
    Wicken Wonder (IRE) (Distant Relative) (36000) **Collins, Saunders & Stewart**
44 **COSMIC DESTINY (IRE)**, b f 16/4 Soviet Star (USA)—
    Cruelle (USA) (Irish River (FR)) (11000) **Mr A. M. Pickering CBE**
45 B c 9/3 King's Best (USA)—Del Deya (IRE) (Caerleon (USA)) **Sheikh Ahmed Al Maktoum**
46 **DILALA (IRE)**, b f 30/4 Barathea (IRE)—Deyaajeer (USA) (Dayjur (USA)) **Mr Hamdan Al Maktoum**
47 **DIMASHQ**, b f 19/5 Mtoto—Agwaas (IRE) (Rainbow Quest (USA)) **Sheikh Ahmed Al Maktoum**
48 **DOONEQ**, b c 3/3 Diktat—Apennina (USA) (Gulch (USA)) (110000) **Mr Hamdan Al Maktoum**
49 **EBAARAAT (IRE)**, b f 13/3 Sinndar (IRE)—Rafif (USA) (Riverman (USA)) **Mr Hamdan Al Maktoum**
50 **EJAAD**, ch c 28/1 Intikhab (USA)—Elshamms (Zafonic (USA)) **Mr Hamdan Al Maktoum**
51 **ELATED (IRE)**, b c 8/5 Erhaab (USA)—
    Elauyun (IRE) (Muhtarram (USA)) (8657) **Gibson, Goddard, Hamer & Hawkes**
52 **ELRAAWY (USA)**, b c 29/4 Red Ransom (USA)—Fatina (Nashwan (USA)) **Mr Hamdan Al Maktoum**
53 **ERTIQAA (USA)**, b c 29/3 Sahm (USA)—Naazeq (Nashwan (USA)) **Mr Hamdan Al Maktoum**
54 B f 27/3 Mtoto—Fair Shirley (IRE) (Shirley Heights) **Sheikh Ahmed Al Maktoum**
55 **FLEURANCE**, br f 8/1 High Estate—Fragrance (Mtoto) **Ms Frances Dakers**
56 **FOREHAND (IRE)**, b f 23/3 Lend A Hand—
    Set Trait (IRE) (Second Set (IRE)) (15000) **Gibson, Goddard, Hamer & Hawkes**
57 **GHOBAAR (IRE)**, b c 25/3 Red Ransom (USA)—
    Najmat Jumairah (USA) (Mr Prospector (USA)) **Sheikh Ahmed Al Maktoum**
58 **HARDDIM**, b c 28/2 Pennekamp (USA)—Ashbilya (USA) (Nureyev (USA)) **Sheikh Ahmed Al Maktoum**
59 Ch c 14/4 Inchinor—Manhattan Sunset (USA) (El Gran Senor (USA)) (40000) **Mrs M. E. Domvile**
60 **MARHOON (USA)**, ch c 15/2 Lion Cavern (USA)—
    United Kingdom (USA) (Danzig (USA)) **Sheikh Ahmed Al Maktoum**
61 **MEASURED RESPONSE**, ch c 6/5 Inchinor—Seal Indigo (IRE) (Glenstal (USA)) (30000) **Racing For Gold**
62 B f 16/2 Dr Fong (USA)—Minute Waltz (Sadler's Wells (USA)) **Lord Hartington**
63 **NASYAAN (IRE)**, b c 29/3 Namid—
    Space Travel (Dancing Dissident (USA)) (170000) **Sheikh Ahmed Al Maktoum**
64 **NOBLE FUTURE**, b c 3/4 Averti (IRE)—
    Gold Luck (USA) (Slew O' Gold (USA)) (31000) **Collins, Kinge & Saunders**
65 B f 6/3 Cadeaux Genereux—One of The Family (Alzao (USA)) **Usk Valley Stud**
66 **TAJAATHUB (USA)**, ch f 22/4 Aljabr (USA)—Tajannub (USA) (Dixieland Band (USA)) **Mr Hamdan Al Maktoum**
67 **TAJAWIZ**, b c 5/3 Zafonic (USA)—Swellegant (Midyan (USA)) (110000) **Sheikh Ahmed Al Maktoum**
68 **TASDEED**, ch c 10/4 Cadeaux Genereux—Miss Universe (IRE) (Warning) (100000) **Sheikh Ahmed Al Maktoum**

Other Owners: Mr G. Blute, Mr D. Boden, Mrs T. Brudenell, Mrs J. Chamberlain, Mr M. Craig, Lord De La Warr, Dr C. Davenport-Jones, Dr C. I. Emmerson, Mr J. Ferguson, Mr H. Fraser, Mr C. J. Gatt, Mr G. Graham, Mr S. J. Hammond, Mrs D. Hampton, Mr & Mrs Handscombe, Mr D. Hounslow, Mrs H. Jinks, Mr R. Kolien, Mr K. J. Mercer, Mrs S. Mercer, Mr N. Palgrave-Brown, Mrs E. Rice, Mr C. B. Robinson, Mr R. Smith, Mr G. Thomas, Mr A. Walters, Mr R. A. Watchman.

Assistant Trainer: Edward Vaughan

519 MRS M. K. STIRK, Ripon
Postal: **Fountains Farm, Aldfield, Ripon, North Yorkshire, HG4 3EB.**
Contact: **PHONE (01765) 606000 MOBILE (07759) 295989 E-MAIL maxinestirk@lineone.net**

1 **ATTICUS FINCH (IRE)**, 7, b g Witness Box (USA)—Dramatic Loop (IRE) **Mrs M. Stirk**
2 **EIGHTY DAYS (IRE)**, 5, b g Air Quest—Valley Hope (IRE) **Mrs M. Stirk**
3 **JETHRO TULL (IRE)**, 5, b g Witness Box (USA)—Country Project (IRE) **Mrs M. Stirk**

Assistant Trainer: A J Stirk

Jockeys (NH): J Crowley (10-0), R Walford (10-0). Conditional: Robert Walford (10-0). Amateurs: Mr S Brewer (10-10), Mr Mark Walford.

520 MR D. R. STODDART, Towcester
Postal: **Highfields, Adstone, Towcester, Northamptonshire, NN12 8DS.**
Contact: **PHONE (01327) 860433 FAX (01327) 860305**

1 **QUAINTON HILLS**, 10, b g Gildoran—Spin Again **Mr D. R. Stoddart**
2 **SERIOUS POSITION (IRE)**, 9, ch g Orchestra—Lady Temba **Mr D. R. Stoddart**

521 MISS ANN STOKELL, Richmond
Postal: **Castle Stables, Gatherley Road, Brompton on Swale, Richmond, North Yorkshire, DL10 7JN.**
Contact: **PHONE (01748) 811873 MOBILE (07768) 436678**

1 6, B g Sea Raven (IRE)—Denby Wood **Mr Tony Longbottom**
2 **DR JULIAN (IRE)**, 4, b g Sesaro (USA)—Toda **Mr R. J. Buxton**
3 **EASTERN GATE**, 4, b g Elmaamul (USA)—Redgrave Design **Ms Caron Stokell**
4 **EAST RIDING**, 4, b f Gothenberg (IRE)—Bettynouche **Ms Caron Stokell**
5 **FLYING TREATY (USA)**, 7, br h You And I (USA)—Cherie's Hope (USA) **Mr R. J. Buxton**
6 **GRASSLANDIK**, 8, b g Ardkinglass—Sophisticated Baby **Mr Paul Byrne**
7 **MESMERISED**, 4, b f Merdon Melody—Gracious Imp (USA) **Ms Caron Stokell**
8 **MISS CEYLON**, 4, b f Brief Truce (USA)—Five Islands **Ms Caron Stokell**
9 **PERCY DOUGLAS**, 4, b c Elmaamul (USA)—Qualitair Dream **Ms Caron Stokell**
10 **SAFRANINE (IRE)**, 7, b m Dolphin Street (FR)—Webbiana **Ms Caron Stokell**
11 **WETHAAB (USA)**, 7, b g Pleasant Colony (USA)—Binntastic (USA) **Ms Caron Stokell**

Assistant Trainer: Caron Stokell

Apprentices: L Enstone (8-2), D Fox (7-5).

522 MR F. S. STOREY, Carlisle
Postal: **Low Dubwath, Kirklinton, Carlisle, Cumbria, CA6 6EF.**
Contact: **PHONE (01228) 675331**

1 **BARRONS PIKE**, 5, ch g Jumbo Hirt (USA)—Bromley Rose **Mr F. S. Storey**
2 **PLENTY COURAGE**, 10, ch g Gildoran—Fastlass **Mr F. S. Storey**

Jockey (NH): B Storey (9-10).

523 MR W. STOREY, Consett
Postal: **Grange Farm & Stud, Muggleswick, Consett, Co. Durham, DH8 9DW.**
Contact: **PHONE (01207) 255259 FAX (01207) 255607 MOBILE (07860) 510441**

1 **BALALAIKA TUNE (IRE)**, 5, b m Lure (USA)—Bohemienne (USA) **Mr W. Storey**
2 **COLWAY RITZ**, 10, b g Rudimentary (USA)—Million Heiress **Mrs M. Tindale & Mr Tom Park**
3 **COPPLESTONE**, 8, b g Second Set (IRE)—Queen of The Brush **Mr J. D. Wright**
4 **DARK SHADOWS**, 9, b g Machiavellian (USA)—Instant Desire (USA) **Mr D. O. Cremin**
5 **DENEISES BLOSSOM (IRE)**, 11, b m Beau Sher—Lindabell **Mr John J. Maguire**
6 **MEGAN'S MAGIC**, 4, b f Blue Ocean (USA)—Hot Sunday Sport **Steve Howard And Tony Peters**
7 **MINSTER BAY**, 6, b g Minster Son—Melaura Belle **Mr J. S. Simpson**
8 **MISS WIZZ**, 4, b f Wizard King—Fyas **Mr Tony McCormick**
9 **PADDY MUL**, 7, ch h Democratic (USA)—My Pretty Niece **Gremlin Racing**

MR W. STOREY—continued

10 **RIVER CANYON (IRE)**, 8, b g College Chapel—Na-Ammah (IRE) **Mr W. Storey**
11 **ROUSING THUNDER**, 7, b g Theatrical—Moss (USA) **Mr John J. Maguire**
12 **SIR EDWARD BURROW (IRE)**, 6, b g Distinctly North (USA)—Alalja (IRE) **Mr W. Storey**
13 **SUGGEST**, 9, b g Midyan (USA)—Awham (USA) **Mrs M. Tindale**
14 **THE WIZARD MUL**, 4, br g Wizard King—Longden Pride **Gremlin Racing**
15 **WEAVER GEORGE**, 14, b g Flash of Steel—Nephrite **Regent Decorators Ltd**

THREE-YEAR-OLDS

16 **BARGAIN HUNT (IRE)**, b g Foxhound (USA)—Atisayin (USA) **Gremlin Racing**
17 **IZZA**, br f Wizard King—Nicholas Mistress **Thistle And Rose Racing**
18 **TIZ WIZ**, b f Wizard King—Dannistar **Thistle And Rose Racing**
19 **WILHEHECKASLIKE**, b g Wizard King—La Ciotat (IRE) **Thistle And Rose Racing**

Other Owners: Mr D. D. Gillies, Mr Steve Howard, Mrs K. J. Hutchinson, Mr Tony Peters, Mr T. Park, Mrs Janet Wardle.

Assistant Trainer: Miss S Storey

---

524 **SIR M. STOUTE, Newmarket**
Postal: Freemason Lodge, Bury Road, Newmarket, Suffolk, CB8 7BY.
Contact: **PHONE (01638) 663801 FAX (01638) 667276**

1 **ARAKAN (USA)**, 4, br c Nureyev (USA)—Far Across **Niarchos Family**
2 **ARGONAUT**, 4, b g Rainbow Quest (USA)—Chief Bee **Mr Saeed Suhail**
3 **ARTISTIC LAD**, 4, ch c Peintre Celebre (USA)—Maid For The Hills **Mr Saeed Suhail**
4 **CHIC**, ch f Machiavellian (USA)—Exclusive **Cheveley Park Stud**
5 **COMFY (USA)**, 5, b h Lear Fan (USA)—Souplesse (USA) **Mr K. Abdulla**
6 **DESERT LORD**, 4, b c Green Desert (USA)—Red Carnival (USA) **Cheveley Park Stud**
7 **DESERT STAR**, 4, b c Green Desert (USA)—Phantom Gold **The Queen**
8 **DISTINCTION (IRE)**, 5, b c Danehill (USA)—Ivy Leaf (IRE) **Highclere Thoroughbred Racing Ltd**
9 **FAAYEJ (IRE)**, 4, b c Sadler's Wells (USA)—Russian Ballet (USA) **Mr Hamdan Al Maktoum**
10 **FAVOURABLE TERMS**, 4, b f Selkirk (USA)—Fatefully (USA) **Maktoum Al Maktoum**
11 **FIRST CHARTER**, 5, b h Polish Precedent (USA)—By Charter **Mr Saeed Suhail**
12 **FREMEN (USA)**, 4, ch c Rahy (USA)—Northern Trick (USA) **Niarchos Family**
13 **GAMUT (IRE)**, 5, b h Spectrum (IRE)—Greektown **Mrs G. Smith**
14 **KALAMAN (IRE)**, 4, b c Desert Prince (USA)—Kalamba (IRE) **H.H. Aga Khan**
15 **MUSANID (USA)**, 4, ch c Swain (IRE)—Siyadah (USA) **Mr Hamdan Al Maktoum**
16 **PIANO STAR**, 4, b g Darshaan—De Stael (USA) **Mr K. Abdulla**
17 **PROMOTION**, 4, b g Sadler's Wells (USA)—Tempting Prospect **The Queen**
18 **RAINBOW QUEEN**, 4, b f Rainbow Quest (USA)—Dazzle **Cheveley Park Stud**
19 **RUSSIAN RHYTHM (USA)**, 4, ch f Kingmambo (USA)—Balistroika (USA) **Cheveley Park Stud**
20 **SUBLIMITY (FR)**, 4, b c Selkirk (USA)—Fig Tree Drive (USA) **Mr Saeed Suhail**
21 **SUPREMACY**, 5, ch g Vettori (IRE)—High Tern **The Royal Ascot Racing Club**

THREE-YEAR-OLDS

22 **ADAIKALI (IRE)**, b c Green Desert (USA)—Adalyka (IRE) **H.H. Aga Khan**
23 **ADMIRAL (IRE)**, b c Alhaarth (IRE)—Coast Is Clear (IRE) **Highclere Thoroughbred Racing XI**
24 **ALMURAAD (IRE)**, b c Machiavellian (USA)—Wellspring (IRE) **Mr Hamdan Al Maktoum**
25 **ALPHECCA (USA)**, b c Kingmambo (USA)—Limbo (USA) **Niarchos Family**
26 **ALWAYS FIRST**, b c Barathea (IRE)—Pink Cristal **Mr Saeed Suhail**
27 **ANTEDILUVIAN (IRE)**, b f Air Express (IRE)—Divina Mia **Lordship Stud**
28 **AUDITORIUM**, b c Royal Applause—Degree **Cheveley Park Stud**
29 **BALAKAN (IRE)**, b g Selkirk (USA)—Balanka (IRE) **H.H. Aga Khan**
30 **BLAZE OF COLOUR**, ch f Rainbow Quest (USA)—Hawait Al Barr **Maktoum Al Maktoum**
31 **BORDER CASTLE**, b c Grand Lodge (USA)—Tempting Prospect **The Queen**
32 **CAPPED FOR VICTORY (USA)**, b c Red Ransom (USA)—Nazoo (IRE) **Maktoum Al Maktoum**
33 **COY (IRE)**, b f Danehill (USA)—Demure **Cheveley Park Stud**
34 **DALISAY (IRE)**, b f Sadler's Wells (USA)—Dabiliya **Mr Philip Newton**
35 **DARING AIM**, b f Daylami (IRE)—Phantom Gold **The Queen**
36 **DAWIYDA (IRE)**, b f Ashkalani (IRE)—Dawala (IRE) **H.H. Aga Khan**
37 **DAY OF RECKONING**, b f Daylami (IRE)—Trying For Gold (USA) **The Queen**
38 **DAZE**, b f Daylami (IRE)—Proud Titania (USA) **Lord Hartington**
39 **DESERT DIPLOMAT (IRE)**, br g Machiavellian (USA)—Desert Beauty (IRE)
40 **DESIGN (FR)**, ch c Machiavellian (USA)—Vitaba (USA) **Highclere Thoroughbred Racing IX**
41 **DEVORE (USA)**, b f Distant View (USA)—Souplesse (USA) **Mr K. Abdulla**

SIR M. STOUTE—continued

42 **DOUBLE ASPECT (IRE)**, b c Dr Fong (USA)—Spring **The Celle Syndicate Incorporated**
43 **DREAMING OF YOU (IRE)**, b f Spectrum (IRE)—Gay Hellene **Mr M. Tabor & Mrs John Magnier**
44 **DUNE RAIDER (USA)**, b c Kingmambo (USA)—Glowing Honor **Mr Saeed Suhail**
45 **EDEN ROCK (IRE)**, b c Danehill (USA)—Marlene-D **The Celle Syndicate Incorporated**
46 **ESTEEMED LADY (IRE)**, b f Mark of Esteem (IRE)—Bareilly (USA) **Mr N. Ahamad**
47 **ESTILHAAM (USA)**, b f Gulch (USA)—Mamlakah (USA) **Mr Hamdan Al Maktoum**
48 **FORT DIGNITY (USA)**, b c Seeking The Gold (USA)—Kitza (IRE) **Britton House Stud Ltd**
49 **GARRYURRA**, gr f Daylami (IRE)—Tropical **Maktoum Al Maktoum**
50 **GIFT VOUCHER (IRE)**, ch c Cadeaux Genereux—Highland Gift (IRE)
51 **GIRONDE**, b c Sadler's Wells (USA)—Sarah Georgina **The Celle Syndicate Incorporated**
52 **GOLDEN KEY**, b c Rainbow Quest (USA)—Keyboogie (USA) **Mr K. Abdulla**
53 **GRANDALEA**, b f Grand Lodge (USA)—Red Azalea **Cheveley Park Stud**
54 **HASAIYDA (IRE)**, b f Hector Protector (USA)—Hasainiya (IRE) **H.H. Aga Khan**
55 **IMPERIAL STRIDE**, b c Indian Ridge—Place de L'Opera **Mr Saeed Suhail**
56 **KELATAKAN (IRE)**, gr c Daylami (IRE)—Kélatéia (USA) **H.H. Aga Khan**
57 **KINGSWORD (USA)**, bl c Dynaformer (USA)—Western Curtsey (USA) **Mr Saeed Suhail**
58 **LEVITATOR**, b c Sadler's Wells (USA)—Cantilever **Mr K. Abdulla**
59 **LIBERTY**, b f Singspiel (IRE)—Virtuous **Cheveley Park Stud**
60 **LORD MAYOR**, b c Machiavellian (USA)—Misleading Lady **Mr J. M. Greetham**
61 **MACLEAN**, b g Machiavellian (USA)—Celtic Cross **The Queen**
62 **MAGNETIC POLE**, b c Machiavellian (USA)—Clear Attraction (USA) **The Queen**
63 **MAHARAAT (USA)**, b c Bahri (USA)—Siyadah (USA) **Mr Hamdan Al Maktoum**
64 **MAJOR EFFORT (USA)**, b c Rahy (USA)—Tethkar **Maktoum Al Maktoum**
65 **MAMBORINA (USA)**, b f Kingmambo (USA)—La Barberina (USA) **Mr Saeed Suhail**
66 **MARAAHEL (IRE)**, b c Alzao (USA)—Nasanice (IRE) **Mr Hamdan Al Maktoum**
67 **MENOKEE (USA)**, b c Cherokee Run (USA)—Meniatarra (USA) **Mr Saeed Maktoum Al Maktoum**
68 **MOTIVE (FR)**, ch c Machiavellian (USA)—Mistle Song **Highclere Thoroughbred Racing X**
69 **NORTH LIGHT (IRE)**, b c Danehill (USA)—Sought Out (IRE)
70 **NOTABLE GUEST (USA)**, b c Kingmambo (USA)—Yenda **Mr K. Abdulla**
71 **ORATION**, b g Singspiel (IRE)—Blush Rambler (IRE) **Sir Evelyn De Rothschild**
72 **PEERESS**, ch f Pivotal—Noble One **Cheveley Park Stud**
73 **POISE (IRE)**, b f Rainbow Quest (USA)—Crepe Ginger (IRE) **Cheveley Park Stud**
74 **PORTMANTEAU**, b f Barathea (IRE)—Dayanata **Maktoum Al Maktoum**
75 **QUEEN OF SCOTS (IRE)**, b f Dr Fong (USA)—Mary Stuart (IRE)
76 **QUIFF**, b f Sadler's Wells (USA)—Wince **Mr K. Abdulla**
77 **RED BLOOM**, b f Selkirk (USA)—Red Camellia **Cheveley Park Stud**
78 **RELAXED (USA)**, b f Royal Academy (USA)—Sleep Easy (USA) **Mr K. Abdulla**
79 **ROEHAMPTON**, b c Machiavellian (USA)—Come On Rosi **The Celle Syndicate Incorporated**
80 **RUSSIAN DANCE (USA)**, br f Nureyev (USA)—Population **Cheveley Park Stud**
81 **SCREENPLAY**, ch g In The Wings—Erudite **Mr K. Abdulla**
82 **SELDEMOSA**, br f Selkirk (USA)—Baldemosa (FR) **Maktoum Al Maktoum**
83 **SHALAYA (IRE)**, b f Marju (IRE)—Shalama (IRE) **H.H. Aga Khan**
84 **SHEIKHMAN (IRE)**, b c Sadler's Wells (USA)—Maria Isabella (USA) **Mr Saeed Suhail**
85 **SHESHALAN (IRE)**, ch c Indian Ridge—Sheshara (IRE) **H.H. Aga Khan**
86 **SHOOTING LODGE (IRE)**, b f Grand Lodge (USA)—Sidama (FR) **Maktoum Al Maktoum**
87 **SION HILL (IRE)**, b g Desert Prince (IRE)—Mobilia **The Celle Syndicate Incorporated**
88 **STREAM OF GOLD (IRE)**, b c Rainbow Quest (USA)—River Dancer
89 **STRIDER**, ch c Pivotal—Sahara Belle **Cheveley Park Stud**
90 **TALWANDI (IRE)**, b c Alhaarth (USA)—Talwara (USA) **H.H. Aga Khan**
91 **TELEFONICA (USA)**, b f Distant View (USA)—Call Account (USA) **Mr K. Abdulla**
92 **TOP FORTY**, b f Rainbow Quest (USA)—Dansara **Mr K. Abdulla**
93 **TOP ROMANCE (IRE)**, ch f Entrepreneur—Heart's Harmony **Mrs Denis Haynes**
94 **TUTULAND (FR)**, b f Green Desert (USA)—Egine (USA) **Niarchos Family**
95 **WEDDING CAKE (IRE)**, ch f Groom Dancer (USA)—Greektown
96 **WHOLE GRAIN**, b f Polish Precedent (USA)—Mill Line **Mr R. Barnett**
97 **ZARINIA (IRE)**, b f Intikhab (USA)—Zariliya (IRE) **H.H. Aga Khan**

TWO-YEAR-OLDS

98 B c King's Best (USA)—Alasana (IRE) (Darshaan) **H.H. Aga Khan**
99 **ALDABRA**, b c Green Desert (USA)—Krisalya (Kris) **Maktoum Al Maktoum**
100 **AMPELIO (IRE)**, ch c Grand Lodge (USA)—Bordighera (Alysheba (USA)) (800000) **Maktoum Al Maktoum**
101 **ANTOINETTE**, b f Silver Hawk (USA)—Excellentadventure (USA) (Slew City Slew (USA)) **Highclere Thoroughbred Racing XXIV**
102 **ASAWER (IRE)**, b f Darshaan—Sassy Bird (USA) (Storm Bird (CAN)) (600000) **Mr Hamdan Al Maktoum**
103 **ATHENS (IRE)**, b c Saddlers' Hall (IRE)—Athene (IRE) (Rousillon (USA)) **Exors of the late Lord Weinstock**

SIR M. STOUTE—continued

104 **AVIEMORE,** b c Selkirk (USA)—Film Script (Unfuwain (USA)) **The Queen**
105 **BASIC SYSTEM (USA),** b c Belong To Me (USA)—Foible (USA) (Riverman (USA)) **Mr K. Abdulla**
106 **BENEDICT,** b c Benny The Dip (USA)—Abbey Strand (Shaded (USA)) **The Queen**
107 B br f Danzig (USA)—Bionic (Zafonic (USA)) **Mr K. Abdulla**
108 **BOLD EAGLE (IRE),** ch c Rainbow Quest (USA)—Britannia (GER) (Tarim) **Gestut Ammerland**
109 Ch c Rainbow Quest (USA)—Bombazine (IRE) (Generous (IRE)) (200000) **Mr Saeed Suhail**
110 B f Sadler's Wells (USA)—Borgia (GER) (Acatenango (GER))
111 **CARISOLO,** b f Dubai Millennium—Solo de Lune (IRE) (Law Society (USA)) **Britton House Stud Ltd**
112 **CELTIQUE,** b f Celtic Swing—Heart's Harmony (Blushing Groom (FR)) **Mrs Denis Haynes**
113 **CHORALIST,** b f Danehill (USA)—Choir Mistress (Chief Singer) **Cheveley Park Stud**
114 B f Giant's Causeway (USA)—Dalara (IRE) (Doyoun) **H.H. Aga Khan**
115 Ch c Alhaarth (IRE)—Datura (Darshaan) **Lord Hartington**
116 **DINNER DATE,** ch c Groom Dancer (USA)—Misleading Lady (Warning) **Mr J. M. Greetham**
117 **ECHELON,** b f Danehill (USA)—Exclusive (Polar Falcon (USA)) **Cheveley Park Stud**
118 **EXHIBIT ONE (USA),** b f Silver Hawk (USA)—Tsar's Pride (Sadler's Wells (USA)) **Mr K. Abdulla**
119 B f Zafonic (USA)—Ferber's Follies (USA) (Saratoga Six (USA)) (110000) **Mr N. Ahamad**
120 **FLAG LIEUTENANT,** b c Machiavellian (USA)—Fairy Godmother (Fairy King (USA)) **The Queen**
121 **FRONT STAGE (IRE),** b br c Grand Lodge (USA)—Dreams (Rainbow Quest (USA)) (65000) **Mr Saeed Suhail**
122 **GALLANTRY,** b c Green Desert (USA)—Gay Gallanta (Woodman (USA)) **Cheveley Park Stud**
123 **GANDALF,** b c Sadler's Wells (USA)—Enchant (Lion Cavern (USA)) **Cheveley Park Stud**
124 **GIFT RANGE (IRE),** b f Spectrum (IRE)—Highland Gift (Generous (IRE)) **Exors of the late Lord Weinstock**
125 **HARD TOP (IRE),** b c Darshaan—Well Head (IRE) (Sadler's Wells (USA)) **Exors of the late Lord Weinstock**
126 B c Danehill (USA)—Hellenic (Darshaan) **Mrs John Magnier**
127 **HIGHLAND DIVA (IRE),** ch f Selkirk (USA)—

Drama Class (IRE) (Caerleon (USA)) **Exors of the late Lord Weinstock**

128 **HORNPIPE,** b c Danehill (USA)—Dance Sequence (USA) (Mr Prospector (USA)) **Cheveley Park Stud**
129 B c Sadler's Wells (USA)—Igreja (ARG) (Southern Halo (USA)) (500000) **The Celle Syndicate Incorporated**
130 **INCH LODGE,** ch c Grand Lodge (USA)—Legaya (Shirley Heights) **Maktoum Al Maktoum**
131 B c Grand Lodge (USA)—In Full Cry (USA) (Seattle Slew (USA)) (250000) **Mr Ahmed BuHaleeba**
132 **INSINUATION (IRE),** b f Danehill (USA)—Hidden Meaning (Gulch (USA)) (260000) **Cheveley Park Stud**
133 Ch c Kingmambo (USA)—Irtifa (Lahib (USA)) (525000) **Mr Hamdan Al Maktoum**
134 Gr c Daylami (IRE)—Kalamba (IRE) (Green Dancer (USA)) **H.H. Aga Khan**
135 Br gr f Rainbow Quest (USA)—Karliyka (IRE) (Last Tycoon) **H.H. Aga Khan**
136 B c Sinndar (IRE)—Kerataka (IRE) (Doyoun) **H.H. Aga Khan**
137 B f Sadler's Wells (USA)—Key Change (IRE) (Darshaan) **Lady Clague**
138 **KINGDOM OF DREAMS (IRE),** b c Sadler's Wells (USA)—

Regal Portrait (IRE) (Royal Academy (USA)) (300000) **Mr Saeed Suhail**

139 **KING'S ADMIRAL (USA),** b br c Danzig (USA)—Bubbles Darlene (USA) (Fappiano (USA)) **Mr Saeed Suhail**
140 **KING'S KAMA,** b c Giant's Causeway (USA)—Maid For The Hills (Indian Ridge) (350000) **Mr Saeed Suhail**
141 B f Danehill (USA)—Lake Victoria (IRE) (Lake Coniston (IRE)) (150000) **Mr Saeed Suhail**
142 B f Montjeu (IRE)—Lalindi (IRE) (Cadeaux Genereux) **Lady Bamford**
143 Ch c Indian Ridge—Lidakiya (IRE) (Kahyasi) **H.H. Aga Khan**
144 **LINE AHEAD (IRE),** b f Sadler's Wells (USA)—Alignment (IRE) (Alzao (USA)) **Exors of the late Lord Weinstock**
145 **LOCHMADDY,** b f Selkirk (USA)—Vaigly Star (Star Appeal) **Maktoum Al Maktoum**
146 B f Silver Hawk (USA)—Mambo Jambo (USA) (Kingmambo (USA)) **Niarchos Family**
147 **MASTER OF THE RACE,** ch c Selkirk (USA)—Dust Dancer (Suave Dancer (USA)) (200000) **Mr Saeed Suhail**
148 **MATINEE IDOL (IRE),** ch c Daylami (IRE)—

Stage Struck (IRE) (Sadler's Wells (USA)) **Exors of the late Lord Weinstock**

149 **MISS TOLERANCE (USA),** ch f Mt Livermore (USA)—Acquiesce (Alleged (USA)) **Miss K. Rausing**
150 **MITRAILLETTE (USA),** ch f Miswaki (USA)—Crockadore (USA) (Nijinsky (CAN)) **Miss K. Rausing**
151 **MOLEM,** b c Green Desert (USA)—Injaad (Machiavellian (USA)) **Mr Hamdan Al Maktoum**
152 B c Sadler's Wells (USA)—Moon Driver (USA) (Mr Prospector (USA)) **Niarchos Family**
153 **NATIONAL TRUST,** b c Sadler's Wells (USA)—National Treasure (Shirley Heights) **Cheveley Park Stud**
154 **NOTNOWCATO,** ch c Inchinor—Rambling Rose (Cadeaux Genereux) **Anthony & David De Rothschild**
155 B f Danehill (USA)—Oriane (Nashwan (USA)) **Lady Clague**
156 B c King's Best (USA)—Park Express (Ahonoora) (775000) **The Celle Syndicate Incorporated**
157 **PHI (USA),** b br c Rahy (USA)—Salchow (USA) (Nijinsky (CAN)) **Niarchos Family**
158 **PLANET (IRE),** b c Soviet Star (USA)—

Laurentia (USA) (St Jovite (USA)) (115000) **Highclere Thoroughbred Racing XX**

159 **PYRAMID,** ch f Pivotal—Mary Cornwallis (Primo Dominie) **Cheveley Park Stud**
160 **RAIDER OF THE EAST (IRE),** b c Darshaan—Convenience (IRE) (Ela-Mana-Mou) (260000) **Mr Saeed Suhail**
161 **READ FEDERICA,** ch f Fusaichi Pegasus (USA)—

Reading Habit (USA) (Half A Year (USA)) (83333) **Newsells Park Stud**

162 **RED DUCHESS,** ch f Halling (USA)—Red Empress (Nashwan (USA)) **Cheveley Park Stud**
163 **RED JAPONICA,** b f Daylami (IRE)—Red Camellia (Polar Falcon (USA)) **Cheveley Park Stud**
164 **REGINA,** b f Green Desert (USA)—Dazzle (Gone West (USA)) **Cheveley Park Stud**

SIR M. STOUTE—continued

165 **RIYMA (IRE)**, b f Dr Fong (USA)—Riyafa (IRE) (Kahyasi) **H.H. Aga Khan**
166 **ROB ROY (USA)**, b br c Lear Fan (USA)—Carnanoe (USA) (Gone West (USA)) **Mr Philip Newton**
167 **SHANGHAI LILY (IRE)**, b f King's Best (USA)—Marlene-D (Selkirk (USA)) (185528) **Cheveley Park Stud**
168 Ch f King's Best (USA)—Sheshara (IRE) (Kahyasi) **H.H. Aga Khan**
169 B c Green Desert (USA)—Shimna (Mr Prospector (USA)) (210000) **The Celle Syndicate Incorporated**
170 **STAMFORD**, b br c Darshaan—Silver Lane (USA) (Silver Hawk (USA)) (400000) **Maktoum Al Maktoum**
171 B c Anabaa (USA)—Steeple (Selkirk (USA)) (230000) **The Celle Syndicate Incorporated**
172 **STELLAR BRILLIANT (USA)**, b br f Kris S (USA)—Subeen (Caerleon (USA)) **Gainsborough Stud**
173 Ch c Cozzene (USA)—Sue Warner (USA) (Forli (ARG)) **Mr Saeed Suhail**
174 Ch c Zafonic (USA)—Tamassos (Dance In Time (CAN)) **Mr Athos Christodoulou**
175 B c King's Best (USA)—Tiavanita (USA) (J O Tobin (USA)) (148422) **Mr Saeed Suhail**
176 **TRIBE**, b c Danehill (USA)—Leo Girl (USA) (Seattle Slew (USA)) (48000) **Highclere Thoroughbred Racing XXII**
177 **TRINNY**, b f Rainbow Quest (USA)—Mall Queen (USA) (Sheikh Albadou) **Maktoum Al Maktoum**
178 **UNDERGRADUATE (IRE)**, b c Unfuwain (USA)—Starlet (Teenoso (USA)) **The Queen**
179 **VILLARRICA (USA)**, ch f Selkirk (USA)—Melikah (IRE) (Lammtarra (USA)) **Maktoum Al Maktoum**
180 **VIRGIL**, b c Machiavellian (USA)—Mystic Goddess (USA) (Storm Bird (CAN)) **Cheveley Park Stud**
181 B f Danehill (USA)—Whakilyric (USA) (Miswaki (USA)) **Niarchos Family**
182 **ZADALRAKIB**, ch c Machiavellian (USA)—Party Doll (Be My Guest (USA)) (240000) **Mr Abdulla BuHaleeba**
183 **ZARABAD (IRE)**, b c King's Best (USA)—Zarannda (IRE) (Last Tycoon) **H.H. Aga Khan**
184 **ZAYNIYA (IRE)**, b f Machiavellian (USA)—Zayana (IRE) (Darshaan) **H.H. Aga Khan**

Other Owners: Mr Anthony De Rothschild, Mr David De Rothschild, The Hon H. Herbert, Mr Pierpont Scott, Mr M. Tabor.

---

525   MR R. M. STRONGE, Newbury
Postal: **Woods Folly, Beedon Common, Newbury, Berkshire, RG20 8TT.**
Contact: **PHONE/FAX (01635) 248710 MOBILE (07887) 521333**

1 **BERLIN BLUE**, 11, b g Belmez (USA)—Blue Brocade **Peter J. Douglas Engineering**
2 4, B g Tragic Role (USA)—Bluebell Miss
3 **COLD ENCOUNTER (IRE)**, 9, ch g Polar Falcon (USA)—Scene Galante (FR) **Anthony Hibbard and Joe Baker**
4 **COOL INVESTMENT (IRE)**, 7, b g Prince of Birds (USA)—Superb Investment (IRE) **Mr A. P. Holland**
5 **CORAL ISLAND**, 10, b g Charmer—Misowni **Mrs Bernice Stronge**
6 **COSMOCRAT**, 6, b g Cosmonaut—Bella Coola **Peter J. Douglas Engineering**
7 **EMARATI'S IMAGE**, 6, b g Emarati (USA)—Choir's Image **Mrs Bernice Stronge**
8 **INDUCEMENT**, 8, ch g Sabrehill (USA)—Verchinina **Mr A. P. Holland**
9 **KRISTOFFERSEN**, 4, ch c Kris—Towaahi (USA) **SirClementFreudAndrewWrightCharlesWilson**
10 **OUR IMPERIAL BAY (USA)**, 5, b g Smart Strike (CAN)—Heat Lightning (USA) **Mrs Bernice Stronge**
11 **PORTICHOL PRINCESS**, 4, b f Bluegrass Prince (IRE)—Barbrallen **Mr Peter J. Allen**
12 **RED RAMONA**, 9, b g Rudimentary (USA)—Apply **Mrs Bernice Stronge**
13 **STORM A BREWING**, 8, ch g Glacial Storm (USA)—Southern Squaw **Peter J. Douglas Engineering**
14 **SURE FUTURE**, 8, b g Kylian (USA)—Lady Ever-So-Sure **The Test Valley Partnership**

Other Owners: Mr Joe Baker, Mr N. Charlton, Mrs L. Douglas, Mr Peter J. Douglas, Sir Clement Freud, Mr Anthony Hibbard, Mr M. G. St Quinton, Mr C. M. Wilson, Mr A. N. Wright.

Assistant Trainer: Bernice Stronge

Jockeys (NH): J Culloty, B Fenton, S Stronge.

---

526   MRS L. STUBBS, Malton
Postal: **Beverley House Stables, Beverley Road, Malton, North Yorkshire, YO17 9PJ.**
Contact: **PHONE (01653) 698731 MOBILES (07747) 613962/(07801) 167707**

1 **AKIRAMENAI (USA)**, 4, br f Salt Lake (USA)—Bold Wench (USA) **Mrs L. Stubbs**
2 **BLUSHING PRINCE (IRE)**, 6, b g Priolo—Eliade (IRE) **Mr Des Thurlby**
3 **DOUBLE RANSOM**, 5, b g Bahamian Bounty—Secrets of Honour **Tyme Partnership**
4 **EASTERN BLUE (IRE)**, 5, ch m Be My Guest (USA)—Stifen **Mr T. C. Chiang**
5 **EASTERN HOPE (IRE)**, 5, b g Danehill Dancer (USA)—Hope And Glory (USA) **Mr T. C. Chiang**
6 **EASTERN MAGENTA (IRE)**, 4, b g Turtle Island (IRE)—Blue Heights (IRE) **Mr T. C. Chiang**
7 **JEZADIL (IRE)**, 6, b m Mujadil (USA)—Tender Time **Mr O. J. Williams**
8 **PAGAN STORM (USA)**, 4, ch g Tabasco Cat (USA)—Melodeon (USA) **Mrs L. Stubbs**
9 **PAINTBRUSH (IRE)**, 4, b f Groom Dancer (USA)—Bristle **Mr O. J. Williams**
10 **PRINCE PROSPECT**, 8, b g Lycius (USA)—Princess Dechtra (IRE) **Mrs L. Stubbs**
11 **SOMERSET WEST (IRE)**, 4, b g Catrail (USA)—Pizzazz **Mrs L. Stubbs**

MRS L. STUBBS—continued

12 ZOOM ZOOM, 4, b c Abou Zouz (USA)—Iltimas (USA) **Mr Des Thurlby**

THREE-YEAR-OLDS

13 ARRAN SCOUT (IRE), b g Piccolo—Evie Hone (IRE) **K. F. F. Potatoes Ltd**
14 DANCING MARQUESSA, b f Danzero (AUS)—Marquante (IRE) **Lavendar Hill Stud**
15 EASTERN FAITH, ch g Perugino (USA)—Bright Fountain (IRE) **Mr T. C. Chiang**
16 EASTERN PEARL, ch f Wolfhound (USA)—Wild Humour (IRE) **Mr T. C. Chiang**
17 TOP ACHIEVER (IRE), ch g Intikhab (USA)—Nancy Maloney (IRE) **Mrs L. Stubbs**

TWO-YEAR-OLDS

18 B g 5/3 Tipsy Creek (USA)—Hotel Street (USA) (Alleged (USA)) (10000) **Mr T. C. Chiang**
19 Br c 31/3 Namid—In Due Course (USA) (A P Indy (USA)) (6500) **Mrs L. Stubbs**
20 KEEPASHARPLOOKOUT (IRE), b c 23/3 Rossini (USA)—Zoyce (Zilzal (USA)) **Mr D. Smith**
21 B c 29/4 Inchinor—Oriel Girl (Beveled (USA)) (3000) **Mrs L. Stubbs**
22 B g 10/5 Comic Strip (USA)—Roxanne (USA) (Woodman (USA)) (7500) **Mrs L. Stubbs**

Other Owners: Mrs J. Cummings, Mr M. S Martin, Mr T. Osborne, Mrs Valerie Pittman, Mr P. G. Shorrock.

Jockeys (Flat): E Áhern, K Fallon (w.a.). **Jockeys (NH):** B Fenton, A P McCoy (w.a.). **Apprentice:** Kristin Stubbs (7-5).

---

527 **MR J. A. SUPPLE, Woodbridge**
Postal: The Dower House, Worlingworth Hall, Worlingworth, Woodbridge, Suffolk, IP13 7NS.
Contact: PHONE (01728) 628554 MOBILE (07775) 943623

1 ANOTHER PROMISE (IRE), 5, b g Presenting—Snape (IRE) **Geoff Hubbard Racing**
2 AUNTIE JACHINTA, 6, b m Governor General—Hopeful Alda **Geoff Hubbard Racing**
3 BALI STRONG (IRE), 10, b g Strong Gale—Greavesfind **Geoff Hubbard Racing**
4 BROUGHTONS MILL, 9, gr g Ron's Victory (USA)—Sandra's Desire **Geoff Hubbard Racing**
5 DAMASK DANCER (IRE), 5, b g Barathea (IRE)—Polish Rhythm (IRE) **Geoff Hubbard Racing**
6 DEAR BOY, 5, ch g Anshan—Kev's Lass (IRE) **Geoff Hubbard Racing**
7 EASTON GALE, 10, b g Strong Gale—Laurello **Geoff Hubbard Racing**
8 FAUNTLEROY (IRE), 5, b g Lord Americo—Ballyroe Ann (IRE) **Mr A. W. K. Merriam**
9 GLORY OF LOVE, 9, b g Belmez (USA)—Princess Lieven **Miss Lorna Preston**
10 LADY INCH, 6, b m Inchinor—Head Turner **The Dyball Partnership**
11 MAJIC DUST, 4, b g Wizard King—Fuchu **Geoff Hubbard Racing**
12 MOSCOW EXECUTIVE, 8, b m Moscow Society (USA)—Stylish Executive (IRE) **Over the Last Partnership**
13 OCCOLD (IRE), 13, b g Over The River (FR)—My Puttens **Geoff Hubbard Racing**
14 RICHIE'S DELIGHT (IRE), 11, br g Phardante (FR)—Johnstown Love (IRE) **Geoff Hubbard Racing**
15 SAXTEAD MILL (IRE), 11, b g King's Ride—Toi Figures **Geoff Hubbard Racing**
16 SUMMER STOCK (USA), 6, b g Theatrical—Lake Placid (IRE) **Mr Peter Botham**
17 TIGER TOPS, 5, ch g Sabrehill (USA)—Rose Chime (IRE) **Mr M. Tilbrook**

THREE-YEAR-OLDS

18 POLISH RHAPSODY (IRE), b f Charnwood Forest (IRE)—Polish Rhythm (IRE) **Geoff Hubbard Racing**

Other Owners: Mr D. Farrow, Mr C. Mangan.

Assistant Trainer: Miss Lorna Preston

Jockey (Flat): W J Supple (8-2). **Jockeys (NH):** B Murphy (10-0), G Supple (10-0). **Conditional:** Lee Barber (10-2). **Amateur:** Mr A Merriam (10-7).

---

528 **MR CHARLIE SWAN, Cloughjordan**
Postal: Modreeny, Cloughjordan, Co. Tipperary, Ireland.
Contact: HOME +353 (0) 505 42221 OFFICE/FAX +353 (0) 505 42128
MOBILE +353 (0) 862 573194 E-MAIL cswan@iol.ie

1 AHEADOFHISTIME (IRE), 5, br g Supreme Leader—Timely Run (IRE) **Mrs T. Hyde**
2 ANNO JUBILO (GER), 7, b g Lando (GER)—Anna Maria (GER) **Mr Noel O'Flaherty**
3 ANXIOUS MOMENTS (IRE), 5, b g Supreme Leader—Mrs Brooks (IRE) **Mr J. P. McManus**
4 ARELLANO (IRE), 6, ch g Erins Isle—Volnost (USA) **Mr J. P. McManus**
5 ARIMERO (GER), 4, b g Monsun (GER)—Averna **Mr Robert Sinclair**

MR CHARLIE SWAN—continued

6 **ASTON (USA)**, 4, b g Bahri (USA)—Halholah (USA) **Mr Jim Ryan**
7 **BALLYGUIDER BRIDGE (IRE)**, 4, b f Accordian—Shannon Dee (IRE) **Mrs Seamus Burns**
8 **BIRTH RITE (IRE)**, 8, ch g Mujtahid (USA)—Park Heiress (IRE) **Mr Noel O'Flaherty**
9 **CLAIR DE LUNE**, 5, ch g Moonax (IRE)—Call Me Over (IRE) **Mr Peter Corcoran**
10 5, Br g Roselier (FR)—Colleen Glen **Mr Michael Ryan**
11 **COLONEL BRADLEY (IRE)**, 10, b g Un Desperado (FR)—Dora Frost **Mr J. P. McManus**
12 **CONTEMPO SUITE (IRE)**, 7, b g Lord Americo—Kintullagh **Mr Dermot Brennan**
13 **CORNICHE (IRE)**, 9, br g Marju (IRE)—Far But Near (USA) **Mr John Marks**
14 **CROOKED THROW (IRE)**, 5, br g Anshan—Mary's View (IRE) **Hogan Woods Whelan Syndicate**
15 **GLENBOGLE**, 5, b g Saddlers' Hall (IRE)—Great Exception **Mr J. P. McManus**
16 **GROUND BALL (IRE)**, 7, b g Bob's Return (IRE)—Bettyhill **MR J. P. McManus**
17 **HASANPOUR (IRE)**, 4, b g Dr Devious (IRE)—Hasainiya (IRE) **Mr Derrick Smith**
18 **HEROIC (IRE)**, 8, b g War Hero—Happy Patter **Capt D. G. Swan**
19 **HE'S MY MAN (IRE)**, 6, b g Be My Native (USA)—That's The Bonus (IRE) **Mr J. P. McManus**
20 **INGRES**, 4, b g Sadler's Wells—Bloudan (USA) **Mr Dermot Cox**
21 **INNISFREE (IRE)**, 6, ch g Presenting—Sweet Peach (IRE) **Coleman County Syndicate**
22 **KIT CARSON (IRE)**, 4, b g Doctor Massini (IRE)—Roses Niece (IRE) **Mrs Sue Magnier**
23 **LACKELLY BLAZE (IRE)**, 6, b m Eurobus—Dancing Melba **Lackelly Syndicate**
24 **LAHINCH LAD (IRE)**, 4, ch g Bigstone (IRE)—Classic Coral (USA) **Mr John Power**
25 **LAKIL BOY (IRE)**, 4, b g Presenting—Tinerana Noble (IRE) **Pat Droney**
26 4, B g Wizard King—Laser Light Lady **Mr Peter Corcoran**
27 **LINCAM (IRE)**, 8, b g Broken Hearted—Nanogan **Miss Rebecca Camlin**
28 5, B g Norwich—Lovemenot (IRE) **Mr Tom Corcoran**
29 **LOVE SUPREME (IRE)**, 4, b f Supreme Leader—Tri Folene (FR) **Mr Derek Mossop**
30 **MAMA JAFFA (IRE)**, 4, ch f In The Wings—Harir **Michael & Karina Healy**
31 **MARIA PIA (IRE)**, 7, b m Bob's Return (IRE)—Blackwater Mist (IRE) **Il Conte Di Montefalco Syndicate**
32 **MASHAMEE (FR)**, 4, ch g Nashamaa—Hisis de Mee (FR) **Mr Richard Walsh**
33 **MASTER OFTHE CHASE (IRE)**, 6, b g Norwich—Beglawella **Mr Tom Keane**
34 **MIDFIELD (IRE)**, 6, br g King's Ride—Celio Lucy (IRE) **Mr J. P. McManus**
35 **MISSINDEPENDENCE (IRE)**, 5, b m Executive Perk—Bonnies Glory **Mr Seamus Mannion**
36 4, B g Alfiora (IRE)—Miss Redlands **Mr Derrick Smith**
37 **MISTER CYRIEN (FR)**, 4, b g Saint Cyrien (FR)—Miss Lady (FR) **Mr Michael Connolly**
38 **MISTER MONTH (IRE)**, 7, ch g Roselier (FR)—Croghan Heather **Mr Noel O'Flaherty**
39 **MOCHARAMOR (IRE)**, 6, b g Distinctly North (USA)—Oso Sure (IRE) **Anne & Andrew Wishant**
40 **MUROLOOK (IRE)**, 9, b g Muroto—French Look (FR) **Mr Peter Corcoran**
41 4, B g Accordion—My Miss Molly (IRE) **Mr Ian Bray**
42 **OH BE THE HOKEY (IRE)**, 6, b g Be My Native (USA)—Lucky Perk (IRE) **Mr J. P. McManus**
43 **OLD FLAME (IRE)**, 5, b g Oscar—Flameing Run **Mr Peter Reilly**
44 **ONE MORE MINUTE (IRE)**, 4, ch g Zaffaran (USA)—Wollongong (IRE) **Mr Robert Butler Racing Ltd**
45 **OODACHEE**, 5, b g Marju—Lady Marguerrite **Modreeny Syndicate**
46 **OVER THE FIRST (IRE)**, 9, b g Orchestra—Ruby Lodge **Mr Michael McKeon**
47 **PILLAR ROCK (USA)**, 8, b g Alysheba—Butterscotch Sauce (USA) **Mr Leo Sharkey**
48 **PORT OSCAR (IRE)**, 4, b g Oscar Schindler—Desert Oasis **Small Syndicate**
49 **PRESENTING MIST (IRE)**, 6, ch m Presenting—Blackwater Mist (IRE) **Capt D. G. Swan**
50 **RANSBORO (IRE)**, 5, b g Needle Gun (IRE)—Moylena **Mr Noel Elliott**
51 **ROCK TROOPER (IRE)**, 4, ch g Rock Hopper—Lady de Hatton (IRE) **Mr Raymond Yeung**
52 **ROESHAN (IRE)**, 5, br m Anshan—Roseocean (IRE) **Mr Sean Harrington**
53 **ROWLANDS DREAM (IRE)**, 4, b f Accordion—Bettyhill **Mr Dermot Brennan**
54 **SAINTLY RACHEL (IRE)**, 6, b m Religiously (USA)—Ursha (IRE) **The Whitethorn Syndicate**
55 **SHANNON ROSE (IRE)**, 5, b m Topanoora—Shannon Dee (IRE) **Mr Louis Van-Beck**
56 4, B g Oscar (IRE)—Shantalla Bay **Charlie McCarthy**
57 **SHELVEN (IRE)**, 5, ch g Accordion—Southcoast Gale (IRE) **Mr Dermot Desmond**
58 **SORRY AL (IRE)**, 4, ch g Anshan—Just A Second **Mr Donal Carby**
59 **STELWONG (IRE)**, 4, b g Blues Traveller (IRE)—Monterana **Long West Syndicate**
60 **STRONG PROJECT (IRE)**, 8, ch g Project Manager—Hurrican Girl (IRE) **Mr J. J. Buckley**
61 **SUN ISLAND (IRE)**, 5, b m Oscar (IRE)—Sun Kiss (IRE) **Modreeny Syndicate**
62 **THANKS A MIL**, 4, b g Charnwood Forest (IRE)—Lundylux
63 **THE DARK FLASHER (IRE)**, 7, b g Lucky Guest—Perpignan **Mr Noel O'Flaherty**
64 **THIS IS SERIOUS (IRE)**, 10, ch g Broken Hearted—Lady Virtue **Mrs Marie Byrne**
65 **TISN'T EASY (IRE)**, 6, b m Mandalus—Gemini Gale **Mr Seamus Mannion**
66 **TODAYSMYDAY**, 6, b g Home Sapien—Tuesdaynightmare **Mr Eugene Kavanagh**
67 **WHAT A NATIVE (IRE)**, 8, b g Be My Native (USA)—Yukon Lil **Mr Mick McKeon**
68 **WHISPERING GRASS (IRE)**, 4, b g Double Trigger (IRE)—Lady Marguerrite **Mr Peter Corcoran**

MR CHARLIE SWAN—continued

THREE-YEAR-OLDS

69 CAVALRY CHARGE (IRE), b g War Hero—Desert Oasis **Capt D. G. Swan**

Assistant Trainer: Mr Danny Barry (Mobile (0866) 179282)

Jockey (NH): David Casey (w.a.). **Conditional:** J F Levins (10-0). **Amateurs:** Mr M T Campbell (9-7), Mr L Flynn (9-7), Mr Eoin Ryan (9-7), Mr David Stratton (9-7), Miss Louisa Williams (9-0).

---

529 MR G. A. SWINBANK, Richmond

Postal: Thorndale Farm, Melsonby, Richmond, North Yorkshire, DL10 5NJ.
Contact: PHONE (01325) 377318 FAX (01325) 377796 MOBILE (07860) 368365/(07711) 488341
E-MAIL info@alanswinbank.com

1 ARCTIC ECHO, 5, b g Alderbrook—Arctic Oats **Mr R. P. Dineen**
2 BLACK FALCON (IRE), 4, ch g In The Wings—Muwasim (USA) **Mr C. N. Barnes**
3 BLUE ETTE (IRE), 4, b g Blues Traveller (IRE)—Princess Roxanne **Elsa Crankshaw & G. Allan II**
4 BLUE MYST, 4, b f Blue Ocean (USA)—Broom Isle **Mr J. Yates**
5 BRANSTON TIGER, 5, b h Mark of Esteem (IRE)—Tuxford Hideaway **Mr J. David Abell**
6 CLASSY LASSIE (IRE), 4, ch f Goldmark (USA)—Okay Baby (IRE) **Mr A. Barnes**
7 COLLIER HILL, 6, ch g Dr Devious (IRE)—Polar Queen **Mr R. H. Hall & Mr Ashley Young**
8 DARK CHARACTER, 5, b g Reprimand—Poyle Jezebelle **Leading Star Racing Group**
9 DIRECT MANDATE (USA), 4, b g Woodman (USA)—Dangora (USA) **Mr M. Sawers**
10 DOROOSS (IRE), 4, b g Charnwood Forest (IRE)—Catherinofaragon (USA) **Mr C. N. Barnes**
11 FAR PAVILIONS, 5, b g Halling (USA)—Flambera (FR) **Mr J. David Abell**
12 FULL TIME (IRE), 5, b g Bigstone (IRE)—Oiche Mhaith **Mrs Michele Rutter**
13 GOLDEN MEASURE, 4, b g Rainbow Quest (USA)—Dawna **Mr R. H. Hall**
14 GRACILIS (IRE), 7, b g Caerleon (USA)—Grace Note (FR) **Mr Michael H. Watt**
15 HARTSHEAD, 5, b g Machiavellian (USA)—Zalitzine (USA) **Mr C. N. Barnes**
16 HELMSLEY, 4, b g Zafonic (USA)—Nesaah (USA) **Mr A. Barnes**
17 LIBERTY SEEKER (FR), 5, ch g Machiavellian (USA)—Samara (IRE) **Mr M. Sawers**
18 LOBLITE LEADER (IRE), 7, b g Tirol—Cyrano Beauty (IRE) **Montequ Bloodstock**
19 LUCKY JUDGE, 7, b g Saddlers' Hall (IRE)—Lady Lydia **Mrs I. Gibson**
20 LUKE AFTER ME (IRE), 4, b g Victory Note (USA)—Summit Talk **Miss T. Waggott**
21 MAGGIE GRAY (IRE), 6, b m Erins Isle—Reenoga **Mr M. Sawers**
22 NORTHERN NEWS, 4, b g Saddlers' Hall (IRE)—Some News (IRE) **Mr D. Souley**
23 OLD BARNS (IRE), 4, b g Nucleon (USA)—Surfer Katie (IRE) **Mr M. Sawers**
24 PAILITAS (GER), 7, b g Lomitas—Pradera (GER) **Mr C. N. Barnes**
25 PEARSON GLEN (IRE), 5, ch g Dolphin Street (FR)—Glendora **The Pearl Divers**
26 POP UP AGAIN, 4, ch f Bahamian Bounty—Bellair **Mrs P. Robinson**
27 SANDS ISLAND (IRE), 4, b g Spectrum (IRE)—Dazzling Fire (IRE) **Mrs B. Watson**
28 SEVEN COLOURS, 4, b g Spectrum (IRE)—Sinking Sun **Miss Sally Haynes**
29 SPECULIGHT, 4, b g Spectrum (IRE)—Sprite **Bransby Racing**
30 TALAMA LADY (IRE), 7, b m Persian Bold—Talama (FR) **Mrs B. Watson**
31 THOUGHT CONTROL, 4, b g Kris—Keyboogie (USA) **Miss Sally R. Haynes**
32 THROUGH THE RYE, 8, ch g Sabrehill (USA)—Baharlilys **Nice to See You Euro-Racing**
33 TOUCH CLOSER, 7, b g Inchinor—Ryewater Dream **Mr C. N. Barnes**
34 VIRGIN SOLDIER (IRE), 8, ch g Waajib—Never Been Chaste **Mr J. David Abell**
35 VITELLI, 4, b g Vettori (IRE)—Mourne Trix **Scotnorth Racing Ltd**
36 WEAVER OF DREAMS (IRE), 4, b g Victory Note (USA)—Daziyra (IRE) **Bonif**
37 WHAT-A-DANCER (IRE), 7, b g Dancing Dissident (USA)—Cool Gales **Mr A. Barnes**

THREE-YEAR-OLDS

38 Ch g Forzando—Manhattan Diamond **Mr J. Kavanagh**
39 POP PLAY AGAIN, ch g Vettori (IRE)—Bellair **Mrs P. Robinson**
40 QUEENSLANDER (IRE), b f Inchinor—Royal Subject (USA) **Mr J. David Abell**
41 RED ROMEO, ch g Case Law—Enchanting Eve **Mr & Mrs G. Yates**
42 RUTTERS REBEL (IRE), b g Entrepreneur—No Quest (IRE) **Mrs M. Rutter**

TWO-YEAR-OLDS

43 BRANSTON LILY, ch f 8/4 Cadeaux Genereux—Indefinite Article (IRE) (Indian Ridge) (25000) **Mr J. David Abell**
44 B c 7/5 Polish Precedent—Gay Fantastic (Ela-Mana-Mou) (10500) **Mr J. David Abell**
45 Ch f 15/3 Trans Island—Persian Danser (IRE) (Persian Bold) (3091) **Mr G. Stephenson**
46 B c 7/3 Entrepreneur—Scrimshaw (Selkirk (USA)) (2500) **Mrs Anne Yates & Miss Sally Haynes**

MR G. A. SWINBANK—continued

47 B f 20/2 Josr Algarhoud (IRE)—Transylvania (Wolfhound (USA)) **Mr J. Hamilton**
48 B f 20/2 Barathea (IRE)—Veronica (Persian Bold) (6500) **Mr C. Bellwood**

Other Owners: Mr T. Bosomworth, Bransby Racing, Mrs Anne Cairns, Mr Tim Finley, I. C. Forsyth, Mr Tim Hawkins, Mr D. Leach, Mr J. McCreanor, Mrs Sue Souley, Star Racing, Mrs A. Sykes, Mr Grant Tuer, Mr B. Valentine, Mr & Mrs D. C. Young.

Assistant Trainer: Miss T Waggott (Headgirl)

Jockeys (Flat): K Fallon (w.a.), R Winston. **Jockeys (NH):** J Crowley, J P McNamara. **Conditional:** C Eddery. **Amateur:** Miss K Russell.

---

530 **MR T. P. TATE, Tadcaster**
Postal: Castle Farm, Hazelwood, Tadcaster, North Yorkshire, LS24 9NJ.
Contact: **PHONE (01937) 836036 FAX (01937) 530011 MOBILE (07970) 122818**
E-MAIL tomtate@castlefarmstables.fsnet.co.uk

1 **BIG BONE (FR)**, 4, b g Zayyani (IRE)—Bone Crasher (FR) **Mr T. P. Tate**
2 **CAGED TIGER**, 5, b g Classic Cliche (IRE)—Run Tiger (IRE) **Mr T. P. Tate**
3 **CUTTHROAT**, 4, ch g Kris—Could Have Been **Mr T. P. Tate**
4 **DR SHARP (IRE)**, 4, ch g Dr Devious (IRE)—Stoned Immaculate (IRE) **The Ivy Syndicate**
5 **EUROPA**, 8, b g Jupiter Island—Dublin Ferry **Mr B. T. Stewart-Brown**
6 **ROBSHAW**, 4, b g Robellino (USA)—Panorama **Mr T. P. Tate**
7 **SHARP WORD (IRE)**, 5, br g Needle Gun (IRE)—Pas de Mot **The Ivy Syndicate**
8 **TEMPLE DOG (IRE)**, 8, ch g Un Desperado (FR)—Shower **The Ivy Syndicate**
9 **WELSH EMPEROR (IRE)**, 5, b g Emperor Jones (USA)—Simply Times (USA) **Mrs Sylvia Clegg**

THREE-YEAR-OLDS

10 **ANOTHER BOTTLE (IRE)**, b g Cape Cross—Aster Aweke (IRE) **Mr J. Hanson**
11 **BABA (IRE)**, ch c Indian Ridge—Theory of Law **Mr Alan Rayne**
12 **BELSHAZZAR (USA)**, b c King of Kings (IRE)—Bayou Bidder **Mrs Sylvia Clegg & Mr T. P. Tate**
13 **MISSION AFFIRMED (USA)**, ch c Stravinsky (USA)—Affirmed Legacy (USA) **Mr T. P. Tate**
14 **OVER THE YEARS (USA)**, b g Silver Hawk (USA)—Sporting Green (USA) **Mr J. Hanson**

TWO-YEAR-OLDS

15 B c 2/5 Xaar—Can Can Lady (Anshan) (15000) **Mr T. P. Tate**
16 **HILL FAIRY**, ch f 27/1 Monsun (GER)—Homing Instinct (Arctic Tern (USA)) (28447) **Mrs Sylvia Clegg**
17 **VISION VICTORY**, b c 7/4 Dashing Blade—Val d'Isere (German (Surumu (GER)) (9894) **Mrs Sylvia Clegg**

Other Owners: Mr D. M. W. Hodgkiss, Mrs S, Hodgkiss, Mr John Krieger.

Assistant Trainer: Mrs F H Tate

Jockey (Flat): Dale Gibson (7-11). **Jockey (NH):** J M Maguire (10-2). **Amateur:** Mr R T A Tate (10-0).

---

531 **MRS L. C. TAYLOR, Upper Lambourn**
Postal: Uplands, Upper Lambourn, Hungerford, Berkshire, RG17 8QJ.
Contact: **HOME (01488) 670046 FAX (01488) 670047 MOBILE (07778) 780592**
E-MAIL lavinia@uplandsracing.com

1 **IDIOME (FR)**, 8, b g Djarvis (FR)—Asterie L'Ermitage (FR) **Mrs L. C. Taylor**
2 **IGLOO D'ESTRUVAL (FR)**, 8, br g Garde Royale—Jalousie (FR) **Mrs L. C. Taylor**
3 **INFRASONIQUE (FR)**, 8, b g Teresio—Quatalina III (FR) **Miss M. Talbot**
4 **JALOUX D'ESTRUVAL (FR)**, 7, b g Kadalko (FR)—Pommette III (FR) **Mrs W. Morrell**
5 **JAMEROSIER (FR)**, 7, b g The Wonder (FR)—Teuphaine (FR) **Mrs L. C. Taylor**
6 **KALI DES OBEAUX (FR)**, 6, b m Panoramic—Alpaga (FR) **Miss M. Talbot**
7 **LATEFA (IRE)**, 4, ch f Among Men (USA)—Kraemer (USA) **Mrs Mette Campbell-Andenaes**
8 **LOTIER (FR)**, 5, b g Dress Parade—Dame d'Onze Heures (FR) **Mrs L. C. Taylor**
9 **MONTE CRISTO (FR)**, 6, ch g Bigstone (IRE)—El Quahirah (FR) **Mrs L. C. Taylor**
10 **ROLEX FREE (ARG)**, 6, ch g Friul (ARG)—Karolera (ARG) **Mrs L. C. Taylor**
11 **TARONGO (FR)**, 6, b g Tel Quel (FR)—Rainbow Rainbow (FR) **Mrs L. C. Taylor**
12 **YVANOVITCH (FR)**, 6, b g Kaldounevees (FR)—County Kerry (FR) **Mr Robert Frosell**

Assistant Trainer: A J Taylor

Jockeys (NH): M Bradburne, A Thornton.

532 MR COLIN TEAGUE, Wingate
Postal: Bridgefield Farm, Trimdon Lane, Station Town, Wingate, Co. Durham, TS28 5NE.
Contact: PHONE (01429) 837087 MOBILE (07967) 330929 E-MAIL colin.teague@btopenworld.com

1 ALWAYS DARING, 5, b m Atraf—Steamy Windows **Collins Chauffeur Driven Executive Cars**
2 CHRISTY JNR (IRE), 10, b g Andretti—Rare Currency **Mrs J. H. Burn**
3 DANZIG TWISTER, 4, b f Danzig Connection (USA)—Early Gales **Mr B. Batey**
4 FORREST GUMP, 4, ch g Zilzal (USA)—Mish Mish **Mrs J. H. Burn**
5 HESTHERELAD (IRE), 5, b g Definite Article—Unbidden Melody (USA) **Mr B. Batey**
6 HIBERNATE (IRE), 10, ch g Lahib (USA)—Ministra (USA) **Collins Chauffeur Driven Executive Cars**
7 HILL TRACK, 10, b g Royal Match—Win Green Hill **Mr B. Batey**
8 MAGICALLY, 4, ch f Ali-Royal (IRE)—Meadmore Magic **Mrs J. Batey**
9 MISS NOTERIETY, 4, b f Victory Note (USA)—Mystic Maid (IRE) **Mrs J. Batey**
10 VICTORY HEIGHTS (IRE), 4, b g Victory Note (USA)—Gulf Girl **Mrs J. Batey**

THREE-YEAR-OLDS

11 MIKES MATE, b g Komaite (USA)—Pitcairn Princess **Mr M. N. Emmerson**
12 SILVER JADE, b f Silver Patriarch (IRE)—Kinraddie **Richardson Kelly O'Gara Partnership**
13 TAPLEON, br f Danzig Connection (USA)—Reem El Fala (FR) **Richardson Kelly O'Gara Partnership**

TWO-YEAR-OLDS

14 ROSS IS BOSS, gr c 4/2 Paris House—Billie Grey (Chilibang) (1000) **Reg Richardson**

Apprentice: T Craggs (8-5). **Amateur:** Mr L Bates (10-5).

533 MRS P. A. TETLEY, Cranleigh
Postal: Norley Farm, Horsham Road, Cranleigh, Surrey, GU6 8EH.
Contact: PHONE (01483) 274013 MOBILE (0411) 867030 E-MAIL btetley@btopenworld.com

1 AMATEUR DRAMATICS, 8, b g Theatrical Charmer—Chaconia Girl **Mrs P. A. Tetley**
2 BARRON BAY (USA), 12, br g Track Barron (USA)—In Bay (ARG) **Mr Brian Tetley**
3 TOMSWAY, 5, b g Relief Pitcher—Thank Yourself **Mr Brian Tetley**

Jockey (NH): Philip Hide.

534 MRS D. THOMAS, Bridgend
Postal: Pen-Y-Lan Farm, Aberkenfig, Bridgend, Mid Glam, CF32 9AN.
Contact: PHONE (01656) 720254 FAX (01656) 722180 MOBILE (07989) 462130
E-MAIL philjones1226@aol.com

1 SAYEH (IRE), 12, b g Fools Holme (USA)—Piffle **Mrs D. Thomas**
2 TIMIDJAR (IRE), 11, b g Doyoun—Timissara (USA) **Mrs D. Thomas**

Assistant Trainer: Miss D C Thomas

Conditional: Colin Bolger.

535 MR K. S. THOMAS, Carlisle
Postal: Murray Holme, Roadhead, Bewcastle, Carlisle, CA6 6PJ.
Contact: PHONE (01697) 748157 MOBILE (07770) 462839 E-MAIL keiththomas@equilaw.co.uk

1 DAYTIME ARRIVAL (IRE), 6, ch g Lucky Guest—Daymer Bay **Ann Holt**
2 NORTHERN ECHO, 7, b g Pursuit of Love—Stop Press (USA) **Mr Keith Thomas**
3 THE CROOKED OAK, 12, ch g Fearless Action (USA)—Life Goes On **Mr Keith Thomas**

Assistant Trainer: Ann Holt

Conditional: Gareth Thomas (9-10). **Amateur:** Mr E Dehashde (9-7).

536   MR D. W. THOMPSON, Darlington
Postal: **South View Racing, South View, Bolam, Darlington, DL2 2UP.**
Contact: **PHONE (01388) 835806 MOBILE (07719) 161657**

1 **BOOK'S WAY,** 8, br g Afzal—In A Whirl (USA) **Mr J. A. Moore**
2 **CANLIS,** 5, b h Halling (USA)—Fajjoura (IRE) **Mr J. A. Moore**
3 **DOUBLE EM,** 5, b g Balnibarbi—Something Speedy (IRE) **Mr David Bartlett**
4 **ESH BRAN GIRL (IRE),** 4, b f Shahrastani (USA)—Logstown (IRE) **Mr P. J. Harle**
5 **LAKE 'O' GOLD,** 5, ch m Karinga Bay—Ginka **Mr D. Holland & Mr A. Davis**
6 **SACSAYHUAMAN,** 5, b m Halling (USA)—La Dolce Vita **Mrs Ann Davis**
7 **SPRING GIFT,** 7, b m Slip Anchor—Belmez Melody **Mr J. Greenbank**
8 **THREE TIMES A LADY,** 4, b f Syrtos—Pure Formality **Mr I. Fox**

Assistant Trainer: J A Moore

Conditional: Declan McGann (9-7).

537   MR RONALD THOMPSON, Doncaster
Postal: **No 2 Bungalow, Haggswood Racing Stable, Stainforth, Doncaster, South Yorkshire, DN7 5PS.**
Contact: **PHONE (01302) 845904 FAX (01302) 845904 MOBILE (0771) 3251141**

1 **COOLING CASTLE (FR),** 8, ch g Sanglamore (USA)—Syphaly (USA) **Mr B. Bruce**
2 **FINNINGLEY CONNOR,** 4, b g Cosmonaut—Arroganza **Mr B. Bruce**
3 **FURNITURE FACTORS (IRE),** 4, b g Magic Ring (IRE)—Make Hay **Mr B. Bruce**
4 **HIGHCAL,** 7, gr g King's Signet (USA)—Guarded Expression **Mr J. Lomas**
5 **LAURA LEA,** 4, b f Bishop of Cashel—Kirriemuir
6 **PERSUETS (IRE),** 6, b m Gildoran—Furry Queen **Mr Ronald Thompson**
7 **WROOT DANIELLE (IRE),** 4, b g Fayruz—Pounding Beat **Mr B. Bruce**

THREE-YEAR-OLDS

8 **HYMNS AND ARIAS,** b f Mtoto—Ewenny **Mr B. Bruce**
9 **KALUSH,** b g Makbul—The Lady Vanishes **Mrs Jan McCabe**

TWO-YEAR-OLDS

10 **BEYOND THE RAINBOW,** b f 21/3 Mind Games—Skyers Flyer (IRE) (Magical Wonder (USA)) **Mr Alan Bell**
11 **ROYALSILVERCHERRY,** b g 20/3 Silver Patriarch—Royal Hanina (Royal Palace) **Mrs S. Thrower**
12 **SKIPPIT JOHN,** b c 21/3 Abou Zouz (USA)—Lady Quinta (IRE) (Gallic League) (2200) **Mr John Thompson**

Other Owners: Mr J. Bradwell, Mr J. M. Phillips, Mr M. Thomas.

Jockeys (Flat): F Lynch, T Williams.

538   MRS B. K. THOMSON, Duns
Postal: **Lambden Burn, Greenlaw, Duns, Berwickshire, TD10 6UN.**
Contact: **PHONE (01361) 810514 MOBILE (07890) 120066 E-MAIL billiethomson@lineone.net**

1 **ASHWORTH VALLEY,** 8, gr m Primitive Rising (USA)—Willow Wood **Mrs B. K. Thomson**
2 **BALISTEROS (FR),** 15, b g Bad Conduct (USA)—Oldbury (FR) **Mrs B. K. Thomson**
3 **INTERDIT (FR),** 8, b br g Shafoun (FR)—Solaine (FR) **Mrs B. K. Thomson**
4 **ROSES ARE WILD (IRE),** 6, gr m Roselier (FR)—Wild Bramble (IRE) **Mrs B. K. Thomson**
5 **SWEET AUBURN (IRE),** 8, b br g Tidaro (USA)—Sweet View **Mrs B. K. Thomson**

539   MR R. W. THOMSON, Hawick
Postal: **Millcourt, Cavers, Hawick, Roxburghshire, TD9 8LN.**
Contact: **PHONE (01450) 372668 MOBILE (07801) 594336**

1 **BALLISTIC BOY,** 7, ch g First Trump—Be Discreet **Mr R. W. Thomson**
2 **MULLER (IRE),** 4, gr g Bigstone (IRE)—Missie Madam (IRE) **Mr R. W. Thomson**
3 **SON OF ROSS,** 10, b g Minster Son—Nancy Ardross **Mr R. W. Thomson**

Conditional: D C Costello (9-7). **Amateurs:** Miss P Robson, Mr E Whillans (9-7).

540 MR C. W. THORNTON, Leyburn

Postal: Dale House, Rectory Garth, Wensley, Leyburn, North Yorkshire, DL8 4HS.
Contact: HOME (01969) 623350 YARD (01969) 625446 FAX (01969) 624374
MOBILE (07976) 648965
E-MAIL christopher.thornton@talk21.com WEBSITE www.chris-thornton.com

1 **CHALFORD MILL**, 4, b g Blushing Flame (USA)—Crambella (IRE) **Mrs Sheila Oakes**
2 **CUSP**, 4, b f Pivotal—Bambolona **Mrs C. Wilson**
3 **GLIMPSE OF GLORY**, 4, b g Makbul—Bright-One **The Challengers**
4 **INGLEWOOD**, 4, ch g Fleetwood (IRE)—Preening **G. B. Turnbull Ltd**
5 **ITALIANO**, 5, b g Emperor Jones (USA)—Elka (USA) **Mr Guy Reed**
6 **QUICKS THE WORD**, 4, b g Sri Pekan (USA)—Fast Tempo (IRE) **Pegasus Team A**
7 **RENO**, 4, ch f Efisio—Los Alamos **Mr Guy Reed**

THREE-YEAR-OLDS

8 **ALPHA ZETA**, b c Primo Dominie—Preening **Ailsa Daniels & Guy Reed**
9 **LETS ROLL**, b g Tamure (IRE)—Miss Petronella **Mr A. Crute & Partners**
10 **SALONIKA SKY**, ch f Pursuit of Love—Willisa **Mrs D. S. Wilkinson**
11 **THE LAVERTON LAD**, ch g Keen—Wyse Folly **Tommy Dod Syndicate**
12 **TIMBUKTU**, b c Efisio—Sirene Bleu Marine (USA) **Mr Guy Reed**

Other Owners: Mr A. Arnold, Mr K. Blakeson, Mr P. Daley, Mrs R. J. Daniels, Mr Brian Dodsworth, Mr B. Gauld, Mr L. Miernik, Mr J. Outridge, Mrs Ros Peck, Mr D. Trevor, Mr Karl Zanft.

Jockey (Flat): Dean McKeown (8-4, w.a.).

541 MRS A. M. THORPE, Carmarthen

Postal: Felinfach, Bronwydd, Carmarthen, Carmarthenshire, SA33 6BE.
Contact: PHONE (01267) 253595/(01267) 253783 MOBILE (07901)528500
E-MAIL amthorpe@racingstables.freeserve.co.uk

1 **BEN THE BRAVE (IRE)**, 5, b g Ridgewood Ben—Shoot The Dealer (IRE) **Just Maybe Club**
2 **CRISTOPHE**, 6, b g Kris—Our Shirley **Mrs A. M. Thorpe**
3 **DENNIS THE MENNIS (IRE)**, 5, b g Fourstars Allstar (USA)—Farm Approach **Mrs A. M. Thorpe**
4 **JEEPERS CREEPERS**, 4, b g Wizard King—Dark Amber **Mrs A. M. Thorpe**
5 **MADAM MOSSO**, 8, b g Le Moss—Rochestown Lass **Mr Aled R. Evans**
6 **MAIDSTONE MONUMENT (IRE)**, 9, b g Jurado (USA)—Loreto Lady **Mr Don Jenkins**
7 **MARMALADE MOUNTAIN**, 9, ch g Lochearnhead (USA)—Lady Seville **Mr Don Jones**
8 **MR DON (IRE)**, 5, b g Mister Lord (USA)—Paradiso (IRE) **Mr Don Jones**
9 **ORBICULARIS (IRE)**, 8, b g Supreme Leader—Liffey Travel **Mrs A. M. Thorpe**
10 **ROBYNS CHANCE**, 5, b m Overbury (IRE)—Caithness Dawn **Mr J. H. Lee**
11 **SEPTEMBER MOON**, 6, b m Bustino—Lunabelle **Mr J. H. Lee**
12 **SOUNDS COOL**, 8, b g Savahra Sound—Lucky Candy **Formula One Racing**
13 **VALLICA**, 5, b m Bishop of Cashel—Vallauris **Mr A. T. Bailey**

Other Owners: Mr W. J. Hunter.

Amateur: Miss P M Hearn.

542 MR C. TINKLER, Compton

Postal: Uplands Stables, Downs Road, Compton, Newbury, Berkshire, RG20 6RE.
Contact: PHONE (01635) 579090 MOBILE (07717) 885204
E-MAIL gatebest@uplandstables.fsnet.co.uk

1 **BOB AR AGHAIDH (IRE)**, 8, b g Bob Back (USA)—Shuil Ar Aghaidh **Mr George Ward**
2 **BOB LE GAOTH (IRE)**, 8, br g Bob Back (USA)—Shuil Le Gaoth (IRE) **Bonusprint**
3 **BONUS TRIX (IRE)**, 8, b g Executive Perk—Black Trix **Team George I**
4 **CLASSY CLARENCE (IRE)**, 7, ch g Un Desperado (FR)—Winscarlet North **Mr J. Fishpool**
5 **CURZON LODGE (IRE)**, 4, ch g Grand Lodge (USA)—Curzon Street **Doubleprint**
6 **DAWN LEADER (IRE)**, 13, b g Supreme Leader—Tudor Dawn **Bonusprint**
7 **DOMINICAN MONK (IRE)**, 5, b g Lord Americo—Ballybeg Katie (IRE) **Mr George Ward**
8 **GLACIAL SUNSET (IRE)**, 9, ch g Glacial Storm (USA)—Twinkle Sunset **Mr George Ward**
9 **ITS ONLY POLITE (IRE)**, 8, b g Roselier (FR)—Decent Debbie **Bonusprint**
10 **MASTER RIDE (IRE)**, 9, b g King's Ride—Cahore **Doubleprint**

MR C. TINKLER—continued

11 **NATIVE IVY (IRE)**, 6, b g Be My Native (USA)—Outdoor Ivy **Mr George Ward**
12 **NORTHAW LAD (IRE)**, 6, ch g Executive Perk—Black Tulip **Mr J. Fishpool**
13 **PHAR GLORY (IRE)**, 9, b g Phardante (FR)—Prudent Rose (IRE) **Mr George Ward**
14 **PRESENT GLORY (IRE)**, 5, br g Presenting—Prudent Rose (IRE)
15 **SMART SAVANNAH**, 8, b g Primo Dominie—High Savannah **Mr George Ward**
16 **STORMING KATE (IRE)**, 4, ch f Lion Cavern (USA)—Try To Catch Me (USA) **Miss K. J. Burnett**
17 **SUNGATES (IRE)**, 8, ch g Glacial Storm (USA)—Live It Up **Team Scruffy II**
18 **SUPREME DAWN (IRE)**, 7, b g Supreme Leader—Tudor Dawn **Mr George Ward**
19 **TROPICAL CORAL (IRE)**, 4, ch f Pennekamp (USA)—Tropical Dance (USA) **Mr George Ward**

THREE-YEAR-OLDS

20 **CRIMSON STAR (IRE)**, b br f Soviet Star (USA)—Crimson Shower **Doubleprint**
21 **DESERT IMAGE (IRE)**, b c Desert King (IRE)—Identical (IRE) **Mr George Ward**
22 **DR CERULLO**, b c Dr Fong (USA)—Precocious Miss (USA) **Doubleprint**
23 **GAYLE STORM (IRE)**, b f Mujadil (USA)—Mercy Bien (IRE) **Mr George Ward**
24 **PLAY THE MELODY (IRE)**, b br c Revoque (IRE)—Dumayla **Doubleprint**
25 **TRY THE AIR (IRE)**, ch f Foxhound (USA)—Try To Catch Me (USA) **Mr W. E. Sturt**

Assistant Trainer: Heidi Leach

---

543 **MR W. H. TINNING, York**
Postal: High Street Farm, Thornton-Le-Clay, York, YO60 7TE.
Contact: **PHONE (01653) 618996 MOBILE (07870) 752748**

1 **COMPTON PLUME**, 4, ch g Compton Place—Brockton Flame **Mr W. H. Tinning**
2 **LIFE IS BEAUTIFUL (IRE)**, 5, b m Septieme Ciel (USA)—Palombella (FR) **W. H. & Mrs J. A. Tinning**
3 **RIGHTY HO**, 10, b g Reprimand—Challanging **Mr W. H. Tinning**

THREE-YEAR-OLDS

4 **SIMPLY SID**, b g Presidium—Chadwick's Ginger **W. H. & Mrs J. A. Tinning**

Other Owners: Mrs J. A. Tinning.

Assistant Trainer: Mrs J A Tinning

---

544 **MR C. L. TIZZARD, Sherborne**
Postal: Venn Farm, Milborne Port, Sherborne, Dorset, DT9 5RA.
Contact: **PHONE (01963) 250598 MOBILE (07976) 778656**

1 **BELSKI**, 11, b g Arctic Lord—Bellekino **The Butterwick Syndicate**
2 **BEYOND CONTROL (IRE)**, 9, b g Supreme Leader—Bucktina **Mr Anthony Knott**
3 **BILLY BALLBREAKER (IRE)**, 8, br g Good Thyne (USA)—Droichead Dhamhile (IRE) **E. Vickery & R. Dibble**
4 **BOB BOB BOBBIN**, 5, gr g Bob Back (USA)—Absalom's Lady **Mrs Sarah Tizzard**
5 **BROOK STREET**, 7, b g Cruise Missile—Sweet Spice **Mr C. L. Tizzard**
6 **DEAR DEAL**, 11, b g Sharp Deal—The Deer Hound **Mr J. A. G. Meaden**
7 **EASIBROOK JANE**, 6, b m Alderbrook—Relatively Easy **Mr R. G. Tizzard**
8 **GAROLSA (FR)**, 10, b g Rivelago (FR)—Rols du Chatelier (FR) **R. G. And C. L. Tizzard**
9 **GEMINI DANCER**, 5, b g Glory of Dancer—Lamloum (IRE) **Mr R. G. Tizzard**
10 **GOOD THYNE GUY (IRE)**, 9, b g Good Thyne (USA)—Mourne Trix **The Wakehill Partnership**
11 **ICARE D'OUDAIRIES (FR)**, 8, ch g Port Etienne (FR)—Vellea (FR) **Mr Anthony Knott**
12 **JUST REUBEN (IRE)**, 9, gr g Roselier (FR)—Sharp Mama VII **Mr Alvin Trowbridge**
13 **KIWI RIVERMAN**, 4, b g Alderbrook—Kiwi Velocity (NZ) **Mr M. L. Stoddart**
14 **LORD KILLESHANRA (IRE)**, 5, br g Mister Lord (USA)—Killeshandra Lass (IRE) **Mr G. F. Gingell**
15 **L'ORPHELIN**, 9, ch g Gildoran—Balula **Mrs John Pope And Friends**
16 **LUCKY CLOVER**, 12, ch g Push On—Winning Clover **Mrs P. O. Perry**
17 **MISTER ONE**, 13, b br g Buckley—Miss Redlands **Mr C. L. Tizzard**
18 **MOORLANDS RETURN**, 5, b g Bob's Return (IRE)—Sandford Springs (USA) **Mrs Lynda M. Williams**
19 **MOTOWN MELODY**, 6, b m Detroit Sam (FR)—Hester Ann **Mr R. G. Tizzard**
20 **NOBLE COMIC**, 13, b g Silly Prices—Barony **Mr R. E. Dimond**
21 **ONLY WALLIS (IRE)**, 7, b g Supreme Leader—Laurdella Lady **Mr D. J. Hinks**
22 **PARIS LATINO (FR)**, 5, b g Nikos—Tarbelissima (FR) **Mr R. G. Tizzard**
23 **SILENT SOUND (IRE)**, 8, b g Be My Guest (USA)—Whist Awhile **Mrs P. Tizzard**

MR C. L. TIZZARD—continued

24 **UNCLE MICK (IRE)**, 9, b g Ikdam—Kandy Kate **Mr D. J. Hinks**
25 **WATCH THE DOVE**, 7, b g Afzal—Spot The Dove **Mrs M. J. Tizzard**

Other Owners: Mrs J. Collier, Mr Roger Dibble, Mr N. W. E. Maynard, Mrs John Pope, Mrs Sarah Purchase, Mrs J. Purdie, The Jam Boys, Mr E. Vickery.

Assistant Trainer: Mrs K. Gingell

Jockey (NH): J Tizzard. **Conditional:** K Burke.

---

545 MR D. M. TODHUNTER, Penrith
Postal: The Park, Orton, Penrith, Cumbria, CA10 3SD.
Contact: **PHONE** (015396) 24314 **FAX** (015396) 24811 **MOBILE** (07976) 440082

1 **ALL SONSILVER (FR)**, 7, b g Son of Silver—All Licette (FR) **Sir Robert Ogden**
2 **BE MY MANAGER (IRE)**, 9, b g Be My Native (USA)—Fahy Quay **Mr Brian Murfin**
3 **BENRAJAH (IRE)**, 7, b g Lord Americo—Andy's Fancy (IRE) **Mr Brian Murfin**
4 **BRAVE EFFECT (IRE)**, 8, b g Bravefoot—Crupney Lass **P. E. Sowerby, K. A. Sowerby, R. E. Bell**
5 **CHEVALIER ERRANT (IRE)**, 11, b br g Strong Gale—Luminous Run **Mr James R. Adam**
6 **CLOONLOO ANNIE**, 5, ch m Be My Chief (USA)—Don't Be Late **Mrs Loretta Kilroe**
7 **DALBLAIR (IRE)**, 5, b g Lake Coniston (IRE)—Cartagena Lady (IRE) **Abbadis Racing Club**
8 **FLORRIES SON**, 9, b g Minster Son—Florrie Palmer **Mrs F. M. Gray**
9 **GERI ROULETTE**, 6, b m Perpendicular—Clashfern **Mr P. Baldwin**
10 **GHADAMES (FR)**, 10, b g Synefos (USA)—Ouargla (FR) **Mrs J. Mandle**
11 **GUNSON HIGHT**, 7, b g Be My Chief (USA)—Glas Y Dorlan **Lord Cavendish**
12 **HARBEN (FR)**, 5, ch g Luchiroverte (IRE)—Dixia (FR) **Mr D. M. Proos**
13 **JUST IN DEBT (IRE)**, 8, br g Montelimar (USA)—No Debt **Mr J. W. Hazeldean**
14 **KARJU (IRE)**, 5, b g Marju (IRE)—Karmisymixa (FR) **Mr B. Batey**
15 **KINGSMARK (IRE)**, 11, gr g Roselier (FR)—Gaye Le Moss **Sir Robert Ogden**
16 **LOCHBUY JUNIOR (IRE)**, 9, b g Saumarez—Chalabiah **The G-Guck Group**
17 **MERLINS PROFIT**, 4, b g Wizard King—Quick Profit **C.P.T.W. Racing**
18 **PROVOCATIVE (FR)**, 6, b br g Useful (FR)—All Blue (FR) **Sir Robert Ogden**
19 **ROCKERFELLA LAD (IRE)**, 4, b g Danetime (IRE)—Soucaro **Mrs Kate Hall**
20 **SACREBLEU (FR)**, 5, b g Epervier Bleu—Sa Majeste (FR) **Sir Robert Ogden**
21 **SILVER JACK (IRE)**, 6, gr g Roselier (FR)—Consharon (IRE) **Mr B. Batey**
22 **TARBOLTON MOSS**, 9, b m Le Moss—Priceless Peril **Mrs David Marshall**
23 **WESTERNMOST**, 6, b g Most Welcome—Dakota Girl **Mr Steve Baron**
24 **YOUNG CHEVALIER**, 7, b g Alflora (IRE)—Mrs Teasdale **Mr James R. Adam**
25 **ZOFFANY (IRE)**, 7, b g Synefos (USA)—Shining Green **Sir Robert Ogden**
26 **ZOLTANO (GER)**, 6, b g In The Wings—Zarella (GER) **Leeds Plywood and Doors Ltd**

THREE-YEAR-OLDS

27 **AYSIDE ALEX**, b g Mistertopogigo (IRE)—Express Girl **Mr P. G. Airey**

Other Owners: Mrs L. Bell, Mr N. Collins, Mr Robert Jackson, Mr D. J. P McWilliams, Mr Bill Parkinson, Mr D. Potter, Mr J. R. Wharton.

Jockey (Flat): G Duffield (w.a.). **Jockeys (NH):** J Crowley, A Dobbin (w.a.), D N Russell (w.a.). **Amateur:** Mr C Thompson (9-7).

---

546 MR J. A. R. TOLLER, Newmarket
Postal: Eve Lodge Stables, Hamilton Road, Newmarket, Suffolk, CB8 0NY.
Contact: **PHONE** (01638) 668918 **HOME** (01638) 730739 **FAX** (01638) 669384
MOBILE (07887) 942234 **E-MAIL** james.toller@virgin.net

1 **COMPLICATION**, 4, b f Compton Place—Hard Task **Miss Julia Staughton**
2 **DUCK ROW (USA)**, 9, ch g Diesis—Sunny Moment (USA) **Duke of Devonshire**
3 **HANAMI**, 4, b f Hernando (FR)—Russian Rose (IRE) **G. B. Partnership**
4 **HARBRIDGE**, 5, ch g Muhtarram (USA)—Beacon **Mr A. Ilsley**
5 **ISLAND RAPTURE**, 4, b f Royal Applause—Gersey **Dr Bridget Drew**
6 **PAGAN PRINCE**, 7, br g Primo Dominie—Mory Kante (USA) **The Gap Partnership**
7 **PAGAN SKY (IRE)**, 5, ch g Inchinor—Rosy Sunset (IRE) **The Gap Partnership**
8 **PEAK PARK (USA)**, 4, br c Dynaformer—Play Po (USA) **Lady Celina Carter**

MR J. A. R. TOLLER—continued

9 **PRIMA STELLA**, 5, gr m Primo Dominie—Raffelina (USA) **Mr John Drew**
10 **RIQUEWIHR**, 4, ch f Compton Place—Juvenilia (IRE) **G. B. Partnership**
11 **SHARP SECRET (IRE)**, 6, b m College Chapel—State Treasure (USA) **Mr John Drew**
12 **STATEROOM (USA)**, 6, ch g Affirmed (USA)—Sleet (USA) **Lady Sophia Topley**

THREE-YEAR-OLDS

13 **ANTIGUA BAY (IRE)**, b f Turtle Island (IRE)—Vilanika (FR) **Buckingham Thoroughbreds I**
14 **BACHELOR DUKE (USA)**, b c Miswaki (USA)—Gossamer (USA) **Duke of Devonshire**
15 **CHAMPION TIPSTER**, b f Pursuit of Love—Halloa **Mr P. J. Smith**
16 **FLAMJICA (USA)**, ch f Real Quiet (USA)—Fiamma (IRE) **The Cadagan Partnership**
17 **HANAZAKARI**, b c Danzero (AUS)—Russian Rose (IRE) **G. B. Partnership**
18 **HINODE (IRE)**, ch c Vettori (IRE)—Juvenilia (IRE) **G. B. Partnership**
19 **NATIVE TURK (USA)**, b c Miswaki (USA)—Churn Dat Butter (USA) **Mr Y. Gelgin**
20 **PAGAN MAGIC (USA)**, b c Diesis—Great Lady Slew (USA) **The Gap Partnership**
21 **RAWALPINDI**, ch c Intikhab (USA)—Just A Treat (IRE) **Mr P. C. J. Dalby**
22 **SFORZANDO**, b f Robellino (USA)—Mory Kante (USA) **Mr P. C. J. Dalby**
23 **SWINBROOK (USA)**, ch g Stravinsky (USA)—Dance Diane (USA) **Lady Sophia Topley**
24 **TRUMAN**, b c Entrepreneur—Sabria (USA) **The Truman Syndicate**
25 **WYATT EARP (IRE)**, b c Piccolo—Tribal Lady **Byculla Thoroughbreds**
26 **WYOMING**, ch f Inchinor—Shoshone **Mr Alan Gibson**

TWO-YEAR-OLDS

27 B c 22/4 Silver Hawk (USA)—Inca Dove (USA) (Mr Prospector (USA)) (26786) **P. Dalby & R. Schuster**
28 **PAGAN QUEST**, b c 20/4 Lujain (USA)—Rohita (IRE) (Waajib) (70000) **Gap Partnership**
29 **PERFECTIONIST**, b f 8/3 In The Wings—
   Lady Donatella (Last Tycoon) (32000) **Mr John Drew and Dr Bridget Drew**
30 **PERFECT STORY (IRE)**, b f 9/4 Desert Story (IRE)—
   Shore Lark (USA) (Storm Bird (CAN)) (25000) **Mr John Drew and Dr Bridget Drew**
31 **RAMSGILL (USA)**, b c 25/3 Prized (USA)—Crazee Mental (Magic Ring (IRE)) (92262) **Duke of Devonshire**
32 **RIGHT TO ROAM (IRE)**, b c 1/3 Namid—Lloc (Absalom) (50000) **Duke Of Devonshire**
33 Ch c 24/3 Rahy (USA)—Rosebrook (USA) (Geiger Counter (USA)) **Y. Gelgin**
34 B c 5/4 In The Wings—Sea Quest (IRE) (Rainbow Quest (USA)) (20000) **M. E. Wates**
35 **TRIBAL CHIEF (IRE)**, b c 2/4 Desert Prince (IRE)—Lehua (IRE) (Linamix (FR)) (35000) **P. Dalby & R. Schuster**

Other Owners: Mr P. R. Anders, Mr Aldred Collard, Mr Joss Collins, Mr E. Dedman, Mrs E. E. Dedman, Mr N. R. R. Drew, Mr P. R. Drew, Mr Jim Glasgow, The Hon R. T. A. Goff, Mr J. A. Grabham, Mr M. G. H. Heald, Mr F. H. Lee, Mrs J. E. Lee-Smith, Mr G. D. P. Materna, Mr J. A. Newman, Mr R. Santilli, Mrs David Staughton, Mr L. Straszewski, Mr G. H. Toller, Mrs J. Toller, Mrs Jacqueline Williams.

Assistant Trainer: Miss J Staughton

---

547 | **MR M. H. TOMPKINS, Newmarket**
Postal: **Flint Cottage Stables, Rayes Lane, Newmarket, Suffolk, CB8 7AB.**
Contact: **PHONE (01638) 661434 FAX (01638) 668107 E-MAIL mht@marktompkins.co.uk**

1 **ASTROCHARM (IRE)**, 5, b m Charnwood Forest (IRE)—Charm The Stars **Mystic Meg Limited**
2 **ASTROMANCER (IRE)**, 4, b br f Silver Hawk (USA)—Colour Dance **Mystic Meg Limited**
3 **BABODANA**, 4, ch c Bahamian Bounty—Daanat Nawal **Mr M. P. Bowring**
4 **CONNECT**, 7, b g Petong—Natchez Trace **Mrs P. R. Bowring**
5 **FRANKLINS GARDENS**, 4, b c Halling (USA)—Woodbeck **Mrs M. Barwell**
6 **INISTRAHULL ISLAND (IRE)**, 4, b g Flying Spur (AUS)—Dolcezza (FR) **Romford Mini Cabs**
7 **JAMES CAIRD (IRE)**, 4, ch g Catrail (USA)—Polish Saga **Mr Kenneth MacPherson**
8 **LANGFORD**, 4, ch g Compton Place—Sharpening **Marlborough Electronics**
9 **LORD EUROLINK (IRE)**, 10, b g Danehill (USA)—Lady Eurolink **Icon-CTT**
10 **MARSHMAN (IRE)**, 5, ch g College Chapel—Gold Fly (USA) **Mr J. H. Ellis**
11 **NIAGARA (IRE)**, 7, b g Rainbows For Life (CAN)—Highbrook (USA) **Pollards Stables**
12 **RETIREMENT**, 5, b g Zilzal (USA)—Adeptation (USA) **Mr Ben Allen**
13 **RICHEMAUR (IRE)**, 4, b f Alhaarth (IRE)—Lady President (IRE) **P. A. & D. G. Sakal**
14 **SKY DOME (IRE)**, 11, ch g Bluebird (USA)—God Speed Her **Pollards Stables**
15 **STEENBERG (IRE)**, 4, ch g Flying Spur (AUS)—Kip's Sister **Mr Kenneth MacPherson**
16 **ST PETERSBURG**, 4, ch g Polar Falcon (USA)—First Law **Mr P. Heath**
17 **THINGMEBOB**, 4, b f Bob Back (USA)—Kip's Sister **Exors of the Late Mr Nick Fuller**

MR M. H. TOMPKINS—continued

THREE-YEAR-OLDS

18 **BUMPTIOUS**, b c Mister Baileys—Gleam of Light (IRE) **Mrs Beryl Lockey**
19 **CANADIAN STORM**, gr c With Approval (CAN)—Sheer Gold (USA) **P. A. & D. G. Sakal**
20 **CEFIRA (USA)**, b f Distant View (USA)—Bold Jessie **Mrs Jane Bailey**
21 **CROCIERA (IRE)**, b c Croco Rouge (IRE)—Ombry Girl (IRE) **Roalco Limited**
22 **FORT CHURCHILL (IRE)**, b g Barathea (IRE)—Brisighella (IRE) **Mr P. H. Betts**
23 **GOLD OF THE DAY (IRE)**, ch f Daylami (IRE)—Please **Mrs Jane Bailey**
24 **ICE DRAGON**, b f Polar Falcon (USA)—Qilin (IRE) **Mr Ian Lochhead**
25 **INCHPAST**, ch c Inchinor—Victor Ludorum **Marcoe Racing Welwyn**
26 **MIKAO (IRE)**, b g Tagula (IRE)—Oumaladia (IRE) **Mr Ben Allen**
27 **PATRIXPRIAL**, gr c Linamix (FR)—Magnificent Star (USA) **Mr P. H. Betts**
28 **PATRIXTOO (FR)**, gr c Linamix (FR)—Maradadi (USA) **Mr P. H. Betts**
29 **RAJAYOGA**, ch c Kris—Optimistic **Mystic Meg Limited**
30 **REEDSMAN (IRE)**, ch c Fayruz—The Way She Moves **Mr Richard R. Flatt**
31 **SALAMBA**, ch c Indian Ridge—Towaahi (IRE) **Mrs Beryl Lockey**
32 **SAND AND STARS (IRE)**, ch f Dr Devious (IRE)—Charm The Stars **Pollards Stables**
33 **SKELTHWAITE**, b g Desert Story (IRE)—Skip To Somerfield **Mr M. H. Tompkins**
34 **THE GADGET MAN**, b g Charnwood Forest (IRE)—Jane Avril (IRE) **Mr Robert Levitt**
35 **TOPARUDI**, b g Rudimentary (USA)—Topatori (IRE) **Mr M. P. Bowring**
36 **TREW CLASS**, ch f Inchinor—Inimitable **Russell Trew Roofing Ltd**
37 **VALENTIA (IRE)**, b f Perugino (USA)—Teide **Mrs Brian Grice**
38 **YASHIN (IRE)**, b g Soviet Star (USA)—My Mariam **Roalco Limited**

TWO-YEAR-OLDS

39 B c 22/2 Rudimentary (USA)—Ardbess (Balla Cove) (9276)
40 B c 28/2 Second Empire (IRE)—Barnabas (ITY) (Slip Anchor) (4328)
41 B c 16/3 Bahhare (USA)—Bodfaridistinction (IRE) (Distinctly North (USA)) (7420)
42 B c 5/2 Mister Baileys—Dusty Shoes (Shareef Dancer (USA)) (6000)
43 B f 19/3 Josr Algarhoud (IRE)—Eileen's Lady (Mtoto) (800) **Ray Smith and Partners**
44 B c 17/2 Trans Island—First Nadia (Auction Ring (USA)) (7420)
45 B f 20/5 Dancing Spree (USA)—Kip's Sister (Cawston's Clown)
46 B c 2/3 Charnwood Forest (USA)—Nairasha (IRE) (Niniski (USA)) (9276)
47 B c 3/4 Victory Note (USA)—Nordic Abu (IRE) (Nordico (USA)) (10821)
48 B c 2/4 Vettori (IRE)—Nordico Princess (Nordico (USA))
49 Ch f 27/1 Docksider (USA)—Pile (USA) (Shadeed (USA)) (3400)
50 **RIVER CARD**, ch f 20/2 Zaha (CAN)—Light Hand (Star Appeal) **Mr Robert Levitt**
51 **ROWAN LODGE (IRE)**, ch c 30/4 Indian Lodge (IRE)—
                     Tirol Hope (IRE) (Tirol) **The Rowan Stud and Clique Partnership**
52 B c 2/3 Bahhare (USA)—Sandystones (Selkirk (USA)) (12986)
53 **SELIKA (IRE)**, ch c 12/4 Daggers Drawn (USA)—
                     Hint-of-Romance (IRE) (Treasure Kay) (11131) **Mrs Beryl Lockey**
54 B c 24/3 General Monash (USA)—Story Time (IRE) (Mansooj) (7111)
55 B c 3/4 Monashee Mountain—Summit Talk (Head For Heights) (8039)
56 B f 16/3 Erhaab (USA)—Tatouma (USA) (The Minstrel (CAN)) (10000)
57 **TIAMO**, ch c 16/3 Vettori (IRE)—Speed To Lead (IRE) (Darshaan) (26000) **P. A. & D. G. Sakal**
58 Br f 5/5 Tipsy Creek (USA)—Tiempo (King of Spain)
59 Ch f 10/4 Bahamian Bounty—Topatori (IRE) (Topanoora) **Mr M. P. Bowring**
60 **TREW FLIGHT (USA)**, b c 27/3 Rahy (USA)—Magdala (IRE) (Sadler's Wells (USA)) (35000) **Mr Russell Trew**
61 **TREW STYLE**, ch c 12/2 Desert King (IRE)—
                     Southern Psychic (USA) (Alwasmi (USA)) (26000) **Mr Russell Trew**
62 **VINIYOGA**, b c 24/2 Cadeaux Genereux—Optimistic (Reprimand) **Mystic Meg Limited**

Other Owners: Mr Bryan Agar, Mr E. K. Cleveland, Mr Pat Cornell, Mr M. Legood, Mr Conrad Lockey, Mr S. R. Powell, Mrs P. M. Rickett, Mr Pat Swayne, Mr & Mrs A. Thompson, Mrs C. Webster, Mr M. Wilkinson.

Assistant Trainer: Steven Avery

Apprentice: Saleem Golam. **Amateurs:** Mr C Musgrave, Mr S Warren.

548 **MRS P. LAXTON TOWNSLEY, Godalming**
Postal: **Mendips, The Common, Dunsfold, Godalming, Surrey, GU8 4LA.**
Contact: **PHONE (01483) 200849 MOBILE (07887) 726363 FAX (01483) 200055**
E-MAIL prutownsley@classicsecurity.co.uk

1 **ALKA INTERNATIONAL,** 12, b g Northern State (USA)—Cachucha **Mr Paul Townsley**
2 **GRUMPYINTMORNING,** 5, b g Magic Ring (IRE)—Grecian Belle **Mr Paul Townsley**
3 **LAGO DI COMO,** 7, b g Piccolo—Farmer's Pet **Mr M. J. Caldwell**
4 **LITTLETON ZEPHIR (USA),** 5, b m Sandpit (BRZ)—Miss Gorgeous (IRE) **Mr Paul Townsley**
5 **SECAM (POL),** 5, gr g Alywar (USA)—Scytia (POL) **Jamie Butler & Paul Townsley**
6 **SIDONIUS (POL),** 4, b c Special Power—Solera (POL) **Steve Johnson & Paul Townsley**
7 **STAR SEVENTEEN,** 6, ch m Rock City—Westminster Waltz **Mr M. J. Caldwell**
8 **VIKING BUOY (IRE),** 12, ch g Pimpernels Tune—Clare's Crystal **Mr Paul Townsley**

Assistant Trainer: Charlotte Thompson

Jockeys (NH): Xavier Aizpuru (w.a.), P Hide (w.a.). **Amateur:** Mrs C Thompson (9-0).

549 **MR M. P. TREGONING, Lambourn**
Postal: **Kingwood House Stables, Lambourn, Berkshire, RG17 7RS.**
Contact: **PHONE (01488) 73300 FAX (01488) 71728 MOBILE (07767) 888100**
E-MAIL enquiries@kingwood-stables.co.uk WEBSITE www.kingwood-stables.co.uk

1 **ALKAADHEM,** 4, b c Green Desert (USA)—Balalaika **Mr Hamdan Al Maktoum**
2 **ALRABAB,** 4, ch f Nashwan (USA)—Jamrat Jumairah (IRE) **Sheikh Ahmed Al Maktoum**
3 **BUSTAN (IRE),** 5, b h Darshaan (USA)—Dazzlingly Radiant **Mr Hamdan Al Maktoum**
4 **GRAND QUEST,** 4, br f Grand Lodge (USA)—Sea Quest (IRE) **Miss A. H. Marshall**
5 **HIGH ACCOLADE,** 4, b c Mark of Esteem (IRE)—Generous Lady **Lady Tennant**
6 **MAC,** 4, ch g Fleetwood (IRE)—Midnight Break
7 **MARGERY DAW (IRE),** 4, b f Sri Pekan (USA)—Suyayeb (USA) **Gaskell, Maccioni, Myers & Tregoning**
8 **MUBTAKER (USA),** 7, ch h Silver Hawk (USA)—Gazayil (USA) **Mr Hamdan Al Maktoum**
9 **PRIORS LODGE (IRE),** 6, br h Grand Lodge (USA)—Addaya (IRE) **Lady Tennant**
10 **SATTAM,** 5, b g Danehill (USA)—Mayaasa (USA) **Mr Hamdan Al Maktoum**
11 **SEVEN YEAR ITCH (IRE),** 4, b c Danehill (USA)—Itching (IRE) **Greenbay Stables Ltd**

THREE-YEAR-OLDS

12 **ALJAAREH (USA),** b br c Storm Cat (USA)—Muhbubh (USA) **Mr Hamdan Al Maktoum**
13 **ALMISQ (USA),** ch f Diesis—Inscrutable Dancer (USA) **Mr Hamdan Al Maktoum**
14 **ALQAAYID,** b c Machiavellian (USA)—One So Wonderful **Mr Hamdan Al Maktoum**
15 **ASAEEIF,** ch c Nashwan (USA)—Swame (USA) **Mrs Mette Campbell-Andenaes**
16 **BIENVENUE,** ch f Bien Bien (USA)—Mossy Rose **Mr Stanley J. Sharp**
17 **COLOUR CODE (IRE),** b c Spectrum (IRE)—Viendra Nur (USA) **Mr Ivan Allan**
18 **DEEP PURPLE,** b g Halling (USA)—Seal Indigo (IRE) **Byculla Thoroughbreds**
19 **DEJEEJE (IRE),** ch c Grand Lodge (USA)—Christan (IRE) **Sheikh Ahmed Al Maktoum**
20 **EKTEBAAT (IRE),** b c Machiavellian (USA)—Dalayil (USA) **Mr Hamdan Al Maktoum**
21 **ELSHADI (IRE),** b c Cape Cross (IRE)—Rispoto **Sheikh Ahmed Al Maktoum**
22 **ESTI AB (IRE),** b c Danehill (USA)—Bintalshaati **Mr Hamdan Al Maktoum**
23 **FERMANN,** b c Fasliyev (USA)—Dayville (USA) **Sheikh Ahmed Al Maktoum**
24 **FIERY ANGEL (IRE),** ch f Machiavellian (USA)—Flaming June (USA) **Sheikh Mohammed**
25 **FLORAGALORE,** b f Dr Fong (USA)—Valagalore **Mrs A. D. Bourne**
26 **KATAYEB (IRE),** b f Machiavellian (USA)—Fair of The Furze **Mr Hamdan Al Maktoum**
27 **KINBRACE,** b f Kirkwall—Cache **Mrs M.Horne,Mrs W.Biggs,Nic de Boinville**
28 **LAABBIJ (USA),** ch c Shuailaan (USA)—United Kingdom (USA) **Sheikh Ahmed Al Maktoum**
29 **MAAKEL (USA),** b f Swain (IRE)—Hiwaya **Mr Hamdan Al Maktoum**
30 **MAAREES,** b f Groom Dancer (USA)—Shemaleyah **Sheikh Ahmed Al Maktoum**
31 **MANNGAH (USA),** b f Silver Hawk (USA)—Magongo **Sheikh Ahmed Al Maktoum**
32 **MANYANA (IRE),** b c Alzao (USA)—Sometime (IRE) **Sheikh Mohammed**
33 **MASNOOD,** b c Selkirk (USA)—Alruccaba **Mr Hamdan Al Maktoum**
34 **MAYAAL,** b g Intikhab (USA)—Balaabel (USA) **Mr Hamdan Al Maktoum**
35 **MENEEF (USA),** b c Kingmambo (USA)—Black Penny (USA) **Mr Hamdan Al Maktoum**
36 **MERWAHA (IRE),** b f Green Desert (USA)—Samheh (USA) **Mr Hamdan Al Maktoum**
37 **MISHALL (USA),** ch c Distant View (USA)—Virgin Stanza (USA) **Sheikh Ahmed Al Maktoum**
38 **MUDAWIN (IRE),** b g Intikhab (USA)—Fida (IRE) **Mr Hamdan Al Maktoum**
39 **MUJAWER (USA),** b g Gulch (USA)—Good Cents (USA) **Mr Hamdan Al Maktoum**
40 **MUKTASB (USA),** b g Bahri (USA)—Maghaarb **Mr Hamdan Al Maktoum**

MR M. P. TREGONING—continued

41 **MUNAAWESH (USA)**, b c Bahri (USA)—Istikbal (USA) **Mr Hamdan Al Maktoum**
42 **MUSTAJED**, b c Alhaarth (IRE)—Jasareh (IRE) **Mr Hamdan Al Maktoum**
43 **NAMAT (IRE)**, b f Daylami (IRE)—Masharik (IRE) **Mr Hamdan Al Maktoum**
44 **NOORA (IRE)**, ch f Bahhare (USA)—Esteraad (IRE) **Mr Khalil Alsayegh**
45 **NOOSHAM (USA)**, gr f Daylami (IRE)—Noushkey **Sheikh Ahmed Al Maktoum**
46 **NOOZHAH**, ch f Singspiel (IRE)—Agwaas **Sheikh Ahmed Al Maktoum**
47 **NUZOOA (USA)**, b br f A P Indy (USA)—Min Alhawa (USA) **Mr Hamdan Al Maktoum**
48 **OKOBOJI (IRE)**, ch c Indian Ridge—Pool Party (USA) **Mr Martin Collins**
49 **ORIENTAL WARRIOR**, b c Alhaarth (IRE)—Oriental Fashion (IRE) **Mr Hadi Al-Tajir**
50 **PLOVERS LANE (IRE)**, b g Dushyantor (USA)—Sweet Alma **Mrs Thomas Wallis and Her Family**
51 **REMAADD (USA)**, gr ro c Daylami (IRE)—Bint Albaadiya (USA) **Sheikh Ahmed Al Maktoum**
52 **SAHOOL**, b f Unfuwain (USA)—Mathaayl (USA) **Mr Hamdan Al Maktoum**
53 **SIAN THOMAS**, ch f Magic Ring (IRE)—Midnight Break **Major & Mrs R. B. Kennard And Partner**
54 **SONGCRAFT**, ch f Singspiel (IRE)—Radiancy (USA) **Sheikh Mohammed**
55 **SO WILL I**, ch c Inchinor—Fur Will Fly **Mr Hamdan Al Maktoum**
56 **STEEL BONNET**, b g Selkirk (USA)—Cask **The Hopeful Partnership**
57 **TAAQAAH**, ch c Grand Lodge (USA)—Belle Ile (USA) **Sheikh Ahmed Al Maktoum**
58 **TAHREEB (FR)**, ch c Indian Ridge—Native Twine **Sheikh Ahmed Al Maktoum**
59 **TAHTHEEB (IRE)**, b f Muhtarram (USA)—Mihnah (IRE) **Mr Hamdan Al Maktoum**
60 **TETCOTT (IRE)**, ch f Definite Article—Charlene Lacy (IRE) **D G Partnership**
61 **THAMINAH (USA)**, b f Danzig (USA)—Bashayer (USA) **Mr Hamdan Al Maktoum**
62 **TORCROSS**, b f Vettori—Sheppard's Cross **Major & Mrs R. B. Kennard & Partner**
63 **TREE CHOPPER (USA)**, ch f Woodman—Gazayil (USA) **Mr Warren Rosenthal**
64 **TRIPLE JUMP**, ch g Inchinor—Meteoric **Mr and Mrs J. D. Cotton**
65 **UNA ROSA PARA TI**, gr f Silver Patriarch (IRE)—Manzanilla **Mrs Mette Campbell-Andenaes**

TWO-YEAR-OLDS

66 **ALMAMOORAH (IRE)**, ch f 4/2 Sinndar (IRE)—Alkaffeyeh (IRE) (Sadler's Wells (USA)) **Mr Hamdan Al Maktoum**
67 **ALSHAMATRY (USA)**, ch f 2/2 Seeking The Gold (USA)—
Mehthaaf (USA) (Nureyev (USA)) **Mr Hamdan Al Maktoum**
68 **ALSHARQ (IRE)**, b f 10/4 Machiavellian (USA)—Balaabel (USA) (Sadler's Wells (USA)) **Mr Hamdan Al Maktoum**
69 **ALSHIMAAL (IRE)**, b 9/2 Namid—Bold As Love (Lomond) (154606) **Mr Hamdan Al Maktoum**
70 **AWAASER (USA)**, ch 24/2 Diesis—Forest Storm (Woodman) (185528) **Mr Hamdan Al Maktoum**
71 **BATTLEDRESS (IRE)**, b c 4/3 In The Wings—Chaturanga (Night Shift (USA)) **Sheikh Mohammed**
72 **BLACK VELVET**, br c 24/2 Inchinor—Three Owls (Warning) (165000) **Lady Tennant**
73 **BLA SHAK (IRE)**, b c 16/2 Alhaarth (IRE)—
Really Gifted (IRE) (Cadeaux Genereux) (75000) **Sheikh Ahmed Al Maktoum**
74 **BLUE LULLABY (IRE)**, b f 7/5 Fasliyev (USA)—Whispering (IRE) (Royal Academy (USA)) **Greenbay Stables Ltd**
75 **CASH ON (IRE)**, ch c 11/5 Spectrum (IRE)—
Lady Lucre (IRE) (Last Tycoon) (17315) **Mr M. Calvert and Mr Colin E. Lewis**
76 **CHANDRA**, b f 4/4 Cape Cross (IRE)—Dom Pennion (Dominion) (44526) **Mrs Amanda Krishnan**
77 **CLAMBAKE (IRE)**, ch f 11/3 Grand Lodge (USA)—
Sometime (IRE) (Royal Academy (USA)) **Greenbay Stables Ltd**
78 **DANAATT (USA)**, b f 18/5 Gulch (USA)—Agama (Nureyev (USA)) **Sheikh Ahmed Al Maktoum**
79 **DAND NEE (USA)**, b br f 10/2 Kabool—Zobaida (IRE) (Green Desert (USA)) **Sheikh Ahmed Al Maktoum**
80 Ch c 17/1 Daggers Drawn (USA)—Dazzling Maid (Tate Gallery (USA)) (24000) **Mr R. C. C. Villers**
81 **DEFINITE DANCER (IRE)**, b g 10/2 Definite Article—
Greeba (Fairy King (USA)) (23000) **Geoffrey and Miss Joan Hayes**
82 **DHELAAL**, b f 25/4 Green Desert (USA)—Irish Valley (USA) (Irish River (FR)) **Mr Hamdan Al Maktoum**
83 **EMILE ZOLA**, b c 31/1 Singspiel (IRE)—Ellie Ardensky (Slip Anchor) **Sheikh Mohammed**
84 **FALEH**, ch f 4/2 Silver Hawk (USA)—Marasem (Cadeaux Genereux) **Mr Hamdan Al Maktoum**
85 **FLAUNT N FLIRT**, b f 20/4 Erhaab (USA)—Lets Fall In Love (USA) (Northern Baby (CAN)) **Miss N. Sexton**
86 B c 7/5 Polish Precedent (USA—Haboobti (Habitat)
87 **HUBOOB (FR)**, b c 16/1 Almutawakel—Atnab (USA) (Riverman (USA)) **Mr Hamdan Al Maktoum**
88 **IMPERIAL RULE (IRE)**, b c 3/5 Second Empire (IRE)—
Alikhlas (Lahib (USA)) (18000) **Imperial Rule Partnership**
89 **ITQAAN (USA)**, b f 9/5 Danzig (USA)—Sarayir (USA) (Mr Prospector (USA)) **Mr Hamdan Al Maktoum**
90 **JAAFI (IRE)**, b c 20/2 Celtic Swing—Bustinetta (Bustino) (52000) **Mr Hamdan Al Maktoum**
91 **JADEERA (IRE)**, b f 4/2 Darshaan—Harayir (USA) (Gulch (USA)) **Mr Hamdan Al Maktoum**
92 **JADIDAH**, ch f 25/3 Pennekamp (USA)—Almuhtarama (IRE) (Rainbow Quest (USA)) **Sheikh Ahmed Al Maktoum**
93 **JALWADA**, b f 13/2 Cadeaux Genereux—Wedoudah (IRE) (Sadler's Wells (USA)) **Sheikh Ahmed Al Maktoum**
94 **KATHEER (USA)**, b c 25/2 Anabaa—Elhida (IRE) (Mujtahid (USA)) **Mr Hamdan Al Maktoum**
95 **KAWN**, b f 4/2 Cadeaux Genereux—Khubza (Green Desert (USA)) (500000) **Mr Hamdan Al Maktoum**
96 **MAGHAZI (USA)**, b c 12/2 Fasliyev—Dalayil (IRE) (Sadler's Wells (USA)) **Mr Hamdan Al Maktoum**
97 **MAYADEEN (IRE)**, b c 28/1 King's Best (USA)—Inaaq (Lammtarra (USA)) **Mr Hamdan Al Maktoum**

MR M. P. TREGONING—continued

98 **MEGGIDO (IRE)**, b c 1/3 Green Desert (USA)—
No Win No Deal (Machiavellian (USA)) **Sheikh Ahmed Al Maktoum**
99 **MENWAAL (USA)**, b c 11/5 Silver Hawk (USA)—Haniya (IRE) (Caerleon (USA)) **Mr Hamdan Al Maktoum**
100 **MERAYAAT (IRE)**, b f 2/2 Darshaan—Maddelina (IRE) (Sadler's Wells (USA)) **Mr Hamdan Al Maktoum**
101 **MOGAAMER (USA)**, b c 30/3 Dixieland Band (USA)—
Dolly Dalbo (USA) (Capote (USA)) **Mr Hamdan Al Maktoum**
102 **MOHAFAZAAT (IRE)**, b f 20/3 Sadler's Wells (USA)—
Wijdan (USA) (Mr Prospector (USA)) **Mr Hamdan Al Maktoum**
103 **MOLLZAM (IRE)**, b c 1/4 Danehill (USA)—
Matilda Bay (IRE) (Indian Ridge) (115000) **Sheikh Ahmed Al Maktoum**
104 **MONDAREJ (IRE)**, b c 17/3 Sinndar (IRE)—Masharik (IRE) (Caerleon (USA)) **Mr Hamdan Al Maktoum**
105 **MONTELEONE (IRE)**, b f 14/2 Montjeu (IRE)—Rainbow Goddess (Rainbow Quest (USA)) **Mr R. J. McCreery**
106 **MOSHKIL (IRE)**, b c 27/4 In The Wings—
Brentsville (USA) (Arctic Tern (USA)) (40000) **Sheikh Ahmed Al Maktoum**
107 **MUSEEB (IRE)**, b c 3/4 Mujadil (USA)—
Island Desert (IRE) (Green Desert (USA)) (43000) **Mr Hamdan Al Maktoum**
108 **MUSHAJER (IRE)**, gr c 14/4 Linamix (FR)—Luxurious (USA) (Lyphard (USA)) (78000) **Mr Hamdan Al Maktoum**
109 **NIGHT HOUR (IRE)**, b c 15/3 Entrepreneur—Witching Hour (IRE) (Alzao (USA)) **Greenbay Stables Ltd**
110 **NOUBIAN (USA)**, ch c 23/3 Diesis—Beraysim (Lion Cavern (USA)) **Sheikh Ahmed Al Maktoum**
111 **OONAGH MACCOOL (IRE)**, ch f 11/2 Giant's Causeway—Alidiva (Chief Singer) **Greenbay Stables Ltd**
112 Br c 12/4 Diktat—Petriece (Mummy's Pet) (45000) **Sheikh Mohammed**
113 **QADAR (IRE)**, b c 8/3 Xaar—Iktidar (Green Desert (USA)) (250000) **Mr Hamdan Al Maktoum**
114 **RAMMAAS (IRE)**, ch c 8/2 Pennekamp—Zeyaarah (USA) (Rahy (USA)) **Sheikh Ahmed Al Maktoum**
115 **RAWAABET (IRE)**, b c 30/4 Bahhare (USA)—Haddeyah (USA) (Dayjur (USA)) **Mr Hamdan Al Maktoum**
116 **REMAAL (IRE)**, ch f 16/3 Unfuwain (USA)—Marah (Machiavellian (USA)) **Mr Hamdan Al Maktoum**
117 **SAREM (USA)**, br c 19/1 Kingmambo (USA)—Storm Beauty (USA) (Storm Cat (USA)) **Mr Hamdan Al Maktoum**
118 **SHAHAMA (IRE)**, gr c 18/2 Daylami (USA)—
Albertville (USA) (Polish Precedent (USA)) **Sheikh Ahmed Al Maktoum**
119 **SHOHRAH (IRE)**, ch f 1/2 Giant's Causeway—Taqreem (IRE) (Nashwan (USA)) **Mr Hamdan Al Maktoum**
120 B f 12/2 Dansili—Shot of Redemption (Shirley Heights) (11000) **Mr R. C. C. Villers**
121 **SNOW PLOUGH (IRE)**, b c 18/4 Indian Ridge—
Snow Princess (IRE) (Ela-Mana-Mou) **Exors of the late Lord Weinstock**
122 **TAKHLEED (USA)**, b c 29/1 Stravinsky (USA)—
Bold Threat (CAN) (Bold Ruckus (USA)) **Mr Hamdan Al Maktoum**
123 **TASIS (USA)**, b c 4/2 Danehill (USA)—Mayaasa (USA) (Lyphard (USA)) **Mr Hamdan Al Maktoum**
124 **TEST THE BEST**, b c 3/3 King's Best (USA)—Um Lardaff (Mill Reef (USA)) **Mr Ziad A. Galadari**
125 **THAKAAFA (USA)**, ch f 21/4 Elnadim (USA)—Istikbal (USA) (Kingmambo (USA)) **Mr Hamdan Al Maktoum**
126 **TO ARMS**, b c 30/4 Mujahid (USA)—Toffee (Midyan (USA))
127 **UMTHOULAH (IRE)**, br f 20/4 Unfuwain (USA)—
Susquehanna Days (USA) (Chief's Crown (USA)) (90000) **Mr Hamdan Al Maktoum**
128 **WAR AT SEA (IRE)**, b c 15/2 Bering—Naval Affair (IRE) (Last Tycoon) **Exors of the late Lord Weinstock**
129 **WELLING (IRE)**, b c 13/1 Darshaan—Felona (Caerleon (USA)) **Sheikh Ahmed Al Maktoum**
130 B c 3/4 Mark of Esteem (IRE)—Whitehaven (Top Ville) **Sheikh Mohammed**
131 B f 6/2 Sadler's Wells (USA)—Will Be Blue (IRE) (Darshaan) (145000) **Mr P. Newton**
132 B c 24/3 In The Wings—Wolf Cleugh (IRE) (Last Tycoon) (29065) **Mr Ivan Allan**
133 **ZEENA (IRE)**, b f 31/3 Unfuwain (USA)—Forest Fire (SWE) (Never So Bold) **Mrs Mette Campbell-Andenaes**

Other Owners: Mrs N. C. Baker, Mr Peter Beaton-Brown, Mr G. C. Blomfield, Miss E. Brown, Mrs Hugh Dalgety, Lady Margaret Fortescue, Mrs A. Hamilton, Capt T. Lucklock, Mr J. Owen, Tessona Racing, Mr J. Tregoning, Mr J. R. Wallis, Mr S. H. Wallis, Mr N. H. T. Wrigley.

Assistant Trainer: Patrick MacEwan

Jockeys (Flat): A Daly (8-0), M Dwyer (7-13), R Hills (8-4), W Supple (8-2). **Apprentices:** C Galbraith, S Parsons.

---

550 | **MR F. G. TUCKER, Wedmore**
Postal: **Mudgley Hill Farm, Mudgley, Wedmore, Somerset, BS28 4TZ.**
Contact: PHONE **(01934) 712684**

1 **DUNNICKS CHANCE**, 9, b m Greensmith—Field Chance **Mr F. G. Tucker**
2 **DUNNICKS FIELD**, 8, b g Greensmith—Field Chance **Mr F. G. Tucker**
3 **DUNNICKS HEAD**, 8, b m Greensmith—Country Magic **Mr F. G. Tucker**
4 **DUNNICKS OPERA**, 5, b m Opera Ghost—Country Magic **Mr F. G. Tucker**
5 **DUNNICKS TRUST**, 6, b g Greensmith—Country Magic **Mr F. G. Tucker**

MR F. G. TUCKER—continued

  6 **DUNNICKS VIEW**, 15, b g Sula Bula—Country Magic **Mr F. G. Tucker**

Assistant Trainer: Mrs C Tucker

---

551 | MR E. W. TUER, Northallerton
Postal: **Home Farm, Great Smeaton, Northallerton, North Yorkshire, DL6 2EP.**
Contact: **PHONE (01609) 881214 MOBILE (07808) 330306**

  1 **AWWAL MARRA (USA)**, 4, ch f King of Kings (IRE)—Secretariat Lass (USA) **Far Distant Partnership**
  2 **BREEZY WARRIOR (IRE)**, 5, b g Commanche Run—Another Crash **Mr E. Tuer**
  3 **COMMANCHE WIND (IRE)**, 9, b g Commanche Run—Delko **Mr E. Tuer**
  4 **FIRST GREY**, 5, gr m Environment Friend—Myrtilla **Mr Nigel E. M. Jones**
  5 **FISHKI'S LAD**, 9, b g Casteddu—Fishki **Far Distant Partnership**
  6 **JOLEWIS**, 6, ch m Sir Harry Lewis (USA)—Askwood (IRE) **Tagwood Syndicate**
  7 **LADY STRATAGEM**, 5, gr m Mark of Esteem (IRE)—Grey Angel **Mr E. Tuer**
  8 **NORMA SPEAKMAN**, 4, ch f Among Men (USA)—Bride Bank (IRE) **Shore Property**
  9 **RIVIERE**, 9, ch m Meadowbrook—Cimarron **Mr R. G. Fairs**
10 **SIMLET**, 9, b g Forzando—Besito **Mr E. Tuer**
11 **SIR HOMO (IRE)**, 10, b g Homo Sapien—Deise Lady **Mr E. Tuer**
12 **SNAILS CASTLE (IRE)**, 5, b g Danehill (USA)—Bean Island (USA) **Shore Property**
13 **TERIMONS DAUGHTER**, 5, b m Terimon—Fun While It Lasts **Mr E. Tuer**

Other Owners: Mr E. Carr, Mr M. Griese, Mrs M. Griese, M. J. Molloy.

Assistant Trainer: G. F. Tuer

---

552 | MR ANDREW TURNELL, Malton
Postal: **Highfield Stables, Beverley Road, Malton, North Yorkshire, YO17 9PJ.**
Contact: **PHONE (01653) 699555 FAX (01653) 699333 MOBILE (07973) 933450**

  1 **ACADEMY (IRE)**, 9, ch g Archway (IRE)—Dream Academy **Mrs M. R. Taylor**
  2 **ARJAY**, 6, b g Shaamit (IRE)—Jenny's Call **Dr John Hollowood**
  3 **BISHOP'S BRIDGE (IRE)**, 6, b g Norwich—River Swell (IRE) **Mrs M. R. Taylor**
  4 **BUYING A DREAM (IRE)**, 7, ch g Prince of Birds (USA)—
                                          Cartagena Lady (IRE) **Robinson Webster (Holdings) Ltd**
  5 **DOCTOR JOHN**, 7, ch g Handsome Sailor—Bollin Sophie **Dr John Hollowood**
  6 **DOWER HOUSE**, 9, ch g Groom Dancer (USA)—Rose Noble (USA) **Mrs Claire Hollowood**
  7 **DUBONAI (IRE)**, 4, ch c Peintre Celebre (USA)—Web of Intrigue **Paradime Ltd**
  8 **ELLO OLLIE (IRE)**, 9, b g Roselier (FR)—Kayanna **Dr John Hollowood**
  9 **GEM BIEN (USA)**, 6, b g Bien Bien (USA)—Eastern Gem (USA) **Mrs Claire Hollowood**
10 **JELANI (IRE)**, 5, b h Darshaan—No Rehearsal (FR) **Mrs Claire Hollowood**
11 **KEW JUMPER (IRE)**, 5, b g Mister Lord—Pharisee (IRE) **Robinson Webster (Holdings) Ltd**
12 **LITTLE TOBIAS (IRE)**, 5, ch g Millkom—Barbara Frietchie (IRE) **Mrs Claire Hollowood**
13 **RED GOLD**, 10, ch g Sula Bula—Ruby Celebration **Mrs C. C. Williams**
14 **ROCHES FLEURIES (IRE)**, 4, b f Barathea (IRE)—Princess Caraboo (IRE) **Paradime Ltd**
15 **SADLER'S PRIDE (IRE)**, 4, b c Sadler's Wells (USA)—Gentle Thoughts **Paradime Ltd**
16 **SIX PACK (IRE)**, 6, ch g Royal Abjar (USA)—Regal Entrance **Mr J. J. Canny**
17 **THE NAMES BOND**, 6, b g Tragic Role (USA)—Artistic Licence **Mrs Claire Hollowood**

THREE-YEAR-OLDS

18 **CELLINO**, b f Robellino (USA)—Celandine **Mrs Claire Hollowood**
19 **INDIBAR (IRE)**, b c Indian Ridge—Barbara Frietchie (IRE) **Paradime Ltd**
20 **KALISHKA (IRE)**, b c Fasliyev (USA)—Andromaque (USA) **Mrs Claire Hollowood**
21 **WASHBROOK**, b c Royal Applause—Alacrity **Mrs Claire Hollowood**

TWO-YEAR-OLDS

22 **BLUE BAJAN (IRE)**, b c 22/2 Montjeu (IRE)—Gentle Thoughts (Darshaan) **Dr John Hollowood**
23 **WARNING GAMES**, b f 4/3 Mind Games—Celandine (Warning) **Mrs Claire Hollowood**

Other Owners: Mr L. G. Kimber, Mr D. Murray.

553 MR D. C. TURNER, Plymouth
Postal: **Higher Collard Farm, Wotter, Plymouth, Devon, PL7 5HU.**
Contact: **PHONE (01752) 839231**

1 **RICCARTON**, 11, b g Nomination—Legendary Dancer **Mrs M. E. Turner**
2 **SILVER MAN**, 10, gr g Silver Owl—What An Experiance **Mrs M. E. Turner**

Jockey (NH): R Greene. **Amateur:** Mrs A Hand (10-0).

554 MR W. G. M. TURNER, Sherborne
Postal: **Sigwells Farm, Sigwells, Corton Denham, Sherborne, Dorset, DT9 4LN.**
Contact: **PHONE (01963) 220523 MOBILE (07932) 100173**

1 **COPPERFIELDS LASS**, 5, b m Milkom—Salveza (IRE) **Mr B. J. Goldsmith**
2 **DUSTY DAZZLER (IRE)**, 4, ch f Titus Livius (FR)—Satinette **T.O.C.S. Ltd**
3 **EDE'IFF**, 7, b m Tragic Role (USA)—Flying Amy **Hawks And Doves Racing Syndicate**
4 **EDE'S**, 4, ch g Bijou d'Inde—Ballagarrow Girl **Mr Tony Smith**
5 **FITTLEWORTH (IRE)**, 4, gr f Bijou d'Inde—Remany **Mrs Lesley Smith**
6 **MAGICAL DAY**, 5, ch m Halling (USA)—Ahla **M J B Racing**
7 **MIZINKY**, 4, b f El Conquistador—Miss Pimpernel **Mr Bob Chandler**
8 **ORAKE PRINCE**, 5, b g Bluegrass Prince (IRE)—Kiri Te **Mr D. A. Drake**
9 **ROJABAA**, 5, b g Anabaa—Slava (USA) **Rojabaa Partnership**
10 **SEE MORE SNOW**, 7, b g Seymour Hicks (FR)—Snow Child **Mr E. Goody**
11 **SIGWELLS CLUB BOY**, 4, b g Fayruz—Run With Pride **Mr Nigel S. Shaw**
12 **THE LORD**, 4, b g Averti (IRE)—Lady Longmead **Mrs M. S. Teversham**

THREE-YEAR-OLDS
13 **EVER CHEERFUL**, b g Atraf—Big Story **Mr E. Goody**
14 **GOLDEN BANKES (IRE)**, ch f Foxhound—Semence d'Or (FR) **Mr T. Lightbowne**
15 **HOLD THE LINE**, b g Titus Livius (FR)—Multi-Sofft **Mr Dermot Gascoyne and Mr Gary Dawkins**
16 **LOOK NO MORE**, ch g First Trump—Jadebelle **Mr Paul Thorman**
17 **RECKLESS MOMENT**, b f Victory Note (USA)—Blue Indigo (FR) **Mr T. E. Pocock**

TWO-YEAR-OLDS
18 **DUSTINI (IRE)**, ch c 12/3 Rossini (USA)—Truly Modest (IRE) (Imp Society (USA)) (21000) **T.O.C.S. Ltd**
19 **EDITH BANKES (IRE)**, ch f 24/4 Woodborough (USA)—Mayday Kitty (Interrex (CAN)) **Mr T. Lightbrown**
20 Ch g 13/5 Bluegrass Prince—Jade's Girl (Emarati (USA)) **Mrs Tracy Turner**
21 **KENTUCKY BANKES (IRE)**, b g 25/4 Bluegrass Prince—Countess Bankes (Son Pardo) **Mr T. Lightbrown**
22 **KISSING A FOOL**, b c 24/4 Tipsy Creek—Amathus Glory (Mummy's Pet) **Mascalis Stud**
23 B c 10/4 Prince Sabo—Lady Mabel (Inchinor) (500) **Mrs Tracy Turner**
24 **NUTTY TIMES**, ch f 24/4 Timeless Times (USA)—Nuthatch (IRE) (Thatching) (800) **Mr R. A. Grant**
25 **PRINCELY VALE (IRE)**, b c 29/4 Princely Heir (IRE)—Lomalou (IRE) (Lightning Dealer) (3000) **Vale Racing**
26 Ch f 15/1 Tagula (IRE)—Rosy Scintilla (IRE) (Thatching) (1904) **Mr Tony Smith**
27 Ch g 18/4 Forzando—St Kitts (Tragic Role (USA)) **Mrs Tracy Turner**
28 Ch c 16/4 Indian Danehill (IRE)—Teer On Eer (Persian Heights) (500) **T.O.C.S. Ltd**
29 Ch f 21/1 Fraam—Tricata (Electric) **Miss C. J. Overton**
30 **TURTLE MAGIC (IRE)**, b f 17/4 Turtle Island (IRE)—Theda (Mummy's Pet) (2473) **Mrs Tracy Turner**
31 **WESTBROOK BLUE**, b c 26/4 Kingsinger (IRE)—Gold And Blue (IRE) (Bluebird (USA)) (4000) **Mr Bob Chandler**
32 Ch f 3/3 Bluebird (USA)—Women In Love (IRE) (Danehill (USA)) (10000) **Mr Tony Smith**

Other Owners: Mr Gary Dawkins, Mr A. G. Drewett, Mrs S. J. Drewett, Mr Dermot Gascoyne, Mr J. P. Rawlins, Mr D. J. Wareham, Mr D. J. B. Woodd.

Apprentices: Colin Haddon, Claire Stretton. **Conditional:** P J Brennan (w.a.), Robert Lucy-Butler, Claire Stretton.

555 MRS K. J. TUTTY, Northallerton
Postal: **Trenholme House Farm, Osmotherley, Northallerton, North Yorkshire, DL6 3QA.**
Contact: **PHONE (01609) 883624 MOBILE (07967) 837406**

1 **DARAK (IRE)**, 8, b g Doyoun—Dararita (IRE) **Mr N. D. Tutty**
2 **ROSEY BOY (IRE)**, 11, gr g Roselier (FR)—Rossian **Mr A. Brook**
3 **SILOGUE (IRE)**, 7, b br g Distinctly North (USA)—African Bloom **Mr N. D. Tutty**
4 **WELSH MARCH (IRE)**, 12, b g Over The River (FR)—Welsh Tan **Mr N. D. Tutty**

Amateur: Mr N D Tutty (10-10).

MR N. A. TWISTON-DAVIES, Cheltenham

556
Postal: **Grange Hill Farm, Naunton, Cheltenham, Gloucestershire, GL54 3AY.**
Contact: **PHONE (01451) 850278 FAX (01451) 850101 MOBILE (07836) 664440**
E-MAIL nigel@nigeltwistondavies.co.uk WEBSITE www.nigeltwistondavies.co.uk561 2

1 **ARDASHIR (FR)**, 5, b g Simon du Desert (FR)—Antea (FR) **Miss Caroline Wilson**
2 **BABY RUN (FR)**, 4, b g Baby Turk—Run For Laborie (FR) **Mr & Mrs Peter Orton**
3 **BARNEYS LYRIC**, 4, ch g Hector Protector (USA)—Anchorage (IRE) **Mr & Mrs Peter Orton**
4 **BARON WINDRUSH**, 6, b g Alderbrook—Dame Scarlet **The Double Octagon Partnership**
5 **BINDAREE (IRE)**, 10, ch g Roselier (FR)—Flowing Tide **Mr H. R. Mould**
6 **BOBBY DAZZLER**, 5, b g Bob's Return (IRE)—Preachers Popsy **Our Friends in the North**
7 **CHAMPAGNE HARRY**, 6, b g Sir Harry Lewis (USA)—Sparkling Cinders **Mr Gavin MacEchern**
8 **CHAMPAGNE LIL**, 7, gr m Terimon—Sparkling Cinders **Mrs Janey Mordaunt**
9 **CORROBOREE (IRE)**, 7, b g Corrouge (USA)—Laura's Toi **The Corroborators**
10 **DARNAYSON (IRE)**, 4, b g Darnay—Nakuru (IRE) **The Son Partnership**
11 **DD'S GLENALLA (IRE)**, 7, b m Be My Native (USA)—Willowho Pride **Mrs Caroline Beresford-Wylie**
12 **DICKENSBURY LAD (FR)**, 4, b g Luchiroverte (IRE)—Voltige de Cotte (FR) **Mr Thomas D. Goodman**
13 **FLORA MUCK**, 8, b m Alflora (IRE)—Muckertoo **The "Yes" - "No" - "Wait"....Sorries**
14 **FULL MINTY**, 9, br g Phardante (FR)—Jouvencelle **Mr H. R. Mould**
15 **FUNDAMENTALIST (IRE)**, 6, b g Supreme Leader—Run For Shelter **Gripen**
16 **GAZUMP (FR)**, 6, b g Iris Noir (FR)—Viva Sacree (FR) **Mr H. R. Mould**
17 **GULABILL**, 5, b g Safawan—Gulsha **Mrs J. K. Powell**
18 **HANOVER SQUARE**, 8, b g Le Moss—Hilly-Down Lass **The Oriental Partnership III**
19 **HENRY THE GREAT (IRE)**, 5, b g Alderbrook—Country Style **The Lodgers**
20 **IDBURY (IRE)**, 6, b g Zaffaran (USA)—Delcarrow **Mr H. R. Mould**
21 **KING'S REIGN (IRE)**, 8, b g King's Ride—Lena's Reign **Mrs Lorna Berryman**
22 **LEWIS ISLAND**, 5, b g Turtle Island (IRE)—Phyllode **Mr & Mrs Peter Orton**
23 **LORD GALE (IRE)**, 6, b g Mister Lord (USA)—Dante Gale (IRE) **Mr C. B. Sanderson**
24 **LORD MAIZEY (IRE)**, 7, b g Mister Lord (USA)—My Maizey **Mr & Mrs Peter Orton**
25 **LUXEMBOURG**, 5, b g Bigstone (IRE)—Princess Borghese (USA) **Mrs Lorna Berryman**
26 **MADAM'S MAN**, 8, b g Sir Harry Lewis (USA)—Madam-M **Mr H. R. Mould**
27 **MASTER PAPA (IRE)**, 5, br g Key of Luck (USA)—Beguine (USA) **The Alchemists 2**
28 **MISTANOORA**, 5, b g Topanoora—Mistinguett (IRE) **Mr A. M. J. Duggan**
29 **MONTEZUMA**, 11, br m Beveled (USA)—Miss Kuwait **Mr A. W. M. Priestley**
30 **NAUNTON BROOK**, 5, b g Alderbrook—Give Me An Answer **Mr David Langdon**
31 **NEV BROWN (IRE)**, 8, b g Executive Perk—Brandy Hill Girl **Geoffrey & Donna Keeys**
32 **OH SO WISLEY**, 9, b g Teenoso (USA)—Easy Horse (FR) **Mr Gavin MacEchern**
33 **OLLIE MAGERN**, 6, b g Alderbrook—Outfield **Mr Roger Nicholls**
34 **ONLY YOU**, 8, b g Gildoran—Outfield **Mr Roger Nicholls**
35 **PETITE MARGOT**, 5, b m Alderbrook—Outfield **Mr Roger Nicholls**
36 **POLAR SUMMIT (IRE)**, 8, br g Top of The World—Blackrath Beauty **The Summit Partnership**
37 **PRANCING BLADE (IRE)**, 8, b g Broadsword (USA)—Sparkling Cinders **Mr Gavin MacEchern**
38 **PRIESTS BRIDGE (IRE)**, 8, ch m Mr Ditton—Paddys Gale **Geoffrey & Donna Keeys**
39 **PRINCESS TESSA**, 8, b m King's Ride—Kathy Cook **Mr M. P. Wareing**
40 **PROMINENT PROFILE (IRE)**, 11, ch g Mazaad—Nakuru **The Son Partnership**
41 **RANDOLPH O'BRIEN (IRE)**, 4, b g Zaffaran (USA)—Gala's Pride **Geoffrey & Donna Keeys**
42 **REDEMPTION**, 9, b g Sanglamore (USA)—Ypha (USA) **Mr John Duggan & Mr Michael Purtill**
43 **ROCKCLIFFE GOSSIP**, 12, ch g Phardante (FR)—Clonmello **Mrs Caroline Beresford-Wylie**
44 **RUSSIAN GIGOLO (IRE)**, 7, b g Toulon—Nanogan **Mrs Caroline Beresford-Wylie**
45 **SCOTCH CORNER (IRE)**, 6, b g Jurado (USA)—Quennie Mo Ghra (IRE) **Mr H. R. Mould**
46 **SHARDAM (IRE)**, 7, b g Shardari—Knockea Hill **Mr Howard Parker**
47 **SHOLAY (IRE)**, 5, b g Bluebird (USA)—Splicing **Mrs S. Trikha**
48 **SIR ROBBO (IRE)**, 10, b g Glacial Storm (USA)—Polly's Slipper **Melton Pets Direct Ltd**
49 **STAGE FRIENDLY (IRE)**, 5, ch g Old Vic—Just Affable (IRE) **Mr I. Guest**
50 **TATES AVENUE (IRE)**, 6, b g Zaffaran (USA)—Tate Divinity (USA) **Mr S. P. Tindall**
51 **THE COCKNEY KID (IRE)**, 9, ch g Glacial Storm (USA)—Rainbow Days **Mr N. A. Twiston-Davies**
52 **THE TALL GUY (IRE)**, 8, b br g Zaffaran (USA)—Mullangale **Mrs Jill Scott & Mrs Sarah MacEchern**
53 **TIGER TIPS LAD (IRE)**, 5, b g Zaffaran (USA)—Halens Match (IRE) **Mr Gary Hopkins**
54 **TIPP TOP LORD (IRE)**, 7, gr g Mister Lord (USA)—Dark Fluff **Mrs R. Vaughan**
55 **TRAMANTANA**, 5, b g Muhtarram (USA)—Hatta Breeze **Mr H. R. Mould**
56 **TWO HUGE**, 6, gr g Norton Challenger—Rainy Miss (IRE) **The Really Huge Partnership**
57 **UNCLE MAX (IRE)**, 4, b g Victory Note (USA)—Sunset Park (IRE) **The "Yes" - "No" - "Wait"....Sorries**
58 **VICAR'S LAD**, 8, b g Terimon—Proverbial Rose **Mrs P. Duncan**
59 **WATER SPORTS (IRE)**, 6, b m Marju (IRE)—Water Splash (USA) **Mr John Duggan**
60 **WHAT DO'IN (IRE)**, 6, b g Good Thyne (USA)—Della Wee **Mr C. Cornes**
61 **WHEREAREYOUNOW (IRE)**, 7, ch g Mister Lord (USA)—Angie's Delight **Mr H. R. Mould**
62 **WITH A DASH**, 6, ch g Afzal—Oh So Ripe **Miss S. Wood**

MR N. A. TWISTON-DAVIES—continued

63 **YOUNG BOUNDER (FR)**, 5, b br g Septieme Ciel (USA)—
Far But Near (USA) **Mrs M. Slade and Mr G. MacEchern**
64 **YOU OWE ME (IRE)**, 7, b g Jurado (USA)—Bodyline **Mr C. Cornes**

Other Owners: Mrs John Arbuthnot, Mrs F. A. Armitage, Mr M. G. Bailey, Mr C. J. Barker, Mrs E. M. Bathurst, Mrs John Bays, G. F. Chesneaux, Mr Chris Coley, Mrs A. Dimmer, Mr I. M. Dimmer, Mr P. H. Earl, Mr John French, Mr Ricky George, Mrs Felicity Griffin, M. P. Grimes, Mr W. Hinshelwood, Mr David Hussey, Mrs Donna Keeys, Mr Geoffrey Keeys, Mrs S. A. Macecheran, Mr John Motson, Mr R. Noy, Mr Peter Orton, Mrs Susan Orton, Mr T. H. Ounsley, Mr Alan Parker, Mr Nigel Payne, Mrs C. M. Pennell, Mr R. G. Perry, Mr K. J. Phillips, Mr O. D. Plunkett, Mr Timothy J. Pope, Mrs Mark Powell, Mr Michael Purtill, Mrs G. C. Robinson, Mr Ian A. Robinson, Mr G. W. Sanders, Mrs C. M. Scott, Mr H. B. Shouler, Mr R. I. Sims, Miss Nicole Skett, Mrs M. E. Slade.

Assistant Trainer: Gemma Emtage

Jockeys (NH): J Goldstein (9-7), C Llewellyn (10-0). **Conditional:** R Biddlecombe (10-4), A Evans (9-10). **Amateur:** Mr Mark Goldstein (9-7).

---

557 **MR J. R. UPSON, Towcester**
Postal: **Glebe Stables, Blakesley Heath, Maidford, Towcester, Northamptonshire, NN12 8HN.**
Contact: **PHONE (01327) 860043 FAX (01327) 860238**

1 **AGINCOURT (IRE)**, 8, b g Alphabatim (USA)—Miss Brantridge **Middleham Park Racing XXI**
2 **ALEXANDER PARK (IRE)**, 7, b g Yashgan—Lady Laramie (IRE) **Middleham Park Racing IV**
3 **ANOTHER GRADUATE (IRE)**, 6, ch g Naheez (USA)—Another Daisy **The Nap Hand Partnership**
4 **BACKSCRATCHER**, 10, b g Backchat (USA)—Tiernee Quintana **The Fourways Partnership**
5 **BEAU COUP**, 7, b g Toulon—Energance (IRE) **Mrs Ann Key**
6 **BLUNHAM HILL (IRE)**, 6, ch g Over The River (FR)—Bronach **The Reserved Judgment Partnership**
7 **BROOKS**, 8, b g Minster Son—Melody Moon **Mr T. L. Brooks**
8 **CLEYMOR HOUSE (IRE)**, 6, ch g Duky—Deise Lady **The Nap Hand Partnership**
9 **ECHO'S OF DAWN (IRE)**, 12, ch g Duky—Nicenames (IRE) **Middleham Park Racing XVII**
10 **GOLDEN AMBER (IRE)**, 5, ch g Glacial Storm (USA)—Rigton Angle **The Peter Partnership**
11 **GRITTI PALACE (IRE)**, 4, b g Duky—Glittering Grit (IRE) **Sir Nicholas Wilson**
12 **LORD OF THE PARK (IRE)**, 7, b g Lord Americo—Wind Chimes **Middleham Park Racing V**
13 **OVER ZEALOUS (IRE)**, 12, b g Over The River (FR)—Chatty Di **Middleham Park Racing X**
14 **REACH THE CLOUDS (IRE)**, 12, b g Lord Americo—Dusky Stream **The Three Horseshoes Sporting Club**
15 **REFLEX COURIER (IRE)**, 12, b g Over The River (FR)—Thornpark Lady **Martin Tucker & Jim Bath**
16 **REGAL RIVER (IRE)**, 7, b g Over The River (FR)—My Friend Fashion **Middleham Park Racing XIX**
17 **STROLLING VAGABOND (IRE)**, 5, ch g Glacial Storm (USA)—Found Again (IRE)
18 **THE RIVER JOKER (IRE)**, 8, ch g Over The River (FR)—Augustaeliza (IRE) **Mr Graeme P. McPherson**
19 **WASTED COSTS (IRE)**, 5, ch g Over The River (FR)—Dream Daisy **The Reserved Judgment Partnership**

Other Owners: Mr Jim Bath, Mr M. H. Beesley, Mr Mike Chapman, Mr G. D. Dalrymple, Mr D. Deveney, Mr Frank Fountain, Mr G. Fowler, Mr S. P. French, Ms S. M. Gilmore, Mr J. D. Horgan, Mr Ian N. Mallett, Mr S. Massey, Mr T. S. Palin, Mrs D. Sanders, Mr Martin Tucker, Mr C. Wallis, Mr Mick White.

Conditional: M Mello (10-0). **Amateurs:** Mr Andrew Cleary (9-7), Mr Liam Payter (9-7).

---

558 **MR M. D. I. USHER, Lambourn**
Postal: **Saxon House Stables, Upper Lambourn, Hungerford, Berkshire, RG17 8QH.**
Contact: **PHONE (01488) 72598 FAX (01488) 72646 MOBILE (07831) 873531**
E-MAIL mark@markusherracing.freeserve.co.uk

1 **AUBURN SPIRIT**, 9, ch g Teamster—Spirit of Youth **Mr G. A. Summers**
2 **JAZZAAM**, 5, ch m Fraam—Aldwick Colonnade **Midweek Racing**
3 4, B g Young Ern—Keepsake (IRE) **Mr Brian Duke**
4 **MOSTAKBEL (USA)**, 5, b br g Saint Ballado (CAN)—Shamlegh (USA) **Midweek Racing**
5 **MRS PICKLES**, 9, gr m Northern Park (USA)—Able Mabel **Midweek Racing**
6 **SCOTTISH RIVER (USA)**, 5, b g Thunder Gulch (USA)—Overbrook **Mr M. D. I. Usher**

THREE-YEAR-OLDS

7 **FORA SMILE**, ch c Forzando—Don't Smile **The Ridgeway Partnership**
8 **IMPERIAL WIZARD**, ch g Magic Ring (IRE)—Paula's Joy **The Ridgeway Partnership**
9 **JINKSONTHEHOUSE**, b f Whittingham (IRE)—Aldwick Colonnade **Midweek Racing**

MR M. D. I. USHER—continued

10 **PLEASURE SEEKER**, b f First Trump—Purse **Mr Bryan Fry**
11 **SWEETEST REVENGE (IRE)**, ch f Daggers Drawn (USA)—Joza **Bryan Fry & The Ridgeway Partnership**

TWO-YEAR-OLDS

12 Ch f 14/2 Bold Edge—Apple Sauce (Prince Sabo) (6500) **The Good Racing Partnership**
13 Ch f 3/3 Whittingham (IRE)—Foxley (Foxhound) **Mr Ian Sheward**
14 Gr c 14/4 Environment Friend—Odyn Dancer (Minshaanshu Amad (USA)) **Mr M. D. I. Usher**
15 B f 22/2 Kingsinger (IRE)—Pure Gold (Dilum (USA)) **The Ridgeway Partnership**
16 B f 15/2 Whittingham (IRE)—Zawdo's Charm (Forzando) **Mr M. D. I. Usher**

Other Owners: Mr M. S. Heath, Miss C. Howard, Mr John Stansfield, Mr Carl West-Meads.

Jockey (NH): W Hutchinson (9-7). **Amateur:** Mr L Newnes (9-0).

---

559 **MR J. WADE, Aycliffe**
Postal: Howe Hills, Mordon, Sedgefield, Cleveland, TS21 2HF.
Contact: PHONE (01325) 313129/315521 FAX (01325) 320660 MOBILE (07831) 686968

1 **COUNT THE COST (IRE)**, 5, ch g Old Vic—Roseaustin (IRE) **Mr John Wade**
2 **DEVIL'S PERK (IRE)**, 6, b g Executive Perk—She Devil **Mr John Wade**
3 **DEVIL'S RUN (IRE)**, 8, b g Commanche Run—She Devil **Mr John Wade**
4 **EISENHOWER (IRE)**, 5, b g Erins Isle—Lyphard Abu (IRE) **Mr John Wade**
5 **EMPEROR'S MONARCH**, 5, ch g Emperor Fountain—Shalta (FR) **Mr John Wade**
6 **FLIGHT WEST (IRE)**, 5, gr g Norwich—Bee In The Rose (IRE) **Mr John Wade**
7 **GUNNER ROYAL**, 6, b g Gunner B—Loadplan Lass **Mr John Wade**
8 **IRON TROOPER (IRE)**, 6, ch g Glacial Storm (USA)—Iron Star **Mr John Wade**
9 **KING OF THE ARCTIC (IRE)**, 6, b g Arctic Lord—Ye Little Daisy **Mr John Wade**
10 **LANHEL (FR)**, 5, ch g Boston Two Step (USA)—Umbrella (FR) **Mr John Wade**
11 **MIDNIGHT MAYHEM (IRE)**, 5, ch m Presenting—Sandy Run (IRE) **Mr John Wade**
12 **ROLLING RIVER (IRE)**, 7, b g Over The River (FR)—Paddy's Dancer **Mr John Wade**
13 **RYMINSTER**, 5, ch g Minster Son—Shultan (IRE) **Mr John Wade**
14 **SHADY BARON (IRE)**, 5, b g Lord Americo—Glint of Baron **Mr John Wade**
15 **STORMY LORD (IRE)**, 8, br g Lord Americo—Decent Shower **Mr John Wade**
16 **TALEBAN**, 9, b g Alleged (USA)—Triode (USA) **Mr John Wade**
17 **TRADING TROUBLE**, 7, b g Petoski—Marielou (FR) **Mr John Wade**

Assistant Trainer: Maria Myco

---

560 **MRS L. A. M. WADHAM, Newmarket**
Postal: The Trainer's House, Moulton Paddocks, Newmarket, Suffolk, CB8 7PJ.
Contact: PHONE (01638) 662411 FAX (01638) 668821 MOBILE (07980) 545776

1 **APRIL MISS (FR)**, 4, bl f Averti (IRE)—Lady of Jakarta (USA) **Dingley Dell Racing Ltd**
2 **BARNEYS REFLECTION**, 4, b g Petoski—Annaberg (IRE) **Mrs C. Bailey**
3 **BOUND**, 6, b g Kris—Tender Moment (IRE) **Dingley Dell Racing Ltd**
4 **BRIGADIER DU BOIS (FR)**, 5, gr g Apeldoorn (FR)—Artic Night (FR) **Hebomapa**
5 **BURGUNDY LACE (USA)**, 5, b m Lord Avie (USA)—Oro Bianco (USA) **The Salmon Racing Partnership**
6 **BURNING SHORE (IRE)**, 4, b f Desert King (IRE)—Gerante (USA) **The Not Over Big Partnership**
7 **EXECUTIVE DECISION (IRE)**, 10, ch g Classic Music (USA)—Bengala (FR) **Ms K. J. Austin**
8 **FANTASTIC CHAMPION (IRE)**, 5, b g Entrepreneur—Reine Mathilde (USA) **Champion And The Fantastics**
9 **FENIX (GER)**, 5, b g Lavirco (GER)—Frille (FR) **P. A. Philipps T. S. Redman J. S. Redman**
10 **HIGHPOINT (GER)**, 6, b m Acatenango (GER)—Holly (GER) **Mrs C. Bailey**
11 **HOMELEIGH MOONCOIN**, 9, ch g Jamesmead—Super Sol **Miss S. Wilson**
12 **KHAYSAR (IRE)**, 6, br g Pennekamp (USA)—Khaytada (IRE) **Dingley Dell Racing Ltd**
13 **LIGHTNING STRIKES (IRE)**, 10, b g Zaffaran (USA)—Nimbi **Mr R. B. Holt**
14 **MR GISBY (USA)**, 6, b g Chief's Crown (USA)—Double Lock **Nightmare Partnership**
15 **NAKED OAT**, 9, b g Imp Society (USA)—Bajina **The Dyball Partnership**
16 **PRINCESS PEA**, 4, b f Shareef Dancer (USA)—Super Sol **Mr J. Short**
17 **RESPLENDENT STAR (IRE)**, 7, b g Northern Baby (CAN)—Whitethroat **Waterhall Racing**
18 **TEALBY**, 7, b m Efisio—Al Raja **The Dyball Partnership**

MRS L. A. M. WADHAM—continued

19 **THE DARK LORD (IRE)**, 7, b g Lord Americo—Khalkeys Shoon **Mr A. E. Pakenham**
20 **VANDAL**, 4, b c Entrepreneur—Vax Star **Mr R. B. Holt**

Other Owners: Mr W. Bottriell, Mr Mark Coley, Mrs C. A. Dyball, Mr D. J. S. Dyball, Mr S. B. Glazer, Mr Alastair Hodge, Mr N. Lewis, Mr Richard Venn, Mr J. J. W. Wadham.

Jockey (NH): L Aspell (10-0).

561 MR N. WAGGOTT, Spennymoor
Postal: Ingledene, Vyners Close, Merrington Lane, Spennymoor, Co. Durham, DL16 7HB.
Contact: **PHONE (01388) 819012**

1 **FRED'S IN THE KNOW**, 9, ch g Interrex (CAN)—Lady Vynz **Mr N. Waggott**
2 **ICEFIRE DANCER**, 11, b m Arctic Lord—Super Gambler **Mrs J. Waggott**
3 **LUKE AFTER ME (IRE)**, 4, b g Victory Note (USA)—Summit Talk **Mrs J. Waggott**
4 **SCIPPIT**, 5, ch g Unfuwain (USA)—Scierpan (USA) **Mrs J. Waggott**
5 **TWILIGHT WORLD**, 7, b g Night Shift (USA)—Masskana (IRE) **Mrs J. Waggott**

Jockey (NH): R Guest.

562 MR J. S. WAINWRIGHT, Malton
Postal: Hanging Hill Farm, Kennythorpe, Malton, North Yorkshire, YO17 9LA.
Contact: **PHONE (01653) 658537 FAX (01653) 658658 MOBILE (07798) 778070**

1 **ALPINE HIDEAWAY (IRE)**, 11, b g Tirol—Arbour (USA) **Mr Peter Easterby**
2 **BEYOND THE CLOUDS (IRE)**, 8, b g Midhish—Tongabezi (IRE) **Mr S. Pederson**
3 **BOBANVI**, 6, b m Timeless Times (USA)—Bobanlyn (IRE) **Mr S. Pedersen**
4 **CATCH THE CAT (IRE)**, 5, b g Catrail (USA)—Tongabezi (IRE) **Mr T. W. Heseltine**
5 **CUT RIDGE (IRE)**, 5, b m Indian Ridge—Cutting Ground (IRE) **Mrs C. Harrington**
6 **DELAWARE TRAIL**, 5, b g Catrail (USA)—Dilwara (IRE) **Mr B. J. Ross**
7 **DORMY TWO (IRE)**, 4, b f Eagle Eyed (USA)—Tartan Lady (IRE) **Mr A. D. Copley & Mr J. S. Wainwright**
8 **EASTERNKING**, 5, ch m Sabrehill (USA)—Kshessinskaya **Mr Peter Easterby**
9 **EDDIES JEWEL**, 4, b g Presidium—Superstream **Mr T. W. Heseltine**
10 **FAIRGAME MAN**, 6, ch g Clantime—Thalya **Mr P. Cooper**
11 **JOYCE'S CHOICE**, 5, b m Mind Games—Madrina **Mr J. S. Wainwright**
12 **LANDOFHEARTSDESIRE (IRE)**, 5, b m Up And At 'em—Ahonita **Mr S. Pedersen**
13 **LE MERIDIEN (IRE)**, 6, ch m Magical Wonder (USA)—Dutch Queen **Mr J. S. Wainwright**
14 **LITTLE TASK**, 6, b g Environment Friend—Lucky Thing **Mr keith Jackson**
15 **PANOORAS LORD (IRE)**, 10, b g Topanoora—Ladyship **Ms Julie French**
16 **RUM DESTINY (IRE)**, 5, b g Mujadil (USA)—Ruby River **Mr J. S. Wainwright**
17 **STAVROS (IRE)**, 4, b g General Monash (USA)—Rivers Rainbow **Mr S. Pederson**
18 **TOMMY SMITH**, 6, ch g Timeless Times (USA)—Superstream **Mr T. W. Hestletine**
19 **TRAVELLING TIMES**, 5, ch g Timeless Times (USA)—Bollin Sophie **Mr S. Pedersen**
20 **ULTRA MARINE (IRE)**, 4, b c Blues Traveller (IRE)—The Aspecto Girl (IRE) **Walker & Briggsy Rules**
21 **VITA SPERICOLATA (IRE)**, 7, b m Prince Sabo—Ahonita **First Class Entertainment**

THREE-YEAR-OLDS

22 **BARON RHODES**, b f Presidium—Superstream **Mr Ian Barron, Mr Paul Rhodes**
23 **CLOUDS OF GOLD (IRE)**, b f Goldmark (USA)—Tongabezi (IRE) **Mr S. Pederson**
24 **LAND SUN'S LEGACY (IRE)**, b g Red Sunset—Almost A Lady (IRE) **Ms Julie French**
25 **LORD WISHINGWELL (IRE)**, b g Lake Coniston (IRE)—Spirito Libro **Mrs Linda O'Sullivan**
26 **MIS CHICAF (IRE)**, b f Prince Sabo—Champagne Season (USA) **Mr A. D. Copley**

TWO-YEAR-OLDS

27 B g 22/4 Mujadil (USA)—Assertive Lass (USA) (Assert) (9894)
28 B g 6/3 Orpen (USA)—Berhala (IRE) (Doyoun) (8000)
29 B f 14/3 Namaqualand (USA)—Denby Wood (Lord Bud) **A. W. Longbottom**
30 Ch f 12/4 Bahamian Bounty—Divine Appeal (El Gran Senor (USA)) (3500)
31 **LA BELLA ROSSA (IRE)**, b f 11/5 Revoque (IRE)—
　　　Tempesta Rossa (IRE) (Persian Heights) (3500) **Hern Racing Club**
32 B f 11/3 King's Theatre (IRE)—Najeyba (Indian Ridge) (3710)
33 B f 9/2 Abou Zouz—Ninfa of Cisterna (Polish Patriot (USA)) (1855)
34 B f 11/5 Factual (USA)—Superstream (Superpower) **Mr Ian Barron, Mr P. Rhodes**

MR J. S. WAINWRIGHT—continued

35 **TIME TO SUCCEED**, b g 5/4 Pennekamp (USA)—Ivory League (Last Tycoon) (10000) **B Selective Partnership**
36 B f 7/3 Rossini (USA)—Two Magpies (Doulab (USA)) (4328)

Other Owners: Mr N. Briggs, Mr D. R. A. King, Mr S. R. Rule.

Jockey (Flat): R Winston (8-3). **Conditional:** L Vickers (9-9).

563 | MR R. B. WALEY-COHEN, Banbury
Postal: Upton Viva, Banbury, Oxon, OX15 6HT.
Contact: PHONE (0044) 020 7244 6022 MOBILE (0044) 07831 888778 E-MAIL rwc@alliance.co.uk

1 **AS DE LA GARENNE (FR)**, 5, b g Sleeping Car (FR)—Maria Theresa (FR) **Mr Robert Waley-Cohen**
2 **MEL IN BLUE (FR)**, 6, b g Pistolet Bleu (IRE)—Calligraphie (FR) **Mr Robert Waley-Cohen**
3 **SOMETHING SMALL**, 4, br g Supreme Leader—Rachel C (IRE) **Mr Robert Waley-Cohen**
4 **STORMING BACK**, 5, b g Bob Back (USA)—Prussian Storm (IRE) **Mr Robert Waley-Cohen**

Assistant Trainer: Cheryl Weller

Amateur: Mr Sam Waley-Cohen (10-7).

564 | MR T. D. WALFORD, Sheriff Hutton
Postal: Cornborough Manor, Sheriff Hutton, York, YO60 6QN.
Contact: PHONE (01347) 878382 FAX (01347) 878547 MOBILE (07904) 237676
E-MAIL g_walford@hotmail.com

1 5, Ch m Minster Son—Buckby Folly **Mrs E. C. York**
2 4, Ch g Minster Son—Joe's Fancy **Mrs R. W. Bromfield**
3 **MASTER JACKSON**, 5, b g Jendali (USA)—Fardella (ITY) **Mr P. Spencer**
4 **PASS ME BY**, 5, b g Balnibarbi—Errol Emerald **Mrs M. Cooper**
5 **PETREA**, 9, b br m St Ninian—Polypodium **Mrs E. C. York**
6 **RO GEMA RI**, 6, b g Perpendicular—Pretty Soon **Mr G. W. Singleton**
7 **SISTER ANNA**, 6, br m Gildoran—Take The Veil **Mr Anthony Preston**
8 **WESTON ROCK**, 5, b g Double Eclipse (IRE)—Mossberry Fair **Mrs H. Spath**

Other Owners: Mr Jim Burns, Mr D. Coates, Mr G. E. Dempsey, Mr David Dickson, Mrs G. B. Walford.

Assistant Trainer: Mrs G B Walford

Conditional: R Walford (9-11). **Amateur:** Mr M Walford (10-4).

565 | MR C. F. WALL, Newmarket
Postal: Induna Stables, Fordham Road, Newmarket, Suffolk, CB8 7AQ.
Contact: HOME (01638) 668896 OFFICE (01638) 661999 FAX (01638) 667279
MOBILE (07764) 940255 E-MAIL christian.wall@btopenworld.com

1 **ACE OF HEARTS**, 5, b g Magic Ring (IRE)—Lonely Heart **Lady Stuttaford & Mr W. G. Bovill**
2 **ASHDOWN EXPRESS (IRE)**, 5, ch g Ashkalani (IRE)—Indian Express **Mr W. J. P. Jackson**
3 **COUNSEL'S OPINION (IRE)**, 7, ch g Rudimentary (USA)—Fairy Fortune **Mrs J. Roberts**
4 **CRAIL**, 4, b g Vettori (IRE)—Tendency **The Crail Partnership**
5 **CZARINA WALTZ**, 5, b m Emperor Jones (USA)—Ballerina Bay **Acorn Racing**
6 **DIDNT TELL MY WIFE**, 5, ch g Aragon—Bee Dee Dancer **Mr G. D. Newton**
7 **FANNY'S FANCY**, 4, b f Groom Dancer (USA)—Fanny's Choice (IRE) **Mr N. Ahamad**
8 **GOLANO**, 4, gr g Linamix (FR)—Dimakya (USA) **Mr Dennis Yardy**
9 **JOROBADEN (FR)**, 4, gr g Poliglote—Mercalle (FR) **The Storm Again Syndicate**
10 **LANDINIUM (ITY)**, 4, b m Lando (GER)—Hollywood Girl **Mr Ettore Landi**
11 **LITTLE VENICE (IRE)**, 4, b f Fumo di Londra (IRE)—Petrine (IRE) **Hintlesham SPD Partners**
12 **PERFECT PUNCH**, 5, b g Reprimand—Aliuska (IRE) **Induna Racing Partners Two**
13 **SHAMARA (IRE)**, 4, b f Spectrum (IRE)—Hamara (FR) **Lady Juliet Tadgell**
14 **SUMMER WINE**, 5, b m Desert King (IRE)—Generous Lady **Mr S. Fustok**

MR C. F. WALL—continued
THREE-YEAR-OLDS

15 **CARLA MOON**, b f Desert Prince (IRE)—Khambani (IRE) **Mr S. Fustok**
16 **CIMYLA (IRE)**, b c Lomitas—Coyaima (GER) **Mr Peter Botham**
17 **GABANA (IRE)**, br f Polish Precedent (USA)—Out West (USA) **Mr S. Fustok**
18 **GENERAL FLUMPA**, b g Vettori (IRE)—Macca Luna (IRE) **Mrs Lucie N. Smith**
19 **INDIAN LILY**, ch f Compton Place—Princess Lily **Stourbank Racing**
20 **KEYAKI (IRE)**, b f Shinko Forest (IRE)—Woodie Dancer (USA) **Hintlesham SPD Partners**
21 **PANSHIR (FR)**, ch g Unfuwain (USA)—Jalcamin (IRE) **Mr Ettore Landi**
22 **PARADISE ISLE**, b f Bahamian Bounty—Merry Rous **The Equema Partnership**
23 **SAMARIA (GER)**, b br f Acatenango (GER)—Suanita (GER) **Dr St John Collier & Mrs Sherry Collier**
24 **SCHOLARSHIP (IRE)**, b g College Chapel—Royal Bracelet (IRE) **Hintlesham Thoroughbreds**
25 **SEAGOLD**, b f Shahrastani—Raeleen **Mr D. A. N. Ross**
26 **WHISTFUL (IRE)**, b f First Trump—Atmospheric Blues (IRE) **Hintlesham Thoroughbreds**
27 **WINSLOW BOY (USA)**, b br g Expelled (USA)—Acusteal (USA) **Mrs Jane Dobie**
28 **ZANGEAL**, ch c Selkirk (USA)—Generous Lady **Mr S. Fustok**

TWO-YEAR-OLDS

29 **ALEYAH**, ch f 23/3 Bachir (IRE)—Silver Peak (FR) (Sillery (USA)) (3500) **The Web Partnership**
30 **ASHDOWN PRINCESS (IRE)**, b f 19/3 King's Theatre (IRE)—
   Indian Express (Indian Ridge) (43289) **Mr W. J. P. Jackson**
31 **CARVOEIRO**, ch f 4/4 Compton Place—Shoshone (Be My Chief (USA)) (35000) **Thoroughbred Farms Ltd**
32 **CUYAMACA (IRE)**, b f 4/4 Desert King (IRE)—
   Surprise Visitor (IRE) (Be My Guest (USA)) **Mr M. Sinclair/Mrs C. J. Walker**
33 **DEEDAY BAY (IRE)**, b f 21/1 Brave Act—Skerries Bell (Taufan (USA)) (22000) **Mr Peter Botham**
34 **DESERT GOOGLE**, b f 7/3 Green Desert (USA)—Khambani (IRE) (Royal Academy (USA)) (32000) **Mr S. Fustok**
35 **KHILKHAAL (IRE)**, b f 12/3 Voleris (FR)—Spinning Star (Arazi (USA)) **Mr S. Fustok**
36 **MON PLAISIR**, br f 13/5 Singspiel (IRE)—Mademoiselle Chloe (Night Shift (USA)) **Mr S. Fustok**
37 **NEW WAVE**, b c 23/3 Woodman (USA)—Vanishing Point (USA) (Caller I D (USA)) **Mr S. Fustok**
38 Ch f 22/3 Royal Applause—Pacifica (Robellino (USA)) (32000) **Mr T. J. Wells**
39 **ROSAPENNA (IRE)**, b f 20/1 Spectrum (IRE)—
   Blaine (USA) (Lyphard's Wish (FR)) (24737) **Thoroughbred Farms Ltd**
40 B f 19/2 Benny The Dip (USA)—Samhat Mtoto (Mtoto) (2400) **Mr T. J. Wells**
41 Ch c 3/3 Daggers Drawn (USA)—Scarlet Woman (Sri Pekan) (45000) **Mr N. Ahamad**
42 **SIEGLINDE**, b f 14/2 High Estate—Carinthia (IRE) (Tirol) (7000) **Hintlesham D. S. Partners**
43 **STAMBAH**, b f 16/4 Pivotal—Double Top (Thatching) (18000) **Lady Juliet Tadgell**
44 Ch c 21/3 Primo Dominie—Tarsa (Ballad Rock) (37000) **The Boardroom Syndicate**
45 **UNRESTRICTED**, ch f 10/5 Mark of Esteem (IRE)—Generous Lady (Generous (IRE)) **Mr S. Fustok**
46 **ZOWINGTON**, gr c 30/1 Zafonic (USA)—Carmela Owen (Owington) **Mr O. Pointing**

Other Owners: Mr David Allan, Mr W. J. Bridge, Mr P. W. Brown, Mr Paul Burnett, Mr John F. Chapman, Mr Roy G. R. Chapman, Mrs Susan Cunningham, Miss Patsy Ede, Mr R. Fraiser, Mr John Fullick, Mr R. T. Goodes, Mr J. N. Gosling, Mrs Jill Kerr-Smiley, Miss Judith Ann Knapman, Mr Roger Nash, Mrs R. M. S. Neave, Mrs Charles Park, Mr D. G. Raffel, Mr Ray Rice, Mr J. Roberts, Prudence Lady Salt, Mr Barry Stewart, Mr D. C. Stuttaford, Mrs P. I. Veenbaas, Mr Peter Veenbaas, Mr R. J. Wayman, Mr H. Webb, Mrs P. H. Williams.

Assistant Trainer: Adrian Rogers

Jockey (Flat): R Mullen. **Apprentice:** S O'Hara. **Amateur:** Miss Melissa Scherer (9-0).

---

566 **MR T. R. WALL, Church Stretton**
Postal: **Harton Manor, Harton, Church Stretton, Shropshire, SY6 7DL.**
Contact: **PHONE** (01694) 724144 **FAX** (01694) 724144 **MOBILE** (07815) 813789

1 **BEVIER**, 10, b g Nashwan (USA)—Bevel (USA) **Mr T. Wall**
2 **E MINOR (IRE)**, 5, b m Blushing Flame (USA)—Watch The Clock **Mr Derek & Mrs Marie Dean**
3 **EXPECTEDTOFLI (IRE)**, 6, b m Mujadil (USA)—Zurarah **Mr E. Young**
4 **GLOWING EMBER**, 4, b f Blushing Flame (USA)—California Dreamin **Mr D. Bunn**
5 **MARGARETS WISH**, 4, gr f Cloudings (IRE)—Gentle Gain **Mr A. H. Bennett**
6 **SCALLYWACE**, 10, br g Wace (USA)—Scally Jenks **Mr K. C. G. Edwards**
7 **SPRING BEE**, 4, b f Parthian Springs—First Bee **Mr D. Pugh**

MR T. R. WALL—continued

    8 SPY GUN (USA), 4, ch g Mt Livermore (USA)—Takeover Target (USA) **Mr Derek & Mrs Marie Dean**
    9 UN AUTRE ESPERE, 5, b g Golden Heights—Drummer's Dream (IRE) **Snax Catering Services Limited**

Other Owners: Mr R. Hargrove, Mr D. B. Roberts, Mr M. Whewell, Mr A. Wright.

Assistant Trainer: Mr D B Roberts

Jockey (NH): R Greene (w.a.).

567	**MR MARK WALLACE, Newmarket** Postal: **Woodland Stables, The Severals, Newmarket, Suffolk, CB8 7BS.** Contact: **PHONE (01638) 560752 FAX (01638) 561387 MOBILE (07771) 532422** E-MAIL mwallace.racing@virgin.net

    1 ARIES (GER), 4, ch f Big Shuffle (USA)—Auenlust (GER)
    2 ETERNAL BEAUTY (USA), 4, b f Zafonic (USA)—Strawberry Roan (IRE)
    3 HARD NOSE (IRE), 4, b c Entrepreneur—Cutlers Corner
    4 4, Ch c Cosmonaut—Highland Spirit
    5 ISMAHAAN, 5, ch m Unfuwain (USA)—River Divine (USA)
    6 KELLS (IRE), 6, b g Dilum (USA)—Elizabethan Air
    7 MAID FOR LIFE (IRE), 4, b f Entrepreneur—Arandora Star (USA)
    8 PERELANDRA (USA), 4, ch f Cadeaux Genereux—Larentia
    9 PRINCE DAYJUR (USA), 5, b br g Dayjur (USA)—Distinct Beauty (USA)

THREE-YEAR-OLDS

   10 ANNIE MILLER (IRE), b f Night Shift (USA)—Lost Dream
   11 ATHBOY, ch c Entrepreneur—Glorious
   12 BALLYBORO (IRE), b f Entrepreneur—Tathkara (USA)
   13 BENBAUN (IRE), b c Stravinsky (USA)—Escape To Victory
   14 BIG BAD BURT, ch c Efisio—Mountain Bluebird (USA)
   15 CEYLON ROUND (FR), b f Royal Applause—Tea Colony (USA)
   16 CLARANETE PRINCESS (IRE), b f Princely Heir (IRE)—Sheryl Lynn
   17 DANCE IDOL, b f Groom Dancer (USA)—Dance To The Top
   18 FIREBELLY, b f Nicolotte—Desert Delight (IRE)
   19 FORTUNE'S PRINCESS, b f Desert Prince (IRE)—Golden Fortune
   20 GAVROCHE (IRE), b c Docksider (USA)—Regal Revolution
   21 GINGER NOT BLONDE (USA), br f Atticus (USA)—Quick To Quibble (USA)
   22 HALF A HANDFUL, b c Victory Note (USA)—Enaam
   23 LADY STRIPES, gr f Alzao (USA)—Shamaya (IRE)
   24 LAKE DIVA, ch f Docksider (USA)—Cutpurse Moll
   25 LASKA (IRE), br f Fasliyev (USA)—Dacian (USA)
   26 LIMIT DOWN (IRE), b g Desert Story (IRE)—Princess Raisa
   27 PANORAMIC VIEW, b f Polar Falcon (USA)—Brush Strokes
   28 SVETLANA (IRE), b f Soviet Star (USA)—Foreign Relation (IRE)
   29 TRINITY FAIR, b f Polish Precedent (USA)—Chita Rivera
   30 WYCHBURY (USA), ch c Swain (IRE)—Garden Rose (IRE)

TWO-YEAR-OLDS

   31 B c 17/2 Monashee Mountain—Arctic Lead (USA) (Arctic Tern (USA)) (15460)
   32 B f 29/4 Xaar—Bea's Ruby (IRE) (Fairy King (USA))
   33 B f 5/3 Orpen (USA)—Cadeau Elegant (Cadeaux Genereux)
   34 CATWALK CLERIC (IRE), b c 27/4 Orpen (USA)—Ministerial Model (IRE) (Shalford (IRE)) (26000)
   35 CHALET, b f 24/2 Singspiel (IRE)—Douce Maison (IRE) (Fools Holme (USA)) (18000)
   36 Ch c 20/3 Namid—Cheeky Weeky (Cadeaux Genereux) (11000)
   37 B c 23/4 Orpen (USA)—Classic Heights (Shirley Heights) (18552)
   38 B f 25/1 Tipsy Creek (USA)—Compton Amber (Puissance) (6000)
   39 B f 15/4 Fraam—Corniche Quest (IRE) (Salt Dome) (5000)
   40 Ch c 23/3 Gold Away (IRE)—Danaide (FR) (Polish Precedent (USA)) (22263)
   41 B f 12/4 Cape Cross (IRE)—Decatur (Deploy) (12000)
   42 B f 11/5 Danehill (USA)—Double Grange (IRE) (Double Schwartz)
   43 Ch f 2/4 Foxhound (USA)—Fiveofive (IRE) (Fairy King (USA)) (9000)
   44 Ch c 11/3 Inchinor—Haste (Halling (USA)) (20000)
   45 Ch f 5/5 Desert Sun—Icefern (Moorestyle) (15460)
   46 B f 4/4 King's Best (USA)—Itab (USA) (Dayjur (USA))

MR MARK WALLACE—continued

47 Ch c 10/3 Namid—Kilshanny (Groom Dancer (USA)) (70000)
48 B f 28/3 Danetime (IRE)—Lila Pedigo (IRE) (Classic Secret (USA)) (3000)
49 Ch c 18/3 Royal Anthem (USA)—Lyphard's Starlite (USA) (Lyphard (USA)) (3000)
50 B c 19/5 Namid—Mamma's Too (Skyliner) (35000)
51 B f 2/5 Night Shift (USA)—Missing Love (IRE) (Thatching) (25973)
52 B f 20/3 Fayruz—Mystique Air (IRE) (Mujadil (USA)) (10000)
53 B c 9/2 Fraam—Norwegian Queen (IRE) (Affirmed (IRE))
54 B c 23/3 Mujahid (USA)—Pain Perdu (IRE) (Waajib) (50000)
55 B c 15/3 Zafonic (USA)—Paradise Soul (Dynaformer (USA)) (19000)
56 B f 16/4 Efisio—Royale Rose (FR) (Bering) (20000)
57 B f 26/2 Mujadil (USA)—Sheezalady (Zafonic (USA)) (25973)
58 B c 25/2 Indian Rocket—Sweet Nature (IRE) (Classic Secret (USA)) (20000)
59 B f 15/3 Rossini (USA)—Touraneena (Robellino (USA)) (5500)
60 Ch f 18/2 Gold Away (IRE)—Turn To Vodka (FR) (Polish Precedent (USA))

Other Owners: H. E. Sheikh Rashid Bin Mohammed, Mr S. Birks, Lee Bollingbrooke & Partners, Mr John Breslin, Brooklands Racing, Mr Jim Brown, Mr C. Campbell, Mr D. Curren, Mr Mel Davies, Anne Dawson & Partners, Mr B. Doyle, Mr C. Dutfield, Favourites Racing, Mrs M. Foreman, Richard Green (Fine Paintings), Grenane House Stud, Mr J. L. Guillambert, Mr D. Hanlon, Hantons Ltd, Mrs R. G. Hillen, Mr T. P. Hyde, Impetious Partnership, Mrs M. Kennel, Mr Adam Kite, Lewis Catering, Lucayan Stud, Mrs J. Magnier, Mr P. Magnier, Mr D. McGovern, Mr N. O'Reilly, Over The Bridge Partnership, Mr P. Player, Mr Liam Queally, Mr P Ransley, Mr J. Roche, Mr Pedro Rosas, Dr K. Sanderson, Mr H. Shepherd, Mr L. Sheridan, Mr A. Skidmore, Mr & Mrs G. Smith, Mr M. Tabor, Mrs S. Thomson-Jones, Mr B. Walsh, Mr D. Walsh & Partners, Major M. G. Wyatt, X Limited Racing.

Jockey (Flat): K Fallon (w.a.). **Apprentice:** K Bowman (8-2).

MRS K. WALTON, Middleham
Postal: **Sharp Hill Farm, Middleham, Leyburn, North Yorkshire, DL8 4QY.**
Contact: **PHONE (01969) 622250 MOBILE (07718) 909356**

1 **ASTRAL PRINCE**, 6, ch g Efisio—Val d'Erica **Mr D. E. Reeves & Mr P. W. Colley**
2 **BILLIE JOHN (IRE)**, 9, ch g Boyne Valley—Lovestream **Mrs Patricia M. Wilson**
3 **FANTASTICO (IRE)**, 4, b f Bahhare (USA)—Minatina (IRE) **The Suffolk Punch Syndicate**
4 **FUSION OF TUNES**, 6, b m Mr Confusion (IRE)—Daleria **Mr Jeff McCarthy**
5 **MARTIN HOUSE (IRE)**, 5, b g Mujadil (USA)—Dolcezza (FR) **Mile High Racing**
6 **ONLY ONE MATTY (IRE)**, 7, b g Satco (FR)—Poundworld (IRE) **The White Liners**
7 **QUEEN CHARLOTTE (IRE)**, 5, ch m Tagula (IRE)—Tisma (FR) **Mr P. W. Colley**
8 **ROMAN OUTLAW**, 12, gr g Alias Smith (USA)—Roman Moor **Mrs K. Walton**
9 **ROMAN REBEL**, 5, ch g Primitive Rising (USA)—Roman Moor **Mr Paul Lawson**
10 **ROYAL CASTLE (IRE)**, 10, b g Caerleon (USA)—Sun Princess **Stan Clough and Dudley Bendall**
11 **TEENAGER**, 4, b f Young Ern—Washita **Mr Guy Reed**
12 **WILDFIELD RUFO (IRE)**, 9, b g Celio Rufo—Jersey Girl **Mrs Carol Holroyd**

Other Owners: Mr James Edwards, Mr Philip Groom, Mr G. Lansbury, Mr G. Pearson, Mr B. Smith, Mr Graham Spall, Mr Rod Squirrel, Mr M. White (Hawick).

Jockey (NH): R McGrath (10-0). **Conditional:** Ashley Dempsey (10-0).

MRS BARBARA WARING, Welford-on-Avon
Postal: **Rumer Farm Stables, Long Marston Road, Welford-on-Avon, Warwickshire, CV37 8AF.**
Contact: **PHONE (01789) 750786 MOBILE (07787) 516723**

1 **BRONHALLOW**, 11, b g Belmez (USA)—Grey Twig **R.Parker,E.Davies,L.Nicholls,Mrs R.Field**
2 **CHARLIESMEDARLIN**, 13, b g Macmillion—Top Cover **Mr E. S. Chivers**
3 **ETTRICK (NZ)**, 9, b g Hereward The Wake (USA)—Kardinia (NZ) **Nicholson McCormack Shapter Frost**
4 **KILCREGGAN (NZ)**, 9, b g Landyap (USA)—Lehmans Lot **Mr B. W. Parren**
5 **LIES AND PHIBBS (IRE)**, 6, gr g Supreme Leader—Rosy Waters
6 **MARTHA REILLY (IRE)**, 8, ch m Rainbows For Life (CAN)—Debach Delight **Mr B. W. Parren**
7 **SMILEAFACT**, 4, br g So Factual (USA)—Smilingatstrangers
8 **SMILING APPLAUSE**, 5, b g Royal Applause—Smilingatstrangers **Eddys A Team**
9 **SOUTHERNCROSSPATCH**, 13, ch g Ra Nova—Southern Bird **Mr E. S. Chivers**

MRS BARBARA WARING—continued

10 **STUNNING MAGIC**, 4, b g Magic Ring (IRE)—Absolutelystunning **R.J.Simmons,D.Patel,S.Gillett,H.Shapter**
11 **TAKEACHANCEONHIM**, 6, b g Dilum (USA)—Smilingatstrangers **Mr A. G. Gibbs**

Other Owners: Mr M. Brewer, Mr G. E. Brunsdon, Mr D. M. Finnigan, Mr M. J. Flint, Mr M. A. Harris, Mrs D. Holman, Mr Robin Keck, Mr M. Mitchell, Mr Kieran P. Ryan, Mr Kenneth Wilson.

Assistant Trainer: H Chisman

Jockey (Flat): T Quinn. **Jockey (NH):** B Hitchcott. **Apprentice:** S Hitchcott. **Conditional:** J P Byrne, R Hobson.

---

570 | **MR L. WARING, Bridgwater**
Postal: **Culverwells Stables, Lower Merridge, Spaxton, Bridgwater, Somerset, TA5 1AS.**
Contact: **PHONE (01278) 671750**

1 **DUAL STAR (IRE)**, 9, b g Warning—Sizes Vary **Mrs J. Waring**
2 **SPANISH ARCHER (IRE)**, 9, b g Spanish Place (USA)—Bow Gello **Mrs J. Waring**

Assistant Trainer: Jenny Waring

Jockey (NH): X Aizpuru.

---

571 | **MR F. WATSON, Sedgefield**
Postal: **Beacon Hill, Sedgefield, Stockton-On-Tees, Cleveland, TS21 3HN.**
Contact: **PHONE (01740) 620582 MOBILES (07973) 614261/(07748) 838331**

1 **ATTILA THE HUN**, 5, b g Piccolo—Katya (IRE) **Mr F. Watson**
2 **BRIDEWELL (USA)**, 3, b g Woodman (USA)—La Alleged (USA) **Mr F. Watson**
3 **DISTINCTLYTHEBEST**, 4, b c Distinctly North (USA)—Euphyllia **Mr F. Watson**
4 **GREAT HOPPER**, 9, b m Rock Hopper—Spun Gold **Mr F. Watson**
5 **GREAT ORATION (IRE)**, 15, b br g Simply Great (FR)—Spun Gold **Mr F. Watson**
6 **QUEEN LOUISA**, 4, b f Piccolo—Queen of Scotland (IRE) **Mr F. Watson**
7 **SHARDDA**, 4, b f Barathea (IRE)—Kronengold (USA) **Mr F. Watson**
8 **THWAAB**, 12, b g Dominion—Velvet Habit **Mr F. Watson**

THREE-YEAR-OLDS

9 Ch f Titus Livius (FR)—Furry Dance (USA) **Mr F. Watson**

TWO-YEAR-OLDS

10 Ch c 20/3 Cayman Kai (IRE)—Bunty's Friend (Highlands) **Mr F. Watson**
11 Ch f 9/5 Cayman Kai (IRE)—Finestatetobein (Northern State (USA)) **Mr F. Watson**

---

572 | **LADY SUSAN WATSON, Bossall**
Postal: **Bossall, York, North Yorkshire, YO60 7NT.**
Contact: **PHONE (01904) 468315**

1 **FRANCKEN (ITY)**, 5, ro g Petit Loup (USA)—Filicaia **Lady Susan Watson**
2 **JUST FLUSTER**, 8, ch g Triune—Flamber **Lady Susan Watson**
3 **JUST SO ELEGANT**, 7, ch g Elegant Monarch—Hollow Wonder **Lady Susan Watson**
4 **KISMET**, 6, b m Tirol—Belamcanda **Lady Susan Watson**
5 **TRIPLEPLAY (IRE)**, 5, br g Tagula (IRE)—Shiyra **Lady Susan Watson**

---

573 | **MRS S. A. WATT, Richmond**
Postal: **Rosey Hill Farm, Scorton Road, Brompton on Swale, Richmond, North Yorkshire, DL10 7EQ.**
Contact: **(01748) 812064 (0797) 0826046 E-MAIL wattfences@aol.com**

1 **FEANOR**, 6, b m Presidium—Nouvelle Cuisine **Mrs S. A. Watt**
2 **NOW THEN SID**, 5, ch g Presidium—Callace **Mrs S. A. Watt**
3 **TOP THE BILL (IRE)**, 4, b c Topanoora—Rio Star (IRE) **Mrs S. A. Watt**

Jockey (NH): Davy Russell (10-4). **Amateur:** Miss Tina Jackson (9-7).

574 MR P. R. WEBBER, Banbury
Postal: **Cropredy Lawn, Mollington, Banbury, Oxfordshire, OX17 1DR.**
Contact: **PHONE (01295) 750226 FAX (01295) 758482 MOBILE (07836) 232465**

1 **ABALVINO (FR)**, 10, ch g Sillery (USA)—Abalvina (FR) **I. M. S. Racing & Noel Cronin**
2 **ATUM RE (IRE)**, 7, br g Be My Native (USA)—Collopy's Cross **Mr Paul Green**
3 **BENBECULA (IRE)**, 7, b g Glacial Storm (USA)—Lough View **Mr J. Dougall**
4 **BODFARI SAUVAGE**, 4, b g Loup Sauvage (USA)—Petite Sonnerie **Bodfari Stud**
5 **BOND DIAMOND**, 7, gr g Prince Sabo—Alsiba
6 **BONNYJO (FR)**, 5, b br g Cyborg (FR)—Argument Facile (FR) **The Branners & Guido Partnership**
7 **BRAD**, 6, b g Deploy—Celia Brady **Mrs David Blackburn**
8 **BUCKBY LANE**, 8, b g Nomadic Way (USA)—Buckby Folly **Mrs P. Starkey**
9 **CLOUDY CLUB (IRE)**, 5, b g Moscow Society (USA)—Glenpatrick Peach (IRE) **Mrs P. Sherwood**
10 **COODLINE KING (IRE)**, 5, b g Germany (USA)—Tara's Serenade (IRE) **Mrs Mary O'Connor**
11 **DECISIVE**, 5, b g Alhaarth (IRE)—Alys **P. Jensen**
12 **DUKE OF BUCKINGHAM (IRE)**, 8, b g Phardante (FR)—Deselby's Choice **Mr C. W. Booth**
13 **EMERALD EXPRESS**, 5, b m Bigstone (IRE)—Nashkara **Economic Security**
14 **FLAME PHOENIX (USA)**, 5, b br g Quest For Fame—Kingscote **The Chamberlain Addiscott Partnership**
15 **FLYING INSTRUCTOR**, 14, gr g Neltino—Flying Mistress **Mrs John Webber**
16 **FROSTY'S COUSIN (IRE)**, 5, b g Arctic Lord—Farojina (USA) **Mrs P. Sherwood**
17 **FULL HOUSE (IRE)**, 5, br g King's Theatre (IRE)—Nirvavita (FR) **The Chamberlain Addiscott Partnership**
18 **GIELGUD**, 5, b g Faustus (USA)—Shirl **Mrs J. K. Powell**
19 **GINGKO**, 7, b g Pursuit of Love—Arboretum (IRE) **Olympic Group of Partners**
20 **HIT ROYAL (FR)**, 9, ch g Montorselli—Valse Royale (FR) **Mr David Czarnetzki**
21 **ICY BLAST (IRE)**, 5, b g Glacial Storm (USA)—Fair Lisselan (IRE) **Mrs P. Sherwood**
22 **IN THE STARS (IRE)**, 6, ch g Definite Article—Astronomer Lady (IRE) **The Fancy Colours Partnership**
23 **IRENE KATE**, 5, b m Bob's Return (IRE)—Shean Deas **Mr Raymond Anderson Green**
24 **JAOKA DU GORD (FR)**, 7, b g Concorde Jr (USA)—Theorie du Cochet (FR) **Mr R. W. Barnett**
25 **JERUFLO (IRE)**, 9, b m Glacial Storm (USA)—Martiness **Mr Raymond Anderson Green**
26 **JUNGLI (IRE)**, 11, b g Be My Native (USA)—Simple Mind **Mrs P. Starkey**
27 **KINGSFOLD FREDDIE**, 6, ch g Rock City—Kingsfold Flame **Mrs Ann Shaw**
28 **LITTLE CHARTRIDGE**, 6, b m Anshan—Auntie Dot **Mrs J. Webber**
29 **LITTLE ED**, 6, b g Shambo—Edina (IRE) **Mr Dennis Yardy**
30 **LORD NORTH (IRE)**, 9, b g Mister Lord (USA)—Mrs Hegarty **Mr D. Allen**
31 **MAN O'MYSTERY (USA)**, 7, b g Diesis—Eurostorm (USA) **B. Nielsen**
32 **MUSICAL STAGE (USA)**, 5, b g Theatrical—Changed Tune (USA) **N. Ruddell & D. Heath**
33 **OPAL RIDGE**, 7, ch g Jupiter Island—The Beginning **Mr D. I. Bare**
34 **OUTLAW EXPRESS (IRE)**, 8, b g Un Desperado (FR)—Surprise Packet **Economic Security 2**
35 **PALMA (IRE)**, 6, b br g Rashar (USA)—Quaybreeze (IRE) **Mr J. Dougall**
36 **PATRICKSNINETEENTH (IRE)**, 7, b g Mister Lord (USA)—Many Miracles **The Large G & T Partnership**
37 **PHILDARI (IRE)**, 8, b g Shardari—Philosophical **Mr Michael Coghlan**
38 **SALT CELLAR (IRE)**, 5, b g Salse—Athene (IRE) **Mr Paul Webber**
39 **STATE OF PLAY**, 4, b g Hernando—Kaprice (GER) **Mrs C. A. Waters**
40 **TANAJI**, 5, b m Marju—Hamsaat (IRE) **The Dream On Partnership**
41 **TARASCO (FR)**, 8, b g Deploy—Moucha (FR) **Mrs D. Ridley**
42 **TELL ME WHY (IRE)**, 8, gr g Roselier (FR)—Clonarctic Slave **Mrs C. A. Waters**
43 **TELMAR FLYER**, 7, gr m Neltino—Flying Mistress **Dodson & Partners**
44 **THE FRIDGE**, 6, ch g Karinga Bay—Sovereign Maiden **S. Hope & J. Dear**
45 **THE GRAND DUKE (IRE)**, 6, ch g Moscow Society (USA)—In For It (IRE) **The Patient Ones**
46 **TIDOUR (FR)**, 8, b g Rahotep (FR)—Softway (FR) **Mrs M. Fisher**
47 **TIGHE CASTER**, 5, b g Makbul—Miss Fire **Mr D. P. Barrie & Mr M. J. Rees**
48 **TISHO**, 8, ch m Sir Harry Lewis (USA)—Sister-In-Law **Mrs P. Scott-Dunn**
49 **ULUNDI**, 9, b g Rainbow Quest—Flit (USA) **Mr D. Heath**
50 **WHALEEF**, 6, br g Darshaan—Wilayif (USA) **Mrs P. Sherwood**
51 **YOUNG GARRICK (IRE)**, 6, b g Old Vic—Youngandfair (IRE) **Mrs Veronica Jones**

Other Owners: Mrs D. L. Addiscott, Mr G. Addiscott, Mr A. M. Armitage, Mrs D. Barnett, Mr B. A. Bell, Mr P. Branigan, Mr G. Bridgford, Mr Nigel Chamberlain, Mrs P.C. Chamberlain, Mrs A. E. Chapman, Major J. L. Damant, Mrs A. J. Davies, Mr Richard Dodson, Mr Michael Fitzgerald, Mr Peter Garnett, Miss H. Gosling, Mrs Miles Gosling, D. Greenall, Mr M. A. Heffernan, Mr D. W. Higgins, Mr R. Kent, Mrs C. M. Kingham, Mr A. S. Lancaster, Mr Richard Lay, Mr I. Magee, Mr A. H. McDonald, Professor David Metcalf, Mr B. E. Nielsen, Mr Martin Pepper, Mrs David Plunkett, Mrs P. A. Potter, Mr G. M. Powell, Mr I. Reynolds, Mr Ian T. Smethurst, Mrs I. M. Steinmann, Mr A. D. Steinmann, Mr Tony Stephens, Mr David A. Taglight, Mr Nigel Titcombe, Mr W. S. Watt, Mrs Giles Weaver, Mrs Anthony West, Mrs E. J. Wilson, Mr Jerry Wright.

Assistant Trainer: George Baker

Jockeys (NH): T Doyle, J McCarthy (10-0), A Thornton. **Amateurs:** Mr J King, D Pebody (9-7).

575 MR M. J. WEEDEN, Weymouth
Postal: **Highfield, Fleet, Weymouth, Dorset, DT3 4EB.**
Contact: **PHONE (01305) 776822 MOBILE (07866) 313914 E-MAIL highfield.fleet@lineone.net**

1 **ADRADEE (IRE)**, 10, b m Ajraas (USA)—Miss Tan A Dee **Mrs E. A. Haycock**
2 **BALIDARE**, 7, b m King's Signet (USA)—Baligay **Just Racing**
3 **CHANTILLY LADY**, 11, ch m Rising—Ladiz **Just Racing**
4 **DUSTY CARPET**, 6, ch g Pivotal—Euridice (IRE) **Mrs M. C. M. Walters**
5 **JAZZ DUKE**, 11, ch g Rising—Gone **Mr M. J. Weeden**
6 **JAZZ JUNIOR**, 5, ch g Romany Rye—Rising's Lass (IRE) **Mr M. J. Weeden**
7 **MADAM FLORA**, 7, b m Afflora (IRE)—Madam's Choice **Mr T. J. Swaffield**
8 **NOBLE DEMAND**, 9, b g Red Ransom (USA)—Noble Nordic (USA) **Mrs E. A. Haycock**
9 **PEVERIL PRIDE**, 6, b g Past Glories—Peveril Princess **Mrs E. A. Haycock**
10 **WINSOME WINNIE**, 9, b m Teamster—G W Supermare **Mrs S. Frost**

THREE-YEAR-OLDS

11 **PITCHER PERFECT**, b f Relief Pitcher—Rising's Lass (IRE) **Mr M. J. Weeden**

TWO-YEAR-OLDS

12 **PEVERIL PARTY GIRL**, ch f 26/2 Classic Cliche (IRE)—Adradee (IRE) (Ajraas (USA)) **Mrs E. A. Haycock**

Other Owners: C. M. Borries, M. G. Green, Mrs W. M. Pope.

Assistant Trainer: Mrs S Weeden

576 MR C. V. WEEDON, Pulborough
Postal: **10 Coppice Place, Combe Lane, Wormley, Godalming, Surrey, GU8 5TY.**
Contact: **PHONE (01428) 683344 MOBILE (07949) 100146**

1 **BANK ON HIM**, 9, b g Elmaamul (USA)—Feather Flower **Vetlab Supplies Ltd**
2 **BORDER TALE**, 4, b g Selkirk (USA)—Likely Story (IRE) **Chadwick, Dyer & Flynn**
3 **CHRISTY'S PRIDE (IRE)**, 12, ch m Kambalda—Caddy Shack **Mr Bill Hinge**
4 **INCHINNAN**, 7, b m Inchinor—Westering **Mr Bill Hinge**
5 5, B m Roscoe Blake—Linen Leaf **Colin Weedon**
6 **OUT OF TUNE**, 4, ch g Elmaamul (USA)—Strawberry Song **Mr Alf Chadwick**

THREE-YEAR-OLDS

7 **BEE DEES LEGACY**, b c Atraf—Bee Dee Dancer **Vetlab Supplies Ltd**
8 **FORGE LANE (IRE)**, b c Desert Style (IRE)—March Fourteenth (USA) **Vetlab Supplies Ltd**
9 B g Orpen (USA)—Green Night Out (IRE) **Colin Weedon**

Other Owners: Mrs Gillian Perry, Simulex Limited.

577 MR P. WEGMANN, Gloucester
Postal: **Maisemore Park, Maisemore, Gloucester, GL2 8HX.**
Contact: **PHONE (01452) 301332 FAX (01452) 505002 MOBILE (07785) 242857**

1 **ALLEGIANCE**, 9, b g Rock Hopper—So Precise (FR) **Mr P. Wegmann**
2 **BLACK SAINT**, 7, b g Perpendicular—Fool's Errand **Mr P. Wegmann**
3 **DALCASSIAN KING (IRE)**, 11, b g King's Ride—Niagara Lass **Mr P. Wegmann**
4 **MONTY'S THEME (IRE)**, 10, b br g Montelimar (USA)—Theme Music **Mr P. Wegmann**
5 **ROYAL ALLEGIANCE**, 9, ch g Kris—Wilayif (USA) **Mr R. Koniger**

Assistant Trainer: Miss V Williams

578 **MR D. K. WELD M.V.B. M.R.C.V.S., The Curragh**
Postal: **Rosewell House, The Curragh, Co. Kildare, Irish Republic.**
Contact: PHONE +353 (0) 45 441273/441476 FAX +353 (0) 45 441119
E-MAIL dkweld@eircom.net

1 **AKSHAR (IRE)**, 5, b h Danehill (USA)—Akilara (IRE) **Dr Ronan Lambe**
2 **AMID THE CHAOS (IRE)**, 4, ch c Nashwan (USA)—Celebrity Style (USA) **Dr M. W. J. Smurfit**
3 **DIRECT BEARING (IRE)**, 7, b g Polish Precedent (USA)—Uncertain Affair (IRE) **Dr M. W. J. Smurfit**
4 **ELITE SOCIETY (IRE)**, 4, gr f Linamix (FR)—Obvious Appeal (IRE) **Moyglare Stud Farm**
5 **EVOLVING TACTICS (IRE)**, 4, b c Machiavellian (USA)—Token Gesture (IRE) **Dr M. W. J. Smurfit**
6 **FORMER SENATOR (IRE)**, 4, b c Sadler's Wells (USA)—Elegance In Design **Moyglare Stud Farm**
7 **GOVAMIX**, 6, b g Linamix (FR)—Segovia **Mr Sean Mulyran**
8 **HYMN OF LOVE (IRE)**, 4, ch f Barathea (IRE)—Perils of Joy (IRE) **Moyglare Stud Farm**
9 **IN TIME'S EYE**, 5, b g Singspiel (IRE)—Irish Edition (USA) **Dr M. W. J. Smurfit**
10 **IVOWEN (USA)**, 4, b br f Theatrical—Shee Cat (USA) **Mrs C. L. Weld**
11 **LEGEND HAS IT (IRE)**, 4, b f Sadler's Wells (USA)—Magical Cliche (USA) **Moyglare Stud Farm**
12 **MAHARIB (IRE)**, 4, b c Alhaarth (IRE)—Diali (USA) **Sheikh Hamden Al Maktoum**
13 **MANDHOOR (IRE)**, 4, b g Flying Spur (AUS)—Moy Water (IRE) **Dr Ronan Lambe**
14 **MEDIA PUZZLE (USA)**, 7, ch g Theatrical—Market Slide (USA) **Dr M. W. J. Smurfit**
15 **MESMERIC (IRE)**, 6, b g Sadler's Wells (USA)—Mesmerize **Fantastic Forecasts**
16 **MULTAZEM (IRE)**, 4, b c Kingmambo—Spirit of Tara (IRE) **Sheikh Hamden Al Maktoum**
17 **MUTAKARRIM**, 7, b g Mujtahid (USA)—Alyakkh (IRE) **Dr M. W. J. Smurfit**
18 **NAYODABAYO (IRE)**, 4, b g Definite Article—Babushka (IRE) **Mr T. P. Ramsden**
19 **ONE MORE ROUND (USA)**, 6, b g Ghazi (USA)—Life of The Party (USA) **Dr M. W. J. Smurfit**
20 **ON THE HORIZON (IRE)**, 4, b f Definite Article—Temporary Lull (USA) **Dr M. W. J. Smurfit**
21 **PRIZE TIME (IRE)**, 5, b g College Chapel—Uncertain Affair (IRE) **Moyglare Stud Farm**
22 **PROMINENT FEATURE (IRE)**, 4, ch c Selkirk (USA)—Looking Brill **M. R. Sinclair**
23 **QUEEN ASTRID (IRE)**, 4, b f Revoque (IRE)—Talina's Law (IRE) **Dr Ronan Lambe**
24 **STAGE AFFAIR (USA)**, 10, b br h Theatrical—Wooing (USA) **Dr M. W. J. Smurfit**
25 **VINNIE ROE (IRE)**, 6, b h Definite Article—Kayu **Mr Seamus Sheridan**
26 **ZEROBERTO (IRE)**, 4, ch g Definite Article—Blazing Soul (IRE) **Dr Ronan Lambe**

THREE-YEAR-OLDS

27 **ABSOLUTELY COOL (IRE)**, gr f Indian Ridge—Absolute Glee (USA) **Moyglare Stud Farm**
28 **ANTIGONE (IRE)**, b f Cape Cross (IRE)—Ashkirk **Mr P. J. O'Shaughnessy**
29 **BEAUTIFUL NOTE (USA)**, b f Red Ransom (USA)—Touch of Truth (USA) **Moyglare Stud Farm**
30 **BINAA (IRE)**, b f Marju (IRE)—Hadeb **Sheikh Hamden Al Maktoum**
31 **CAIRDEAS (IRE)**, b c Darshaan—Sabaah (USA) **Irish National Stud**
32 **CELTIC QUEEN (IRE)**, b f Sadler's Wells (USA)—Sweeten Up **Mrs John Magnier**
33 **CLEVER MYTH (IRE)**, b f Green Desert (USA)—Magical Cliche (USA) **Moyglare Stud Farm**
34 **EASE THE WAY**, b c Nashwan (USA)—Desert Ease (IRE) **Moyglare Stud Farm**
35 **EASY LAUGHTER (IRE)**, b c Danehill (USA)—All To Easy **Moyglare Stud Farm**
36 **FANDANGO DANCER (IRE)**, ch c Selkirk (USA)—Dance By Night **Dr M. W. J. Smurfit**
37 **FAVOURITE NATION (IRE)**, ch c Cadeaux Genereux—Fernanda **Dr M. W. J. Smurfit**
38 **FLOSCULA (USA)**, b f Theatrical—Comfort And Style **Moyglare Stud Farm**
39 **FORTY GRAND (IRE)**, b c Red Ransom (USA)—Sue's Ruby (USA) **Mr Sean Mulyran**
40 **GENUINE CHARM (IRE)**, b f Sadler's Wells (USA)—Market Slide (USA) **Moyglare Stud Farm**
41 **GREY SWALLOW (IRE)**, gr c Daylami (IRE)—Style of Life (USA) **Mrs Rochelle Quinn**
42 **HAY BURN STREET (IRE)**, ch c Barathea (IRE)—Always Far (USA) **Mrs E Berry Lynch Long**
43 **ICARUS DREAM (IRE)**, b c Intikhab (USA)—Nymphs Echo (IRE) **Lady O'Reilly**
44 **INDIAN PACE (IRE)**, ch c Indian Ridge—Blend of Pace (IRE) **Moyglare Stud Farm**
45 **IRISH DESIGN (IRE)**, ch f Alhaarth (IRE)—Idara **Mr B. R. Firestone**
46 **KENTUCKY HOME (USA)**, b c Kingmambo—Miss Carolina (IRE) **C.A.M.M.A. di sas Schiavi**
47 **KHULASAH (IRE)**, b f Darshaan—Hawas **Sheikh Hamdan Al Maktoum**
48 **KING JOCK (USA)**, b c Ghazi (USA)—Glen Kate **Mrs E. Berry Lynch Long**
49 **LIGHTER SPIRIT (IRE)**, b c Green Desert (USA)—Epicure's Garden (USA) **Moyglare Stud Farm**
50 **LISIEUX ORCHID (IRE)**, b f Sadler's Wells (USA)—Clear Issue (USA) **Moyglare Stud Farm**
51 **LOYAL FOCUS**, ch c Definite Article—Temporary Lull (USA) **Moyglare Stud Farm**
52 **MADAME MOONSHINE**, gr f Machiavellian (USA)—Vadsagreya (FR) **Mr Cathal Ryan**
53 **MEDIA ASSET (IRE)**, ch c Polish Precedent—Lady Luck (IRE) **Mr G. Olivero**
54 **MEGEC BLISS (IRE)**, b f Soviet Star (USA)—Machaera **Mr D. O'Flynn**
55 **METISSE (IRE)**, b br f Indian Ridge—Across The Ice (USA) **Dr M. W. J. Smurfit**
56 **MISTY HEIGHTS**, b f Fasliyev (USA)—Mountains of Mist **Lady O'Reilly**
57 **MOHAWK STAR (IRE)**, ch c Indian Ridge—Searching Star **Mrs T. V. Ryan**
58 **MONASER (IRE)**, b c Sadler's Wells (USA)—Copper Creek **Sheikh Hamden Al Maktoum**
59 **MUNTALIQ**, b c Muhtarram (USA)—Bawader (USA) **Sheikh Hamden Al Maktoum**

MR D. K. WELD M.V.B. M.R.C.V.S.—continued

60 **MUNTAMI (IRE)**, gr c Daylami (IRE)—Bashashah (IRE) **Sheikh Hamden Al maktoum**
61 **NOAHS ARK (IRE)**, b f Charnwood Forest (IRE)—Abstraction **Mr D. O'Flynn**
62 **ORPINGTON**, b c Hernando (FR)—Oops Pettie **Mr J. Higgins**
63 **OUT OF THANKS (IRE)**, b f Sadler's Wells (USA)—Trust In Luck (IRE) **Moyglare Stud Farm**
64 **PHAROAH PRINCE**, b c Desert Prince (IRE)—Kinlochewe **Dr M. W. J. Smurfit**
65 **PULITSER (IRE)**, br c Grand Lodge (USA)—Proskona (USA) **Mr J. Higgins**
66 **REHAM (IRE)**, b f Lear Fan (USA)—Stylized **Mr Haif Mohammed Aboud Al Qhatani**
67 **RELAXED GESTURE (IRE)**, ch c Indian Ridge—Token Gesture (IRE) **Moyglare Stud Farm**
68 **RICH SENSE (IRE)**, ch f Mt Livermore (USA)—Seasonal Style (IRE) **Moyglare Stud Farm**
69 **RUSSIAN TSAR (IRE)**, b c King of Kings (IRE)—Kardashina (FR) **Mr Seamus Sheridan**
70 **SIMPLE EXCHANGE (IRE)**, b c Danehill (USA)—Summer Trysting (USA) **Moyglare Stud Farm**
71 **SOARINGWITHEAGLES (USA)**, b c Woodman (USA)—Memories of Pam (USA) **Kenneth L. & Sarah K. Ramsey**
72 **SPIRIT OF AGE (IRE)**, b f Indian Ridge—Minstrels Folly (USA) **Moyglare Stud Farm**
73 **STEEL LIGHT (USA)**, ch c Stravinsky (USA)—Idilic Calm (IRE) **Moyglare Stud Farm**
74 **STOLEN LIGHT (IRE)**, ch c Grand Lodge (USA)—Spring To Light (USA) **Moyglare Stud Farm**
75 **STYLIST (IRE)**, b f Sadler's Wells (USA)—Filia Ardross **Dr M. W. J. Smurfit**
76 **SUMMER SUNSET (IRE)**, ch f Grand Lodge (USA)—Elegant Bloom (IRE) **Mrs C. L. Weld**
77 **TANWIR**, b f Unfuwain (USA)—Al Amlah (USA) **Sheikh Hamden Al Maktoum**
78 **TARKEEZ (USA)**, b c Lear Fan (USA)—Mr Morna (USA) **Sheikh Hamden Al Maktoum**
79 **UPPERVILLE (IRE)**, ch f Selkirk (USA)—Alyakkh (IRE) **Mr B. R. Firestone**
80 **WATHAB (IRE)**, b c Cadeaux Genereux—Bally Souza (IRE) **Mr Haif Mohammed Aboud Al Qhatani**
81 **WOW THE CRITICS (IRE)**, b f Danehill (USA)—Trusted Partner (USA) **Moyglare Stud Farm**

TWO-YEAR-OLDS

82 **ABSOLUTE IMAGE (IRE)**, gr c 31/5 Indian Ridge—Absolute Glee (USA) (Kenmare (FR)) **Moyglare Stud Farm**
83 **B c** 3/5 Giant's Causeway—Across The Ice (USA) (General Holme (USA)) (46381) **Dr M. W. J. Smurfit**
84 **ALL IN A MIX (IRE)**, b c 3/2 Definite Article—Super Gift (IRE) (Darshaan) **Moyglare Stud Farm**
85 **ALTA GRACIA (IRE)**, ch f 7/5 Danehill Dancer (IRE)—Nora Yo Ya (Ahonoora (USA)) (23500) **Mr F. Hinojosa**
86 **AMALTEA**, b f 21/3 Nashwan (USA)—Ballykett Lady (USA) (Sir Ivor) **Mr F. Hinojosa**
87 **ATTEND (IRE)**, b f 23/2 Giant's Causeway—Ashkirk (Selkirk (USA)) **Mr B. R. Firestone**
88 **AURA OF CALM (IRE)**, ch c 19/5 Grand Lodge—
                              Perils of Joy (IRE) (Rainbow Quest (USA)) **Moyglare Stud Farm**
89 **AWAY WITH IT (IRE)**, b c 16/5 Sadler's Wells (USA)—
                              Celebrity Style (USA) (Seeking The Gold (USA)) **Moyglare Stud Farm**
90 **BAWAADER (IRE)**, b c 5/5 Indian Ridge—Alyakkh (IRE) (Sadler's Wells (USA)) **Sheikh Hamdam Al Maktoum**
91 **BOBS PRIDE (IRE)**, b c 30/3 Marju (IRE)—Vyatka (Lion Cavern (USA)) (27828) **Robert Blacoe**
92 **BURREN ROSE (USA)**, ch f 1/2 Storm Cat (USA)—Lisieux Rose (IRE) (Generous (IRE)) **Moyglare Stud Farm**
93 **CASUAL REMARK (IRE)**, b f 5/3 Trans Island—Cidaris (IRE) (Persian Bold) (46381) **Mr B. R. Firestone**
94 **CHEYENNE'S SPIRIT (IRE)**, b f 17/4 Sadler's Wells (USA)—
                              Looking For Gold (Mr Prospector (USA)) **Mrs Rochelle Quinn**
95 **CLEARING THE WATER (IRE)**, b c 21/2 Sadler's Wells (USA)—
                              Leave Me Alone (IRE) (Nashwan (USA)) **Moyglare Stud Farm**
96 **Ch c** 4/2 In The Wings—Continuous (IRE) (Darshaan) (197897) **Dr M. W. J. Smurfit**
97 **CREAM OF SOCIETY (IRE)**, b f 22/4 Selkirk (USA)—All To Easy (Alzao (USA)) **Moyglare Stud Farm**
98 **B f** 23/4 Imperial Ballet (IRE)—Cutlers Corner (Sharpen Up) (37105) **Mr B. R. Firestone**
99 **DATELINE**, ch c 30/1 Namid—Graten (IRE) (Zieten (USA)) (77302) **Mr B. R. Firestone**
100 **DECADES OF STYLE (IRE)**, ch f 23/4 A P Indy (USA)—
                              Gloriously Bright (USA) (Nureyev (USA)) **Moyglare Stud Farm**
101 **DESCRIPTIVE (IRE)**, ch f 27/4 Desert King (IRE)—Ridiya (IRE) (Last Tycoon) (30920) **Mr B. R. Firestone**
102 **B c** 28/2 Machiavellian (USA)—Desert Magic (Green Desert (USA)) (75000) **Dr M. W. J. Smurfit**
103 **DICTATION**, b f 13/2 Diktat—Monaiya (Shareef Dancer (USA)) (49474) **Lady O'Reilly**
104 **DREAM TO DRESS (IRE)**, ch f 19/4 Theatrical—
                              Journey of Hope (USA) (Slew O'Gold (USA)) **Moyglare Stud Farm**
105 **EKTISHAAF (IRE)**, b f 30/1 Mujahid (USA)—Tahnee (Cadeaux Genereux) (41434) **Sheikh Hamdan Al Maktoum**
106 **ELUSIVE DOUBLE (IRE)**, ch c 12/4 Grand Lodge (USA)—Lady Luck (USA) (Kris) **Moyglare Stud Farm**
107 **ESTATE**, b c 11/5 Montjeu (IRE)—Fig Tree Drive (USA) (Miswaki (USA)) (85000) **Highclere Syndicate**
108 **ETIJAHAAT (IRE)**, b c 31/3 King's Best (USA)—
                              Dance Ahead (Shareef Dancer (USA)) (55658) **Sheikh Hamdam Al Maktoum**
109 **Ch c** 16/4 Desert Prince (IRE)—Factice (USA) (Known Fact (USA)) (34013) **Mr David Prentice**
110 **B c** 24/4 Definite Article—Feather 'n Lace (Green Desert (USA)) **Mr S. Sheridan**
111 **B f** 10/2 Indian Ridge—Gipsy Rose Lane (IRE) (Marju (IRE)) (50000) **Mr Derek Weld**
112 **HAPPY TO CHAT**, b f 20/1 Alzao (USA)—Air of Approval (USA) (Diesis) **Moyglare Stud Farm**
113 **HARD WARRIOR (USA)**, ch c 14/4 Gulch (USA)—Seasonal Style (IRE) (Generous (IRE)) **Moyglare Stud Farm**
114 **INSAANI (IRE)**, b c 22/2 Soviet Star (USA)—Ezilla (IRE) (Darshaan) **Sheikh Hamdan Al Maktoum**

MR D. K. WELD M.V.B. M.R.C.V.S.—continued

115 **JUBILANT NOTE**, b c 31/5 Sadler's Wells (USA)—
    Hint of Humour (USA) (Woodman (USA)) **Moyglare Stud Farm**
116 **KHETAAB (IRE)**, b c 4/2 Alhaarth (IRE)—Liberi Versi (IRE) (Last Tycoon) (61842) **Sheikh Hamdan Al Maktoum**
117 **LEADING ARTICLE (IRE)**, ch c 10/3 Definite Article—Jameela (IRE) (Danehill (USA)) (55658) **Dr Ronan Lambe**
118 **LUNAR DANCE (IRE)**, b c 9/2 Fasliyev (USA)—Darkling (IRE) (Grand Lodge (IRE)) (61842) **Dr Ronan Lambe**
119 **MAX ALMIGHTY**, ch c 28/2 Polish Precedent—God Speed (USA) (Be My Guest (USA)) **Mrs Rochelle Quinn**
120 **MERMAID ISLAND**, b f 14/3 Mujadil (USA)—Caumshinaun (IRE) (Indian Ridge) (100000) **Dr Ronan Lambe**
121 **MIDNIGHT MIST (IRE)**, b f 19/1 Green Desert (USA)—Mountains of Mist (IRE) (Shirley Heights) **Lady O'Reilly**
122 **MOONLIGHT DANCE (IRE)**, ch f 26/3 Sinndar (IRE)—
    Style of Life (USA) (The Minstrel (CAN)) (179343) **Dr M. W. J. Smurfit**
123 **MORNING GLOW**, b c 14/4 King Of Kings (IRE)—Colourful Coast (IRE) (Nashwan (USA)) **Moyglare Stud Farm**
124 **MOSAWAT**, b f 8/3 Machiavellian (USA)—Ta Awun (USA) (Housebuster (USA)) **Sheikh Hamdan Al Maktoum**
125 **MOTAFARRED (IRE)**, ch c 15/4 Machiavellian (USA)—Thurayya (Nashwan (USA)) **Sheikh Hamdan Al Maktoum**
126 **MUSAHIM**, b c 28/2 Marju (IRE)—Joonayh (Warning) (85000) **Sheikh Hamdan Al Maktoum**
127 Ch c 8/4 Nashwan (USA)—My Emma (Marju (IRE)) (86580) **Dr M. W. J. Smurfit**
128 Ch c 10/2 Sinndar (IRE)—Navajo Love Song (IRE) (Dancing Brave) (22000) **Eurostrait Ltd**
129 **NOBLE CONCORDE**, gr c 21/3 Daylami (IRE)—
    Place de L'Opera (Sadler's Wells (USA)) (80000) **Dr Ronan Lambe**
130 B c 6/1 Theatrical—Personal Love (USA) (Diesis) (130000) **Six C Racing Ltd**
131 B c 12/3 Desert Prince (IRE)—Play With Fire (FR) (Priolo (USA)) **Dr M. W. J. Smurfit**
132 **QUEEN'S LACE (IRE)**, b br f 23/3 King's Best (USA)—Staff Approved (Teenoso (USA)) (61842) **Lady O'Reilly**
133 B c 5/4 Spinning World (USA)—Rihan (USA) (Dayjur (USA)) (80395) **Mr B. Heiligbrodt**
134 **ROKOCOKO (IRE)**, b c 3/3 Fasliyev (USA)—Early Memory (USA) (Devil's Bag (USA)) **Moyglare Stud Farm**
135 **RUSSIAN WALTZ (IRE)**, b f 19/4 Spectrum (IRE)—
    Russian Countess (USA) (Nureyev (USA)) (74211) **Mr B. R. Firestone**
136 B c 15/4 Alhaarth (IRE)—Sail By Night (USA) (Nureyev (USA)) **Mr Daniele Campanogili**
137 B c 15/3 Royal Anthem (USA)—Search Committee (USA) (Roberto (USA)) (74211) **Mr B. Heiligbrodt**
138 **SET IN MOTION (IRE)**, ch c 3/2 Grand Lodge (USA)—
    Sudden Stir (USA) (Woodman (USA)) **Moyglare Stud Farm**
139 **SOCIETY HOSTESS (USA)**, b f 16/3 Seeking The Gold—
    Touch of Truth (USA) (Storm Cat (USA)) **Moyglare Stud Farm**
140 **SOCIETY MILLINER**, b c 21/3 Sadler's Wells (USA)—Elegance In Design (Habitat) **Moyglare Stud Farm**
141 **SOURCE OF LIFE (IRE)**, b f 12/4 Fasliyev (USA)—Asnieres (USA) (Spend A Buck (USA)) **Mr Robert Sangster**
142 **SPECTACULAR DANCER**, b c 16/4 Fasliyev (USA)—
    Committal (USA) (Chief's Crown (USA)) (61842) **Dr Ronan Lambe**
143 **SPRING OF PEARLS (IRE)**, br f 15/4 Big Shuffle (USA)—
    Foreign Love (USA) (Gulch (USA)) **Moyglare Stud Farm**
144 **STEP IT OUT**, ch c 11/5 King Of Kings (USA)—
    Missing The Beat (USA) (Green Dancer (USA)) **Moyglare Stud Farm**
145 **STRIKING FORCE**, b c 10/5 Danehill (USA)—Trusted Partner (USA) (Affirmed (USA)) **Moyglare Stud Farm**
146 B f 12/3 Xaar—Stylized (USA) (Sovereign Dancer (USA)) (27828) **Hait Mohammed Aboud Al Qatani**
147 **SUMMER SOUL**, b c 23/4 Danehill (USA)—Blend of Pace (IRE) (Sadler's Wells (USA)) **Moyglare Stud Farm**
148 B f 18/4 Deputy Commander—Take Heart (USA) (Secretariat (USA)) **Mr Denis O'Flynn**
149 **TINY PETAL (IRE)**, ch f 4/5 Grand Lodge (USA)—Trust In Luck (IRE) (Nashwan (USA)) **Moyglare Stud Farm**
150 **TRUE JEWEL (USA)**, ch f 12/3 Rahy (USA)—Believe In Myths (USA) (Nijinsky (CAN)) **Moyglare Stud Farm**
151 **UNDERCOVER GLAMOUR (USA)**, b f 30/3 Kingmambo (USA)—
    Well Designed (IRE) (Sadler's Wells (USA)) **Moyglare Stud Farm**
152 **UNIQUE POSE**, b f 4/3 Sadler's Wells (USA)—Desert Ease (IRE) (Green Desert) **Moyglare Stud Farm**
153 **UTTERLY HEAVEN**, b f 4/5 Danehill (USA)—Epicure's Garden (USA) (Affirmed (USA)) **Moyglare Stud Farm**
154 B c 29/4 Darshaan—Wellspring (IRE) (Caerleon (USA)) (420000) **Six C Racing Ltd**
155 **WILDERNESS BAY (IRE)**, b f 28/1 Fasliyev (USA)—Pleine Lune (IRE) (Alzao (USA)) (65000) **Dr Ronan Lambe**
156 **ZAITOON (IRE)**, b f 8/2 Soviet Star (USA)—
    Rise And Fall (Mill Reef (USA)) (210000) **Sheikh Hamdan Al Maktoum**

Jockeys (Flat): P Shanahan (8-5). P J Smullen (8-6). **Jockey (NH):** D T Evans (10-0).

579	**MR D. R. WELLICOME, Llandeilo** Postal: **Beili Llwyd Farm, Manordeilo, Llandeilo, Carmarthenshire, SA19 7BL.** Contact: **PHONE (01550) 779061 MOBILE (07976) 426421**

1 5, B m Tulwar—Fair Seas **Mr D. R. Wellicome**
2 **PANAMA (IRE)**, 4, b c Peintre Celebre (USA)—Bay Queen **Mr D. R. Wellicome**

580 MR MARK WELLINGS, Bridgnorth

Postal: **Broad Acre Stables, Broadlanes, Quatt, Bridgnorth, Shropshire, WV15 6EG.**
Contact: **PHONE (01746) 781019 MOBILE (07973) 763469 E-MAIL mark@broadacre.fsnet.co.uk**

1 DANCING DANOLI, 4, b f Bin Ajwaad (IRE)—Wave Dancer **Mr G. K. Gordon**
2 D-DAY-SMOKE, 10, ch g Cigar—Little Pockthorpe **Mr Norman Wolstencroft**
3 ESPERE D'OR, 7, b g Golden Heights—Drummer's Dream (IRE) **Snax Catering Services Limited**
4 GWENS GIRL, 4, b f Wizard King—Russian Project (IRE) **Mr J. C. Bradbury**
5 HILL FARM CLASSIC, 4, ch g Meqdaam (USA)—Wing of Freedom **Mr Dennis Newton**
6 LITTLE RICHARD, 5, b g Alhaarth (IRE)—Intricacy **The 1471 Racing Partnership**
7 OLD GOLDEN GREY, 7, gr g Thethingaboutitis (USA)—Modina April **Mr Stephen Williams**
8 PLATINUM BOY (IRE), 4, b g Goldmark (USA)—Brown Foam **The 1471 Racing Partnership**
9 POLKA PRINCESS, 4, b f Makbul—Liberatrice (FR) **The Fun Run Partnership**

TWO-YEAR-OLDS

10 KATIE KILLANE, ch f Komaite (USA)—Efficacy (Efisio) **Mr D. Timmins**

Other Owners: Mr T. C. J. Heston, Mr A. M. H. Kendrick, Mrs G. Lancina, Mr A. Tranter.

Assistant Trainer: Mrs L A Wellings

581 MR L. WELLS, Billingshurst

Postal: **Pallingham Manor Farm, Wisborough Green, Billingshurst, West Sussex, RH14 0EZ.**
Contact: **HOME (01403) 700679 OFFICE (01403) 700119 FAX (01403) 700899**
MOBILE (07977) 144949
E-MAIL pmf@btinternet.com WEBSITE www.lawrencewells.co.uk

1 COWBOYBOOTS (IRE), 6, b g Lord Americo—Little Welly **Mr David Gower**
2 ELVIS, 11, b g Southern Music—Tyqueen **The Chap Quartet**
3 GOLDEN NOUGAT (IRE), 6, ch g Montelimar (USA)—Serenade Run **Mr D. W. Cox & Mr Paul Zetter**
4 GOOD BONE (FR), 7, b g Perrault—Bone Crasher (FR) **Mr L. Wells**
5 HIDDEN WEAPON, 7, b g Charmer—Bustellina **Hills, Smith and Wearne**
6 JUST ANVIL (IRE), 6, ch g Baron Blakeney—Amy Just (IRE) **Mr David Cox**
7 KILBREADY BOY (IRE), 9, ch g Beau Sher—Ginger Dee **Hills, Smith and Wearne**
8 KILDORRAGH (IRE), 10, b g Glacial Storm (IRE)—Take A Dare **Mrs Carrie Zetter-Wells**
9 LEASE BACK (FR), 5, b g Sleeping Car (FR)—Salse Pareille (FR) **Mrs Carrie Zetter-Wells**
10 MARIE DE MARSAL (IRE), 5, ch m Zaffaran (USA)—Crabtreejazz (IRE) **Mr Randal Mawhinney**
11 MOSS CAMPIAN, 6, ch g Le Moss—Rose Rambler **Mr W. A. Scott**
12 MULTI TALENTED (IRE), 8, b g Montelimar (USA)—Boro Glen **Mr David Cox**
13 ONE CORNETTO (IRE), 5, b g Eurobus—Costenetta (IRE) **Mrs Carrie Zetter-Wells**
14 RUSINGA, 6, gr g Homo Sapien—Royal Blaze **Mrs Carrie Zetter-Wells**
15 SPIRIT OFTHE GREEN (IRE), 6, br g Detroit Sam (FR)—Golden Hearted **Jazz Knight Partnership**
16 STARSHIPENTERPRISE, 6, b g The Star of Orion VII—Lequest **Mr L. Wells**
17 STONED (IRE), 4, b g Bigstone (IRE)—Lady Celina (FR) **Mr L. Wells**
18 SUPER ROAD TRAIN, 5, b g Petoski—Foehn Gale (IRE) **Mr David Knox**
19 SUPERROLLERCOASTER, 4, b g Classic Cliche (IRE)—Foehn Gale (IRE) **Mr David Knox**
20 TOP DOG (IRE), 5, b g Topanoora—Dun Oengus (IRE) **Mrs Carrie Zetter-Wells**
21 WITHTHELADS (IRE), 6, b g Tidaro (USA)—Quayside Charm **Mr L. Wells**
22 ZERO RISK (IRE), 8, ch g Insan (USA)—Serenade Run **Mr Paul Zetter**

THREE-YEAR-OLDS

23 THE STAFFORD (IRE), b g Selkirk (USA)—Bint Zamayem (IRE) **Sir Eric Parker**

Other Owners: Mr R. E. Greatorex, Mr M. J. Hills, Mr D. L. C. Longden, Mr Julian Smith, Mr P. Wearne.

Assistant Trainer: Mrs C Zetter-Wells

Amateurs: Mr J J King (9-12), Miss Claire Milne (9-0), Mr Justin Morgan (10-0).

582

MR J. R. WEYMES, Middleham
Postal: **Ashgill, Coverham, Leyburn, North Yorkshire, DL8 4TJ.**
Contact: **PHONE (01969) 640420 FAX (01969) 640505 MOBILE (07753) 792516**
E-MAIL johnweymes@aol.com WEBSITE www.johnweymes.co.uk

1 **BRIGADORE**, 5, b g Magic Ring (IRE)—Music Mistress (IRE) **White Rose Poultry Ltd**
2 **CROSBY DON**, 9, b g Alhijaz—Evening Star **Mr Don Raper**
3 **CROSBY DONJOHN**, 7, ch g Magic Ring (IRE)—Ovideo **Mr Don Raper**
4 **DANAKIM**, 7, b g Emarati (USA)—Kangra Valley **Miss K. A. Buckle**
5 **GOTYA**, 4, b f Gothenberg (IRE)—Water Well **Mrs M. Hills**
6 **GRACIOUS AIR (USA)**, 6, b m Bahri (USA)—Simply Bell (USA)
7 **GRAND VIEW**, 8, ch g Grand Lodge (USA)—Hemline **Sporting Occasions**
8 5, B m Primitive Rising (USA)—Hinton Bairn **Mr Ron Lilly**
9 4, B g Gothenberg (IRE)—Hobbs Choice **Mr J. J. Crossier**
10 **IMPERIAL SHO**, 5, ch g Royal Abjar (USA)—Magnetic Point (USA) **White Rose Poultry Ltd**
11 **LAPADAR (IRE)**, 5, b br m Woodborough (USA)—Indescent Blue **Mr J. Weymes**
12 **LINDEN'S LADY**, 4, b f Compton Place—Jubilee Place (IRE) **Lonsdale Racing**
13 **LITTLETON VALAR (IRE)**, 4, ch g Definite Article—Fresh Look (IRE) **Miss K. A. Buckle**
14 **MILDON**, 8, ch g Dolphin Street (FR)—Lycia **Mr Don Raper**
15 **STANLEY PARK**, 6, ch g Bold Arrangement—Queen Buzzard **Miss K. A. Buckle**
16 **VINTAGE STYLE**, 5, ch g Piccolo—Gibaltarik (IRE) **Sporting Occasions**

THREE-YEAR-OLDS

17 **ATTACCA**, b c Piccolo—Jubilee Place (IRE) **J. K. Brown & Partners**
18 **BLUE VIKING (IRE)**, b g Danetime (IRE)—Jenny Spinner (IRE) **Three J's Racing**
19 **CROSBY JUBILEE (IRE)**, b g Shinko Forest (IRE)—Quicksand (IRE) **Mr Don Raper**
20 **FOXIES FUTURE (IRE)**, b f General Monash (USA)—Indescent Blue **Dandyjack Racing**
21 **GOLD CARD**, b g First Trump—Fleuve d'Or (IRE) **Mrs R. L. Heaton**
22 **GRACEFUL AIR (IRE)**, b f Danzero (AUS)—Samsung Spirit **T. A. Scothern**
23 B f Magic Ring (IRE)—Kirkadian **R. Burton**
24 **MYANNABANANA (IRE)**, ch c Woodborough (USA)—Raging Storm **T. A. Scothern**
25 **MYTHICAL AIR (IRE)**, b f Magic Ring (IRE)—Legendary Dancer **T. A. Scothern & Partners**
26 **UPTHEDALE (IRE)**, b g General Monash (USA)—Pimpinella **Middleham Park Racing**
27 **VALIANT AIR (IRE)**, b g Spectrum (IRE)—Shining Desert (IRE) **T. A. Scothern & Partners**

TWO-YEAR-OLDS

28 **AQUA**, b f 14/4 Mister Baileys—Water Well (Sadler's Wells (USA)) (1600) **Mrs M. Hills**
29 B f 2/3 Bluegrass Prince—Brac Princess (IRE) (Nicolette) (1500) **Sporting Occasions**
30 **FENRIR**, ch c 12/3 Loup Solitaire (USA)—Whoops (Shernazar) **Mr A. Moorey**
31 B f 1/3 Tipsy Creek (USA)—Grandads Dream (Never So Bold) **J. K. Brown & Partners**
32 **HRYMR**, b c 23/3 Trempolino (USA)—Ten To Six (Night Shift (USA)) **Mr W. Pooleman**
33 **MORNING WORLD**, b c 29/1 Bahamian Bounty—Snap Cracker (Inchinor) (16000) **Mr N. Palamountain**
34 B f 22/3 Charnwood Forest—Mubadara (IRE) (Lahib (USA)) (1400) **Sporting Occasions**
35 **REGAL LUSTRE**, b f 2/2 Averti (IRE)—Noble Lustre (USA) (Lyphard's Wish (FR)) (11500) **Mrs A. Birkett**
36 B f 19/4 Bold Fact (USA)—Sky Lover (Ela-Mana-Mou) (3000) **Web Racing**
37 B g 15/3 Rock City—Thieves Welcome (Most Welcome) (2000) **Mr J. Isteed**
38 B c 15/3 Polish Precedent—Trick (IRE) (Shirley Heights) (7500) **Mrs N. Naiper**

Other Owners: Mrs D. Catlow, Mr Mel Catlow, Mr I. A. Gregg, Mrs E. Palamountain, Mr C. A. Watson.

Assistant Trainer: Kirsty Buckle

Jockeys (Flat): P Hanagan, R Winston. **Jockey (NH):** J Crowley. **Apprentice:** D Fentiman (7-5). **Conditional:** P Whelan.

583

MR E. A. WHEELER, Pangbourne
Postal: **Coombe Park Stables, Whitchurch on Thames, Pangbourne, Oxfordshire, RG8 7QT.**
Contact: **PHONE (01189) 841317 FAX (01189) 841924 MOBILE (07712) 880966**

1 **BATCHWORTH BREEZE**, 6, ch m Beveled (USA)—Batchworth Dancer **Mr G. W. Witheford**
2 **CATCHTHEBATCH**, 8, b g Beveled (USA)—Batchworth Dancer **Four Of A Kind Racing**
3 **DANCING MYSTERY**, 10, b g Beveled (USA)—Batchworth Dancer **Astrod TA Austin Stroud & Co**
4 **DIAPHANOUS**, 6, b m Beveled (USA)—Sharp Venita **The Red Square Partnership**
5 **DUNEDIN RASCAL**, 7, b g Piccolo—Thorner Lane **Halewood International Ltd**
6 **KUMAKAWA**, 6, ch g Dancing Spree (USA)—Maria Cappuccini **Mr Mike Smith**

MR E. A. WHEELER—continued

  7 MASTER MCGHEE, 5, ch g Beveled (USA)—Sandra Dee (IRE) **Mr E. A. Wheeler**
  8 4, B g Nomination—Princess Kelly **Mr G. Witheford**
  9 RATHMULLAN, 5, ch g Bluegrass Prince (IRE)—National Time (USA) **You're Having A Laugh Racing Club**
10 YOUNG DYNASTY, 4, ch g Young Ern—Miss Michelle **You're Having A Laugh Racing Club**

THREE-YEAR-OLDS

11 B g Young Ern—A Little Hot **Mr E. Wheeler**
12 BATCHWORTH BEAU, ch g Bluegrass Prince (IRE)—Batchworth Belle **Mrs Diana Price**
13 Ch f Young Ern—Batchworth Dancer **Mrs Diana Price**
14 B f Young Ern—Treasurebound **Mrs Diana Price**

TWO-YEAR-OLDS

15 B f 15/3 Fraam—Clued Up (Beveled (USA)) **Four Of A Kind Racing**

Other Owners: Mr T. Arnold, Mr T. M. Bowser, Mrs K. Francis, Mr Neale Sadlier.

Jockey (Flat): S Carson (8-2). **Apprentice:** Liam Jones (7-2). **Amateur:** Mr C Witheford (9-10).

---

584 **MR A. C. WHILLANS, Hawick**
Postal: **Esker House, Newmill-On-Slitrig, Hawick, TD9 9UQ.**
Contact: **PHONE (01450) 376642 MOBILE (07771) 550555**

  1 ABLE MIND, 4, b g Mind Games—Chlo-Jo **Mrs L. Irving**
  2 ASTAFORT (FR), 5, ch g Kendor (FR)—Tres Chic (USA) **Mrs Murray Scott**
  3 BRAVE VISION, 8, b g Clantime—Kinlet Vision (IRE) **Mrs S. Harrow**
  4 CHAKA ZULU, 7, b g Muhtarram (USA)—African Dance (USA) **Mrs L. Irving**
  5 CRYSTAL GIFT, 12, b g Dominion—Grain Lady (USA) **Mrs L. M. Whillans**
  6 CUTHILL HOPE (IRE), 13, gr g Peacock (FR)—Sicilian Princess **Mr Stephen Gilchrist**
  7 EASTERN TRIBUTE (USA), 8, b g Affirmed (USA)—Mia Duchessa (USA) **Mr John J. Elliot**
  8 GOFAGOLD, 9, ch g Tina's Pet—Golden Della **Mrs L. M. Whillans**
  9 KIVOTOS (USA), 6, gr g Trempolino (USA)—Authorized Staff (USA) **Mr C. Bird**
10 KRACK DE L'ISLE (FR), 6, b g Kadalko (FR)—Ceres de L'Isle (FR) **Mr John J. Elliot**
11 MINSTER FAIR, 6, b m Minster Son—Fair Echo **Mr E. Waugh**
12 NAUTICAL STAR, 9, b g Slip Anchor—Comic Talent **Mrs Helen Greggan**
13 REFLECTIVE WAY, 11, ch m Mirror Boy—Craigie Way **Mr Robert Robinson**
14 SCURRA, 5, b g Spectrum (IRE)—Tamnia **Mrs L. M. Whillans**
15 UNDER WRAPS (IRE), 10, b g In The Wings—Wrapping **Mr G. Brown**

Other Owners: Mr J. Waugh.

Amateur: Mr Ewan Whillans (9-10).

---

585 **MR R. M. WHITAKER, Scarcroft**
Postal: **Hellwood Racing Stables, Hellwood Lane, Scarcroft, Leeds, West Yorkshire, LS14 3BP.**
Contact: **PHONE (0113) 2892265 FAX (0113) 2893680 MOBILE (07831) 870454**

  1 ALCHEMIST MASTER, 5, b g Machiavellian (USA)—Gussy Marlowe **Mr T. L. Adams**
  2 JAKEAL (IRE), 5, b g Eagle Eyed (USA)—Karoi (FR) **Mr James Marshall & Mrs Susan Marshall**
  3 LORD OF METHLEY, 5, gr g Zilzal (USA)—Paradise Waters **Mr R. M. Whitaker**
  4 MYND, 4, b g Atraf—Prim Lass **Derek and Jean Clee**
  5 NEVADA DESERT (IRE), 4, b g Desert King (USA)—Kayanga **Mr J. Barry Pemberton**
  6 SALLY TRAFFIC, 5, b m River Falls—Yankeedoodledancer **Mr J. Barry Pemberton**
  7 SOLARTISTE, 4, b f Danzig Connection (USA)—Shaft of Sunlight **Mr R. M. Whitaker**
  8 STEEL BLUE, 4, b g Atraf—Something Blue **Country Lane Partnership**
  9 VICIOUS PRINCE (IRE), 5, b g Sadler's Wells—Sunny Flower (FR) **Mr Alan Crossan**
10 VICIOUS ROSIE, 5, ch m Dancing Spree (USA)—Spinner **Mr J. Samuel**
11 VICIOUS WARRIOR, 5, b g Elmaamul (USA)—Ling Lane **Mr J. Samuel**

THREE-YEAR-OLDS

12 ACCA LARENTIA (IRE), gr f Titus Livius (FR)—Daisy Grey **Mr Ken Lewis**
13 BISCAR TWO (IRE), b g Daggers Drawn (USA)—Thoughtful Kate **Mr M. J. O'Dwyer**
14 CARIBBEAN BLUE, b f First Trump—Something Blue **Mrs Jill Willows**

MR R. M. WHITAKER—continued

15 **HARRINGTON BATES**, ch g Wolfhound (USA)—Fiddling **Mr Paul Davies (H'gte)**
16 B f Danzig Connection (USA)—Ling Lane **Mr R. M. Whitaker**
17 **NEON BLUE**, b br g Atraf—Desert Lynx (IRE) **Country Lane Partnership**
18 Ch g Wolfhound (USA)—Parfait Amour **Mr R. M. Whitaker**
19 **SCOOBY DOOBY DO**, b f Atraf—Redgrave Design **Mr Paul Davies (H'gte)**

TWO-YEAR-OLDS

20 **AFRICAN BREEZE**, b f 21/2 Atraf—Luanshya (First Trump) **T. L. Adams & G. F. Pemberton**
21 B g 12/5 Vettori (IRE)—Alacrity (Alzao (USA)) (3300)
22 **CHINGOLA**, b f 15/2 Atraf—Sulaka (Owington) (5200) **T. L. Adams**
23 **DESERTINA (IRE)**, b f 5/4 Spectrum (IRE)—Kayanga (Green Desert (USA)) (7500) **J. B. Pemberton**
24 B g 17/4 Mind Games—Fairy Ring (IRE) (Fairy King (USA))
25 **JUST WAZ (USA)**, ch c 13/3 Woodman—Just Tops (USA) (Topsider (USA)) (45000) **Mrs L. Ziegler**
26 **LUCKY LIL**, ch f 7/3 Cadeaux Genereux—Amalia (IRE) (Danehill (USA)) (8000) **Mrs L. Ziegler**
27 **MR MAXIM**, ch g 13/3 Lake Coniston (IRE)—White Hare (Indian Ridge) **J. Englehart**
28 **PARIS HEIGHTS**, gr g 15/2 Paris House—Petra Nova (First Trump) **Mr W. M. Ellis**
29 B g 8/5 Factual (USA)—Tugra (FR) (Baby Turk) (500)
30 B c 20/3 Second Empire (IRE)—Ultimate Beat (USA) (Go And Go) (8000) **Mr R. M. Whitaker**

Other Owners: Mr & Mrs R. Bell, Mr G. Rayner.

Assistant Trainer: Simon R Whitaker

Jockeys (Flat): Vince Halliday (8-4), Dean McKeown (8-4).

---

586 **MR A. J. WHITEHEAD, Craven Arms**
Postal: **Lawn Farm, Beambridge, Aston on Clun, Craven Arms, Shropshire, SY7 0HA.**
Contact: **PHONE (01588) 660424**

1 **CITIMAN (AUS)**, 7, b g Citidancer—Taimian (NZ) **Mr A. J. Whitehead**
2 **JOCKER DU SAPIN (FR)**, 7, br g Franc Parler—Nymphe Rose (FR) **Mr A. J. Whitehead**
3 **LORD DAL (FR)**, 11, b g Cadoudal (FR)—Lady Corteira (FR) **Mr A. J. Whitehead**
4 **MEILLEUR (NZ)**, 6, ch g Mellifont (USA)—Petite Cheval (NZ) **Mr A. J. Whitehead**

Jockey (NH): O McPhail (10-0, w.a.).

---

587 **MR A. J. WHITING, Dursley**
Postal: **38 Barrs Lane, North Nibley, Dursley, Gloucestershire, GL11 6DT.**
Contact: **PHONE (01453) 546375 MOBILE (07786) 152539**

1 **APPLE JOE**, 8, b g Sula Bula—Hazelwain **Mr A. J. Whiting**
2 **BALLOFASOP (IRE)**, 7, b g Shalford (IRE)—Sosalolomome (IRE) **Mr A. J. Whiting**
3 **FOREST MAZE**, 8, b m Arzanni—Forest Nymph (NZ) **Mr A. J. Whiting**
4 **HAZELJACK**, 9, b g Sula Bula—Hazelwain **Mr A. J. Whiting**

---

588 **MR M. S. WILESMITH, Dymock**
Postal: **Bellamys Farm, Dymock, Gloucestershire, GL18 2DX.**
Contact: **PHONE (01531) 890410 MOBILE (07970) 411638 FAX (01684) 893428**
E-MAIL martin@m.s.wilesmith.com

1 4, B f Alflora (IRE)—Annicombe Run **Mr M. S. Wilesmith**
2 **CLARAS PRIDE (IRE)**, 12, b g Be My Native (USA)—Our Hollow **Mr M. S. Wilesmith**
3 **COTTON ON**, 7, b g Henbit (USA)—Linen Leaf **Mr M. S. Wilesmith**
4 5, B g Carroll House—Mountain Grove **Mr M. S. Wilesmith**
5 **OLE GUNNAR (IRE)**, 12, b g Le Bavard (FR)—Rareitess **Mr M. S. Wilesmith**
6 **THIS ONE IS A BOY (IRE)**, 8, b g Executive Perk—Belinda Vard **Mr M. S. Wilesmith**

Assistant Trainer: Miss E C Wilesmith

Amateur: Mr M C Wilesmith (10-9).

589 MR. M S. C. WILLCOCK, Tavistock
Postal: **3 Townhead Cottages, Mary Tavy, Tavistock, Devon, PL19 9PR.**
Contact: **PHONE (01822) 810839**

1 5, Ch m Past Glories—Flira **Ms Sue Willcock**
2 PIPERSLAND, 7, b g Lir—Celtic Mist **Ms Sue Willcock**

Amateur: Mr Darren Edwards.

590 MR D. L. WILLIAMS, Chilton
Postal: **Hillside Stud, Great Shefford, Nr Hungerford, Berkshire, RG17 7DL.**
Contact: **HOME (01488) 638636 FAX (01488) 638121 MOBILE (07747) 864739**

1 AUTUMN RAIN (USA), 7, br g Dynaformer (USA)—Edda (USA) **Ridgeway Farm Racing**
2 COMPTON EXPERT (IRE), 4, b g Cadeaux Genereux—Samira **Mr Gareth Cheshire**
3 GOLLY (IRE), 8, b g Toulon—Tor-Na-Grena **Reliance Car Hire Services Ltd**
4 LUNARDI (IRE), 6, b g Indian Ridge—Gold Tear (USA) **Miss L. Horner**
5 MISS KOEN (IRE), 5, b m Barathea (IRE)—Fanny Blankers (IRE) **D. L. Williams**
6 MR COSPECTOR, 7, b g Cosmonaut—L'Ancressaan **The Eight Prospectors Syndicate**
7 NADOUR AL BAHR (IRE), 9, b g Be My Guest (USA)—Nona (GER) **D. L. Williams**
8 PEPETA, 7, b m Presidium—Mighty Flash **Miss L. Horner**
9 RELIANCE LEADER, 8, ch g Weld—Swift Messenger **Reliance Car Hire Services Ltd**
10 SHARP SPICE, 8, b m Lugana Beach—Ewar Empress (IRE) **Symbol Of Success Racing**
11 SPARKLING WATER (USA), 5, b h Woodman (USA)—Shirley Valentine **Mrs Jeffrey Robinson**
12 YORKSHIRE (IRE), 10, ch g Generous (IRE)—Ausherra (USA) **Girls On Top Racing 2000**

Other Owners: R. J. Barker, Mr J. Darby, Mrs N. C. Diment, James Fry, Mr John S. C. Fry, Mrs K. A. Fry, Gumbriggs Racing Partnership, Mr K. L. Pollington.

Assistant Trainer: Miss Victoria Flood

Jockey (NH): James Diment (10-0). **Amateurs:** Miss V M L Flood (10-7), Capt. Lucy Horner (9-0).

591 MR I. P. WILLIAMS, Alvechurch
Postal: **Hob Hill Farm, Seafield Lane, Portway, Birmingham, B48 7HL.**
Contact: **PHONE (01564) 822392 FAX (01564) 829475 E-MAIL info@ianwilliamsracing.com**

1 ARCTIC PLAYBOY, 8, b g Petoski—Arctic Oats **Mr R. P. Dineen**
2 BAIKALINE (FR), 5, b m Cadoudal (FR)—Advantage (FR) **Mr Ian Williams**
3 BATMAN SENORA (FR), 8, b g Chamberlin (FR)—Cartza (FR) **Mr G. Polinski**
4 BLACK FALCON (IRE), 4, ch g In The Wings—Muwasim (USA) **Mr C. N. Barnes**
5 BLUE RONDO (IRE), 4, b g Hernando (FR)—Blueberry Walk **Sky Blues Racing**
6 BOB'S THE BUSINESS (IRE), 10, b g Bob Back (USA)—Kiora **Mr Christopher Harris**
7 BRAVE SPIRIT (FR), 6, b g Legend of France (USA)—Guerre Ou Paix (FR) **Sir Robert Ogden**
8 BREWSTER (IRE), 7, b g Roselier (FR)—Aelia Paetina **Mr & Mrs John Poynton**
9 BROOKLYN'S GOLD (USA), 9, b g Seeking The Gold (USA)—Brooklyn's Dance (FR) **Mr Terry Warner**
10 BUCCANEER BOY (IRE), 11, b g Buckskin (FR)—Shady Miss **Mrs Rosemary Paterson**
11 CAUCASIAN (IRE), 6, gr g Leading Counsel (USA)—Kemal's Princess **Mr Ian Williams**
12 CHRISTMAS TRUCE (IRE), 5, b g Brief Truce (USA)—Superflash **Mr M. Murphy**
13 CIRCUS MAXIMUS (USA), 7, b g Pleasant Colony (USA)—Crockadore (USA) **Mr Chris McHale**
14 COLVADA, 8, b m North Col—Prevada **Mr & Mrs M. R. Paul**
15 COMPTON COMMANDER, 6, ch g Barathea (IRE)—Triode (USA) **Mr Mark Gichero**
16 COOLBYTHEPOOL, 4, b c Bijou d'Inde—Alchi (USA) **Mr Paul Morrison**
17 DOROOSS (IRE), 4, b g Charnwood Forest (IRE)—Catherinofaragon (USA) **Mr C. N. Barnes**
18 DOWNPOUR (USA), 6, b g Torrential (USA)—Juliac (USA) **Favourites Racing**
19 EDGINSWELL LASS, 6, b m Morpeth—Oribi Gorge (IRE) **Mr Terry Sanders**
20 ELUNA, 6, ch m Unfuwain (USA)—Elisha (GER) **Mr & Mrs John Poynton**
21 FASHION VICTIM, 9, b g High Estate—Kirkby Belle **Mr J. A. Simpson**
22 FORTUNATE DAVE (USA), 5, b g Lear Fan (USA)—Lady Ameriflora (USA) **Mr M. N. Dennis**
23 FRENCH ENVOY (FR), 5, bl g Cadoudal (FR)—Miss Merry (FR) **Sir Robert Ogden**
24 GOVERNOR DANIEL, 13, b g Governor General—Princess Semele **DSM Demolition Limited**
25 GRANDE BRETAGNE (FR), 5, b g Legend of France (USA)—L'Epicurienne (FR) **Sir Robert Ogden**
26 HI FI, 6, b g Homo Sapien—Baroness Orkzy **Mrs Rosemary Paterson**
27 HIGH ACTION (USA), 4, ch c Theatrical—Secret Imperatrice (USA) **Mr C. N. Barnes**

MR I. P. WILLIAMS—continued

28 **HORS LA LOI (FR)**, 8, ch g Exit To Nowhere (USA)—Kernia (IRE) **The Not So Risky Partnership**
29 **IDEALKO (FR)**, 8, b g Kadalko (FR)—Belfaster (FR) **Mrs Maggie Bull**
30 **IMPERATIVE (USA)**, 4, ch c Woodman (USA)—Wandesta **Mr Paul Morrison**
31 **JARDIN DE BÉAULIEU (FR)**, 7, ch g Rough Magic (FR)—Emblem (FR) **Mr & Mrs John Poynton**
32 **KASSEL (USA)**, 4, ch g Swain (IRE)—Gretel **Mr Patrick Kelly**
33 **KORAKOR (FR)**, 10, ch g Nikos—Aniflore (FR) **Mr and Mrs J. D. Cotton**
34 **LATE CLAIM**, 4, ch g King of Kings (IRE)—Irish Flare (USA) **Pertemps Group Limited**
35 **MAJESTIC (IRE)**, 9, b g Belmez (USA)—Noble Lily (USA) **Mr Patrick Kelly**
36 **MANORAM (GER)**, 5, ch g Zinaad—Mayada (USA) **Willsford Racing Incorporated**
37 **MAZILEO**, 11, b g Mazilier (USA)—Embroglio (USA) **Mr T. J. & Mrs H. Parrott**
38 **MISTER MANORAM (IRE)**, 7, b g Norwich—Monalma (IRE) **Favourites Racing**
39 **MONEY CRAZY (FR)**, 5, ch g Green Tune (USA)—Value For Money (FR) **J. M. Boodle Esq & A. H. M. White Esq**
40 **MONSIEUR TAGEL (FR)**, 8, b g Tagel (USA)—Miss Zonissa (FR) **J. Cullen Thermals Ltd**
41 **MULHACEN (IRE)**, 8, br m Supreme Leader—Lancaster Lady (IRE) **The Mulhacen Partnership**
42 **NAGANO (FR)**, 6, b g Hero's Honor (USA)—Sadinskaya (FR) **Allan Stennett & Terry Warner**
43 **NAVARONE**, 10, b g Gunner B—Anamasi **Mr A. J. Cresser**
44 **NORVIN (IRE)**, 7, b g Nashwan (USA)—Percy's Lass **Mr Ian Williams**
45 **NOT AMUSED (UAE)**, 4, ch g Indian Ridge—Amusing Time (IRE) **Mr Ian Williams**
46 **OATIS BROOK**, 6, b g Alderbrook—Lagrimass **McMahon (Contractors Services) Ltd**
47 **PERTEMPS PROFILE**, 8, b g Petoski—Peristyle **Pertemps Group Limited**
48 **PILLAR OF FIRE (IRE)**, 10, gr g Roselier (FR)—Cousin Flo **Mr Paul Robson**
49 **PILLAR TO POST**, 5, b g Bluegrass Prince (IRE)—Parisana (FR) **Mr T. J. & Mrs H. Parrott**
50 **PLANTAGANET (FR)**, 6, br g Cadoudal (FR)—Ever Young (FR) **Sir Robert Ogden**
51 **PRIMATICCIO (IRE)**, 9, b g Priolo (USA)—Martiniva **Mr Ian Williams**
52 **QUITE REMARKABLE**, 5, b g Danzig Connection (USA)—Kathy Fair (IRE) **Mr J. Tredwell**
53 **RIVER PHANTOM (IRE)**, 5, b g Over The River (FR)—Cathilda (IRE) **Mr Graham Ketley**
54 **ROYALEETY (FR)**, 5, b g Garde Royale—La Grive (FR) **Mr & Mrs John Poynton**
55 **ROYAL TRIGGER**, 4, b c Double Trigger (IRE)—Jeronime (USA) **Lady Caffyn-Parsons & Mrs E. E. Dedman**
56 **SAINT REVERIEN (FR)**, 5, b g Silver Rainbow—La Briganderie (FR) **Hill Fuels Limited**
57 **SHARMY (IRE)**, 8, b g Caerleon (USA)—Petticoat Lane **Mr T. J. & Mrs H. Parrott**
58 **SHARPATEN (IRE)**, 9, b g Scenic—Sloane Ranger **The Baron Rouge Partnership**
59 **SMOOTHIE (IRE)**, 6, gr g Definite Article—Limpopo **Miss S. Howell**
60 **SNIPE**, 6, ch g Anshan—Flewwing **Mr C. J. Tipton**
61 **TEST OF FRIENDSHIP**, 7, br g Roselier (FR)—Grease Pot **Mr M. F. Barraclough**
62 **THE PRINCE**, 10, b g Machiavellian (USA)—Mohican Girl **Mr Patrick Kelly**
63 **UNGARETTI (GER)**, 7, b g Law Society (USA)—Urena (GER) **PEL Project Management**
64 **WAR OWL (USA)**, 7, gr g Linamix (FR)—Ganasheba (USA) **Mrs Glennie Braune**
65 **WAR TUNE**, 8, b g Warrshan (USA)—Keen Melody (USA) **The Five Nations Partnership**
66 **WHITE DOVE (FR)**, 6, b m Beaudelaire (USA)—Hermine And Pearls (FR) **Creme de la Creme**
67 **WILD POWER (FR)**, 6, br g Turtle Island (IRE)—White On Red (GER) **Direct Sales UK Ltd**

Other Owners: Mr J. M. Boodle, Lady Caffyn-Parsons, Mr Anthony Callaghan, Mr G. Clinton, Mrs J. E. Clinton, Mr K. Collins, Mr D. G. Conyers, Mrs B. Cotton, Mr J. D. Cotton, Mrs E. E. Dedman, Mr Tony Eaves, Mr Adrian Johnstone, Mr H. R. Johnstone, Mr P. Kendall, Mr T. C. Marshall, Mr John Nash, Mr R. J. Newbery, Mr N. E. Newbold, Dr R. D. P Newland, Mrs H. Parrott, Mr T. J. Parrott, Mr M. R. Paul, Mrs S. M. Paul, Mrs Anne Poynton, Mr John Poynton, Mr P. A. Rose, Mr Allan Stennett, Mr R. Trow, Mr A. H. M. White.

Assistant Trainer: Chris Kinane

Jockey (NH): D R Dennis. **Conditional:** N Carter, R I Mackenzie, W A Worthington. **Amateur:** Mr Thomas Messenger (9-7).

---

592 **MR N. S. L. WILLIAMS, South Molton**
Postal: **Culverhill Farm, George Nympton, South Molton, Devon, EX36 4JE.**
Contact: **HOME (01769) 574174 FAX (01769) 573661 MOBILE (07855) 450379**

1 **COMPLETE OUTSIDER**, 6, b g Opera Ghost—Alice Passthorn **Mr Mike Ford**
2 **DEAD-EYED DICK (IRE)**, 8, b g Un Desperado (FR)—Glendale Charmer **Mrs Jane Williams**
3 **DOM D'ORGEVAL (FR)**, 4, ch g Belmez (USA)—Marie d'Orgeval (FR) **Mrs Jane Williams**
4 **FABREZAN (FR)**, 5, b g Nikos—Fabulous Secret (FR) **Mr J. D. Cox**
5 **FEAR SIUIL (IRE)**, 11, b g Strong Gale—Astral River **Mrs Jane Williams**
6 **HE'S THE BIZ (FR)**, 5, b g Nikos—Irun (FR) **Mrs Jane Williams**
7 **KINGS BROOK**, 4, br g Alderbrook—Kins Token **Mr Tony Gale**
8 **MR CRAWFORD**, 5, gr g Opera Ghost—Alice Passthorn **Gale Force Two**
9 **PHILSON RUN (IRE)**, 8, b g Un Desperado (FR)—Isis **Gale Force One**

MR N. S. L. WILLIAMS—continued

THREE-YEAR-OLDS

10 **BLANDINGS CASTLE**, b g Cloudings (IRE)—Country House **Mr J. D. Cox**
11 B g Flemensfirth (USA)—Cheryls Pet (IRE) **Mrs Jane Williams**
12 B g Oscar (IRE)—Cush Maid **Mrs Jane Williams**
13 B g Taipan (IRE)—Forest Mist (USA) **Mrs Jane Williams**
14 **LADY LOVEDAY**, b br f Panoramic—Cadal Queen (FR) **Mrs Jane Williams**
15 B g Supreme Leader—Stormy Miss (IRE) **Mrs Jane Williams**

TWO-YEAR-OLDS

16 **DIZZY LIZZY**, gr f 11/3 Sendawar (IRE)—Black Velvet (FR) (Black Tie Affair) **Mrs Jane Williams**

Other Owners: Mr Peter Norris.

Assistant Trainer: Mrs Jane Williams

---

593 MR S. C. WILLIAMS, Newmarket
Postal: 133 Tulyar Walk, Newmarket, Suffolk, CB8 7AX.
Contact: YARD (01638) 560143 HOME (01638) 560143 FAX (01638) 560143
MOBILE (07730) 314102 E-MAIL scwilliams@ntlworld.com

1 **AITANA**, 4, b f Slip Anchor—Tsungani **Mr D. Burge**
2 **BOB'S BUZZ**, 4, ch g Zilzal (USA)—Aethra (USA) **Mr M. J. Peacock**
3 **CONCER ETO**, 5, ch g Sabrehill (USA)—Drudwen **Bainey Racing Partnership**
4 **COTE QUEST (USA)**, 4, b f Green Desert (USA)—West Brooklyn (USA) **Ronvalon UK Ltd**
5 **DISABUSE**, 4, ch g Fleetwood (IRE)—Agony Aunt **J. R. and T. J. Allenby**
6 **EXPECTED BONUS (USA)**, 5, b g Kris S (USA)—Nidd (USA) **T. D. Racing**
7 **INDIVIDUAL TALENTS (USA)**, 4, ch f Distant View (USA)—Indigenous (USA) **Mr D. A. Shekells**
8 **IPSA LOQUITUR**, 4, b f Unfuwain (USA)—Plaything **Mr A. Simpson**
9 **MR SMITHERS JONES**, 4, br g Emperor Jones (USA)—Phylian **The Lager Khan**
10 **OUT FOR A STROLL**, 5, g Zamindar (USA)—The Jotter **The Suffolk Ramblers Racing Club**
11 **PRETTY KOOL**, 4, b f Inchinor—Carrie Kool **Mr D. A. Shekells**
12 **SCARROTTOO**, 6, ch g Zilzal (USA)—Bold And Beautiful **Mr M. P. Peacock**
13 **SENDINTANK**, 4, ch g Halling (USA)—Colleville **Steve Jones and Phil McGovern**
14 **TYCHY**, 5, ch m Suave Dancer (USA)—Touch of White **Mr P. Ellinas**

THREE-YEAR-OLDS

15 **BOLD BUNNY**, b f Piccolo—Bold And Beautiful **Mr J. Miller**
16 **BUNINO VEN**, gr c Silver Patriarch (IRE)—Plaything **Mr A. Simpson**
17 **DONT CALL ME DEREK**, b g Sri Pekan (USA)—Cultural Role **J. Lloyd and E. Warder**
18 **DULCE DE LECHE**, b g Cayman Kai (IRE)—Give Us A Treat **Mr Chris Wright**
19 **FIRECRACKER (FR)**, b br f Mark of Esteem (IRE)—Green Emerald **Mrs V. Vilain**
20 **KILLMOREY**, ch c Nashwan (USA)—Zarma (FR) **Wood Farm Stud (Waresley) Partnership**
21 **KOOL ACCLAIM**, b f Royal Applause—Carrie Kool **Mrs C. Shekells**
22 **MISS SINGSPIEL**, ch f Singspiel (IRE)—Dunkellin (USA) **Mr and Mrs J. Etchells**
23 **PICKLE**, b f Piccolo—Crackle **Mr S. P. Tindall**
24 **STRANGELY BROWN (IRE)**, b g Second Empire (IRE)—Damerela (IRE) **J. T. and K. Worsley**
25 **THE KING'S BISHOP**, b g Bishop of Cashel—Kennedys Prima **The K P Partnership**
26 **TREVIAN**, ch g Atraf—Ascend (IRE) **The Little Trev Partnership**
27 **WONKY DONKEY**, b g Piccolo—Salinas **The Wonky Donkey Partnership**

TWO-YEAR-OLDS

28 **FAIRLEE ROYAL**, gr f 31/1 King Of Kings (IRE)—Fairlee Mixa (FR) (Linamix (FR)) (12000) **Mr S. J. Mear**
29 B f 15/4 Groom Dancer (USA)—Happy Omen (Warning) (4000) **Mr A. Baxter**
30 B c 24/3 Dansili—Kalindi (Efisio) (60000) **Mrs S. Roy**
31 **LANKAWI**, ch c 13/2 Unfuwain (USA)—Zarma (FR) (Machiavellian (USA)) **Mr S. J. Mear**
32 **NODINA**, b c 10/5 Primo Dominie—Princess Tara (Prince Sabo) (28000) **The Throcking Partnership**
33 Br c 6/2 Josr Algarhoud (IRE)—Real Popcorn (IRE) (Jareer (USA)) (9000) **Mr M. North**
34 **SHOTGUN CHARLIE**, b c 24/4 Groom Dancer (USA)—
    Twilight Patrol (Robellino (USA)) (22000) **Mr & Mrs M. Ballamy**

MR S. C. WILLIAMS—continued

35 **SMOOTH MOVER**, b g 24/4 Mister Baileys—Dancing Heights (IRE) (High Estate) (3000) **Flintloch Stud**
36 B c 15/2 Mister Baileys—Wannaplantatree (Niniski (USA)) (20000) **Mrs M. North**

Other Owners: Mr K. Armit, Mr A. G. Axton, Mr M. Ayres, Mr J. R. Baigent, Basicstyle Limited, Mr P. Brook, Mr A. Chandler, Mrs B. Childs, Mr K. Childs, Mr J. Clifton, Miss C. Curry, Mr T. Dorrington, Mrs A. Dowler, Mr G. Dowler, Mr W. E. Enticknap, Mr P. Geoghan, Mr C. J. Harper, Mr J. Harrison, Mr M. Head, Ms B. Heard, Mrs Fiona Heeney, Mr A. Hodge, Mr T. Jacobs, Miss V. Lawson, Mr Patrick Madelein, Wendy Middleton, Miss P. Newman, Mr J. W. Parry, Mrs J. Power, Mr B. H. Prebble, Mr H. Reed, Dr P. Rossdale, Mrs M. Saunders, Mr A. Snell, Mrs S. Snell, Mr M. Wakefield, Mr I. Wallace, Mr M. Webster, Mr L. Westwood.

Assistant Trainer: Conan McLynn

Apprentice: Brian Reilly (8-2).

---

594 **MRS S. D. WILLIAMS, South Molton**
Postal: Hilltown Farm, Mariansleigh, South Molton, Devon, EX36 4NS.
Contact: PHONE (01769) 550291 FAX (01769) 550291 MOBILE (07813) 985683
E-MAIL sarahdaphnewilliams@hotmail.com

1 **BLUE BROOK**, 5, ch g Alderbrook—Connaught's Pride **Mrs Angela Tincknell**
2 **BURNING GOLD**, 6, b g Gildoran—Regan (USA) **Mr William Peto**
3 **COOKIES BANK**, 6, b g Broadsword (USA)—Kitty Come Home **Berry Racing**
4 **DOUBLE HEADER (IRE)**, 5, b g Old Vic—Ballybeggan Lady (IRE) **Mr Dick Williamson**
5 **ESSEX BIRD**, 5, b m Primitive Rising (USA)—L'Hawaienne (USA) **Berry Racing**
6 **FAROUK (IRE)**, 6, b g Fourstars Allstar (USA)—Clontinty Queen **Berry Racing**
7 **HOLLAND PARK (IRE)**, 7, gr g Roselier (FR)—Bluebell Avenue **Mr B. M. Yin**
8 **MASTER BILLYBOY (IRE)**, 6, b g Old Vic—Clonodfoy **Mr William Peto**
9 **RYDON LANE (IRE)**, 8, br g Toca Madera—Polocracy (IRE) **Mr D. C. Coard**
10 **SUPER BLUE (IRE)**, 7, b m Supreme Leader—Tip Marie (IRE) **Mrs Angela Tincknell**
11 **SWORD LADY**, 6, b m Broadsword (USA)—Speckyfoureyes **Berry Racing**

Other Owners: Mr J. M. Barlow, Mrs Ann Whitten, Mr J. L. Whitten.

---

595 **MISS V. M. WILLIAMS, Hereford**
Postal: Aramstone, Kings Caple, Hereford, HR1 4TU.
Contact: PHONE (01432) 840646 FAX (01432) 840830 MOBILE (07770) 627108

1 **ALCOPOP**, 5, b g Alderbrook—Albacizna **P. S. & Mrs B. M. Willcocks**
2 **ALVA GLEN (USA)**, 7, b g Gulch (USA)—Domludge (USA) **Exors of the Late Mr M. J. Morris**
3 **ANGEL DELIGHT**, 8, gr m Seymour Hicks (FR)—Bird's Custard **Croome Cavaliers**
4 **ASK ME WHAT (IRE)**, 7, b m Shernazar—Laffan's Bridge (IRE) **The Turf Club**
5 **A TOI A MOI (FR)**, 4, ch g Cyborg (FR)—Peperonelle (FR) **Mr T. England**
6 **AVITTA (IRE)**, 5, b m Pennekamp (USA)—Alinova (USA) **Mr P. A. Deal**
7 **BALLYCONNELL (IRE)**, 8, b g Insan (USA)—Stormy Skies **Gallant Denco Wallace Whittle**
8 **BANKER COURT**, 12, b g Lord Bud—Gilzie Bank **Mrs H. Brown & Mr O. P. Dakin**
9 **BLEU SUPERBE (IRE)**, 9, b g Epervier Bleu—Brett's Dream (FR) **P.A. Deal, A. Hirschfeld & J. Tyndall**
10 **BRAMBLEHILL DUKE (IRE)**, 12, b g Kambalda—Scat-Cat **Mr Mel Davies**
11 **BRAMLYNN BROOK (FR)**, 6, ch g Apple Tree (FR)—Sainte Lys (FR) **Mr Christopher Drury**
12 **BUNTER BARLOW (SAF)**, 8, b g Fine Edge—Jungle Creature (SAF) **P. A. Deal**
13 **CHEM'S TRUCE (IRE)**, 7, b g Brief Truce—In The Rigging (USA) **Mr O. P. Dakin**
14 **CHIEF YEOMAN**, 4, b g Machiavellian (USA)—Step Aloft **B. Moore & E. C. Stephens**
15 **COTOPAXI (IRE)**, 8, b g Turtle Island (IRE)—Ullapool **Mrs Kathy Stuart**
16 **DERIVATIVE (IRE)**, 6, b br g Erins Isle—Our Hope **Mr P. Ryan**
17 **DIAMONDS WILL DO (IRE)**, 7, b m Bigstone (IRE)—Clear Ability (IRE) **Geraldine Mapp & Lawrence Degville**
18 **DICKENS (USA)**, 4, ch g King of Kings (IRE)—Dellagrazia (USA) **Mr George Houghton**
19 **FABULOUS JET (FR)**, 4, ch g Starborough—Jetty (FR) **Mr Malcolm Edwards**
20 **FAIR QUESTION (IRE)**, 6, b g Rainbow Quest (USA)—Fair of The Furze **The MerseyClyde Partnership**
21 **FANTASTIC ARTS (FR)**, 4, b g Royal Applause—Magic Arts (USA) **Knightsbridge BC**
22 **FLYING FALCON**, 5, b g Polar Falcon (USA)—Lemon Balm **Mr Peter Diamond**
23 **GAN EAGLA (IRE)**, 5, b g Paris House—Mafiosa **Mr T. Hywel Jones**
24 **GODS TOKEN**, 6, gr g Gods Solution—Pro-Token **The Silver Cod Partnership**
25 **GOLDEN REWARD (SAF)**, 6, ro g Goldmark (SAF)—Enticement (SAF) **P. A. Deal & J. Tyndall**
26 **GRAND FINALE (IRE)**, 7, b h Sadler's Wells (USA)—Final Figure (USA) **Leinster Bar**
27 **HERON'S GHYLL (IRE)**, 7, b g Simply Great (FR)—Leisure Centre (IRE) **Mrs Vida Bingham**

MISS V. M. WILLIAMS—continued

28 **HESCONDIDO (FR)**, 9, gr g Dadarissime (FR)—Vahine de Prairie (FR) **Mrs C. A. T. Swire**
29 **HIS NIBS (IRE)**, 7, b g Alflora (IRE)—Mrs Jennifer **Mr John Galvanoni**
30 **IDOLE FIRST (IRE)**, 5, b g Flemensfirth (USA)—Sharon Doll (IRE) **Direct Sales UK Ltd**
31 **IMAGINAIRE (USA)**, 9, b g Quest For Fame—Hail The Dancer (USA) **Miss J.Davies,Mr L.Jakeman,Mr W.Fenn**
32 **INNER SANCTUM (IRE)**, 7, ch g Bob's Return (IRE)—Princess Wager **Mr P. Ryan**
33 **ITSONLYME (IRE)**, 11, b g Broken Hearted—Over The Arctic **Mr Mel Davies**
34 **JARRO (FR)**, 8, b g Pistolet Bleu (IRE)—Junta (FR) **Mrs P. A. H. Hartley**
35 **JASMIN GUICHOIS (FR)**, 7, ch g Dom Alco (FR)—Lady Belle (FR) **Seasons Holidays**
36 **JAVELOT D'OR (FR)**, 7, b br g Useful (FR)—Flika d'Or (FR) **John Nicholls (Banbury) Ltd**
37 **JIMMY TENNIS (FR)**, 7, b br g Video Rock (FR)—Via Tennise (FR) **Derek and Jean Clee**
38 **JOES EDGE (IRE)**, 7, b br g Supreme Leader—Right Dark **Chemipetro Limited**
39 **JUST MAYBE (IRE)**, 10, b g Glacial Storm (USA)—Purlace **Mr W. E. Prichard**
40 **KEEP SMILING (IRE)**, 8, b g Broken Hearted—Laugh Away **Mrs Kathy Stuart**
41 **KELREV (FR)**, 6, ch g Video Rock (FR)—Bellile II (FR) **Len Jakeman, Flintham, King & Roberts**
42 **KETY STAR (FR)**, 6, b g Bojador (FR)—Danystar (FR) **Mrs S. A. J. Kinsella-Hurley**
43 **KINDLE BALL (FR)**, 6, gr m Kaldounevees (FR)—Scala IV (FR) **Miss V. M. Williams**
44 **KING ON THE RUN (IRE)**, 11, b g King's Ride—Fly Run **Lady Harris**
45 **KING SOLOMON (FR)**, 5, gr h Simon du Desert (FR)—All Square (FR) **Seasons Holidays**
46 **KNOCKTOPHER ABBEY (IRE)**, 7, ch g Pursuit of Love—Kukri **Seasons Holidays**
47 **KOCK DE LA VESVRE (FR)**, 6, b g Sassanian (USA)—Csardas (FR) **Mr O. P. Dakin**
48 **LAZERITO (IRE)**, 6, b g Shernazar—Nemova (IRE) **Mr T. Wilson**
49 **LIMERICK BOY (GER)**, 6, b h Alwuhush (USA)—Limoges (GER) **Favourites Racing**
50 **LORD OLYMPIA (IRE)**, 5, b g Lord Americo—Mooreshill (IRE) **Mrs Sally-Anne Ryan**
51 **MARRASIT (IRE)**, 8, b g Mazffaran (USA)—Alligator Crawl (IRE) **The Blondie Partnership**
52 **MEGGIE'S DREAM (FR)**, 5, b g Silver Rainbow—Cystar (FR) **Mr T. England**
53 **MEGGIES GAMBLE (FR)**, 7, b g Zaffaran (USA)—Glaskerbeg Lady (IRE) **Mr T. England**
54 **MEGGIE'S LAD (IRE)**, 7, b g Beau Sher—Kambaya (IRE) **Mr T. England**
55 **MENDOSINO (GER)**, 5, b g Acatenango (GER)—Maji **Direct Sales UK Ltd**
56 **MISTY DANCER**, 5, gr g Vettori (IRE)—Light Fantastic **Pinks Gym & Leisure Wear Ltd**
57 **MISTY FUTURE**, 6, b g Sanglamore (USA)—Star of The Future (USA) **The Mystics**
58 **MOBASHER (IRE)**, 5, b g Spectrum (IRE)—Danse Royale (IRE) **The 1961 Partnership**
59 **MR BAXTER BASICS**, 13, b g Lighter—Phyll-Tarquin **Mr P. Ryan**
60 **MY LADY LINK (FR)**, 5, b m Sleeping Car (FR)—Cadoudaline (FR) **Six Diamonds Partnership**
61 **NETHERLEY (FR)**, 5, gr g Beyssac (FR)—Lessons In Love (FR) **Mr P. Ryan**
62 **NOISETINE (FR)**, 6, ch m Mansonnien (FR)—Notabilite (FR) **Mrs Jean F. P. Yeomans**
63 **NORDANCE PRINCE (IRE)**, 13, b g Nordance (USA)—Shirleys Princess **Mr D. C. Pierce**
64 **OLD MARSH (IRE)**, 8, b g Grand Lodge (USA)—Lolly Dolly **Seasons and Paradise**
65 **OLIVIER (USA)**, 6, ch g Theatrical—Izara (USA) **You Can Be Sure**
66 **PHARPOST (IRE)**, 9, b g Phardante (FR)—Branstown Lady **Direct Sales UK Ltd**
67 **POUGATCHEVA (FR)**, 5, ch m Epervier Bleu—Notabilite (FR) **Direct Sales UK Ltd**
68 **PRINCE HOLING**, 4, ch g Halling (USA)—Ella Mon Amour **FF Racing Services**
69 **RADCLIFFE (IRE)**, 7, b g Supreme Leader—Marys Course **Mr M. L. Shone**
70 **RANELAGH GRAY (IRE)**, 7, gr g Roselier (FR)—Bea Marie **Mr Christopher Drury**
71 **REAL CRACKER (IRE)**, 5, b g Lahib (USA)—Loreo (IRE) **Mr Peter Diamond**
72 **RESEARCHER**, 5, ch m Cosmonaut—Rest **Mrs Kathy Stuart**
73 **RIDERS REVENGE (IRE)**, 6, b g Norwich—Paico Ana **Dr Moira Hamlin**
74 **ROYAL ROCKET (IRE)**, 7, b m King's Ride—Carols Cracker (IRE) **Miss L. M. Rochford**
75 **RUNNING MACHINE (IRE)**, 7, b g Classic Memory—Foxborough Lady **Favourites Racing**
76 **SONEVAFUSHI (FR)**, 6, b g Ganges (USA)—For Kicks (FR) **Mr B. C. Dice**
77 **SPRING LOVER (FR)**, 5, b g Fijar Tango (FR)—Kailasa (FR) **Mr Malcolm Edwards**
78 **SUPERB LEADER (IRE)**, 10, b g Supreme Leader—Emmagreen **The Geisha Girls**
79 **TAMING (IRE)**, 8, ch g Lycius (USA)—Black Fighter (USA) **Oakview Racing**
80 **THE OUTLIER (IRE)**, 6, br g Roselier (FR)—Shuil A Cuig **Mr P. Murphy**
81 **THESIS (IRE)**, 6, ch g Definite Article—Chouette **The 1961 Partnership**
82 **TIGHTEN YOUR BELT (IRE)**, 7, b g Phardante (FR)—Hi' Upham **The MerseyClyde Partnership**
83 **TRIBAL DANCER (IRE)**, 10, ch g Commanche Run—Cute Play **You Can Be Sure**
84 **TRIGGERLINO**, 4, b f Double Trigger (IRE)—Voolino **Mrs Valerie Nock-Sampson**
85 **TROUBLE AHEAD (IRE)**, 13, b g Cataldi—Why 'o' Why **Mrs Sharon C. Nelson**

MISS V. M. WILLIAMS—continued

86 **WINTER STAR**, 4, b g Overbury (IRE)—Pepper Star (IRE) **M. Crabb, B. Ead, P. May & M. Moore**
87 **WISCALITUS (GER)**, 5, b g Lead On Time (USA)—Wiscaria (GER) **Direct Sales UK Ltd**

Other Owners: Mr J. H. A. Bennett, Dr Martin Booth, Mr Andrew Brown, Mr A. W. Buller, Mr Frank Clarke, Countess Coventry, Dr Chris Cowell, Mr J. S. Dale, Mrs Christine Davies, Mr C. R. Elliott, Mrs Douglas Graham, Mr Martin P. Graham, Mr P. A. H. Hartley, Mr Tony Hirschfeld, Mr L. C. Hooper, Mr D. Jinks, Mr N. Kemp, Mr Stephen Lanigan-O'Keeffe, Mrs Caroline Perry, Mrs Jane Pilkington, Mrs C. E. Rich, Mr A. J. Roberts, Mr T. D. Rose, Mr G. Siden, Mrs H. Spencer, Mrs Nicholas Stephens, Mr R. J. Stevenson, Mr D. M. Stuart, Mr G. D. W. Swire, Mr D. A. Thorpe, Mr John Tyndall.

Jockey (NH): Brian Crowley. **Conditional:** A O'Keeffe, S Thomas.

---

596 MRS L. V. WILLIAMSON, Chester
Postal: **Saighton Hall, Saighton, Chester, Cheshire, CH3 6EE.**
Contact: **PHONE (01244) 314254 MOBILE (0797) 0437679**

1 **ALPHA IMAGE (IRE)**, 5, b g Alphabatim (USA)—Happy Image **John Riley**
2 **BOLD AFFAIR**, 5, ch g Bold Arrangement—So Curious **Denis Hutchinson**
3 **CLASSIC QUARTET**, 4, b f Classic Cliche (IRE)—Carolside **Mr K. Carbery**
4 **COLLIERS COURT**, 7, b g Puget (USA)—Rag Time Belle **Castlebend Syndicate**
5 **ELFEET BAY (IRE)**, 9, b g Yashgan—Marjoram **Mr K. Rigby**
6 **HAREM SCAREM (IRE)**, 13, b g Lord Americo—River Rescue **Halewood International Ltd**
7 **HEIDI III (FR)**, 9, b m Bayolidaan (FR)—Irlandaise (FR) **Turner Technology Ltd**
8 **HOW RAN ON (IRE)**, 13, b br g Mandalus—Kelly's Bridge **Halewood International Ltd**
9 **ICE CUBE**, 8, b g Rakaposhi King—Arctic Rymes **Mrs Lisa Williamson**
10 **KILT (FR)**, 6, b m Luchiroverte (IRE)—Unite II (FR) **Halewood International Ltd**
11 **LADY LAMBRINI**, 4, b f Overbury (IRE)—Miss Lambrini **Halewood International Ltd**
12 **LAMBRINI BIANCO (IRE)**, 6, br g Roselier (FR)—Darjoy **Halewood International Ltd**
13 **LAMBRINI PRINCE**, 10, b g Derrylin—Flying Faith **Halewood International Ltd**
14 **LOST IN NORMANDY (IRE)**, 7, b g Treasure Hunter—Auntie Honnie (IRE) **Blush Syndicate**
15 **RED ALERT MAN (IRE)**, 9, ch g Sharp Charter—Tukurua **Halewood International Ltd**
16 **RED SQUARE KNIGHT (IRE)**, 9, b g Roselier (FR)—Suny Salome **Halewood International Ltd**
17 **RED SQUARE LAD (IRE)**, 8, ch g Toulon—Tempestuous Girl **Halewood International Ltd**
18 **RIVER MERE**, 10, b h River God (USA)—Rupert's Daughter **Mrs J. E. Webster**
19 **SHERANI**, 4, b f Cigar—Aquainted **Visay De Lanerolle**
20 **WELSH CRYSTAL**, 5, gr m Muqarab (USA)—Rupert's Daughter **Mrs Lisa Williamson**
21 **WEST POINT**, 7, ch g Unfuwain (USA)—Western Reel (USA) **Turner Technology Ltd**

Other Owners: Mr J. Clarke, Mr Michael Medcalf, Mrs K. Pinarbasi, Mr M. Roberts.

Assistant Trainer: Mark Williamson

Jockey (NH): P Flynn. **Amateurs:** Mr C Ellingham, Mr D Gater.

---

597 MR A. J. WILSON, Cheltenham
Postal: **Glenfall Stables, Ham, Charlton Kings, Cheltenham, Gloucestershire, GL52 6NH.**
Contact: **PHONE (01242) 244713 FAX (01242) 226319 MOBILE (07932) 157243**
E-MAIL ajwglenfall@aol.com

1 **BOB'S TEMPTATION**, 5, br g Bob's Return (IRE)—Temptation (IRE) **The Cotswold Partnership**
2 **CERULEAN**, 6, ch g Polar Falcon (USA)—Billie Blue **J. A. Cover**
3 **LORD THOMAS (IRE)**, 6, b g Grand Lodge (USA)—Noble Rocket **Mr Tim Leadbeater**
4 **OSOSHOT**, 11, b g Teenoso (USA)—Duckdown **Favourites Racing**
5 **PERFECT VENUE (IRE)**, 11, b g Danehill (USA)—Welsh Fantasy **Mrs M. J. Wilson**
6 **SALLIEMAK**, 6, b m Makbul—Glenbrook Fort **Mr Tim Leadbeater**
7 **SKIORA**, 7, br m Petoski—Coral Delight **Mrs T. D. Pilkington**
8 **TROCHILIDAE (IRE)**, 8, b m Alphabatim (USA)—Quincy Bay **Mrs M. J. Wilson**
9 **VIVANTE (IRE)**, 6, b m Toulon—Splendidly Gay **P. A. Deal**

598 MR C. R. WILSON, Darlington

Postal: **Manor Farm, Manfield, Darlington, Co. Durham, DL2 2RW.**
Contact: **PHONE (01325) 374595 MOBILES (07815) 952306/ (07721) 379277**

1 **CELTIC FLOW**, 6, b m Primitive Rising (USA)—Celtic Lane **Mr W. R. Wilson**
2 5, B m Primitive Rising (USA)—Celtic Lane **Mr W. R. Wilson**
3 5, B g Environment Friend—La Princesse **Mrs J. Wilson**
4 **ONCE AGAIN (IRE)**, 8, ch m John French—Marsharon **Mrs J. Wilson**
5 **QUARTERSTAFF**, 10, b g Charmer—Quaranta **Mrs J. Wilson (Durham)**
6 **RED CRYSTAL**, 6, b m Presidium—Crystallography **Mrs V. C. Sugden**
7 **RIVER RISING**, 10, br g Primitive Rising (USA)—Dragons Daughter **Mr W. R. Wilson**
8 **SEA MAIZE**, 6, b m Sea Raven (IRE)—Dragons Daughter **Mr W. R. Wilson**

TWO-YEAR-OLDS

9 B f 18/2 Tipsy Creek (USA)—So Bold (Never So Bold) (1100) **Mr S. R. Bainbridge**

Other Owners: Mr A. Lea, Mr W. Martin.

Assistant Trainer: Julie Wilson

599 MISS S. J. WILTON, Stoke-on-Trent

Postal: **Round Meadow Racing Stables, Rownal Road, Wetley Rocks, Stoke-On-Trent, Staffordshire, ST9 0BP.**
Contact: **HOME (0782) 550861 OFFICE 550115 FAX 550158 MOBILE (07771) 650010**

1 **ANDY'S BIRTHDAY (IRE)**, 13, ch g King Luthier—Clonroche Abendego **John Pointon and Sons**
2 **ARAGLIN**, 5, b g Sadler's Wells (USA)—River Cara (USA) **John Pointon and Sons**
3 **BACHELORS PAD**, 10, b g Pursuit of Love—Note Book **John Pointon and Sons**
4 **BARON DE PICHON (IRE)**, 8, b g Perugino (USA)—Ariadne **John Pointon and Sons**
5 **BOING BOING (IRE)**, 4, b g King's Theatre (IRE)—Limerick Princess (IRE) **John Pointon and Sons**
6 **COUNT DE MONEY (IRE)**, 9, b g Last Tycoon—Menominee **John Pointon and Sons**
7 **CRIMSON DANCER**, 4, b f Groom Dancer (USA)—Crimson Rosella **John Pointon and Sons**
8 **DANTON (IRE)**, 6, ch g Cadeaux Genereux—Royal Circle **John Pointon and Sons**
9 **FINE FRENZY (IRE)**, 4, b f Great Commotion (USA)—Fine Project (IRE) **John Pointon and Sons**
10 **FIRST DYNASTY (USA)**, 4, br b c Danzig (USA)—Willow Runner (USA) **John Pointon and Sons**
11 **FORTY FORTE**, 8, b g Pursuit of Love—Cominna **John Pointon and Sons**
12 **HARBOUR BOUND (IRE)**, 5, b g Sadler's Wells (USA)—Argon Laser **John Pointon and Sons**
13 **IMPREVUE (IRE)**, 10, ch m Priolo (USA)—Las Bela **Mr P. W. Saunders**
14 **LEGION OF HONOUR (IRE)**, 5, b h Danehill (USA)—Total Chic (USA) **John Pointon and Sons**
15 **LOVE'S DESIGN (IRE)**, 7, b br g Pursuit of Love—Cephista **John Pointon and Sons**
16 **MELLEDGAN (IRE)**, 7, b m Catrail (USA)—Dark Hyacinth (IRE) **John Pointon and Sons**
17 **NZAME (IRE)**, 6, b g Darshaan—Dawnsio (IRE) **John Pointon and Sons**
18 **RELATIVE HERO (IRE)**, 4, ch g Entrepreneur—Aunty (IRE) **John Pointon and Sons**
19 **REVELINO (IRE)**, 5, b g Revoque (IRE)—Forelino (USA) **John Pointon and Sons**
20 **SOFISIO**, 7, ch g Efisio—Legal Embrace (CAN) **John Pointon and Sons**
21 **THE FLYER (IRE)**, 7, b g Blues Traveller (IRE)—National Ballet **John Pointon and Sons**
22 **THE IMPOSTER (IRE)**, 9, ch g Imp Society (USA)—Phoenix Dancer (IRE) **John Pointon and Sons**
23 **THE RENDERER**, 8, b g Homo Sapien—Kingsley **John Pointon and Sons**
24 **VITELUCY**, 5, b m Vettori (IRE)—Classic Line **John Pointon and Sons**

Conditional: Tom Burrows (9-4).

600 MR K. G. WINGROVE, Bridgnorth

Postal: **6 Netherton Farm Barns, Netherton Lane, Highley, Bridgnorth, Shropshire, WV16 6NJ.**
Contact: **HOME (01746) 861534 MOBILE (07974) 411267**

1 **AFTER THE BLUE (IRE)**, 7, b g Last Tycoon—Sudden Interest (FR) **Mr L. T. Woodhouse**
2 **AMACITA**, 6, b m Shareef Dancer (USA)—Kina (USA) **Mr M. M. Foulger**
3 **AMRITSAR**, 7, ch g Indian Ridge—Trying For Gold (USA) **Mr L. T. Woodhouse**
4 **BANNERET**, 11, b g Imperial Falcon (CAN)—Dashing Partner **Mr A. Bourne**
5 **BEAUCHAMP MAGIC**, 9, b g Northern Park (USA)—Beauchamp Buzz **Mr S. J. Westwood**
6 **EWAR BOLD**, 11, b g Bold Arrangement—Monaneigue Lady **Mr A. F. Maiden**
7 **MANIKATO (USA)**, 10, b g Clever Trick (USA)—Pasampsi (USA) **Mr S. J. Westwood**
8 **NERINA PRINCESS (IRE)**, 5, b m Key of Luck (USA)—Finessing **First In Racing Partnership**

MR K. G. WINGROVE—continued
9 **RUDIK (USA)**, 7, b g Nureyev (USA)—Nervous Baba (USA) **Mr L. T. Woodhouse**
10 **YELLOW SKY**, 6, b m Gildoran—Summer Sky **Mr L. T. Woodhouse**

Assistant Trainer: Isobel Willer

Jockeys (NH): A Evans, W Marston.

---

601 MR P. L. WINKWORTH, Godalming
Postal: **Robins Farm Racing Stables, Fisher Lane, Chiddingfold, Surrey, GU8 4TB.**
Contact: **PHONE (01428) 685025 FAX (01483) 200878 MOBILE (07968) 799950**
E-MAIL peter.winkworth@cbcf.com

1 **AT THE DOUBLE**, 8, b g Sure Blade (USA)—Moheli **Adrian Lindsay Smith**
2 **BANDIT BROWN (IRE)**, 8, b g Supreme Leader—Parkroe Lady (IRE) **R. D. Barber & R. J. B. Blake**
3 **BEAU CHASSEUR (FR)**, 6, ch g Cyborg (FR)—Safari Girl (FR) **Mr I. Russell**
4 **BED HOPPER**, 8, b g Rock Hopper—Rodney's Sister **Mr P. Winkworth**
5 **CHAMPAGNE SUNDAE (IRE)**, 6, b g Supreme Leader—Partners In Crime **Sundae Best**
6 **CONCERT PIANIST**, 9, b g Rakaposhi King—Divine Affair (IRE) **Ms J. P. Segal**
7 **DERVALLOC (IRE)**, 7, b g Zaffaran (USA)—Keeping Company **Mr P. Winkworth**
8 **DRY OLD PARTY (IRE)**, 5, ch g Un Desperado (FR)—The Vine Browne (IRE) **Mr P. Winkworth**
9 **DUNSFOLD DUKE**, 4, b g Cloudings (IRE)—Rositary (FR) **Mr P. Winkworth**
10 **FIELD OF BLUE**, 5, b g Shambo—Flashing Silks **Mr A. G. Russell**
11 **GEORGE BLEST**, 6, ch g Safawan—Praise The Lord **Miss Katie Powell**
12 **GROUSE MOOR (USA)**, 5, b g Distant View (USA)—Caithness (USA) **Tweenhills Racing (Cleeve Hill)**
13 **INAKI (FR)**, 7, b g Dounba (FR)—Incredule (FR) **Robert Scott & Partners**
14 **INSTANT APPEAL**, 7, gr g Terimon—Free Travel **G. Clark, C. Haycock, M. Rogerson**
15 **IRISH GOLD (IRE)**, 9, b g Good Thyne (USA)—Ardfallon (IRE) **Mr R. R. A. Eadie**
16 **JUST A TOUCH**, 8, ch g Rakaposhi King—Minim **R N Scott, R G Robinson, Peter Broste**
17 **KEN SCOTT (FR)**, 6, b g Kendor (FR)—Scottish Bride (FR) **Help - Yourself**
18 **LEVALLOIS (IRE)**, 6, b g Trempolino (USA)—Broken Wave **Tweenhills Racing (Cleeve Hill)**
19 **MUNCH MUNCH (IRE)**, 4, b f High Roller (IRE)—Tatlock **Mrs Tessa Winkworth**
20 **NURSERYMAN (IRE)**, 7, b g Mandalus—The Mighty Midge **Mr P. Winkworth**
21 **ROZNIC (FR)**, 6, b g Nikos—Rozamie (FR) **Mr P. Winkworth**
22 **SIGNATURE TUNE (IRE)**, 5, b g Gothland (FR)—Divine Affair (IRE) **Mr Simon Martyn**
23 **SOSSUS VLEI**, 8, b g Inchinor—Sassalya **Mr P. Winkworth**
24 **SUPER TIP (IRE)**, 6, b g Supreme Leader—Tip Marie (IRE) **Mr P. Winkworth**
25 **TORPICA**, 8, br g Be My Native (USA)—Irish Mint **Miss Jessica Winkworth**
26 **TUCK IN**, 7, b g Good Thyne (USA)—Always Shining **Help - Yourself**
27 **WALTER (IRE)**, 5, ch g Presenting—Siberian Princess **Mr P. Winkworth**
28 **WENGER (FR)**, 4, b c Unfuwain (USA)—Molly Dance **Mrs Tessa Winkworth**

TWO-YEAR-OLDS
29 **IT'S A HOTTIE**, b g 28/1 Bahamian Bounty—Laser Light Lady (Tragic Role (USA)) **Team Safari**
30 **RIDE SAFARI**, b c 2/4 Fraam—Vocation (IRE) (Royal Academy (USA)) (11000) **Team Safari**
31 **SAFARI ADVENTURES (IRE)**, b g 12/4 King's Theatre (IRE)—
                        Persian Walk (FR) (Persian Bold) (15000) **Team Safari**
32 **SAFARI SUNSET (IRE)**, b c 25/3 Fayruz—Umlani (IRE) (Great Commotion (USA)) (15460) **Team Safari**

Other Owners: Mr Patrick Allen, Mrs Bridget Bagnall, Mrs C. Barber, Mrs Rosie Brough, Mr D. E. Chambers, Mr Ed Clarkson, Mrs Cax Du Pon, Mrs Lois Eadie, Mrs Jo Farrant, Mr N. Fyler, Mrs Rosemary Gourlay, Mrs Gillian Hayward, Mrs Victoria Lowrie, Mrs Sal Marks, Mr Richard Muddle, Mr D. R. Obank, Miss R. E. O'Connell, Mr J. Palmer-Brown, Mr Graham Pasquill, Mr D. Redvers, Mrs Laura Redvers, Mrs Anne Scales, Mr B. T. Stewart-Brown, Mrs Y. C. Timberlake, Mr Matthew Turner, Mrs Uschi Williams, Mr Piers Winkworth.

Assistant Trainer: Anton Pearson

Jockeys (NH): L Aspell (10-0), P Hide (10-0). **Conditional:** C Bolger (9-7), R Flavin (9-7).

602 MR D. J. WINTLE, Cheltenham

Postal: **Lavender Hill Stud, Naunton, Cheltenham, Gloucestershire, GL54 3AZ.**
Contact: **PHONE (01451) 850893 FAX (01451) 850187 MOBILE (07900) 933197**
E-MAIL info@lavenderhillstud.co.uk

1 **AWESOME WELLS (IRE)**, 10, b g Sadler's Wells (USA)—Shadywood **Mr M. Tuerks**
2 **BLASKET SOUND (IRE)**, 12, b g Lancastrian—June's Friend **Mr R. H. L. Barnes**
3 **BUSTISU**, 7, b m Rakaposhi King—Tasmin Gayle (IRE) **Mr John W. Egan**
4 **CAMILLE PISSARRO (USA)**, 4, b g Red Ransom (USA)—Serenity **Lavender Hill Stud L.L.C.**
5 **CELTIC TANNER (IRE)**, 5, b g Royal Abjar (USA)—Mills Pride (IRE) **Mr G. M. McGuinness**
6 **DILEER (IRE)**, 5, b g Barathea (IRE)—Stay Sharpe (USA) **Court Roof Tiling Ltd**
7 **ERIN ALLEY (IRE)**, 11, ch g Be My Native (USA)—Cousin Flo **Lavender Hill Stud L.L.C.**
8 **FAIRTOTO**, 8, b g Mtoto—Fairy Feet **Mr John W. Egan**
9 **FIERY CREEK**, 7, ch m Moscow Society (USA)—Deep Creek **Mr John W. Egan**
10 **FIRST BOY (GER)**, 5, b h Bering—First Smile **Lavender Hill Stud L.L.C.**
11 5, Ch m Executive Perk—Golden Mela **Mr John W. Egan**
12 **GOOD POTENTIAL (IRE)**, 8, b g Petardia—Steel Duchess (IRE) **Brigadier Racing 2000**
13 **HARBOUR ROCK (IRE)**, 5, b g Midhish—Annie's Glen (IRE) **Mrs B. Grainger**
14 **HERECOMESPAPIN (IRE)**, 7, b m Naheez (USA)—Bold Kim **Mick Coulson, John Bull, John Gent**
15 **KNOTTY ASH GIRL (IRE)**, 5, ch m Ashkalani (IRE)—Camisha (IRE) **Mr John W. Egan**
16 **LOUISES GLORY (IRE)**, 9, ch g Executive Perk—Ring-Em-All **Mr D. J. Wintle**
17 **MIGWELL (FR)**, 4, b g Assessor (IRE)—Uguette IV (FR) **DGM Partership**
18 **REAL DEFINITION**, 5, gr g Highest Honor (FR)—Segovia **Lady Blyth**
19 **RIDAPOUR (IRE)**, 5, b g Kahyasi—Ridiyara (IRE) **Frinton Bloodstock**
20 **ROYAL NIECE (IRE)**, 5, b m Rakaposhi King—Sister Stephanie (IRE)
21 **ROYMILLON (GER)**, 10, b g Milesius (USA)—Royal Slope (USA) **John W. Egan/Mr Graham Brown**
22 **SHINING KNIGHT (IRE)**, 8, b g Mister Lord (USA)—Yes Your Honour **Mr G. Brain**
23 **STERN LEADER (IRE)**, 5, b g Supreme Leader—Strong Stern (IRE) **D.Bishop,J.Bull,T.Hickman & Friends**
24 **STORM CLEAR (IRE)**, 5, b h Mujadil (USA)—Escape Path **Mr D. Boocock**
25 **TANTICO (IRE)**, 7, b g Lord Americo—Tanti's Last **The Lavender Hill Mob**
26 **THE GERRY MAN (IRE)**, 5, b g Arctic Lord—Soldeu Creek (IRE) **Mr G. M. McGuinness**
27 **TRAGIC DANCER**, 8, b g Tragic Role (USA)—Chantallee's Pride **Mr E. Treadwell/Miss M. Butler**
28 **WILD ROMANCE (IRE)**, 9, b g Accordion—Mandy's Last **B. E. T. Partnership**
29 **YAKIMOV (USA)**, 5, ch g Affirmed (USA)—Ballet Troupe (USA) **B. E. T. Partnership**
30 **YASSAR (IRE)**, 9, b g Yashgan—Go Hunting (IRE) **Lavender Hill Stud L.L.C.**

Other Owners: Mr Philip F. Banks, Mr Stephen Bell, Mr David Bishop, Mr Graham Brown, Mr J. R. Bull, Mr H. Burford, Mr D. J. Bussell, Miss M. M. Butler, Mr Daniel Charlesworth, Mr Gregory Charlesworth, Mr Mick Coulson, Mr R. P. Deane, Mr J. A. Gent, Mr Ian Johnson, Mr D. A. Thorpe, Mr E. Treadwell.

Assistant Trainer: Michael Finn

Jockeys (NH): W Marston (10-0), J Mogford (10-0). **Amateurs:** Mr Keith Dodd (10-7), Mr T McCourt, Mr A Wintle (11-7).

603 MR R. D. E. WOODHOUSE, York

Postal: **Teal House Racing Stables, Chestnut Avenue, Welburn, York, YO60 7EH.**
Contact: **PHONE (01653) 618637 FAX (01653) 619481 MOBILE (07885) 651348**

1 **BOSTON LASS**, 7, b m Terimon—Larksmore **Mr M. K. Oldham**
2 **CHEEKY BOY DANNY**, 6, ch g Formidable (USA)—Moments Joy **Mr R. D. E. Woodhouse**
3 **DONNYBROOK (IRE)**, 11, ch g Riot Helmet—Evening Bun **R.Smith,D.Hall,D.Thompson,Mrs C.Clarke**
4 **DOWN TO THE WOODS (USA)**, 6, ch g Woodman (USA)—Riviera Wonder (USA) **Mr Mark Sawyer & Mr Geoff Button**
5 **ELLIE BEE**, 5, b m Primitive Rising (USA)—Hutcel Loch **Mr R. D. E. Woodhouse**
6 **FAR GLEN (IRE)**, 9, b g Pharndante (FR)—Asigh Glen **Mr R. D. E. Woodhouse**
7 **GOLLINGER**, 8, b g St Ninian—Edith Rose **Mr R. D. E. Woodhouse**
8 **HITCHHIKER**, 10, b h Picea—Lady Lax **Mrs Jan Slater**
9 4, Ch c Emperor Fountain—Mary Hand (IRE) **Mr R. D. E. Woodhouse**
10 **MISS FOSS**, 5, b m Primitive Rising (USA)—Crammond Brig **The Rumpole Partnership**
11 **MOOR SPIRIT**, 7, b g Nomadic Way (USA)—Navos **Mrs C. M. Clarke**
12 **MR MAHDLO**, 10, b g Rakaposhi King—Fedelm **Mr R. D. E. Woodhouse**
13 **SIR NORMAN**, 9, b g Arctic Lord—Moy Ran Lady **Mr M. A. Sawyer**
14 **SUPER BOSTON**, 4, b g Saddlers' Hall (IRE)—Nasowas (IRE) **Mr M. K. Oldham**
15 **WINDFOLA**, 5, b m Sovereign Water (FR)—Sainte Martine **Miss J. M. Slater**

MR R. D. E. WOODHOUSE—continued
THREE-YEAR-OLDS

16 B f Bal Harbour—Grindalythe **Mr M. K. Oldham**
17 B f Cloudings (IRE)—Hutcel Loch **Mr R. D. E. Woodhouse**
18 B f Bob's Return (IRE)—Mary Hand (IRE) **Mr R. D. E. Woodhouse**
19 **ROCKY RAMBO**, b g Sayaarr (USA)—Kingston Girl **Mr R. D. E. Woodhouse**

Jockey (Flat): Robert Winston. **Jockey (NH):** Tony Dobbin. **Conditional:** Darren Harold (9-7), P Whelan.

---

604 **MISS J. WORMALL, Ibstock**
Postal: **Ibstock Grange, Ibstock, Leicester, LE67 6LN.**
Contact: **PHONE (01530) 260224 MOBILE (07761) 947524**

1 5, B g Makbul—Derring Floss **Mrs R. Wormall**
2 **JAFFA**, 12, ch g Kind of Hush—Sip of Orange **Mrs R. Wormall**
3 5, Ch g Alflora (IRE)—Red Dust **Mrs R. Wormall**

---

605 **MR GEOFFREY WRAGG, Newmarket**
Postal: **Abington Place, Bury Road, Newmarket, Suffolk, CB8 7BT.**
Contact: **OFFICE (01638) 662328 FAX (01638) 663576 E-MAIL gwragg@btclick.com**

1 **ALWAYS ESTEEMED (IRE)**, 4, b g Mark of Esteem (IRE)—Always Far (USA) **Mollers Racing**
2 **AUTUMN GLORY (IRE)**, 4, b c Charnwood Forest (IRE)—Archipova (IRE) **Mollers Racing**
3 **DESERT DANCE (IRE)**, 4, b g Desert Story (IRE)—Cindy's Star (IRE) **Mollers Racing**
4 **GRAND PASSION (IRE)**, 4, b g Grand Lodge (USA)—Lovers' Parlour **Mr H. H. Morriss**
5 **ISLAND HOUSE (IRE)**, 8, ch g Grand Lodge (USA)—Fortitude (IRE) **Mollers Racing**
6 **JACK OF TRUMPS (IRE)**, 4, b c King's Theatre (IRE)—Queen Caroline (USA) **Mollers Racing**
7 **JUBILEE TREAT (USA)**, 4, b f Seeking The Gold (USA)—Dance Treat (USA) **Mr Peter R. Pritchard**
8 **MEZUZAH**, 4, b g Barathea (IRE)—Mezzogiorno **Mrs R. Philipps**
9 **MISS IVANHOE (IRE)**, 4, b f Selkirk (USA)—Robellino Miss (USA) **The Eclipse Partnership**
10 **MONTURANI (IRE)**, 5, b m Indian Ridge—Mezzogiorno **Mrs R. Philipps**
11 **MR MISTRAL**, 5, b g Zilzal (USA)—Miss Sancerre **Howard Spooner and Partners (II)**
12 **PROXIMA (IRE)**, 4, b f Cadeaux Genereux—Alusha **Mr A. E. Oppenheimer**
13 **QUIET STORM (IRE)**, 4, b f Desert Prince (IRE)—Hertford Castle **Mr Howard Spooner**
14 **THE WHISTLING TEAL**, 8, b g Rudimentary (USA)—Lonely Shore **Mrs F. A. Veasey**
15 **TORCELLO (IRE)**, 6, b g Royal Academy (USA)—Vanya **Mollers Racing**

THREE-YEAR-OLDS

16 **CHORUS BEAUTY**, b f Royal Applause—Happy Lady (FR) **Mrs Claude Lilley**
17 **COQUETERIA (USA)**, b f Cozzene (USA)—Miss Waikiki (USA) **Miss K. Rausing**
18 **DAY ONE**, ch c Daylami (IRE)—Myself **Bloomsbury Stud**
19 **FELICIA'S JOURNEY (IRE)**, ch f Alhaarth (IRE)—Queen Caroline (USA) **Mr Trevor C. Stewart**
20 **GOLDEN DRIFT**, ch f Inchinor—Carpet of Leaves (USA) **The Eclipse Partnership**
21 **GRAHAM ISLAND**, b c Acatenango (GER)—Gryada **Mollers Racing**
22 **HALABALOO (IRE)**, b f Intikhab (USA)—Outcry **Mr A. E. Oppenheimer**
23 **HIDDEN HOPE**, ch f Daylami (IRE)—Nuryana **Mrs Stephen Lussier**
24 **INCHENI (IRE)**, b f Nashwan (USA)—Inchmurrin **Mrs Emily Oppenheimer Turner**
25 **LARKWING (IRE)**, b c Ela-Mana-Mou—The Dawn Trader (USA) **Mollers Racing**
26 **LOCHBUIE (IRE)**, b c Definite Article—Uncertain Affair (IRE) **Mollers Racing**
27 **MISS LANGKAWI**, gr f Daylami (IRE)—Miss Amanpuri **Mr J. L. C. Pearce**
28 **MISS SHANGRI LA**, b f Rainbow Quest (USA)—Miss Rinjani **Mr J. L. C. Pearce**
29 **NICE COTE D'AZUR**, ch c Hernando (FR)—Miss Beaulieu **Mr J. L. C. Pearce**
30 **PICK A BERRY**, b f Piccolo—Bonne de Berry **Mrs Mary Watt**
31 **RIVER TREAT (FR)**, ch c Irish River (FR)—Dance Treat (USA) **Mr Peter R. Pritchard**
32 **RUBAIYAT (IRE)**, b g Desert Story (IRE)—Lovers' Parlour **Mrs H. H. Morriss**
33 **SILK CRAVAT (IRE)**, ch c Dr Devious (IRE)—Dances With Dreams **Dr Anne J. F. Gillespie**
34 **SPEEDBIRD (USA)**, ch f Sky Classic (CAN)—Egoli (USA) **The Sporting Partnership**

TWO-YEAR-OLDS

35 **BARATARIA**, ch c 13/2 Barathea (IRE)—Aethra (USA) (Trempolino (USA)) (150000) **Mollers Racing**
36 B f 7/3 In The Wings—Dananira (High Top) (70000) **Mr Ali Saaed**
37 **ELLE NINO**, b f 23/4 Inchinor—Robellino Miss (USA) (Robellino (USA)) **The Eclipse Partnership**
38 **HERITIERE**, b f Hernando (FR)—Subjective (USA) (Secretariat (USA)) **Miss K. Rausing**

MR GEOFFREY WRAGG—continued

39 **LOCHRANZA (IRE)**, b c 30/4 Fasliyev (USA)—Mysistra (FR) (Machiavellian (USA)) (92763) **Mollers Racing**
40 **MARLION (FR)**, gr c 6/4 Linamix (FR)—Marzipan (FR) (Green Desert (USA)) (30921) **Mollers Racing**
41 **MISS KATMANDU (IRE)**, ch f 16/4 Rainbow Quest (USA)—Miss Rinjani (Shirley Heights) **Mr J. L. C. Pearce**
42 **MISS L'AUGEVAL**, b f 17/3 Zilzal (USA)—Miss Sancerre (Last Tycoon) **Mr J. L. C. Pearce**
43 **MONT SAINT MICHEL (IRE)**, b c 2/3 Montjeu (IRE)—
    Band of Angels (Alzao (USA)) (62000) **Mr J. L. C. Pearce**
44 **NEVERLETME GO (IRE)**, b f 13/3 Green Desert (USA)—Cassandra Go (IRE) (Indian Ridge) **Mr Trevor C. Stewart**
45 B f 26/2 Night Shift (USA)—Pray (IRE) (Priolo (USA)) (40197) **Mr Howard Spooner**
46 **ROYAL MOUGINS**, br c 21/1 Daylami (IRE)—Miss Riviera Golf (Hernando (FR)) **Mr J. L. C. Pearce**
47 **SANIBONA**, ch f 27/2 Hernando (FR)—Miss Penton (Primo Dominie) **Mr A. E. Oppenheimer**
48 **TAYMAN (IRE)**, b br c 4/4 Sinndar (IRE)—Sweet Emotion (IRE) (Bering) (95000) **Mollers Racing**
49 B f 12/3 Inchinnor—Twitcher's Delight (Polar Falcon (USA)) **Mr A. E. Oppenheimer**
50 **WATERSILK (IRE)**, b f 20/3 Fasliyev (USA)—Dances With Dreams (Be My Chief (USA)) **Dr Anne J. F. Gillespie**

Other Owners: Mr Anthony Cane, Mr James Charrington, Mr M. A. Clark, Mr D. W. Dennis, Mr N. J. Forman Hardy, Mr C. Hellyer, Mr Ian McNicol, Mr J. A. Porteous, Lady De Ramsey, Mr Anthony Richmond-Watson, Mr Stuart Richmond-Watson, Mr Gerard Strahan, Mr R. L. Tappin.

Jockey (Flat): D Holland.

606 **MR W. G. YOUNG, Carluke**
Postal: **Overton Farm, Crossford, Carluke, Lanarkshire, ML8 5QF.**
Contact: **PHONE (01555) 860226 MOBILE (07889) 442584/(07779) 954590**
E-MAIL wgyoung@fsbdial.co.uk

1 **JAMIE BROWNE (IRE)**, 7, ch g Sayaarr (USA)—Glowing Embers **Mr W. G. Young**
2 **LORD OF THE LOCH (IRE)**, 13, b b g Lord Americo—Loughamaire **Mr W. G. Young**
3 **NUZUM ROAD MAKERS (IRE)**, 13, b g Lafontaine (USA)—Dark Gold **Mr W. G. Young**
4 **POPPERS**, 11, ch g Germont—Night Profit **Mr W. G. Young**
5 **SON OF SNURGE (FR)**, 8, b g Snurge—Swift Spring (FR) **Mr W. G. Young**
6 **TREBLE VISION (IRE)**, 10, ch g Down The Hatch—General Vision **Mr W. G. Young**
7 **TURBO MOWER**, 6, b g Turbo Speed—Fruids Park **Mr W. G. Young**
8 **UNSHAKEN**, 10, b h Environment Friend—Reel Foyle (USA) **Mr W. G. Young**

Assistant Trainer: W G Young Jnr

Conditional: B Orde-Powlett. **Amateur:** Mr T Davidson (10-5).

ADDITIONAL TEAMS

607 **MR F. T. J. JORDAN, Towcester**
Postal: **Highfields Stables, Adstone, Towcester, Northamptonshire, NN12 8DS.**
Contact: **OFFICE (01327) 860840 HOME (01327) 861162 FAX (01327) 860810**
MOBILE (07831) 101632 E-MAIL jordyracer27@hotmail.com

1 **ACE IN THE HOLE**, 4, br f So Factual (USA)—Timely Raise (USA) **Mr R. K. Betts**
2 **BLOW ME DOWN**, 5, b m Overbury (IRE)—Chinook's Daughter (IRE) **Mrs K. Roberts-Hindle**
3 **BUALADHBOS (IRE)**, 5, b g Royal Applause—Goodnight Girl (IRE) **Mr F, K, Jennings**
4 **FIRSTFLOR**, 5, b m Alflora (IRE)—First Crack **Mr F. Jordan**
5 **HIDDEN SMILE (USA)**, 7, b m Twilight Agenda (USA)—Smooth Edge (USA) **The Bhiss Partnership**
6 **IRISH BLESSING (USA)**, 7, b g Ghazi (USA)—Win For Leah (USA) **The Bhiss Partnership**
7 **KITTE OU DOUBLE (FR)**, 6, b g Agent Bleu (FR)—Briffault (FR) **Le Tricolore**
8 **LABELTHOU (FR)**, 5, b m Saint Preuil (FR)—Suzy de Thou (FR) **Le Tricolore**
9 **LERUBIS (FR)(,** 5, b g Ragmar (FR)—Perle de Saisy (FR)
10 **LET'S CELEBRATE**, 4, b g Groom Dancer (USA)—Shimmer **Mr F. Jordan**
11 **LUBINAS (IRE)**, 5, b g Grand Lodge (USA)—Liebesgirl **Mr Paul Ratcliffe**
12 **MARON**, 7, b g Puissance—Will Be Bold **Mr G. E. Gibson**
13 **MEDKHAN (IRE)**, 7, ch g Lahib (USA)—Safayn (USA) **Miss L. M. Rochford**
14 **SHADY ANNE**, 6, ch m Derrylin—Juno Away **Mr D. Pugh**
15 **SUMMER BOUNTY**, 8, b g Lugana Beach—Tender Moment (IRE) **Mr Tim Powell**

MR F. T. J. JORDAN—continued

16 **TURTLE RECALL (IRE)**, 5, b g Turtle Island (IRE)—Nora Yo Ya **Mr F. Jordan**
17 **WELSH MAIN**, 7, br g Zafonic (USA)—Welsh Daylight **Mr M. A. Reeder**

Other Owners: Mr D. A. Charlesworth, Mrs Henrietta Charlet, Mr Tony Cocum, Mr M. W. Doyle, Mr R. A. Hancocks, Mrs S. J. Le Gros, Mr David M. Thornton.

Amateur: Mr P Cowley (10-2).

---

608 **MR D. MCCAIN, Cholmondeley**
Postal: **Bankhouse, Cholmondeley, Malpas, Cheshire, SY14 8AL.**
Contact: **PHONE (01829) 720352 FAX (01829) 720475 MOBILES (07939) 126544 (07947) 583961**
E-MAIL gingermccain@cholmondeley.fsbusiness.co.uk

1 **AMBERLEIGH HOUSE (IRE)**, 12, br g Buckskin (FR)—Chancy Gal **Halewood International Ltd**
2 **ANOTHER CLUB ROYAL**, 5, b g Overbury (IRE)—Miss Club Royal **Halewood International Ltd**
3 **BALMORAL QUEEN**, 4, br f Wizard King—Balmoral Princess **Mrs S. K. Maan**
4 **BEGSY'S BULLET**, 9, b m Primitive Rising (USA)—Seeker's Sister **Mrs D. McCain**
5 **BETTERTHEDEVILUNO**, 5, b g Hector Protector (USA)—Aquaglow **Mr D. McCain**
6 **BINNY BAY**, 8, b m Karinga Bay—Binny Grove **Mr D. McCain**
7 **CASAYANA**, 4, b f Sir Harry Lewis (USA)—Five And Four (IRE) **W. Carrier, S. Naylor, G. Salter, C. Yarney**
8 **S**, B m Superlative—Castle Rouge **Mr D. McCain**
9 **CLUB ROYAL**, 7, b g Alflora (IRE)—Miss Club Royal **Halewood International Ltd**
10 **5**, Ch m Master Willie—Coquette **Mr D. McCain**
11 **DICKIE LEWIS**, 6, b g Well Beloved—Moneyacre **Mr D. McCain**
12 **EBONY LIGHT (IRE)**, 8, br g Buckskin (FR)—Amelioras Daughter **Mr Roger Bellamy**
13 **FATHER MULCAHY**, 8, b g Safawan—Constant Delight **Mr D. McCain**
14 **4**, Ch f Weldnaas (USA)—Go Gipsy **Mr D. McCain**
15 **HEAVENLY STRIDE**, 8, b g Karinga Bay—Chapel Hill (IRE) **Helshaw Grange, E. O'Malley, D. McCain**
16 **INVESTMENT AFFAIR (IRE)**, 4, b g Sesaro (USA)—Superb Investment (IRE) **Mr R. Fuller**
17 **JUST LAMBRINI**, 5, br m Overbury (IRE)—Lambrini (IRE) **Mr D. McCain**
18 **LAMBRINI GOLD**, 10, b g Gildoran—Fille de Soleil **Halewood International Ltd**
19 **4**, B f Double Eclipse (IRE)—Let Me Finish **Mr D. McCain**
20 **4**, Ch c Unfuwain (USA)—Light Ship **Mr D. McCain**
21 **4**, B c Overbury (IRE)—Miss Club Royal **Halewood International Ltd**
22 **MISTER CLUB ROYAL**, 8, b g Alflora (IRE)—Miss Club Royal **Mr John Singleton**
23 **MITRASH**, 4, b c Darshaan—L'Ideale (USA) **Mr B. Dunn**
24 **PARISIENNE GALE (IRE)**, 5, b m Lapierre—Elegant Gale (IRE) **Mr Ray Pattison**
25 **PINK HARBOUR**, 6, b m Rakaposhi King—Let Me Finish **Mr D. McCain**
26 **THE EENS**, 12, b g Rakaposhi King—Snippet **Shaw Hill Golf Club and Partners.**
27 **THE GINGER PRINCE**, 4, ch g Alderbrook—Chapel Haven (IRE) **Mr R. Pattison**
28 **THE TALLET**, 6, ch g Alflora (IRE)—Bustle'em (IRE) **Mr D. McCain**

THREE-YEAR-OLDS

29 Ch c Pursuit of Love—Constant Delight **Mr D. McCain**
30 B f Classic Cliche (IRE)—Hard Love **Mr D. McCain**
31 Ch c Karinga Bay—Miss Club Royal **Halewood International Ltd**
32 B f Overbury (IRE)—Nevermind Hey **Mr J. Singleton**
33 **REEM TWO**, b f Mtoto—Jamrat Samya (IRE) **Mr D. McCain**
34 B f Sir Harry Lewis (USA)—Tyrilda (FR) **Mr D. McCain**

TWO-YEAR-OLDS

35 B f 5/2 Lake Coniston (IRE)—Common Cause (Polish Patriot (USA)) **Mr D. McCain**
36 B f 26/4 Titus Livius (FR)—Cossack Princess (IRE) (Lomond (USA)) **Mr D. McCain**
37 B f 6/6 Environment Friend—Heathyards Gem (Governor General) **L. A. Morgan**

Other Owners: Mr I. N. Meadows, Mr R. J. Rossiter, Mr G. Gary Salters **Sage Cott Props Ltd., Pressure & Temperature Ltd.**

Assistant Trainer: Mrs B McCain, D R McCain (Jnr)

Jockey (NH): G Lee (w.a.). **Conditional:** G Grogan (9-4). **Amateur:** Mr D F Williams (9-7).

609 MR B. A. MCMAHON, Tamworth
Postal: **Woodside Farm, Hopwas Hill, Tamworth, Staffordshire, B78 3AR.**
Contact: PHONE (01827) 62901 FAX (01827) 68361

1 **BACK IN SPIRIT**, 4, ch g Primo Dominie—Pusey Street Girl **The Oakley**
2 **BAND**, 4, b g Band On The Run—Little Tich **D. J. Allen**
3 **BRANTWOOD (IRE)**, 4, b g Lake Coniston (IRE)—Angelic Sounds (IRE) **Mr J. C. Fretwell**
4 **DR RAJ**, 5, ch g In The Wings—Tawaaded (IRE) **Mr C. G. Conway**
5 **FLASHING BLADE**, 4, b f Inchinor—Finlaggan **Mr R. L. Bedding**
6 **LOOK HERE'S CAROL (IRE)**, 4, ch f Safawan—Where's Carol **S. L. Edwards**
7 **RAHJEL SULTAN**, 6, b g Puissance—Dalby Dancer **Mrs J. McMahon**
8 **ROYAL CASCADE (IRE)**, 10, b g River Falls—Relative Stranger **Mrs J. McMahon**
9 **WHITE O' MORN**, 5, gr m Petong—I'm Your Lady **Mrs A. H. Stokes**

THREE-YEAR-OLDS
10 **COTOSOL**, b g Forzando—Emerald Dream (IRE) **J. P. Hames, G. Pickering, RJH Limited**
11 **DESERT LEADER (IRE)**, b c Green Desert (USA)—Za Aamah (USA) **Mr J. C. Fretwell**
12 **FICTIONAL**, b c Fraam—Manon Lescaut **Mr J. C. Fretwell**
13 **INCHLOSS (IRE)**, b g Imperial Ballet (IRE)—Earth Charter **R. Thornhill**
14 **INDIAN CALL**, ch c Classic Cliche (IRE)—Crees Sqaw **Mr Michael Sturgess**
15 **KEEPER'S LODGE (IRE)**, ch f Grand Lodge (USA)—Gembira (USA) **Mr W. D. McClennon**
16 **LAKE GARDA**, b c Komaite (USA)—Malcesine (IRE) **Mr J. C. Fretwell**
17 **LOCAL POET**, b c Robellino (USA)—Laugharne **Mr J. C. Fretwell**
18 **LUPINE HOWL**, b c Wolfhound (USA)—Classic Fan (USA) **Mr J. C. Fretwell**
19 **NOW LOOK AWAY (IRE)**, b g Dushyantor (USA)—Where's Carol **S. L. Edwards**
20 **WITHORWITHOUTYOU (IRE)**, b f Danehill (USA)—Morningsurprice (USA) **Mr J. C. Fretwell**

TWO-YEAR-OLDS
21 **ALLIZAM**, b c 23/2 Tragic Role (USA)—Mazilla (Mazilier (USA)) **M. Rhodes**
22 **APOLOGIES**, b c 17/2 Robellino (USA)—Mistook (Phone Trick (USA)) **Mr J. C. Fretwell**
23 **AUTHENTICATE**, b f 29/4 Dansili—Exact Replica (Darshaan) **Mr J. C. Fretwell**
24 **CASTELLETTO**, b f 14/4 Komaite (USA)—Malcesine (IRE) (Auction Ring (USA)) **Mr J. C. Fretwell**
25 **DANCE NIGHT (IRE)**, b f 27/3 Danehill Dancer (IRE)—Tiger Wings (IRE) (Thatching) **Mr J. C. Fretwell**
26 **EL POTRO**, b c 14/3 Forzando—Gaelic Air (Ballad Rock) **J. P. Hames, G. Pickering, RJH Limited**
27 **ENGLISH FELLOW**, b c 30/1 Robellino (USA)—Q Factor (Tragic Role (USA)) **Mr J. C. Fretwell**
28 **INGLETON**, b c 14/2 Komaite (USA)—Dash Cascade (Absalom) **Mr J. C. Fretwell**
29 **LOOK HERE'S MAY**, b f 1/5 Revoque (IRE)—Where's Carol (Anfield) **S. L. Edwards**
30 **MADAM BUTLER**, b f 1/3 Night Shift (USA)—Inflation (Primo Dominie) **R. Butler**
31 **MONKSTOWN ROAD**, b c 12/2 Makbul—Carolside (Music Maestro) **J. J. Staunton**
32 **PIVOTAL'S PRINCESS (IRE)**, ch f 12/2 Pivotal—
Art Princess (IRE) (Fairy King (USA)) **Mr R. L. Bedding & Mrs J. McMahon**
33 **PIVOTAL FLAME**, b c 3/5 Pivotal—Reddening (Blushing Flame (USA)) **Mr R. L. Bedding**
34 **ROCK TAIL BAY**, b f 23/4 Band On The Run—Elsocko (Swing Easy) (USA)) **D. J. Allen**
35 **SUPERSTITIOUS (IRE)**, b c 25/2 Bluebird (USA)—
Stellar Empress (USA) (Star de Naskra (USA)) **Mr J. C. Fretwell**
36 **WENDY WINDBLOWS**, ch f Band On The Run—Breezy Day (Day Is Done) **Mrs J. McMahon**

Assistant Trainer: Edward McMahon

Jockey (Flat): G Gibbons. **Apprentice:** Richard Hodson (8-2). **Amateurs:** Miss Elizabeth George, Miss Sarah Phizacklea.

610 MR J. F. P. O'REILLY, Barnsley
Postal: **Burntwood Racing Stables, Brierley Common, Brierley, Barnsley, South Yorkshire, S72 9ET.**
Contact: PHONE (01302) 724795 MOBILE (07810) 307482

1 **DIZZY IN THE HEAD**, 5, b g Mind Games—Giddy **Burntwood Sports Ltd**
2 **MY BAYARD**, 5, ch g Efisio—Bay Bay **Burntwood Sports Ltd**
3 **NITEOWL DREAM**, 4, ch f Colonel Collins (USA)—Nite-Owl Dancer **Mr J. Saul**
4 **NITE-OWL FIZZ**, 6, b g Efisio—Nite-Owl Dancer **Mr J. Saul**
5 **SHOLTO**, 5, b g Tragic Role (USA)—Rose Mill **Denny Mansell Racing Partnership**
6 **SUDRA**, 7, g g Indian Ridge—Bunting **Mr J. Morris**
7 **TANTRIC**, 5, br g Greensmith—Petunia (GER) **Mr J. Saul**
8 **WENTBRIDGE BOY**, 4, gr g Keen—Wentbridge Girl **Mrs K. Morrell**

MR J. F. P. O'REILLY—continued
THREE-YEAR-OLDS

  9 EMBASSY LORD, b g Mind Games—Keen Melody (USA) **Denny Mansell Racing Partnership**
 10 NITEOWL EXPRESS (IRE), b f Royal Applause—Nordan Raider **Mr J. Saul**
 11 ROYAL NITE OWL, b g Royal Applause—Nite-Owl Dancer **Mr J. Saul**

TWO-YEAR-OLDS

 12 Ch f 13/5 Timeless Times (USA)—Cashmirie (Domynsky) **Mr J. P. O'Reilly**
 13 HIATS, b c 25/4 Lujain (USA)—Naulakha (Bustino) **Mr Andrew Skelton**
 14 Ch c 17/4 Tagula (IRE)—Mareha (IRE) (Cadeaux Genereux) **Mr J. Saul**
 15 B f 29/3 Royal Applause—Nite-Owl Dancer (Robellino (USA)) **Mr J. Saul**
 16 B c 7/2 Spectrum (IRE)—Rush Hour (IRE) (Night Shift (USA)) **Mr Pete Smith**
 17 RUSSIANNIGHTINGALE, b c 24/2 Fraam—Nightingale Song (Tina's Pet) **Denny Mansell Racing**
 18 SADLERS SENOR, b c 9/2 Imperial Ballet (IRE)—Mechilie (Belmez (USA)) **Denny Mansell Racing**

Assistant Trainer: Michael Harris

Apprentices: D Allan (w.a.), J D O'Reilly (8-0). **Amateur:** Miss T O'Brian (8-11).

---

611 **MRS J. A. SAUNDERS, Teeton**
Postal: **Teeton Grange Farm, Teeton, Northampton, NN6 8LW.**
Contact: **PHONE (01604) 505739 MOBILE (07970) 667852**

 1 HOMELIFE (IRE), 6, b g Persian Bold—Share The Vision **Mrs J. Saunders**
 2 STANMORE (IRE), 12, b g Aristocracy—Lady Go Marching (USA) **Mr & Mrs Simon E. Bown**

---

612 **MR I. A. WOOD, Upper Lambourn**
Postal: **Neardown Stables, Upper Lambourn, Hungerford, Berkshire, RG17 8QP.**
Contact: **PHONE (01488) 72324 FAX (01488) 72877 MOBILE (07775) 508111**

 1 ALIMISTE (IRE), 4, b f Ali-Royal—Miss Senate (IRE) **Mr M. I. Forbes**
 2 CLANN A COUGAR, 4, ch g Bahamian Bounty—Move Darling **Mrs Sue Pidcock**
 3 DISTINCTIVE DANCER (IRE), 6, b br h Distinctly North (USA)—Resiusa (ITY) **Neardown Stables**
 4 DISTINCTLYSPLENDID, 4, b g Distinctly North (USA)—Shelley Marie **Mrs E. P. Smith**
 5 FIDELIS SEMPER (IRE), 4, b f College Chapel—Reflection Time (IRE) **Eric Ryder**
 6 HEFIN, 7, ch g Red Rainbow—Summer Impressions (USA) **Mr Christopher Shankland**
 7 4, B f The West (USA)—Kumzar
 8 MERELY A MONARCH, 5, b g Reprimand—Ruby Princess (IRE) **Miss Jacqueline Goodearl**
 9 MOST-SAUCY, 8, br m Most Welcome—So Saucy **Mrs A. M. Riney**
 10 PAY THE SILVER, 6, gr g Petong—Marjorie's Memory (IRE) **Mr Christopher Shankland**
 11 REBANNA, 4, ch f Rock City—Fuwala **Eric Ryder**
 12 RIVA ROYALE, 4, b f Royal Applause—Regatta **Tyrnest Ltd**
 13 SPECIAL ELLIE (FR), 4, b f Celtic Swing—Recherchee **Mr K. P. Joseph**
 14 THAAYER, 9, b g Wolfhound (USA)—Hamaya (USA) **Neardown Stables**
 15 TRAVEL TARDIA (IRE), 6, br b h Petardia—Annie's Travels (IRE) **Neardown Stables**
 16 TWELI, 7, b g Deploy—Flying Fantasy **Mrs A. M. Riney**
 17 VICTORIA PARK (IRE), 4, b f Victory Note (USA)—Break For Tee (IRE) **Eric Ryder**

THREE-YEAR-OLDS

 18 BELLA TUTRICE (IRE), b f Woodborough (USA)—Institutrice (IRE) **Brooklands Racing**
 19 CATCH THE WIND, b f Bahamian Bounty—Tinkerbird **Mr C. S. Tateson**
 20 DESERT DAISY (IRE), gr f Desert Prince (IRE)—Pomponette (USA) **Mrs Julie Mitchell**
 21 LADY XANTHIA, ch f Bien Bien (USA)—Carmosa (USA) **The Dunnet Lads**
 22 MAYBE SOMEDAY, ch g Dr Fong (USA)—Shicklah (USA) **Mr Nigel Shields**
 23 MORAG, b f Aragon—Minnehaha **Mr D. Miller**
 24 PERERIN, b c Whittingham (IRE)—Antithesis (IRE) **Tyrnest Ltd**
 25 PINK SUPREME, ch f Night Shift (USA)—Bright Spells **Mr C. S. Tateson**
 26 Ch c Opening Verse (USA)—Pola Star (IRE), **Ms Patricia Watson**
 27 RED SOVEREIGN, b f Danzig Connection (USA)—Ruby Princess (IRE) **Miss Jacqueline Goodearl**
 28 SAHARA SCIROCCO (IRE), b c Spectrum (IRE)—St Bride's Bay **Mr R. K. Arrowsmith**
 29 SAYRIANNA, br f Sayaarr (USA)—Arianna **Mrs J. Gawthorpe**
 30 SWEET REPLY, ch f Opening Verse (USA)—Sweet Revival **Mr C. S. Tateson**
 31 WALTZING BEAU, ch c Dancing Spree (USA)—Blushing Belle **Mr Christopher Shankland**

MR I. A. WOOD—continued
TWO-YEAR-OLDS

32 **AHAZ,** b c 17/2 Zaha—Classic Faster (IRE) (Running Steps (USA)) (6666) **Mrs E. Smith**
33 B f 28/4 Soviet Star (USA)—Avantage Service (IRE) (Exactly Sharp (USA)) (2473) **Brooklands Racing**
34 B c 20/3 Dr Fong (USA)—Bathwick Babe (IRE) (Sri Pekan (USA)) (14000) **Mr W. Clifford**
35 **BEAU MARCHE,** b c 9/5 My Best Valentine—
Beau Dada (IRE) (Pine Circle (USA)) (3047) **Mr Christopher Shankland**
36 B f 14/2 Imperial Ballet—Bebe Auction (IRE) (Auction Ring (USA)) (3091) **Neardown Stables**
37 **BE BOP ALOHA,** b f 3/4 Most Welcome—Just Julia (Natroun (FR)) (3200) **Mr K. P. Joseph**
38 B f 20/4 Namaqualand (USA)—Breakfast Creek (Hallgate) (2000) **Neardown Stables**
39 B c 1/4 Mind Games—Bron Hilda (IRE) (Namaqualand (USA)) (1500) **Mr John Purcell**
40 B c 16/4 Namaqualand (USA)—Captivating (IRE) (Wolfhound (USA)) (800) **Mr John Purcell**
41 **EXCELERATOR,** ch c 28/4 Compton Place—Dance The Swans (IRE) (Try My Best (USA)) (11000) **A1 Racing**
42 B f 27/3 Royal Applause—Foreign Mistress (Darshaan) **Harold Duery**
43 Ch f 27/2 Royal Anthem (USA)—Hide The Bride (USA) (Runaway Groom (CAN)) (8000) **Neardown Stables**
44 B f 25/3 Xaar—Hill of Doon (IRE) (Fairy King (USA)) **Brooklands Racing**
45 B f 1/3 Second Empire (IRE)—Home Comforts (Most Welcome) (5256) **Caerphilly Building Supplies Ltd**
46 B f Tipsy Creek (USA)—Joe's Dancer (Shareef Dancer (USA)) (1000) **Neardown Stables**
47 **JUSTAQUESTION,** b f 3/2 Pursuit of Love—Queenbird (Warning) (6476) **Mr Christopher Shankland**
48 **KATANA,** b f 5/2 Spectrum (IRE)—Karlaska (Lashkari) (10000) **Mr D. Bass**
49 B f 28/1 Danetime (IRE)—Kavana (IRE) (Marju (IRE)) (3091) **Neardown Stables**
50 **KAYF ARAMIS,** b c 27/4 Kayf Tara—Ara (Birthright) **Mrs Isobel Phipps-Coltman**
51 Ch c 5/4 Tomba—Lady In White (Shareef Dancer (USA)) **Stampede Racing**
52 B f 26/3 Josr Algarhoud (IRE)—Lady of Limerick (IRE) (Thatching) (1600) **Neardown Stables**
53 B c 10/4 Fasliyev (USA)—Lioness (Lion Cavern (USA)) (2473) **Brooklands Racing**
54 B c 9/5 Lake Coniston (IRE)—Minnehaha (Be My Chief (USA)) **Mr D. Miller**
55 B f 4/4 Definite Article—Mistress Mine (IRE) (King of Clubs) (1855) **Mr & Mrs L. Harris**
56 Ch f 16/3 Zaha (CAN)—Mother Molly (USA) (Irish River (FR)) **Neardown Stables**
57 B c 6/5 Almaty (IRE)—Nest Egg (Prince Sabo) (3809) **Neardown Stables**
58 **PERSIAN CARPET,** b f 9/2 Desert Style (IRE)—Kuwah (IRE) (Be My Guest (USA)) (3000) **Mr C. S. Tateson**
59 **PIDDIES PRIDE (IRE),** b f 7/4 Indian Lodge (IRE)—Fairybird (FR) (Pampabird) (4000) **Mrs Sue Pidcock**
60 B f 13/4 Spectrum (Sadler's Wells (USA)) **Mr Richard Lewis**
61 Ch f 13/4 Compton Place—Polar Peak (Polar Falcon (USA)) (3333) **Mrs A. M. Rincy**
62 B c 14/4 Mind Games—Possessive Lady (Dara Monarch) (7500) **Mr John Purcell**
63 **SARAH BROWN (IRE),** b f 4/4 Benny The Dip (USA)—
Lalique (IRE) (Lahib (USA)) **Belmore Lane Stud Racing Partnership**
64 Ch f 7/3 Wolfhound (USA)—Seven Sisters (USA) (Shadeed (USA)) (5565) **Neardown Stables**
65 B f 21/2 Docksider (USA)—Solar Flare (IRE) (Danehill (USA)) **Mr Richard Lewis**
66 **SWEET COINCIDENCE,** b f 1/3 Mujahid (USA)—Sibilant (Selkirk (USA)) (2200) **Mr S. A. Douch**
67 B f 10/5 Lake Coniston (IRE)—Tower Glades (Tower Walk) **Neardown Stables**
68 Ch f 2/4 Inchinor—Trojan Desert (Troy) **Mr Paddy Barrett**
69 **ZAHARA,** ch c 28/3 Zaha (CAN)—Maria Cappuccini (Siberian Express (USA)) **Mr D. Bass**

Other Owners: Mr M. H. Bates, Mr R. H. Brookes, Mrs L. Clark, Mr J. J. Collard, Mr J. L. Dunlop, Mr P. Friend, Mr A. P. Hartley, Mr A. M. Hession, Mr D. T. Horn, Mr J. A. Leavett-Shenley, Mr D. S. Lovatt, Mr Edward Matthews, Mr V. W. Oubridge, Mr S. J. Pembroke, Mr R. Robinson, Mrs Joyce Wood, Mr John Wright.

INDEX TO HORSES

The Figure before the name of the horse refers to the number of the team in which it appears and **The Figure after** the horse supplies a ready reference to each animal. Horses are indexed strictly alphabetically, e.g. THE FUND MANAGER appears in the T's, MR WONG in the MR's, ST CLAIR C in the ST's etc.

262 **ALPINE SPECIAL** (IRE) 16
222 **ALPINE STAR** 2
549 **ALQAAYID** 14
373 **AL QUDRA** (IRE) 67
549 **ALRABAB** 2
383 **ALRAFID** (IRE) 5
192 **ALRIDA** (IRE) 1
420 **ALRIYAAH** F 42
119 **AL SAQIYA** (USA) C 66
253 **ALSHAKR** F 16
549 **ALSHAMATRY** (USA) 67
169 **ALSHAWAMEQ** (IRE) 26
549 **ALSHIMAAL** (IRE) 69
67 **AL SHUUA** 16
16 **ALSU** (IRE) 77
79 **ALSYATI** 2
578 **ALTA GRACIA** (IRE) 85
301 **ALTAREEK** (USA) 2
290 **ALTARES** 18
192 **ALTAY** 2
347 **ALTHREY RULER** (IRE) 1
49 **ALTITUDE DANCER** (IRE) 2
277 **ALUMNI** 11
329 **ALUSHA C** 32
595 **ALVA GLEN** (USA) 2
361 **ALVAREZ** 4
265 **ALVARINHO LADY** 21
446 **ALVARITA** 30
331 **ALVINO** 3
207 **ALWAYS BELIEVE** (USA) 2
532 **ALWAYS DARING** 1
605 **ALWAYS ESTEEMED** (IRE) 1
524 **ALWAYS FIRST** 26
254 **ALWAYS MINE** 9
475 **ALWAYS RAINBOWS** (IRE) 2
465 **ALWAYS SOMETHING** (IRE) 1
169 **ALYOUSUFEYA** (IRE) 27
287 **ALZOLA** (IRE) 1
600 **AMACITA** 2
135 **AMALFI COAST** 1
578 **AMALTEA** 86
410 **AMANDA KASAKOVA** 2
106 **AMANDA'S LAD** (IRE) 2
349 **AMANDUS** (USA) 2
36 **AMANKILA** 15
49 **AMAR** (CZE) 31
26 **AMARETTO EXPRESS** (IRE) 2
429 **AMARYLLIS** (IRE) C 31
533 **AMATEUR DRAMATICS** 1
160 **AMAYA SILVA** 23
66 **AMAZONA** (IRE) F 100
351 **AMAZONE DU BERLAIS** (FR) 92
67 **AMBER FIZZ** (USA) C 40
37 **AMBER FOX** (IRE) 24
380 **AMBER GO GO** 1
308 **AMBER GOLD** 1
186 **AMBER LEGEND** 4
323 **AMBER MOSS** 1
205 **AMBER SKY** (IRE) 3
94 **AMBERSONG** 2
476 **AMBER STARLIGHT** 3
17 **AMBER WAVES** 54
391 **AMBIENCE LADY** 1
272 **AMBITION ROYAL** (FR) 3
286 **AMBITIOUS ANNIE** 1
114 **AM BROSE** 2
512 **AMBRY** 2

381 **AMBUSHED** (IRE) 2
66 **AMELIA** (IRE) 5
411 **AMELLNAA** (IRE) C 33
210 **AMERAS** (IRE) 1
403 **AMERICAN COUSIN** 2
288 **AMERICAN DUCHESS** (IRE) 2
373 **AMERICAN DUKE** (USA) 19
269 **AMERICAN POST** 11
104 **AMEYRAH** (IRE) 31
361 **AMICELLI** (GER) 5
578 **AMID THE CHAOS** (IRE) 2
191 **AMIE DE MIX** (FR) 15
277 **AMIRA** 11
302 **AMIR ZAMAN** 2
376 **AMJAD** 1
378 **AMMENAYR** (IRE) 1
361 **AMMONIAS** (GER) 6
221 **AMNESIA** (USA) F 35
383 **AMNESTY** 6
420 **AMONG DREAMS** 14
421 **AMONG FRIENDS** (IRE) 1
39 **A MONK SWIMMING** (IRE) 13
221 **AMOROSA BRI** 36
524 **AMPELIO** (IRE) 100
29 **AMPHYCLES** (FR) 12
309 **AMPITHEATRE** (IRE) 21
280 **AMPLIFI** (IRE) 3
67 **AMPOULE** 1
600 **AMRITSAR** 3
64 **AMUSEMENT** 1
302 **AMWELL BRAVE** 38
302 **AMWELL STAR** (USA) 3
88 **AMY HUNTER** (USA) F 27
460 **AMY LEIGH** (IRE) G 10
353 **AMY LEWIS** 2
204 **AMYROSEISUPPOSE** 1
299 **ANAAMIL** 43
159 **ANABAA REPUBLIC** (FR) 53
135 **ANACAPRI** 2
489 **ANACLONE** (IRE) 2
478 **ANADIYLA** (IRE) 2
299 **ANAK PEKAN** 1
392 **ANALAMPI** (GR) C 90
361 **ANALOGY** (IRE) 7
445 **ANALYZE** (FR) 1
168 **ANANI** (USA) 1
435 **ANATAR** (IRE) 2
49 **ANATASE** C 58
185 **ANATOLIAN QUEEN** (USA) 11
425 **ANA WINTA** (FR) 1
141 **ANDALEER** (IRE) 1
133 **ANDALUZA** 9
29 **ANDEAN** 21
404 **ANDREAS** (FR) 6
227 **ANDREYEV** (IRE) 1
17 **ANDROMACHE** 2
118 **ANDRONIKOS** 56
190 **AND TOTO TOO** 3
185 **ANDURIL** 12
280 **ANDY GIN** (FR) 4
599 **ANDY'S BIRTHDAY** (IRE) 1
431 **ANEEDA** C 75
173 **ANELYN'S GIFT** 84
221 **ANESTASIA** (IRE) 37
288 **A NEW STORY** (IRE) 3
373 **ANEYDIA** (IRE) C 68
119 **ANGE GARDIEN** (IRE) 41

223 **ANGEL ANNIE** 1
56 **ANGELA'S GIRL** 40
595 **ANGEL DELIGHT** 3
141 **ANGELENA BALLERINA** 4
457 **ANGELICA PICKLES** (IRE) 3
192 **ANGEL ISA** (IRE) 3
418 **ANGELLO** 2
17 **ANGEL MAID** 55
420 **ANGELO'S PRIDE** 15
84 **ANGEL RAYS** 45
125 **ANGEL SPRINTS** 10
302 **ANGELS VENTURE** 4
16 **ANGEL WING** 78
107 **ANGIE'S DOUBLE** 1
436 **ANGLANIT** (CZE) 2
349 **ANGLO SAXON** (USA) 3
29 **ANGRY BARK** (USA) 13
142 **ANGUILLA** 2
157 **ANICAFLASH** 22
161 **ANIMAL MAGIC** 2
221 **ANIMATRICE** (USA) F 38
443 **ANISETTE** 30
421 **ANITA'S LOVE** (IRE) F 26
141 **ANKLES BACK** (IRE) 5
114 **ANKLET** (USA) F 35
438 **ANN'S DELIGHT** (IRE) 17
98 **ANNABEE** 2
456 **ANNA KARIETTA C** 9
396 **ANNAKITA** 1
92 **ANNALS** 42
349 **ANNAMBO** 4
259 **ANNA PALLIDA** 30
92 **ANNA PANNA** 17
36 **ANNAPURNA** (IRE) F 50
221 **ANNEE LUMIERE** (IRE) 39
349 **ANNE OF CLEVES** 61
408 **ANNETTES STAR** 16
446 **ANNIBALE CARO** 31
588 **ANNICOMBE RUN F** 1
442 **ANNIE BYERS** 1
235 **ANNIE DIPPER** 2
504 **ANNIE HARVEY** 6
567 **ANNIE MILLER** (IRE) 10
84 **ANNISHIRANI** 1
82 **ANNITAS DREAM** (IRE) 13
195 **ANNIVERSARY GUEST** (IRE) 1
146 **ANNODYCE** 2
528 **ANNO JUBILO** (GER) 2
119 **ANODE** 3
141 **ANOTHER BALLY** 6
468 **ANOTHER BARGAIN** (IRE) 1
530 **ANOTHER BOTTLE** (IRE) 10
301 **ANOTHER CHANCE** 3
344 **ANOTHER CHOICE** (IRE) 20
391 **ANOTHER CONQUEST** 2
161 **ANOTHER COPPER** 3
281 **ANOTHER DEAL** (FR) 2
161 **ANOTHER DIAMOND** (IRE) 4
257 **ANOTHER DOLLAR** (IRE) 1
306 **ANOTHER DUDE** (IRE) 2
432 **ANOTHER GENERAL** (IRE) 4
482 **ANOTHER GLIMPSE** 1
557 **ANOTHER GRADUATE** (IRE) 3
301 **ANOTHER GROUSE** F 4
399 **ANOTHER JOKER** 1
335 **ANOTHER MOOSE** (IRE) 1
205 **ANOTHER NATIVE** (IRE) 4
527 **ANOTHER PROMISE** (IRE) 1

524 **ASAWER** (IRE) 102
485 **ASBO** 1
206 **ASCARI** 1
344 **ASCERTAIN** (IRE) 21
67 **ASCOT CYCLONE** (USA) F 42
563 **AS DE LA GARENNE** (FR) 1
185 **ASHALA** (FR) 3
478 **ASHARA** (IRE) C 81
24 **ASH BRANCH** (IRE) 1
234 **ASHDALI** (IRE) 63
565 **ASHDOWN EXPRESS** (IRE) 2
565 **ASHDOWN PRINCESS** (IRE) 30
185 **ASHFIELD** 13
252 **ASHGAR** (USA) 1
517 **ASHJAAN** (USA) C 20
82 **ASHKADIMA** (IRE) 14
478 **ASHKARA** (IRE) F 82
5 **ASH LADDIE** (FR) 2
350 **ASHLEYBANK HOUSE** (IRE) 3
46 **ASHLEY BROOK** (IRE) 1
219 **ASHLEY MARSH** 2
384 **ASHNAYA** (FR) 6
299 **ASHSTANZA** 16
478 **ASHTARKA** C 83
106 **ASHTAROUTE** (USA) 3
25 **ASHTON VALE** 1
265 **ASHTREE BELLE** 1
169 **ASHWAAQ** (USA) 29
32 **ASHWELL** 2
538 **ASHWORTH VALLEY** 1
427 **ASIAN PERSUASION** (IRE) 1
254 **ASIAN TIGER** (IRE) 92
277 **ASIA WINDS** (IRE) 21
442 **ASK FOR LUCK** (IRE) 1
277 **ASK FOR RAIN** 113
595 **ASK ME WHAT** (IRE) 4
42 **ASKNINTH** (IRE) 18
120 **ASK THE CLERK** (IRE) 20
198 **ASK THE DRIVER** 8
404 **ASK THE GATHERER** (IRE) 9
443 **AS MUSTARD** F 38
119 **ASO ROCK** (IRE) 4
495 **ASPARAGUS** (IRE) 1
194 **ASPIRED** (IRE) 33
404 **ASPIRING ACTOR** (IRE) 10
221 **ASPOLINA** (IRE) 41
277 **ASRAR** 114
562 **ASSERTIVE LASS** (USA) G 27
392 **ASSESSED** (IRE) 5
383 **ASSOON** 9
238 **ASSUMETHEPOSITION** (FR) 4
432 **ASSUMPTALINA** 7
584 **ASTAFORT** (FR) 2
309 **ASTEEM** 22
29 **ASTERIE** 15
78 **ASTON MARA** 3
528 **ASTON** (USA) 6
360 **ASTOUGHASOLDBOOTS** (IRE) 1
324 **ASTRAC** (IRE) 1
452 **ASTRAL AFFAIR** (IRE) 1
568 **ASTRAL PRINCE** 1
82 **ASTRILLE** (IRE) 15
547 **ASTROCHARM** (IRE) 1
409 **ASTRO GLIDE** (IRE) 4
547 **ASTROMANCER** (USA) 2
338 **ASTRONOMER LADY** (IRE) F 1
306 **ASTRONOMIC** 4
277 **ASTRONOMICAL** (IRE) 115

100 **ASTUCE** 14
446 **ASTYANAX** (IRE) 2
54 **ASWAN** (IRE) 2
77 **ATALANTA SURPRISE** (IRE) 3
341 **ATALYA** 2
364 **ATAVUS** 2
290 **A TEEN** 2
567 **ATHBOY** 1
118 **ATHENS BELLE** (IRE) C 57
524 **ATHENS** (IRE) 103
424 **ATHNOWEN** (IRE) 1
174 **ATHOLLBROSE** (USA) 47
299 **A THOUSAND SMILES** (IRE) 46
29 **ATLANDO** (IRE) 16
504 **ATLANTIC ACE** 1
352 **ATLANTIC BREEZE** 24
241 **ATLANTIC CITY** 17
33 **ATLANTIC CROSSING** (IRE) 2
393 **ATLANTIC HAWK** 5
492 **ATLANTIC LADY** (GER) 2
255 **ATLANTIC QUEST** (USA) 1
232 **ATLANTICUS** (IRE) 1
403 **ATLANTIC VIKING** (IRE) 3
494 **ATLANTIC WALTZ** 1
219 **ATLASTABOY** (IRE) 1
595 **A TOI A MOI** (FR) 5
209 **ATOMIC BREEZE** (IRE) 1
582 **ATTACCA** 17
297 **ATTACK MINDED** 5
300 **ATTASLIYAH** (IRE) C 29
578 **ATTEND** (IRE) 87
601 **AT THE DOUBLE** 1
383 **AT THE READY** (IRE) 82
269 **ATTICUS BOY** (USA) 13
519 **ATTICUS FINCH** (IRE) 1
571 **ATTILA THE HUN** 1
269 **ATTIRINA** 72
493 **ATTORNEY** 2
418 **ATTORNEY GENERAL** (IRE) 3
373 **ATTUNE** 21
574 **ATUM RE** (IRE) 2
168 **AT YOUR REQUEST** 15
351 **AUBANE** (FR) 4
303 **AUBURN DUKE** 1
558 **AUBURN SPIRIT** 1
1 **AUDIENCE** 2
17 **AUDIOSTREETDOTCOM** 3
298 **AUDITION** F 21
341 **AUDITOR** 3
524 **AUDITORIUM** 28
303 **AUDITTY** (IRE) 1
259 **AUENLUST** (GER) C 64
391 **AU LAC** 3
435 **AULD NICK** (IRE) 6
313 **AULD THYNES SAKE** (IRE) 1
475 **AUNTIE FAY** (IRE) C 20
527 **AUNTIE JACHINTA** 2
373 **AUNT JEMIMA** C 71
254 **AUNT JULIA** 93
67 **AUNT PEARL** (USA) C 43
578 **AURA OF CALM** (IRE) 88
178 **AURAZURE** (IRE) 1
446 **AURELIA** 11
277 **AU REVOIR** 116
329 **AURIGA** F 33
160 **AURORA BAY** (IRE) C 24
36 **AUROVILLE** 16
411 **AUSONE** 34

221 **AUSTRALIE** (IRE) 8
273 **AUTHORITY** (IRE) 1
225 **AUTUMN FALL** (USA) F 83
180 **AUTUMN FANTASY** (USA) 2
127 **AUTUMN FLYER** (IRE) 11
605 **AUTUMN GLORY** (IRE) 2
590 **AUTUMN RAIN** (USA) 1
431 **AUTUMN WEALTH** (IRE) 27
141 **AVADI** (IRE) 7
41 **AVALANCHE** (FR) 3
335 **AVANTI EXPRESS** (IRE) 2
32 **AVANTI TIGER** (IRE) 3
4 **AVAS DELIGHT** (IRE) 2
384 **AVEBURY** 7
205 **AVEC PLAISIR** (GER) 5
445 **AVEIRO** (IRE) 4
438 **AVENTURA** (IRE) 1
119 **AVENUE MONTAIGNE** (FR) 5
16 **AVERAMI** 42
148 **AVERLLINE** 18
468 **AVERSE** (USA) 2
408 **AVESA** 2
110 **AVESSIA** 15
524 **AVIEMORE** 104
595 **AVITTA** (IRE) 6
311 **AVOCET** (IRE) 24
110 **AVONBRIDGE** 1
338 **AVRIL BLAKE** F 14
549 **AWAASER** (USA) 70
403 **AWAKE** 4
29 **AWAKEN** 17
333 **AWAKENING** 35
309 **AWARDING** 1
100 **AWASH** 45
578 **AWAY WITH IT** (IRE) 89
602 **AWESOME WELLS** (IRE) 1
482 **A WOMAN IN LOVE** 2
37 **AWTAAR** (USA) C 39
551 **AWWAL MARRA** (USA) 1
114 **AXE CREEK** (USA) C 36
168 **AYAAM** (IRE) 16
257 **AYE AYE POPEYE** (IRE) 3
227 **AYR CLASSIC** C 20
545 **AYSIDE ALEX** 27
465 **AZAHARA** 93
194 **AZAROLE** (IRE) 34
404 **AZERTYUIOP** (FR) 11
358 **AZOLA** (IRE) C 26
118 **AZRA** (IRE) C 58
41 **AZULA** C 31
169 **AZYAA** C 87
404 **AZZEMOUR** (FR) 12

298 **BAALBEK** c 22
104 **BAAWRAH** 33
530 **BABA** (IRE) 11
269 **BABBLING ON** (FR) 73
547 **BABODANA** 3
194 **BABOON** (IRE) 35
89 **BABOUSHKA** (IRE) 6
460 **BABY BARRY** 1
237 **BABY BE** 1
81 **BABY COME BACK** 28

533 **BARRON BAY** (USA) 2
522 **BARRONS PIKE** 1
393 **BARROW** (SWI) 7
181 **BARRY ISLAND** 1
388 **BARSHAM C** 54
318 **BARTON BARON** (IRE) 2
124 **BARTON BOG** (IRE) 1
173 **BARTON FLOWER** 67
318 **BARTON GATE** 3
174 **BARTON HILL** 2
318 **BARTON NIC** 4
435 **BARTON SANDS** (IRE) 8
54 **BARZAK** (IRE) 3
429 **BASEMAH** (FR) 32
518 **BASHRRI** 42
524 **BASIC SYSTEM** (USA) 105
77 **BASIL** 4
457 **BASINET** 5
342 **BASMAT** (USA) C 3
83 **BASSANO** (USA) 3
277 **BASSERAH** (IRE) 118
392 **BASSETT TIGER** (IRE) 7
583 **BATCHWORTH BEAU** 12
583 **BATCHWORTH BREEZE** 1
583 **BATCHWORTH DANCER F** 13
8 **BATHE IN LIGHT** (USA) C 28
44 **BATH HOUSE BOY** (IRE) 1
46 **BATHSHEBA** 2
318 **BATHWICK ANNIE** 5
377 **BATHWICK BILL** (USA) 24
377 **BATHWICK BRUCE** (IRE) 2
377 **BATHWICK DREAM** 3
591 **BATMAN SENORA** (FR) 3
219 **BATON CHARGE** (IRE) 5
403 **BATOOL** (USA) 10
180 **BATSWING** 4
134 **BATTENBURG** (IRE) 2
549 **BATTLEDRESS** (IRE) 71
52 **BATTLE WARNING** 2
384 **BATTO** 8
429 **BAVARIA STREET** (FR) 33
578 **BAWAADER** (IRE) 90
225 **BAY BIANCA** (IRE) F 84
431 **BAYEUX DE MOI** (IRE) 77
16 **BAY HAWK** 82
299 **BAYHIRR** 11
14 **BAY KENNY** 3
225 **BAYLANDS SUNSHINE** (IRE) C 85
18 **BAYLAW STAR** 22
436 **BAY LEGEND** (IRE) 3
134 **BAYLETTA** (IRE) 4
479 **BAY MAGIC** (IRE) 1
250 **BAY OF DREAMS** 1
148 **BAYOU PRINCESS** 19
478 **BAYRIKA** (IRE) C 84
465 **BAYROUGE** (IRE) F 94
174 **BAY SOLITAIRE** 4
349 **BAY TREE** (IRE) 23
493 **BAZELLE** 30
98 **BDELLIUM** 3
567 **BEA'S RUBY** (IRE) F 32
36 **BEACH PARTY** (IRE) 17
393 **BEACON OF LIGHT** (IRE) 8
504 **BEADY** (IRE) 2
162 **BEAMING F** 8
384 **BEAMISH PRINCE** 9
384 **BEAMSLEY BEACON** 37
134 **BEANCOUNTER** (IRE) 5

141 **BEARAWAY** (IRE) 8
183 **BEARE NECESSITIES** (IRE) 1
325 **BEAR ON BOARD** (IRE) 5
496 **BEAT THE BANK** (IRE) 2
413 **BEAT THE HEAT** (IRE) 1
306 **BEAU ARTISTE** 2
306 **BEAUCHAMP GIGI** (IRE) 9
600 **BEAUCHAMP MAGIC** 5
57 **BEAUCHAMP PRINCESS** 4
311 **BEAUCHAMP Q** 1
311 **BEAUCHAMP SPARK** 25
84 **BEAUCHAMP STAR** 20
84 **BEAUCHAMP SUN** 21
84 **BEAUCHAMP SURPRISE** 22
84 **BEAUCHAMP TESS** 47
84 **BEAUCHAMP TIGER** 48
84 **BEAUCHAMP TRUMP** 49
84 **BEAUCHAMP TURBO** 50
84 **BEAUCHAMP TWIST** 51
601 **BEAU CHASSEUR** (FR) 3
557 **BEAU COUP** 5
295 **BEAUFORT** 27
103 **BEAU GESTE** (IRE) 1
147 **BEAU JAZZ** 5
50 **BEAU LARGESSE** 6
416 **BEAULY** (IRE) 2
241 **BEAUNE** 48
445 **BEAUSEJOUR** (USA) 8
161 **BEAU SUPREME** (IRE) 6
37 **BEAUTEOUS** (IRE) 1
333 **BEAUTIFIX** (GER) 36
278 **BEAUTIFUL MOVER** (USA) 31
578 **BEAUTIFUL NOTE** (USA) 29
439 **BEAU TORERO** (FR) 3
457 **BEAUVRAI** 6
66 **BEAVER DIVA** 87
31 **BEAVER LODGE** (IRE) 1
309 **BEAVER PATROL** (IRE) 23
445 **BEBOPSKIDDLEY** 10
201 **BECKERMET** (IRE) 15
248 **BECKY'S HILL** 10
349 **BEDAZZLING** (IRE) C 63
272 **BED BUG** (IRE) 7
311 **BEDFORD LEADER** 2
601 **BED HOPPER** 4
300 **BEDLAM** 30
226 **BEDTIME BLUES** 12
219 **BEE AN BEE** (IRE) 6
338 **BEECH BRAMBLE** (IRE) F 15
331 **BEECHWOOD** 6
248 **BEECHY BANK** (IRE) 1
576 **BEE DEES LEGACY** 7
288 **BEEF OR SALMON** (IRE) 6
436 **BEE IN THE ROSE** (IRE) G 4
118 **BEEJAY** 23
244 **BEETLE BUG** 1
36 **BE EXCITING** (IRE) F 52
141 **BEFORE DARK** (IRE) 9
103 **BEFORE THE MAST** (IRE) 2
169 **BEFORE TIME** 89
131 **BEHAN** 3
28 **BEHARI** (IRE) 1
478 **BEHARIYA** (IRE) C 85
422 **BEHAVINGBADLY** (IRE) 1
478 **BEHKARA** (IRE) 4
478 **BEHLAYA** (IRE) 36
29 **BEKLA** (FR) 18
129 **BELALCAZAR** 1

82 **BELALZAO** (IRE) 1
246 **BELAMCANDA G** 11
361 **BELCARO** (GER) 9
392 **BELINKIN** 8
173 **BELISARIO** (IRE) 4
431 **BELISCO** (USA) 28
431 **BELITA** 78
435 **BELLA BAMBINA** 9
13 **BELLA BEGUINE** 3
49 **BELLA BOY ZEE** (IRE) 33
442 **BELLA HELENA F** 27
349 **BELLA LAMBADA F** 64
423 **BELLA LIANA** (IRE) 2
437 **BELLA MARY** 1
66 **BELLA PAVLINA** 3
398 **BELLAPORT GIRL** 1
443 **BELLE DE NUIT** (IRE) F 39
50 **BELLE LARGESSE** 7
290 **BELLESOEUR** 3
474 **BELLEVUE HERO** (NZ) 4
290 **BELLS BEACH** (IRE) 4
480 **BELLS BOY'S** 3
217 **BELL TOR** (IRE) 3
496 **BEL OMBRE** (IRE) 1
530 **BELSHAZZAR** (USA) 12
544 **BELSKI** 1
147 **BELTANE** 2
194 **BELUGA BAY** 3
436 **BELUGA** (IRE) 5
66 **BE MY ALIBI** (IRE) 88
382 **BE MY BETTER HALF** (IRE) 3
436 **BE MY DESTINY** (IRE) 6
141 **BE MY FRIEND** (IRE) 10
205 **BE MY LEADER** (IRE) 6
545 **BE MY MANAGER** (IRE) 2
77 **BE MY OWN** (IRE) 5
567 **BENBAUN** (IRE) 13
574 **BENBECULA** (IRE) 3
95 **BENBYAS** 1
524 **BENEDICT** 106
500 **BENEFIT** 1
215 **BENEKING** 7
169 **BENEVENTA** 4
136 **BEN EWAR** 1
452 **BEN GORM** (IRE) 2
66 **BEN HUR** 9
178 **BENJAMIN BUCKRAM** (IRE) 2
513 **BENJAMIN** (IRE) 1
207 **BEN KENOBI** 3
166 **BEN LOMOND** 1
326 **BEN MORE** 1
83 **BENNANABAA** 4
377 **BENNY BATHWICK** (IRE) 25
344 **BENNY THE BALL** (USA) 22
230 **BENO** (IRE) 1
545 **BENRAJAH** (IRE) 3
541 **BEN THE BRAVE** (IRE) 1
373 **BENTINCK** (IRE) 73
254 **BENTLEY'S BALL** (USA) 19
254 **BENTLEY'S BUSH** (IRE) 95
351 **BEN VETO** (FR) 94
420 **BE PREPARED** (IRE) F 43
257 **BE QUIET** (IRE) 4
83 **BERENGARIO** (IRE) 5
480 **BERENICE** (ITY) C 48
517 **BERENSON** (IRE) 21
295 **BERESFORD BOY** 16
180 **BERGAMO** 5

119 **BLEU D'ECOSSE** (FR) 7
595 **BLEU SUPERBE** (FR) 9
335 **BLINDED BY LOVE** (IRE) 34
431 **BLING BLING** 79
300 **BLOFELD** 9
344 **BLONDE EN BLONDE** (IRE) 1
27 **BLONDE STREAK** (USA) 2
88 **BLOOD MONEY** 30
290 **BLOSSOMING C** 26
11 **BLOSSOM WHISPERS** 1
431 **BLOUDAN** (USA) F 80
435 **BLOWING WIND** (FR) 10
404 **BLUE AMERICO** (IRE) 1
552 **BLUE BAJAN** (IRE) 22
525 **BLUEBELL MISS G** 2
358 **BLUEBERRY RHYME** 1
92 **BLUE BOY** 43
594 **BLUE BROOK** 1
404 **BLUE BUSINESS** 16
173 **BLUE BUSTER** 6
29 **BLUE CANARI** (FR) 9
159 **BLUE CANYON** (FR) 4
148 **BLUE CANYON** (IRE) 2
312 **BLUE CASCADE** (IRE) 1
280 **BLUE DERBY** (IRE) 6
49 **BLUE EMPEROR** (IRE) 34
262 **BLUE EMPIRE** (IRE) 17
404 **BLUE ENDEAVOUR** (IRE) 17
529 **BLUE ETTE** (IRE) 3
309 **BLUEFIELD** (IRE) 13
281 **BLUE GALE** (IRE) 5
110 **BLUE GENTIAN** (USA) F 62
17 **BLUEGRASS BOY** 7
145 **BLUE HAWK** (IRE) 1
388 **BLUE JAVA** 29
298 **BLUE KNIGHT** (IRE) 1
73 **BLUE LEADER** (IRE) 1
356 **BLUE LINE** 14
393 **BLUE LIZARD** (IRE) 11
549 **BLUE LULLABY** (IRE) 74
274 **BLUE MAEVE** 1
259 **BLUE MARINER** 5
110 **BLUE MONDAY** 19
529 **BLUE MYST** 4
165 **BLUE NUN** 10
239 **BLUE OASIS** (IRE) 16
185 **BLUE PATRICK** 1
81 **BLUE POWER** (IRE) 29
287 **BLUE QUIVER** (IRE) 3
209 **BLUE RINSE G** 2
393 **BLUE RISING** 95
591 **BLUE RONDO** (IRE) 5
442 **BLUE SAVANNA** 3
402 **BLUE SHANNON** (IRE) 1
333 **BLUE SILK** (FR) 38
148 **BLUE SIOUX F** 20
81 **BLUE SKY THINKING** (IRE) 7
173 **BLUE SPINNAKER** (IRE) 7
208 **BLUES STORY** (FR) 3
383 **BLUE STREAK** (IRE) 12
118 **BLUE TOMATO** 24
226 **BLUETORIA** 6
329 **BLUE TROJAN** (IRE) 1
262 **BLUE VENTURE** (IRE) 1
582 **BLUE VIKING** (IRE) 18
29 **BLUE WING** 20
492 **BLUE YONDER** 3
241 **BLUFF** 49

106 **BLUNHAM** 4
557 **BLUNHAM HILL** (IRE) 6
404 **BLUSHING BULL** 18
333 **BLUSHING IRISH** (FR) 8
526 **BLUSHING PRINCE** (IRE) 2
262 **BLUSHING RUSSIAN** (IRE) 37
168 **BLYTHE KNIGHT** (IRE) 2
192 **BLYTHE SPIRIT** 6
78 **BO' BABBITY F** 20
114 **BOA ESTRELA** (IRE) 37
56 **BOANERGES** (IRE) 2
93 **BOARDROOM DANCER** (IRE) 1
335 **BOARDROOM FIDDLE** (IRE) 6
465 **BOARD WALK** (IRE) 4
190 **BOAVISTA** (IRE) 6
593 **BOB'S BUZZ** 2
66 **BOB'S SHERIE** 11
386 **BOBALONG** (IRE) 1
57 **BOBANLYN** (IRE) G 5
562 **BOBANVI** 3
542 **BOB AR AGHAIDH** (IRE) 1
271 **BOBAWAY** (IRE) 2
102 **BOB BAILEYS** 31
234 **BOBBELLA** (IRE) F 64
104 **BOBBIE LOVE** 102
142 **BOBBI ROSE RED** 4
544 **BOB BOB BOBBIN** 4
145 **BOBBY BLAKENEY** 2
485 **BOBBY CHARLES** 7
556 **BOBBY DAZZLER** 6
31 **BOBERING** 2
542 **BOB LE GAOTH** (IRE) 2
277 **BOBO** 119
269 **BOBOMAN** (USA) 14
152 **BOBOSH** 3
451 **BOBSBEST** (IRE) 1
307 **BOB'S BUSTER** 1
391 **BOB'S FINESSE** 5
510 **BOB'S GONE** (IRE) 1
431 **BOBSLEIGH** 2
169 **BOBSPIN** (IRE) 91
578 **BOBS PRIDE** (IRE) 91
17 **BOB'S PRINCESS G** 56
597 **BOB'S TEMPTATION** 1
591 **BOB'S THE BUSINESS** (IRE) 6
468 **BOB THE PILER** 4
234 **BOCACCIO** (IRE) 4
442 **BODFARI CREEK** 3
547 **BODFARIDISTINCTION** (IRE) C 41
13 **BODFARI ROSE** 2
574 **BODFARI SAUVAGE** 4
55 **BODFARI SIGNET** 3
350 **BOGUS DREAMS** (IRE) 6
436 **BOHEMIAN BOY** (IRE) 8
254 **BOHOLA FLYER** (IRE) 21
599 **BOING BOING** (IRE) 5
403 **BOISDALE** (IRE) 12
72 **BOJANGLES** (IRE) 3
405 **BOLANEY GIRL** (IRE) M 2
29 **BOLAS F** 58
92 **BOLD ACT** (IRE) 44
135 **BOLD AMUSEMENT** 5
414 **BOLD BISHOP** (IRE) 5
504 **BOLD BLADE** 27
593 **BOLD BUNNY** 15
83 **BOLD CENTURY** 6
104 **BOLD CHEVRAK** 103

232 **BOLD CLASSIC** (IRE) 4
36 **BOLD DESIRE** 54
390 **BOLD DIKTATOR** 29
524 **BOLD EAGLE** (IRE) 108
136 **BOLD EFFORT** (FR) 2
29 **BOLD EMPRESS** (USA) F 59
254 **BOLD GEM C** 96
189 **BOLD HUNTER** 3
269 **BOLDINI** (USA) 15
134 **BOLD LILLIAN** (IRE) F 30
148 **BOLD MOMENTO** 3
518 **BOLD PHOENIX** (IRE) 13
329 **BOLD RIDGE** (IRE) 2
10 **BOLD TRUMP** 9
515 **BOLD WOLF** 26
377 **BOLERO C** 36
423 **BOLESLAV** (USA) 4
378 **BOLEYN CASTLE** (USA) 2
269 **BOLITHO** (FR) 74
191 **BOLIVAR** (GER) 22
174 **BOLLIN ANNABEL** 50
174 **BOLLIN ARCHIE** 51
174 **BOLLIN EDWARD** 3
174 **BOLLIN JANET** 4
174 **BOLLIN JEANNIE** 5
174 **BOLLIN MICHAEL** 85
174 **BOLSHEVIK** (IRE) 52
353 **BOLSHOI BALLET** 3
238 **BOLTON BARRIE** (IRE) 8
255 **BOLTON CASTLE** 2
210 **BOLTON FOREST** (IRE) 2
524 **BOMBAZINE** (IRE) C 109
192 **BO MCGINTY** (IRE) 56
277 **BON BON** 120
504 **BOND BABE** 49
504 **BOND BECKS** (IRE) 3
504 **BOND BOY** 4
504 **BOND BROOKLYN** 28
504 **BOND CAT** 50
574 **BOND CITY** (IRE) 51
504 **BOND DIAMOND** 5
504 **BOND DOMINGO** 5
504 **BOND FINESSE** 52
504 **BOND MAY DAY** 6
504 **BOND MILLENNIUM** 7
504 **BOND MOONLIGHT** 29
504 **BOND PLAYBOY** 8
504 **BOND PUCCINI** 53
504 **BOND ROCKERFELLA** 54
504 **BOND ROMEO** 30
504 **BOND ROYALE** 9
504 **BOND SHAKIRA** 31
349 **BONECRUSHER** 6
392 **BONEYARROW** (IRE) 3
152 **BONFIRE NIGHT** (IRE) 4
435 **BONGO FURY** (FR) 11
504 **BONJOUR BOND** (IRE) 32
504 **BONNE DE FLEUR** 33
503 **BONNE FOI** 37
502 **BONNET'S PIECES** 1
92 **BONNETTS** (IRE) 18
391 **BONNIE FLORA** 6
429 **BONNIE MEMORIES** (FR) 14
393 **BONNIE PARKER** (IRE) 12
459 **BONNY BOY** (IRE) 3
116 **BONNY BUSONA** 2
489 **BONNY GLEN** (IRE) 3
255 **BONNY GROVE** 3

432 **BROOKING** (IRE) 13
391 **BROOKLANDS LAD** 7
49 **BROOKLANDS LODGE** (USA) 35
370 **BROOKLANDS TIME** (IRE) 10
301 **BROOKLYN BROWNIE** (IRE) 10
591 **BROOKLYN'S GOLD** (USA) 9
557 **BROOKS** 7
544 **BROOK STREET** 5
448 **BROOKSY DOVE** 1
140 **BROOMERS HILL** (IRE) 1
41 **BROOM ISLE C** 32
479 **BRORA SUTHERLAND** (IRE) 3
82 **BROSNA BELLE** 33
258 **BROTHER CADFAEL** 17
130 **BROTHER TED** 1
388 **BROUGH SUPREME** 30
396 **BROUGHTON BOUNTY** 34
396 **BROUGHTON KNOWS** 4
396 **BROUGHTON MELODY** 5
396 **BROUGHTONS FLUSH** 6
396 **BROUGHTON'S GOLD** (IRE) G 7
527 **BROUGHTONS MILL** 4
396 **BROUGHTON SUNNY** 35
318 **BROWN BEN** 4
265 **BROWN DRAGON** 10
143 **BROWN FLYER** 5
266 **BROWN HOLLY** 1
387 **BROWNIE RETURNS** (IRE) 4
173 **BROWNINGS EXPRESS** 9
288 **BROWN PADDY** 9
208 **BROWN TEDDY** 5
517 **BRUEGEL** (IRE) 1
248 **BRUREN** (IRE) 2
241 **BRUNEL** (IRE) 18
377 **BRUNSTON CASTLE** 4
437 **BRUSH A KING** 5
499 **BRUSH AND GO** (IRE) 1
191 **BRUSH STROKES C** 90
507 **BRUSH THE ARK** 1
257 **BRUTISH FACIE** (IRE) 8
342 **BRUZELLA** 1
76 **BRYANTS ROONEY** 1
387 **BUACHAILL HAZE** (IRE) 5
168 **BUBBLING FUN** 17
269 **BUBBLING RING** (FR) 18
503 **BUBBLY MOLLY** (FR) 19
591 **BUCCANEER BOY** (IRE) 10
88 **BUCHANAN STREET** (IRE) 12
564 **BUCKBY FOLLY M** 1
574 **BUCKBY LANE** 8
299 **BUCKEYE WONDER** (USA) 18
295 **BUCKS** 1
492 **BUCKSKIN LAD** (IRE) 4
436 **BUDDHI** (IRE) 10
71 **BUDE** 3
136 **BUGLE CALL** 3
231 **BUKHOOR** (IRE) 10
118 **BUKIT FRASER** (IRE) 25
462 **BULAWAYO** 2
431 **BULAXIE C** 81
349 **BULL RUN** (IRE) 25
442 **BULLYRAG** 18
547 **BUMPTIOUS** 18
275 **BUNDABERG** 1
157 **BUNDY** 5
593 **BUNINO VEN** 16
392 **BUNKERS HILL** (IRE) 11
340 **BUNKUM** 6

595 **BUNTER BARLOW** (SAF) 12
571 **BUNTY'S FRIEND C** 10
168 **BUNYAH** (IRE) 18
143 **BURDENS BOY** 6
143 **BURDENS GIRL** 7
560 **BURGUNDY LACE** (USA) 5
334 **BURKEES GRAW** (IRE) 11
225 **BURLEY FIREBRAND** 3
225 **BURLEY FLAME** 30
329 **BURLINGTON PLACE** 17
36 **BURN** 19
594 **BURNING GOLD** 2
411 **BURNING MOON** 13
560 **BURNING SHORE** (IRE) 6
495 **BURNING TRUTH** (USA) 2
192 **BURNLEY AL** (IRE) 79
41 **BURNT COPPER** (IRE) 4
578 **BURREN ROSE** (USA) 92
225 **BURTON ASH** 90
94 **BURUNDI** (IRE) 8
219 **BURWOOD BREEZE** (IRE) 8
66 **BUSCADOR** (USA) 13
512 **BUSHIDO** 2
270 **BUSHIE BILL** 1
4 **BUSH PARK** (IRE) 5
465 **BUSINESS CLASS** (NZ) 6
503 **BUSINESSMAN** (FR) 2
212 **BUSINESS MATTERS** (IRE) 1
451 **BUSINESS TRAVELLER** (IRE) 2
422 **BUSTAMANTE** 3
549 **BUSTAN** (IRE) 3
465 **BUSTED FLAT** (IRE) 7
194 **BUSTER HYVONEN** (IRE) 77
602 **BUSTISU** 9
388 **BUSTLING NELLY C** 3
262 **BUSTLING RIO** (IRE) 2
257 **BUST OUT** 9
173 **BUTTRESS** 10
552 **BUYING A DREAM** (IRE) 4
390 **BUY ON THE RED** 11
94 **BUZ KIRI** (USA) 9
124 **BUZYBAKSON** (IRE) 2
67 **BUZZ BUZZ** 19
49 **BY ALL MEN** (IRE) 3
420 **BY CANDLELIGHT** (IRE) F 45
29 **BY FAR** (FR) 1
274 **BYGONE** 8
241 **BYGONE DAYS** 19
320 **BYINCHKA** 2
385 **BYLAND** 4
468 **BYRON LAMB** 7
109 **BYWELL BEAU** (IRE) 1

496 **CABER** (IRE) 4
122 **CABIN BOY** 2
338 **CABRIOLET** (IRE) 16
191 **CACIQUE** (IRE) 24
17 **CA'D'ORO** 9
567 **CADEAU ELEGANT F** 33
239 **CADEAU SPECIALE** 1
29 **CADEAUX D'ETE** (IRE) 61
225 **CADEAUX DES MAGES** 4
382 **CADOU ROYAL** (FR) 6

80 **CADWALLADER** (USA) 1
92 **CAESAR BEWARE** (IRE) 46
432 **CAESAREAN HUNTER** (USA) 14
479 **CAESAR'S PALACE** (GER) 4
493 **CAFE SOLO F** 32
530 **CAGED TIGER** 2
297 **CAILIN CIARRAI** (IRE) G 1
578 **CAIRDEAS** (IRE) 31
146 **CAIRDE NUA** (IRE) F 21
381 **CAITRIONA'S CHOICE** (IRE) 4
89 **CALACHUCHI** (IRE) G 7
435 **CALAMINTHA** 13
66 **CALARA HILLS** 89
301 **CALATAGAN** (IRE) 11
334 **CALCAR** (IRE) 3
325 **CALCOT FLYER** 8
460 **CALCULATE** 8
277 **CALCUTTA** 2
201 **CALDERBRIDGE** (IRE) 16
104 **CALDY DANCER** (IRE) 35
181 **CALEDONIAN** (IRE) 21
358 **CALENDAR GIRL** 3
67 **CALIFORNIA GIRL** 46
234 **CALIFORNIA SPIRIT** (IRE) 5
351 **CALISSON** (FR) 95
444 **CALIWAG** (IRE) 5
8 **CALKE PARK** 1
466 **CALLED TO THE BAR** 2
92 **CALLED UP** 19
325 **CALL FOR TAYLOR G** 9
272 **CALLING BRAVE** (IRE) 10
436 **CALLMARTEL** (IRE) G 11
274 **CALL ME JACK** (IRE) 3
68 **CALL ME LUCKY C** 15
168 **CALL ME MAX** 70
262 **CALL ME SUNSHINE** 5
426 **CALL MY GUEST** (IRE) 1
192 **CALL OF THE WILD** 8
34 **CALOMERIA** 7
100 **CALONNOG** (IRE) 2
17 **CALUSA LADY** (IRE) 10
219 **CALVIC** (IRE) 9
397 **CAMADERRY** (IRE) 1
372 **CAMAIR CRUSADER** (IRE) 3
316 **CAMARADERIE** 3
118 **CAMBERLEY** (IRE) 3
378 **CAMBERWELL** 11
222 **CAMDENATION** (IRE) 3
84 **CAMELOT** 2
280 **CAMERON BRIDGE** (IRE) 9
376 **CAMERON JACK** 3
518 **CAMERONS FUTURE** (IRE) 43
602 **CAMILLE PISSARRO** (USA) 4
414 **CAMPAIGN TRAIL** (IRE) 7
37 **CAMPBELLS LAD** 27
202 **CAMPBELL'S TALE** (IRE) 1
67 **CAMP COMMANDER** (IRE) 3
243 **CAMP HILL** 3
132 **CAMPLI** (IRE) 63
169 **CAMROSE** 31
212 **CAMROSS** 2
259 **CAMZO** (USA) 2
161 **CAN'T BE SCRABBLE** 7
435 **CANADA** 14
510 **CANADA ROAD** (IRE) 3
126 **CANADIAN DANEHILL** (IRE) 20
435 **CANADIANE** (FR) 15
547 **CANADIAN STORM** 19

173 **DENBY** (IRE) 17
521 **DENBY WOOD G** 1
29 **DENEBOLA** (USA) 24
523 **DENEISES BLOSSOM** (IRE) 5
192 **DENE VIEW** 15
81 **DENIAL F** 51
288 **DENMARK** 18
208 **DENNEY'S WELL** (IRE) 8
262 **DENNICK** 40
541 **DENNIS THE MENNIS** (IRE) 3
391 **DENNY ISLAND** 13
100 **DENONORE** 17
369 **DEN'S-JOY** 1
373 **DENVER** (IRE) 30
272 **DEOCH AN DORAIS** (IRE) 21
436 **DEO GRATIAS** (POL) 17
110 **DEPORTIVO** 3
462 **DEPRESSED** 24
102 **DEPTFORD** (IRE) 3
360 **DEPUTY FAIRFAX** 3
118 **DEPUTY OF WOOD** (USA) 63
168 **DERAASAAT** 20
292 **DERAMORE** (IRE) 17
382 **DERAWAR** (IRE) 9
595 **DERIVATIVE** (IRE) 16
104 **DERNIER DANSE** 41
402 **DERREEN BOY** (IRE) 5
308 **DERRING BRIDGE** 3
604 **DERRING FLOSS G** 1
497 **DERRINTOGHER YANK** (IRE) 5
321 **DERRY ANN** 2
437 **DERRY DICE** 3
601 **DERVALLOC** (IRE) 7
42 **DERWENT** (USA) 2
17 **DESAILLY** 15
578 **DESCRIPTIVE** (IRE) 101
435 **DESERT AIR** (JPN) 29
66 **DESERT ARC** (IRE) 21
48 **DESERT BATTLE** (IRE) 12
100 **DESERT BLUEBELL C** 47
274 **DESERT BUZZ** (IRE) 22
29 **DESERT CHILD** 63
168 **DESERT CLASSIC** 74
605 **DESERT DANCE** (IRE) 4
225 **DESERT DAWN F** 95
277 **DESERT DEMON** (IRE) 132
524 **DESERT DIPLOMAT** (IRE) 39
277 **DESERT DREAMER** (IRE) 34
186 **DESERT FERN** (IRE) 16
30 **DESERT FURY** 1
565 **DESERT GOOGLE** 34
254 **DESERT HAWK** 33
490 **DESERT HEAT** 5
542 **DESERT IMAGE** (IRE) 21
585 **DESERTINA** (IRE) 23
159 **DESERT JIM** (FR) 78
493 **DESERT LIGHT** (IRE) 26
524 **DESERT LORD** 6
578 **DESERT MAGIC** (IRE) C 102
104 **DESERT MOVE** (IRE) 112
234 **DESERT OF GOLD** (IRE) 38
16 **DESERT QUEST** (IRE) 10
66 **DESERT QUILL** (IRE) 22
298 **DESERT REIGN** 8
168 **DESERT ROYALTY** (IRE) 4
119 **DESERT SAND** (FR) 10
312 **DESERT SPA** (USA) 2
524 **DESERT STAR** 7

82 **DESERT STREAM** (IRE) 18
119 **DESERT THREAT** (IRE) 11
378 **DESERT TOMMY** 13
125 **DESERT VALENTINE** 2
191 **DESIDERATUM** 94
37 **DESIGNER CITY** (IRE) 30
436 **DESIGNER LABEL** (IRE) 18
524 **DESIGN** (FR) 40
257 **DESIGN TO WIN** (IRE) 18
39 **DESIREE** (IRE) 14
68 **DESIRES DESTINY** 2
420 **DESPERATE DAN** 18
254 **DESTINATE** (IRE) 110
512 **DESTINO** 13
392 **DETONANTE** (FR) 19
280 **DEUX DONS AMIS** 21
110 **DEUXIEME** (IRE) 23
420 **DEVASTATING F** 51
292 **DEVERED** (IRE) 19
361 **DEVIL'S TEARDROP** 15
29 **DEVIL DANCER** (FR) 64
277 **DEVIL'S BITE** 35
559 **DEVIL'S PERK** (IRE) 2
559 **DEVIL'S RUN** (IRE) 3
294 **DEVINE COMMAND** 13
354 **DEVINE LIGHT** (IRE) 5
84 **DEVIOUS AYERS** (IRE) 25
483 **DEVISE** (IRE) 5
281 **DEVON MAID** 7
404 **DEVON VIEW** (IRE) 26
524 **DEVORE** (USA) 41
214 **DEVOTE** 6
301 **DEWASENTAH** (IRE) 16
434 **DEXILEOS** (IRE) 1
478 **DEYNIZI** (IRE) 45
119 **DEZIRING** (IRE) 42
253 **DHABYAN** (USA) 1
231 **DHAKAA** (IRE) 12
192 **DHAUDELOUP** (FR) 16
277 **DHAULAR DHAR** (IRE) 133
253 **DHEFAAF** (IRE) 17
231 **DHEHDAAH** 11
549 **DHELAAL** 82
119 **DIABLE MIX** 12
392 **DIACONATE** (IRE) 84
290 **DIAL SQUARE** 21
432 **DIAMANIKOS** (FR) 28
414 **DIAMANT NOIR** 19
277 **DIAMOND CIRCLE** 134
104 **DIAMOND DAN** (IRE) 113
470 **DIAMOND DARREN** (IRE) 5
318 **DIAMOND DAZZLER** 9
139 **DIAMOND DREAM** (FR) C 4
45 **DIAMOND DYNASTY** 3
191 **DIAMOND FOR EVER** (FR) 27
39 **DIAMOND GEORGE** (IRE) 15
191 **DIAMOND GREEN** (FR) 28
278 **DIAMOND HOMBRE** (USA) 34
514 **DIAMOND JOSHUA** (IRE) 2
239 **DIAMOND KATIE** (IRE) 37
411 **DIAMOND LODGE** 15
39 **DIAMOND MAXINE** (IRE) 4
190 **DIAMOND MAX** (IRE) 8
325 **DIAMOND MERCHANT** 14
272 **DIAMOND MONROE** (IRE) 22
190 **DIAMOND ORCHID** (IRE) 9
105 **DIAMOND RACKET** 3
190 **DIAMOND RIBBY** (IRE) 30

91 **DIAMOND RING** 7
465 **DIAMOND SAL** 16
95 **DIAMOND SHANNON** (IRE) 9
595 **DIAMONDS WILL DO** (IRE) 17
191 **DIAMOND TANGO** (FR) 29
237 **DIAMOND VEIN** 3
349 **DIAMOND WAY** (USA) 29
191 **DIAMPILINA** (FR) 95
583 **DIAPHANOUS** 4
512 **DICEMAN** (IRE) 14
556 **DICKENSBURY LAD** (FR) 12
595 **DICKENS** (USA) 18
17 **DICKIE DEADEYE** 16
184 **DICKINSONS BAY** 2
510 **DICK THE TAXI** 5
578 **DICTATION** 103
407 **DICTUM** (GER) 3
248 **DIDBROOK** 11
367 **DIDIFON** 2
565 **DIDNT TELL MY WIFE** 6
191 **DIEGO CAO** (IRE) 30
392 **DIEGO GARCIA** (IRE) 20
444 **DIEQUEST** (USA) 21
191 **DIEVOTCHKA C** 96
262 **DIFFERENTGEAR** 22
504 **DIFFERENTIAL** (USA) 12
278 **DIFFERENT PLANET** 16
110 **DIFFERENT STORY** (USA) 66
393 **DIGGING DEEP** 21
104 **DIGITAL** 7
465 **DIKLERS ROSE** (IRE) 17
104 **DIKTATIT** 114
352 **DIL** 4
191 **DILAG** (IRE) 97
518 **DILALA** (IRE) 46
602 **DILEER** (IRE) 6
4 **DILETIA** 10
22 **DILIGENT LAD** 4
17 **DILIZA** 17
480 **DILSAA** 7
330 **DILYS** 1
518 **DIMASHQ** 47
477 **DIMINUTIVE** (USA) 1
229 **DIMITRI** (IRE) 8
435 **DINARELLI** (FR) 30
465 **DING DONG BELLE** 18
156 **DINGO DANCER** 2
524 **DINNER DATE** 116
66 **DINOFELIS** 23
306 **DIONN RIGH** (IRE) 19
4 **DIONYSIAN** (IRE) 11
295 **DIOSCOREA** (IRE) F 28
217 **DIPLOMATIC DAISY** (IRE) 7
169 **DIPPERS** (USA) C 98
350 **DIRECT ACCESS** (IRE) 15
578 **DIRECT BEARING** (IRE) 3
457 **DIRECT DESCENDANT** (IRE) 9
103 **DIRECT FLIGHT** (IRE) 9
385 **DIRECTION** 9
529 **DIRECT MANDATE** (USA) 9
476 **DIRK COVE** (IRE) 9
593 **DISABUSE** 5
241 **DISCIPLE** 55
48 **DISCO DIVA** 13
110 **DISCOMATIC** (USA) C 67
458 **DISCRIMINATION F** 25
32 **DI'S DILEMMA** 9
169 **DISH DASH** (IRE) 99

126 **ESTIMATION** 3
6 **ESTRELA VERMELHA** F 2
383 **ESTRELLA LEVANTE** 29
100 **ESTRELLE** (GER) 50
253 **ESWARAH** 18
231 **ETAAR** 13
194 **ETCHING** (USA) 7
191 **ETENDARD INDIEN** (FR) 34
567 **ETERNAL BEAUTY** (USA) 2
68 **ETERNAL BLOOM** 3
126 **ETERNALLY** 1
361 **ETERNAL NIGHT** (FR) 18
578 **ETIJAHAAT** (IRE) 108
277 **ETLAALA** 139
286 **ETMA ROSE** (IRE) C 48
82 **ETOILE D'INDE** (IRE) 35
403 **ETON** (GER) 21
569 **ETTRICK** (NZ) 3
132 **ETTRICK WATER** 2
478 **EUBEA** (FR) 7
254 **EUGENIE** 38
225 **EUIPPE** 37
268 **EUNICE CHOICE** 5
373 **EUPHORIA** 86
218 **EURADREAM** (IRE) 4
306 **EURO CAT** (IRE) 20
288 **EURO FLYER** (IRE) 22
392 **EURO LEADER** (IRE) 22
80 **EUROLINK VIRAGO** C 6
530 **EUROPA** 5
201 **EURYALUS** (IRE) 2
388 **EVA JEAN** 32
378 **EVALUATOR** (IRE) 14
343 **EVANGELIST** (IRE) 2
349 **EVASIVE QUALITY** (FR) 80
331 **EVA SO CHARMING** 19
383 **EVEN EASIER** 85
514 **EVENING FALLS** C 21
111 **EVENING FRAGRANCE** 11
419 **EVENING SPLASH** (IRE) 1
4 **EVEN MORE** (IRE) 14
12 **EVE PET F** 3
554 **EVER CHEERFUL** 13
180 **EVEREST** (IRE) 11
198 **EVERGREEN** (IRE) C 15
111 **EVERLAND** (IRE) 1
333 **EVERLAST** (IRE) 13
280 **EVERREADY** 26
457 **EVERY NOTE COUNTS** 11
302 **EVIYRN** (IRE) 10
578 **EVOLVING TACTICS** (IRE) 5
120 **EVOQUE** 21
49 **EVROBI** (IRE) C 60
600 **EWAR BOLD** 6
393 **EWE BEAUTY** (FR) 23
138 **EXALTED** (IRE) 1
169 **EXCELSIUS** (IRE) 10
122 **EXCEPTIONNEL** (FR) 6
277 **EXCLUSIVE DANIELLE** 37
560 **EXECUTIVE DECISION** (IRE) 7
341 **EXECUTIVE OFFICE** (IRE) 7
524 **EXHIBIT ONE** (USA) 118
269 **EXIMIUS** 27
404 **EXISTENTIAL** (FR) 33
404 **EXIT SWINGER** (FR) 34
404 **EXIT TO WAVE** (FR) 35
39 **EX MILL LADY** 16
418 **EXODOUS** (ARG) 13

414 **EXOTIC DANCER** (FR) 21
593 **EXPECTED BONUS** (USA) 6
566 **EXPECTEDTOFLI** (IRE) 3
251 **EXPENSIVE FOLLY** (IRE) 1
59 **EXPLICIT** (IRE) 4
500 **EXPLODE** 4
517 **EXPLOSIVE FOX** (IRE) 13
257 **EXPRESS EXIT** 22
255 **EXPRESS LILY** 6
192 **EXSTOTO** 18
431 **EXTERIOR** (USA) 37
403 **EXTINGUISHER** 22
60 **EXTRA CACHE** (NZ) 5
110 **EXTRA COVER** (IRE) 24
6 **EXTRA PROUD** 3
174 **EXTREMELY RARE** (IRE) 61
14 **EXTREMIST** (USA) 7
194 **EYECATCHER** 8
408 **EYES DONT LIE** (IRE) 3
100 **EYES ONLY** 19
354 **EYZE** (IRE) 7
425 **EZZ ELKHEIL** 3

524 **FAAYEJ** (IRE) 9
290 **FABRANESE** 5
592 **FABREZAN** (FR) 4
320 **FABUCO** (IRE) 10
503 **FABULEUX DESTIN** (FR) 42
333 **FABULIST** (USA) C 14
595 **FABULOUS JET** (IRE) 9
91 **FABULOUS MOLLY** G 26
485 **FABULOUS NIGHT** (FR) C 13
269 **FABULOUS SPEED** (USA) 28
413 **FACE THE LIMELIGHT** (IRE) 3
578 **FACTICE** (USA) C 109
306 **FACTOR FIFTEEN** 21
377 **FACTUAL LAD** 3
412 **FADDAD** (USA) 2
104 **FADING** F 116
382 **FADOUDAL DU COCHET** (FR) 11
277 **FAHLAWI** (IRE) 38
344 **FAILED TO HIT** 2
140 **FAILTE** (IRE) 2
300 **FAIR ALONG** (GER) 34
191 **FAIRBATHE** (FR) 100
476 **FAIR ENOUGH** (IRE) 10
89 **FAIREY FIREFLY** F 11
562 **FAIRGAME MAN** 10
593 **FAIRLEE ROYAL** 28
458 **FAIRLIE** 14
87 **FAIRLY GLORIOUS** 8
191 **FAIRLY RUN** (FR) 35
496 **FAIR MAJORITY** (IRE) 11
466 **FAIRMEAD PRINCESS** 4
139 **FAIR OPTIONS** 5
595 **FAIR QUESTION** (IRE) 20
579 **FAIR SEAS M** 1
176 **FAIR SHAKE** (IRE) 4
518 **FAIR SHIRLEY** (IRE) F 54
202 **FAIR TEST** F 20
602 **FAIRTOTO** 8
329 **FAIR VERONA** (USA) C 36
191 **FAIRWUALA** (IRE) 101

458 **FAIRY FLAX** (IRE) G 28
67 **FAIRY GARDEN** (USA) F 50
67 **FAIRY HEIGHTS** (IRE) F 51
22 **FAIRY HIGHLANDS** (IRE) F 21
375 **FAIRY MONARCH** (IRE) 1
503 **FAIRY NOTE** (FR) 3
585 **FAIRY RING** (IRE) G 24
255 **FAIRY SKIN MAKER** (IRE) 7
333 **FAIRY WEST** (USA) F 44
137 **FAIRY WIND** (GER) 3
288 **FAITHEN GRAND** (IRE) 23
277 **FAITHFUL WARRIOR** (USA) 6
373 **FAKHIRA** (IRE) C 87
549 **FALEH** (USA) 84
446 **FALL IN LINE** 5
225 **FALL OF THE HAMMER** F 98
169 **FALSAFI** 103
132 **FAMCAPII** (IRE) 70
277 **FAME AT LAST** (USA) C 140
14 **FAMFONI** (FR) 8
504 **FAMILIAR AFFAIR** 39
393 **FAMILY VENTURE** (IRE) 24
361 **FAMOUS GROUSE** 19
443 **FANCIER BIT F** 40
456 **FANCIFUL** (IRE) F 13
277 **FANCY BOOTS** (IRE) F 141
373 **FANCY FOXTROT** 32
67 **FANCY RULER** (USA) C 52
192 **FANCY WRAP** C 84
578 **FANDANGO DANCER** 36
240 **FANION DE NOURRY** (FR) 2
403 **FANLING LADY** 71
565 **FANNY'S FANCY** 7
446 **FANTAISISTE** 39
169 **FANTASIA'S FOREST** (IRE) 104
504 **FANTASMIC RIVER** (IRE) 13
595 **FANTASTIC ARTS** (FR) 21
117 **FANTASTIC BLOOM** (VEN) C 9
560 **FANTASTIC CHAMPION** (IRE) 8
169 **FANTASTIC LUCK** (IRE) 105
568 **FANTASTICO** (IRE) 3
254 **FANTASTIC VIEW** (USA) 39
457 **FANTASY BELIEVER** 12
223 **FANTASY CRUSADER** 2
457 **FANTASY DEFENDER** (IRE) 40
375 **FANTASY FEELING** 16
292 **FANTASY WORLD M** 24
377 **FANTAZIA** F 41
36 **FARAWAY ECHO** 21
416 **FARAWAY LOOK** (USA) 5
213 **FARD DU MOULIN MAS** (FR) 1
169 **FARDI** (IRE) 106
517 **FARDUS** (IRE) C 24
511 **FAREWELL CHILD** 3
254 **FAREWELL GIFT** 40
390 **FAR FOR LULU** 14
603 **FAR GLEN** (IRE) 6
272 **FAR HORIZON** (IRE) 25
382 **FARINEL** 12
232 **FARINGTON LODGE** (IRE) 10
306 **FARLINGTON** 22
280 **FARMER JACK** 27
145 **FARMER JOSH** 3
515 **FARMERS SWING** (IRE) F 31
496 **FARNAHEEZVIEW** (IRE) 12
181 **FARNBOROUGH** (USA) 24
255 **FARNE ISLE** 8
54 **FAR NOTE** (USA) 6

350 **KABARDA g** 33
100 **KABIS AMIGOS** 55
100 **KABIS BOOIE** (IRE) 26
168 **KABREET** 30
404 **KADAM** (IRE) 56
4 **KADARA** (IRE) 24
404 **KADARANN** (IRE) 57
431 **KADDASAN** 91
351 **KADISCOT** (FR) 103
152 **KADITO** 19
124 **KADOUKO** (FR) 3
143 **KADOUN** (FR) 24
325 **KADOUNY** (FR) 33
432 **KAFRI D'AIRY** (FR) 46
410 **KAGOSHIMA** (IRE) 5
254 **KAHLA C** 126
349 **KAHRAMANA** 91
340 **KAID** (IRE) 12
373 **KAIETEUR** (USA) 6
432 **KAISER** (IRE) 47
287 **KAJUL** 9
401 **KALI CRAZY** (FR) 3
29 **KALABAR** 4
478 **KALAJANA** (USA) C 93
364 **KALAMANSI** (IRE) 25
524 **KALAMBA** (IRE) C 134
231 **KALANISHA** (IRE) 2
280 **KALCA MOME** (FR) 49
221 **KALDEVEES** (FR) F 56
454 **KALHMERA** (IRE) 16
110 **KALI** 29
511 **KALIC D'ALM** (FR) 6
531 **KALI DES OBEAUX** (FR) 6
351 **KALIMIE** (FR) 24
432 **KALIN DE THAIX** (FR) 48
593 **KALINDI C** 30
552 **KALISHKA** (IRE) 20
145 **KALISKO** (FR) 4
478 **KALIYOUN** (IRE) 52
221 **KALKARA** (IRE) 18
104 **KALMINI** (USA) 129
137 **KALOU** (GER) 5
83 **KALUGA** (IRE) 12
537 **KALUSH** 9
254 **KAMAKIRI** (IRE) 127
72 **KAMALA** 6
277 **KAMANDA LAUGH** 60
191 **KAMARITA** (IRE) 45
258 **KAMA'S WHEEL** 4
132 **KAMA TASHOOF** F 75
67 **KAMEEZ** (IRE) C 56
192 **KAMENKA** 61
351 **KAMI DES OBEAUX** (FR) 25
392 **KAMPALA II** (FR) 34
67 **KANDIDATE** 57
153 **KANDYLE** (IRE) 5
458 **KANGARILLA ROAD** 10
446 **KANGRINA** 43
517 **KANISFLUH** 15
411 **KANSA** (FR) F 50
94 **KANZ WOOD** (USA) 21
386 **KAOLIN DE PERCHE** (FR) 5
382 **KAOUTCHOU** (FR) 30
24 **KAPAJE** 130
431 **KAPAROLO** (USA) 6
467 **KAPPELHOFF** (IRE) 3

232 **KAPPILLAN** (IRE) 14
114 **KAP VERDE** 4
367 **KARAHISAR** (IRE) 3
384 **KARAJAN** (IRE) 19
169 **KARAMEA** (SWI) 46
478 **KARANI** (FR) 11
144 **KARANJA** 6
329 **KARAOKE** (IRE) 7
239 **KARASHINKO** (IRE) 21
192 **KARASHINO** (IRE) 85
350 **KARATCHI** (FR) 34
278 **KARATHAENA** (IRE) 7
299 **KARDASHINA** (FR) F 66
168 **KARDELLE C** 89
396 **KAREEB** (FR) 18
191 **KARELIAN** 46
37 **KAREN BLIXEN** F 52
411 **KAREN S** (USA) C 51
356 **KARIBEE** 2
152 **KARIBLUE** 20
8 **KARINA'S CARBON G** 4
463 **KARINGA CITY** 4
161 **KARINGA COIN** 22
46 **KARING KENDA** 9
351 **KARIO KA** (FR) 26
545 **KARJU** (IRE) 14
524 **KARLIYKA** (IRE) F 135
169 **KARLU** (GER) 117
278 **KARMA CHAMELIAN** (USA) 20
393 **KA ROSE** (FR) 45
299 **KARRNAK** (FR) 7
376 **KARYON** (IRE) 6
478 **KASAKIYA** (IRE) 12
478 **KASALI** (IRE) 53
159 **KASBAH BLISS** (FR) 84
277 **KASKA** (IRE) 61
503 **KASLIK** (FR) 27
591 **KASSEL** (USA) 32
306 **KASTHARI** (IRE) 35
13 **KATALI** 11
411 **KATAVI** (USA) 20
549 **KATAYEB** (IRE) 26
400 **KATE O'KIRKHAM M** 2
549 **KATHEER** 94
11 **KATHELLA** (IRE) 3
411 **KATHLEEN'S DREAM** (USA) F 52
181 **KATHOLOGY** (IRE) 9
505 **KATHY FAIR** (FR) F 10
182 **KATIE'S BISCUIT** 1
152 **KATIE'S JEWEL** F 21
368 **KATIE DALY** (IRE) M 6
475 **KATIE DICK** (IRE) G 6
580 **KATIE KILLANE** 10
353 **KATIE SAVAGE** 14
182 **KATIE'S BATH TIME** 9
190 **KATIE SCARLETT M** 15
307 **KATIES DOLPHIN** (IRE) 7
182 **KATIE'S EMPIRE** (IRE) 10
214 **KATIES HERO** 11
182 **KATIE'S ROLE** 11
482 **KATIYPOUR** (IRE) 8
306 **KATMANDU** 36
418 **KATOOF** (USA) 16
118 **KATRINA** (IRE) C 71
63 **KATTEGAT** 3
103 **KATY JONES** 16
246 **KATY O'HARA** 3
107 **KATZ PYJAMAS** (IRE) 6

194 **KAURI FOREST** (USA) 47
351 **KAUTO RAY** (FR) 104
172 **KAVI** (IRE) 4
501 **KAWADER** (USA) 2
549 **KAWAK** 95
29 **KAYAK** 32
107 **KAY BEE VENTURE** 4
351 **KAYSERI** (FR) 27
194 **KAZATZKA** 86
392 **KEAVENEY** 35
420 **KEBABS** (IRE) F 65
208 **KEBREYA** (USA) 14
299 **KEELUNG** (USA) 28
468 **KEEN AND ABLE** 22
414 **KEEN LEADER** (IRE) 35
104 **KEEN MELODY** (USA) C 131
33 **KEEN SKIMMER** 20
512 **KEEN TO THE LAST** (FR) 29
526 **KEEPASHARPLOOKOUT** (IRE) 20
387 **KEEPATEM** (FR) 11
118 **KEEPERS KNIGHT** (IRE) 37
4 **KEEPERS MEAD** (IRE) 25
378 **KEEP ON MOVIN'** (IRE) 18
558 **KEEPSAKE** (IRE) G 3
595 **KEEP SMILING** (IRE) 40
77 **KEEPTHEDREAMALIVE** 15
214 **KEETCHY** (IRE) 12
357 **KEHAAR** 6
64 **KEIMAR** 10
283 **KEIRAN** (IRE) 6
234 **KEITHARA** (IRE) 13
159 **KELAMI** (FR) 16
14 **KELANTAN** 20
524 **KELATAKAN** (IRE) 56
13 **KELBROOK** 12
567 **KELLS** (IRE) 6
392 **KELLY'S CRAFT** 36
512 **KELLY PRIDE** 30
288 **KELLYS LEADER** (IRE) 35
595 **KELREV** (FR) 41
226 **KELSEAS KOLBY** (IRE) 3
373 **KELSO MAGIC** (USA) C 95
361 **KELTIC BARD** 34
152 **KELTIC BLUE** (IRE) 22
195 **KELTIC FLUTE** 4
140 **KELTIC HERITAGE** (IRE) 10
265 **KELTIC RAINBOW** (IRE) 15
17 **KELTIC ROCK** 31
227 **KELUCIA** (IRE) 19
148 **KEMCHEE M** 6
406 **KEMPSKI** 3
170 **KENNINGTON** 3
91 **KENNY THE TRUTH** (IRE) 15
601 **KEN SCOTT** (FR) 17
225 **KEN SHABBY** 48
239 **KENSINGTON** (IRE) 22
391 **KENTFORD GREBE** 22
98 **KENTISH WARRIER** (IRE) 6
254 **KENTMERE** (FR) C 128
554 **KENTUCKY BANKES** 21
174 **KENTUCKY BLUE** (IRE) 19
401 **KENTUCKY BULLET** (USA) 4
191 **KENTUCKY CHARM** (FR) 47
174 **KENTUCKY EXPRESS** 67
272 **KEN'TUCKY** (FR) 50
159 **KENTUCKY GOLD** (FR) 17
578 **KENTUCKY HOME** (USA) 46
84 **KENTUCKY LILL** (USA) C 64

329 **MICHELLE MA BELLE** (IRE) 9
189 **MICHIGAN BLUE** 4
387 **MICK DIVINE** (IRE) 14
37 **MICKEY BOGGITT** 58
178 **MICKEY CROKE** 9
13 **MICKLEDO** 37
157 **MICKLEDOR** 12
42 **MICKLEGATE** 15
270 **MICKLEY** (IRE) 8
110 **MIDAS WAY** 6
277 **MIDCAP** (IRE) 161
262 **MIDDLEHAM PARK** (IRE) 9
262 **MIDDLEHAM ROSE** 27
227 **MIDDLEMARCH** 37
391 **MIDDLEMISS** (IRE) 26
73 **MIDDLE POND** 5
173 **MIDDLETHORPE** 34
401 **MIDDLETON GREY** 9
376 **MIDDLEWAY** 9
528 **MIDFIELD** (IRE) 34
165 **MIDGES PRIDE** 6
331 **MIDLAND FLAME** (IRE) 42
121 **MIDLEM MELODY** 3
504 **MIDNIGHT ALLURE** C 62
309 **MIDNIGHT BALLARD** (USA) 17
95 **MIDNIGHT FLOTILLA** F 17
233 **MIDNIGHT GOLD** 3
448 **MIDNIGHT GUNNER** 5
239 **MIDNIGHT MAMBO** (USA) 4
559 **MIDNIGHT MAYHEM** (IRE) 11
578 **MIDNIGHT MIST** (IRE) 121
5 **MIDNIGHT PARKES** 8
173 **MIDNIGHT PRINCE** 71
226 **MIDNIGHT PROMISE** 9
162 **MIDNIGHT ROMANCE** F 7
83 **MIDNIGHT SPIRIT** 15
94 **MIDSHIPMAN** 25
259 **MIDSHIPMAN EASY** (USA) 48
478 **MIDSOU** (FR) 58
383 **MID SUSSEX SPIRIT** 54
159 **MIEUX MIEUX** (IRE) 62
159 **MIG** 36
67 **MIGHTY FLYER** (IRE) F 63
94 **MIGHTY GLEN** (IRE) 26
414 **MIGHTY KILCASH** (IRE) 43
60 **MIGHTY MAN** (IRE) 9
247 **MIGHTY MAX** 10
51 **MIGHTY PIP** 17
272 **MIGHTY STRONG** 69
602 **MIGWELL** (FR) 17
205 **MIJAS LADY** (IRE) 25
518 **MIJDAAF** (FR) 25
393 **MIJICO** (FR) 58
325 **MIKADO MELODY** (IRE) 42
547 **MIKAO** (IRE) 26
201 **MIKASA** (IRE) 5
298 **MIKATI MAID** 12
233 **MIKE SIMMONS** 4
532 **MIKES MATE** 11
210 **MIKE STAN** (IRE) 6
119 **MIKOS** (FR) 27
191 **MILADY'S PRIDE** 58
298 **MILADY LILLIE** (IRE) F 33
348 **MILAN KING** (IRE) 6
285 **MILDAN GRACE** 7
582 **MILDON** 14
67 **MILITARY TUNE** (IRE) F 64

81 **MILITARY TWO STEP** (IRE) 35
66 **MILK AND SULTANA** 51
392 **MILKAT** (IRE) 57
420 **MILK IT MICK** 26
132 **MILLAFONIC** 13
490 **MILLAGROS** (IRE) 12
104 **MILLBAG** (IRE) 64
360 **MILL BANK** 4
161 **MILLCROFT REDROCK** 30
161 **MILLCROFT SEASCAPE** 31
4 **MILLCROFT SEASPRAY** 33
365 **MILLE ET UNE NUITS** (FR) 8
261 **MILL EMERALD** 5
414 **MILLENAIRE** (FR) 44
169 **MILLENARY** 17
173 **MILL END CHATEAU** 100
349 **MILL END** (IRE) 96
173 **MILL END TEASER** 72
159 **MILLENIUM ROYAL** (FR) 37
104 **MILLENNIUM FORCE** 19
381 **MILLENNIUM HALL** 17
264 **MILLENNIUM TALE** (FR) G 6
254 **MILLER'S MELODY** F 137
109 **MILLERBURN** (IRE) 5
331 **MILLER'S BAY** 43
225 **MILLIBIEN** 52
329 **MILLIE'S LADY** (IRE) C 41
240 **MILLIE MILLION** G 5
156 **MILLIESOME** 4
480 **MILLIETOM** (IRE) 38
192 **MILLIGAN** (FR) 33
239 **MILLINSKY** (USA) 28
262 **MILLION HEIRESS** C 52
81 **MILLION PERCENT** 14
349 **MILLITRIX** F 97
480 **MILLKOM ELEGANCE** 14
104 **MILLSTREAM** (USA) F 149
406 **MILL TOWER** 5
299 **MILLVILLE** 5
239 **MILLYBAA** (USA) 5
456 **MILLY HA HA** C 21
91 **MILLY'S LASS** 16
66 **MILLY WATERS** 93
91 **MILNER BE GOOD** 17
91 **MILNER BE GREAT** 18
119 **MILORD DES BORDES** (FR) 28
435 **MILORD LESCRIBAA** (FR) 87
159 **MILRANE** (FR) 63
92 **MIMAS GIRL** 10
239 **MIMIC** 7
174 **MIMI MOUSE** 9
104 **MIN ASL WAFI** (IRE) 150
174 **MIND ALERT** 70
350 **MINDANAO** 45
239 **MINDFULNESS** 29
514 **MIND PLAY** 18
274 **MIND THE TIME** 21
41 **MINE BEHIND** 15
42 **MINE** (IRE) 6
288 **MINELLA VIC** (IRE) 44
514 **MINELLY** 9
445 **MINERS DANCE** (IRE) 41
225 **MING THE MERCILESS** 15
95 **MING VASE** 24
432 **MINIBALLIST** (IRE) 56
496 **MINI DARE** 21
191 **MINIMIZE** (USA) 117
414 **MINI SENSATION** (IRE) 45

174 **MINIVET** 25
411 **MINNIE HABIT** C 59
34 **MINNESINGER** 41
92 **MINNESOTA** (USA) 52
454 **MINNIE BLOO MIN** (IRE) 7
439 **MINNIE SECRET** 6
402 **MINORA BLUE** 9
382 **MINOR RUMPUS** 40
351 **MINOS DES OBEAUX** (FR) 60
499 **MINOUCHKA** (FR) 2
419 **MINSGILL GLEN** 5
523 **MINSTER BAY** 7
395 **MINSTER BLUE** 13
584 **MINSTER FAIR** 11
173 **MINSTER GLORY** 35
101 **MINSTER MEADOW** 9
465 **MINSTER MISSILE** 48
83 **MINSTER PARK** 16
232 **MINSTER SHADOW** 18
252 **MINSTER YORK** 11
381 **MINSTREL HALL** 18
395 **MINSTREL'S DOUBLE** 21
286 **MINSTRELS FOLLY** (IRE) F 52
351 **MINUIT DE COTTE** (FR) 61
518 **MINUTE WALTZ** F 62
358 **MINYA KONKA** F 21
103 **MIO CARO** (FR) 23
435 **MIOCHE D'ESTRUVAL** (FR) 88
352 **MI ODDS** 7
243 **MIRABAD** 7
191 **MIRABILIS** (USA) 118
66 **MIRAGE PRINCE** (IRE) 105
435 **MIRANT** 89
295 **MIRASOL PRINCESS** 21
350 **MIRJAN** (IRE) 46
54 **MIRROR FOUR SPORT** C 22
49 **MISARO** (GER) 45
85 **MISBEHAVIOUR** 6
562 **MIS CHICAF** (IRE) 26
35 **MISCHIEF** 6
29 **MISCUT** (IRE) 38
29 **MISDIRECT** 85
114 **MISE EN PLACE** 29
549 **MISHALL** (USA) 37
443 **MISHKA** 17
66 **MISKINA** 94
277 **MISS ADELAIDE** (IRE) 70
59 **MISS AMOUR** 13
101 **MISS ARAGONT** 7
146 **MISS ARK ROYAL** G 10
104 **MISSATTITUDE** 65
159 **MISS BEHAVIOUR** (FR) 64
146 **MISS BORDEAUX** (IRE) C 11
121 **MISS BROOK** F 5
320 **MISS BUSSELL** C 16
228 **MISS CAVO** G 7
268 **MISS CELERITY** 4
521 **MISS CEYLON** 8
190 **MISS CHAMPERS** (IRE) 16
60 **MISS CHINCHILLA** 10
304 **MISS COLMESNIL** (FR) 3
435 **MISS COOL** 90
87 **MISS COSPECTOR** 5
300 **MISSCOSTALOT** 6
94 **MISS COTSWOLD LADY** 53
331 **MISS CYNTHIA** G 44
169 **MISSED AGAIN** F 125
265 **MISSED OPPORTUNITY** (IRE) F 26

305 **MONASH GIRL** (IRE) 11
414 **MONBONAMI** (IRE) 46
549 **MONDAREJ** (IRE) 104
327 **MONDEED** 4
5 **MONDESIR DU COCHET** (FR) 65
351 **MONDIAL JACK** (FR) 91
383 **MONDURU** 56
468 **MONET'S GARDEN** (IRE) 27
269 **MONEVASSIA** (USA) F 95
591 **MONEY CRAZY** (FR) 39
254 **MONEY MARKET** (IRE) 139
418 **MONEY MOUNTAIN** 25
46 **MONGER LANE** 12
387 **MONIFETH MAN** (IRE) 15
280 **MONKERHOSTIN** (FR) 59
393 **MONKEY ISLAND** 59
375 **MONKEY OR ME** (IRE) 13
345 **MONKSFORD** 7
350 **MONOLITH** 47
438 **MON PETIT DIAMANT** 5
565 **MON PLAISIR** 36
345 **MONSAL DALE** (IRE) 8
504 **MON SECRET** (IRE) 17
504 **MONSIEUR BOND** (IRE) 18
55 **MONSIEUR POIROT** (IRE) 10
222 **MONSIEUR ROSE** (IRE) 14
591 **MONSIEUR TAGEL** (FR) 40
436 **MONSIGNOR** (FR) 40
66 **MONSTER JAWBREAKER** (IRE) 52
84 **MONTAGE** (IRE) 67
51 **MONTAGNETTE** 8
333 **MONTECARMELO** (USA) 55
259 **MONTECASSINO ABBEY** (IRE) 13
254 **MONTECITO** 140
239 **MONTECRISTO** 8
531 **MONTE CRISTO** (FR) 9
392 **MONTEEPA** (IRE) 58
418 **MONTEFORTE** 26
549 **MONTELEONE** (IRE) 105
368 **MONTEL GIRL** (IRE) 7
299 **MONTE MAJOR** (FR) 33
265 **MONTE MAYOR LAD** (IRE) 9
469 **MONTEMOSS** (IRE) 9
500 **MONTE ROUGE** (IRE) 9
238 **MONTESINO** 22
208 **MONTESSORI MIO** (FR) 21
414 **MONTEVIDEO** 47
556 **MONTEZUMA** 29
404 **MONTIFAULT** (FR) 77
404 **MONT FLYER** 78
306 **MONTMARTRE** (IRE) 50
351 **MONT MISERE** (FR) 66
272 **MONTPELIER** (IRE) 70
257 **MONT PUTTENS** (FR) 43
435 **MONTREAL** (FR) 92
605 **MONT SAINT MICHEL** (IRE) 43
605 **MONTURANI** (IRE) 10
33 **MONTY'S QUEST** (IRE) 24
272 **MONTY'S SALVO** (USA) 71
99 **MONTY BE QUICK** 1
393 **MONTY FLOOD** (IRE) 60
360 **MONTY'S PASS** (IRE) 5
577 **MONTY'S THEME** (IRE) 4
272 **MON VILLEZ** (FR) 72
159 **MONZON** (FR) 39
174 **MOON** 27
333 **MOON CATCHER** (IRE) 21

206 **MOON COLONY** 3
241 **MOON DAZZLE** (USA) 32
524 **MOON DRIVER** (USA) C 152
302 **MOON EMPEROR** 22
197 **MOONGLADE** (USA) 10
215 **MOON GLOW** (IRE) 7
29 **MOON IS UP** F 86
300 **MOON LEGEND** 19
429 **MOONLIGHT'S BOX** F 44
578 **MOONLIGHT DANCE** (IRE) 122
267 **MOONLIGHT GOLD** 3
254 **MOONLIGHT MAN** 62
344 **MOONLIGHT PATH** (IRE) F 46
173 **MOONLIT HARBOUR** 36
104 **MOONMAIDEN** 152
2 **MOON MIST** 8
352 **MOON ROYALE** 10
168 **MOONSHAFT** (USA) 36
316 **MOON SHOT** 7
17 **MOONSIDE** 76
517 **MOONSILK** C 31
351 **MOON SIR** (GER) 146
272 **MOONSTREAM** 73
185 **MOONSTRUCK** 31
45 **MOONZIE LAIRD** (IRE) 6
33 **MOORAMANA** 25
478 **MOORE'S MELODY** (IRE) 59
234 **MOORE'S LAW** (USA) 21
495 **MOOR HALL HOPPER** 6
214 **MOORLAND MONARCH** 21
544 **MOORLANDS RETURN** 18
16 **MOOR LANE** 22
420 **MOORLAW** (IRE) 27
277 **MOORS MYTH** 72
603 **MOOR SPIRIT** 11
321 **MORCAT** C 7
272 **MORE HANKY PANKY** (IRE) 74
14 **MORELUCK** (IRE) 28
478 **MORE MAGIC** (GER) C 100
174 **MORE SLEEPERS** (USA) 72
382 **MORE THAN A STROLL** (IRE) 41
351 **MORGANE DU BOST** (FR) 67
17 **MORGAN LEWIS** (IRE) 64
457 **MORGANNWG** F 43
349 **MORINA** (USA) C 98
398 **MORLESS** 14
194 **MORNING AFTER** 16
269 **MORNING ECLIPSE** 3
578 **MORNING GLOW** 123
264 **MORNING** (IRE) 2
136 **MORNING SUN** 7
582 **MORNING WORLD** 33
420 **MOROCCO** (IRE) 7
3 **MOROZOV** (USA) 7
31 **MORRIS DANCING** (USA) 10
420 **MORSE** (IRE) 28
225 **MORVERN** (IRE) 16
578 **MOSAWAT** 124
257 **MOSCOW COURT** (IRE) 44
381 **MOSCOW DANCER** (IRE) 19
527 **MOSCOW EXECUTIVE** 12
331 **MOSCOW FIELDS** (IRE) 46
257 **MOSCOW FLYER** (IRE) 45
448 **MOSCOW GOLD** (IRE) 6
238 **MOSCOW LEADER** (IRE) 23
401 **MOSCOW MARY** 21
288 **MOSCOW PARADE** (IRE) 45
181 **MOSCOW TIMES** 28

280 **MOSCOW WHISPER** (IRE) 60
549 **MOSHKIL** (IRE) 106
431 **MOSS C** 95
183 **MOSSAR** (FR) 6
581 **MOSS CAMPIAN** 11
292 **MOSSEY TUNE H** 50
301 **MOSS HARVEY** 27
304 **MOSS RUN** (IRE) 4
506 **MOSSTOWIE** 1
277 **MOSS VALE** (IRE) 73
392 **MOSSY GREEN** (IRE) 59
558 **MOSTAKBEL** (USA) 4
168 **MOSTANAD** 94
383 **MOSTARSIL** (USA) 57
174 **MOST DEFINITELY** (IRE) 28
300 **MO STOPHER C** 40
578 **MOTAFARRED** (IRE) 125
169 **MOTARASSED** 128
4 **MOTCOMBE** (IRE) 34
361 **MOTCOMB JAM** (IRE) 39
10 **MOTHER SAYS** 5
36 **MOTIVATOR** 73
524 **MOTIVE** (FR) 68
110 **MOTORWAY** (IRE) 35
544 **MOTOWN MELODY** (IRE) 19
169 **MOTU** (IRE) 60
277 **MOUFTARI** (USA) 74
351 **MOUILLEURDEPONGES** (FR) 108
159 **MOULIN RICHE** (FR) 40
280 **MOUNSEY CASTLE** 61
420 **MOUNTAIN BLUEBIRD** (USA) F 76
181 **MOUNTAIN DANCER** (IRE) C 52
588 **MOUNTAIN GROVE G** 4
497 **MOUNTAIN MAN** (FR) 10
431 **MOUNTAIN MEADOW** 46
191 **MOUNTAIN TOP** 60
34 **MOUNT BENGER** 4
3 **MOUNTCHARGE** (IRE) 15
144 **MOUNT CLERIGO** (IRE) 8
141 **MOUNT COOK** (FR) 25
225 **MOUNT COTTAGE** 55
201 **MOUNT EPHRAM** (IRE) 19
173 **MOUNT HILLABY** (IRE) 37
354 **MOUNTHOOLEY** 11
404 **MOUNT KARINGA** 79
382 **MOUNT KIMBLE** 42
269 **MOUNT PAGET** (USA) 96
227 **MOUNT PEKAN** (IRE) 11
14 **MOUNT PRAGUE** (IRE) 29
257 **MOUNT PROSPECT** (IRE) 46
281 **MOUNTS BAY** 15
458 **MOUNT VETTORE** 17
351 **MOUSSU LESCRIBAA** (FR) 109
229 **MOVIE KING** (IRE) 18
413 **MOVIELAND** (USA) F 28
100 **MOVIE QUEEN** 30
94 **MOVING EARTH** (IRE) 27
383 **MOWBRAY** (USA) 58
411 **MOY WATER** (IRE) C 60
104 **MOZAFIN** 153
169 **MPENZI** 129
174 **MR ALBERT** (IRE) 29
350 **MR AUCHTERLONIE** (IRE) 48
392 **MR BABBAGE** (IRE) 60
595 **MR BAXTER BASICS** 59
196 **MR BOO** (IRE) 5
238 **MR BOSSMAN** (IRE) 24
157 **MR BOUNTIFUL** (IRE) 13

254 **REFERENCE** (IRE) 150
414 **REFINEMENT** (IRE) 59
54 **REFLECTED LIFE** 19
584 **REFLECTIVE WAY** 13
451 **REFLEX BLUE** 9
557 **REFLEX COURIER** (IRE) 15
239 **REGAL ACT** (IRE) 46
239 **REGAL AFFECTION** (USA) 44
247 **REGAL ALI** (IRE) 13
359 **REGAL ALI** (IRE) 4
331 **REGAL BANDIT** (IRE) 62
325 **REGAL CHANCE** 49
327 **REGAL CUSTOM** 6
449 **REGAL EMPRESS** 3
272 **REGAL EXIT** (FR) 88
281 **REGAL GALLERY** (IRE) 7
361 **REGAL HOLLY** 47
85 **REGAL JONES** (IRE) 7
582 **REGAL LUSTRE** 35
329 **REGAL PERFORMER** (IRE) 26
557 **REGAL RIVER** (IRE) 16
446 **REGAL SETTING** (IRE) 23
152 **REGAL TERM** (IRE) 33
232 **REGAL VINTAGE** (USA) 21
361 **REGAL VISION** (IRE) 48
503 **REGARDEZ MOI** (USA) 30
300 **REGENT'S FOLLY** (IRE) F 44
227 **REGENT'S SECRET** (USA) 14
148 **REGENTS WALK** (IRE) 13
43 **REGGAE RHYTHM** (IRE) 8
524 **REGINA** 164
431 **REGISTRAR** 101
420 **REGULATED** (IRE) 33
578 **REHAM** (IRE) 66
127 **REHEARSAL** 15
278 **REHIA** 26
225 **REIDIES CHOICE** 64
373 **REIGN OF FIRE** (IRE) 50
29 **REINE D'AVRIL** (FR) 91
241 **REINE DE LA CIEL** (USA) F 67
191 **REINE WELLS** (IRE) C 129
6 **REIVERS MOON** 6
280 **REIZIGER** (FR) 75
431 **REJUVENATE** (IRE) 14
599 **RELATIVE HERO** (IRE) 18
401 **RELAX** 12
578 **RELAXED GESTURE** (IRE) 67
524 **RELAXED** (USA) 78
590 **RELIANCE LEADER** 9
393 **RELIX** (FR) 70
49 **RELLIM** 22
549 **REMAADD** (USA) 51
549 **REMAAL** (IRE) 116
224 **REMEMBRANCE** 12
309 **REMINISCENT** (IRE) 8
29 **REMOTE ROMANCE** (USA) F 92
306 **RENADA** 75
476 **RENALOO** (IRE) 27
208 **RENDARI** (IRE) 27
254 **RENDORO** (USA) 71
16 **RENDOVA** 30
226 **RENE BARBIER** (IRE) 11
540 **RENO** 7
33 **RENSHAW WOOD** G 28
302 **REN'S MAGIC** 28
414 **RENVYLE** (IRE) 60
211 **RENVYLE SOCIETY** (IRE) 12
258 **RENZO** (IRE) 9

299 **REPEAT WARNING** F 80
443 **REPENT AT LEISURE** 22
483 **REPERTORY** 10
136 **REPERTOIRE** (FR) 8
36 **REPIQUE** (USA) F 81
289 **REPLACEMENT PET** (IRE) 5
163 **REPUBLICAN LADY** 3
218 **REPUNZEL** 8
37 **REQUENA** F 66
413 **RESCIND** (IRE) 11
595 **RESEARCHER** 72
432 **RESEDA** (IRE) 66
241 **RESERVOIR** (IRE) 39
300 **RESHUFFLE** 21
431 **RESIDENTIAL** 55
247 **RESISTANCE** (IRE) 14
401 **RESONATE** (IRE) 13
259 **RESPLENDENT CEE** (IRE) 18
378 **RESPLENDENT GLORY** (IRE) 30
378 **RESPLENDENT KING** (USA) 20
259 **RESPLENDENT NOVA** 95
378 **RESPLENDENT ONE** (IRE) 21
259 **RESPLENDENT PRINCE** 96
560 **RESPLENDENT STAR** (IRE) 17
383 **RESSOURCE** (FR) 67
262 **RESTART** (IRE) 29
17 **RESTLESS WIND** (IRE) 46
78 **RETAIL THERAPY** (IRE) 13
547 **RETIREMENT** 12
512 **RETURNED UN PAID** (IRE) 44
132 **RETURN OF THE KING** 80
432 **RETURN TICKET** 67
392 **REVE DE ROSE** 69
333 **REVE D'IMAN** (FR) 27
194 **REVEILLEZ** 21
599 **REVELINO** (IRE) 19
518 **REVENIR** (IRE) 35
173 **REVERSIONARY** 79
263 **REVERSO** (FR) 9
36 **REVIVALIST** 82
190 **REWARDIA** (IRE) F 54
253 **REWAYAAT** 11
351 **REXLOR** (IRE) 134
81 **REX ROMELIO** 19
259 **REZZAGO** (USA) 19
382 **RHEINDROSS** (IRE) 48
446 **RHETORICAL** 24
64 **RHETORIC** (IRE) 15
414 **RHINESTONE COWBOY** (IRE) 61
114 **RIBOT'S GUEST** (IRE) F 53
351 **RIB PILE** (FR) 76
415 **RICARDO'S CHANCE** 6
553 **RICCARTON** 1
299 **RICHELIEU** 81
547 **RICHEMAUR** (IRE) 13
299 **RICHIE BOY** 38
527 **RICHIE'S DELIGHT** (IRE) 14
373 **RICHLY DESERVED** (IRE) C 112
351 **RICH ROMEO** (GER) 156
578 **RICH SENSE** (IRE) 68
192 **RICHTEE** (IRE) 68
466 **RICHWAY** 7
266 **RICKHAM GLORY** 6
59 **RICKY MARTAN** 8
272 **RICO HOMBRE** (FR) 89
478 **RIDAAR** (FR) 20
478 **RIDAFA** (IRE) 21
602 **RIDAPOUR** (IRE) 19

117 **RIDDER** 11
429 **RIDDLE** (FR) 47
161 **RIDEAWAY ROSE** (IRE) 37
595 **RIDERS REVENGE** (IRE) 73
601 **RIDE SAFARI** 30
490 **RIDGEBACK** 13
442 **RIDICULE** (IRE) 66
82 **RIFFLE** (FR) 9
53 **RIFFLES** 6
165 **RIFLEMAN** (IRE) 8
280 **RIFT VALLEY** (IRE) 76
277 **RIGHTFUL RULER** 178
306 **RIGHT ON TARGET** (IRE) 54
546 **RIGHT TO ROAM** (IRE) 32
543 **RIGHTY HO** 3
404 **RIGMAROLE** 91
174 **RIGONZA** 77
351 **RIGOUREUX** (FR) 77
578 **RIHAN** (USA) C 133
225 **RILEY BOYS** (IRE) 65
345 **RILEYS DREAM** 10
16 **RIMBA** (USA) C 113
311 **RIMOSA** 17
104 **RIMSKY** (IRE) 75
331 **RINGAROSES** 89
259 **RING OF DESTINY** 20
110 **RING OF FIRE** (IRE) 94
349 **RING OF KERRY** (IRE) C 110
17 **RING OF LOVE** G 68
173 **RING OF ROSES** 47
390 **RING QUEEN** C 40
193 **RINGSIDE JACK** 13
84 **RINGSIDER** (IRE) 35
299 **RING THE RELATIVES** C 82
257 **RINGTOWN MINE** (IRE) 63
254 **RINNEEN** (IRE) 72
67 **RIO DE JUMEIRAH** 33
353 **RIO REAL** (IRE) 23
393 **RIOTHAMUS** (IRE) 71
273 **RIPCORD** (IRE) 8
171 **RIPPLE EFFECT** 4
546 **RIQUEWIHR** 10
265 **RISALAH** G 27
462 **RISE** 20
192 **RISING SHADOW** (IRE) 69
192 **RISKA KING** 44
190 **RISK FREE** 20
254 **RISK THE WITCH** F 151
475 **RISKY WAY** 11
104 **RISQUE LADY** F 171
257 **RITA'S STAR** 64
512 **RIVAL BIDDER** 45
341 **RIVAL** (IRE) 17
384 **RIVERAIN** C 47
85 **RIVER AMORA** (IRE) 8
216 **RIVER BANN** (USA) 5
444 **RIVER BUG** (IRE) 16
523 **RIVER CANYON** (IRE) 10
547 **RIVER CARD** 50
103 **RIVER CITY** (IRE) 37
276 **RIVER GROUND** (IRE) 3
38 **RIVER GROVE** (IRE) 15
181 **RIVER GYPSY** 30
388 **RIVERINE** F 49
195 **RIVER IRIS** 9
78 **RIVER LARK** (IRE) 14
193 **RIVER LINE** (USA) 21
193 **RIVER MAIDEN** (USA) F 23

468 **VIC THE PILER** (IRE) 46
254 **VICTIM OF LOVE** C 165
288 **VICTORIAN LADY** 66
265 **VICTORIA REGIA** (IRE) F 29
410 **VICTORIA RYAN** (IRE) 12
311 **VICTORY BELL** 72
286 **VICTORY FLIP** (IRE) 29
532 **VICTORY HEIGHTS** (IRE) 10
104 **VICTORY HYMN** 199
104 **VICTORY LAP** (GER) 91
334 **VICTORY QUEST** (IRE) 9
335 **VICTORY ROLL** 31
76 **VICTORY SIGN** (IRE) 6
48 **VICTORY VEE** 10
159 **VIC TOTO** (IRE) 52
288 **VIC VILLE** (IRE) 67
238 **VIDI CAESAR** (NZ) 44
254 **VIENNA'S BOY** (IRE) 83
119 **VIE PRIVEE** (FR) 63
278 **VIEUX CARRE F** 47
490 **VIEWFORTH** 22
403 **VIGOROUS** (IRE) 62
229 **VIGOUREUX** (FR) 32
490 **VIJAY** (IRE) 23
548 **VIKING BUOY** (IRE) 8
390 **VIKING'S COVE** (IRE) C 47
82 **VIKING STAR** (IRE) 32
48 **VILANY** C 37
351 **VILA REAL** (FR) 89
36 **VILAS** 13
435 **VILLA** 150
280 **VILLAGE KING** (IRE) 105
361 **VILLAIR** (IRE) 61
119 **VILLA MINERVA** (FR) 64
524 **VILLARRICA** (USA) 179
351 **VILLENTIN** (IRE) 161
350 **VILLON** (IRE) 75
191 **VIMY RIDGE** (FR) 81
178 **VINANDO** 23
258 **VINCENT** 15
281 **VINCENT VAN GOGH** (IRE) 28
351 **VINDESROIS** (FR) 90
194 **VINDICATION** 28
48 **VIN DU PAYS** 11
144 **VINGIS PARK** (IRE) 16
547 **VINIYOGA** 62
578 **VINNIE ROE** (IRE) 25
192 **VINTAGE PREMIUM** 51
582 **VINTAGE STYLE** 16
351 **VINTOX** (GER) 162
225 **VIOLET AVENUE** 78
269 **VIOLET LANE** 121
373 **VIOLET PARK** 60
381 **VIRAGO** 29
524 **VIRGIL** 180
92 **VIRGIN'S TEARS** 62
529 **VIRGIN SOLDIER** (IRE) 34
349 **VIRGIN STANZA** (USA) C 143
110 **VIRTUE** 104
82 **VIRTUE REWARDED** (IRE) C 50
295 **VISCOUNT ROSSINI** 33
435 **VISIBILITY** (IRE) 151
530 **VISION VICTORY** 17
191 **VISORAMA** (IRE) 11
257 **VISSI D'ARTE** (IRE) 89
299 **VISTA BELLA** 90
325 **VISTA VERDE** 65
513 **VITAL LASER** (USA) F 9

562 **VITA SPERICOLATA** (IRE) 21
529 **VITELLI** 35
599 **VITELUCY** 24
216 **VITO ANDOLINI** 6
482 **VIVA ATLAS ESPANA** 13
244 **VIVA FOREVER** (FR) 14
597 **VIVANTE** 9
221 **VIVE LA VIE** (USA) 32
94 **VIZULIZE** 42
56 **VLASTA WEINER** 37
221 **VOCATAINE** (IRE) 33
262 **VOCATIVE** (GER) 65
435 **VODKA BLEU** (FR) 152
16 **VOICE MAIL** 38
254 **VOILE** (IRE) 84
503 **VOIX DU NORD** (FR) 35
403 **VOLATICUS** (IRE) 78
191 **VOLISIX** (IRE) 82
29 **VOL SAUVAGE** (FR) F 108
87 **VOLUPTUOUS** 7
241 **VONADAISY** 44
358 **VOODOO ROCKET** C 37
221 **VOVAN** (IRE) 79
351 **VOY POR USTEDES** (FR) 139
114 **VRACCA** 60
300 **VRENNAN F** 49
475 **VULCAN BELLE M** 15
238 **VULCAN LANE** (NZ) 45
269 **VULNERABLE** 65

104 **WAAEDAH** (USA) 92
254 **WAATHEB** (USA) 166
43 **WAFFLING M** 9
138 **WAFIR** (IRE) 6
81 **WAFT** (USA) F 62
497 **WAGGY** (IRE) 17
414 **WAGNER** (IRE) 88
435 **WAHIBA SANDS** 153
27 **WAHOO SAM** (USA) 24
270 **WAIMEA BAY** 18
479 **WAINAK** (USA) 11
418 **WAIN MOUNTAIN** 43
49 **WAINWRIGHT** (IRE) 28
383 **WAIT FOR THE WILL** (USA) 78
114 **WAITING FOR FAME** (IRE) 34
191 **WAJD** (USA) F 149
388 **WAKEFUL NIGHT** (IRE) F 73
110 **WAKE UP HENRY** 55
335 **WAKEUP SMILING** (IRE) 32
373 **WAKE** (USA) 17
269 **WAKIRED** (USA) 66
183 **WALCOT LAD** (IRE) 10
212 **WALKER BAY** (IRE) 13
338 **WALK IN MY SHADOW** (IRE) 25
205 **WALK OVER** (IRE) 37
238 **WALLY WONDER** (IRE) 46
280 **WALSINGHAM** (IRE) 106
601 **WALTER** (IRE) 27
316 **WALTER PLINGE** 11
379 **WALTER'S DESTINY** 4
385 **WALTHAM DOVE** 28
82 **WALTING MATILDA F** 51
350 **WALTZING ALONG** (IRE) 76

37 **WALTZING WIZARD** 23
403 **WANCHAI LAD** 79
228 **WANJIB'S SONG** (IRE) G 4
349 **WANNABE GRAND** (IRE) C 144
593 **WANNAPLANTATREE** C 36
152 **WANNA SHOUT** 41
311 **WANSFORD LADY** 23
315 **WARAQA** (USA) 2
549 **WAR AT SEA** (IRE) 128
178 **WARBRECK** 24
194 **WARDEN COMPLEX** 73
170 **WARDEN WARREN** 7
277 **WARED** (USA) 104
81 **WARES HOME** (IRE) 43
77 **WAREYTH** (USA) 28
432 **WARJAN** (FR) 83
290 **WARLINGHAM** (IRE) 17
273 **WARNINGCAMP** (GER) 23
552 **WARNING GAMES** 23
67 **WARNING SHADOWS** (IRE) C 81
84 **WARNING STAR** C 83
387 **WAR OF ATTRITIAN** (IRE) 25
591 **WAR OWL** (USA) 64
84 **WARRAD** (USA) 42
392 **WARRENS CASTLE** (IRE) 82
359 **WARRIORS PATH** (IRE) 7
193 **WARRLIN** 16
67 **WARRSAN** (IRE) 14
169 **WAR SHANTY** C 153
326 **WARTORN** (IRE) 16
591 **WAR TUNE** 65
376 **WAS A DRIVE** (IRE) 15
104 **WASALAT** (USA) 200
552 **WASHBROOK** 21
232 **WASHINGTON PINK** (IRE) 28
340 **WASSL STREET** (IRE) 27
557 **WASTED COSTS** (IRE) 19
442 **WASTED TALENT** (IRE) 17
358 **WATAMU** (IRE) 24
383 **WATCHFUL WITNESS** 79
403 **WATCHING** 63
544 **WATCH THE DOVE** 25
143 **WATERBERG** (IRE) 50
385 **WATERCRESS** 29
331 **WATER JUMP** (IRE) 82
73 **WATER KING** (USA) 7
435 **WATERLAW** (IRE) 154
257 **WATERLILY** (IRE) 79
190 **WATERLINE BLUE** (IRE) 46
190 **WATERLINE DANCER** (IRE) 26
190 **WATERLINE SPIRIT** 27
191 **WATERMARK** 83
152 **WATERMOUSE** 42
272 **WATER NYMPH** (IRE) 112
128 **WATERPARK** 4
431 **WATER PISTOL** 113
480 **WATER PIXIE** (IRE) F 65
278 **WATERSIDE** (IRE) 11
605 **WATERSILK** (IRE) 50
556 **WATER SPORTS** (IRE) 59
515 **WATERSPRAY** (AUS) 23
392 **WATER STORM** (IRE) 83
110 **WATER TAXI** 56
578 **WATHAB** (IRE) 80
277 **WATHEEQAH** (USA) C 184
276 **WAVE BACK** (IRE) 8
356 **WAVERLEY ROAD** 11
280 **WAVE ROCK** 107

LOCATION OF TRAINING QUARTERS

References show squares as on map

IN SEVERAL CASES THE NEAREST MAIN CENTRE IS SHOWN TO LOCATE SITUATION OF STABLES

JOHNSON HOUGHTON, R. F., Didcot............................F4
JONES, A. E., Hungerford............................F4
JONES, A. P., Eastbury............................F4
JONES, G. ELWYN, Lampeter............................E2
JONES, MRS M. A., Lambourn............................F4
JONES, R. W., Newmarket............................F6
JONES, T. M., Guildford............................G5
JUCKES, A. G., Abberley............................E3

KAVANAGH, H. M., Llandrindod Wells............................E2
KEANE, D. P., Limpley Stoke............................F3
KEDDY, T., Newmarket............................F6
KEIGHTLEY, S. L., Newmarket............................D5
KELLY, G. P., Sheriff Hutton............................
KELSALL, P., Hanley Swan............................F3
KERR, C. J., Aberfeldy............................A3
KING, ALAN, Barbury Castle............................F4
KING, MRS A. L. M., Stratford-on-Avon............................F4
KING, J. S., Swindon............................F4
KING, N. B., Newmarket............................F6
KIRBY, F., Northallerton............................C5
KIRK, SYLVESTER, Upper Lambourn............................F4
KITTOW, WILLIAM S., Cullompton............................G2
KNIGHT, MISS H. C., Wantage............................F4
KNIPE, R. F., Allensmore............................E3

LAMYMAN, MRS S., Louth............................E6
LAVELLE, MISS E. C., Andover............................F4
LAY, B. L., Chipping Norton............................F4
LEAVY, B. D., Stoke-on-Trent............................F4
LEE, R., Presteigne............................E3
LEWIS, S. T., Upton-on-Severn............................F3
LIDDERDALE, A. J. D., Newbury............................F4
LIDDIARD, MRS S. A., Hungerford............................F4
LITTMODEN, N. P., Newmarket............................F6
LLEWELLYN, B. J., Bargoed............................F2
LLOYD, D. M., Bridgend............................F2
LLOYD, F., Bangor-on-Dee............................E3
LOCKWOOD, ALAN, Malton............................D6
LODER, D. R., Newmarket............................F6
LUNGO, L., Carrutherstown............................C3

MACAULEY, MRS N. J., Melton Mowbray............................E5
MACKIE, W. J. W., Church Broughton............................E4
MACTAGGART, A. B., Hawick............................B4
MACTAGGART, A. H., Hawick............................B4
MADGWICK, M. J., Denmead............................G4
MAGNUSSON, MIKAEL, Upper Lambourn,............................F4
MAKIN, P. J., Marlborough............................F4
MANN, C. J., Upper Lambourn............................F4
MANN, MRS J. M. E., Leamington Spa............................F4
MANNERS, H. J., Swindon............................F4
MARGARSON, G. G., Newmarket............................F6
MARKS, MISS K., Tenbury Wells............................E3
MARVIN, R. F., Southwell............................E5
MCCAIN, D., Cholmondeley............................D3
MCCORMACK, N. P., Medomsley............................C5
MCGOVERN, T. P., Lewes............................G5
MCHALE, MISS D. A., Newmarket............................F6
MCINNES, I. W., Westow............................D5
MCINNES-SKINNER, MRS C., Melton Mowbray............................E5
MCKEOWN, W. J., Newcastle-upon-Tyne............................C5
MCMAHON, B. A., Tamworth............................E4
MCMILLAN, M. D., Cheltenham............................F4
MCWILLIAMS, H. A., Cockerham............................D3
MEEHAN, B. J., Upper Lambourn............................F4
MEEK, MRS M., Eastbury............................F4
MIDGLEY, P. T., Weston............................D5
MILLIGAN, MISS M. K., Middleham............................D5
MILLMAN, B. R., Cullompton............................G2
MILLS, T. G., Epsom............................G5
MITCHELL, C. W., Dorchester............................G3
MOFFATT, D. J., Cartmel............................C4
MONTEITH, PETER, Rosewell............................B4
MOORE, G. L., Brighton............................G5
MOORE, G. M., Middleham............................D5
MOORE, J. A., Darlington............................C4
MORGAN, K. A., Melton Mowbray............................E5
MORLOCK, C. P. H., Wantage............................F4
MORRISON, H., East Ilsley............................F4
MUGGERIDGE, M. P., Crawley Down............................G5

MUIR, WILLIAM R., Lambourn............................F4
MULLINS, J. W., Amesbury............................F4
MURPHY, F., Leyburn............................C5
MURPHY, P. G., Hungerford............................F4
MURTAGH, F. P., Carlisle............................C4
MUSSON, W. J., Newmarket............................F6

NAUGHTON, MRS A. M., Richmond............................C5
NAYLOR, DR J. R. J., Shrewton............................G4
NEEDHAM, J. L., Ludlow............................E3
NEEDHAM, P., Barnard Castle............................C2
NEWCOMBE, A. G., Barnstaple............................F2
NICHOLLS, D., Thirsk............................D5
NICHOLLS, P. F., Shepton Mallet............................F3
NIVEN, P. D., Malton............................D6
NIXON, G. R. S., Selkirk............................B3
NOCK, MRS R., Stow-on-the-Wold............................F4
NOLAN, D. A., Wishaw............................B3
NORMILE, MRS L. B., Glenfarg............................A4
NORTON, J. R., Barnsley............................D5
NOSEDA, J. J., Newmarket............................F6

O'BRIEN, D. C., Tonbridge............................G6
O'KEEFFE, J., Leyburn............................C5
OLD, J. A. B., Wroughton............................F4
OLIVER, MRS J. K. M., Hawick............................B4
O'NEILL, J. J., Cheltenham............................F4
O'NEILL, O., Cheltenham............................F4
O'REILLY, J. F. P., Newmarket............................D5
OSBORNE, J. A., Upper Lambourn............................F4
O'SHEA, J. G. M., Westbury-on-Severn............................F3

PALLING, BRYN, Cowbridge............................F2
PARKER, ANDREW, Lockerbie............................C3
PARKES, J. E., Malton............................D6
PAYNE, J. R., Dulverton............................F2
PAYNE, J. W., (PIP) Newmarket............................F6
PEACOCK, R. E., Malmesbury............................F4
PEARCE, B. A., Lingfield............................G5
PEARCE, K. R., Laugharne............................E2
PERRATT, MISS L. A., Ayr............................B3
PERRETT, MRS A. J., Pulborough............................G5
PHILLIPS, R. T., Moreton-in-Marsh............................F4
PIKE, S. L., Sidmouth............................G2
PINDER, ANTHONY D., Wantage............................F4
PIPE, C. B. E., MARTIN C., Wellington............................F3
PITMAN, M. A., Upper Lambourn............................F4
POGSON, C. T., Newark............................E5
POLGLASE, M. J., Southwell............................E5
POLLOCK, B. N., Market Harborough............................E5
POMFRET, N. J., Tilton-on-the-Hill............................E5
POPHAM, C. L., Taunton............................F3
PORTMAN, J. G. B., Compton............................F4
POULTON, C. J., Newmarket............................F6
POULTON, J. R., Lewes............................G5
POWELL, B. G., Winchester............................G4
PRESCOTT, BT, SIR MARK, Newmarket............................F6
PRICE, A. E., Leominster............................E3
PRICE, MRS A., Presteigne............................E3
PRICE, C. J., Leominster............................E3
PRICE, J. K., Ebbw Vale............................F2
PRICE, RICHARD J., Hereford............................F3
PRITCHARD, DR. P. J., Purton............................F3
PRITCHARD, P. A., Shipston-on-Stour............................F3
PRODROMOU, G., East Harling............................E7
PURDY, P. D., Bridgwater............................F3

QUINLAN, M., Newmarket............................F6
QUINN, J. J., Malton............................D6

RAMSDEN, MRS J. R., Thirsk............................D5
REES, D., Haverfordwest............................E1
REES, MRS G. S., Preston............................D3
REES, MRS H. E., Dorchester............................G3
REID, A. S., Mill Hill............................F5
RETTER, E. R., South Brent............................F2
RETTER, MRS J. G., Swindon............................F4
REVELEY, MRS G. R., Saltburn............................C5
RICH, P. M.,Usk............................F3
RICHARDS, MRS LYDIA, Chichester............................G5
RICHARDS, N. G., Greystoke............................C4

TRAINERS' VAT NUMBERS

TRAINER	REG NUMBER
JONATHAN AKEHURST	563964796
C. N. ALLEN	637912028
AUVRAY, JEAN-RENE	797413783
K. C. BAILEY	314664563
A. M. BALDING	199094119
J. BALDING	457758887
D. W. BARKER	633223080
M. A. BARNES	621400401
T. D. BARRON	772206343
J. C. DE P BERRY	638100758
P. BEAUMONT	171124988
R. N. BEVIS	713204777
S. R. BOWRING	509278724
J. M. BRADLEY	274664333
M. F. BRADSTOCK	491470535
G. C. BRAVERY	571294237
D. G. BRIDGWATER	650994018
C. E. BRITTAIN	102592304
M. A. BRITTAIN	599146977
H. R. BUCKLER	398770975
M. A. BUCKLEY	721353368
N. BYCROFT	171213794
N. A. CALLAGHAN	102933011
A. M. CAMPION	587879646
A. W. CARROLL	704895219
D. CARROLL	796883545
N. T. CHANCE	724408546
M. CHANNON	189661117
DAVID W. CHAPMAN	168959983
M. C. CHAPMAN	344208574
J. I. A. CHARLTON	746465407
G. C. H. CHUNG	711369745
P. F. I. COLE	314293378
H. J. COLLINGRIDGE	104254807
J. R. CORNWALL	745692595
C. G. COX	718184818
I. E. L. CRAIG	806250260
R. CRAGGS	602268958
P. D. CUNDELL	614824055
T. A. K. CUTHBERT	330488857
L. A. DACE	712064377
P. T. DALTON	616881224
V. R. A. DARTNALL	631092665
B. DE HAAN	314859934
R. DICKIN	650226565
M. J. K. DODS	257933133
B. N. DORAN	748198976
S. L. DOW	413544574
M. W. EASTERBY	169069725
C. R. EGERTON	569752780
BRIAN ELLISON	660293245
D. R. C. ELSWORTH	355785023
G. P. ENRIGHT	435943923
J. M. P. EUSTACE	521219779
P. D. EVANS	489174986
C. W. FAIRHURST	602285861
J. R. FANSHAWE	521042309
MISS J. D. FEILDEN	776710308
G. FIERRO	536880711
M. E. D. FRANCIS	314910188
N. A. GASELEE	200779676
T. R. GEORGE	571312270
J. A. GLOVER	570900256
J. S. GOLDIE	556428423
ROBERT H. GOLDIE	264621953
RAE GUEST	521042211
W. J. HAGGAS	442932451
J. S. HALDANE	271440773
MISS S. E. HALL	602277467
B. HANBURY	103810125
PATRICK HASLAM	199936189
N. J. HAWKE	679656268
J. C. HAYNES	621426962

M. J. HAYNES	211231925
P. R. HEDGER	503611295
N. J. HENDERSON	314065590
LADY HERRIES	321820494
J. HETHERTON	598972355
P. W. HIATT	119746644
B. W. HILLS	385437325
J. W. HILLS	569940094
P. J. HOBBS	357220859
R. J. HODGES	379438207
R. HOLLINSHEAD	100714234
H. S. HOWE	763022162
DON E. INCISA	602257083
E. L. J. D. JAMES	200940804
A. P. JARVIS	569954274
M. A. JARVIS	344445361
W. JARVIS	410611119
J. N. JEFFERSON	347619039
J. R. W. JENKINS	321802888
W. P. JENKS	632098837
J. H. JOHNSON	532645354
R. F. JOHNSON HOUGHTON	199189886
MRS A. L. M. KING	398488080
MISS H. C. KNIGHT	200516720
B. J. LLEWELLYN	691545413
ALAN LOCKWOOD	317079458
D. R. LODER	571447728
MRS N. J. MACAULEY	520735078
W. J. W. MACKIE	390480447
C. J. MANN	614848525
H. J. MANNERS	195320658
G. G. MARGARSON	632698317
T. P. MCGOVERN	620849049
MISS M. K. MILLIGAN	633271164
T. G. MILLS	564116061
PETER MONTEITH	271087168
G. M. MOORE	602113509
H. MORRISON	614830161
WILLIAM R. MUIR	569863572
J. W. MULLINS	504372669
F. MURPHY	634496811
F. P. MURTAGH	686608000
W. J. MUSSON	213080024
A. G. NEWCOMBE	320610613
J. O'NEILL	257253650
J. A. B. OLD	501801302
MRS J. K. M. OLIVER	270373273
J. A. OSBORNE	537599688
J. W. PAYNE	521068184
R. T. PHILLIPS	614622855
MARTIN C. PIPE	794117903
M. A. PITMAN	614846825
J. G. B. PORTMAN	642435647
P. D. PURDY	529855403
MRS J. R. RAMSDEN	754555901
MRS G. S. REES	324906951
A. S. REID	511129591
M. J. ROBERTS	621655551
B. S. ROTHWELL	599172585
R. ROWE	397611812
MISS M. E. ROWLAND	684046620
A. M. SADIK	715381149
J. J. SHEEHAN	237456547
R. SHIELS	593090919
MISS L. C. SIDDALL	431044695
O. M. C. SHERWOOD	363042676
MRS P. M. SLY	486255319
B. SMART	450209482
M. E. SOWERSBY	698398155
J. L. SPEARING	275942326
A. C. STEWART	428074648
MISS ANN STOKELL	687860179
MRS L. STUBBS	685582192
R. M. STRONGE	757205428
MRS L. C. TAYLOR	623648926

J. A. R. TOLLER	684781191
M. H. TOMPKINS	334108488
E. W. TUER	721823061
N. A. TWISTON-DAVIES	713747237
J. R. UPSON	623653839
J. WADE	602275669
C. F. WALL	496701221
MARK WALLACE	811681052
F. WATSON	789399537
C. V. WEEDON	212347206
J. R. WEYMES	734217450
R. M. WHITAKER	170674459
M. S. WILESMITH	771353725
A. J. WILSON	286154441
MRS S. D. WILLIAMS	631020504
MISS V. M. WILLIAMS	655596100
GEOFFREY WRAGG	102855589

Foaling dates are shown for two-year-olds
where these are provided, and the purchase
price (in guineas) as a yearling.

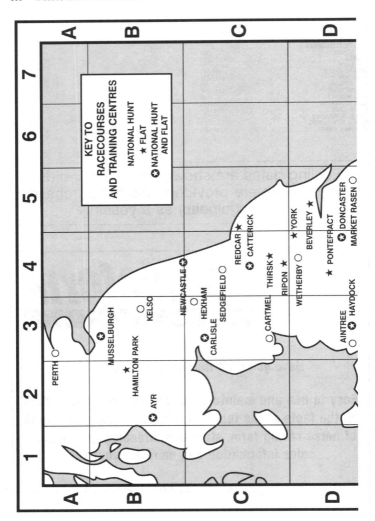

KEY TO RACECOURSES
AND TRAINING CENTRES

NATIONAL HUNT
★ FLAT
✪ NATIONAL HUNT
AND FLAT

PERTH ○
MUSSELBURGH ✪
KELSO ○
HAMILTON PARK ★
AYR ✪
NEWCASTLE ✪
HEXHAM ○
CARLISLE ✪
SEDGEFIELD ○
REDCAR ★
CATTERICK ✪
CARTMEL ○
THIRSK ★
RIPON ★
WETHERBY ○
YORK ★
BEVERLEY ○
PONTEFRACT ★
DONCASTER ✪
MARKET RASEN ○
AINTREE ✪
HAYDOCK ○

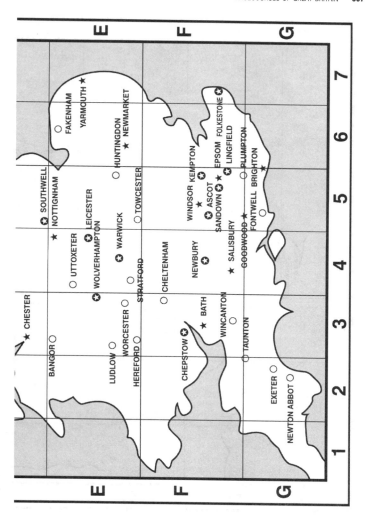

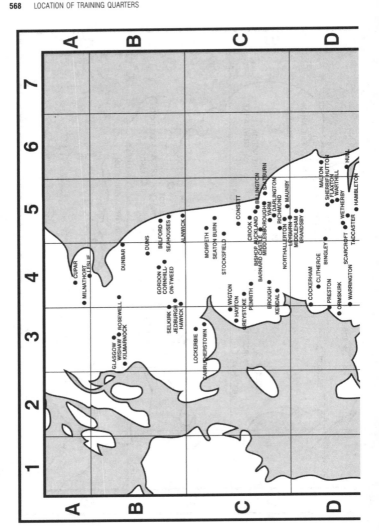

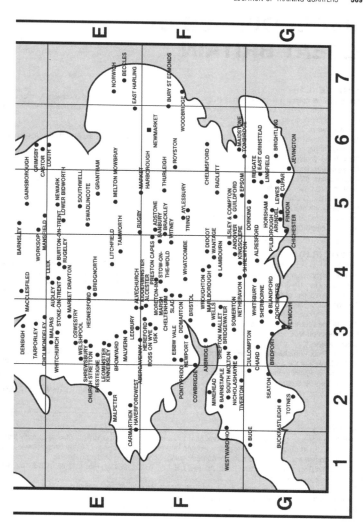

RACECOURSES OF GREAT BRITAIN

AINTREE (L.H)
Grand National Course: Triangular, 2m 2f (16) 494y run-in with elbow. Perfectly flat. A severe test for both horse and rider, putting a premium on jumping ability, fitness and courage, although some of the fences were recently modified.
Mildmay Course: Rectangular, 1m 4f (8) 260y run-in. A very fast course with sharp bends.
Address: Aintree Racecourse, Aintree, Liverpool, L9 5AS Tel: (0151) 523 2600 Fax: (0151) 522 2920E-mail: aintree@rht.net
Clerk Of The Course: Mr A Tulloch
Managing Director: Mr C. H. Barnett
Going Reports: (0151) 523 2600.
Stabling: 176 boxes allocated in strict rotation. Facilities are available on the course for up to 100 stable staff. (0151) 523 2600.
By Road: North of the City, near the junction of the M57 and M58 with the A59 (Preston).
By Rail: Aintree Station is adjacent to the Stands, from Liverpool Central.
By Air: Liverpool (Speke) Airport is 10 miles. Helicopter landing facility by prior arrangement.

ASCOT (R.H)
Flat: Right-handed triangular course of 1m 6f 34y, with a run-in of two and half furlongs. Ascot is galloping and stiff, slightly undulating with easy turns. All races up to 7f take place on the straight course.
N.H. Triangular, 1m 6f (10) 240y run-in mostly uphill. A galloping course with an uphill finish, Ascot provides a real test of stamina. The fences are stiff and sound jumping is essential, especially for novices.
Address: Ascot Racecourse, Ascot, Berkshire SL5 7JN Tel: (01344) 622211 Fax: (01344) 628299 Internet: http://www.ascot.co.uk
Clerk Of The Course: Mr N. Cheyne Tel: (01344) 874567, Fax: (01344) 624978
Chief Executive: Mr D. Erskine-Crum.
Going Reports: Day: (01344) 874567
Stabling: Free, with shavings, straw or paper provided. Tel: (01344) 625630 Fax: (01344) 873751
By Road: West of the town on the A329. Easy access from the M3 (Junction 3) and the M4 (Junction 6). Car parking adjoining the course and Ascot Heath.
By Rail: Regular service from Waterloo to Ascot (500y from the racecourse).
By Air: Helicopter landing facility at the course. London (Heathrow) Airport 15 miles, White Waltam Airfield 12 miles.

AYR (L.H)
Flat: A left-handed, galloping, flat oval track of 1m 4f with a 4f run-in. The straight 6f is essentially flat.
N.H. Oval, 1m 6f (9) 210y run-in. Relatively flat and one of the fastest tracks in Great Britain. It is a well-drained course and the ground rarely becomes testing. Suits the long-striding galloper.
Address: Ayr Racecourse, Whitletts Road, Ayr KA8 0JE Tel: (01292) 264179 Fax: (01292) 610140 Internet: www.ayr-racecourse.com
Clerk Of The Course: Mr C R Kennedy Tel: (01292) 264179. Mobile: (07796) 443481
Going Reports: Contact Clerk of the Course as above.
Stabling: Free stabling and accommodation for lads and lasses. Tel: (01292) 264179.
By Road: East of the town on the A758. Free parking for buses and cars.

By Rail: Ayr Station (trains on the half hour from Glasgow Central). Journey time 55 minutes. Buses and taxis also to the course.

By Air: Prestwick International Airport (10 minutes), Glasgow Airport (1 hour).

BANGOR-ON-DEE (L.H)

N.H. Circular, 1m 4f (9) 325y run-in. Apart from some 'ridge and furrow', this is a flat course notable for three sharp bends, especially the paddock turn. Suits handy, speedy sorts and is ideal for front-runners.

Address: Bangor-On-Dee Racecourse, Overton Road, Bangor-On-Dee, Wrexham. LL13 0DATel: (01978) 780323, Fax: (01978) 780985

Clerk of the Course & Manager: Major R. M. O. Webster Tel: (01978) 780323 orMobile (07781) 780576. Fax: (01978) 780985.

Going Reports: Contact Clerk of the Course as above.

Stabling: 84 stables, allotted on arrival. Shavings (straw on request). Applications to the Manager. Tel: (01978) 780323.

By Road: 5 miles South-East of Wrexham, off the B5069.

By Rail: Wrexham Station (bus or taxi to the course).

By Air: Helicopters may land by prior arrangement with Clerk of the Course at entirely their own risk.

BATH (L.H)

Flat: Galloping, left-handed, level oval of 1m 4f 25y, with long, stiff run-in of about 4f which bends to the left. An extended chute provides for races over 5f 11y and 5f 161y.

Address: The Racecourse, Lansdown, Bath. (01225) 424609 Fax: (01225) 444415. Internet: www.bath-racecouse.co.uk

Clerk Of The Course: Major D. McAllister. Tel: (01283) 711233 (Office), (01889) 562221 (Home)or (0860) 286003 (Mobile).

Going Reports: Contact Clerk of the Course as above.

Stabling: Free stabling and accommodation for lads and lasses. Tel: (01225) 444274

By Road: 2 miles North-West of the City (M4 Junction 18) at Lansdown. Unlimited free car and coach parking space immediately behind the stands. Special bus services operate from Bath to the racecourse.

By Rail: Bath Station (from Paddington), regular bus service from Bath to the course (3 miles).

By Air: Bristol or Colerne Airports. (no landing facilities at the course).

BEVERLEY (R.H)

Flat: A right-handed oval of 1m 3f, generally galloping, with an uphill run-in of two and a half furlongs. The 5f course is very stiff.

Address: Beverley Race Co. Ltd., York Road, Beverley, Yorkshire HU17 9QZ Tel: (01482) 867488/882645.

Clerk Of The Course: Mr J. M. Hutchinson. Tel: (01765) 602156. Mobile (07860) 679904.

Racecourse Manager: Sally Iggulden

Going Reports: Tel: (01482) 867488/882645 or Head Groundsman (Mr. S Jessop) mobile 07885 678186

Stabling: Free stabling. Accommodation available for lads and lasses Tel: (01482) 867488/882645.

By Road: 7 miles from the M62 (Junction 38) off the A1035. Free car parking opposite the course. Owners and Trainers use a separate enclosure.

By Rail: Beverley Station (Hull-Scarborough line). Occasional bus service to the course (1 mile).

By Air: Helicopter landings by prior arrangement. Light aircraft landing facilities at Linley Hill, Leven airport.

BRIGHTON (L.H)

Flat: Left-handed, 1m 4f horseshoe with easy turns and a run-in of three and a half furlongs. Undulating and sharp, the track suits handy types.

Address: Brighton Racecourse, Brighton, Sussex BN2 2XZ Tel: (01273) 603580 Fax: (01273) 673267.

Clerk Of The Course: Mr Geoffrey Stickels Tel: (01273) 603580. Mobile: (07973 737006)

Going Reports: Available on brighton-racecourse.co.uk or contact main office/Clerk Of Course as above
Stabling: Stabling & accommodation: Tel: (01273) 603580, available on request.
By Road: East of the city on the A27 (Lewes Road). There is a car park adjoining the course.
By Rail: Brighton Station (from Victoria on the hour, London Bridge or Portsmouth). Special bus service to the course from the station (approx 2 miles).
By Air: No racecourse facilities.

CARLISLE (R.H)

Flat: Right-handed, 1m 4f pear-shaped track. Galloping and undulating with easy turns and a stiff uphill run-in of three and a half furlongs. 6f course begins on an extended chute.
N.H. Pear-shaped, 1m 5f (9) 300y run-in uphill. Undulating and a stiff test of stamina, ideally suited to the long-striding thorough stayer. Three mile chases start on a chute, and the first fence is only jumped once. Ground tends to be either very fast or very soft.
Address: Carlisle Racecourse, Durdar Road, Carlisle CA2 4TS Tel: (01228) 554700 Office: (01228) 554747.
Clerk Of The Course: Mr J. E. Fenwicke-Clennell. Tel: Office (01228) 554700. Home (016974) 76589. Mobile: (07860) 737729.
Going Reports: (01228) 554700 (recorded) or contact Clerk Of The Course above
Stabling: Stabling and accommodation available on request. Please phone Head Groundsman on (01228) 546188, or Stable Office on (01228) 549489 from 3pm day before racing.
By Road: 2 miles south of the town (Durdar Road). Easy access from the M6 (Junction 42). The car park is free (adjacent to the course). Trackside car parking £3 (except Saturdays & Bank Holidays £5).
By Rail: Carlisle Station (2 miles from the course).
By Air: Helicopter landing facility by prior arrangement.

CARTMEL (L.H)

N.H.: Oval, 1m 1f (6) 800y run-in. Almost perfectly flat but very sharp, with the longest run-in in the country, approximately half a mile. The fences are stiff but fair.
Address: Cartmel Racecourse, Cartmel, nr Grange-Over-Sands, Cumbria LA11 6QFTel: (015395) 36340. Out of season (015395) 33335
Clerk Of The Course: Mr A. J. A. Tulloch Tel: (0151) 523 2600 Fax: (0151) 522 2920 Car: (0411) 880123 Racedays: (01539) 536340.
Club Secretary: Mrs Bray (015395) 33434
Going Reports: (015395) 36340 or contact Clerk Of Course as above.
Stabling: Boxes and accommodation for lads and lasses is limited. Prior booking is advisable.
By Road: 1 mile West of the town, 2 miles off the B5277 (Grange-Haverthwaite road). M36 (Junction 36).
By Rail: Cark and Cartmel Station (2½ miles) (Carnforth-Barrow line).
By Air: Light aircraft facilities available at Cark Airport (4 miles from the course). Helicopter landing facility at the course, by prior arrangement only.

CATTERICK (L.H)

Flat: A sharp, left-handed, undulating oval of 1m 180y with a downhill run-in of 3f.
N.H. Oval, 1m 1f (9) 240y run-in. Undulating, sharp track that favours the handy, front-running sort, rather than the long-striding galloper.
Address: The Racecourse, Catterick Bridge, Richmond, North Yorkshire DL10 7PETel: (01748) 811478 Fax: (01748) 811082
Clerk Of The Course (Flat): International racecourse management
Clerk of the Course (jumps): Mr C.M.Tetley. Manor Farm, Little Habton, Malton, N.Yorkshire YO17 OUA. Tel: (01302) 320066 (racedays), Home (01904) 489669. Mobile (07860) 919661.
Going Reports: Contact Clerk Of Course as above
Stabling: Boxes are allotted on arrival.

By Road: The course is adjacent to the A1, 1 mile North-West of the town on the A6136. There is a free car park.

By Rail: Darlington Station (special buses to course - 14 mile journey).

By Air: Helicopters can land by prior arrangement. Fixed wing planes contact RAF Leeming Tel: 01677 423041

CHELTENHAM (L.H)

Old Course: Oval, 1m 4f (9) 350y run-in. A testing, undulating track with stiff fences. The ability to stay is essential.

New Course: Oval, 1m 5f (10) 220y run-in. Undulating, stiff fences, testing course, uphill for the final half-mile.

Address: Cheltenham Racecourse, Prestbury Park, Cheltenham, Gloucestershire GL50 4SHTel (01242) 513014 Fax: (01242) 224227 Internet: http://www.cheltenham.co.uk

Managing Director: E. W. Gillespie

Clerk Of The Course: Mr S. J. Claisse

Going Reports: Available from 6 days before racing (01242) 517900

Stabling: Ample stabling and accommodation for lads. Apply to the Stable Manager (01242) 513014 or 521950.

By Road: 1.5 miles North of the town on the A435. M5 (Junction 10 or 11).

By Rail: Cheltenham (Lansdowne) Station. Buses and taxis to course.

By Air: Helicopter landing site to the North-East of the stands.

CHEPSTOW (L.H)

Flat: A left-handed, undulating oval of about 2m, with easy turns, and a straight run-in of 5f. There is a straight track of 1m 14y.

N.H. Oval, 2m (11) 240y run-in. Many changing gradients, five fences in the home straight. Favours the long-striding front-runner, but stamina is important.

Address: Chepstow Racecourse, Chepstow, Gwent NP6 5YH Tel: (01291) 622260Fax: (01291) 627061 Internet: www.chepstow-racecourse.co.uk

Clerk Of The Course: Major D. McAllister. Tel: (01283) 711233 (Office), (01889) 562221 (Home) or (0860) 286003 (Mobile).

Going Reports: Contact Clerk of the Course as above.

Stabling: 40 boxes, allotted on arrival. Limited accommodation for lads and lasses. Apply:(01291) 623414.

By Road: 1 mile North-West of the town on the A466. (1 mile from Junction 22 of the M4 (Severn Bridge). There is a Free public car park opposite the Stands entrance.

By Rail: Chepstow Station (from Paddington, change at Gloucester or Newport). The course is 1 mile from station.

By Air: Helicopter landing facility in the centre of the course.

CHESTER (L.H)

Flat: A level, sharp, left-handed, circular course of 1m 73y, with a short run-in of 230y. Chester is a specialists track which generally suits the sharp-actioned horse.

Address: The Racecourse, Chester CH1 2LY Tel: (01244) 304600 Fax: (01244) 304649

Clerk Of The Course: Major R M O Webster

Going Reports: Contact Main Office (01244) 304600

Stabling: (175 boxes) and accommodation. Tel: (01244) 324880

By Road: The course is near the centre of the city on the A548 (Queensferry Road). The Owners and Trainers car park is adjacent to the County Stand. There is a public car park in the centre of the course.

By Rail: Chester Station (3/4 mile from the course). Services from Euston, Paddington and Northgate.

By Air: Hawarden Airport (2 miles).

DONCASTER (L.H)

Flat: A left-handed, flat, galloping course of 1m 7f 110y, with a long run-in which extends to a straight mile.
N.H. Conical, 2m (11) 247y run-in. A very fair, flat track ideally suited to the long-striding galloper.
Address: Doncaster Racecourse, Leger Way, Doncaster DN2 6BB Tel: (01302) 304200, Fax: (01302) 323271 E-mail: info@britishracing.com, Internet: www.britishracing.com
Chief Executive & Clerk of Course (Flat): Mr J. Sanderson.
Clerk of the Course (jumps): Mr C.M.Tetley. Manor Farm, Little Habton, Malton, N.Yorkshire YO17 OUA. Tel: (01302) 304200 (racedays), Home (01904) 489669. Mobile (07860) 919661.
Going Reports: Contact Clerk of the Course as above.
Stabling: Free stabling and accommodation. Mr M Taylor Tel: (01302) 349337
By Road: East of the town, off the A638 (M18 Junctions 3 & 4). Club members car park reserved. Large public car park free and adjacent to the course.
By Rail: Doncaster Central Station (from King's Cross). Special bus service from the station (1 mile).
By Air: Helicopter landing facility by prior arrangement only.

EPSOM (L.H)

Flat: Left-handed and undulating with easy turns, and a run-in of just under 4f. The straight 5f course is also undulating and downhill all the way, making it the fastest 5f in the world.
Address: The Racecourse, Epsom Downs, Surrey, KT18 5LQ. Tel: (01372) 726311, Fax (01372) 748253
Clerk Of The Course: Mr A. J. Cooper. Tel: (01372) 726311, Mobile (07774) 230850.
Going Reports: Contact Clerk of the Course as above.
Stabling: Free stabling and accommodation. Tel: (01372) 460454
By Road: 2 miles South of the town on the B290 (M25 Junctions 8 & 9). For full car park particulars apply to: The Club Secretary, Epsom Grandstand, Epsom Downs, Surrey KT18 5LQ.Tel: (01372) 726311.
By Rail: Epsom, Epsom Downs or Tattenham Corner Stations (trains from London Bridge, Waterloo, Victoria). Regular bus services run to the course from Epsom and Morden Underground Station.
By Air: London (Heathrow) and London (Gatwick) are both within 20 miles of the course. Heliport (Derby Meeting only) apply to Hascombe Aviation. Tel: (01279) 680291.

EXETER (R.H)

N.H.: Oval, 2m (11) 300y run-in uphill. Undulating with a home straight of half a mile. A good test of stamina, suiting the handy, well-balanced sort.
Address: Exeter Racecourse, Kennford, Exeter, Devon EX6 7XS Tel: (01392) 832599Fax: (01392) 833454 Email: exeter-racecourse@eclipse.co.uk. Internet: www.exeter-racecourse.co.uk
Clerk Of The Course: Mr Barry Johnson
Managing Director: Mr G. K. Billson
Raceday Manager: Mr B. W. Soper
Club Secretary: Mrs Robinson
Going Reports: Contact Clerk of the Course as above.
Stabling: 81 loose boxes on the course. Sleeping accommodation and canteen for both lads and lasses by prior arrangement. Apply to Mrs J. Browning. Tel: (01392) 832816 or (01392) 832599.
By Road: The course is at Haldon, 5 miles South-West of Exeter on the A38 (Plymouth) road, 2 miles East of Chudleigh.
By Rail: Exeter (St Davids) Station.
By Air: Helicopters can land by prior arrangement.

FAKENHAM (L.H)

N.H.: Square, 1m (6) 200y run-in. On the turn almost throughout and undulating, suiting the handy front-runner. The going rarely becomes heavy.
Address: The Racecourse, Fakenham, Norfolk NR21 7NY Tel: (01328) 862388 Fax: (01328) 855908 email: info@fakenhamracecourse.co.uk Internet: www.fakenhamracecourse.co.uk
Clerk of the Course & Racecourse Manager: Mr D. J. Hunter Tel: (01328) 862388Mobile (07767) 802206.
Going Reports: Contact Clerk of the Course as above.
Stabling: 68 boxes available. Tel: (01328) 862388 Fax (01328) 855908.
By Road: 1 mile South of the town on the B1146 (East Dereham) road.
By Rail: Norwich Station (26 miles) (Liverpool Street line), King's Lynn (22 miles) (Liverpool Street).
By Air: Helicopter landing facility in the centre of the course.

FOLKESTONE (R.H)

Flat: Right-handed, undulating, circuit of 1m 3f, with a two and a half furlong run-in. There is a straight 6f course.
N.H. Oval, 1m 3f (8) chases 220y run-in, hurdles 250y run-in. An undulating course with easy fences, not particularly suitable for the long-striding galloper.
Address: Folkestone Racecourse, Westenhanger, Hythe, Kent CT21 4HX Tel (0870) 2200022Fax: (01303) 260185 Internet: www.folkestone-racecourse.co.uk
Director of Racing: Mr I Renton Tel: (01753) 498442
Clerk Of The Course: Mr C Stickels Tel: (01342) 831720.
Going Reports: Contact Clerk Of The Course as above
Stabling: 90 boxes allotted in rotation. Advance notice required for overnight accommodation, from 2pm on the day prior to racing. Tel: (01303) 266407 or 268449 (racedays).
By Road: 6 miles West of town at Westenhanger. Easy access from Junction 11 of the M20.Car park adjoins stands. (Free, except course enclosure £4).
By Rail: Westenhanger Station adjoins course. Trains from Charing Cross.
By Air: Helicopter landing facility by prior arrangement.

FONTWELL (Fig. 8)

N.H.: 2m (7) 230y run-in with left-hand bend close home. The figure-of-eight chase course suits handy types and is something of a specialists' track. The hurdle course is oval, one mile round with nine hurdles per two and a quarter miles.
Address: Fontwell Park Racecourse, nr Arundel, West Sussex BN18 0SX Tel: (01243) 543335Fax: (01243) 543904
Clerk Of The Course: Mr Geoffrey Stickels Tel: (01273) 603580. Mobile: (07973) 737006
Going Reports: (01243) 543335 during office hours.
Stabling: 77 boxes. Limited accommodation. If arriving the day before the meeting, contact:Tel: (01243) 543370.
By Road: South of village at the junction of the A29 (Bognor) and A27 (Brighton-Chichester) roads.
By Rail: Barnham Station (2 miles). Brighton-Portsmouth line (access via London Victoria).
By Air: Helicopter landing facility by prior arrangement with the Clerk of the Course.

GOODWOOD (R.H)

Flat.: A sharp, undulating, essentially right-handed track with a long run-in. There is also a straight six furlong course.
Address: Goodwood Racecourse Ltd., Goodwood, Chichester, West Sussex PO18 0PXTel: (01243) 755022, Fax: (01243) 755025 Internet: http://www.goodwood.co.uk/racenews/goodwood
Clerk of the Course and General Manager: Mr R. N. Fabricius Tel: Mobile (07836) 321254
Going Reports: (01243) 755022 (recorded message)

Stabling: Free stabling and accommodation for runners (115 well equipped boxes at Goodwood House). Subsidised canteen and recreational facilities. Tel: (01243) 755022/755036.
By Road: 6 miles North of Chichester between the A286 & A285. There is a car park adjacent to the course. Ample free car and coach parking.
By Rail: Chichester Station (from Victoria or London Bridge). Regular bus service to the course(6 miles).
By Air: Helicopter landing facility by prior arrangement with Martin Fiddler. Tel: (01279) 850750.Fax (01279) 850459 Goodwood Airport 2 miles (taxi to the course).

HAMILTON (R.H)

Flat.: Sharp, undulating, right-handed course of 1m 5f with a five and a half furlong, uphill run-in. There is a straight track of 6f.
Address: Hamilton Park Racecourse, Bothwell Road, Hamilton, Lanarkshire ML3 0DWTel: (01698) 283806 Fax: (01698) 286621.
Clerk Of The Course: Hazel Peplinski (01698) 283806. Mobile (07774) 116733. Fax (01698) 286621
Chief Executive: Morag Gray Tel: (01698) 283806. Mobile: (07776) 136677
Going Reports: Head Groundsman: (07850) 609037 (mobile).
Stabling: Free stabling (120 boxes) and accommodation on request. Tel: (01698) 248892 or Office.
By Road: Off the A74 on the B7071 (Hamilton-Bothwell road). (M74 Junction 5). Free parking for cars and buses.
By Rail: Hamilton West Station (1 mile).
By Air: Glasgow Airport (20 miles).

HAYDOCK (L.H)

Flat: A galloping, almost flat, oval track, 1m 5f round, with a run-in of four and a half furlongs and a straight six furlong course.
N.H. Oval, 1m 5f (10) 440y run-in. Flat, galloping chase course with stiff drop fences. The hurdle track, which is sharp, is inside the chase course and has some tight bends.
Address: Haydock Park Racecourse, Newton-le-Willows, Merseyside WA12 0HQ Tel: (01942) 725963 Fax: (01942) 270879
Clerk Of The Course: Mr W. K. Tellwright.
General Manager: Mr A. J. P. Waterworth.
Going Reports: Contact Clerk Of The Course as above
Stabling: Applications to be made to the Racecourse for stabling and accommodation.Tel (01942) 725963 or (01942) 402615 (racedays).
By Road: The course is on the A49 near Junction 23 of the M6.
By Rail: Newton-le-Willows Station (Manchester-Liverpool line) is 2.5 miles from the course. Earlstown 3 miles from the course. Warrington Bank Quay and Wigan are on the London to Carlisle/ Glasgow line.
By Air: Landing facilities in the centre of the course for helicopters and planes not exceeding 10,000lbs laden weight. Apply to the Sales Office.

HEREFORD (R.H)

N.H.: Square, 1m 4f (9) 300y run-in. The turns, apart from the final one that is on falling ground, are easily negotiated, placing the emphasis on speed rather than stamina. A handy position round the home turn is vital, as winners rarely come from behind. The hurdle track is on the outside of the chase course. The fences have a reputation of being pretty stiff, but at the same time fair.
Address: Hereford Racecourse, Roman Road, Holmer, Hereford HR4 9 QU Tel: (01432) 273560,Fax (01432) 352807 Internet: www.hereford-racecourse.co.uk
Clerk of the Course and Secretary: Mr J. Pullin
Going Reports: (01432) 352807 (Recorded) or web site as listed above
Stabling: 90 boxes allocated on arrival. Apply to the Stabling Manager, The Racecourse House, Roman Road, Holmer, Hereford. Tel: (01432) 273560.

By Road: 1 mile North West of the City centre off the A49 (Leominster) road.
By Rail: Hereford Station (1 mile from the course).
By Air: Helicopter landing facility in the centre of the course by arrangement with the Clerk of the Course, and entirely at own risk.

HEXHAM (L.H)

N.H.: Oval, 1m 4f (10) 220y run-in. An undulating course that becomes very testing when the ground is soft, it has easy fences and a stiff uphill climb to the finishing straight, which is on a separate spur.
Address: Hexham Racecourse, The Riding, Hexham, Northumberland NE46 4PF Tel: (01434) 606881 Fax (01434) 605814, Racedays (01434) 603738. Email: hexrace@aol.com Internet: www.hexham-racecourse.co.uk
Clerk of the Course and Secretary: Mr S. C. Enderby
Going Reports: Contact Clerk Of The Course as above
Stabling: Boxes allocated in rotation. Tel: (01434) 603738.
By Road: 1.5 miles South-West of the town off the B6305.
By Rail: Hexham Station (Newcastle-Carlisle line). Free bus to the course.
By Air: Helicopter landing facility in centre of course (by special arrangement only).

HUNTINGDON (R.H)

N.H.: Oval, 1m 4f (9) 200y run-in. Perfectly flat, galloping track with a tricky open ditch in front of the stands. The two fences in the home straight can cause problems for novice chasers. Suits front runners.
Address: The Racecourse, Brampton, Huntingdon, Cambridgeshire PE18 8NN Tel: (01480) 453373 Fax: (01480) 455275
Clerk Of The Course: Mr M Prosser
Manager: Mrs T Dawson
Going Reports: Tel: (01480) 453373
Stabling: 100 boxes available. Allotted on arrival. Tel Racecourse Office.
By Road: The course is situated at Brampton, 2 miles West of Huntingdon on the A14. Easy access from the A1 (1/2 mile from the course).
By Rail: Huntingdon Station. Buses and taxis to course.
By Air: Helicopter landing facility by prior arrangement.

KELSO (L.H)

N.H.: Oval, 1m 3f (9) 440y run-in uphill. Rather undulating with two downhill fences opposite the stands, Kelso suits the nippy, front-running sort, though the uphill run to the finish helps the true stayer. The hurdle course is smaller and very sharp with a tight turn away from the stands.
Address: Kelso Racecourse, Kelso, Roxburghshire. Tel: (01573) 22767.
Clerk Of The Course: Mr J. E. Fenwicke-Clennell. The Grandstand Office, The Racecourse, Durdar Road, Carlisle, CA2 4TS. Tel: Office (01228) 554700. Home (016974) 76589. Mobile: (07860) 737729.
Secretary: Mr Richard M. Landale, c/o Sale & Partners, 18-20 Glendale Road, Wooler, Northumberland NE71 6DW. Tel: (01668) 281611. Fax: (01668) 281113
Going Reports: Racecourse: (01573) 22767 Groundsman Tel: (07774) 172527
Stabling: Boxes allotted in rotation. Reservations for stabling and accommodation for lads and lasses at the racecourse. Please phone Head Groundsman Tel: (01573) 224767 or Racecourse stables: (01573) 224822 from 3pm the day before racing.
By Road: 1 mile North of the town, off the B6461.
By Rail: Berwick-upon-Tweed Station. 23 mile bus journey to Kelso.
By Air: Helicopters can land at course by arrangement, fixed wing aircraft Winfield, regular aircraft Edinburgh

KEMPTON (R.H)

Flat: A sharp, level, right-handed course of 1m 5f, with a three and a half furlong run-in. The 1m 2f Jubilee Course starts on an extension to the round course, and there is a straight 6f track.

N.H. Triangular, 1m 5f (10) 175y run-in. Practically flat; sharp course where the long run between the last obstacle on the far side and the first in the home straight switches the emphasis from jumping to speed.

Address: Kempton Park Racecourse, Sunbury-on-Thames, Middlesex TW16 5AQ Tel: (01932) 782292 Fax: (01932) 782044 Raceday Fax: (01932) 779525 Internet: www.kempton.co.uk Email: kempton@rht.net

Clerk Of The Course: Mr B Clifford Mobile (07880) 784484

Going Reports: (01932) 782292 if unavailable contact Clerk Of The Course as above

Stabling: Allocated on arrival. Prior booking required for overnight stay. Tel: (01932) 783334

By Road: On the A308 near Junction 1 of the M3. Main car park £2, Silver Ring and centre car park free.

By Rail: Kempton Park Station (from Waterloo).

By Air: London (Heathrow) Airport 6 miles.

LEICESTER (R.H)

Flat: Stiff, galloping, right-handed oval of 1m 5f, with a 5f run-in. There is a straight course of 1m 8y.

N.H. Rectangular, 1m 6f (10) 250y run-in uphill. An undulating course with an elbow 150y from the finish, Leicester can demand a high degree of stamina, for the going can become extremely heavy and the last three furlongs are uphill.

Address: Leicester Racecourse, Oadby, Leicester LE2 3QH. Tel: (0116) 2716515 Fax (0116) 2711746

Clerk Of The Course: Captain N. E. S. Lees. Home (01284) 386889.

Going Reports: Recorded message (0116) 2710875 or contact Head Groundsman (0116) 2712115 (07774) 497281 (mobile).

Stabling: Allocated on arrival. canteen opens at 7.30a.m. tel: (0116) 271 2115.

By Road: The course is 2.5 miles South-East of the City on the A6 (M1, Junction 21). The car park is free.

By Rail: Leicester Station (from St Pancras) is 2.5 miles.

By Air: Helicopter landing facility in the centre of the course.

LINGFIELD (L.H)

Flat, Turf: A sharp, undulating left-handed circuit, with a 7f 140y straight course.

Flat, Polytrack: The left-handed all-weather polytrack is 1m 2f round, with an extended chute to provide a 1m 5f start. It is a sharp, level track with a short run-in.

N.H. Conical, 1m 5f (10) 200y run-in. Severely undulating with a tight downhill turn into the straight, the chase course suits front runners and those of doubtful resolution.

Address: Lingfield Park Racecourse, Lingfield, Surrey RH7 6PQ Tel: (01342) 831720Fax: (01342) 832833 Internet: www.lingfieldpark.co.uk

Director of Racing: Mr I Renton Tel: (01753) 498442

Clerk Of The Course: Mr C Stickels Tel: (01342) 831720.

Going Reports: Contact Clerk Of The Course as above

Stabling: 180 boxes. For details of accommodation tel (01342) 831720. Advance notice for overnight accommodation required before 12 noon on the day before racing.

By Road: South-East of the town off the A22 (M25 Junction 6). Ample free parking. Reserved car park £3.

By Rail: Lingfield Station (regular services from London Bridge and Victoria). 1/2m walk to the course.

By Air: London (Gatwick) Airport 10 miles. Helicopter landing facility south of wind-sock.

LUDLOW (R.H)

N.H.: Oval, 1m 4f (9) 185y run-in. The chase course is flat and has quite sharp bends into and out of the home straight, although long-striding horses never seem to have any difficulties. The hurdle course is on the outside of the chase track and is not so sharp.

Address: Ludlow Race Club Ltd, The Racecourse, Bromfield, Ludlow, Shropshire SY8 2BTTel: (01584) 856221 (Racedays) or see below.

Secretary & Clerk Of The Course: Mr B. R. Davies. Tel: (01981) 580260 (Home),Mobile (07970) 861533, Fax (01981) 580181 (home), 01584 856217 (course)Email: bobdavies@ludlowracecourse.co.uk

Going Reports: Contact Clerk Of Course as above or Groundsman Tel: (01584) 856269

Stabling: Free and allocated on arrival. 100 stables, mainly shavings with a limited number of paper and straw. Tel: (01584) 856269.

By Road: The course is situated at Bromfield, 2 miles North of Ludlow on the A49.

By Rail: Ludlow Station (Hereford-Shrewsbury line) 2 miles.

By Air: Helicopter landing facility in the centre of the course by arrangement with the Clerk of the Course and entirely at own risk.

MARKET RASEN (R.H)

N.H.: Oval, 1m 2f (8) 250y run-in. A sharp, undulating course with a long run to the straight, Market Rasen favours the handy, front-running type. The fences are not as easy as they used to be.

Address: Market Rasen Racecourse, Legsby Road, Market Rasen, Lincolnshire LN8 3EATel: (01673) 843434 Fax: (01673) 844532

Clerk Of The Course: Mr E Gretton Tel: (07775) 704822

Going Reports: Contact Clerk Of The Course as above.

Stabling: 90 boxes at the course, allocated on arrival. Accommodation for lads and lasses is by reservation only. Tel: (01673) 842307 (racedays only)

By Road: The town is just off A46, and the racecourse is one mile East of the town on the A631. Free car parks and racecards.

By Rail: Market Rasen Station 1 mile (King's Cross - Cleethorpes line).

By Air: Helicopter landing facility by prior arrangement only.

MUSSELBURGH (R.H)

Flat: A sharp, level, right-handed oval of 1m 2f, with a run-in of 4f. There is an additional 5f straight course.

N.H. Rectangular, 1m 3f (8) 150y run-in (variable). A virtually flat track with sharp turns, suiting the handy, front-running sort. Drains well.

Address: Musselburgh Racecourse, Linkfield Road, Musselburgh, East Lothian EH21 7RGTel: (0131) 665 2859 (Racedays) Fax: (0131) 653 2083

Clerk Of The Course: Mrs Anthea Morshead Tel: (07789) 697241.

Going Reports: Contact main office as above.

Stabling: Free stabling. Accommodation provided. Tel: (0131) 665 4955, Stables (racedays) (0131) 665 2796.

By Road: The course is situated at Musselburgh, 5 miles East of Edinburgh on the A1. Car park, adjoining course, free for buses and cars.

By Rail: Waverley Station (Edinburgh). Local Rail service to Musselburgh.

By Air: Edinburgh (Turnhouse) Airport 30 minutes

NEWBURY (L.H)

Flat: Left-handed, oval track of about 1m 7f, with a slightly undulating straight mile. The round course is level and galloping with a four and a half furlong run-in. Races over the round mile and 7f 60y start on the adjoining chute.

N.H. Oval, 1m 6f (11) 255y run-in. Slightly undulating, wide and galloping in nature. The fences are stiff and sound jumping is essential. One of the fairest tracks in the country.

Address: The Racecourse, Newbury, Berkshire RG14 7NZ Fax: (01635) 528354

Clerk Of The Course: Mr M. Kershaw Racecourse Office (01635) 40015 or 550354.

Going Reports: Clerk of the Course as above.

Stabling: Free stabling and accommodation for lads and lasses. Tel: (01635) 40015.

By Road: East of the town off the A34 (M4, Junction 12 or 13). Car park, adjoining enclosures, free.

By Rail: Newbury Racecourse Station, adjoins course.

By Air: Light Aircraft landing strip East/West. 830 metres by 30 metres wide. Helicopter landing facilities.

NEWCASTLE (L.H)

Flat: Galloping, easy, left-handed oval of 1m 6f, with an uphill 4f run-in. There is a straight course of 1m 8y.

N.H. Oval, 1m 6f (11) 220y run-in. A gradually rising home straight of four furlongs makes this galloping track a true test of stamina, especially as the ground can become very heavy. The fences are rather stiff.

Address: High Gosforth Park, Newcastle-Upon-Tyne NE3 5HP Tel: (0191) 236 2020Fax 0191 236 7761

Clerk Of The Course: Mr J Armstrong

Chairman: Mr S. W. Clarke C.B.E.

Stabling: Stabling Free. It is essential to book accommodation in advance. Apply via the Racecourse Office.

Going Reports: Contact Clerk of the Course as above.

By Road: 4 miles North of city on the A6125 (near the A1). Car and coach park free.

By Rail: Newcastle Central Station (from King's Cross), a free bus service operates from South Gosforth and Regent Centre Metro Station.

By Air: Helicopter landing facility by prior arrangement. The Airport is 4 miles from the course.

NEWMARKET (R.H)

Rowley Course: There is a straight ten furlong course, which is wide and galloping. Races over 12f or more are right-handed. The Rowley course has a long run-in and a stiff finish.

July Course: Races up to a mile are run on the Bunbury course, which is straight. Races over 10f or more are right-handed, with a 7f run-in. Like the Rowley course, the July track is stiff.

Address: Newmarket Racecourse, Newmarket, Suffolk CB8 0TG Tel: (01638) 663482 (Main Office), (01638) 663762 (Rowley), (01638) 662752 (July) Fax: Rowley (01638) 675340. Fax: July (01638) 667839

Clerk Of The Course: Mr M. Prosser, Westfield House, The Links, Newmarket. Tel: (01638) 662933

Manager: Mrs Lisa Hancock

Going Reports: Contact main office or Clerk Of Course as above

Stabling: Free accommodation available at the Links Stables. Tel: (01638) 662200

By Road: South-West of the town on the A1304 London Road (M11 Junction 9). Free car parking at the rear of the enclosure. Members car park £1 all days; Free courtesy bus service from Newmarket Station, Bus Station and High Street, commencing 90 minutes prior to the first race, and return trips up to 60 minutes after the last race.

By Rail: Infrequent rail service to Newmarket Station from Cambridge (Liverpool Street) or direct bus service from Cambridge (13 mile journey).

By Air: Landing facilities for light aircraft and helicopters on racedays at both racecourses. See Flight Guide. Cambridge Airport 11 miles.

NEWTON ABBOT (L.H)

N.H.: Oval, 1m 2f (7) 300y run-in. Flat with two tight bends and a water jump situated three fences from home. The nippy, agile sort is favoured. The run-in can be very short on the hurdle course.

Address: Newton Abbot Races Ltd., Kingsteignton Road, Newton Abbot, Devon TQ12 3AFTel: (01626) 353235 Fax: (01626) 336972

Clerk Of The Course/Estate Manager: Mr J Loosemoore

Managing Director: Mr P. G. Masterson. Tel: (01626) 353235 Fax: (01626) 336972Mobile: (07778) 463207.

Going reports: Clerk of the Course as above, or Head Groundsman: (0374) 914403

Stabling: 90 boxes, allocated on arrival. Tel: (07467) 264796

By Road: North of the town on the A380. Torquay 6 miles, Exeter 17 miles.

By Rail: Newton Abbot Station (from Paddington) 3/4 mile. Buses and taxis operate to and from the course.

By Air: Helicopter landing pad in the centre of the course.

NOTTINGHAM (L.H)

Flat: Left-handed, galloping, oval of about 1m 4f, and a run-in of four and a half furlongs. Flat with easy turns.

Address: Nottingham Racecourse, Colwick Park, Nottingham NG2 4BE Tel: (0115) 958 0620 Fax: (0115) 958 4515

Clerk Of The Course: Post vacant going to press

Going Reports: Contact main office as above

Racecourse Manager: Miss Nina Coverley

Stabling: 120 boxes allotted on arrival. Hostel for lads and lasses. Tel: (0115) 950 1198

By Road: 2 miles East of the City on the B686. The car park is free. Silver Ring Picnic Car Park £12 (admits car and four occupants).

By Rail: Nottingham (Midland) Station. Regular bus service to course (2 miles).

By Air: Helicopter landing facility in the centre of the course.

PERTH (R.H)

N.H.: Rectangular, 1m 2f (8) 283y run-in. A flat, easy track with sweeping turns. Not a course for the long-striding galloper. An efficient watering system ensures that the ground rarely gets hard.

Address: Perth Racecourse, Scone Palace Park, Perth PH2 6BB Tel (01738) 551597 Fax: (01738) 553021 Internet: www.perth-races.co.uk

Clerk Of The Course: Mrs Anthea Morshead Tel: (07789) 697241

General Manager: Mr S. R. Morshead Tel: (01738) 551597 Mobile: (07768) 868848 Home: (01764) 652658.

Secretary: Mrs Lucy Normile

Going Reports: Groundsman: (07899 034 012) or contact Clerk of the Course as above.

Stabling: 96 boxes and accommodation for lads and lasses Tel: (01738) 551597. Stables Tel: (01738) 621604 (racedays only).

By Road: 4 miles North of the town off the A93.

By Rail: Perth Station (from Dundee) 4 miles. There are buses to the course.

By Air: Scone Airport (3.75 miles). Edinburgh Airport 45 minutes.

PLUMPTON (L.H)

N.H.: Oval, 1m 1f (7) 200y run-in uphill. A tight, undulating circuit with an uphill finish, Plumpton favours the handy, fast jumper. The ground often gets heavy, as the course is based on clay soil.

Address: Plumpton Racecourse, Plumpton, East Sussex, BN7 3AL Tel: (01273) 891550/890383 Fax: (01273) 891557.

Clerk Of The Course: Mr D Mcharg Tel: (01273) 891550, Fax: (01273) 891557 (07771) 660115

Going Reports: Tel: (01273) 891550, or (07771) 660115.

Stabling: 75 boxes. Advance notice required for overnight arrival. Tel: (01273) 890522
By Road: 2 miles North of the village off the B2116.
By Rail: Plumpton Station (from Victoria) adjoins course.
By Air: Helicopter landing facility by prior arrangement with the Clerk of the Course.

PONTEFRACT (L.H)

Flat: Left-handed oval, undulating course of 2m 133y, with a short run-in of 2f. It is a particularly stiff track with the last 3f uphill.
Address: Pontefract Park Race Co. Ltd., The Park, Pontefract, West Yorkshire Tel: (01977) 703224 (Admin Office) (01977) 702210 (Racedays)
Clerk of the Course, Managing Director & Secretary: Mr J. N. Gundill, 33 Ropergate, Pontefract, West Yorkshire. WF8 1LE. Tel: (01977) 703224 (Office), (01977) 620649 (Home), (01977) 702210 (racedays)
Going Reports: Contact Admin Office as above, or Racedays number
Stabling: Stabling and accommodation must be reserved. They will be allocated on a first come-first served basis. Tel: (01977 702323)
By Road: 1 mile North of the town on the A639. Junction 32 of M62. Free car park adjacent to the course.
By Rail: Pontefract Station (Tanshelf, every hour to Wakefield), 1½ miles from the course. Regular bus service from Leeds.
By Air: Helicopters by arrangement only. (Nearest Airfields: Doncaster, Sherburn-in-Elmet, Yeadon (Leeds/Bradford).

REDCAR (L.H)

Flat: Left-handed, level, galloping, oval course of 2 miles with a straight run-in of 5f. There is also a straight 8f.
Address: Redcar Racecourse, Redcar, Cleveland TS10 2BY Tel: (01642) 484068 Fax: (01642) 488272
Clerk of the Course & General Manager: Mr J. N. Gundill Tel: (01642) 484068 Mobile (07770) 613049
Going Reports: Contact main office as above
Stabling: 142 Boxes available. Tel Stables (01642) 484068 or racedays only (01642) 484254).
By Road: In town off the A1085. Free parking adjoining the course for buses and cars.
By Rail: Redcar Station (¼ mile from the course).
By Air: Landing facilities at Turners Arms Farm (600y runway) Yearby, Cleveland. 2 miles South of the racecourse - transport available. Teeside airport (18 miles west of Redcar).

RIPON (R.H)

Flat: A sharp, undulating, right-handed oval of 1m 5f, with a 5f run-in. There is also a 6f straight course.
Address: Ripon Racecourse, Boroughbridge Road, Ripon, North Yorkshire HG4 1UG Tel: (01765) 602156 Fax: (01765) 690018 E-mail: cwpy@hutchbutch.co.ukInternet: www.ripon-races.co.uk
Clerk Of The Course: Mr J. M. Hutchinson, 77 North Street, Ripon HG4 1DS. Tel: (01765) 602156, Mobile (07860) 679904. Racedays (01765) 603696
Going Reports: Tel: (01765) 603696
Stabling: Trainers requiring stabling (104 boxes available) are requested to contact Stable Manager prior to 11a.m. the day before racing. Tel: (01765) 604135/603696
By Road: The course is situated 2 miles South-East of the city, on the B6265. There is ample free parking for cars and coaches. For reservations apply to the Secretary.
By Rail: Harrogate Station (11 miles), or Thirsk (15 miles). Bus services to Ripon.
By Air: Helicopters only on the course. Otherwise Leeds/Bradford airport.

SALISBURY (R.H)

Flat: Right-handed and level, with a run-in of 4f. There is straight 8f track. The last half mile is uphill, providing a stiff test of stamina.

Address: Salisbury Racecourse, Netherhampton, Salisbury, Wiltshire SP2 8PN Tel: (01722) 326461 Fax: 01722 412710

Clerk Of The Course: Mr J Martin

Going Reports: Contact main office as above

Stabling: Free stabling (112 boxes) and accommodation for lads and lasses, apply to the Stabling Manager (01722) 327327.

By Road: 3 miles South-West of the city on the A3094 at Netherhampton. Free car park adjoins the course.

By Rail: Salisbury Station is 3.5 miles (from London Waterloo). Bus service to the course.

By Air: Helicopter landing facility near the ten furlong start.

SANDOWN (R.H)

Flat: An easy right-handed oval course of 1m 5f with a stiff straight uphill run-in of 4f. Separate straight 5f track is also uphill. Galloping.

N.H. Oval, 1m 5f (11) 220y run-in uphill. Features seven fences on the back straight, the last three (Railway Fences) are very close together and can often decide the outcome of races. The stiff uphill climb to the finish puts the emphasis very much on stamina, but accurate-jumping, free-running sorts are also favoured. Hurdle races are run on the Flat course.

Address: Sandown Park Racecourse, Esher, Surrey KT10 9AJ Tel: (01372) 463072 Fax: (01372) 470427

Clerk Of The Course: Mr A. J. Cooper, Sandown Park, Esher, Surrey. Tel: (01372) 463072 Mobile (0374) 230850.

Going Reports: (01372) 461212.

Stabling: Free stabling and accommodation for lads and lasses. Tel: (01372) 463511.

By Road: 4 miles South-West of Kingston-on-Thames, on the A307 (M25 Junction 10). The members' car park in More Lane £2. All other car parking is free.

By Rail: Esher Station (from Waterloo) adjoins the course.

By Air: London (Heathrow) Airport 12 miles.

SEDGEFIELD (L.H)

N.H.: Oval, 1m 2f (8) 200y run-in: Hurdles 200y run-in. Undulating with fairly tight turns and does not suit the big, long-striding horse.

Address: Sedgefield Racecourse, Sedgefield, Stockton-on-Tees, Cleveland TS21 2HW Tel: (01740) 621925 (Office) Fax: (01740) 620663

Clerk Of The Course: Mr J Armstrong Tel: (07801) 166820

Going Reports: Tel: (01740) 621925 or contact Clerk Of Course as above

Stabling: 115 boxes filled in rotation. No forage. Accommodation for horse attendants: Tel: (01740) 621925

By Road: 3/4 mile South-West of the town, near the junction of the A689 (Bishop Auckland) and the A177 (Durham) roads. The car park is free.

By Rail: Darlington Station (9 miles). Durham Station (12 miles).

By Air: Helicopter landing facility in car park area by prior arrangement only.

SOUTHWELL (L.H)

Flat, Turf: Tight left-handed track.
Flat, Fibresand: Left-handed oval, Fibresand course of 1m 2f with a 3f run-in. There is a straight 5f. Sharp and level, Southwell suits front-runners.
N.H. Oval, 1m 1f (7) 220y run-in. A tight, flat track with a short run-in, suits front-runners.
Address: Southwell Racecourse, Rolleston, Newark, Nottinghamshire NG25 0TS Tel: (01636) 814481 Fax: (01636) 812271.
Clerk Of The Course: Mr F Cameron, Wolverhampton Racecourse. Tel: (07971) 531162.
Going Reports: Contact Clerk Of The Course as above.
Stabling: 110 boxes at the course. Applications for staff and horse accommodation to be booked by noon the day before racing on (01636) 814481.
By Road: The course is situated at Rolleston, 3 miles South of Southwell, 5 miles from Newark.
By Rail: Rolleston Station (Nottingham-Newark line) adjoins the course.
By Air: Helicopters can land by prior arrangement with Mr David Williams Tel: (07968) 306373

STRATFORD-ON-AVON (L.H)

N.H.: Triangular, 1m 2f (8) 200y run-in. Virtually flat with two tight bends, and quite a short home straight. A sharp and turning course, Stratford-on-Avon suits the well-balanced, handy sort.
Address: Stratford Racecourse, Luddington Road, Stratford-upon-Avon, Warwickshire CV37 9SE Tel: (01789) 267949 Fax: (01789) 415850
Clerk Of The Course: Mr Stephen Lambert. Mobile (07836) 384932. Home (01608) 674354
Going reports: Contact main office as above or Head Groundsman Tel: (07770) 623366.
Stabling: Allotted on arrival. Advance notice must be given for overnight stays. Tel: (01789) 267949.
By Road: 1 mile from the town centre, off the A429 (Evesham road).
By Rail: Stratford-on-Avon Station (from Birmingham New Street or Leamington Spa) 1 mile.
By Air: Helicopter landing facility by prior arrangement.

TAUNTON (R.H)

N.H.: Elongated oval, 1m 2f (8) 150y run-in uphill. Sharp turns, especially after the winning post, with a steady climb from the home bend. Suits the handy sort.
Address: Taunton Racecourse, Orchard Portman, Taunton, Somerset TA3 7BL Tel: (01823) 337172 (Office) Fax: (01823) 325881
Clerk Of The Course: Mr M. Trickey, The Racecourse, Taunton, Somerset TA3 7BL. Tel: (01823) 337172.
Going reports: Contact Clerk of the Course as above, or head Groundsman (after 4.30pm) (07971) 695132.
Stabling: 98 boxes allotted on arrival. Advance bookings for long journeys. Apply to the Stable Manager, c/o The Racecourse (01823) 337172
By Road: 2 miles South of the town on the B3170 (Honiton) road (M5 Junction 25). Free car park for Members. The public car parks are free or £3 on course.
By Rail: Taunton Station 2.5 miles. There are buses and taxis to course.
By Air: Helicopter landing facility by prior arrangement.

THIRSK (L.H)

Flat: Left-handed, oval of 1m 2f with sharp turns and an undulating run-in of 4f. There is a straight 6f track.
Address: The Racecourse, Station Road, Thirsk, North Yorkshire YO7 1QL Tel: (01845) 522276 Fax: (01845) 525353.
Clerk Of The Course: Mr C.M. Tetley
Going reports: Contact main office as above
Club Secretary: Mr D. Whitehead
Stabling: For stabling and accommodation apply to the Racecourse Tel: (01845) 522276 or (01845) 522096 (racedays).

By Road: West of the town on the A61. Free car park adjacent to the course for buses and cars.
By Rail: Thirsk Station (from King's Cross). 1/2 mile from the course.
By Air: Helicopters can land by prior arrangement. Tel: Racecourse (01845) 522276. Fixed wing aircraft can land at RAF Leeming. Tel: (01677) 423041. Light aircraft at Bagby. Tel: (01845) 597385 or (01845) 537555.

TOWCESTER (R.H)

N.H.: Square, 1m 6f (10) 200y run-in uphill. The final six furlongs are uphill. One of the most testing tracks in the country with the emphasis purely on stamina.
Address: The Racecourse, Easton Neston, Towcester, Northants NN12 7HS Tel: (01327) 353414 Fax: (01327) 358534 Internet: www.towcester-racecourse.co.uk
Clerk Of The Course: Mr D. Henson, Tel: (01327) 861061 Mobile (07740) 853170
Racecourse Manager: Mr P Robinson.
Going Reports: Tel: (01327) 353414 or contact Clerk Of The Course as above.
Stabling: Being re-built at time of going to press. Contact racecourse office for details
By Road: 1 mile South-East of the town on the A5 (Milton Keynes road). M1 (Junction 15) (from the South), M1 (Junction 16) (from the North).
By Rail: Northampton Station (Euston) 9 miles, buses to Towcester; or Milton Keynes (Euston) 12 miles, taxis available.
By Air: Helicopters can land by prior arrangement with the Racecourse Manager.

UTTOXETER (L.H)

N.H.: Oval, 1m 2f (8) 170y run-in. Few undulations, easy bends and fences and a flat home straight of over half a mile. Suits front-runners, especially on the two mile hurdle course.
Address: The Racecourse, Wood Lane, Uttoxeter, Staffordshire ST14 8BD Tel: (01889) 562561Fax: (01889) 562786 Internet: www.uttoxeter-racecourse.co.uk
Clerk Of The Course: Mr John Pullin Mobile: (07974) 646090
Going Reports: Contact main office or Clerk of the Course, as above.
Stabling: 90 boxes, allotted on arrival. Tel: (01889) 562561.
By Road: South-East of the town off the B5017 (Marchington Road).
By Rail: Uttoxeter Station (Crewe-Derby line) adjoins the course.
By Air: Helicopters can land by prior arrangement with the raceday office.

WARWICK (L.H)

Flat: Left-handed, sharp, level track of 1m 6f 32y in circumference, with a run-in of two and a half furlongs. There is a dog-leg 5f course.
N.H. Circular, 1m 6f (10) 240y run-in. Undulating with tight bends, five quick fences in the back straight and a short home straight, Warwick favours handiness and speed rather than stamina.
Address: Warwick Racecourse, Hampton Street, Warwick CV34 6HN Tel: (01926) 491553 Fax: (01926) 403223
Clerk Of The Course: Mr R Bellamy
Racecourse Manager: Mr C. R. Leech Tel Racedays (01926) 491553 Mobile (0788) 0788464
Going Reports: Contact main office as above
Stabling: 112 boxes allocated on arrival or by reservation (01926) 493803.
By Road: West of the town on the B4095 adjacent to Junction 15 of the M40. Free parking (except the Members' Car Park, £5 to Daily Club Members).
By Rail: Warwick or Leamington Spa Station.
By Air: Helicopters can land by prior arrangement with the Clerk Of The Course.

WETHERBY (L.H)

N.H.: Oval, 1m 4f (9) 200y run-in slightly uphill. A flat, very fair course which suits the long-striding galloper.

Address: The Racecourse, York Road, Wetherby, LS22 5EJ Tel: (01937) 582035 Fax: (01937) 588021

Clerk Of The Course: Mr C. M. Tetley

Chief Executive: Mr T Betteridge

Going reports: Tel: (01937) 582035, or Course Foreman: (07880) 722586

Stabling: 98 boxes allocated on arrival. Accommodation available. Tel: (01937) 582035 or from 2pm day before racing (01937) 582074.

By Road: East of the town off the B1224 (York Road). Adjacent to the A1. Excellent bus and coach facilities. Car park free.

By Rail: Leeds Station 12 miles. Buses to Wetherby.

By Air: Helicopters can land by prior arrangement

WINCANTON (R.H)

N.H.: Rectangular, 1m 3f (9) 200y run-in. Good galloping course where the going rarely becomes heavy. The home straight is mainly downhill.

Address: Wincanton Racecourse, Wincanton, Somerset BA9 8BJ Tel: (01963) 32344 Fax: (01963) 34668

Clerk Of The Course: Mr B Clifford.

Going Reports: Contact Racecourse Office as above.

Stabling: 92 boxes allocated on arrival, overnight accommodation must be booked in advance. Apply to the Stable Manager, Wincanton Racecourse. Tel: (01963) 32344.

By Road: 1 mile North of the town on the B3081.

By Rail: Gillingham Station (from Waterloo) or Castle Cary Station (from Paddington). Buses and taxis to the course.

By Air: Helicopter landing area is situated in the centre of the course.

WINDSOR (Fig. 8)

Flat: Figure eight track of 1m 4f 110y. The course is level and sharp with a long run-in. The 6f course is essentially straight.

Address: Royal Windsor Racecourse, Maidenhead Road, Windsor, Berkshire SL4 5JJ Tel: (01753) 498400 Fax: (01753) 830156. Internet: www.windsor-racecourse.co.uk

Clerk Of The Course/Racecourse Manager: Mr D Mackinnon Mobile: (07776) 135965

Going Reports: Contact Clerk Of The Course as above.

Stabling: 120 boxes available. Reservation required for overnight stay and accommodation only. Tel: (01753) 498400 or (01753) 498405 (racedays).

By Road: North of the town on the A308 (M4 Junction 6). Car parks adjoin the course (£1, £1.50, £2).

By Rail: Windsor Central Station (from Paddington) or Windsor & Eton Riverside Station (from Waterloo).

By Air: London (Heathrow) Airport 15 minutes

By Road: via the M4. Also White Waltham Airport (West London Aero Club) 15 minutes.

River Bus: 7mins from Barry Avenue promenade at Windsor £2 fare each way

WOLVERHAMPTON (L.H)

Flat: Left-handed oval of 1m, with a run-in of 380y. A level track with sharp bends, the Fibresand surface usually rides slower than the all-weather surfaces at Lingfield and Southwell.

Address: Wolverhampton Racecourse, Dunstall Park, Gorsebrook Road, Wolverhampton WV6 0PE Tel: (01902) 421421 Fax: 0870 220 0107

Clerk Of The Course: Mr F Cameron Mobile (07971) 531162

Going Reports: Contact Main Office as above

Stabling: 100 boxes allotted on arrival. Applications for lads and lasses, and overnight stables must be made to Racecourse by noon on the day before racing. Tel: (01902) 421421. Fax: (01902) 421621.

By Road: 1 mile North of city on the A449 (M54 Junction 2 or M6 Junction 12). Car parking free of charge.
By Rail: Wolverhampton Station (from Euston) 1 mile.
By Air: Halfpenny Green Airport 8 miles.

WORCESTER (L.H)

N.H.: Elongated oval, 1m 5f (9) 220y run-in. Flat with easy turns, Worcester is a very fair, galloping track.
Address: Worcester Racecourse, Pitchcroft, Worcester WR1 3EJ Tel: (01905) 25364 (racedays) Fax:
(01905) 617563.
Clerk Of The Course: Mr F Cameron, Wolverhampton Racecourse. Tel: (07971) 531162.
Manager: Mr D. Roberts Tel: (01905) 25364.
Going Reports: Contact Clerk of the Course as above, or (01905) 25364.
Stabling: 100 boxes allotted on arrival. Overnight accommodation for lads and lasses in Worcester. Tel:
(01905) 25364.
By Road: West of the city off the A449 (Kidderminster road) (M5 Junc 8).
By Rail: Foregate Street Station, Worcester (from Paddington) 3/4 mile.
By Air: Helicopter landing facility in the centre of the course, by prior arrangement only.

YARMOUTH (L.H)

Flat: Left-handed, level circuit of 1m 4f, with a run-in of 5f. The straight course is 8f long.
Address: The Racecourse, Jellicoe Road, Great Yarmouth, Norfolk NR30 4AU Tel: (01493) 842527 Fax:
(01493) 843254
Clerk Of The Course: Major Charlie Moore.
Manager: Mr David Thompson
Going Reports: Contact Main Office as above
Stabling: Allocated on arrival. Tel: (01493) 855651.
By Road: 1 mile East of town centre (well sign-posted from A47 & A12). Large car park adjoining course £1.
By Rail: Great Yarmouth Station (1 mile). Bus service to the course.
By Air: Helicopter landing available by prior arrangement with Racecourse Office

YORK (L.H)

Flat: Left-handed, level, galloping track, with a straight 6f. There is also an adjoining course of 6f 214y.
Address: The Racecourse, York YO23 1EX Tel: (01904) 620911 Fax: (01904) 611071
Manager, Clerk of the Course and Secretary: Mr W Darbey
Going Reports: Contact Main Office as above
Stabling: 200 boxes available Tel: (01904) 706317 (Racedays).
By Road: 1 mile South-East of the city on the A1036.
Car parking: Car Park 'D': £5 per space, available all meetings bar May & August. Car Park 'D2': £2 per
space. All other parking is free.
By Rail: 1.5 miles York Station (from King's Cross). Special bus service from station to the course.
By Air: Light aircraft and helicopter landing facilities available at Rufforth aerodrome (5,000ft tarmac
runway). £20 landing fee-transport arranged to course. Leeds/Bradford airport (25 miles).

THE VODAFONE DERBY STAKES (CLASS A)
EPSOM, SATURDAY, JUNE 5th

HORSE	TRAINER
ABBEYGATE	T. Keddy
ABLAJ (IRE)	E. A. L. Dunlop
ABSOLUTELYTHEBEST (IRE)	E. A. L. Dunlop
ACE (IRE)	A. P. O'Brien, Ireland
ACROPOLIS (IRE)	A. P. O'Brien, Ireland
ADJAMI (IRE)	A. de Royer Dupre, France
ADMIRAL (IRE)	Sir Michael Stoute
ADVICE	A. Fabre, France
AFRICAN STAR	Mrs A. J. Perrett
AKAREM	
AKIMBO (USA)	H. R. A. Cecil
AKRITAS	P. F. I. Cole
ALBINUS	A. M. Balding
ALGERNON TALMAGE (USA)	
ALGHAAZY	L. M. Cumani
ALMAHAB	
ALMURAAD	Sir Michael Stoute
ALPHECCA	Sir Michael Stoute
ALQAAYID	M. P. Tregoning
ALWAYS FIRST	Sir Michael Stoute
AMALIE BAY (IRE)	A. P. O'Brien, Ireland
AMERICAN POST	Mme C. Head-Maarek, France
ANCHOR	A. P. O'Brien, Ireland
ANDEAN	D. R. Loder
ANDURIL	J. M. P. Eustace
ANTONIUS PIUS	A. P. O'Brien, Ireland
ANYWHO	Mme C. Head-Maarek, France
APSIS	
AQLAHUM (USA)	
ARAN ISLE (IRE)	A. P. O'Brien, Ireland
ARCH REBEL (USA)	P. Garvey, Ireland
ARMFELT (IRE)	
ARRGATT (IRE)	
ARTICULATION	H. R. A. Cecil
ARTISTICIMPRESSION (IRE)	E. A. L. Dunlop
ARTISTS LICENCE	R. Charlton
ART MASTER (USA)	
ART TRADER (USA)	Mrs A. J. Perrett
ASAEEIF	M. P. Tregoning
ASIA MINOR (UAE)	
ASIATIC	M. Johnston
ATID (USA)	
AT YOUR REQUEST	E. A. L. Dunlop
AUGUSTINE	
AUSTRIA (IRE)	A. P. O'Brien, Ireland
AWESOME LOVE (USA)	M. Johnston
AZAMOUR (IRE)	
BAAWRAH	M. R. Channon
BACKGAMMON	D. R. Loder
BADR (USA)	
BAGO (FR)	J. E. Pease, France
BAKHTYAR	R. Charlton
BALAKAN (IRE)	Sir Michael Stoute
BALLYDUFF (UAE)	John M. Oxx, Ireland
BARATHEA BLUE	P. W. Harris
BARATI	
BARRANCO (IRE)	A. Fabre, France
BASIC HERO	
BASK IN GLORY (USA)	
BATRAAN (USA)	
BAYEUX (USA)	
BELISCO (USA)	Mrs A. J. Perrett
BIRKSPIEL (GER)	A. Wohler, Germany
BLUE MONDAY	A. M. Balding
BOBBY CHARLES	Dr J. D. Scargill
BOOK OF KINGS (USA)	A. P. O'Brien, Ireland
BORDER CASTLE	Sir Michael Stoute
BOUNDARY	A. P. O'Brien, Ireland
BRUNEL (IRE)	W. J. Haggas
BUCKEYE WONDER (USA)	M. A. Jarvis
BUENA VISTA (IRE)	A. P. O'Brien, Ireland

HORSE	TRAINER
BULL RUN (IRE)	D. R. Loder
BURNING MOON	J. Noseda
CAIRDEAS (IRE)	D. K. Weld, Ireland
CALEDONIAN (IRE)	D. R. C. Elsworth
CANADIAN STORM	M. H. Tompkins
CANNON FIRE (FR)	
CAPO FERRO (USA)	J. H. M. Gosden
CAPPED FOR VICTORY (USA)	Sir Michael Stoute
CARADAK (IRE)	
CARTE DIAMOND (USA)	M. Johnston
CARTE SAUVAGE (IRE)	
CELTIC CAT (IRE)	A. P. O'Brien, Ireland
CHARING CROSS (IRE)	A. P. O'Brien, Ireland
CHARMED BY FIRE (USA)	Mrs A. J. Perrett
CHESTER LE STREET (USA)	
CHOIR LEADER	W. J. Haggas
CIRCASSIAN (IRE)	
CIVIL RIGHTS (USA)	
CLASS KING (USA)	Mme C. Head-Maarek, France
COBALT BLUE (IRE)	W. J. Haggas
COBRA (IRE)	A. P. O'Brien, Ireland
COCONUT BEACH	A. P. O'Brien, Ireland
CODE (IRE)	
COHN BLUE (IRE)	
COLOSSAL (IRE)	A. P. O'Brien, Ireland
COMING AGAIN (IRE)	B. W. Hills
CONVICTION	J. R. Fanshawe
COPPICE (IRE)	L. M. Cumani
CORNWALL (IRE)	A. P. O'Brien, Ireland
COUNT OF ANJOU (UAE)	
COURT CAVE (IRE)	
CREDIT (IRE)	R. Hannon
CROCIERA (IRE)	M. H. Tompkins
CRYSTAL KING (USA)	
CUTTING CREW (USA)	P. W. Harris
DABIROUN (IRE)	John M. Oxx, Ireland
DALAYAN (IRE)	A. de Royer Dupre, France
DALLDOL	M. A. Jarvis
DALTON (FR)	Mme C. Head-Maarek, France
DANDY JIM	D. W. Chapman
DANTSU SPRING (IRE)	
DANZIG RIVER (IRE)	B. W. Hills
DARSALAM (IRE)	
DARYAL (IRE)	
DAWN SURPRISE (USA)	
DAY CARE	Mrs A. J. Perrett
DAY FLIGHT	J. H. M. Gosden
DAY OF THE CAT (USA)	A. P. O'Brien, Ireland
DAY TO REMEMBER	A. C. Stewart
DEEP PURPLE	M. P. Tregoning
DEJEEJE (IRE)	M. P. Tregoning
DELFOS (IRE)	
DESERT DREAMER (IRE)	B. W. Hills
DESERT TOMMY	T. G. Mills
DESIGN (FR)	Sir Michael Stoute
DESTINATION DUBAI (USA)	
DEYNIZI (IRE)	
DHEHDAAH	N. A. Graham
DIAMOND GEORGE (IRE)	John Berry
DICTATOR (IRE)	John M. Oxx, Ireland
DIVINE GIFT	M. A. Jarvis
DOSTOIEVSKY (IRE)	John M. Oxx, Ireland
DOUBLE ASPECT (IRE)	Sir Michael Stoute
DOWNING STREET (IRE)	A. M. Balding
DRESS SWORD (UAE)	A. Fabre, France
DUBAI ACE (USA)	J. S. Bolger, Ireland
DUBAI SUNDAY (JPN)	D. R. Loder
DUBOIS	
DUKE'S VIEW (IRE)	Mrs A. J. Perrett
DUKE OF VENICE (USA)	
DUMFRIES	J. H. M. Gosden

DUNE RAIDER (USA)	Sir Michael Stoute
EBAZIYAN (IRE)	John M. Oxx, Ireland
ECOLE D'ART (USA)	A. Fabre, France
ECOMIUM (IRE)	J. Noseda
EDEN ROCK (IRE)	Sir Michael Stoute
ELBASAR (IRE)	
ELMUSTANSER	
ELSHAAN (USA)	
ELSHADI (IRE)	M. P. Tregoning
ELUSIVE DREAM	Sir Mark Prescott
EMIRATES FLYER (IRE)	
ERSHAAD (USA)	J. E. Hammond, France
ESHAADEH (USA)	
ESPERANTO (IRE)	A. P. O'Brien, Ireland
ESTI AB (IRE)	M. P. Tregoning
EVALUATOR (IRE)	T. G. Mills
EXPLICIT (IRE)	G. C. Bravery
EZZO JAH	
FAASEL (IRE)	
FAHLAWI (IRE)	B. W. Hills
FANCY FOXTROT	B. J. Meehan
FANTASTICAT (USA)	A. P. O'Brien, Ireland
FAR AWAY TREE (USA)	J. H. M. Gosden
FARREES	
FENDER	H. R. A. Cecil
FIDDLERS FORD (IRE)	J. Noseda
FIFTH EDITION (USA)	
FINDERS KEEPERS	E. A. L. Dunlop
FIRE DRAGON (IRE)	A. P. O'Brien, Ireland
FIRE OF KEN (FR)	W. P. Mullins, Ireland
FIRST CENTURION	J. W. Hills
FIVE DYNASTIES (USA)	A. P. O'Brien, Ireland
FLAMBOYANT LAD	B. W. Hills
FLICKERING	C. E. Brittain
FLYING PATRIARCH	
FOCUS GROUP (USA)	H. R. A. Cecil
FOREIGN EXCHANGE	J. E. Hammond, France
FOREVER FANTASY (IRE)	J. L. Dunlop
FORGED (IRE)	L. M. Cumani
FORT	
FORT CHURCHILL (IRE)	M. H. Tompkins
FORTHRIGHT	C. E. Brittain
FOUR PENCE (IRE)	B. W. Hills
FRANKIES WINGS (IRE)	T. G. Mills
FRANKLINS TRAIL (IRE)	W. P. Mullins, Ireland
FRANK SONATA	M. G. Quinlan
FURTHER FORTUNE (USA)	
FUTURE LEGEND	
GAMESET'N'MATCH	M. L. W. Bell
GANYMEDE	A. P. O'Brien, Ireland
GATO DEL MAR (USA)	A. P. O'Brien, Ireland
GAZZARINI (USA)	P. Schiergen, Germany
GENTLE TIGER (GER)	Sir Michael Stoute
GIFT VOUCHER (IRE)	Sir Michael Stoute
GIRONDE	B. J. Meehan
GJOVIC	J. Noseda
GLIDE	R. Charlton
GO FOR GOLD	A. P. O'Brien, Ireland
GOLDEN EMPIRE	E. A. L. Dunlop
GOLDEN GRACE	E. A. L. Dunlop
GOLDEN KEY	Sir Michael Stoute
GOLDEN QUEST	M. Johnston
GOLD WELL	M. Johnston
GOLD HISTORY	J. E. Hammond, France
GOVERNMENT (IRE)	J. H. M. Gosden
GRAND BAY (USA)	J. E. Hammond, France
GRAND BUT ONE (IRE)	B. W. Hills
GRAND REWARD (USA)	A. P. O'Brien, Ireland
GRAND RICH KING (IRE)	
GREAT EXHIBITION	
GREAT MAN (FR)	Mme C. Head-Maarek, France
GREY FOX (UAE)	John M. Oxx, Ireland
GREY SWALLOW (IRE)	D. K. Weld, Ireland
GUN TOTE (USA)	
HAADEF	J. H. M. Gosden
HAAFHD	B. W. Hills
HABITUAL (IRE)	Sir Mark Prescott
HAMAIRI (IRE)	
HANAZAKARI	J. A. R. Toller
HANOVERIAN (JPN)	John M. Oxx, Ireland

HAPPINESS MOMENT (USA)	
HATHLEN (IRE)	M. R. Channon
HAYAJAAN (IRE)	
HAYDN (USA)	P. W. Chappie-Hyam
HAZEWIND	P. D. Evans
HEARTHSTEAD DREAM	M. Johnston
HECTOR'S LAW	
HEIR TO THE THRONE (IRE)	
HELENSBURGH (IRE)	P. Bary, France
HELIKE (USA)	L. M. Cumani
HELM (IRE)	M. A. Jarvis
HENNDEY (IRE)	
HERE TO ETERNITY (IRE)	T. G. Mills
HIGH CHARTER	J. R. Fanshawe
HIGHER STATE	
HILLS SPITFIRE (IRE)	P. W. Harris
HUE	
IDRIS (GER)	M. Johnston
IKTIBAS	
IKTITAF (IRE)	J. H. M. Gosden
ILWADOD	M. R. Channon
IMPARTIAL	P. F. I. Cole
IMPERIALISM (IRE)	
IMPERIAL STRIDE	Sir Michael Stoute
IMPRINT (UAE)	
INDIAN DAGGER (FR)	
INNOCENT REBEL (USA)	E. A. L. Dunlop
INSPECTOR POWELL (IRE)	John M. Oxx, Ireland
INSTRUCTOR	R. Hannon
INTILAAQ (USA)	
INTO THE DARK	
INVESTMENT PRINCE (IRE)	
IQTE SAAB (USA)	J. L. Dunlop
IRISH BLADE (IRE)	H. Candy
ISIDORE BONHEUR (IRE)	B. W. Hills
JACKIE KIELY	T. G. Mills
JOE LIEBERMAN	G. B. Balding
JOHNNY ROOK (USA)	E. A. L. Dunlop
JUNIPER PARK (IRE)	A. P. O'Brien, Ireland
JUST A FLUKE (IRE)	M. Johnston
KALIYOUN (IRE)	
KASEH (USA)	
KHARMANI (IRE)	John M. Oxx, Ireland
KHUDABAD (IRE)	John M. Oxx, Ireland
KIBRYAA (USA)	M. A. Jarvis
KING DAVID'S SON (USA)	
KING HESPERUS (USA)	A. P. O'Brien, Ireland
KING MAXIMUS (USA)	
KING OF DREAMS (IRE)	M. Johnston
KING RAMA (USA)	A. P. O'Brien, Ireland
KINGSWORD (USA)	Sir Michael Stoute
KIRKSTONE (IRE)	
KOOL KARMA	H. J. Cyzer
KYATIKYO	P. Bary, France
LAAYEQ (USA)	
LATE OPPOSITION	E. A. L. Dunlop
LAWAAHEB (IRE)	
LEICESTER SQUARE (IRE)	
LESS OF A MYSTERY (USA)	J. L. Dunlop
LET THE LION ROAR	Sir Michael Stoute
LEVITATOR	H. Morrison
LIQUIDATE	D. R. Loder
LOMMEL (UAE)	
LORD ADMIRAL (USA)	Charles O'Brien, Ireland
LORD DARNLEY (IRE)	A. Fabre, France
LORD MAYOR	Sir Michael Stoute
LORENTZ (JPN)	A. Fabre, France
LOST SOLDIER THREE (USA)	L. M. Cumani
LOVE DEPARTMENT (IRE)	
LUCKY STORY (USA)	M. Johnston
MAALOOF	J. L. Dunlop
MACLEAN	Sir Michael Stoute
MAGNETIC POLE	Sir Michael Stoute
MAGRITTE (IRE)	A. P. O'Brien, Ireland
MAHARAAT (USA)	Sir Michael Stoute
MAHMOOM	M. R. Channon
MAHOGANY (IRE)	A. P. O'Brien, Ireland
MAIDSTONE MIDAS (IRE)	W. S. Kittow
MAJLIS (JPN)	A. Fabre, France
MAJORCA	J. H. M. Gosden
MAKFOOL (FR)	M. R. Channon

MANAYER (IRE)	
MANDATUM	L. M. Cumani
MANDOBI (IRE)	A. C. Stewart
MANNTAB (USA)	D. R. Loder
MAN OF REPUTE	John M. Oxx, Ireland
MARAAHEL (IRE)	Sir Michael Stoute
MARAAKEB (FR)	J. H. M. Gosden
MARBUSH (IRE)	M. A. Jarvis
MARCH (IRE)	A. P. O'Brien, Ireland
MASAFI (IRE)	Sir Mark Prescott
MASEER (USA)	
MASKED (IRE)	J. W. Hills
MASNOOD	M. P. Tregoning
MASSIF CENTRALE	
MASTER MARVEL (IRE)	M. Johnston
MASTER WILLIAM (CAN)	
MATLOOB	
MA YAHAB	L. M. Cumani
MBOSI (USA)	M. Johnston
MEADAAF (IRE)	A. C. Stewart
MEATH (IRE)	A. P. O'Brien, Ireland
MEDIC (IRE)	Ms Joanna Morgan, Ireland
MEGATON	
MENEEF (USA)	M. P. Tregoning
MENELAUS	D. R. Loder
MESAYAN (IRE)	A. C. Stewart
MESOPOTAMIA (IRE)	A. P. O'Brien, Ireland
MESSE DE MINUIT (IRE)	R. Charlton
MICHABO (IRE)	D. R. C. Elsworth
MIDSHIPMAN EASY (USA)	P. W. Harris
MIKADO	A. P. O'Brien, Ireland
MILLEMIX (FR)	Mme C. Head-Maarek, France
MILLIBIEN	
MISHALL (IRE)	M. P. Tregoning
MISTER MONET (IRE)	M. Johnston
MITH HILL	E. A. L. Dunlop
MONASER (IRE)	D. K. Weld, Ireland
MONCRIEFF (IRE)	Edward Lynam, Ireland
MOREZ	
MOSCOW BALLET (IRE)	A. P. O'Brien, Ireland
MOTIVE (FR)	Sir Michael Stoute
MOTORWAY (IRE)	R. Charlton
MOUFTARI (USA)	B. W. Hills
MR TAMBOURINE MAN (IRE)	P. F. I. Cole
MUHAYMIN (USA)	J. L. Dunlop
MUKAFEH (USA)	J. L. Dunlop
MULLINS BAY (IRE)	A. P. O'Brien, Ireland
MUNAAHEJ (IRE)	
MUNAAWESH (USA)	M. P. Tregoning
MUNTALIQ (USA)	D. K. Weld, Ireland
MUNTAMI (USA)	D. K. Weld, Ireland
MUSAAYER (USA)	
MUSTAJEEB (USA)	
MUTADAREK	E. A. L. Dunlop
MUTAFANEN	J. L. Dunlop
MUTAHAYYA (IRE)	B. W. Hills
MUTAWAFFER	B. W. Hills
MUTAWASSEL (USA)	M. R. Channon
NAADDEY (IRE)	
NAHANE (IRE)	
NAMED AT DINNER	
NAMROC (IRE)	A. C. Stewart
NAPOLEON (IRE)	A. P. O'Brien, Ireland
NATION STATE	
NATIVE TURK (USA)	J. A. R. Toller
NECROPOLIS (USA)	A. P. O'Brien, Ireland
NEWNHAM (IRE)	L. M. Cumani
NEWS SKY (USA)	B. W. Hills
NEWTON (IRE)	A. P. O'Brien, Ireland
NEW YORK CITY (IRE)	L. M. Cumani
NICK THE SILVER	G. B. Balding
NIETZSCHE (IRE)	J. Noseda
NINCSEN (HUN)	
NORDWIND (IRE)	P. W. Harris
NORTH LIGHT (IRE)	Sir Michael Stoute
NOTABLE GUEST (USA)	Sir Michael Stoute
NUNKI (USA)	H. R. A. Cecil
OBAY	E. A. L. Dunlop
OLD DEUTERONOMY (USA)	A. P. O'Brien, Ireland
OMAN GULF (USA)	B. W. Hills
ONCE AROUND (IRE)	T. G. Mills

ONE COOL CAT (USA)	A. P. O'Brien, Ireland
ON EVERY STREET	H. J. Cyzer
ORATION	Sir Michael Stoute
ORCADIAN	
OVATION (IRE)	A. P. O'Brien, Ireland
OVER THE RAINBOW (IRE)	B. W. Hills
PAGAN CEREMONY (USA)	Mrs A. J. Perrett
PAGAN MAGIC (USA)	J. A. R. Toller
PARLIAMENT SQUARE (IRE)	D. R. Loder
PATRIXPRIAL	M. H. Tompkins
PATRIXTOO (FR)	M. H. Tompkins
PEARL ISLAND (USA)	D. R. Loder
PEARL OF LOVE (IRE)	M. Johnston
PEER GYNT (USA)	
PENZANCE	J. R. Fanshawe
PERCUSSIONIST (IRE)	J. H. M. Gosden
PERSIAN DAGGER (IRE)	J. L. Dunlop
PHANTASOS (USA)	W. P Mullins, Ireland
PHILOSOPHY	D. R. Loder
PIANO CONCERTO (UAE)	
PIAZZA NAVONA (USA)	
PIPER HALL (UAE)	John M. Oxx, Ireland
PLECTRUM (USA)	
PLOVERS LANE (IRE)	M. P Tregoning
POST AND RAIL (USA)	E. A. L. Dunlop
POWER STRIKE (USA)	R. Charlton
PRE EMINANCE (IRE)	C. R. Egerton
PREMIER ROUGE	A. C. Stewart
PRIMUS INTER PARES (IRE)	J. R. Fanshawe
PROVENANCE (IRE)	John M. Oxx, Ireland
PUKKA (IRE)	L. M. Cumani
QAADIMM	
QUDRAAT (IRE)	A. C. Stewart
RAAKAAN	A. C. Stewart
RAVEL (IRE)	M. L. W. Bell
RAWDON (IRE)	J. H. M. Gosden
RED DAMSON (IRE)	
REEFSCAPE	
REGAL SETTING (IRE)	C. G. Cox
REHEARSAL	M. P Tregoning
REMAADD (USA)	W. J. Haggas
RESERVOIR (IRE)	T. G. Mills
RESPLENDENT KING (USA)	
RETURN IN STYLE (IRE)	A. C. Stewart
REVENIR (USA)	
RINJANI (USA)	
RIO DE JANEIRO (IRE)	A. P. O'Brien, Ireland
RIVER GYPSY	D. R. C. Elsworth
ROCK OF CASHEL (IRE)	A. P. O'Brien, Ireland
ROEHAMPTON	Sir Michael Stoute
ROMARIC (USA)	
ROYAL LUSTRE	J. H. M. Gosden
RULE OF LAW (USA)	
RUSSIAN TSAR (IRE)	D. K. Weld, Ireland
RUSSIAN VALOUR (IRE)	M. Johnston
SABBAAG (USA)	D. R. Loder
SABBEEH (USA)	
SABRE'S EDGE (IRE)	J. H. M. Gosden
SAILMAKER (IRE)	R. Charlton
SAINT LAZARE (IRE)	J. G. Given
SALFORD CITY (IRE)	D. R. C. Elsworth
SALISBURY PLAIN	D. R. Loder
SAVILLE ROW (USA)	A. Fabre, France
SCHUMANN	J. H. M. Gosden
SCIENTIST	J. H. M. Gosden
SCREENPLAY	Sir Michael Stoute
SCRIPTORIUM	L. M. Cumani
SEATTLE (USA)	A. P. O'Brien, Ireland
SEQUESTRO (USA)	A. Fabre, France
SERENGETI SKY (USA)	D. R. Loder
SERGE	
SETTLEMENT CRAIC (IRE)	T. G. Mills
SHAABAN (IRE)	M. R. Channon
SHARAAB (USA)	B. Hanbury
SHARADI (IRE)	John M. Oxx, Ireland
SHEIKHMAN (IRE)	Sir Michael Stoute
SHIROCCO (GER)	A. Schutz, Germany
SILVER ISLAND	
SILVER SILENCE (JPN)	J. S. Bolger, Ireland
SILVERSTEIN (USA)	J. H. M. Gosden
SILVER SWORD	

SINGING POET (IRE)
SINGLET — H. J. Collingridge
SINTARAJAN (IRE) — John M. Oxx, Ireland
SKIDMARK — D. R. C. Elsworth
SKYHAWK (IRE) — M. J. Grassick, Ireland
SKYSTHELIMIT (IRE)
SLAVONIC (USA) — J. H. M. Gosden
SLEEPING INDIAN — J. H. M. Gosden
SNAP JUDGEMENT (IRE)
SNOW RIDGE (IRE) — Saeed bin Suroor, United Arab Emirates
SOARINGWITHEAGLES (USA)
SOLOR — D. J. Coakley
SONG OF VALA — R. Charlton
SON OF GREEK MYTH (USA)
SOULACROIX — Mrs A. J. Perrett
SPANISH LORD (IRE)
SPIN KING (IRE) — M. L. W. Bell
STAGE RIGHT — D. R. C. Elsworth
STATE DILEMMA (IRE) — B. W. Hills
STATE PERFORMANCE (USA) — J. H. M. Gosden
STRAW HAT — J. Noseda
STREAM OF GOLD (IRE) — Sir Michael Stoute
STREETLIGHT
STRIDENT (USA) — G. A. Butler
STRIKE — J. H. M. Gosden
SUNDAY CITY (JPN) — D. R. Loder
SUN OF SPEED (IRE)
SUSSEX
SUTTER'S FORT (IRE)
SWAHILI DANCER (USA) — L. M. Cumani
SWAINSON (USA) — P. Mitchell
SWIFT SAILING (USA) — B. W. Hills
SWIFT SAILOR — M. Johnston
TAAQAAH — M. P. Tregoning
TAFAAHUM (USA) — M. Johnston
TALWANDI (IRE) — Sir Michael Stoute
TANNENBERG (IRE) — A. Fabre, France
TANNOOR (USA) — M. A. Jarvis
TARKEEZ (USA) — D. K. Weld, Ireland
TEAM PLAYER — L. M. Cumani
TELEMANN (IRE) — A. Fabre, France
TEMPLE PLACE (IRE) — M. L. W. Bell
THE MIGHTY TIGER (USA) — A. P. O'Brien, Ireland
THESPIS (IRE)
THE WAY WE WERE — T. G. Mills
THINK TANK
THREE COUNTIES (IRE) — D. R. Loder
TIGANELLO (GER) — F. Head, France
TIMBREL
TORLEY GRANGE (IRE) — P. W. Harris
TREASURE HOUSE (IRE)
TREBELLO — M. Johnston
TREFFLICH (GER) — John M. Oxx, Ireland

TRIGGERS DOUBLE — K. Bell
TROFAIN
TROUBADOUR (IRE) — A. P. O'Brien, Ireland
TRUE PATRIOT
TRUMAN — J. A. R. Toller
TSARBUCK — R. M. H. Cowell
TUCKERMAN — John M. Oxx, Ireland
TUMBAGA (USA) — R. Charlton
TUMBLEBRUTUS (USA) — A. P. O'Brien, Ireland
TUNGSTEN STRIKE (USA) — Mrs A. J. Perrett
TURN 'N BURN — C. A. Cyzer
TURNER — W. M. Brisbourne
TURNSTILE — R. Hannon
TWOFAN (USA) — M. Johnston
TWO MILES WEST (IRE) — A. P. O'Brien, Ireland
TYCOON — A. P. O'Brien, Ireland
UNITED NATIONS — D. R. Loder
VARAN (IRE) — A. de Royer Dupre, France
VAUGHAN — Mrs A. J. Perrett
VIBE — M. Johnston
VINANDO — C. R. Egerton
VINTAGE FIZZ (IRE) — Patrick Mullins, Ireland
VIVE LA VIE (USA) — R. Gibson, France
WARED (USA) — B. W. Hills
WARIF (USA)
WATER GLANCE (USA)
WEST COUNTRY (UAE)
WEST HILL (IRE) — A. Fabre, France
WHITE HAWK — D. R. Loder
WINSLOW HOMER (FR) — J. H. M. Gosden
WISTMAN (UAE) — D. R. Loder
WITH DISTINCTION (USA) — A. P. O'Brien, Ireland
WOLFE TONE (IRE) — A. P. O'Brien, Ireland
WORCESTER LODGE — R. Charlton
WYVERN (GER) — W. J. Haggas
YAAHOMM — D. R. Loder
YEATS (IRE) — Mrs David Nagle) A. P. O'Brien, Ireland
YOSHKA — M. Johnston
ZAIYAD (IRE) — A. de Royer Dupre, France
ZANGEAL — C. F. Wall
ZARAD (IRE)
ZARGHARI (IRE) — John M. Oxx, Ireland
ZEITGEIST (IRE) — L. M. Cumani
ZOUAVE (IRE)
ZUMA (IRE) — R. Hannon
EX BU HAGAB (IRE) — G. B. Balding
EX DOATING (IRE)
EX KRUGUY DANCER (FR)
EX KSHESSINSKAYA

DISTANCE CONVERSION

5f	1,000m	10f	2,000m	15f	3,000m	20f	4,000m
6f	1,200m	11f	2,200m	16f	3,200m	21f	4,200m
7f	1,400m	12f	2,400m	17f	3,400m	22f	4,400m
8f	1,600m	13f	2,600m	18f	3,600m		
9f	1,800m	14f	2,800m	19f	3,800m		

EUROPEAN FREE HANDICAP
NEWMARKET CRAVEN MEETING 2004
(ON THE ROWLEY MILE COURSE)
WEDNESDAY, APRIL 14TH

The Victor Chandler European Free Handicap (Class A) (Listed race) with £30,000 added for two-years old only of 2003 (including all two-years-old in the 2003 International Classification), to run as three-year-olds; lowest weight 7st 12lb; highest weight 9st 7lb. Penalty for winner after December 31, 2003, 5lb. Seven furlongs.

Rating		st	lb
121	BAGO (FR)	9	7
119	ATTRACTION	9	5
119	GREY SWALLOW (IRE)	9	5
118	LUCKY STORY (USA)	9	4
118	MILK IT MICK	9	4
118	ONE COOL CAT (USA)	9	4
118	THREE VALLEYS	9	4
117	AMERICAN POST	9	3
117	WHIPPER (USA)	9	3
116	MAJESTIC MISSILE (IRE)	9	2
115	BALMONT (USA)	9	1
115	HAAFHD	9	1
115	WATHAB (IRE)	9	1
114	BACHELOR DUKE (USA)	9	0
114	DENEBOLA (USA)	9	0
114	FOKINE (USA)	9	0
114	HOLBORN (UAE)	9	0
114	OLD DEUTERONOMY (USA)	9	0
114	PEARL OF LOVE (IRE)	9	0
114	VOIX DU NORD (FR)	9	0
113	APSIS	8	13
113	AUDITORIUM	8	13
113	CHINEUR (FR)	8	13
113	COLOSSUS (IRE)	8	13
113	DIAMOND GREEN (FR)	8	13
113	FANTASTIC VIEW (USA)	8	13
113	GREEN NOON (FR)	8	13
113	IMPERIAL STRIDE	8	13
113	MUCH FASTER (IRE)	8	13
113	RED BLOOM	8	13
113	RUSSIAN VALOR (IRE)	8	13
113	SNOW RIDGE (IRE)	8	13
113	TROUBADOUR (IRE)	8	13
112	BAYEUX (USA)	8	12
112	CARRY ON KATIE (USA)	8	12
112	HOWICK FALLS (USA)	8	12
112	SPIRIT OF DESERT (IRE)	8	12
112	THE MIGHTY TIGER (USA)	8	12
111	BYRON	8	11
111	GRAND REWARD (USA)	8	11
111	MAGRITTE (IRE)	8	11
111	MAJESTIC DESERT	8	11
111	NEVISIAN LAD	8	11
111	PEAK TO CREEK	8	11
111	SIMPLEX (IRE)	8	11
110	BARBAJUAN (IRE)	8	10
110	CAPE FEAR	8	10
110	CARRIZO CREEK (IRE)	8	10
110	GLAD LION (GER)	8	10
110	MOSCOW BALLET (IRE)	8	10
110	PASTORAL PURSUITS	8	10
110	PUNCTILIOUS	8	10
110	RULE OF LAW (USA)	8	10
110	SABBEEH (USA)	8	10
110	SUNDROP (JPN)	8	10
110	TULIPE ROYALE (FR)	8	10
110	VILLADOLIDE (FR)	8	10
109	NYRAMBA	8	9
108	ANTONIUS PIUS (USA)	8	8
108	AZAROLE (IRE)	8	8
108	CAIRNS (UAE)	8	8
108	CEDARBERG (UAE)	8	8
108	KHELEYF (USA)	8	8
108	PEARL GREY	8	8
108	RIVER BELLE	8	8
108	TAHREEB (FR)	8	8
108	TOP SEED (IRE)	8	8
107	BADMINTON	8	7
107	BOOGIE STREET	8	7
107	CATSTAR (USA)	8	7
107	DEVIL MOON (IRE)	8	7
107	GWAIHIR (USA)	8	7
107	KINGS POINT (IRE)	8	7
107	KINNAIRD (IRE)	8	7
107	LEICESTER SQUARE (IRE)	8	7
107	MENHOUBAH (USA)	8	7
107	MOKABRA (IRE)	8	7
107	NERO'S RETURN (IRE)	8	7
106	CHESTER LE STREET (USA)	8	6
106	CHINA EYES (IRE)	8	6
106	DUKE OF VENICE (USA)	8	6
106	KING HESPERUS (USA)	8	6
106	MAC LOVE	8	6
106	MATLOOB	8	6
106	SPANISH ACE	8	6
106	TASHKIL (IRE)	8	6
106	TUMBLEBRUTUS (USA)	8	6
106	VENABLES (USA)	8	6
105	BAY TREE (IRE)	8	5
105	BRUNEL (IRE)	8	5
105	CALDY DANCER (USA)	8	5
105	CASTLETON	8	5
105	CELTIC CAT (IRE)	8	5
105	CLIFDEN	8	5
105	DIOSYPROS BLUE (IRE)	8	5
105	GRACEFULLY (IRE)	8	5
105	MALAICA (FR)	8	5
105	MOONLIGHT MAN	8	5
105	NEEDLES AND PINS (IRE)	8	5
105	PRIVY SEAL (IRE)	8	5
105	PSYCHIATRIST	8	5
105	RUBY ROCKET (IRE)	8	5

105	**SNOW GOOSE**	8	5
105	**VOILE** (IRE)	8	5
104	**BLUE TOMATO**	8	4
104	**CARTOGRAPHY** (IRE)	8	4
104	**HAPPY CRUSADER** (IRE)	8	4
104	**JOSEPHUS** (IRE)	8	4
104	**KELUCIA** (IRE)	8	4
104	**MUTAHAYYA** (IRE)	8	4
104	**NIGHTS CROSS** (IRE)	8	4
104	**PARKVIEW LOVE** (USA)	8	4
104	**SECRET CHARM** (IRE)	8	4
104	**TAROT CARD**	8	4
103	**COP HILL LAD**	8	3
103	**DUNLOSKIN**	8	3
103	**HATHRAH** (IRE)	8	3
103	**LUCKY PIPIT**	8	3
103	**MANNTAB** (USA)	8	3
103	**NEW MEXICAN**	8	3
103	**NEWTON** (IRE)	8	3
103	**ORCADIAN**	8	3
103	**SILCA'S GIFT**	8	3
103	**TYCOON**	8	3
102	**ALMURAAD** (IRE)	8	2
102	**BIRTHDAY SUIT** (IRE)	8	2
102	**COHN BLUE** (IRE)	8	2
102	**ITHACA** (USA)	8	2
102	**NATALIYA**	8	2
102	**NOTABLE LADY** (IRE)	8	2
102	**QASIRAH** (IRE)	8	2
102	**ROMANCERO** (IRE)	8	2
102	**TOP ROMANCE** (IRE)	8	2
101	**CARTE SAUVAGE** (IRE)	8	1
101	**PHILHARMONIC**	8	1
101	**SPOTLIGHT**	8	1
100	**BOTANICAL** (USA)	8	0
100	**CAPPED FOR VICTORY** (USA)	8	0
100	**CHINSOLA** (IRE)	8	0
100	**FIRST ORDER**	8	0
100	**IF PARADISE**	8	0
100	**MILLBAG** (IRE)	8	0
100	**MOSS VALE** (IRE)	8	0
100	**ORIENTAL WARRIOR**	8	0
100	**PETIT CALVA** (FR)	8	0
100	**ROSEHEARTY** (USA)	8	0
100	**SGT PEPPER** (IRE)	8	0
100	**WHITE HAWK**	8	0

Last Year: Indian Haven 9-1 (J F Egan)
P D'Arcy 9/2 6 ran 1m 27.00s

Owners names are shown against their horses where this information is available.
In the case of Partnerships and Syndicates, the nominated owner is given alongside the horse with other owners listed below the team.

INTERNATIONAL CLASSIFICATION THREE-YEAR-OLDS 2003

For three-year-olds rated 116 or greater by the International Classification Committee handicappers

Rating		Trained
132	**DALAKHANI** (IRE)	IRE
131	**ALAMSHAR** (IRE)	IRE
125	**OASIS DREAM**	GB
122	**DAI JIN**	GER
122	**EMPIRE MAKER** (USA)	USA
122	**FUNNY CIDE** (USA)	USA
122	**KRIS KIN** (USA)	GB
121	**DOYEN** (IRE)	FR
121	**MAGISTRETTI** (USA)	GB
121	**ZAFEEN** (FR)	GB
120	**CAJUN BEAT** (USA)	USA
120	**PEACE RULES** (USA)	USA
120	**ROOSEVELT** (IRE)	IRE
120	**TEN MOST WANTED** (USA)	USA
120	**TRADE FAIR**	GB
119	**DYNEVER** (USA)	USA
119	**KALAMAN** (IRE)	GB
119	**L'ANCRESSE** (IRE)	IRE
119	**THE GREAT GATSBY** (IRE)	IRE
119	**VESPONE** (IRE)	GB
118	**REFUSE TO BEND** (IRE)	IRE
118	**SUPER CELEBRE** (FR)	FR
117	**AIRWAVE**	GB
117	**ATSWHATIMTALKNABOUT** (USA)	USA
117	**BIRD TOWN** (USA)	USA
117	**BRIAN BORU**	IRE
117	**IKHTYAR** (IRE)	GB
117	**INDIAN HAVEN**	GB
117	**NEBRASKA TORNADO** (USA)	FR
117	**NEO UNIVERSE** (JPN)	JPN
117	**NORSE DANCER** (IRE)	GB
117	**POWERSCOURT**	IRE
117	**RANSOM O'WAR** (USA)	GER
117	**RUSSIAN RHYTHM** (USA)	GB
117	**SIX PERFECTIONS** (FR)	FR
117	**SOMNUS**	GB
117	**STRONG HOPE** (USA)	USA
116	**BALESTRINI** (IRE)	IRE
116	**BUDDY GIL** (USA)	USA
116	**COMPOSURE** (USA)	GB
116	**ELLOLUV** (USA)	USA
116	**GHOSTZAPPER** (USA)	USA
116	**HIGH ACCOLADE**	GB
116	**LE VIE DEI COLORI**	ITY
116	**MAIDEN TOWER**	FR
116	**MARTILLO** (GER)	FR
116	**STROLL** (USA)	USA
116	**VINTAGE TIPPLE** (IRE)	IRE
116	**YESTERDAY** (IRE)	IRE

FOUR-YEAR-OLDS AND UP OF 2003

For four-year-olds and up rated 118 or greater by the International Classification Committee handicappers

Rating		Age	Trained
133	**HAWK WING** (USA)	4	IRE
130	**MUBTAKER** (USA)	6	GB
127	**CANDY RIDE** (ARG)	4	USA
127	**FALBRAV** (IRE)	5	GB
127	**HIGH CHAPARRAL** (IRE)	4	IRE
127	**JOHAR** (USA)	4	USA
127	**MINESHAFT** (USA)	4	USA
126	**MOON BALLAD** (IRE)	4	GB
125	**DUBAI DESTINATION** (USA)	4	GB
125	**NAYEF** (USA)	5	GB
125	**SULAMANI** (IRE)	4	GB
124	**PLEASANTLY PERFECT** (USA)	5	USA
124	**SYMBOLI KRIS S** (USA)	4	JPN
123	**ANGE GABRIEL** (FR)	5	FR
123	**AZERI** (USA)	5	USA
123	**TAP DANCE CITY** (USA)	6	JPN
122	**CONGAREE** (USA)	5	USA
122	**GOOD JOURNEY** (USA)	7	USA
122	**MEDAGLIA D'ORO** (USA)	4	USA
122	**STORMING HOME**	5	GB
121	**ALDEBARAN** (USA)	5	USA
121	**BOLLIN ERIC**	4	GB
121	**CHOISIR** (AUS)	4	AUS
121	**SILENT WITNESS** (AUS)	4	HK
121	**RAKTI**	4	GB
121	**ELTIRA** (AUS)	4	HK
120	**DURANDAI** (JPN)	4	JPN
120	**HISHI MIRACLE** (JPN)	4	JPN
120	**ISLINGTON** (IRE)	4	GB
120	**LONHRO** (AUS)	5	AUS
120	**PERFECT DRIFT** (USA)	4	USA
120	**REDATTORE** (BRZ)	8	USA
120	**SIGHTSEEK** (USA)	4	USA
120	**SPECIAL RING** (AUS)	6	USA
119	**DENON** (USA)	5	USA
119	**DOMEDRIVER** (IRE)	5	FR
119	**IPI TOMBE** (ZIM)	5	SFA
119	**LEADERSHIP**	4	GB
119	**LOHENGRIN** (JPN)	4	JPN
119	**MAMOO** (IRE)	4	GB
119	**MR DINOS** (IRE)	4	GB
119	**TSURUMARU BOY** (JPN)	5	JPN
119	**VINNIE ROE** (IRE)	5	IRE
119	**WILD SPIRIT** (CHI)	4	USA
119	**XTRA HEAT** (USA)	5	USA
118	**BLACK SAM BELLAMY**	4	IRE
118	**EISHIN PRESTON** (USA)	6	USA
118	**EKRAAR** (USA)	6	GB
118	**HARLAN'S HOLIDAY** (USA)	4	USA
118	**NEXT DESERT**	4	GER
118	**TATES CREEK** (USA)	5	USA
118	**THE TIN MAN** (USA)	5	USA

GODOLPHIN HORSES IN THE INTERNATIONAL CLASSIFICATIONS

THREE-YEAR-OLDS

MOON BALLAD (IRE)	Singspiel (IRE) - Velvet Moon (IRE)	120
KAZZIA (GER)	Zinaad - Khoruna (GER)	119
IMPERIAL GESTURE (USA)	Langfuhr (CAN) - Honor An Offer (USA)	117
DUBAI DESTINATION (USA)	Kingmambo (USA) - Mysterial (USA)	114
FIREBREAK	Charnwood Forest (IRE) - Breakaway	114
ESSENCE OF DUBAI (USA)	Pulpit (USA) - Epitome (USA)	113
JILBAB (USA)	A P Indy (USA) - Headline	113
MESHAHEER (USA)	Nureyev (USA) - Race The Wild Wind (USA)	113
NAHEEF (IRE)	Marju (IRE) - Golden Digger (USA)	113
IMTIYAZ (USA)	Woodman (USA) - Shadayid (USA)	112
HERO'S JOURNEY	Halling (USA) -Zahwa	110
MAMOOL (IRE)	In The Wings - Genovefa (USA)	110
AL MOULATHAM	Rainbow Quest (USA) - High Standard	105

FOUR-YEAR-OLDS AND UP

MARIENBARD (IRE), 5	Caerleon (USA) - Marienbad (FR)	127
GRANDERA (IRE), 4	Grand Lodge (USA) - Bordighera (USA)	126
STREET CRY (IRE), 4	Machiavellian (USA) - Helen Street	124
BEST OF THE BESTS (IRE), 5	Machiavellian (USA) - Sueboog (IRE)	121
NOVERRE (USA), 4	Rahy (USA) - Danseur Fabuleux (USA)	120
EKRAAR (USA), 5	Red Ransom (USA) - Sacahuista (USA)	118
KUTUB (IRE), 5	In The Wings - Minnie Habit (IRE)	118
E DUBAI (USA), 4	Mr Prospector (USA) - Words Of War (USA)	116
PUGIN (IRE), 4	Darshaan - Gothic Dream (IRE)	116
SAKHEE (USA), 5	Bahri (USA) - Thawakib (IRE)	116
NARRATIVE (IRE), 4	Sadler's Wells (USA) - Barger (USA)	115
WAREED (IRE), 4	Sadler's Wells (USA) - Truly Special (IRE)	114
EQUERRY (USA), 4	St Jovite (USA) - Colour Chart (USA)	113
SLICKLY (FR), 6	Linamix (FR) - Slipstream Queen (USA)	113
THREE POINTS, 5	Bering - Trazl (IRE)	113
EXPRESS TOUR (USA), 4	Tour d'Or (USA) - Express Fashion (USA)	112
BEEKEEPER, 4	Rainbow Quest (USA) - Chief Bee	111
ATLANTIS PRINCE, 4	Tagula (IRE) - Zoom Lens (IRE)	110
HATHA ANNA (IRE), 5	Sadler's Wells (USA) - Moon Cactus	110
MASTERFUL (USA), 4	Danzig (USA) - Moonlight Serenade (FR)	109
SYDENHAM (USA), 4	A P Indy (USA) - Crystal Shard (USA)	109
TOBOUGG (IRE), 4	Barathea (IRE) - Lacovia (USA)	109
DIVINE TASK, 4	Irish River (FR) - Set In Motion (USA)	107
TEMPTING FATE (IRE), 4	Persian Bold (IRE) - West Of Eden (IRE)	105

AIDAN O'BRIEN-TRAINED HORSES IN THE INTERNATIONAL CLASSIFICATIONS

TWO-YEAR-OLDS

ONE COOL CAT (USA)	Storm Cat (USA) - Tacha (USA)	**119**
OLD DEUTERONOMY (USA)	Storm Cat (USA) - Jewel In The Crown (USA)	**114**
COLOSSUS (IRE)	Danehill (USA) - Mira Adonde (USA)	**113**
TROUBADOUR (IRE)	Danehill (USA) - Taking Liberties (IRE)	**113**
THE MIGHTY TIGER (USA)	Storm Cat (USA) - Clear Mandate (USA)	**112**
GRAND REWARD (USA)	Storm Cat (USA) - Serena's Song (USA)	**111**
MAGRITTE (IRE)	Sadler's Wells (USA) - Ionian Sea	**111**
MOSCOW BALLET (IRE)	Sadler's Wells (USA) - Fire The Groom (USA)	**110**
ANTONIUS PIUS (USA)	Danzig (USA) - Catchascatchcan	**108**
DEVIL MOON (IRE)	Danehill (USA) - Moon Drop	**108**
KING HESPERUS (USA)	Kingmambo (USA) - Victoria (USA)	**106**
TUMBLEBRUTUS (USA)	Storm Cat (USA) -Mariah's Storm (USA)	**106**
CELTIC CAT (IRE)	Danehill (USA) - Golden Cat (USA)	**105**
NEWTON (IRE)	Danehill (USA) - Elite Guest (IRE)	**103**
TYCOON	Sadler's Wells (USA) - Fleeting Glimpse	**103**

THREE-YEAR-OLDS

ROOSEVELT (IRE)	Danehill (USA) - Star Begonia	**120**
L'ANCRESSE (IRE)	Darshaan - Solo de Lune (IRE)	**119**
THE GREAT GATSBY (IRE)	Sadler's Wells (USA) - Ionian Sea	**119**
BRIAN BORU	Sadler's Wells (USA) - Eva Luna (USA)	**117**
POWERSCOURT	Sadler's Wells (USA) - Rainbow Lake	**117**
BALESTRINI (IRE)	Danehill (USA) - Welsh Love (IRE)	**116**
YESTERDAY (IRE)	Sadler's Wells (USA) - Jude	**116**
FRANCE	Desert Prince (IRE) - Hyperspectra	**115**
HOLD THAT TIGER (USA)	Storm Cat (USA) - Beware Of The Cat (USA)	**115**
MINGUN (USA)	A P Indy (USA) - Miesque (USA)	**115**
ALBERTO GIACOMETTI (IRE)	Sadler's Wells (USA) - Sweeten Up	**114**
STATUE OF LIBERTY (USA)	Storm Cat (USA) - Charming Lassie (USA)	**114**
CATCHER IN THE RYE (USA)	Danehill (IRE) - Truly A Dream (USA)	**113**

FOUR-YEAR-OLDS AND UP

HAWK WING (USA), 4	Woodman (USA) - La Lorgnette (CAN)	**133**
HIGH CHAPARRAL (IRE), 4	Sadler's Wells (USA) - Kasora (IRE)	**127**
BLACK SAM BELLAMY (IRE), 4	Sadler's Wells (USA) - Urban Sea (USA)	**118**

RACEFORM CHAMPIONS 2003
THREE-YEAR-OLDS AND UP

5f-6f

OASIS DREAM	131	CAPE OF GOOD HOPE	124
SILENT WITNESS	130	AIRWAVE	123
CHOISIR	128	CAJUN BEAT	123
NATIONAL CURRENCY	126	SOMNUS	123
GHOSTZAPPER	125		

7f-9f

HAWK WING	134	FUNNY CIDE	125
ALDEBARAN	128	VALID VIDEO	125
DOMEDRIVER	126	NAYYIR	123
DUBAI DESTINATION	126	RUSSIAN RHYTHM	123
KALAMAN	126	SIX PERFECTIONS	123
LEADERSHIP	126	TELEGNOSIS	123
REFUSE TO BEND	126	TOUCH OF THE BLUES	123
TRADE FAIR	126	ZAFEEN	123
EMPIRE MAKER	125		

10f-12f

DALAKHANI	134	KRIS KIN	125
ALAMSHAR	133	MAGISTRETTI	125
FALBRAV	132	MEDAGLIA D'ORO	125
MUBTAKER	132	BOLLIN ERIC	124
CANDY RIDE	131	DYNEVER	124
MOON BALLAD	131	IKHTYAR	124
NAYEF	129	MAMOOL	124
HIGH CHAPARRAL	128	ANGE GABRIEL	123
JOHAR	128	BLACK SAM BELLAMY	123
MINESHAFT	128	DENON	123
PLEASANTLY PERFECT	128	HIGH ACCOLADE	123
SULAMANI	128	ISLINGTON	123
CONGAREE	127	MOON BALLAD	123
RAKTI	126	VESPONE	123
TEN MOST WANTED	126		

13f+

BRIAN BORU	125	MR DINOS	123
WARRSAN	124		

Owners names are shown against their horses where this information is available. In the case of Partnerships and Syndicates, the nominated owner is given alongside the horse with other owners listed below the team.

RACEFORM CHAMPIONS 2003
TWO-YEAR-OLDS

5f-6f

MAJESTIC MISSILE	118	OLD DEUTERONOMY	113
ATTRACTION	117	COLOSSUS	112
THREE VALLEYS	117	FOKINE	112
WHIPPER	117	GRAND REWARD	112
BALMONT	115	MUCH FASTER	112
HOLBORN	113		

7f+

ONE COOL CAT	121	HAAFHD	114
GREY SWALLOW	119	SPIRIT OF DESERT	114
BAGO	118	VOIX DU NORD	114
MILK IT MICK	118	ACTION THIS DAY	113
AMERICAN POST	117	AUDITORIUM	112
BIRDSTONE	117	BARBAJUAN	112
LUCKY STORY	117	CHAPEL ROYAL	112
CUVEE	116	HALFBRIDLED	112
NIELLO	115	IMPERIAL STRIDE	112
PEARL OF LOVE	115	SNOW RIDGE	112
WATHAB	115	TROUBADOUR	112
BACHELOR DUKE	114		

RACEFORM FASTEST PERFORMERS
THREE-YEAR-OLDS AND UP 2003

5f-6f Turf

MISS EMMA	118
DUBAIAN GIFT	117
NEEDWOOD BLADE	117
OASIS DREAM	117
BEYOND THE CLOUDS	116
PATAVELLIAN	116
SMART PREDATOR	116
THE TATLING	116
ACCLAMATION	115
BAHAMIAN PIRATE	115
BALI ROYAL	115
BORDER SUBJECT	115
CAPRICHO	115
CARIBBEAN CORAL	115
CHOISIR	115
DAZZLING BAY	115
FRUIT OF GLORY	115
HENRY HALL	115
LOYAL TYCOON	115
OLIVIA GRACE	115
PERUVIAN CHIEF	115
PORLEZZA	115
RATIO	115
ROYAL MILLENNIUM	115
SMOKIN BEAU	115
SOMNUS	115
STRIKING AMBITION	115
TWILIGHT BLUES	115

5f-6f AW

DUSTY DAZZLER	115

7f-9f Turf

REFUSE TO BEND	124
LATINO MAGIC	121
HAWK WING	120
MIDDLEMARCH	119
SALSELON	119
ALMOND MOUSE	118
CHARMING GROOM	118
MASSIGANN	118
NEBRASKA TORNADO	118
TERFEL	118
BLUE SPINNAKER	117
ETOILE MONTANTE	117
JUST JAMES	117
LOHENGRIN	117
LUGNY	117
OCEAN VICTORY	117
PENTECOST	117
SIX PERFECTIONS	117
SPECIAL KALDOUN	117
VESPONE	117

7f-9f AW

NIMELLO	115

10f-12f Turf

ALAMSHAR	121
DALAKHANI	121
FAIR MIX	121
MUBTAKER	120
ANA MARIE	119
CARNIVAL DANCER	119
EXECUTE	119
FALBRAV	119
HIGH CHAPARRAL	119
NAYEF	119
CHANCELLOR	118
IKHTYAR	118
INGLIS DREVER	118
ISLINGTON	118
MILLENARY	118
ROOSEVELT	118
SUNSTRACH	118
VALENTINO	118
WITHOUT CONNEXION	118

10f-12f AW

PARASOL	118
ADIEMUS	117
BOURGAINVILLE	116
COMPTON BOLTER	116
GOBLET OF FIRE	116
NORTON	115
PAWN BROKER	115

13f+ Turf

MR DINOS	117
DARASIM	116
KASTHARI	115
KING CAREW	115
MAMOOL	115
POLE STAR	115

13f+ AW

NO QUALIFIERS

RACEFORM FASTEST PERFORMERS TWO-YEAR-OLDS OF 2003

5f-6f Turf

PETERS CHOICE	111
WHIPPER	111
OLD DEUTERONOMY	110

7f+

DENEBOLA	117
BAGO	116
GREEN NOON	116
GREEN SWALLOW	114
MICK IT MICK	114
TULIPE ROYALE	114
VALIXIR	114
ONE COOL CAT	113
THREE VALLEYS	113
BACHELOR DUKE	112
GRANDES ILLUSIONS	112
HAAFHD	112
HAPPY CRUSADER	112
VOIX DU NORD	112
BRIGHT ABUNDANCE	111
GREY SWALLOW	111
IMPERIAL STRIDE	111
NECKLACE	111
PEARL OF LOVE	111
TROUBADOUR	111

WEIGHT CONVERSION TABLE

Great Britain st lbs	France kilos	U.S.A. pounds	Great Britain st lbs	France kilos	U.S.A. pounds
7 7	47.5	105	8 11	56.0	123
7 8	48.0	106	8 12	56.0	124
7 9	48.5	107	8 13	56.5	125
7 10	49.0	108	9 0	57.0	126
7 11	49.5	109	9 1	57.5	127
7 12	50.0	110	9 2	58.0	128
7 13	50.5	111	9 3	58.5	129
8 0	51.0	112	9 4	59.0	130
8 2	51.5	114	9 5	59.5	131
8 3	52.0	115	9 6	60.0	132
8 4	52.5	116	9 7	60.5	133
8 5	53.0	117	9 8	61.0	134
8 6	53.5	118	9 10	61.5	136
8 7	54.0	119	9 11	62.0	137
8 8	54.5	120	9 12	62.5	138
8 9	55.0	121	9 13	63.0	139
8 10	55.5	122	10 0	63.5	140

1 Pound = 0.453592 Kilogrammes 1 Kilogramme = 2.2 lbs 14lbs = 1 Stone

MEDIAN TIMES 2003

The following Raceform median times are used in the calculation of the Split Second speed figures. They represent a true average time for the distance, which has been arrived at after looking at the winning times for all races over each distance within the past five years, except for those restricted to two or three-year-olds.

Some current race distances have been omitted as they have not yet had a sufficient number of races run over them to produce a reliable average time.

ASCOT

5f	1m 01.94	1m Straight ... 1m 41.91	2m 4f ... 4m 24.53
6f	1m 16.11	1m 2f ... 2m 08.80	2m 6f 34yds ... 4m 56.73
7f	1m 29.84	1m 4f ... 2m 33.66	
1m Round	1m 43.06	2m 45yds ... 3m 34.84	

AYR

5f	1m 00.46	1m ... 1m 43.24	1m 5f 13yds ... 2m 55.90
6f	1m 13.75	1m 1f ... 1m 55.20	1m 7f ... 3m 23.71
7f	1m 29.38	1m 2f ... 2m 12.29	2m 1f 105yds ... 3m 54.77
7f 50yds	1m 33.83	1m 2f 192yds ... 2m 23.64	

BATH

5f 11yds	1m 02.50	1m 2f 46yds ... 2m 11.10	1m 5f 22yds ... 2m 51.20
5f 161yds	1m 11.30	1m 3f 144yds ... 2m 30.30	2m 1f 34yds ... 3m 49.50
1m 5yds	1m 41.10		

BEVERLEY

5f	1m 04.00	1m 100yds ... 1m 47.40	1m 4f 16yds ... 2m 40.40
7f 100yds	1m 34.30	1m 1f 207yds ... 2m 07.30	2m 35yds ... 3m 39.40

BRIGHTON

5f 59yds	1m 02.30	6f 209yds ... 1m 22.70	1m 1f 209yds ... 2m 2.60
5f 213yds	1m 10.10	7f 214yds ... 1m 35.00	1m 3f 196yds ... 2m 32.10

CARLISLE

5f	1m 1.60	7f 200yds ... 1m 40.00	1m 6f 32yds ... 3m 7.30
5f 193yds	1m 15.20	1m 1f 61yds ... 1m 58.60	2m 1f 52yds ... 3m 49.90
6f 192yds	1m 27.20	1m 3f 206yds ... 2m 33.60	

CATTERICK

5f	1m 00.70	1m 3f 214yds ... 2m 40.20	1m 5f 175yds ... 3m 04.90
5f 212yds	1m 14.10	1m 4f 44yds ... 2m 39.70	1m 7f 177yds ... 3m 31.60
7f	1m 27.60		

CHEPSTOW

5f 16yds	59.50	1m 14yds ... 1m 35.90	2m 49yds ... 3m 38.30
6f 16yds	1m 12.30	1m 2f 36yds ... 2m 9.40	2m 2f ... 4m 0.20
7f 16yds	1m 23.20	1m 4f 23yds ... 2m 38.30	

CHESTER

5f 16yds	1m 02.0	1m 2f 75yds ... 2m 12.93	1m 7f 195yds ... 3m 33.78
6f 18yds	1m 15.90	1m 3f 79yds ... 2m 25.79	2m 2f 147yds ... 4m 05.57
7f 2yds	1m 28.36	1m 4f 66yds ... 2m 40.52	
7f 122yds	1m 34.92	1m 5f 89yds ... 2m 55.42	

DONCASTER

5f.....................................1m 01.26	7f...................................1m 27.81	1m 4f...............................2m 35.38
5f 140yds.......................1m 08.09	1m Round.......................1m 40.52	1m 6f 132yds..................3m 10.17
6f.....................................1m 14.28	1m Straight....................1m 41.61	2m 110yds......................3m 42.11
6f 110yds.......................1m 20.48	1m 2f 60yds...................2m 11.83	2m 2f..............................3m 57.93

EPSOM

5f..55.68	7f...................................1m 23.95	1m 2f 18yds....................2m 8.74
6f.....................................1m 10.64	1m 114yds......................1m 45.76	1m 4f 10yds....................2m 38.72

FOLKESTONE

5f.....................................1m 00.70	7f...................................1m 27.90	1m 7f 92yds....................3m 27.20
6f.....................................1m 13.60	1m 1f 149yds..................2m 5.00	2m 93yds........................3m 40.60
6f 189yds Round.............1m 25.70	1m 4f..............................2m 40.30	

GOODWOOD

5f..59.05	1m1f...............................1m 56.94	2m...................................3m 30.79
6f.....................................1m 12.91	1m 1f 192yds..................2m 07.75	2m 4f..............................4m 20.89
7f.....................................1m 28.15	1m 4f..............................2m 39.10	
1m....................................1m 40.39	1m 6f..............................3m 03.97	

HAMILTON

5f 4yds...........................1m 01.20	1m 1f 36yds....................1m 59.40	1m 4f 17yds....................2m 39.00
6f 5yds...........................1m 13.00	1m 3f 16yds....................2m 25.90	1m 5f 9yds......................2m 52.80
1m 65yds........................1m 49.20		

HAYDOCK

5f.....................................1m 02.13	1m 30yds........................1m 45.70	1m 6f..............................3m 06.37
6f.....................................1m 14.89	1m 2f 120yds..................2m 17.88	2m 45yds........................3m 38.65
7f 30yds.........................1m 32.21	1m 3f 200yds..................2m 35.18	

KEMPTON

5f.....................................1m 01.36	1m Jubilee......................1m 40.47	1m 3f 30yds....................2m 22.61
6f.....................................1m 13.17	1m...................................1m 40.47	1m 4f..............................3m 35.00
7f Jubilee.......................1m 27.25	1m 1f..............................1m 54.80	1m 6f 92yds....................3m 10.66
7f.....................................1m 26.61	1m 2f Jubilee..................2m 06.2	2m...................................3m 30.57

LEICESTER

5f 2yds...........................1m 01.10	7f 9yds...........................1m 26.10	1m 1f 218yds..................2m 08.70
5f 218yds.......................1m 13.4	1m 9yds..........................1m 42.70	1m 3f 183yds..................2m 35.20

LINGFIELD (TURF)

5f..58.94	7f 140yds........................1m 31.33	1m 3f 106yds..................2m 29.37
6f.....................................1m 11.61	1m 1f..............................1m 55.29	1m 6f..............................3m 06.92
7f.....................................1m 24.20	1m 2f..............................2m 09.46	2m...................................3m 33.19

LINGFIELD (AW)

5f..59.78	1m...................................1m 39.51	1m 5f..............................2m 48.08
6f.....................................1m 12.92	1m 2f..............................2m 07.39	2m...................................3m 28.58
7f.....................................1m 26.00	1m 4f..............................2m 33.98	

MUSSELBURGH

5f.....................................1m 00.50	1m 1f..............................1m 53.30	1m 6f..............................3m 06.10
7f 30yds.........................1m 29.40	1m 4f..............................2m 38.80	2m...................................3m 33.90
1m....................................1m 42.80		

NEWBURY

5f 34yds 1m 02.92	1m 1m 41.08	1m 3f 5yds 2m 22.83
6f 8yds 1m 14.49	1m 7yds Round 1m 38.73	1m 4f 5yds 2m 36.43
7f 1m 27.57	1m 1f 1m 54.59	1m 5f 61yds 2m 51.43
7f 64yds Round 1m 31.26	1m 2f 6yds 2m 08.78	2m 3m 36.15

NEWCASTLE

5f 1m 01.53	1m Round 1m 43.48	1m 2f 32yds 2m 11.80
6f 1m 15.13	1m 3yds 1m 41.90	1m 4f 93yds 2m 43.20
7f 1m 28.04	1m 1f 9yds 1m 57.80	2m 19yds 3m 34.77

NEWMARKET (ROWLEY)

5f 1m 00.41	1m 1f 1m 51.91	1m 6f 3m 00.79
6f 1m 13.08	1m 2f 2m 05.63	2m 3m 26.22
7f 1m 26.45	1m 4f 2m 33.50	2m 2f 3m 52.62
1m 1m 39.45		

NEWMARKET (JULY)

5f 59.72	1m 1m 40.46	1m 6f 175yds 3m 11.10
6f 1m 13.38	1m 2f 2m 06.48	2m 24yds 3m 27.35
7f 1m 26.81	1m 4f 2m 33.23	

NOTTINGHAM

5f 13yds 1m 01.90	1m 54yds 1m 46.50	1m 6f 15yds 3m 07.20
6f 15yds 1m 14.90	1m 1f 213yds 2m 09.70	2m 9yds 3m 33.50

PONTEFRACT

5f 1m 03.80	1m 2f 6yds 2m 14.10	2m 1f 216yds 4m 03.60
6f 1m 17.40	1m 4f 8yds 2m 40.40	2m 5f 122yds 5m 00.80
1m 4yds 1m 45.80	2m 1f 22yds 3m 51.22	

REDCAR

5f 58.70	1m 1f 1m 53.40	1m 6f 19yds 3m 05.00
6f 1m 11.70	1m 2f 2m 06.80	2m 3m 31.50
7f 1m 24.90	1m 3f 2m 21.00	
1m 1m 37.70		

RIPON

5f 1m 00.20	1m 1f 1m 53.80	1m 4f 60yds 2m 39.90
6f 1m 12.90	1m 2f 2m 07.80	2m 3m 32.80
1m 1m 41.10		

SALISBURY

5f 1m 01.59	1m 1m 43.17	1m 4f 2m 36.28
6f 1m 15.06	1m 1f 198yds 2m 08.46	1m 6f 15yds 3m 06.00
6f 212yds 1m 29.06		

SANDOWN

5f 6yds 1m 02.22	1m1f 1m 56.45	1m 6f 3m 04.51
7f 16yds 1m 31.14	1m 2f 7yds 2m 10.30	2m 78yds .... 3m 38.23.
1m 14yds 1m 43.95	1m 3f 91yds 2m 28.07	

SOUTHWELL (TURF)

6f 1m 16.10	1m 2f 2m 15.00	2m 3m 41.50
7f 1m 29.20	1m 4f 2m 40.30	

SOUTHWELL (AW)

5f	1m 00.30	1m	1m 44.60	1m 6f	3m 09.60
6f	1m 16.80	1m 3f	2m 28.90	2m	3m 52.50
7f	1m 30.80	1m 4f	2m 42.10		

THIRSK

5f	59.90	7f	1m 27.10	1m 4f	2m 35.20
6f	1m 12.50	1m	1m 39.70	2m	3m 30.90

WARWICK

5f	1m 00.20	1m 22yds	1m 39.30	1m 4f 134yds	2m 43.60
6f 21yds	1m 12.90	1m 2f 188yds	2m 19.90	2m 39yds	3m 32.20
7f 26yds	1m 25.50				

WINDSOR

5f 10yds	1m 01.20	1m 67yds	1m 45.50	1m 3f 135yds	2m 30.00
6f	1m 13.70	1m 2f 7yds	2m 08.20		

WOLVERHAMPTON (AW)

5f	1m 02.6	1m 100yds	1m 51.00	1m 6f 166yds	3m 20.80
6f	1m 15.70	1m 1f 79yds	2m 02.90	2m 46yds	3m 42.30
7f	1m 30.20	1m 4f	2m 41.50		

YARMOUTH

5f 43yds	1m 02.70	1m 3yds	1m 39.70	1m 6f 17yds	3m 05.20
6f 3yds	1m 13.50	1m 2f 21yds	2m 07.90	2m	3m 31.80
7f 3yds	1m 26.50	1m 3f 101yds	2m 27.30	2m 2f 51yds	4m 06.90

YORK

5f	59.28	7f 202yds	1m 39.51	1m 3f 195yds	2m 31.49
6f	1m 12.57	1m 205yds	1m 52.31	1m 5f 194yds	2m 58.78
6f 214yds	1m 25.40	1m 2f 85yds	2m 11.81	1m 7f 195yds	3m 24.40

If an entry is incorrect or has been omitted, please notify the editor by January 3rd, 2005.

This will ensure it appears correctly in the 2005 edition.

RACEFORM RECORD TIMES (FLAT)

ASCOT

DISTANCE	TIME	AGE	WEIGHT	GOING	HORSE	DATE		
5f	59.7 secs	2	8-8	Good To Firm	LYRIC FANTASY	Jun	17	1992
5f	59.1 secs	3	8-8	Firm	ORIENT	Jun	21	1986
6f	1m 13.6	2	8-12	Good To Firm	THREE VALLEYS	Jun	17	2003
6f	1m 12.1	4	9-6	Firm	FAYR JAG	Jun	21	2003
6f	1m 12.1	5	9-3	Firm	RATIO	Jun	21	2003
7f	1m 27.2	2	8-11	Good To Firm	CELTIC SWING	Oct	8	1994
7f	1m 25.8	4	8-2	Good To Firm	MASTER ROBBIE	Sep	27	2003
1m (Rnd)	1m 40.8	2	8-10	Good To Firm	RED BLOOM	Sep	27	2003
1m (Str)	1m 38.0	4	7-8	Good To Firm	COLOUR SERGEANT	Jun	17	1992
1m (Rnd)	1m 38.5	3	9-0	Good To Firm	RUSSIAN RHYTHM	Jun	20	2003
1m 2f	2m 02.7	4	9-3	Good To Firm	FIRST ISLAND (IRE)	Jun	18	1996
1m 4f	2m 26.9	5	8-9	Firm	STANERRA	Jun	17	1983
2m 45y	3m 25.2	3	8-11	Good To Firm	LANDOWNER	Jun	17	1992
2m 4f	4m 15.3	5	9-0	Good To Firm	ROYAL GAIT (DISQ)	Jun	16	1988
2m 6f 34y	4m 47.8	5	8-9	Firm	COVER UP	Jun	23	2003

AYR

DISTANCE	TIME	AGE	WEIGHT	GOING	HORSE	DATE		
5f	56.9 secs	2	8-11	Good	BOOGIE STREET	Sep	18	2003
5f	57.2 secs	4	9-5	Good To Firm	SIR JOEY	Sep	16	1993
6f	1m 09.7	2	7-10	Good To Firm	BERT	Sep	17	1969
6f	1m 08.9	7	8-8	Good To Firm	SOBERING THOUGHTS	Sep	18	1993
7f 50y	1m 28.9	2	9-0	Good	TAFAAHUM (USA)	Sep	19	2003
7f 50y	1m 28.2	4	9-2	Good To Firm	FLU NA H ALBA	Jun	21	2003
1m	1m 39.2	2	9-0	Good To Firm	KRIBENSIS	Sep	17	1986
1m	1m 36.0	4	7-13	Firm	SUFI	Sep	16	1959
1m 1f 20y	1m 50.3	4	9-3	Good	RETIREMENT	Sep	19	2003
1m 2f	2m 04.0	4	9-9	Good To Firm	ENDLESS HALL	Jly	17	2000
1m 2f 192y	2m 13.3	4	9-0	Good To Firm	AZZAAM	Sep	18	1991
1m 5f 13y	2m 45.8	4	9-7	Good To Firm	EDEN'S CLOSE	Sep	18	1993
1m 7f	3m 13.1	3	9-4	Good	ROMANY RYE	Sep	19	1991
2m 1f 105y	3m 45.0	4	6-13	Good	CURRY	Sep	16	1955

BATH

DISTANCE	TIME	AGE	WEIGHT	GOING	HORSE	DATE		
5f 11y	1m 00.1	2	8-11	Firm	DOUBLE FANTASY	Aug	25	2000
5f 11y	59.9 secs	6	9-2	Firm	CAUDA EQUINA	Aug	25	2000
5f 161y	1m 09.1	2	8-7	Firm	SIBLA	Aug	25	2000
5f 161y	1m 08.1	6	9-0	Firm	MADRACO	May	22	1989
1m 5y	1m 40.3	2	8-12	Good To Firm	KHASSAH	Sep	9	1999
1m 5y	1m 37.2	5	8-12	Good To Firm	ADOBE	Jun	17	2000
1m 2f 46y	2m 05.6	3	9-0	Good To Firm	CONNOISSEUR BAY (USA)	May	29	1998
1m 3f 144y	2m 26.1	3	8-12	Firm	ANTICIPATE	Sep	10	2001
1m 5f 22y	2m 47.2	4	10-0	Firm	FLOWN	Aug	13	1991
2m 1f 34y	3m 43.4	6	7-9	Firm	YAHESKA (IRE)	Jun	14	2003

BEVERLEY

DISTANCE	TIME	AGE	WEIGHT	GOING	HORSE	DATE		
5f	1m 01.0	2	8-2	Good To Firm	ADDO (IRE)	Jly	17	2001
5f	1m 00.1	4	9-5	Firm	PIC UP STICKS	Apr	16	2003
7f 100y	1m 31.1	2	9-0	Firm	MAJAL (IRE)	Jly	30	1991
7f 100y	1m 29.5	3	7-8	Firm	WHO'S TEF	Jly	30	1991
1m 100y	1m 43.3	2	9-0	Firm	ARDEN	Sep	24	1986
1m 100y	1m 42.2	3	8-4	Firm	LEGAL CASE	Jun	14	1989
1m 1f 207y	2m 01.3	3	9-7	Firm	ROSE ALTO	Jly	5	1991
1m 3f 216y	2m 30.8	3	8-1	Hard	COINAGE	Jun	18	1986
2m 35y	3m 29.5	4	9-2	Good To Firm	RUSHEN RAIDER	Aug	14	1996

BRIGHTON

DISTANCE	TIME	AGE	WEIGHT	GOING	HORSE	DATE		
5f 59y	1m.00.1	2	9-0	Firm	BID FOR BLUE	May	6	1993
5f 59y	59.3 secs	3	8-9	Firm	PLAY HEVER GOLF	May	26	1993
5f 213y	1m 08.1	2	8-9	Firm	SONG MIST (IRE)	Jly	16	1996
5f 213y	1m 07.3	3	8-9	Firm	THIRD PARTY	Jun	3	1997
5f 213y	1m 07.3	5	9-1	Good To Firm	BLUNDELL LANE	May	4	2000
6f 209y	1m 19.9	2	8-11	Hard	RAIN BURST	Sep	15	1988
6f 209y	1m 19.4	4	9-3	Good To Firm	SAWAKI	Sep	3	1991
7f 214y	1m 32.8	2	9-7	Firm	ASIAN PETE	Oct	3	1989
7f 214y	1m 30.5	5	8-11	Firm	MYSTIC RIDGE	May	27	1999
1m 1f 209y	2m 04.7	2	9-0	Good To Soft	ESTEEMED MASTER	Nov	2	2001
1m 1f 209y	1m 57.2	3	9-0	Firm	GET THE MESSAGE	Apr	30	1984
1m 3f 196y	2m 25.8	4	8-2	Firm	NEW ZEALAND	Jly	4	1985

CARLISLE

DISTANCE	TIME	AGE	WEIGHT	GOING	HORSE	DATE		
5f	1m 00.1	2	8-5	Firm	LA TORTUGA	Aug	2	1999
5f	59.3 secs	5	8-12	Firm	FRIAR TUCK	Jly	21	2000
5f 207y	1m 12.8	2	8-9	Hard	PARFAIT ARMOUR	Sep	10	1991
5f 193y	1m 11.7	5	8-6	Good To Firm	CHAIRMAN BOBBY	Jun	15	2003
6f 206y	1m 26.5	2	9-4	Hard	SENSE OF PRIORITY	Sep	10	1991
6f 206y	1m 25.3	4	9-1	Firm	MOVE WITH EDES	Jly	6	1996
7f 214y	1m 44.6	2	8-8	Firm	BLUE GARTER	Sep	9	1980
7f 214y	1m 37.4	4	9-8	Good To Firm	GIFTED FLAME	Jun	15	2003
1m 1f 61y	1m 55.0	4	8-13	Firm	SHIPLEY GLEN	May	7	1999
1m 3f 206y	2m 29.4	8	8-13	Firm	SILVERTOWN	Jun	26	2003
1m 6f 32y	3m 02.2	6	8-10	Firm	EXPLOSIVE SPEED	May	26	1994

CATTERICK

DISTANCE	TIME	AGE	WEIGHT	GOING	HORSE	DATE		
5f	57.7 secs	2	9-0	Good To Firm	VERDE ALITALIA	Sep	21	1991
5f	57.1 secs	4	8-7	Fast	KABCAST	Jly	7	1989
5f 212y	1m 11.4	2	9-4	Firm	CAPTAIN NICK	Jly	11	1978
5f 212y	1m 09.8	9	8-13	Good To Firm	SHARP HAT	May	30	2003
5f 212y	1m 10.4	3	8-8	Firm	TRIAD TREBLE	May	31	1984
7f	1m 24.1	2	8-11	Firm	LINDAS FANTASY	Sep	18	1982
7f	1m 22.5	6	8-7	Firm	DIFFERENTIAL (USA)	May	31	2003
1m 3f 214y	2m 30.5	3	8-8	Good To Firm	RAHAF	May	30	2003
1m 5f 175y	2m 54.8	3	8-5	Firm	GERYON	May	31	1984
1m 7f 177y	3m 20.8	4	7-11	Firm	BEAN BOY	Jly	8	1982

CHEPSTOW

DISTANCE	TIME	AGE	WEIGHT	GOING	HORSE	DATE		
5f 16y	57.6 secs	2	8-11	Firm	MICRO LOVE	Jly	8	1986
5f 16y	56.8 secs	3	8-4	Firm	TORBAY EXPRESS	Sep	15	1979
6f 16y	1m 09.4	2	9-0	Fast	ROYAL FIFI	Sep	9	1989
6f 16y	1m 08.8	4	8-6	Fast	AFRICAN REX	May	12	1987
7f 16y	1m 20.8	2	9-0	Good To Firm	ROYAL AMARETTO (IRE)	Sep	12	1996
7f 16y	1m 19.3	3	9-0	Firm	TARANAKI	Sep	18	2001
1m 14y	1m 33.1	2	8-11	Good To Firm	SKI ACADEMY (IRE)	Aug	28	1995
1m 14y	1m 31.6	3	8-13	Firm	STOLI (IRE)	Sep	18	2001
1m 2f 36y	2m 04.1	5	8-9	Hard	LEONIDAS	Jly	5	1983
1m 2f 36y	2m 04.1	5	7-8	Good To Firm	IT'S VARADAN	Sep	9	1989
1m 2f 36y	2m 04.1	3	8-5	Good To Firm	ELA ATHENA	Jly	23	1999
1m 4f 23y	2m 31.0	3	8-9	Good To Firm	SPRITSAIL	Jly	13	1989
1m 4f 23y	2m 31.0	7	9-6	Hard	MAINTOP	Aug	27	1984
2m 49y	3m 27.7	4	9-0	Good To Firm	WIZZARD ARTIST	Jly	1	1989
2m 2f	3m 56.4	5	8-7	Good To Firm	LAFFAH	Jly	8	2000

CHESTER

DISTANCE	TIME	AGE	WEIGHT	GOING	HORSE	DATE		
5f 16y	1m 00.2	2	9-0	Good To Firm	MAJESTIC MISSILE (IRE)	Jly	11	2003
5f 16y	59.2 secs	3	10-0	Firm	ALTHREY DON	Jly	10	1964
6f 18y	1m 13.2	2	8-11	Good To Firm	ACE OF PARKES	Jly	11	1998
6f 18y	1m 12.7	3	8-3	Good To Firm	PLAY HEVER GOLF	May	4	1993
6f 18y	1m 12.7	6	9-2	Good	STACK ROCK	Jun	23	1993
7f 2y	1m 26.2	2	8-4	Good To Firm	BY HAND	Aug	31	1991
7f 2y	1m 24.5	3	8-11	Good To Firm	MONNAVANNA	May	9	2001
7f 122y	1m 35.0	2	9-0	Firm	DOUBLE VALUE	Sep	1	1972
7f 122y	1m 31.5	3	8-12	Good To Firm	STEAL 'EM	Jly	12	1996
1m 2f 75y	2m 7.9	3	8-10	Good To Firm	BENEFICIAL	May	6	1993
1m 3f 79y	2m 22.5	3	8-9	Good To Firm	ROCKERLONG	May	9	2001
1m 4f 66y	2m 34.2	3	8-11	Good To Firm	OLD VIC	May	9	1989
1m 5f 89y	2m 45.4	5	8-11	Firm	RAKAPOSHI KING	May	7	1987
1m 7f 195y	3m 24.5	7	7-11	Good To Firm	MOONLIGHT QUEST	Jly	30	1995
2m 2f 147y	4m 00.6	4	9-0	Good To Firm	RAINBOW HIGH	May	5	1999

DONCASTER

DISTANCE	TIME	AGE	WEIGHT	GOING	HORSE	DATE		
5f	58.4 secs	2	9-5	Firm	SING SING	Sep	11	1959
5f	57.5 secs	6	8-10	Good To Firm	ABSENT FRIENDS	Jun	29	2003
5f 140y	1m 07.2	2	9-0	Good To Firm	CARTOGRAPHY (IRE)	Jun	29	2003
5f 140y	1m 06.2	3	9-2	Good	WELSH ABBOT	Sep	12	1958
6f	1m 09.7	2	8-11	Firm	PADDY'S SISTER	Sep	9	1959
6f	1m 09.7	3	8-9	Good To Firm	ILTIMAS (USA)	Jly	26	1995
6f 110y	1m 18.2	2	8-13	Good To Firm	MY BRANCH	Sep	6	1995
7f	1m 23.2	2	8-10	Good To Firm	BAHHARE (USA)	Sep	13	1996
7f	1m 22.6	3	9-4	Hard	PINOLLI	Jun	3	1963
1m	1m 37.5	2	9-5	Good To Firm	LEND A HAND	Sep	11	1997
1m	1m 37.4	2	9-0	Good To Firm	MIDNIGHT LINE (USA)	Sep	11	1997
1m	1m 36.6	9	9-9	Good	INVADER	Jun	29	2003
1m	1m 36.7	3	8-10	Good To Firm	MUSHAHID (USA)	Jly	17	1996
1m 2f 60y	2m 13.4	2	8-8	Good	YARD BIRD	Nov	6	1981
1m 2f 60y	2m 05.4	3	8-8	Good To Firm	CARLITO BRIGANTE	Jly	26	1995
1m 4f	2m 27.7	3	8-12	Good To Firm	TAKWIN (IRE)	Sep	9	2000
1m 6f 132y	3m 02.2	3	8-3	Good To Firm	BRIER CREEK	Sep	10	1992
2m 110y	3m 34.4	4	9-12	Good To Firm	FARSI	Jun	12	1992
2m 2f	3m 52.1	4	9-0	Good To Firm	CANON CAN (USA)	Sep	11	1997

EPSOM

DISTANCE	TIME	AGE	WEIGHT	GOING	HORSE	DATE		
5f	55.0 secs	2	8-9	Good To Firm	PRINCE ASLIA	Jun	9	1995
5f	53.6 secs	4	9-5	Firm	INDIGENOUS	Jun	2	1960
6f	1m 07.8	2	8-11	Good To Firm	SHOWBROOK	Jun	5	1991
6f	1m 07.3	5	8-12	Good	LOYAL TYCOON	Jun	7	2003
7f	1m 22.1	2	8-9	Good To Firm	SHAMROCK FAIR (IRE)	Aug	30	1994
7f	1m 20.1	4	8-7	Firm	CAPISTRANO	Jun	7	1972
1m 114y	1m 42.8	2	8-5	Good To Firm	NIGHTSTALKER	Aug	30	1988
1m 114y	1m 40.7	3	8-6	Good To Firm	SYLVA HONDA	Jun	5	1991
1m 2f 18y	2m 03.5	5	7-13	Good	CROSSBOW	Jun	7	1967
1m 4f 10y	2m 32.3	3	9-0	Good To Firm	LAMMTARRA	Jun	10	1995

FOLKESTONE

DISTANCE	TIME	AGE	WEIGHT	GOING	HORSE	DATE		
5f	58.4 secs	2	9-2	Good To Firm	PIVOTAL	Nov	6	1995
5f	58.65 secs	3	9-0	Good To Firm	ZARZU	Jun	28	2002
6f	1m 10.8	2	8-9	Good	BOOMERANG BLADE	Jly	16	1998
6f	1m 09.5	4	8-12	Good To Firm	DOUBLE OSCAR (IRE)	Jly	14	1997
6f 189y	1m 23.7	2	8-11	Good	HEN HARRIER	Jly	3	1996
6f 189y	1m 20.2	4	10-0	Firm	NEUWEST	Jun	28	1996
7f	1m 21.4	3	8-9	Firm	CIELAMOUR (USA)	Aug	9	1988
1m 1f 149y	1m 59.7	3	8-6	Good To Firm	DIZZY	Jly	23	1991
1m 4f	2m 38.5	4	8-8	Hard	SNOW BLIZZARD	Jun	30	1992
1m 7f 92y	3m 23.1	3	9-11	Firm	MATA ASKARI	Sep	12	1991
2m 93y	3m 34.9	3	8-12	Good To Firm	CANDLE SMOKE (USA)	Aug	20	1996

GOODWOOD

DISTANCE	TIME	AGE	WEIGHT	GOING	HORSE	DATE		
5f	57.5 secs	2	8-12	Good To Firm	POETS COVE	Aug	3	1990
5f	56.0 secs	5	9-0	Good To Firm	RUDI'S PET	Jly	27	1999
6f	1m 09.8	2	8-11	Good To Firm	BACHIR (IRE)	Jly	28	1999
6f	1m 09.5	4	8-3	Firm	FOR THE PRESENT	Jly	30	1994
7f	1m 24.9	2	8-11	Good To Firm	EKRAAR	Jly	29	1999
7f	1m 23.8	3	8-7	Firm	BRIEF GLIMPSE (IRE)	Jly	25	1995
1m	1m 38.5	2	8-11	Good To Firm	SELKIRK (USA)	Sep	14	1990
1m	1m 35.6	3	8-13	Good To Firm	ALJABR (USA)	Jly	28	1999
1m 1f	1m 52.8	3	9-6	Good	VENA (IRE)	Jly	27	1995
1m 1f 192y	2m 04.5	3	8-9	Firm	AZOUZ PASHA (USA)	Jly	30	1999
1m 2f	2m 04.9	3	8-6	Firm	KARTAJANA	Aug	4	1990
1m 3f	2m 23.0	3	8-8	Firm	ASIAN HEIGHTS	May	22	2001
1m 4f	2m 31.5	3	8-10	Firm	PRESENTING	Jly	25	1995
1m 6f	2m 58.5	4	9-2	Good To Firm	MOWBRAY	Jly	27	1999
2m	3m 21.63	5	9-2	Good To Firm	JARDINES LOOKOUT (IRE)	Aug	1	2002
2m 4f	4m 11.7	3	7-10	Firm	LUCKY MOON	Sep	2	1990

HAMILTON

DISTANCE	TIME	AGE	WEIGHT	GOING	HORSE	DATE		
5f 4y	58.0 secs	3	7-8	Firm	FAIR DANDY	Sep	25	1972
5f 4y	58.0 secs	5	8-6	Firm	GOLDEN SLEIGH	Sep	6	1972
6f 5y	1m 10.0	2	8-12	Good To Firm	BREAK THE CODE	Aug	24	1999
6f 5y	1m 09.3	4	8-7	Firm	MARCUS GAME	Jly	11	1974
1m 65y	1m 45.8	2	8-11	Firm	HOPEFUL SUBJECT	Sep	24	1973
1m 65y	1m 42.7	6	7-7	Firm	CRANLEY	Sep	25	1972
1m 1f 36y	1m 54.1	5	9-4	Good To Firm	JEDI KNIGHT	Aug	24	1999
1m 3f 16y	2m 20.7	8	9-9	Firm	DESERT FIGHTER	Jly	9	1999
1m 3f 16y	2m 20.7	5	9-8	Good To Firm	WADI	Jly	20	2000
1m 4f 17y	2m 32.0	4	7-4	Firm	FINE POINT	Aug	24	1981
1m 5f 9y	2m 45.1	6	9-6	Firm	MENTALASANYTHIN	Jun	14	1995

HAYDOCK

DISTANCE	TIME	AGE	WEIGHT	GOING	HORSE	DATE		
5f	59.2 secs	2	9-4	Firm	**MONEY FOR NOTHING**	Aug	21	1964
5f	58.5 secs	6	8-9	Good To Firm	**WHISTLER**	Aug	9	2003
6f	1m 09.9	4	9-0	Good To Firm	**IKTAMAL** (USA)	Sep	7	1996
7f 30y	1m 29.4	2	9-0	Good To Firm	**APPREHENSION**	Sep	7	1996
7f 30y	1m 27.2	3	9-4	Firm	**INDIAN KING**	Jun	5	1982
1m 30y	1m 40.6	2	8-12	Good To Firm	**BESIEGE**	Sep	7	1996
1m 30y	1m 40.1	3	9-2	Firm	**UNTOLD RICHES** (USA)	Jly	11	1999
1m 2f 120y	2m 08.5	3	8-7	Good To Firm	**FAHAL** (USA)	Aug	5	1995
1m 3f 200y	2m 26.4	3	8-2	Firm	**NEW MEMBER**	Jly	4	1970
1m 6f	2m 59.5	3	8-3	Good To Firm	**CASTLE SECRET**	Sep	30	1989
2m 45y	3m 27.0	4	8-13	Firm	**PRINCE OF PEACE**	May	26	1984
2m 1f 130y	3m 55.0	3	8-12	Good	**CRYSTAL SPIRIT**	Sep	8	1990

KEMPTON

DISTANCE	TIME	AGE	WEIGHT	GOING	HORSE	DATE		
5f	58.3 secs	2	9-0	Firm	**SCHWEPPESHIRE LAD**	Jun	3	1978
5f	57.4 secs	4	9-3	Good To Firm	**ALMATY** (IRE)	May	31	1997
6f	1m 10.6	2	8-10	Good To Firm	**DON PUCCINI**	May	29	1999
6f	1m 09.5	3	8-11	Good To Firm	**INDIAN TRAIL**	Jun	25	2003
7f	1m 26.7	2	8-8	Good	**EXCLUSIVE**	Sep	10	1997
7f	1m 24.7	2	9-0	Good To Firm	**CANONS PARK**	Jun	28	1995
7f	1m 23.5	3	9-2	Good	**WILD RICE**	Aug	2	1995
7f	1m 23.6	3	9-0	Good To Firm	**SHAHEEN** (USA)	May	31	1997
1m	1m 43.4	2	7-0	Good	**FASCINATING**	Nov	3	1956
1m	1m 38.7	2	9-0	Good To Firm	**TAVERNER SOCIETY** (IRE)	Sep	22	1997
1m	1m 35.8	4	9-1	Firm	**COUNTY BROKER**	May	23	1984
1m	1m 35.3	3	8-12	Good To Firm	**PRIVATE LINE**	Jun	28	1995
1m 1f	1m 50.0	4	9-11	Good To Firm	**BAHRQUEEN** (USA)	Jun	25	2003
1m 2f	1m 59.5	4	9-6	Firm	**BATSHOOF**	Apr	6	1990
1m 3f 30y	2m 16.2	4	9-2	Firm	**SHERNAZAR**	Sep	6	1985
1m 4f	2m 30.1	6	8-5	Firm	**GOING GOING**	Sep	7	1985
1m 6f 92y	3m 06.5	4	9-8	Good To Firm	**RENZO** (IRE)	Sep	21	1997
2m	3m 24.3	4	8-9	Good To Firm	**EMINENCE GRISE** (IRE)	May	29	1999

LEICESTER

DISTANCE	TIME	AGE	WEIGHT	GOING	HORSE	DATE		
5f 2y	58.4 secs	2	9-0	Firm	**CUTTING BLADE**	Jun	9	1986
5f 2y	58.0 secs	3	7-13	Good To Firm	**EMERALD PEACE** (IRE)	Sep	5	2000
5f 218y	1m 10.1	2	9-0	Firm	**THORDIS** (IRE)	Oct	24	1995
5f 218y	1m 09.4	3	8-12	Good To Firm	**LAKELAND BEAUTY**	May	29	1990
7f 9y	1m 22.8	2	8-6	Good	**MISS DRAGONFLY** (IRE)	Sep	22	1997
7f 9y	1m 20.8	3	8-7	Firm	**FLOWER BOWL**	Jun	9	1986
1m 8y	1m 34.5	2	8-9	Firm	**LADY CARLA**	Oct	24	1995
1m 8y	1m 33.6	5	7-13	Good To Firm	**DERRYQUINN**	Aug	13	2000
1m 9y	1m 39.2	4	8-11	Firm	**NASHAAB** (USA)	May	28	2001
1m 1f 218y	2m 05.3	2	9-1	Good To Firm	**WINDSOR CASTLE**	Oct	14	1996
1m 1f 218y	2m 02.4	3	8-11	Firm	**EFFIGY**	Nov	4	1985
1m 1f 218y	2m 02.4	4	9-6	Good To Firm	**LADY ANGHARAD** (IRE)	Jun	18	2000
1m 3f 183y	2m 27.1	5	8-12	Good To Firm	**MURGHEM** (IRE)	Jun	18	2000

LINGFIELD (TURF)

DISTANCE	TIME	AGE	WEIGHT	GOING	HORSE	DATE		
5f	57.1 secs	2	8-9	Good	EMERALD PEACE	Aug	6	1999
5f	56.2 secs	3	9-1	Good To Firm	EVENINGPERFORMANCE	Jly	25	1994
6f	1m 08.6	2	9-3	Firm	THE RITZ	Jun	11	1965
6f	1m 08.2	6	9-10	Firm	AL AMEAD	Jly	2	1986
7f	1m 21.3	2	7-6	Firm	MANDAV	Oct	3	1980
7f	1m 20.1	3	8-7	Good To Firm	ZELAH (IRE)	May	13	1998
7f 140y	1m 29.9	2	8-12	Firm	RATHER WARM	Nov	7	1978
7f 140y	1m 26.7	3	8-6	Fast	HIAAM	Nov	7	1978
1m 1f	1m 52.4	4	9-2	Good To Firm	QUANDARY (USA)	Jly	15	1995
1m 2f	2m 04.6	3	9-3	Firm	USRAN	Jly	15	1989
1m 3f 106y	2m 23.9	3	8-5	Firm	NIGHT-SHIRT	Jly	14	1990
1m 6f	2m 59.1	5	9-5	Firm	IBN BEY	Jly	1	1989
2m	3m 23.7	3	9-5	Good To Firm	LAURIES CRUSADOR	Aug	13	1988

LINGFIELD (A.W)

DISTANCE	TIME	AGE	WEIGHT	GOING	HORSE	DATE		
5f	58.6 secs	2	9-7	Standard	CLASSY CLEO (IRE)	Nov	28	1997
5f	58.0 secs	3	8-2	Standard	DUSTY DAZZLER	Feb	8	2003
6f	1m 11.5	2	8-8	Standard	TWO STEP KID (USA)	Oct	27	2003
6f	1m 10.5	4	9-4	Standard	J CHEEVER LOOPHOLE	Nov	23	1989
7f	1m 24.0	2	8-12	Standard	SCOTTISH CASTLE	Nov	2	1990
7f	1m 22.9	3	9-3	Standard	CONFRONTER	Jly	18	1992
1m	1m 36.5	2	9-5	Standard	SAN PIER NICETO	Nov	30	1989
1m	1m 36.3	5	9-5	Standard	VANROY	Nov	30	1989
1m 2f	2m 02.6	3	8-10	Standard	COMPTON BOLTER	Nov	18	2000
1m 4f	2m 29.2	6	8-13	Standard	URSA MAJOR	Dec	28	2000
1m 5f	2m 42.9	3	9-7	Standard	GLOBAL DANCER	Dec	7	1994
2m	3m 20.0	3	9-0	Standard	YENOORA	Aug	8	1992

MUSSELBURGH

DISTANCE	TIME	AGE	WEIGHT	GOING	HORSE	DATE		
5f	57.7 secs	2	8-2	Firm	ARASONG	May	16	1994
5f	57.3 secs	3	8-12	Firm	CORUNNA	Jun	3	2000
7f 30y	1m 28.4	2	8-8	Firm	SAND BANKES	Jun	26	2000
7f 30y	1m 27.1	5	8-12	Good	DIAMOND DECORUM	Jun	18	2001
1m	1m 40.6	2	9-0	Good To Firm	RUTTERS REBEL (IRE)	Sep	13	2003
1m	1m 39.2	6	9-10	Firm	PRINCE MINATA	Jun	3	2000
1m	1m 39.2	4	8-4	Firm	SWYNFORD ELEGANCE	Sep	4	2001
1m 1f	1m 51.7	4	9-7	Firm	KID'Z'PLAY	Jun	3	2000
1m 4f	2m 33.7	3	9-11	Firm	ALEXANDRINE	Jun	26	2000
1m 5f	3m 00.6	9	7-5	Soft	CRAIGARY	Oct	26	2000
1m 6f	2m 59.2	3	9-7	Firm	FORUM CHRIS	Jly	3	2000
2m	3m 28.1	3	8-1	Good To Firm	WARRING KINGDOM	Sep	13	1999

NEWBURY

DISTANCE	TIME	AGE	WEIGHT	GOING	HORSE	DATE		
5f 34y	59.1 secs	2	8-6	Good To Firm	SUPERSTAR LEO	Jly	22	2000
5f 34y	59.2 secs	3	9-5	Good To Firm	THE TRADER (IRE)	Aug	18	2001
6f 8y	1m 11.4	2	8-6	Good To Firm	ASCENSION	Jly	22	2000
6f 8y	1m 09.8	3	8-12	Good To Firm	AUENKLANG (GER)	Jly	22	2000
7f	1m 24.1	2	8-11	Good To Firm	HAAFHD	Aug	15	2003
7f	1m 21.5	3	8-4	Good To Firm	THREE POINTS	Jly	21	2000
7f 64y	1m 28.8	2	8-10	Good To Firm	DUTY TIME	Aug	14	1993
7f 64y	1m 26.1	4	9-12	Good To Firm	GREEN PERFUME (USA)	Jly	19	1996
1m	1m 37.7	2	8-10	Good	ETHMAAR (USA)	Sep	17	1999
1m	1m 35.1	3	8-11	Good To Firm	DANCING TRIBUTE (USA)	Sep	23	1989
1m 7y	1m 37.2	2	8-11	Firm	MASTER WILLIE	Oct	1	1979
1m 7y	1m 34.9	3	8-9	Good To Firm	PHILIDOR	May	16	1992
1m 1f	1m 49.6	3	8-0	Good To Firm	HOLTYE	May	21	1995
1m 2f 6y	2m 1.2	3	8-7	Good To Firm	WALL STREET (USA)	Jly	20	1996
1m 3f 5y	2m 16.5	3	8-9	Good To Firm	GRANDERA (IRE)	Sep	22	2001
1m 4f 5y	2m 29.2	4	8-9	Hard	VIDI VIC	Jun	21	1951
1m 5f 61y	2m 44.9	5	10-0	Good To Firm	MYSTIC HILL	Jly	20	1996
2m	3m 25.4	8	9-12	Good To Firm	MOONLIGHT QUEST	Jly	19	1996

NEWCASTLE

DISTANCE	TIME	AGE	WEIGHT	GOING	HORSE	DATE		
5f	58.8 secs	2	9-0	Firm	ATLANTIC VIKING (IRE)	Jun	4	1997
5f	58.0 secs	4	9-2	Firm	PRINCESS OBERON	Jly	23	1994
6f	1m 12.6	2	9-0	Firm	SUNDANCE KID	Oct	3	1989
6f	1m 10.6	8	9-5	Firm	TEDBURROW	Jly	1	2000
7f	1m 24.2	2	9-0	Good To Firm	ISCAN (IRE)	Aug	31	1998
7f	1m 23.3	4	9-2	Good To Firm	QUIET VENTURE	Aug	31	1998
1m	1m 38.9	2	9-0	Good To Firm	STOWAWAY	Oct	2	1996
1m	1m 38.9	3	8-12	Firm	JACAMAR	Jly	22	1989
1m 3y	1m 37.1	2	8-3	Good To Firm	HOH STEAMER (IRE)	Aug	31	1998
1m 3y	1m 37.3	3	8-8	Good To Firm	ITS MAGIC	May	27	1999
1m 1f 9y	2m 03.2	2	8-13	Soft	RESPONSE	Oct	30	1993
1m 1f 9y	1m 58.4	3	8-8	Good To Firm	INTRODUCING	Aug	6	2003
1m 2f 32y	2m 06.5	3	8-11	Fast	MISSIONARY RIDGE	Jly	29	1990
1m 4f 93y	2m 37.3	5	8-12	Firm	RETENDER	Jun	25	1994
1m 6f 97y	3m 06.4	3	9-6	Good To Firm	ONE OFF	Aug	6	2003
2m 19y	3m 24.3	4	8-10	Good	FAR CRY (IRE)	Jun	26	1999

NEWMARKET (ROWLEY)

DISTANCE	TIME	AGE	WEIGHT	GOING	HORSE	DATE		
5f	58.76 secs	2	8-5	Good To Firm	VALIANT ROMEO	Oct	3	2002
5f	56.8 secs	6	9-2	Good To Firm	LOCHSONG	Apr	30	1994
6f	1m 09.61	2	8-11	Good To Firm	OASIS DREAM	Oct	3	2002
6f	1m 10.2	4	9-8	Good To Firm	LAKE CONISTON	Apr	18	1995
7f	1m 23.02	2	8-9	Firm	KHULOOD (USA)	Oct	5	2002
7f	1m 22.2	4	9-5	Good To Firm	PERFOLIA	Oct	17	1991
1m	1m 36.7	2	9-0	Good To Firm	BOLD PURSUIT	Oct	17	1991
1m	1m 34.54	4	9-0	Good To Firm	DESERT DEER	Oct	3	2002
1m 1f	1m 47.28	4	9-5	Firm	BEAUCHAMP PILOT	Oct	5	2002
1m 2f	2m 04.6	2	9-4	Good	HIGHLAND CHIEFTAIN	Nov	2	1985
1m 2f	2m 01.0	3	8-10	Good	PALACE MUSIC	Oct	20	1984
1m 4f	2m 27.1	5	8-12	Good To Firm	EASTERN BREEZE	Oct	3	2003
1m 6f	2m 54.3	5	8-6	Good To Firm	TUDOR ISLAND	Sep	30	1994
2m	3m 19.5	5	9-5	Good To Firm	GREY SHOT	Oct	4	1997
2m 2f	3m 47.5	3	7-12	Hard	WHITEWAY	Oct	15	1947

NEWMARKET (JULY)

DISTANCE	TIME	AGE	WEIGHT	GOING	HORSE	DATE		
5f	58.5 secs	2	8-10	Good	**SEDUCTRESS**	Jly	10	1990
5f	57.3 secs	6	8-12	Good To Firm	**RAMBLING BEAR**	Jan	1	1999
6f	1m 10.6	2	8-10	Good To Firm	**MUJTAHID**	Jly	11	1990
6f	1m 09.5	3	8-13	Good To Firm	**STRAVINSKY** (USA)	Jly	8	1999
7f	1m 24.1	2	8-11	Good	**MY HANSEL**	Aug	27	1999
7f	1m 22.5	3	9-7	Firm	**HO LENG** (IRE)	Jly	9	1998
1m	1m 39.0	2	8-11	Good	**TRACEABILITY**	Aug	25	1995
1m	1m 35.5	3	8-6	Good To Firm	**LOVERS KNOT**	Jly	8	1998
1m 110y	1m 44.1	3	8-11	Good	**GOLDEN SNAKE**	Apr	15	1999
1m 2f	2m 00.9	4	9-3	Good To Firm	**ELHAYQ** (IRE)	May	1	1999
1m 4f	2m 25.2	4	9-2	Good	**CRAIGSTEEL**	Jly	6	1999
1m 6f 175y	3m 04.2	3	8-5	Good	**ARRIVE**	Jly	11	2001
2m 24y	3m 20.2	7	9-10	Good	**YORKSHIRE**	Jly	11	2001

NOTTINGHAM

DISTANCE	TIME	AGE	WEIGHT	GOING	HORSE	DATE		
5f 13y	57.9 secs	2	8-9	Firm	**HOH MAGIC**	May	13	1994
5f 13y	58.4 secs	4	7-7	Firm	**VILGORA**	Apr	12	1976
5f 13y	58.4 secs	6	8-8	Good	**MINSTREL KING**	Mar	29	1960
6f 15y	1m 11.4	2	8-11	Firm	**JAMEELAPI**	Aug	8	1983
6f 15y	1m 10.0	4	9-2	Firm	**AJANAC**	Aug	8	1988
1m 54y	1m 40.8	2	9-0	Good To Firm	**KING'S LOCH**	Sep	2	1991
1m 54y	1m 39.6	4	8-2	Good To Firm	**BLAKE'S TREASURE**	Sep	2	1991
1m 1f 213y	2m 02.3	2	9-0	Firm	**AYAABI**	Jly	21	1984
1m 6f 15y	2m 57.8	3	8-10	Firm	**BUSTER JO**	Oct	1	1985
2m 9y	3m 24.0	5	7-7	Firm	**FET**	Oct	5	2036
2m 2f 18y	3m 55.1	9	9-10	Good To Firm	**PEARL RUN**	May	1	1990

PONTEFRACT

DISTANCE	TIME	AGE	WEIGHT	GOING	HORSE	DATE		
5f	1m 01.1	2	9-0	Firm	**GOLDEN BOUNTY**	Sep	20	2001
5f	1m 01.1	5	7-7	Hard	**REGAL BINGO**	Sep	29	1971
6f	1m 14.0	2	9-3	Firm	**FAWZI**	Sep	6	1983
6f	1m 12.6	3	7-13	Firm	**MERRY ONE**	Aug	29	1970
1m 4y	1m 42.8	2	9-13	Firm	**STAR SPRAY**	Sep	6	1970
1m 4y	1m 41.3	7	8-9	Firm	**NIGRASINE**	Sep	20	2001
1m 2f 6y	2m 12.8	2	9-0	Good To Firm	**WARBROOK**	Oct	2	1995
1m 2f 6y	2m 08.2	4	7-8	Hard	**HAPPY HECTOR**	Jly	9	1979
1m 4f 8y	2m 34.1	3	9-5	Good To Firm	**HIGH ACTION**	Aug	6	2003
2m 1f 22y	3m 42.1	3	9-2	Firm	**NIGHT EYE**	Sep	6	1983
2m 1f 216y	3m 51.1	3	8-8	Firm	**KUDZ**	Sep	9	1986
2m 5f 122y	4m 47.8	4	8-4	Firm	**PHYSICAL**	May	14	1984

REDCAR

DISTANCE	TIME	AGE	WEIGHT	GOING	HORSE	DATE		
5f	56.9 secs	2	9-0	Firm	**MISTER JOEL**	Oct	24	1995
5f	56.5 secs	3	9-7	Firm	**NAZELA**	Aug	10	1980
6f	1m 09.4	2	8-7	Good To Firm	**PROUD NATIVE** (IRE)	Oct	17	1996
6f	1m 08.6	3	9-2	Good To Firm	**SIZZLING SAGA**	Jun	21	1991
7f	1m 21.9	2	8-11	Firm	**NAGWA**	Sep	27	1975
7f	1m 21.0	3	9-1	Firm	**EMPTY QUARTER**	Oct	3	1995
1m	1m 36.1	2	7-11	Good To Soft	**MASTER SODEN**	Nov	1	1999
1m	1m 33.1	3	9-5	Firm	**NIGHT WINK** (USA)	Oct	24	1995
1m 1f	1m 52.6	2	9-0	Firm	**YOSHKA**	Sep	15	2003
1m 1f	1m 48.5	5	8-12	Firm	**MELLOTTIE**	Jly	25	1990
1m 2f	2m 10.1	2	8-11	Good	**ADDING**	Nov	10	1989
1m 2f	2m 01.4	5	9-2	Firm	**ERADICATE**	May	28	1990
1m 3f	2m 17.2	3	8-9	Firm	**PHOTO CALL**	Aug	7	1990
1m 5f 135y	2m 54.7	6	9-10	Firm	**BRODESSA**	Jun	20	1992
1m 6f 19y	2m 59.9	6	8-7	Firm	**TRAINGLOT**	Jly	25	1990
2m 4y	3m 24.9	3	9-3	Good To Firm	**SUBSONIC**	Oct	8	1991

RIPON

DISTANCE	TIME	AGE	WEIGHT	GOING	HORSE	DATE		
5f	57.8 secs	2	8-8	Firm	**SUPER ROCKY**	Jly	5	1991
5f	57.6 secs	5	8-5	Good	**BROADSTAIRS BEAUTY**	May	21	1995
6f	1m 10.9	2	8-11	Good	**KAHIR ALMAYDAN** (IRE)	Aug	28	1995
6f	1m 09.8	4	9-8	Good To Firm	**TADEO**	Aug	16	1997
6f	1m 09.8	5	7-10	Firm	**QUOIT**	Jly	23	1966
1m	1m 41.1	2	9-0	Good To Firm	**RAPHAEL** (IRE)	Sep	1	2001
1m	1m 37.0	4	7-10	Firm	**CROWN WITNESS**	Aug	25	1980
1m 1f	1m 50.4	3	9-2	Good To Firm	**BOLD WORDS** (CAN)	Apr	9	1997
1m 2f	2m 02.6	3	9-4	Firm	**SWIFT SWORD**	Jly	20	1990
1m 4f 60y	2m 32.2	6	8-7	Firm	**CHOLO**	Sep	27	1941
2m	3m 27.8	6	9-0	Good To Firm	**SAMAIN**	Aug	31	1993

SALISBURY

DISTANCE	TIME	AGE	WEIGHT	GOING	HORSE	DATE		
5f	59.8 secs	2	8-5	Good To Firm	**TARF** (USA)	Aug	17	1995
5f	59.4 secs	3	8-11	Firm	**BELLSABANGING**	May	5	1993
6f	1m 12.1	2	8-0	Good To Firm	**PARISIAN LADY** (IRE)	Jun	10	1997
6f	1m 11.5	4	8-7	Good To Firm	**PRINCE SKY**	Jun	25	1986
6f 212y	1m 25.9	2	9-0	Firm	**MORE ROYAL** (USA)	Jun	29	1995
6f 212y	1m 24.9	3	9-7	Firm	**HIGH SUMMER** (USA)	Sep	5	1996
1m	1m 40.48	2	8-13	Firm	**CHOIR MASTER**	Sep	17	2002
1m	1m 38.6	4	8-8	Firm	**TAKE HEART**	Jly	14	1990
1m 1f 198y	2m 04.9	3	8-6	Good To Firm	**ZANTE**	Aug	12	1998
1m 4f	2m 31.6	3	9-5	Good To Firm	**ARRIVE**	Jun	27	2001
1m 6f 15y	2m 59.4	3	8-6	Good To Firm	**TABAREEH**	Sep	2	1999

SANDOWN

DISTANCE	TIME	AGE	WEIGHT	GOING	HORSE	DATE		
5f 6y	59.4 secs	2	9-3	Firm	TIMES TIME	Jly	22	1982
5f 6y	58.8 secs	6	8-9	Good To Firm	PALACEGATE TOUCH	Sep	17	1996
7f 16y	1m 27.8	2	8-12	Good To Firm	RED CAMELLIA	Jly	25	1996
7f 16y	1m 26.3	3	9-0	Firm	MAWSUFF	Jun	14	1983
1m 14y	1m 41.1	2	8-11	Fast	REFERENCE POINT	Sep	23	1986
1m 14y	1m 39.0	3	8-8	Firm	LINDA'S FANASTY	Aug	19	1983
1m 1f	1m 54.6	2	8-8	Good To Firm	FRENCH PRETENDER	Sep	20	1988
1m 1f	1m 52.6	3	8-9	Good To Firm	DARNELLE	Aug	19	1988
1m 2f 7y	2m 02.1	4	8-11	Firm	KALAGLOW	May	31	1982
1m 3f 91y	2m 21.6	4	8-3	Fast	AYLESFIELD	Jly	7	1984
1m 6f	2m 56.9	4	8-7	Good To Firm	LADY ROSANNA	Jly	19	1989
2m 78y	3m 29.9	6	9-2	Firm	SADEEM	May	29	1989

SOUTHWELL (TURF)

DISTANCE	TIME	AGE	WEIGHT	GOING	HORSE	DATE		
6f	1m 15.6	2	8-11	Good To Firm	YASELDA	Jly	4	2001
6f	1m 14.1	4	9-12	Good To Firm	MISS HAGGIS	Jly	26	1993
7f	1m 29.1	2	9-0	Good To Firm	DULCET SPEAR	Jly	4	2001
7f	1m 26.5	3	9-5	Good To Firm	SEA STORM (IRE)	Jly	5	2001
1m 2f	2m 10.0	3	9-4	Good	BRONZE MAQUETTE (IRE)	Jly	26	1993
1m 4f	2m 34.4	5	9-3	Good To Firm	CORN LILY	Aug	10	1991
2m	3m 34.1	5	9-1	Good To Firm	TRIPLICATE	Sep	20	1991

SOUTHWELL (A.W)

DISTANCE	TIME	AGE	WEIGHT	GOING	HORSE	DATE		
5f	58.5 secs	2	8-1	Standard	PRIMROSE AND ROSE	Apr	4	2001
5f	57.4 secs	4	9-4	Standard	WOODLAND BLAZE	May	8	2003
6f	1m 14.0	2	8-5	Standard	PANALO	Nov	8	1989
6f	1m 13.3	3	9-2	Standard	RAMBO EXPRESS	Dec	18	1990
7f	1m 27.1	2	8-2	Standard	MYSTIC CRYSTAL (IRE)	Nov	20	1990
7f	1m 26.8	5	8-4	Standard	AMENABLE	Dec	13	1990
1m	1m 38.0	2	8-9	Standard	ALPHA RASCAL	Nov	13	1990
1m	1m 38.0	2	8-10	Standard	ANDREW'S FIRST	Dec	30	1989
1m	1m 37.2	3	8-6	Standard	VALIRA	Nov	3	1990
1m 3f	2m 21.5	4	9-7	Standard	TEMPERING	Dec	5	1990
1m 4f	2m 33.9	4	9-12	Standard	FAST CHICK	Nov	8	1989
1m 6f	3m 01.6	3	7-7	Standard	QUALITAIR AVIATOR	Dec	1	1989
1m 6f	3m 01.6	3	7-8	Standard	EREVNON	Dec	29	1990
2m	3m 37.6	9	8-12	Standard	OLD HUBERT	Dec	5	1990

THIRSK

DISTANCE	TIME	AGE	WEIGHT	GOING	HORSE	DATE		
5f	57.2 secs	2	9-7	Good To Firm	PROAD BOAST	Aug	5	2000
5f	56.1 secs	7	8-0	Firm	SIR SANDROVITCH (IRE)	Jun	26	2003
6f	1m 09.2	2	9-6	Good To Firm	WESTCOURT MAGIC	Aug	25	1995
6f	1m 08.8	6	9-4	Firm	JOHAYRO	Jly	23	1999
7f	1m 23.7	2	8-9	Firm	COURTING	Jly	23	1999
7f	1m 22.8	4	8-5	Firm	SILVER HAZE	May	21	1988
1m	1m 38.5	2	8-9	Good To Firm	IVAN LUIS (FR)	Sep	7	1996
1m	1m 34.8	4	8-13	Firm	YEARSLEY	May	5	1990
1m 4f	2m 29.9	5	9-12	Firm	GALLERY GOD	Jun	4	2001
2m	3m 22.3	3	8-10	Firm	TOMASCHEK (USA)	Aug	1	1964

WARWICK

DISTANCE	TIME	AGE	WEIGHT	GOING	HORSE	DATE		
5f	58.4 secs	2	9-7	Good To Firm	PRENONAMOSS	Oct	9	1990
5f	57.8 secs	5	9-4	Good To Firm	ANOTHER EPISODE (IRE)	Aug	29	1994
6f 21y	1m 11.3	2	8-6	Good To Firm	KNIGHT ON THE TILES (IRE)	Aug	25	2003
6f 21y	1m 10.3	4	9-5	Good To Firm	MILLION PERCENT	Jun	22	2003
6f 21y	1m 12.1	3	8-6	Good To Firm	GEMTASTIC	Jun	18	2001
7f 26y	1m 23.6	2	9-3	Good To Firm	HOAX (IRE)	Jun	27	2001
7f 26y	1m 22.0	4	8-13	Good To Firm	MASTER ROBBIE	Jun	16	2003
1m 22y	1m 37.1	3	8-11	Firm	ORINOCOVSKY (IRE)	Jun	26	2002
1m 2f 188y	2m 16.2	6	7-12	Good To Firm	SCENTED AIR	Apr	21	2003
1m 4f 134y	2m 39.5	3	8-13	Good To Firm	MAIMANA (IRE)	Jun	22	2002
1m 6f 135y	3m 07.5	3	9-7	Good To Firm	BURMA BAY (USA)	Jly	2	1999
2m 39y	3m 30.6	5	8-1	Good To Firm	RENAISSANCE LADY (IRE)	Jun	27	2001

WINDSOR

DISTANCE	TIME	AGE	WEIGHT	GOING	HORSE	DATE		
5f 10y	58.9 secs	2	9-0	Firm	STRICTLY PRIVATE	Jly	22	1974
5f 10y	59.1 secs	4	8-13	Good	BEYOND THE CLOUDS	Jly	17	2000
5f 217y	1m 09.0	2	8-7	Good To Firm	OPTIONS OPEN	Jly	25	1994
5f 217y	1m 10.1	3	8-4	Firm	SWEET RELIEF	Sep	11	1978
6f	1m 10.5	2	9-5	Good To Firm	CUBISM (USA)	Aug	17	1998
6f	1m 10.3	4	8-12	Good To Firm	CARLTON (IRE)	Jun	22	1998
1m 67y	1m 44.4	2	9-0	Good To Firm	TEMPLE PLACE	Sep	29	2003
1m 67y	1m 41.2	5	9-1	Good	POLISH SPIRIT	Apr	10	2000
1m 2f 7y	2m 03.0	3	9-1	Firm	MOOMBA MASQUERADE	May	19	1990
1m 3f 135y	2m 21.5	3	9-2	Firm	DOUBLE FLORIN	May	19	1980

WOLVERHAMPTON (A.W)

DISTANCE	TIME	AGE	WEIGHT	GOING	HORSE	DATE		
5f	1m 01.4	2	9-0	Standard	DANEHURST	Oct	3	2000
5f	1m 00.1	7	8-7	Standard	SIR TASKER	Jan	4	1995
6f	1m 13.8	2	9-0	Standard	SHOUF AL BADOU (USA)	Oct	2	1999
6f	1m 13.8	2	8-9	Standard	NOZOMI (IRE)	Oct	3	1998
6f	1m 13.8	2	8-7	Standard	REACTIVE (IRE)	Oct	17	1998
6f	1m 13.2	6	9-4	Standard	REDOUBTABLE (USA)	Dec	26	1997
6f	1m 13.2	7	9-8	Standard	SEA-DEER	Aug	31	1996
7f	1m 28.0	2	8-1	Standard	ASWHATILLDOIS (IRE)	Oct	17	2000
7f	1m 26.8	4	9-11	Standard	MUSAFI (USA)	Jan	10	1998
1m 100y	1m 48.2	2	9-0	Standard	GRALMANO (IRE)	Dec	29	1997
1m 100y	1m 45.7	5	9-0	Standard	CASHMERE LADY	Jun	21	1997
1m 1f 79y	2m 00.2	2	8-11	Standard	BOUND	Oct	20	2000
1m 1f 79y	1m 57.5	3	9-7	Standard	HAL'S PAL	Aug	17	1996
1m 4f	2m 35.0	4	9-7	Standard	STATE APPROVAL	Jun	21	1997
1m 6f 166y	3m 11.4	4	8-11	Standard	NOUFARI	Jan	4	1995
2m 46y	3m 36.7	4	9-6	Standard	FAR CRY (IRE)	Mar	13	1999

YARMOUTH

DISTANCE	TIME	AGE	WEIGHT	GOING	HORSE	Date		
5f 43y	1m 00.4	2	8-6	Good To Firm	**EBBA**	Jly	26	1999
5f 43y	1m 00.2	3	8-11	Firm	**CHARM BIRD**	Sep	15	1988
6f 3y	1m 10.4	2	9-0	Fast	**LANCHESTER**	Aug	15	1988
6f 3y	1m 10.0	3	8-10	Good To Firm	**TIPSY CREEK** (USA)	Aug	10	1997
7f 3y	1m 22.2	2	9-0	Good To Firm	**WARRSHAN**	Sep	14	1988
7f 3y	1m 22.2	3	8-7	Firm	**CIELAMOUR**	Sep	15	1988
1m 3y	1m 36.3	2	8-2	Good To Firm	**OUTRUN**	Sep	15	1988
1m 3y	1m 33.9	3	8-8	Firm	**BONNE ETOILE**	Jun	27	1995
1m 2f 21y	2m 03.1	4	8-9	Good To Firm	**SUPREME SOUND**	Aug	9	1998
1m 3f 101y	2m 23.1	3	8-9	Firm	**RAHIL**	Jly	1	1993
1m 6f 17y	2m 57.8	3	8-2	Good To Firm	**BARAKAT**	Jly	24	1990
2m	3m 26.7	4	8-2	Good To Firm	**ALHESN** (USA)	Jly	26	1999
2m 2f 51y	3m 56.8	4	9-10	Firm	**PROVENCE**	Sep	19	1991

YORK

DISTANCE	TIME	AGE	WEIGHT	GOING	HORSE	Date		
5f 3y	58.4 secs	2	8-11	Good To Firm	**HOWICK FALLS** (USA)	Aug	20	2003
5f 3y	56.2 secs	3	9-9	Good To Firm	**OASIS DREAM**	Aug	21	2003
6f 3y	1m 10.6	2	9-0	Good To Firm	**CARRY ON KATIE** (USA)	Aug	21	2003
6f 3y	1m 09.4	3	8-2	Good To Firm	**DAZZLING BAY**	Jun	14	2003
6f 217y	1m 22.6	2	9-0	Good To Firm	**MOONLIGHT MAN**	Oct	9	2003
6f 217y	1m 22.0	4	9-0	Good To Firm	**VANDERLIN**	Aug	21	2003
7f 202y	1m 37.2	2	9-4	Good To Firm	**THE WIFE**	Sep	2	1999
7f 205y	1m 36.0	5	8-7	Good To Firm	**FAITHFUL WARRIOR** (USA)	Jul	11	2003
1m 205y	1m 52.4	2	8-1	Good To Firm	**ORAL EVIDENCE**	Oct	6	1988
1m 208y	1m 48.9	4	8-5	Good To Firm	**KRUGERRAND** (USA)	Jun	14	2003
1m 2f 88y	2m 06.5	4	9-4	Good To Firm	**FAR LANE** (USA)	Jly	12	2003
1m 3f 198y	2m 27.4	4	9-4	Good To Firm	**ISLINGTON** (IRE)	Aug	20	2003
1m 5f 197y	2m 52.5	4	8-9	Good To Firm	**MAMOOL** (USA)	May	15	2003
1m 7f 195y	3m 18.4	3	8-0	Good To Firm	**DAM BUSTERS**	Aug	16	1988

TOP FLAT JOCKEYS IN BRITAIN 2003

WINS-RUNS	%	JOCKEY	2ND	3RD	TOTAL PRIZE	WIN PRIZE
221-1055	21%	K FALLON	164	143	5,259,588	3,692,215
157-989	16%	D HOLLAND	136	108	3,211,618	2,166,351
125-871	14%	K DARLEY	114	98	1,862,454	1,081,185
121-751	16%	R HUGHES	88	80	2,061,804	1,346,115
112-862	13%	A CULHANE	107	88	919,100	623,993
110-1018	11%	DANE O'NEILL	109	111	1,339,131	755,659
109-1022	11%	S DROWNE	104	99	1,308,130	737,706
107-852	13%	E AHERN	103	90	1,408,431	851,695
102-597	17%	J P SPENCER	96	62	1,875,039	1,212,498
101-495	20%	L DETTORI	90	62	2,715,872	1,652,947
101-860	12%	S SANDERS	106	90	1,046,800	650,972
93-912	10%	R WINSTON	80	85	761,336	456,479
90-789	11%	MARTIN DWYER	87	73	1,949,889	1,268,119
86-709	12%	G DUFFIELD	59	67	751,308	528,830
84-753	11%	J FANNING	60	77	844,979	598,417
82-587	14%	T QUINN	80	66	1,307,164	774,547
80-739	11%	I MONGAN	82	80	593,777	329,676
78-621	13%	PAT EDDERY	62	51	2,011,064	1,165,792
75-374	20%	R HILLS	58	32	1,401,625	881,450
70-486	14%	P ROBINSON	53	60	1,555,538	1,016,842
68-799	9%	P NORTON	72	99	626,802	356,979
64-533	12%	K DALGLEISH	46	40	762,866	518,934
64-705	9%	P HANAGAN	56	71	750,810	425,526
62-522	12%	W SUPPLE	56	51	758,112	497,764
61-719	8%	J F EGAN	66	77	701,758	455,695
59-627	9%	R L MOORE	66	58	515,799	318,280
59-947	6%	C CATLIN	57	67	502,462	300,626
58-433	13%	M HILLS	49	50	948,363	595,335
55-758	7%	M FENTON	77	64	582,814	312,296
52-640	8%	N CALLAN	70	62	385,921	217,062
51-653	8%	S WHITWORTH	58	48	357,024	210,310
49-442	11%	R FFRENCH	41	35	341,958	227,273
49-644	8%	J QUINN	61	65	546,920	327,417
46-380	12%	J FORTUNE	55	46	750,409	368,242
45-322	14%	S HITCHCOTT	31	30	435,089	319,244
43-411	10%	R MULLEN	25	35	483,395	350,897
43-519	8%	LISA JONES	32	46	316,458	219,891
43-559	8%	D ALLAN	56	59	386,850	199,369
41-604	7%	L FLETCHER	45	62	315,019	193,486
38-312	12%	R MILES	35	25	283,187	189,679
38-463	8%	J MACKAY	31	30	321,241	214,203
38-532	7%	DEAN MCKEOWN	41	39	397,025	264,054
37-347	11%	J-P GUILLAMBERT	33	33	202,775	136,913
37-444	8%	DARREN WILLIAMS	40	49	244,066	151,874
36-251	14%	N MACKAY	28	22	378,706	294,235
36-362	10%	D MERNAGH	46	24	321,471	179,005
35-316	11%	B DOYLE	21	31	236,446	161,835
34-444	8%	G GIBBONS	43	48	277,936	126,714
32-383	8%	S W KELLY	40	40	330,954	233,729
32-417	8%	F LYNCH	38	42	341,183	204,204

TOP FLAT TRAINERS IN BRITAIN 2003

TRAINER	LEADING HORSE	WINS-RUNS	2ND	3RD	4TH	TOTAL PRIZE	WIN PRIZE
SIR MICHAEL STOUTE	Kris Kin	115–482	74	69	44	3,754,850	2,760,765
M JOHNSTON	Lucky Story	139-758	105	72	62	2,049,041	1,410,772
M R CHANNON	Zafeen	144–1136	126	149	94	2,029,345	1,174,784
R HANNON	Reel Buddy	122–1031	118	101	95	1,688,075	1,028,947
B W HILLS	Far Lane	107–640	72	76	56	1,458,827	931,417
M P TREGONING	Nayef	56–260	47	22	28	1,387,277	928,240
J H M GOSDEN	Oasis Dream	71–391	69	49	40	1,356,380	881,783
A P O'BRIEN	The Great Gatsby	6–58	10	7	4	1,247,495	463,189
T D EASTERBY	Somnus	58–829	80	86	81	1,177,970	678,868
L M CUMANI	Falbrav	57–268	29	33	17	1,156,252	1,009,172
A M BALDING	Casual Look	54–521	55	56	52	1,141,821	703,047
D R C ELSWORTH	Persian Punch	40–301	29	38	25	1,092,328	599,654
D R LODER	With Reason	70–225	50	19	22	1,088,309	705,296
J L DUNLOP	Millenary	86–570	68	50	50	1,085,325	673,566
C E BRITTAIN	Warrsan	41–395	42	38	47	991,501	597,878
SAEED BIN SUROOR	Sulamani	23–98	17	8	5	986,310	529,431
J NOSEDA	Balmont	38–191	31	14	17	928,218	689,340
B J MEEHAN	Cape Fear	54–521	74	57	42	922,475	541,126
M A JARVIS	Rakti	57–298	37	31	19	909,150	604,631
R CHARLTON	Patavellian	56–269	42	17	23	850,189	597,050
G A BUTLER	Compton Bolter	62–406	44	45	23	838,762	566,258
P F I COLE	Mr Dinos	56–407	50	50	32	819,414	583,063
J R FANSHAWE	Macadamia	46–289	45	39	31	817,129	458,617
MRS A J PERRETT	Tillerman	55–395	50	61	32	762,442	377,399
D NICHOLLS	Fire Up The Band	65–782	70	52	38	740,891	450,829
E A L DUNLOP	Hold To Ransom	50–443	56	65	38	620,234	326,891
JOHN M OXX	Alamshar	1–9	0	2	1	615,325	435,000
J A OSBORNE	Milk It Mick	48–365	42	50	20	595,340	410,789
P W HARRIS	Leporello	46–448	37	48	47	578,264	411,656
M L W BELL	Shabernak	35–300	36	34	20	540,469	359,263
J G GIVEN	Hugs Dancer	47–419	35	38	20	539,134	337,046
J M BRADLEY	The Tatling	37–750	68	58	35	533,566	257,681
T D BARRON	Axis	71–436	67	44	27	528,869	316,755
R A FAHEY	Lady Bear	50–465	41	45	31	526,707	346,111
SIR MARK PRESCOTT	No Refuge	67–283	36	29	11	517,734	426,271
N A CALLAGHAN	Magistretti	34–194	19	21	11	489,230	296,976
N P LITTMODEN	Peruvian Chief	54–648	58	64	38	487,940	260,028
W J HAGGAS	Chorist	44–259	35	28	16	447,954	307,851
H MORRISON	Baltic King	46–321	31	25	23	437,198	286,830
K A RYAN	Halmahera	41–418	31	37	35	372,798	252,725
H R A CECIL	Tuning Fork	25–156	36	22	14	353,687	176,183
T G MILLS	Where Or When	27–188	23	22	15	353,305	151,308
W M BRISBOURNE	Milly Waters	48–458	52	37	25	348,855	232,306
P D EVANS	The Kiddykid	42–534	40	53	19	331,379	206,745
G WRAGG	Asian Heights	16–166	18	20	21	331,097	161,913
M H TOMPKINS	Franklins Gardens	27–306	33	35	24	330,941	183,522
K R BURKE	Million Percent	46–563	69	75	34	325,323	178,917
C F WALL	Ashdown Express	32–217	22	32	13	318,690	199,282
A C STEWART	Tarjman	26–182	29	26	18	310,590	173,747

TOP FLAT OWNERS IN BRITAIN 2003

OWNER	LEADING HORSE	WINS-RUNS	2ND	3RD	4TH	TOTAL PRIZE	WIN PRIZE
K ABDULLA	Oasis Dream	78-357	60	53	29	1,796,464	1,221,515
HAMDAN AL MAKTOUM	Nayef	103-524	79	49	64	1,728,757	1,125,862
CHEVELEY PARK STUD	Russian Rhythm	48-237	32	28	18	1,413,349	1,023,300
SHEIKH MOHAMMED	With Reason	96-366	77	45	29	1,389,385	834,559
SAEED SUHAIL	Kris Kin	17-57	5	13	7	1,180,847	1,018,579
GODOLPHIN	Sulamani	23-98	17	8	5	986,310	529,431
H H AGA KHAN	Alamshar	15-51	4	7	2	867,816	581,887
MRS JOHN MAGNIER	The Great Gatsby	5-21	5	0	1	853,916	455,486
SCUDERIA RENCATI SRL	Falbrav	5-20	1	1	1	728,161	698,401
J C SMITH	Persian Punch	23-179	19	21	21	645,955	300,861
SAEED MANANA	Warrsan	15-119	12	9	18	554,747	411,576
EXORS OF THE LATE LORD WEINSTOCK	Islington	14-50	9	4	5	510,405	393,712
MAKTOUM AL MAKTOUM	Shanty Star	32-233	30	32	21	498,724	308,372
PAUL J DIXON	Milk It Mick	36-419	30	40	27	475,756	360,832
JABER ABDULLAH	Zafeen	13-111	14	18	17	469,975	273,436
SHEIKH AHMED AL MAKTOUM	Tarjman	44-215	36	30	20	453,457	274,401
ABDULLA BUHALEEBA	Lucky Story	16-76	17	9	8	375,123	259,394
LADY TENNANT	High Accolade	5-13	4	1	1	358,385	224,935
GARY A TANAKA	Rakti	1-5	1	0	1	311,850	232,000
W S FARISH III	Casual Look	4-16	4	0	0	299,938	285,276
T W WALLACE & PARTNERS	Choisir	2-3	1	0	0	281,200	226,200
ELITE RACING CLUB	New Seeker	9-70	9	11	6	280,968	156,720
M TABOR	Magistretti	9-61	7	9	3	275,255	131,760
NIARCHOS FAMILY	Arakan	10-38	10	4	5	274,085	100,084
SANFORD R ROBERTSON	Balmont	6-19	3	0	2	252,097	225,897
R E SANGSTER	Ocean Silk	8-45	5	3	4	227,757	89,758
ERIK PENSER	Compton Bolter	20-131	14	9	2	226,086	147,552
SPEEDLITH GROUP	Reel Buddy	3-22	3	7	0	225,073	173,051
MOYGLARE STUD FARM	Refuse To Bend	2-5	0	1	0	220,100	214,600
RAYMOND TOOTH	Psychiatrist	15-102	14	10	5	216,331	102,045
C SHIACOLAS	Mr Dinos	4-11	1	0	0	210,519	209,629
SEYMOUR COHN	Indian Creek	5-17	3	5	1	208,450	128,977
MRS P W HARRIS	Leporello	15-74	3	9	9	208,014	188,373
LUCAYAN STUD	Just James	10-144	13	11	8	206,208	86,562
MOUNTGRANGE STUD	Move It	14-76	16	9	6	200,763	136,290
H R H SULTAN AHMAD SHAH	Putra Pekan	12-68	13	5	4	200,360	146,132
LORD VESTEY	Macadamia	5-12	3	0	2	196,632	159,344
SHEIKH MARWAN AL MAKTOUM	Dutch Gold	9-49	7	8	3	190,729	80,796
MOHAMMED RASHID	Carry On Katie	7-25	2	0	4	189,427	180,605
MRS SUSAN ROY	Twilight Blues	10-71	10	5	8	183,104	130,371
C FOX & J WRIGHT	Peak To Creek	7-13	2	1	1	175,416	162,325
THE QUEEN	Right Approach	11-73	8	9	9	174,167	78,521
KENNET VALLEY THOROUGHBRED II	Cape Fear	1-1	1	0	0	170,609	147,684
LEGARD SIDEBOTTOM & SYKES	Somnus	3-7	1	0	1	170,365	158,775
D J DEER	Patavellian	6-62	3	4	7	168,653	136,755
HENRY CANDY & PARTNERS	Airwave	1-5	1	2	0	166,750	58,000
GUY REED	Pablo	14-94	10	5	10	166,420	131,168
SALEM SUHAIL	Nyramba	3-17	1	1	0	165,690	155,496
SIR NEIL WESTBROOK	Bollin Eric	2-23	2	3	5	162,787	63,652
MALIH L AL BASTI	Fantastic View	7-44	11	8	0	148,967	60,454

TOP FLAT HORSES IN BRITAIN & IRELAND 2003

HORSE (AGE)	WIN & PLACE £	W-R	TRAINER	OWNER	BREEDER
ALAMSHAR (3)	1,172,764	3-7	John M Oxx	H H Aga Khan	H H Aga Khan's Studs
KRIS KIN (3)	978,500	2-3	Sir Michael Stoute	Saeed Suhail	Flaxman Holdings Ltd
FALBRAV (5)	820,127	3-6	L M Cumani	S Rencati & T Yoshida	A A Francesca
RUSSIAN RHYTHM (3)	539,700	3-5	Sir Michael Stoute	Cheveley Park Stud	Brushwood Stable
HIGH CHAPARRAL (4)	433,116	2-2	A P O'Brien	Michael Tabor	S Coughlan
THE GREAT GATSBY (3)	358,984	0-3	A P O'Brien	Mrs John Magnier	Orpendale
NAYEF (5)	335,000	1-5	M P Tregoning	Hamdan Al Maktoum	Shadwell Farm Inc
OASIS DREAM (3)	325,900	2-4	J H M Gosden	K Abdulla	Juddmonte Farms
RAKTI (4)	309,000	1-2	M A Jarvis	Gary A Tanaka	A A Rosati Colareti
BRIAN BORU (3)	308,584	1-5	A P O'Brien	Mrs John Magnier	Juddmonte Farms
WARRSAN (5)	303,050	3-5	C E Brittain	Saeed Manana	Saeed Manana
HIGH ACCOLADE (3)	281,385	4-9	M P Tregoning	Lady Tennant	Deerfield Stud
CHOISIR (4)	281,200	2-3	Paul Perry	T W Wallace & Partners	R M Daisley
CASUAL LOOK (3)	269,655	1-4	N J Howard	W S Farish III	W S Farish
ONE COOL CAT (2)	265,786	4-5	A P O'Brien	Mrs John Magnier	Winstar Farm Llc
ZAFEEN (3)	252,250	1-5	Saeed Bin Suroor	Godolphin	Gainsborough Stud
YESTERDAY (3)	251,332	1-4	A P O'Brien	Mrs J Magnier/ R Henry	Premier Bloodstock
ISLINGTON (4)	246,842	1-4	Sir Michael Stoute	Exors Lord Weinstock	Ballymacoll Stud Fm Ltd
REFUSE TO BEND (3)	236,249	3-4	D K Weld	Moyglare Stud Farm	Moyglare Stud Farm Ltd
PERSIAN PUNCH (10)	214,840	4-8	D R C Elsworth	J C Smith	Adstock Manor Stud
MILK IT MICK (3)	214,565	5-12	J A Osborne	Paul J Dixon	Mrs Yvette Dixon
MAGISTRETTI (3)	203,860	2-4	N A Callaghan	M Tabor	Tri-County Farms LLC
REEL BUDDY (5)	203,300	1-6	R Hannon	Speedlith Group	Stronach Stables
MR DINOS (4)	203,000	2-2	P F I Cole	C Shiacolas	Mocklerstown Hse Stud
BALMONT (2)	189,239	4-6	J Noseda	S R Robertson	S R Robertson
INDIAN CREEK (5)	187,661	2-8	D R C Elsworth	Exors S Cohn	Mrs Rebecca Philipps
MACADAMIA (4)	176,530	3-7	J R Fanshawe	Lord Vestey	Lord Vestey
PEAK TO CREEK (2)	171,666	7-11	J Noseda	C Fox & J Wright	Compton Down Stud
CAPE FEAR (2)	170,609	2-6	B J Meehan	Kennett Valley T'breds	Mascalls Stud
SOMNUS (3)	170,365	3-7	T D Easterby	L Sidebottom & Sykes	Lady Legard
AIRWAVE (3)	166,750	1-5	H Candy	Henry Candy & Partners	R T & Mrs Watson
SULAMANI (4)	165,000	0-1	Saeed Bin Suroor	Godolphin	The Niarchos Family
INDIAN HAVEN (3)	164,793	2-5	P W D'Arcy	Gleeson/Smith/Conway	Cliveden Stud Ltd
DALAKHANI (3)	163,051	0-1	A De Royer-Dupre	H H Aga Khan	H H Aga Khan's Studs
NYRAMBA (2)	160,996	3-5	J H M Gosden	Salem Suhail	Five Horses Ltd
BLACK SAM BELLAMY (4)	158,779	2-4	A P O'Brien	Michael Tabor	Sunderland Holdings Ltd
BOLLIN ERIC (4)	157,633	1-7	T D Easterby	Sir Neil Westbrook	Sir Neil & Lady Westbrook
VINTAGE TIPPLE (3)	156,720	1-4	P Mullins	Patrick J O'Donovan	Sir E J Loder
DUBAI DESTINATION (4)	154,504	2-3	Saeed Bin Suroor	Godolphin	Calumet Farm
CARRY ON KATIE (2)	153,308	3-3	J Noseda	Mohammed Rashid	Swordlestown Stud
AMERICAN POST (2)	151,500	1-1	Mme C Head-Maarek	K Abdulla	Juddmonte Farms
FAR LANE (4)	149,931	3-8	B W Hills	K Abdulla	Airlie Stud
ACCLAMATION (4)	148,745	3-7	L G Cottrell	Liam Cashman	Tedwood Bloodstock Ltd
LIVADIYA (7)	148,376	5-14	H Rogers	Gerard McStay	H H Aga Khans Studs
NORSE DANCER (3)	146,950	0-6	D R C Elsworth	J C Smith	R Egnist & B Faust
MAJESTIC DESERT (2)	145,980	2-5	M R Channon	Jaber Abdullah	Bloodhorse Inter. Ltd
NECKLACE (2)	141,493	2-3	A P O'Brien	M Tabor & Mrs J Magnier	Meon Valley Stud
NEW SEEKER (3)	141,056	3-6	C G Cox	Elite Racing Club	Shadwell Estate Inc
LEPORELLO (3)	139,271	6-7	P W Harris	Mrs P W Harris	Pendley Farm
VINNIE ROE (5)	138,376	2-2	D K Weld	Seamus Sheridan	Mrs Virginia Moeran
SAINT ALEBE (4)	136,573	2-6	D R C Elsworth	The Howarting's Pship	Mrs M J Hills
THE TATLING (6)	133,692	2-14	J M Bradley	Dab Hand Racing	Patrick J Power
LUCKY STORY (2)	132,593	4-5	M Johnston	Abdulla Buhaleeba	Winstar Farm Llc
MEMBERSHIP (3)	126,730	3-13	C E Brittain	Saeed Manana	Darley Stud
COMPTON BOLTER (6)	126,686	4-17	G A Butler	Erik Penser	Rathasker Stud
POWERSCOURT (3)	126,577	2-4	A P O'Brien	Mrs John Magnier	Juddmonte Farms

TOP JUMP JOCKEYS IN BRITAIN 2002/3

WINS-RUNS	%	JOCKEY	2ND	3RD	TOTAL PRIZE
257-840	31%	A P MCCOY	132	118	2,599,546
147-725	20%	R JOHNSON	116	111	1,735,272
109-478	23%	A DOBBIN	65	43	832,830
77-295	26%	R WALSH	49	32	1,530,000
77-448	17%	M A FITZGERALD	71	45	962,824
66-548	12%	G LEE	60	66	569,096
62-521	12%	A THORNTON	95	65	672,573
61-445	14%	W MARSTON	39	55	539,188
60-358	17%	B FENTON	46	36	471,485
59-493	12%	L ASPELL	59	64	616,086
56-388	14%	J CULLOTY	46	41	900,899
50-486	10%	R THORNTON	69	59	535,251
48-249	19%	L COOPER	32	25	517,453
48-317	15%	B J CROWLEY	42	42	388,512
46-357	13%	S DURACK	40	37	410,515
42-409	10%	T J MURPHY	53	39	615,557
41-298	14%	M FOLEY	36	26	342,239
41-314	13%	P FLYNN	38	26	326,401
36-514	7%	R GREENE	40	50	440,952
35-317	11%	D R DENNIS	39	40	299,336
35-352	10%	N FEHILY	54	50	379,636
33-330	10%	K RENWICK	36	38	257,367
33-384	9%	M BRADBURNE	41	39	351,773
32-293	11%	R GARRITTY	45	51	296,169
32-354	9%	T SCUDAMORE	34	34	294,651
31-211	15%	W HUTCHINSON	20	29	177,932
29-292	10%	P ROBSON	38	36	224,297
29-361	8%	C LLEWELLYN	41	45	314,493
28-190	15%	D ELSWORTH	28	21	273,263
28-259	11%	J CROWLEY	28	31	182,270
28-328	9%	T DOYLE	35	32	271,537
28-330	8%	R MCGRATH	30	41	297,418
27-152	18%	R P MCNALLY	20	18	152,697
27-310	9%	P HIDE	37	16	207,694
26-104	25%	B J GERAGHTY	9	7	1,260,920
24-184	13%	P WHELAN	25	21	159,679
24-248	10%	J M MAGUIRE	28	24	209,413
24-268	9%	B HITCHCOTT	25	25	152,098
23-112	21%	CHRISTIAN WILLIAMS	16	10	134,531
23-231	10%	J P MCNAMARA	28	23	206,344
23-238	10%	P ASPELL	20	36	168,820
23-261	9%	A DEMPSEY	29	36	246,541
23-292	8%	B HARDING	36	25	217,294
22-216	10%	D N RUSSELL	17	34	340,983
21-137	15%	A O'KEEFFE	11	21	142,884
20-101	20%	N WILLIAMSON	9	8	527,966
20-124	16%	J TIZZARD	17	11	224,803
20-208	10%	B STOREY	16	27	143,771
19-147	13%	F KING	18	21	146,820
19-149	13%	R FLAVIN	17	11	132,263

TOP JUMP TRAINERS IN BRITAIN 2002/3

TRAINER	LEADING HORSE	WINS-RUNS	2ND	3RD	4TH	TOTAL PRIZE	WIN PRIZE
M C PIPE	Stormez	189-941	114	108	53	2,490,700	1,579,846
P F NICHOLLS	Azertyuiop	151-576	104	69	39	2,088,925	1,465,746
JONJO O'NEILL	Iris's Gift	114-544	77	50	32	1,545,414	1,198,144
P J HOBBS	Rooster Booster	134-616	99	84	37	1,464,359	1,075,242
N J HENDERSON	Fondmort	69-392	63	56	26	1,069,207	614,239
MISS H C KNIGHT	Best Mate	42-275	36	28	21	886,027	600,447
MISS VENETIA WILLIAMS	Limerick Boy	78-475	63	67	28	702,907	449,414
MRS S J SMITH	Ardent Scout	74-352	52	38	31	641,896	445,481
MRS M REVELEY	A Piece Of Cake	56-448	54	69	40	504,122	307,570
FERDY MURPHY	Truckers Tavern	43-415	44	56	34	472,914	244,601
H D DALY	Behrajan	28-203	27	30	12	422,298	306,637
A KING	Jaboune	39-272	46	34	24	398,467	205,211
IAN WILLIAMS	Brooklyn's Gold	50-340	48	42	26	390,210	261,877
L LUNGO	Laouen	63-274	37	18	8	364,506	297,545
R T PHILLIPS	La Landiere	32-125	19	15	5	361,726	286,106
MRS JOHN HARRINGTON	Spirit Leader	5-10	1	0	0	354,276	350,900
JAMES JOSEPH MANGAN	Monty's Pass	1-1	0	0	0	348,000	348,000
N A TWISTON-DAVIES	Shardam	31-317	37	42	29	324,436	161,265
C J MANN	Regal Holly	28-245	42	36	28	312,757	154,313
R H ALNER	Peccadillo	35-271	38	35	23	299,216	190,321
P R WEBBER	Frosty Canyon	19-191	24	24	24	240,137	115,906
N G RICHARDS	Lord Jack	36-139	29	13	9	237,263	148,702
F DOUMEN	Baracouda	4-27	3	3	2	236,939	205,360
J HOWARD JOHNSON	Covent Garden	33-153	10	12	9	205,459	172,807
G L MOORE	Tikram	25-184	28	19	16	202,548	121,342
MRS H DALTON	Quality First	25-188	23	17	15	184,905	133,091
J W MULLINS	Farmer Jack	20-197	21	23	13	183,784	111,607
P G MURPHY	Supreme Glory	6-67	11	7	2	175,744	23,123
MISS E C LAVELLE	Tana River	17-105	14	9	7	175,537	111,246
T R GEORGE	Royal Beluga	21-201	16	27	12	175,368	112,097
E J O'GRADY	Sacundai	2-13	1	0	1	169,185	145,000
D McCAIN	Amberleigh House	10-150	14	21	21	166,012	44,691
K C BAILEY	Famfoni	22-192	13	19	13	164,914	110,514
B G POWELL	Eau De Cologne	22-218	21	25	14	163,237	111,405
T D EASTERBY	Edmo Heights	19-156	28	24	9	154,690	80,127
A L T MOORE	Native Upmanship	1-13	1	2	0	149,917	87,000
R ROWE	Native New Yorker	22-149	10	22	9	148,740	119,219
J T GIFFORD	Telimar Prince	12-117	15	17	9	145,847	89,266
A CROOK	Ryalux	7-78	15	12	6	144,024	90,174
M TODHUNTER	Kingsmark	17-103	22	14	6	142,290	91,814
C ROCHE	Youlneverwalkalone	2-24	3	3	2	141,501	66,700
G M MOORE	Jungle Jinks	20-158	21	25	5	141,442	82,503
R LEE	Suspendid	19-128	24	8	11	139,339	88,994
P BOWEN	Swansea Bay	18-96	11	5	7	130,797	101,003
NOEL T CHANCE	Flame Creek	20-91	9	11	3	127,409	103,442
J M JEFFERSON	Noel's Pride	20-121	15	18	11	125,961	84,878
P MONTEITH	Cita Verda	18-119	8	10	9	120,470	94,477
P BEAUMONT	Hunters Tweed	8-135	12	16	17	119,915	41,121
R DICKIN	Jacdor	18-173	23	13	11	118,192	73,404
M W EASTERBY	The Nomad	23-193	26	16	11	117,617	69,100

TOP JUMP OWNERS IN BRITAIN 2002/3

OWNER	LEADING HORSE	WINS-RUNS	2ND	3RD	4TH	TOTAL PRIZE	WIN PRIZE
D A JOHNSON	Stormez	46-166	21	20	16	873,101	577,881
JOHN P MCMANUS	Baracouda	33-185	30	18	12	753,036	568,935
JIM LEWIS	Best Mate	11-27	4	3	1	491,528	413,294
TERRY WARNER	Rooster Booster	14-38	4	4	4	383,698	334,682
DEE RACING SYNDICATE	Monty's Pass	1-1	0	0	0	348,000	348,000
TREVOR HEMMINGS	Goguenard	23-164	31	15	14	316,667	162,874
SIR ROBERT OGDEN	Marlborough	22-116	18	13	7	307,653	184,449
MRS J STEWART	Cenkos	4-24	5	1	6	267,655	195,760
MRS JOHN MAGNIER	Native Upmanship	6-10	1	1	0	250,977	159,227
MRS G SMITH	Spectroscope	14-33	6	3	3	205,324	168,849
MR & MRS R ANDERSON GREEN	Star Jack	23-104	16	13	4	195,509	143,269
MRS R J SKAN	La Landiere	11-24	5	1	1	192,959	170,305
N B MASON	Xaipete	27-258	21	33	21	192,380	119,885
ASHLEYBANK INVESTMENTS LTD	Paco Venture	37-98	10	4	4	189,881	165,231
C G ROACH	Shotgun Willy	9-31	6	1	3	165,155	124,566
KEITH NICHOLSON	Nickel Sun	23-72	9	5	8	157,422	128,119
B A KILPATRICK	Tarxien	8-38	4	5	3	152,556	130,548
D THOMPSON	Spirit Leader	3-3	0	0	0	147,900	147,900
BRIAN KEARNEY	Moscow Flyer	1-2	0	0	0	145,000	145,000
PAUL K BARBER	Valley Henry	9-23	2	2	3	143,678	98,727
ROBERT LESTER	Iris's Gift	6-7	2	1	0	141,397	109,057
J HALES	Azertyuiop	9-20	3	4	0	138,387	133,127
C J L MOORSOM	Supreme Glory	0-5	1	0	1	135,750	0
MRS M B SCHOLEY	Truckers Tavern	1-22	4	5	2	127,798	34,800
B C MARSHALL	Vol Solitaire	8-28	5	3	3	121,386	74,105
W J BROWN	Fondmort	4-12	2	3	0	118,599	81,544
M ARCHER & MISS J BROADHURST	Westender	6-34	4	6	3	117,588	19,160
R GIBBS	One Knight	4-5	0	1	0	112,847	109,547
INTERSKYRACING.COM & MRS O'NEILL	Intersky Falcon	3-4	0	0	0	111,900	104,400
HALEWOOD INTERNATIONAL LTD	Amberleigh House	3-78	9	12	10	111,848	10,833
THE MACCA & GROWLER P'SHIP	Seebald	1-17	6	1	1	106,635	13,897
AXOM	Deano's Beeno	3-7	2	1	0	106,150	87,200
WILLIAM LOMAS	Ryalux	2-6	2	2	0	104,633	73,880
MRS BELINDA HARVEY	Chicuelo	9-27	2	1	0	100,067	96,262
MRS STEWART CATHERWOOD	Keen Leader	5-19	1	5	0	96,423	75,113
MRS ALICIA SKENE & W S SKENE	Ardent Scout	3-11	3	2	0	95,458	66,153
THE BEHRAJAN PARTNERSHIP	Behrajan	3-10	0	3	0	94,664	84,171
FAVOURITES RACING	Limerick Boy	9-62	7	13	5	94,402	59,547
DARREN C MERCER	Sudden Shock	8-31	7	3	1	90,992	69,714
TERRY NEILL	Puntal	11-25	2	1	0	88,915	73,845
MALM SYNDICATE	Sacundai	1-2	0	0	0	87,000	87,000
D J & F A JACKSON	Epervier D'Or	8-35	10	3	4	86,854	50,150
MARK TINCKNELL	Poliantas	4-13	3	3	0	86,616	53,074
THE HON MRS TOWNSHEND	Santenay	3-5	1	0	0	81,558	65,058
NOTALOTTERY	Kadarann	3-8	0	2	1	77,612	58,592
P BARBER, M COBURN, C LEWIS 2	Young Devereaux	2-3	0	0	0	77,400	77,400
THURLOE FINSBURY	Geos	1-10	1	2	2	77,355	26,800
MRS E ROBERTS & NICK ROBERTS	Chauvinist	2-5	0	2	0	75,652	62,290
MAJOR CHRISTOPHER HANBURY	Irish Hussar	3-13	1	1	1	75,431	55,776
MRS F MONTAUBAN	Jair Du Cochet	3-5	1	0	0	74,377	43,577

TOP JUMP HORSES IN BRITAIN & IRELAND 2002/03

HORSE (AGE)	WIN & PLACE £	W-R	TRAINER	OWNER	BREEDER
MONTY'S PASS (10)	408,773	2-10	James Joseph Mangan	Dee Racing Syndicate	G Slattery
BEST MATE (8)	322,725	3-3	Miss H C Knight	Jim Lewis	Jacques Van't Hart
ROOSTER BOOSTER (9)	299,831	5-6	P J Hobbs	Terry Warner	Mrs E Mitchell
NATIVE UPMANSHIP (10)	205,657	3-6	A L T Moore	Mrs John Magnier	John Noonan
MOSCOW FLYER (9)	200,993	4-5	Mrs John Harrington	Brian Kearney	Edward Joyce
STORMEZ (6)	173,620	7-12	M C Pipe	D A Johnson	Satwa Farm
BEEF OR SALMON (7)	165,296	4-5	Michael Hourigan	B J Craig	John Murphy
SPIRIT LEADER (7)	157,096	3-6	Mrs John Harrington	D Thompson	Miss E Kennedy
LA LANDIERE (8)	151,055	7-8	R T Phillips	Mrs R J Skan	Hubert Carion
INTERSKY FALCON (6)	143,801	4-5	Jonjo O'Neill	Intersky/Mrs J O'Neill	Fulling Mill Fm & Stud
IRIS'S GIFT (6)	141,397	6-7	Jonjo O'Neill	Robert Lester	Mrs R Crank
SUPREME GLORY (10)	135,750	0-5	P G Murphy	C J L Moorsom	Hugh B Hodge
BARROW DRIVE (7)	131,187	6-11	Anthony Mullins	Mrs B Lenihan	Mrs R E Hambor
SEEBALD (8)	130,340	1-6	M C Pipe	Macca & Growler	Dr Werner Spangler
LIMESTONE LAD (11)	129,018	5-7	James Bowe	James Bowe	James Bowe
CENKOS (9)	127,500	1-5	P F Nicholls	Mrs J Stewart	Gerard Samama
SACUNDAI (6)	127,264	4-5	E J O'Grady	Malm Syndicate	A A Patrizia
TRUCKERS TAVERN (8)	121,550	1-5	Ferdy Murphy	Mrs M B Scholey	J J Manning
DEANO'S BEENO (11)	117,150	3-8	M C Pipe	Axom	E Gregory
BARACOUDA (8)	117,060	2-3	F Doumen	John P McManus	R Dupuis
AZERTYUIOP (6)	115,736	4-4	P F Nicholls	J Hales	P De M Melun
ONE KNIGHT (7)	112,847	4-5	P J Hobbs	R Gibbs	Geoffrey Thompson
SOLERINA (6)	112,681	7-9	James Bowe	John P Bowe	Michael J Bowe
AD HOC (9)	109,458	2-7	P F Nicholls	Sir Robert Ogden	M Doran
HARDY EUSTACE (6)	109,130	3-6	D T Hughes	Laurence Byrne	Patrick Joyce
YOULNEVERWALKALONE (9)	105,957	3-5	C Roche	John P McManus	Buckley Osborne Partnership
VALLEY HENRY (8)	105,422	3-6	P F Nicholls	Paul K Barber	Bill Ronayne
RHINESTONE COWBOY (5)	105,227	5-6	Jonjo O'Neill	Mrs John Magnier	Mrs Frances Whelan
RYALUX (10)	104,633	2-6	A Crook	William Lomas	Danny Doran
INTELLIGENT (9)	97,833	3-9	Mrs John Harrington	Norman Moore	Miss J McClements
MORE THAN A STROLL (11)	97,120	3-6	A L T Moore	Mrs D Grehan	Owen O'Leary
XENOPHON (7)	96,902	2-3	A J Martin	Lane Syndicate	Patrick Cannon
FIRST GOLD (10)	96,369	1-5	F Doumen	John P McManus	Roger Chaignon
BE MY ROYAL (9)	94,924	4-5	W P Mullins	Mrs Violet O'Leary	Kenneth Parkhill
SPECTROSCOPE (4)	91,957	3-6	Jonjo O'Neill	Mrs G Smith	Mrs M Campbell-Andenaes
MINI SENSATION (10)	91,939	2-5	Jonjo O'Neill	John P McManus	T McKeever
BEHRAJAN (8)	89,350	2-5	H D Daly	The Behrajan Partnership	H H Aga Khan's Studs
FONDMORT (7)	88,899	1-6	N J Henderson	W J Brown	Hubert Carion
AMBERLEIGH HOUSE (11)	85,563	0-8	D McCain	Halewood Inter Ltd	Robert McCarthy
VOL SOLITAIRE (5)	83,995	5-9	P F Nicholls	B C Marshall	Antoine Bozo
KADARANN (6)	83,161	3-8	P F Nicholls	Notalotterry	H H Aga Khan's Studs
SANTENAY (5)	81,558	3-5	P F Nicholls	Hon Mrs Townshend	M-F Graffard/M Bertran
BACK IN FRONT (6)	81,393	3-4	E J O'Grady	D Cox	Miss Noreen Hayes
LE COUDRAY (9)	80,558	3-6	C Roche	John P McManus	N Pelat
LE ROI MIGUEL (5)	80,420	1-4	P F Nicholls	Mrs J Stewart	B Dutruel & E Vielly
EDREDON BLEU (11)	80,330	3-6	Miss H C Knight	Jim Lewis	Lucien Chevrollier
CLASSIFIED (7)	79,773	2-4	M C Pipe	D A Johnson	J H Walsh
GEOS (7)	78,100	1-7	N J Henderson	Thurloe Finsbury	Haras Des Coudraies
YOUNG DEVEREAUX (6)	77,400	2-3	P F Nicholls	P Barber/M Coburn/C Lewis	P J Walsh
POLIANTAS (6)	77,214	2-6	P F Nicholls	Mark Tincknell	M E Van Haaren
TARXIEN (9)	76,840	3-6	M C Pipe	B A Kilpatrick	Sheikh Rashid Al Maktoum

LEADING SIRES OF 2003 IN GREAT BRITAIN AND IRELAND

STALLION	BREEDING	RNRS	WNRS	WINS	WIN MONEY	PLACES	PLACE MONEY	TOTAL
SADLER'S WELLS (USA) (1981)	by Northern Dancer	173	76	104	2244697	222	1214920	3459617
DANEHILL (USA) (1986)	by Danzig	136	58	89	902557	203	573984	1476542
KEY OF LUCK (USA) (1991)	by Chief's Crown	47	12	20	1161785	49	249861	1411646
KRIS S (USA) (1977)	by Roberto	14	9	17	1142705	34	161145	1303850
INDIAN RIDGE (1985)	by Ahonoora	106	49	70	882558	177	416263	1298821
CADEAUX GENEREUX (1985)	by Young Generation	121	41	71	817699	186	429337	1247036
GREEN DESERT (USA) (1983)	by Danzig	83	35	52	784748	149	389556	1174304
GRAND LODGE (USA) (1991)	by Chief's Crown	140	43	72	658780	201	417242	1076022
SELKIRK (USA) (1988)	by Sharpen Up	88	33	59	551105	163	486349	1037454
DARSHAAN (1981)	by Shirley Heights	76	36	46	522894	120	507130	1030024
NIGHT SHIFT (USA) (1980)	by Northern Dancer	114	45	71	729656	223	295708	1025364
KINGMAMBO (USA) (1990)	by Mr Prospector	43	16	30	786084	68	217695	1003779
MACHIAVELLIAN (USA) (1987)	by Mr Prospector	88	43	66	594915	140	304694	899609
FAIRY KING (USA) (1982)	by Northern Dancer	11	4	8	735178	14	164295	899472
PIVOTAL (GB) (1993)	by Polar Falcon	80	30	48	638945	140	253758	892703
DANEHILL DANCER (IRE) (1993)	by Danehill	89	21	32	498440	116	353093	851534
POLAR FALCON (USA) (1987)	by Nureyev	84	36	62	462826	153	337429	800255
MARK OF ESTEEM (IRE) (1993)	by Darshaan	66	25	46	489388	107	307971	797359
ZAFONIC (USA) (1990)	by Gone West	73	25	37	456050	113	313648	769698

LEADING BRITISH AND IRISH BASED SIRES OF 2003
(GREAT BRITAIN, IRELAND AND OVERSEAS)

STALLION	BREEDING	DOMESTIC WNRS	WINS	WIN MONEY	OVERSEAS WNRS	WINS	WIN MONEY	TOTAL
SADLER'S WELLS (USA) (1981)	by Northern Dancer	76	104	2244697	48	72	2024925	4269623
SINGSPIEL (IRE) (1992)	by In The Wings	20	25	192190	28	42	3513518	3705708
DANEHILL USA (1986)	by Danzig	58	89	902557	64	110	2720043	3622600
HERNANDO (FR) (1990)	by Niniski	20	40	333722	31	57	1890281	2224002
DARSHAAN (1981)	by Shirley Heights	36	46	522894	21	33	1428290	1951184
DESERT KING (IRE) (1994)	by Danehill	20	29	424696	30	50	1385118	1809814
FAIRY KING (USA) (1982)	by Northern Dancer	4	8	735178	14	21	992320	1727498
GREEN DESERT (USA) (1983)	by Danzig	35	52	784748	33	61	935283	1720031
MACHIAVELLIAN (USA) (1987)	by Mr Prospector	43	66	594915	43	65	1078743	1673658
PEINTRE CELEBRE (USA) (1994)	by Nureyev	19	29	273587	19	30	1309279	1582866
CADEAUX GENEREUX (1985)	by Young Generation	41	71	817699	28	47	651086	1468785
PIVOTAL (GB) (1993)	by Polar Falcon	30	48	638945	23	45	793513	1432457
SRI PEKAN (USA) (1992)	by Red Ransom	34	43	241471	71	136	1175806	1417278
IN THE WINGS (1986)	by Sadler's Wells	25	34	467092	32	53	825973	1293065
MARJU (IRE) (1988)	by Last Tycoon	35	43	282739	45	95	966236	1248974
INDIAN RIDGE (1985)	by Ahonoora	49	70	882558	33	54	341767	1224325
KEY OF LUCK (USA) (1988)	by Chief's Crown	12	20	1161785	7	12	38419	1200204
SELKIRK (USA) (1988)	by Sharpen Up	33	59	551105	30	47	624222	1175327
NIGHT SHIFT (USA) (1980)	by Northen Dancer	45	71	729656	49	90	418651	1148307
KRIS S (USA) (1977)	by Roberto	9	17	1142705	0	0	0	1142705

LEADING TWO-YEAR-OLD SIRES OF 2003 IN GREAT BRITAIN AND IRELAND

STALLION	BREEDING	RNRS	WNRS	WINS	WIN MONEY	PLACES	PLACE MONEY	TOTAL
CAPE CROSS (IRE) (1994)	by Green Desert	44	20	35	367376	77	155802	523178
ROYAL APPLAUSE (GB) (1993)	by Waajib	40	16	32	385607	56	127917	513524
FASLIYEV (USA) (1997)	by Nureyev	48	19	29	388815	65	102022	490836
STORM CAT (USA) (1983)	by Storm Bird	13	9	12	318051	20	154860	472911
STRAVINSKY (USA) (1996)	by Nureyev	30	16	26	333345	48	61964	395309
DANEHILL (USA) (1986)	by Danzig	39	18	25	237128	50	135143	372271
NIGHT SHIFT (USA) (1980)	by Night Shift	33	12	21	293849	49	50298	344147
CADEAUX GENEREUX (1985)	by Young Generation	31	13	17	155259	48	137823	293082
GREEN DESERT (USA) (1983)	by Danzig	32	16	21	166425	42	120770	287195
SADLER'S WELLS (USA) (1981)	by Northern Dancer	55	15	16	130724	36	99518	230242
DAGGERS DRAWN (USA) (1995)	by Diesis	42	16	23	104344	68	124447	228791
MILLKOM (GB) (1991)	by Cyrano De Bergerac	1	1	5	193316	5	21250	214566
DANEHILL DANCER (IRE) (1993)	by Danehill	28	8	13	132912	36	74933	207844
INDIAN RIDGE (1985)	by Ahonoora	22	9	11	137473	24	69859	207332
SELKIRK (USA) (1988)	by Sharpen Up	21	6	9	159817	18	39832	199649
ORPEN (USA) (1996)	by Lure	47	13	18	112553	75	85508	198061
DR FONG (USA) (1995)	by Kris S	40	11	15	140870	38	49872	190741
INTIKHAB (USA) (1994)	by Red Ransom	31	18	24	126269	40	61454	187723
MARJU (IRE) (1988)	by Last Tycoon	33	14	16	91905	44	94749	166654
PEINTRE CELEBRE (USA) (1994)	by Nureyev	24	6	9	113049	27	63057	176106

LEADING FIRST CROP SIRES OF 2003 IN GREAT BRITAIN AND IRELAND

STALLION	BREEDING	RNRS	WNRS	WINS	WIN MONEY	PLACES	PLACE MONEY	TOTAL
CAPE CROSS (IRE) (1994)	by Green Desert	44	20	35	367376	77	155802	523178
FASLIYEV (USA) (1997)	by Nureyev	48	19	29	388815	65	102022	490836
STRAVINSKY (USA) (1996)	by Nureyev	30	16	26	333345	48	61964	395309
DAGGERS DRAWN (USA) (1995)	by Diesis	42	16	23	104344	68	124447	228791
ORPEN (USA) (1996)	by Lure	47	13	18	112553	75	85508	198061
DR FONG (USA) (1995)	by Kris S	40	11	15	140870	38	49872	190741
INTIKHAB (USA) (1994)	by Red Ransom	31	18	24	126269	40	61454	187723
DAYLAMI (IRE) (1994)	by Doyoun	26	8	11	93992	15	18542	112534
GOLD AWAY (IRE) (1995)	by Goldneyev	2	2	5	63440	5	14980	78421
SHINKO FOREST (IRE) (1993)	by Green Desert	22	6	9	31584	41	42182	73766
INDIAN ROCKET (GB) (1994)	by Indian Ridge	19	5	7	34331	23	31767	66098
STORMIN FEVER (USA) (1994)	by Storm Cat	1	1	3	57557	1	4400	61957
DOCKSIDER (USA) (1995)	by Diesis	32	7	8	31928	28	29045	60973
CROCO ROUGE (IRE) (1995)	by Rainbow Quest	15	5	6	28220	14	30600	58820
SECOND EMPIRE (IRE) (1995)	by Fairy King	19	6	7	22727	24	22268	44995
DUSHYANTOR (USA) (1993)	by Sadler's Wells	4	2	2	11992	10	16365	28357
GREAT DANE (IRE) (1995)	by Danehill	9	2	3	13337	15	9723	23061
HORSE CHESTNUT (SAF) (1995)	by Fort Wood	5	2	2	8735	6	12057	20792
HIGHEST HONOR (FR) (1983)	by Kenmare	3	2	3	8951	11	11304	20254
PRINCELY HEIR (IRE) (1995)	by Fairy King	7	2	3	11729	8	7925	19654

LEADING MATERNAL GRANDSIRES OF 2003 IN GREAT BRITAIN AND IRELAND

STALLION	BREEDING	RNRS	WNRS	WINS	WIN MONEY	PLACES	PLACE MONEY	TOTAL
RAINBOW QUEST (USA) (1981)	by Blushing Groom	111	39	62	1878137	142	522191	2400328
DARSHAAN (1981)	by Shirley Heights	120	53	78	1229137	160	458085	1687221
SADLER'S WELLS (USA) (1981)	by Northern Dancer	152	64	95	985265	225	507248	1492513
SHAHRASTANI (USA) (1983)	by Nijinsky	19	6	8	1003233	29	221424	1224657
ALLEGED (USA) (1974)	by Hoist The Flag	55	25	46	727725	80	403215	1130940
NIGHT SHIFT (USA) (1980)	by Northern Dancer	110	41	73	736067	170	345906	1081973
SHIRLEY HEIGHTS (1975)	by Mill Reef	138	56	84	587330	236	449366	1036696
MR PROSPECTOR (USA) (1970)	by Raise A Native	69	32	43	577921	108	277501	855422
ALZAO (USA) (1980)	by Lyphard	138	43	60	443654	182	394831	838484
DANCING BRAVE (USA) (1983)	by Lyphard	61	21	34	551763	107	285761	837524
SLEWPY (USA) (1980)	by Seattle Slew	1	1	3	669900	3	150227	820127
NIJINSKY (CAN) (1967)	by Northern Dancer	44	15	18	563180	63	235316	798496
NUREYEV (USA) (1977)	by Northern Dancer	78	37	53	556385	114	233507	789892
CAERLEON (USA) (1980)	by Nijinsky	120	44	64	487529	192	298172	785701
SLIP ANCHOR (1982)	by Shirley Heights	78	26	39	188831	94	560850	749681
GREEN DESERT (USA) (1983)	by Danzig	134	35	53	365245	212	380282	745527
RIVERMAN (USA) (1969)	by Never Bend	80	26	39	361707	123	360040	721747
KRIS (1976)	by Sharpen Up	120	38	58	470270	184	235175	705445
LAST TYCOON (1983)	by Try My Best	98	34	54	501686	153	189068	690754
DIESIS (1980)	by Sharpen Up	81	38	50	412477	136	266220	678697

STALLIONS EARNINGS FOR 2003

(includes every stallion who sired a winner on the flat in Great Britain and Ireland in 2003)

STALLIONS	RNRS	STARTS	WNRS	WINS	PLACES	TOTAL
ABOU ZOUZ (USA)	16	64	1	1	10	13139.53
ACAMBARO (GER)	1	3	1	1	1	3596.50
ACATENANGO (GER)	11	47	4	10	10	142911.15
ACCONDY (IRE)	1	6	1	1	1	4016.25
AFFIRMED (USA)	11	80	5	8	19	57466.71
AIR EXPRESS (IRE)	12	50	4	4	17	208502.68
AIR QUEST (GB)	1	9	1	1	1	4487.02
AKARAD (FR)	3	15	1	2	4	55465.74
ALHAARTH (IRE)	71	314	22	36	91	592860.05
ALHIJAZ (GB)	10	59	5	7	12	39141.95
ALI-ROYAL (IRE)	75	362	11	14	76	206948.82
ALLEGED (USA)	1	20	1	1	4	7261.25
ALLIED FORCES (USA)	6	23	1	2	1	9731.00
ALPHABATIM (USA)	2	11	1	2	3	12055.20
ALYDEED (CAN)	2	16	1	1	2	4366.40
ALZAO (USA)	82	407	28	41	113	474175.18
AMONG MEN (USA)	41	190	5	8	24	47665.19
ANABAA (USA)	27	114	6	9	37	196669.72
ANITA'S PRINCE	9	76	4	6	20	54585.08
ANSHAN	9	57	4	6	13	85784.83
A P INDY (USA)	8	30	5	7	10	132260.72
A P JET (USA)	1	15	1	1	4	8819.00
ARAGON	12	82	5	8	22	53268.80
ARAZI (USA)	7	31	3	4	5	22294.75
ARCH (USA)	5	12	2	2	5	12958.58
ARCHWAY (IRE)	13	97	5	8	19	70793.56
ARDKINGLASS (GB)	7	66	2	2	10	19150.80
ASHKALANI (IRE)	61	335	19	31	105	349805.01
ATRAF (GB)	56	341	16	23	90	266734.76
ATTICUS (USA)	3	30	2	3	10	29545.50
AVERTI (IRE)	28	198	7	13	56	132887.21
AWESOME (GB)	2	12	1	1	1	4185.00
BAHAMIAN BOUNTY (GB)	42	261	16	27	61	288469.60
BAHHARE (USA)	52	270	20	37	77	323067.06
BAHRI (USA)	16	67	4	4	24	54748.39
BALNIBARBI (GB)	2	12	1	1	3	5781.00
BANDMASTER (USA)	3	33	2	4	11	23025.10
THE BART (USA)	123	581	37	55	176	736799.89
BARYSHNIKOV (AUS)	2	7	1	2	0	15457.79
BATSHOOF	2	11	2	4	3	21167.75
BAY TERN (USA)	7	32	2	3	7	22751.75
BELONG TO ME (USA)	1	16	1	1	7	12703.00
BE MY CHIEF (USA)	4	23	3	5	9	139302.50
BE MY GUEST (USA)	14	97	3	4	21	35857.40
BE MY NATIVE (USA)	32	180	11	16	57	231901.30
BENEFICIAL (GB)	15	30	4	4	6	36971.86
BENNY THE DIP (USA)	2	3	1	1	1	4613.63
BERING	7	30	4	6	10	135816.68
BETTERGETON (GB)	24	125	9	16	29	298558.97
BEVELED (USA)	3	13	1	2	0	7339.00
BIEN BIEN (USA)	39	287	11	21	74	193501.30
BIG SHUFFLE (USA)	12	52	2	2	11	16890.25
BIGSTONE (IRE)	7	39	4	4	17	69335.65
BIJOU D'INDE (GB)	29	167	6	13	31	82110.53
BIN AJWAAD (IRE)	31	176	5	11	30	80432.66
BINARY STAR (USA)	30	176	8	10	39	113117.94
BISHOP OF CASHEL (GB)	5	31	1	2	7	11989.00
BLUEBIRD (USA)	39	288	19	34	80	395062.14
BLUEGRASS PRINCE (IRE)	64	344	16	22	74	315187.89
	39	212	6	10	43	90292.80

STALLIONS	RNRS	STARTS	WNRS	WINS	PLACES	TOTAL
BLUE OCEAN (USA)	7	63	2	2	23	24952.15
BLUES TRAVELLER (IRE)	20	107	3	5	30	41067.20
BLUSHING FLAME (USA)	12	60	2	2	16	26305.05
BLUSH RAMBLER (USA)	1	8	1	1	4	6037.85
BOB BACK (USA)	10	37	3	4	12	57818.82
BOBINSKI (GB)	1	3	1	1	1	4615.75
BOLD ARRANGEMENT	3	32	1	1	5	13989.50
BOTANIC (USA)	7	35	3	5	11	33306.37
BOUNDARY (USA)	6	33	1	2	10	16155.83
BRIEF TRUCE (USA)	45	310	17	27	73	200959.17
BRUNSWICK (USA)	1	19	1	1	6	14297.00
CADEAUX GENEREUX	121	597	41	71	186	1247035.56
CAERLEON (USA)	18	86	6	12	19	450256.43
CAJETANO (USA)	1	1	1	1	0	8441.56
CALLER I D (USA)	1	10	1	2	1	7312.00
CAPE CROSS (IRE)	44	190	20	35	77	523177.86
CAPOTE (USA)	5	26	1	1	4	20291.00
CARNEGIE (IRE)	5	14	3	3	5	21007.89
CASE LAW	26	145	4	8	22	68768.31
CASTEDDU (GB)	7	48	3	3	9	18222.25
CATRAIL (USA)	44	270	14	19	64	270259.69
CAT'S CAREER (USA)	1	6	1	2	1	14562.30
CAYMAN KAI (IRE)	8	42	2	3	8	18025.50
CELIO RUFO	2	3	1	1	0	4928.57
CELTIC SWING (GB)	24	118	5	8	31	202840.89
CHADDLEWORTH (IRE)	5	31	1	2	4	9694.55
CHARENTE RIVER (IRE)	1	7	1	1	2	7775.00
CHARNWOOD FOREST (IRE)	76	411	25	37	83	334793.30
CHEROKEE RUN (USA)	5	19	2	2	6	20454.95
CHIEF'S CROWN (USA)	2	15	2	2	3	9519.00
CIGAR	4	21	1	1	6	15451.80
CLANTIME	21	206	9	15	56	138977.65
CLASSIC CLICHE (IRE)	16	79	4	6	18	194542.50
CLASSIC SECRET (USA)	5	16	1	1	3	6307.51
CLOUDINGS (IRE)	11	61	1	2	12	15550.30
COBRA KING (USA)	1	6	1	1	2	5506.25
COIS NA TINE (IRE)	4	18	1	1	5	18930.50
COLLEGE CHAPEL (GB)	73	465	22	28	98	250902.19
COLONEL COLLINS (USA)	4	28	2	2	5	17784.25
COMMON GROUNDS	44	257	10	17	55	152183.79
COMPTON PLACE (GB)	63	402	19	29	130	377654.07
CONTRACT LAW (USA)	4	18	1	2	1	14809.00
COZZENE (USA)	12	44	5	6	12	41799.82
CRAFTY PROSPECTOR (USA)	4	27	3	5	9	40915.09
CROCO ROUGE (IRE)	15	65	5	6	14	58820.24
CRYPTOCLEARANCE (USA)	5	40	2	2	11	29654.19
CYRANO DE BERGERAC	17	103	2	3	21	41747.79
DAGGERS DRAWN (USA)	42	198	16	23	68	228790.70
DANCING DISSIDENT (USA)	5	40	1	2	12	19458.70
DANCING SPREE (USA)	27	145	7	8	27	42450.95
DANEHILL (USA)	136	632	58	89	203	1476541.76
DANEHILL DANCER (IRE)	89	455	21	32	116	851533.85
DANETIME (IRE)	56	344	20	33	84	413734.89
DANZERO (AUS)	30	111	11	14	35	142630.38
DANZIG (USA)	19	76	11	14	34	306690.03
DANZIG CONNECTION (USA)	42	229	10	13	63	95372.99
DARNAY (GB)	9	34	2	3	8	61562.62
DARSHAAN	76	309	36	46	120	1030023.68
DAYJUR (USA)	8	51	4	7	12	48970.26
DAYLAMI (IRE)	26	58	8	11	15	112533.96
DEFINITE ARTICLE (GB)	61	365	17	29	92	449427.41
DELTA DANCER (GB)	1	17	1	3	8	26489.20
DEMOCRATIC (USA)	4	19	1	1	4	6092.00
DEPLOY	38	173	13	19	41	127640.39

STALLIONS	RNRS	STARTS	WNRS	WINS	PLACES	TOTAL
DEPUTY MINISTER (CAN)	5	14	1	1	4	8816.10
DESERT KING (IRE)	75	327	20	29	110	546565.88
DESERT PRINCE (IRE)	70	291	22	32	92	548631.93
DESERT STORY (IRE)	51	292	6	9	73	109590.51
DESERT STYLE (IRE)	54	288	19	26	71	263013.13
DESERT SUN (GB)	35	128	10	11	27	126398.71
DEVIL'S BAG (USA)	4	9	1	1	3	27139.61
DIESIS	56	199	16	22	56	562846.17
DILUM (USA)	10	63	1	1	14	14142.70
DISTANT RELATIVE	30	254	7	13	56	149870.44
DISTANT VIEW (USA)	48	233	19	38	60	377231.91
DISTINCTLY NORTH (USA)	39	158	3	5	15	23464.79
DIXIELAND BAND (USA)	8	37	3	3	13	65261.47
DOCKSIDER (USA)	32	104	7	8	28	60972.61
DOLPHIN STREET (FR)	38	212	9	17	47	112999.79
DON CORLEONE (GB)	1	5	1	2	1	6480.00
DON'T FORGET ME	6	22	1	1	3	6655.70
DOUBLE BED (FR)	1	7	1	2	1	6362.00
DOUBLE ECLIPSE (IRE)	4	17	1	1	2	5926.26
DOUBLETOUR (USA)	4	15	1	1	7	9503.25
DOUBLE TRIGGER (IRE)	14	53	2	2	9	12085.80
DOWSING (USA)	5	35	1	1	9	16246.70
DOYOUN	14	47	4	4	14	46640.38
DR DEVIOUS (IRE)	58	253	15	26	57	339850.40
DR FONG (USA)	40	130	11	15	38	190741.44
DUMAANI (USA)	1	7	1	2	3	12803.00
DUNBEATH (USA)	1	3	1	1	1	3971.25
DUSHYANTOR (USA)	4	29	2	2	10	28357.09
DYNAFORMER (USA)	7	32	4	5	15	139056.86
EAGLE EYED (USA)	63	455	17	32	111	221180.80
EDITOR'S NOTE (USA)	1	6	1	1	1	12636.36
EFISIO	92	627	37	58	159	565892.92
ELA-MANA-MOU	20	98	5	8	24	136119.55
ELBIO	15	116	5	5	32	65752.53
EL GRAN SENOR (USA)	4	32	1	4	10	41943.00
ELMAAMUL (USA)	32	213	14	18	56	154275.69
EL PRADO (IRE)	13	64	4	5	22	124636.53
ELUSIVE QUALITY (USA)	6	26	2	2	19	49754.75
EMARATI (USA)	38	346	15	23	82	201708.31
EMPEROR JONES (USA)	52	291	14	21	72	167660.21
ENTREPRENEUR (GB)	98	474	32	44	115	592732.19
ENVIRONMENT FRIEND (GB)	9	32	1	1	5	5910.50
ERHAAB (USA)	3	9	1	1	2	9190.50
ERINS ISLE	27	86	2	3	17	34632.77
EXECUTIVE PERK	2	4	1	1	3	13896.11
EXIT TO NOWHERE (USA)	13	52	2	2	16	30370.92
EXPELLED (USA)	3	10	1	1	5	8091.80
EZZOUD (IRE)	13	90	5	9	33	119382.11
FACTUAL (USA)	10	57	2	5	12	34833.50
FAIRY KING (USA)	11	55	4	8	14	899472.19
FALTAAT (USA)	1	8	1	1	4	32598.00
FARFELU	4	25	1	1	4	5618.50
FASLIYEV (USA)	48	191	19	29	65	490836.03
FAUSTUS (USA)	3	21	1	1	3	5376.75
FAYRUZ	71	367	19	31	89	326003.93
FIRST TRUMP (GB)	79	506	17	23	136	250021.42
FITZCARRALDO (ARG)	2	18	1	4	5	14669.00
FLEETWOOD (IRE)	36	191	9	17	37	122358.68
FLYING SPUR (AUS)	40	286	18	23	76	278432.11
FOOLS HOLME (USA)	1	9	1	1	3	4644.00
FOREST WIND (USA)	9	47	2	4	10	54478.64
FORZANDO	49	281	15	23	65	188089.38
FOURSTARS ALLSTAR (USA)	12	51	3	4	13	88582.06
FOXHOUND (USA)	61	325	11	16	85	190292.43

STALLIONS	RNRS	STARTS	WNRS	WINS	PLACES	TOTAL
FRAAM (GB)	39	209	12	20	40	257441.55
FUMO DI LONDRA (IRE)	15	93	5	6	24	45943.42
GENERAL MONASH (USA)	65	296	8	11	55	81469.57
GENEROUS (IRE)	6	31	2	2	7	9220.65
GENTLEMEN (ARG)	1	4	1	1	2	4312.50
GERMANY (USA)	3	13	1	1	5	9993.50
GILDED TIME (USA)	4	22	1	1	13	20368.50
GLACIAL STORM (USA)	2	3	1	1	0	8441.56
GLORY OF DANCER (GB)	5	43	2	5	14	53906.50
GOLD AWAY (IRE)	2	12	2	5	5	78420.62
GOLDEN HEIGHTS	3	21	1	1	4	7687.50
GOLD FEVER (USA)	2	10	1	1	2	5600.75
GOLDMARK	35	184	9	9	48	83594.22
GONE WEST (USA)	28	101	11	13	37	148714.77
GOTHENBERG (IRE)	8	54	2	5	9	29702.00
GRAN ALBA (USA)	1	7	1	1	0	2982.00
GRAND LODGE (USA)	140	683	43	72	201	1076021.89
GRAND SLAM (USA)	5	23	2	2	11	34029.12
GREAT COMMOTION (USA)	19	128	5	8	28	140843.23
GREAT DANE (IRE)	9	46	2	3	15	23060.79
GREEN DANCER (USA)	5	38	1	1	12	10338.47
GREEN DESERT (USA)	83	431	35	52	149	1174304.87
GREENSMITH	11	93	5	11	21	68180.58
GREEN TUNE (USA)	3	5	1	2	1	9987.00
GREY DESIRE	2	9	1	1	0	2713.20
GROOM DANCER (USA)	71	376	25	38	108	337793.21
GULCH (USA)	32	157	10	13	45	440506.47
HALLING (USA)	52	223	22	32	73	708269.85
HAMAS (IRE)	30	192	7	14	37	115172.94
HANSEL (USA)	4	16	1	1	1	3514.70
HECTOR PROTECTOR (USA)	70	310	15	22	86	294022.71
HENNESSY (USA)	10	45	2	2	12	24052.10
HERNANDO (FR)	48	246	20	40	71	645724.73
HIGH ESTATE	4	28	2	3	12	61858.71
HIGHEST HONOR (FR)	16	98	7	10	31	145312.98
HIGH KICKER (USA)	4	23	1	1	4	3543.35
HORSE CHESTNUT (SAF)	5	13	2	2	6	20792.05
HOUMAYOUN (FR)	8	22	1	1	7	27844.15
HOUSEBUSTER (USA)	4	24	1	3	9	33746.80
HURRICANE SKY (AUS)	9	93	6	12	25	64784.95
IDRIS (IRE)	15	75	1	1	9	12971.66
IMPERIAL BALLET (IRE)	37	204	15	19	60	141698.37
IMPERIAL FRONTIER (USA)	10	73	5	6	17	50044.54
IMP SOCIETY (USA)	5	22	1	4	1	23796.20
INCHINOR (GB)	80	471	26	41	114	408450.88
IN COMMAND (IRE)	10	38	1	1	6	6968.74
INDIAN RIDGE	106	565	49	70	177	1298820.59
INDIAN ROCKET (GB)	19	95	5	7	23	66097.63
IN THE WINGS	64	270	25	34	99	713079.80
INTIKHAB (USA)	31	110	18	24	40	187722.75
INZAR (USA)	20	118	4	8	26	70428.49
IRISH RIVER (FR)	21	99	6	8	20	88878.65
IS IT TRUE (USA)	1	8	1	1	2	3738.00
JADE HUNTER (USA)	3	23	2	3	7	13701.50
JAMBALAYA JAZZ (USA)	1	4	1	1	3	17012.00
JUPITER ISLAND	1	3	1	1	0	9750.00
KAHYASI	35	170	11	21	61	243812.57
KARINGA BAY	5	15	1	1	0	3643.25
KARLINSKY (USA)	1	5	1	1	3	4890.80
KASAKOV (GB)	2	15	1	2	0	14673.56
KEFAAH (USA)	1	13	1	1	2	4889.75
KENDOR (FR)	7	10	1	1	2	8166.50
KEY OF LUCK (USA)	47	190	12	20	49	1411645.64
KINGMAMBO (USA)	43	157	16	30	68	1003778.60

STALLIONS	RNRS	STARTS	WNRS	WINS	PLACES	TOTAL
KING OF KINGS (IRE)	44	196	17	19	63	170052.34
KINGSINGER (IRE)	4	12	1	1	3	3599.00
KING'S SIGNET (USA)	16	133	7	13	51	186042.35
KING'S THEATRE (IRE)	54	267	15	22	74	178339.35
KIRKWALL (GB)	8	33	2	2	9	18957.43
KNOWN FACT (USA)	9	46	4	9	5	62351.70
KOMAITE (USA)	59	392	16	24	97	183851.88
KRIS	45	172	10	14	45	125371.87
KRIS S (USA)	14	81	9	17	34	1303850.35
KYLIAN (USA)	10	48	4	8	15	58658.61
LABEEB (GB)	5	31	2	2	13	39314.41
LAHIB (USA)	46	243	12	16	64	276573.91
LAKE CONISTON (IRE)	57	318	10	11	51	146484.83
LAST TYCOON	6	34	1	1	6	7890.52
LEAR FAN (USA)	30	133	13	23	45	348732.77
LINAMIX (FR)	45	177	15	21	70	280136.56
LION CAVERN (USA)	41	241	13	23	53	283467.73
LIT DE JUSTICE (USA)	4	35	1	1	13	14939.79
LOMITAS (GB)	10	37	4	4	12	31897.06
LORD AVIE (USA)	2	14	1	1	3	4350.23
LUCKY GUEST	11	43	2	2	12	22879.88
LUGANA BEACH	19	159	6	10	30	117342.14
LURE (USA)	5	33	2	2	5	8759.26
LYCIUS (USA)	28	164	7	16	41	122882.84
LYPHARD (USA)	1	11	1	1	5	10481.75
MACHIAVELLIAN (USA)	88	426	43	66	140	899609.12
MAGICAL STRIKE (USA)	4	31	1	1	8	12493.52
MAGICAL WONDER (USA)	13	49	3	5	12	53898.96
MAGIC RING (IRE)	73	489	24	39	116	370514.98
MAJOR JACKO	1	12	1	1	4	6836.50
MAKBUL	31	165	12	15	40	127801.56
MARJU (IRE)	87	432	35	43	124	586617.22
MARK OF ESTEEM (IRE)	66	353	25	46	107	797359.29
MASTER WILLIE	6	22	2	2	5	15314.70
MATTY G (USA)	1	4	1	1	2	3703.00
MERDON MELODY	14	101	3	3	15	21739.36
MIDHISH (GB)	21	140	5	9	36	114954.37
MIDYAN (USA)	10	47	2	8	10	46883.33
MILLKOM (GB)	18	99	7	15	25	277856.96
MIND GAMES (GB)	74	397	16	19	88	236578.14
MINSHAANSHU AMAD (USA)	4	43	2	2	6	11646.50
MINSTER SON	2	7	1	1	0	4192.50
MISTER BAILEYS (GB)	15	81	6	11	30	112508.39
MISWAKI (USA)	18	78	6	8	30	193054.66
MIZORAM (USA)	4	16	1	2	1	7263.00
MONDRIAN (GER)	2	9	1	1	1	3867.00
MONSUN (GER)	4	11	1	1	3	10574.82
MOST WELCOME	43	269	16	35	57	222144.56
MR GREELEY (USA)	1	6	1	1	3	203300.00
MR PROSPECTOR (USA)	7	38	3	9	16	51362.05
MT LIVERMORE (USA)	12	70	5	5	21	47159.21
MTOTO	45	194	11	12	44	105260.36
MUHARIB (USA)	2	14	1	1	4	8531.00
MUHTARRAM (USA)	44	277	9	17	80	165617.64
MUJADIL (USA)	105	644	34	47	161	370497.21
MUJTAHID (USA)	17	151	7	8	26	114494.25
MUKADDAMAH (USA)	39	234	14	22	69	296947.16
MY BEST VALENTINE (GB)	12	61	1	1	9	8626.10
NAHEEZ (USA)	5	20	1	1	4	9380.52
NAMAQUALAND (USA)	31	188	9	13	38	92174.08
NASHWAN (USA)	53	227	20	35	76	355551.79
NESHAD (USA)	2	6	1	1	0	2968.00
NEVER SO BOLD	10	88	3	4	14	21601.82
NICHOLAS (USA)	2	11	1	1	2	4935.50

STALLIONS	RNRS	STARTS	WNRS	WINS	PLACES	TOTAL
NICOLOTTE (GB)	28	118	9	12	32	92082.08
NIGHT SHIFT (USA)	114	782	45	71	223	1025363.63
NORDICO (USA)	4	26	2	5	8	18567.50
NORTHERN FLAGSHIP (USA)	2	21	1	2	7	10746.00
NUREYEV (USA)	18	75	8	9	30	158699.48
OCTAGONAL (NZ)	17	62	3	5	24	73226.79
OPENING VERSE (USA)	8	37	2	2	7	10997.53
ORPEN (USA)	47	201	13	18	75	198060.75
OWINGTON (GB)	4	19	1	2	9	113469.26
PARIS HOUSE (GB)	38	209	8	10	43	92250.26
PEINTRE CELEBRE (USA)	55	204	19	29	76	398497.15
PELDER (IRE)	2	11	1	1	0	2093.00
PENNEKAMP (USA)	41	224	18	27	54	278435.29
PERPENDICULAR (GB)	8	44	2	4	13	22217.25
PERSIAN BOLD	26	117	6	10	31	92241.13
PERSIAN HEIGHTS	2	9	1	4	4	214840.00
PERSONAL FLAG (USA)	1	11	1	1	4	9522.73
PERUGINO (USA)	89	440	21	28	119	357446.97
PETARDIA (GB)	45	260	10	12	35	114579.77
PETONG	41	273	11	16	51	127760.80
PETORIUS	22	120	4	5	17	45119.39
PETOSKI	4	32	1	5	9	28303.25
PHARDANTE (FR)	5	12	1	1	1	5071.43
PHARLY (FR)	10	28	1	2	10	16111.15
PHONE TRICK (USA)	3	12	1	2	5	18367.00
PICCOLO (GB)	100	630	37	60	129	486201.15
PIPS PRIDE (GB)	15	119	6	12	26	61641.99
PISTOLET BLEU (IRE)	4	14	1	1	4	5494.23
PIVOTAL (GB)	80	450	30	48	140	892703.11
POLAR FALCON (USA)	84	544	36	62	153	800254.74
POLAR PRINCE (IRE)	15	94	5	12	25	70182.20
POLIGLOTE (GB)	2	9	1	2	0	29522.00
POLISH NUMBERS (USA)	1	4	1	1	2	22692.47
POLISH PATRIOT (USA)	7	61	4	8	13	54442.46
POLISH PRECEDENT (USA)	63	285	19	25	92	641808.93
PORTRAIT GALLERY (IRE)	2	15	1	1	5	14144.94
PRESENTING (GB)	2	9	2	2	2	13490.26
PRESIDIUM	42	318	10	20	55	114855.34
PRIMO DOMINIE	78	494	28	53	100	460747.56
PRINCELY HEIR (IRE)	7	35	2	3	8	19653.83
PRINCE OF BIRDS (USA)	14	77	3	6	12	131907.64
PRINCE SABO	39	242	15	17	64	213200.58
PRIOLO (USA)	28	127	10	13	29	132210.55
PUISSANCE	35	240	8	13	55	126194.31
PURSUIT OF LOVE (GB)	64	367	23	38	84	295175.80
QUEST FOR FAME (GB)	13	81	5	7	28	62050.23
QUIET AMERICAN (USA)	7	26	1	1	6	8922.70
RAHY (USA)	24	125	13	20	50	241876.78
RAINBOW QUEST (USA)	63	241	20	30	71	470329.77
RAINBOWS FOR LIFE (CAN)	14	64	2	3	12	21262.65
RAMBO DANCER (CAN)	6	31	1	1	11	13902.45
RAPHANE (USA)	9	51	3	5	12	27883.14
REAL QUIET (USA)	3	11	1	2	7	13212.00
RED RAINBOW (GB)	2	19	1	3	6	13814.70
RED RANSOM (USA)	31	152	20	29	57	618666.65
RED SUNSET	6	52	4	7	18	150430.81
REPRIMAND	19	111	6	8	29	83998.72
REVOQUE (IRE)	76	398	15	25	89	226452.05
RIDGEWOOD BEN (GB)	9	41	1	1	7	8182.86
RISK ME (FR)	12	50	2	7	6	28134.78
RIVER FALLS (GB)	11	45	1	1	4	6141.00
ROBELLINO (USA)	60	292	15	20	73	238005.10
ROCK CITY	10	50	2	7	12	54908.89
ROCK HOPPER	13	53	3	4	19	29486.75

STALLIONS	RNRS	STARTS	WNRS	WINS	PLACES	TOTAL
ROLFE (USA)	2	9	1	2	3	10293.50
ROY (USA)	1	6	1	3	0	10277.50
ROYAL ABJAR (USA)	18	128	6	13	33	155408.75
ROYAL ACADEMY (USA)	58	324	14	23	82	323032.17
ROYAL APPLAUSE (GB)	90	537	33	59	155	935832.15
ROYAL FOUNTAIN	1	7	1	2	2	9980.52
RUBIANO (USA)	2	20	1	2	2	41580.72
RUDIMENTARY (USA)	25	225	8	16	62	166279.80
RUNAWAY GROOM (CAN)	2	6	1	1	1	3880.75
RUSSIAN REVIVAL (USA)	9	38	1	1	6	12212.76
SABREHILL (USA)	24	177	7	9	46	75135.28
SADDLERS' HALL (IRE)	15	69	4	7	6	39815.55
SADLER'S WELLS (USA)	173	581	76	104	222	3459617.04
SAFAWAN (USA)	7	74	7	11	28	131427.85
SAHM (USA)	4	12	1	1	6	14303.65
SAINT BALLADO (CAN)	3	11	2	2	3	30492.83
SALSE (USA)	29	214	12	18	66	175919.08
SALT DOME (USA)	3	15	1	1	4	9915.61
SANDPIT (BRZ)	2	13	1	1	4	5273.75
SANGLAMORE (USA)	4	23	2	3	9	56468.30
SAUMAREZ (USA)	3	13	1	2	4	17165.38
SAVAHRA SOUND	2	15	1	2	2	7520.25
SCENIC	7	60	4	6	17	55791.39
SEA RAVEN (IRE)	4	18	1	1	2	15631.80
SEATTLE SLEW (USA)	4	14	1	1	4	28405.33
SECOND EMPIRE (IRE)	19	87	6	7	24	44995.31
SECOND SET (IRE)	4	38	2	2	8	14448.92
SEEKING THE GOLD (USA)	28	105	15	20	44	227607.91
SELKIRK (USA)	88	440	33	59	163	1037453.87
SEPTIEME CIEL (USA)	8	36	1	1	4	5343.37
SESARO (USA)	32	235	7	11	61	107436.07
SEYMOUR HICKS (FR)	1	8	1	1	1	2406.00
SHAAMIT (IRE)	16	103	5	12	34	247668.94
SHALFORD (IRE)	12	87	4	8	22	78099.13
SHAMBO	2	20	1	2	9	16150.75
SHAREEF DANCER (USA)	25	135	5	12	39	98028.01
SHARP VICTOR (USA)	4	23	2	4	6	18294.50
SHAVIAN	1	28	1	6	6	26107.50
SHEIKH ALBADOU (GB)	20	137	7	10	26	73491.95
SHERNAZAR	6	23	1	5	6	148376.63
SHINKO FOREST (IRE)	22	109	6	9	41	73766.09
SHIRLEY HEIGHTS	7	45	2	6	15	82815.00
SILLERY (USA)	5	30	2	4	5	23489.10
SILVER DEPUTY (CAN)	5	21	2	2	7	25526.95
SILVER HAWK (USA)	35	124	10	14	40	240659.06
SIMPLY GREAT (FR)	8	25	1	1	4	7938.31
SIMPLY MAJESTIC (USA)	1	15	1	1	4	7089.50
SINGSPIEL (IRE)	44	168	20	25	68	381239.09
SIPHON (BRZ)	1	2	1	1	0	2254.00
SIR CAT (USA)	2	15	2	3	5	14349.80
SKY CLASSIC (CAN)	6	40	1	1	9	12173.13
SLIP ANCHOR	30	121	5	6	23	58157.08
SO FACTUAL (USA)	20	119	5	6	30	54050.09
SORBIE TOWER (IRE)	1	15	1	1	4	5412.00
SOUTHERN HALO (USA)	11	45	2	3	10	22778.19
SOUVENIR COPY (USA)	2	2	1	1	1	4192.00
SOVIET LAD (USA)	9	57	3	5	13	40362.84
SOVIET STAR (USA)	26	100	11	13	24	91057.34
SPANISH PLACE (USA)	2	9	1	1	4	6220.78
SPECIAL POWER	2	18	1	1	5	6091.75
SPECTRUM (IRE)	121	578	35	46	158	649621.81
SPINNING WORLD (USA)	21	112	7	9	28	163495.95
SRI PEKAN (USA)	110	638	34	43	171	464318.24
STARBOROUGH (GB)	7	68	4	8	17	61907.12

STALLIONS	RNRS	STARTS	WNRS	WINS	PLACES	TOTAL
STAR QUEST	1	7	1	1	3	6137.50
STATOBLEST	5	40	1	1	7	10220.60
ST JOVITE (USA)	2	8	1	1	4	5547.00
STORM BIRD (CAN)	4	12	1	1	4	25767.10
STORM CAT (USA)	25	74	11	14	32	604891.03
STORMIN FEVER (USA)	1	5	1	3	1	61957.25
STRAVINSKY (USA)	30	123	16	25	49	395309.22
STROLLING ALONG (USA)	1	14	1	1	3	5647.50
SUAVE DANCER (USA)	8	50	3	6	10	53408.95
SUBORDINATION (USA)	1	7	1	1	1	3350.25
SULTRY SONG (USA)	1	3	1	1	0	4338.75
SUNDAY SILENCE (USA)	4	10	3	3	5	58578.38
SUNSHINE FOREVER (USA)	1	20	1	5	5	30526.50
SUPERLATIVE	4	20	1	1	4	6456.30
SUPERPOWER	16	109	3	4	18	26576.10
SUPREME LEADER	7	12	1	1	3	11012.98
SURE BLADE (USA)	12	63	4	12	13	76176.70
SWAIN (IRE)	21	87	9	12	40	145643.72
SWORD DANCE	1	23	1	3	8	13621.50
TABASCO CAT (USA)	4	17	1	1	7	12211.97
TAGULA (IRE)	50	293	19	39	85	346604.63
TAKE RISKS (FR)	3	7	1	1	1	7367.00
TALE OF THE CAT (USA)	5	15	2	2	6	18397.74
TAMARISK (IRE)	1	15	1	1	4	6957.25
TAMURE (IRE)	5	32	3	3	14	37386.45
TEMPORAL (GER)	1	3	1	1	1	5525.97
TENBY (GB)	7	55	2	2	12	27886.27
THATCHING	12	86	5	7	19	35931.80
THEATRICAL	34	150	18	22	38	277323.41
THUNDER GULCH (USA)	5	22	1	1	7	21949.43
TIMELESS TIMES (USA)	28	172	4	4	29	47435.64
TINA'S PET	2	17	1	1	6	10992.00
TIROL	5	19	2	2	1	12101.15
TITUS LIVIUS (FR)	63	372	19	24	99	306795.70
TOULON (GB)	6	13	3	4	1	18311.69
TRAGIC ROLE (USA)	23	101	3	7	20	47862.90
TREASURE KAY	3	16	2	2	1	11902.59
TREMPOLINO (USA)	11	63	5	8	25	70313.68
TURTLE ISLAND (IRE)	67	378	16	30	83	249207.30
TWINING (USA)	2	19	2	2	6	10581.18
UNBLEST (GB)	5	41	3	5	9	82119.89
UNBRIDLED'S SONG (USA)	1	8	1	2	2	21428.58
UN DESPERADO (FR)	3	10	1	3	4	61733.76
UNFUWAIN (USA)	56	242	14	17	53	212080.25
UP AND AT 'EM (GB)	26	177	9	13	35	79599.10
VETTORI (IRE)	60	287	26	37	77	275416.36
VICTORY NOTE (USA)	67	405	14	19	108	181961.47
WAAJIB	3	10	1	1	2	6786.10
WARNING	11	95	3	3	31	66047.41
WARRSHAN (USA)	4	28	2	6	8	20731.40
WASHINGTON STATE (USA)	1	9	1	1	3	5014.25
WELDNAAS (USA)	5	34	1	1	9	10151.25
THE WEST (USA)	15	73	2	2	22	23556.50
WHITTINGHAM (IRE)	33	225	6	9	37	76580.40
WILD AGAIN (USA)	4	18	1	1	5	26322.70
WINNING GALLERY	2	18	1	5	4	30076.30
WIZARD KING (GB)	50	211	6	8	30	75319.71
WOLFHOUND (USA)	58	389	17	30	91	259498.14
WOODBOROUGH (USA)	68	386	14	24	75	160914.93
WOODMAN (USA)	38	189	13	15	57	259381.36
WOODS OF WINDSOR (USA)	5	25	1	3	6	26394.24
YOU AND I (USA)	1	15	1	3	4	28806.90
YOUNG ERN (GB)	24	105	4	5	15	26887.73
ZABEEL (NZ)	1	8	1	2	0	17630.10

STALLIONS	RNRS	STARTS	WNRS	WINS	PLACES	TOTAL
ZAFONIC (USA)	73	371	25	37	113	769698.13
ZAMINDAR (USA)	30	158	6	10	21	62792.83
ZIETEN (USA)	12	80	6	7	29	90064.05
ZILZAL (USA)	38	205	10	16	53	186618.47

BY KIND PERMISSION OF WEATHERBYS

Foaling dates are shown for two-year-olds
where these are provided, and the purchase
price (in guineas) as a yearling.

JUMP STALLIONS EARNINGS FOR 2002/2003

(includes every stallion who sired a winner on the jump in Great Britain and Ireland in 2002/2003)

STALLIONS	RNRS	STARTS	WNRS	WINS	PLACES	TOTAL
AAHSAYLAD	9	33	2	2	9	19863.50
ABARY (GER)	1	8	1	2	3	14414.30
ABEDNEGO	8	29	4	4	6	23192.04
ABSALOM	10	39	3	3	10	13913.45
ACATENANGO (GER)	7	26	1	1	13	15531.89
ACCORDION	53	182	12	16	49	195252.14
ACCOUNTANT (NZ)	1	9	1	1	3	6212.75
AFFIRMED (USA)	7	21	1	1	7	16312.09
AFZAL	39	106	7	8	20	39026.00
AIR DISPLAY (USA)	5	12	1	1	2	5207.80
AJDAYT (USA)	4	11	1	3	2	29700.10
AKARAD (FR)	4	13	1	1	3	6668.22
ALA HOUNAK	9	49	1	1	14	33523.50
ALDERBROOK (GB)	24	67	4	7	17	46482.10
ALESSO (USA)	1	3	1	2	1	117060.00
ALFIE DICKINS	1	9	1	1	1	4129.00
ALFLORA (IRE)	83	278	19	33	72	300420.76
ALHAARTH (IRE)	5	29	3	4	12	26901.48
ALHIJAZ (GB)	19	58	4	6	14	33676.00
ALIAS SMITH (USA)	2	13	1	2	0	9072.00
ALI-ROYAL (IRE)	11	42	3	3	10	33140.15
ALLEGED (USA)	13	55	3	3	13	20630.65
ALL HASTE (USA)	5	28	2	2	11	27385.13
ALMOOJID	7	33	1	1	4	5623.10
ALPHABATIM (USA)	61	263	15	23	54	193320.51
ALWUHUSH (USA)	2	6	1	2	2	45033.26
ALYDEED (CAN)	1	10	1	1	3	7938.65
ALZAO (USA)	18	57	2	2	19	17159.56
AMBOISE	1	10	1	1	2	5126.00
ANABAA (USA)	5	18	1	2	6	18914.89
ANDRETTI	6	33	1	2	4	16297.53
ANSHAN	33	128	9	14	25	96354.92
APELDOORN (FR)	5	22	3	4	6	31051.71
APRIL NIGHT (FR)	2	12	3	5	2	25090.75
ARAPAHOS (FR)	3	12	1	1	2	5806.89
ARAZI (USA)	7	32	2	4	10	98317.03
ARCANE (USA)	2	6	1	1	0	3542.50
ARCHITECT (USA)	4	11	1	1	1	5729.00
ARCHWAY (IRE)	15	55	3	6	22	142671.41
ARCTIC CIDER (USA)	8	38	3	6	8	33434.20
ARCTIC LORD	67	280	15	23	85	219404.31
ARCTIC TERN (USA)	4	17	1	1	5	13309.00
ARDKINGLASS (GB)	6	19	1	1	5	13491.03
ARDROSS	19	53	4	4	14	85228.05
ARISTOCRACY	40	183	10	21	50	254756.64
ART FRANCAIS (USA)	2	14	1	1	6	7169.00
ARZANNI	15	46	3	6	14	55844.35
ASHKALANI (IRE)	13	47	2	4	15	23987.52
ASHMOLEAN (USA)	5	30	1	1	10	15323.65
ASIR	9	54	5	8	18	74741.85
ASTRONEF	3	26	1	2	7	13340.20
BABY TURK	5	24	3	6	9	150364.59
BAD CONDUCT (USA)	4	18	3	5	4	45261.25
BAHRI (USA)	2	7	1	1	2	7447.25
BAKHAROFF (USA)	2	10	1	1	0	3066.00
BAL HARBOUR (GB)	2	5	1	1	2	3049.00
BALINGER	6	21	1	1	8	8653.27

STALLIONS	RNRS	STARTS	WNRS	WINS	PLACES	TOTAL
BALLACASHTAL (CAN)	7	40	2	3	6	15564.50
BALLAD ROCK	3	14	1	1	4	7848.25
BALLEROY (USA)	2	9	2	3	0	18079.25
BALLET ROYAL (USA)	7	21	1	1	3	5538.25
BALNIBARBI (GB)	4	11	1	1	0	2975.00
BALSAMO (FR)	1	5	1	4	1	24874.50
BARATHEA (IRE)	24	76	4	5	14	41721.96
THE BART (USA)	13	66	3	4	23	32688.64
BATSHOOF	12	69	3	3	21	36672.50
BAYOLIDAAN (FR)	3	11	1	1	2	8160.40
BEAUDELAIRE (USA)	3	15	2	4	3	17828.40
BEAU SHER	38	170	12	16	44	136258.82
BEDFORD	7	20	2	2	5	18559.10
BE MY CHIEF (USA)	25	90	6	14	23	93304.02
BE MY GUEST (USA)	22	90	6	9	20	68519.30
BE MY NATIVE (USA)	367	1383	102	158	370	2024166.36
BENEFICIAL (GB)	15	60	2	2	12	20201.57
BENNY THE DIP (USA)	3	8	1	3	2	31271.50
BEREG (USA)	1	13	1	2	7	16469.83
BERING	15	85	7	10	29	108423.34
BEVELED (USA)	22	75	2	2	11	9926.05
BEYSSAC (FR)	13	42	4	8	11	121112.91
BIEN BIEN (USA)	3	29	3	6	14	42633.20
BIG SINK HOPE (USA)	5	23	2	2	2	13512.13
BIGSTONE (IRE)	33	137	11	18	36	178577.36
BIN AJWAAD (IRE)	10	39	2	3	4	15140.30
BINARY STAR (USA)	1	3	1	1	0	2217.60
BLACK MINSTREL	11	42	2	3	11	36424.86
BLACK MONDAY	12	53	5	8	14	46091.00
BLAKENEY	3	10	1	1	1	2308.00
BLUEBIRD (USA)	16	56	1	2	15	18869.50
BLUES TRAVELLER (IRE)	20	71	4	4	17	39565.82
BLUSHING FLAME (USA)	10	38	2	5	10	38492.60
BOB BACK (USA)	76	268	20	31	73	453315.85
BOB'S RETURN (IRE)	34	125	7	10	27	78805.34
BOLD FOX	3	19	1	4	5	23099.71
BOSTON TWO STEP (USA)	2	8	1	2	2	9001.00
BOTANIC (USA)	2	6	1	2	3	9801.75
BOYNE VALLEY	11	30	2	3	4	15816.84
BRAVEFOOT (GB)	10	43	3	3	5	19999.28
BRIEF TRUCE (USA)	36	143	10	12	42	92894.85
BROADSWORD (USA)	24	104	7	10	34	98139.60
BROADWAY FLYER (USA)	3	18	1	1	6	8742.00
BROKEN HEARTED	60	238	14	20	59	201543.82
BROTHERLY (USA)	1	7	1	1	1	3991.00
BRUSH ASIDE (USA)	22	74	4	7	17	45655.93
BUCKSKIN (FR)	54	202	11	16	63	262882.90
BULLDOZER	3	23	2	2	5	17032.07
BUSTINO	17	57	8	10	18	114360.29
BYBICELLO	1	4	1	1	2	2300.00
CACHE OF GOLD (USA)	2	9	1	3	3	16422.05
CADEAUX GENEREUX	18	79	5	10	15	56970.17
CADOUDAL (FR)	23	76	7	9	21	155419.97
CAERLEON (USA)	20	61	4	10	4	52192.70
CAJETANO (USA)	3	8	1	4	1	163704.57
CAMDEN TOWN	54	177	9	12	44	127316.37
CAPOTE (USA)	4	23	2	3	7	15818.55
CARDINAL FLOWER	8	36	3	4	7	26739.45
CARLINGFORD CASTLE	25	89	5	10	14	61831.08
CARLTON (GER)	5	15	2	2	3	6410.75
CARMELITE HOUSE (USA)	4	16	1	2	4	21510.26
CARROLL HOUSE	20	47	2	2	5	9850.72
CASE LAW	10	35	1	2	9	14294.14
CASHEL COURT	3	14	2	2	7	23704.53
CASTEDDU (GB)	5	22	2	5	5	29441.70
CASTLE KEEP	22	85	2	3	21	44722.44

STALLIONS	RNRS	STARTS	WNRS	WINS	PLACES	TOTAL
CATALDI	26	86	5	5	18	38551.43
CATRAIL (USA)	16	60	3	3	10	24900.68
CELIO RUFO	23	140	12	20	49	214568.81
CELTIC ARMS (FR)	1	1	1	1	0	3584.42
CELTIC SWING (GB)	9	29	2	3	8	14026.40
CHAKIRIS (USA)	1	8	1	2	3	10476.14
CHAMBERLIN (FR)	7	35	2	3	14	43173.00
CHARLIE BARLEY (USA)	1	4	1	1	1	5379.49
CHARMER	14	77	6	9	13	61877.00
CHARNWOOD FOREST (IRE)	24	77	1	1	10	12167.29
CHEF DE CLAN II (FR)	4	21	2	4	7	73687.05
CISTO (FR)	1	5	1	1	1	4880.50
CLANTIME	6	27	1	2	7	12677.50
CLASSIC CHEER (IRE)	2	19	1	3	7	19010.47
CLASSIC MEMORY	4	15	1	1	4	7310.00
CLASSIC MUSIC (USA)	2	9	1	1	5	12540.50
CLASSIC SECRET (USA)	8	37	1	1	6	13209.19
CLEARLY BUST	10	49	3	4	9	27249.01
COLLEGE CHAPEL (GB)	22	71	3	3	8	13736.63
COMMANCHE RUN	106	445	27	34	118	371647.26
COMMON GROUNDS	26	71	2	2	20	20321.25
CONQUERING HERO (USA)	6	23	1	1	7	9232.81
CONTRACT LAW (USA)	18	73	4	5	11	32833.90
CONVINCED	6	32	1	1	14	43311.64
COOL JAZZ (GB)	1	10	1	2	4	13299.75
CORONADO (IRE)	2	11	1	2	5	20949.63
CORROUGE (USA)	18	46	1	1	2	4833.96
COSMONAUT (GB)	12	32	2	2	6	12826.05
COZZENE (USA)	3	10	2	3	4	58361.21
CRESTED LARK	8	25	2	4	4	53249.60
CRICKET BALL (USA)	2	11	1	1	4	68830.80
CRUISE MISSILE	12	22	1	1	2	5653.50
CYBORG (FR)	17	73	7	8	24	223108.41
DAHAR (USA)	1	8	1	1	4	11228.25
DANCING DISSIDENT (USA)	11	37	1	2	7	15360.75
DANCING HIGH	5	21	2	2	9	17509.50
DANCING SPREE (USA)	8	29	2	3	6	15807.99
DANEHILL (USA)	16	78	5	8	23	67431.64
DANEHILL DANCER (IRE)	12	34	2	2	4	19013.94
DANZIG CONNECTION (USA)	12	43	5	7	12	42985.50
DARK STONE (FR)	1	6	1	1	3	10211.80
DARSHAAN	23	98	7	10	31	147407.90
DASHING BLADE	7	30	3	4	7	23068.50
DAUPHIN DU BOURG (FR)	1	5	1	1	4	21789.89
DAYJUR (USA)	3	11	1	3	1	14920.55
DEFENSIVE PLAY (USA)	2	11	1	2	3	19981.88
DEFINITE ARTICLE (GB)	24	86	6	14	23	121249.49
DELTIC (USA)	1	5	1	1	1	4897.50
DEMOCRATIC (USA)	7	26	1	1	6	8264.87
DENEL (FR)	21	73	6	6	18	47019.09
DEPLOY	36	119	7	14	41	88231.27
DERRING ROSE	6	18	2	2	5	11561.00
DERRYLIN	35	139	10	16	40	145043.02
DESERT KING (IRE)	6	21	2	2	5	11836.55
DESERT OF WIND (USA)	2	8	1	2	3	11400.79
DESSE ZENNY (USA)	7	27	2	2	3	11551.93
DIESIS	17	91	6	8	33	72992.17
DILUM (USA)	6	35	3	5	9	26356.84
DISTANT RELATIVE	12	50	1	1	15	12788.62
DISTANT VIEW (USA)	7	25	1	1	1	4031.00
DISTINCTLY NORTH (USA)	36	116	5	9	22	66071.78
DJARVIS (USA)	2	8	1	1	4	18077.75
DOLPHIN STREET (FR)	31	127	6	6	34	53034.52
DOM ALCO (FR)	3	16	2	3	6	38609.00
DOMITOR (USA)	2	7	1	1	3	6137.80
DOMYNSKY	4	10	1	1	0	2268.00

STALLIONS	RNRS	STARTS	WNRS	WINS	PLACES	TOTAL
DON'T FORGET ME	12	41	1	2	9	19805.48
DOUBLE BED (FR)	4	12	1	1	4	9124.30
DOUNBA (FR)	1	6	1	1	2	7645.75
DOWSING (USA)	3	17	1	1	7	8290.00
DOYOUN	20	79	4	8	18	85963.50
DR DEVIOUS (IRE)	14	60	3	3	8	21353.52
DROMOD HILL	13	37	1	1	7	9711.59
DRY DOCK	9	38	2	5	3	31669.15
DUKY	8	28	1	1	5	10874.21
DUNBEATH (USA)	5	16	1	1	3	3933.00
DURGAM (USA)	7	21	1	1	1	4555.63
DYNAFORMER (USA)	6	21	2	5	9	32739.31
EAGLE EYED (USA)	17	57	4	5	9	57578.50
EFISIO	20	56	4	5	9	29904.90
ELA-MANA-MOU	20	91	7	11	29	61583.33
ELBIO	11	40	1	1	9	13787.48
EL CONQUISTADOR	3	8	2	2	3	18300.00
ELECTRIC	9	33	1	1	2	8401.17
EL GRAN SENOR (USA)	4	12	1	1	1	3655.00
ELMAAMUL (USA)	14	63	2	2	16	18422.08
EMARATI (USA)	11	29	3	3	6	15853.25
EMPEROR FOUNTAIN	6	24	1	1	10	12905.70
EMPEROR JONES (USA)	22	82	5	7	17	50887.68
EN CALCAT (FR)	4	23	2	4	13	45773.10
ENTREPRENEUR (GB)	7	26	2	2	9	15701.01
ENVIRONMENT FRIEND (GB)	14	64	6	8	15	46593.50
EPERVIER BLEU (FR)	11	43	5	9	10	112158.93
ERDELISTAN (FR)	8	37	3	5	6	63160.33
ERIN'S HOPE	2	17	2	3	5	24752.50
ERINS ISLE	45	169	13	24	39	217146.31
EUPHEMISM	11	34	1	5	5	30582.60
EUROBUS	34	95	3	3	17	22245.27
EVE'S ERROR	14	72	2	4	16	82779.41
EXECUTIVE PERK	106	366	14	19	75	215761.15
EXIT TO NOWHERE (USA)	15	66	6	8	29	107131.08
EZZOUD (IRE)	21	94	4	12	38	219860.88
FACTUAL (USA)	5	7	1	1	1	4672.00
FAIRYDEL (IRE)	3	8	1	1	2	6800.61
FAIRY KING (USA)	12	56	7	11	20	78003.22
FAMOUS STAR	1	8	1	1	3	7838.50
FARHAAN	10	42	1	2	5	11639.19
FARMA WAY (USA)	1	9	1	1	4	8750.09
FAR NORTH (CAN)	1	8	1	3	5	112893.14
FAUSTUS (USA)	14	61	3	5	12	28643.00
FAVOURED NATIONS (IRE)	1	6	1	2	3	22017.50
FAYRUZ	15	54	2	4	10	22789.77
FEELINGS (FR)	3	12	1	1	5	7192.15
FIJAR TANGO (FR)	5	22	1	2	8	20396.90
FIRST NORMAN (USA)	4	12	1	1	3	9642.00
FIRST TRUMP (GB)	21	76	2	3	14	18445.95
FIT TO FIGHT (USA)	1	9	1	2	3	12991.33
FLASH OF STEEL	1	14	1	1	3	10038.00
FLORIDA SON	10	34	2	2	6	26977.31
FLYING SPUR (AUS)	16	34	2	3	5	19645.20
FOREST WIND (USA)	20	62	2	2	15	24592.69
FORZANDO	8	24	1	1	9	7285.52
FOURSTARS ALLSTAR (USA)	56	191	8	11	38	72397.32
FOXHOUND (USA)	15	77	7	13	22	80497.19
FRAAM (GB)	7	25	1	1	5	5978.75
FREDDIE'S STAR	2	6	1	2	0	10474.00
FREEDOM'S CHOICE (USA)	1	5	1	1	1	4451.00
FRESH BREEZE (USA)	6	23	1	1	14	16710.80
FRIMAIRE (GB)	4	12	1	1	2	5056.77
FUNAMBULE (FR)	2	14	1	1	5	6115.50
FUNNY BABY (FR)	1	7	1	5	1	33094.50
GANGES (USA)	2	13	1	1	8	22900.20

STALLIONS	RNRS	STARTS	WNRS	WINS	PLACES	TOTAL
GARDE ROYALE	15	59	6	11	16	75589.34
GASPARD DE LA NUIT (FR)	1	8	1	3	2	50811.15
GENERAL HOLME (USA)	2	6	1	2	2	16182.00
GENERAL MONASH (USA)	13	32	2	2	5	14759.90
GENERAL VIEW	1	5	1	2	0	11843.00
GENEROUS (IRE)	17	96	6	11	32	141636.90
GERI (USA)	1	6	1	3	2	34235.44
GERMANY (USA)	10	40	1	2	6	14521.30
GILDORAN	44	167	9	12	44	147797.29
GLACIAL STORM (USA)	157	642	49	76	170	660248.56
GLAIEUL (USA)	2	8	1	1	2	6814.29
GLORY OF DANCER (GB)	2	5	1	2	2	12434.80
GODS SOLUTION	3	6	1	1	1	2129.00
GOLD AND IVORY (USA)	1	3	1	1	2	6144.75
GOLDMARK (USA)	28	88	11	13	24	123469.99
GOLDNEYEV (USA)	3	11	2	4	3	62895.97
GONE FISHIN	12	28	1	1	2	3788.36
GOOD THYNE (USA)	157	610	43	60	147	476471.43
GOOFALIK (USA)	3	12	2	2	3	10799.59
GOTHLAND (USA)	14	36	2	2	8	14634.47
GOVERNOR GENERAL	3	17	1	6	5	18652.50
GRAND LODGE (USA)	26	81	5	6	19	35327.83
GRAND PLAISIR (IRE)	29	61	2	3	8	23424.21
GRAND TRESOR (FR)	9	43	3	5	19	112702.26
GRAVERON (FR)	1	11	1	1	2	3881.00
GREAT COMMOTION (USA)	9	31	1	1	7	6510.79
GREAT MARQUESS	7	16	2	2	3	5739.27
GREEN ADVENTURE (USA)	5	22	1	1	9	13937.40
GREEN DANCER (USA)	13	40	2	2	12	19723.49
GREEN DESERT (USA)	12	41	3	4	6	20963.50
GREENSMITH	19	64	2	2	16	16718.81
GREEN TUNE (USA)	3	12	1	2	2	18578.75
GULCH (USA)	7	22	2	2	6	14141.20
GUNNER B	46	179	14	35	63	584652.78
HALLING (USA)	8	38	4	9	8	56568.05
HAMAS (IRE)	13	42	4	4	12	29166.22
HATIM (USA)	9	25	1	1	8	19438.48
HAWKSTONE (IRE)	4	15	2	4	5	23488.36
HECTOR PROTECTOR (USA)	4	10	1	1	4	7833.25
HEIGHTS OF GOLD	1	4	1	1	0	3521.00
HELLIOS (USA)	1	5	1	1	4	11684.50
HENBIT (USA)	51	159	7	8	33	66765.74
HERNANDO (FR)	16	63	4	8	19	175595.71
HERO'S HONOR (USA)	3	11	1	4	3	15851.48
HIGH ESTATE	7	31	1	1	8	9771.00
HIGHEST HONOR (FR)	9	52	5	12	14	120639.90
HIGH ICE (USA)	1	8	1	1	3	8250.00
HOLLOW HAND	19	71	4	5	16	63189.33
HOMME DE LOI (IRE)	2	7	2	2	3	14426.37
HOMO SAPIEN	43	155	2	7	34	71841.16
HOUMAYOUN (FR)	18	61	1	1	11	39255.58
HOUSAMIX (FR)	2	13	1	1	1	4688.00
HOUSE RULES (USA)	1	8	1	1	5	6263.50
HUBBLY BUBBLY (USA)	12	59	3	7	10	53406.59
HULA TOWN (NZ)	1	7	1	1	3	20605.00
HUSYAN (USA)	49	167	9	10	47	181567.95
HYMNS ON HIGH	2	3	1	1	0	5152.60
IADES (FR)	1	6	1	2	1	14428.00
IDIOT'S DELIGHT	7	31	2	2	8	18807.00
IDRIS (IRE)	8	33	1	1	5	7978.01
IKDAM	18	72	4	4	17	43306.07
IMPERIAL FRONTIER (USA)	6	25	2	3	5	27321.93
IMPORT	1	13	1	1	5	8191.64
IMP SOCIETY (USA)	9	23	1	1	5	5239.50
INCHINOR (GB)	17	56	2	3	19	67950.61
INDIAN RIDGE	21	98	9	11	32	80142.86

STALLIONS	RNRS	STARTS	WNRS	WINS	PLACES	TOTAL
INFANTRY	11	21	1	1	3	4645.35
INSAN (USA)	54	190	10	17	56	169487.86
INTERREX (CAN)	11	68	5	8	23	50099.30
IN THE WINGS	28	106	6	7	31	152638.06
INZAR (USA)	7	30	2	4	7	106773.74
IRON DUKE (FR)	2	5	1	2	0	19587.25
JAMESMEAD	5	24	3	5	7	36611.68
JAPE (USA)	3	10	2	2	3	10775.50
JENDALI (USA)	7	23	2	2	3	7226.50
JOHANN QUATZ (FR)	3	32	3	12	10	85363.45
JOHN FRENCH	13	40	3	3	6	24116.56
JOLLY JAKE (NZ)	37	185	15	26	59	290190.52
JUMBO HIRT (USA)	12	50	2	2	9	10103.75
JUPITER ISLAND	29	105	9	10	21	103910.57
JURADO (USA)	102	426	21	30	95	252876.18
KADALKO (FR)	9	37	5	6	8	27574.00
KADOUNOR (FR)	2	8	2	2	2	11394.00
KADROU (FR)	1	6	1	2	4	9806.15
KAHYASI	31	146	7	14	38	128278.53
KALDOUN (FR)	3	15	1	1	3	9940.65
KAMBALDA	13	44	5	6	12	50707.99
KARINGA BAY	45	161	12	16	43	93918.30
KASHTAN (FR)	1	5	1	1	3	5570.75
KEDELLIC (FR)	1	2	1	1	0	2551.50
KEEN	13	47	1	4	8	33765.40
KEFAAH (USA)	4	16	3	3	0	21151.06
KENDOR (FR)	5	29	2	4	9	85687.50
KENMARE (FR)	2	9	1	1	3	24497.93
KEY OF LUCK (USA)	10	41	2	3	15	29351.73
KING AMONG KINGS	3	19	2	3	5	16603.00
KING LUTHIER	13	50	2	2	13	17084.56
KINGMAMBO (USA)	4	12	1	2	4	11131.86
KING PERSIAN	5	31	1	1	12	25693.42
KINGS LAKE (USA)	1	2	1	1	1	2742.50
KING'S RIDE	94	306	17	24	87	255076.89
KING'S THEATRE (IRE)	20	77	10	20	23	231883.79
KLIMT (FR)	1	8	1	2	5	16591.30
KNOWN FACT (USA)	2	10	1	3	5	18703.25
KOMAITE (USA)	7	21	3	3	4	19488.95
KRIS	29	141	12	18	53	177816.19
KYLIAN (USA)	7	19	1	2	10	18525.50
LAFONTAINE (USA)	18	80	4	7	22	46268.51
LAHIB (USA)	17	54	3	4	14	42402.57
LAKE CONISTON (IRE)	6	17	1	1	3	4719.91
LAMPON (FR)	2	8	2	2	3	15647.65
LANCASTRIAN	29	110	3	5	33	65485.30
LANDO (GER)	4	15	2	4	6	29868.43
LANDYAP (USA)	6	29	2	2	8	29615.25
LASHKARI	20	97	8	9	24	86655.74
LAST TYCOON	8	33	1	1	3	3917.45
LAW SOCIETY (USA)	8	41	2	2	12	21338.55
LEADING COUNSEL (USA)	40	175	7	9	36	66791.00
LEAR FAN (USA)	13	76	8	11	26	68679.61
LE BAVARD (FR)	11	40	1	1	9	8036.31
LE COQ D'OR	3	25	1	2	7	12055.50
LEGAL CIRCLES (USA)	1	12	1	1	4	9931.65
LE MOSS	21	108	7	12	39	101451.07
LE NAIN JAUNE (FR)	8	25	2	2	8	48942.13
LE RIVERAIN (FR)	3	22	2	4	10	31257.35
LESOTHO (FR)	4	18	1	1	5	16095.10
LIGHTER	10	58	5	6	23	57708.85
LIGHTS OUT (FR)	2	13	1	2	4	8606.00
LINAMIX (FR)	11	38	5	6	11	37893.63
LION CAVERN (USA)	18	62	3	5	11	27472.85
LIR	9	29	2	2	8	24949.95
LITTLE BIGHORN	21	71	4	4	18	28577.64

STALLIONS	RNRS	STARTS	WNRS	WINS	PLACES	TOTAL
LITTLE BROWN JUG (NZ)	1	1	1	1	0	4075.50
LITTLE WOLF	7	29	2	3	8	25746.96
LOCHNAGER	1	9	1	1	0	1958.60
LOMITAS (GB)	4	21	2	2	7	10627.60
LONG POND	5	12	1	1	2	3432.67
LORD AMERICO	172	722	34	55	187	560619.69
LORD AT WAR (ARG)	1	6	1	2	2	7655.10
LORD BALLINA (AUS)	1	3	1	1	2	17421.60
LORD BUD	16	43	2	3	10	16217.25
LOUP SOLITAIRE (USA)	1	9	1	5	3	83995.80
LUCKY GUEST	10	46	1	1	11	20140.62
LUGANA BEACH	6	21	1	1	3	3499.00
LURE (USA)	4	13	2	4	4	23040.75
LUTE ANTIQUE (FR)	8	34	4	6	15	119525.51
LUTH DANCER (USA)	1	5	1	1	1	14423.32
LYCIUS (USA)	19	108	5	12	19	124301.33
LYPHENTO (USA)	8	25	2	4	5	17255.85
MACHIAVELLIAN (USA)	10	49	3	5	15	71328.64
MAGICAL STRIKE (USA)	11	50	2	3	8	16329.90
MAGICAL WONDER (USA)	27	123	9	15	38	120691.53
MAGIC RING (IRE)	13	36	1	1	2	4402.00
MAKBUL	11	40	2	2	4	8060.60
MANDALUS	125	508	25	35	114	284181.39
MANGO EXPRESS	2	7	1	2	4	15493.08
MANSONNIEN (FR)	6	26	2	5	8	82712.28
MARIGNAN (USA)	1	13	2	5	6	19643.75
MARJU (IRE)	21	69	2	2	26	34658.41
MARK OF ESTEEM (IRE)	7	17	1	1	2	5885.00
MASTER WILLIE	8	19	1	2	5	18311.20
MATAHAWK	2	8	1	1	3	8239.00
MATCHING PAIR	1	5	1	1	2	7022.00
MAZAAD	16	79	2	4	19	24092.24
MAZILIER (USA)	3	9	1	1	0	8307.00
MBAIKI (FR)	1	5	1	1	2	5445.00
MEADOWBROOK	10	32	3	4	8	16328.10
MESLEH	2	16	1	1	4	6775.00
MICHELOZZO (USA)	11	37	3	4	11	35127.15
MIDHISH (GB)	6	18	1	2	0	10219.98
MIDNIGHT LEGEND (GB)	2	8	2	2	1	5061.40
MIDYAN (USA)	11	50	5	10	15	49027.00
MIESQUE'S SON (USA)	1	8	1	1	3	4983.50
MILESIUS (USA)	1	3	1	1	1	2497.90
MILIEU	15	59	1	5	9	47148.00
MILLFONTAINE	4	31	3	5	5	47055.85
MILLKOM (GB)	6	19	1	1	4	6223.27
MIND GAMES (GB)	5	19	1	1	2	7204.17
MINDS MUSIC (USA)	1	9	1	5	2	43702.40
MINER'S LAMP	11	23	1	1	1	4010.66
MINSHAANSHU AMAD (USA)	7	19	1	1	5	5548.90
MINSTER SON	55	225	10	19	64	132337.42
MIRROR BOY	3	21	2	3	9	19132.10
MISSED FLIGHT (GB)	12	42	1	2	1	6840.50
MISSOLONGHI (USA)	1	5	1	1	3	9155.40
MISTER BAILEYS (GB)	5	19	2	3	6	17016.61
MISTER LORD (USA)	104	399	33	51	93	353952.62
MISTER MAT (FR)	3	8	1	3	2	82813.00
MISTER SICY (FR)	2	8	1	1	2	6203.50
MISTIGRI	1	2	1	1	0	10725.00
MOLLICONE JUNIOR (FR)	1	5	1	1	0	4810.00
MONDRIAN (GER)	2	13	2	3	4	12767.50
MONSUN (GER)	8	31	5	9	10	74226.00
MONTEKIN	3	16	1	1	4	11174.84
MONTELIMAR (USA)	146	607	46	64	181	1203625.81
MONTORSELLI	2	5	1	2	1	10418.50
MOONAX (IRE)	2	3	1	1	0	3416.00
MORESPEED	3	9	1	1	3	37414.20

STALLIONS	RNRS	STARTS	WNRS	WINS	PLACES	TOTAL
MORPETH (GB)	10	27	3	4	8	18952.50
MOSCOW SOCIETY (USA)	69	245	11	18	59	330650.70
MOST WELCOME	14	55	4	5	12	26665.44
MOTIVATE	2	5	1	1	1	3255.00
MOTLEY (USA)	2	15	1	1	3	38381.00
MR CONFUSION (IRE)	4	16	1	1	3	10304.27
MR DITTON	2	10	1	3	4	25650.95
MTOTO	32	120	9	13	29	101463.89
MUHARIB (USA)	15	59	1	2	21	27116.01
MUHTARRAM (USA)	7	28	2	2	13	25510.99
MUJADIL (USA)	20	80	3	4	16	25805.53
MUJTAHID (USA)	11	45	4	7	14	70911.62
MUKADDAMAH (USA)	18	65	2	2	10	12767.69
MULBERRY (FR)	1	6	1	1	4	130340.00
MUROTO	5	15	1	2	4	11856.94
MYSTIKO (USA)	7	32	2	2	12	15010.75
NAHEEZ (USA)	24	70	3	4	17	41699.30
NAIYLI (IRE)	1	4	1	1	1	4896.10
NALCHIK (USA)	7	21	1	2	2	7437.50
NAMAQUALAND (USA)	32	131	4	5	30	51222.62
NASHAMAA	4	12	1	1	3	8798.75
NASHWAN (USA)	16	63	6	8	18	62700.26
NEARLY A HAND	14	45	2	2	9	19261.50
NELTINO	16	55	1	3	15	17866.25
NEUSTRIEN (FR)	2	12	2	3	5	26627.13
NEVER SO BOLD	8	25	1	2	2	10645.75
NEWSKI (USA)	3	21	2	2	4	10080.50
NICHOLAS BILL	25	104	10	15	32	121309.10
NICOLOTTE (GB)	14	38	1	2	10	17001.28
NIGHT SHIFT (USA)	21	93	4	6	23	95594.41
NIKOS	13	68	5	12	29	239074.75
NINISKI (USA)	5	19	3	4	8	48514.15
NOBLE PATRIARCH	6	19	2	4	6	20777.75
THE NOBLE PLAYER (USA)	2	6	2	2	0	7707.65
NOMADIC WAY (USA)	29	112	9	16	32	103636.20
NOMINATION	6	22	1	1	8	10992.50
NORDANCE (USA)	2	11	1	2	5	15168.25
NORTH BRITON	1	20	1	8	8	84358.55
NORTH COL	8	23	1	2	4	9894.70
NORTHERN CRYSTAL (GB)	2	13	1	2	3	9771.07
NORTHERN FLAGSHIP (USA)	4	10	1	2	3	11965.68
NORTHERN PARK (USA)	3	12	1	1	4	5857.50
NORTHERN STATE (USA)	3	9	1	4	3	16430.00
NORTON CHALLENGER	12	26	1	1	4	4980.75
NORWICH	42	148	8	11	34	84635.92
NUCLEON (USA)	11	33	2	3	9	23356.90
NUREYEV (USA)	3	10	1	2	4	17001.28
OCTAGONAL (NZ)	1	3	1	1	0	5824.68
OLD VIC	52	148	8	15	40	164026.71
OPENING VERSE (USA)	2	10	2	2	0	7372.50
ORCHESTRA	39	156	13	22	50	268701.30
ORE	8	28	4	5	7	34455.05
OREGON (USA)	1	3	1	1	1	5127.00
OVAC (ITY)	2	21	1	1	13	19615.50
OVER THE RIVER (FR)	88	366	24	35	118	350953.21
OWINGTON (GB)	4	19	2	4	2	20198.09
PAMPONI (FR)	1	1	1	1	0	19314.00
PARIS HOUSE (GB)	11	31	1	1	1	2941.18
PARLIAMENT	5	16	1	1	3	7988.92
PAROLE	1	5	1	1	3	22950.57
THE PARSON	7	21	1	3	6	18986.15
PARTHIAN SPRINGS (GB)	6	23	2	2	5	9915.33
PASSING SALE (FR)	11	46	5	6	15	66745.64
PAST GLORIES	10	37	2	2	13	13179.50
PEACOCK (FR)	12	47	4	5	10	33582.33
PELDER (IRE)	1	3	1	1	1	5354.50

STALLIONS	RNRS	STARTS	WNRS	WINS	PLACES	TOTAL
PENNEKAMP (USA)	14	36	1	1	9	10468.40
PENNINE WALK	3	12	2	4	3	111918.01
PERPENDICULAR (GB)	17	64	2	3	15	17818.10
PERRAULT	9	36	6	9	12	70052.99
PERSIAN BOLD	31	143	12	18	53	161287.29
PERSIAN MEWS	27	86	5	5	14	32265.66
PERUGINO (USA)	30	115	8	11	28	94664.06
PETARDIA (GB)	28	95	5	6	12	39822.71
PETIT LOUP (USA)	4	20	1	1	7	31628.27
PETOSKI	46	165	9	11	41	72783.26
PHANTOM BREEZE	4	17	2	4	7	90549.69
PHARDANTE (FR)	233	925	52	69	245	758950.41
PHARLY (FR)	10	43	2	2	20	52516.75
PICCOLO (GB)	11	44	1	2	11	12847.00
PICEA	3	20	1	1	6	7423.80
PISTOLET BLEU (IRE)	12	72	7	13	33	176438.88
PISTOLS AND ROSES (USA)	1	6	1	1	3	5376.79
PIVOTAL (GB)	5	9	2	2	0	7729.32
PLATINI (GER)	2	6	2	1	2	19204.25
PLEASANT TAP (USA)	3	14	2	3	4	34521.88
POET'S DREAM (IRE)	2	6	3	2	1	6786.52
POINT OF NO RETURN (FR)	1	5	1	2	2	114640.78
POLAR FALCON (USA)	14	54	4	9	11	157855.72
POLISH PATRIOT (USA)	7	34	3	4	12	45750.44
POLISH PRECEDENT (USA)	23	104	5	7	35	75579.25
PORT LUCAYA (GB)	5	21	1	1	6	7681.32
PRAGMATIC	1	8	1	2	2	9818.75
PRESENTING (GB)	38	94	5	8	18	40317.45
PRESIDIUM	32	106	1	1	23	19243.59
PRIMITIVE RISING (USA)	53	207	10	15	63	122149.48
PRINCE DANIEL (USA)	3	18	1	1	8	11665.09
PRINCE DES COEURS (USA)	2	7	1	1	1	3095.00
PRINCE FERDINAND (GB)	1	4	1	2	1	9536.75
PRINCE OF BIRDS (USA)	13	52	4	9	19	89925.30
PRINCE SABO	6	19	1	2	2	5658.62
PRIOLO (USA)	10	46	4	5	17	37109.30
PROFESSIONAL (IRE)	2	11	2	2	5	12077.75
PROJECT MANAGER	14	34	1	1	4	13511.79
PROTEKTOR (GER)	1	2	1	1	0	4480.52
PROUD PANTHER (FR)	1	6	1	4	1	35760.75
PUISSANCE	11	36	1	1	9	8287.60
PURSUIT OF LOVE (GB)	20	73	3	3	13	30082.69
PYRAMUS (USA)	4	13	1	1	2	5758.15
QUART DE VIN (FR)	4	11	2	3	3	23919.82
QUEST FOR FAME	8	24	1	1	9	8516.11
RAGMAR (FR)	3	6	1	1	3	15446.25
RAHOTEP (FR)	1	5	1	3	1	75125.00
RAHY (USA)	2	18	1	3	4	24776.04
RAINBOW QUEST (USA)	22	85	5	9	24	95823.96
RAINBOWS FOR LIFE (CAN)	24	110	9	12	43	111068.75
RAKAPOSHI KING	67	247	9	22	50	107476.47
RAMBO DANCER (CAN)	9	31	2	4	8	48166.50
RA NOVA	5	40	2	2	13	19273.85
RASHAR (USA)	31	105	3	3	16	60807.73
RASI BRASAK	2	9	1	2	4	78450.50
RED RANSOM (USA)	4	25	1	3	7	22478.10
RED SUNSET	5	22	1	1	4	9631.91
REGAL INTENTION (CAN)	1	8	1	1	1	5824.00
RELIEF PITCHER	4	20	1	3	7	14985.00
RELIGIOUSLY (USA)	27	102	6	12	29	213717.92
REMAINDER MAN	1	4	1	2	2	13656.75
REPRIMAND	13	45	3	4	8	14009.00
REVOQUE (IRE)	13	34	3	3	12	20918.19
RIBERETTO	7	26	1	1	4	13356.50
RIDGEWOOD BEN (GB)	10	34	2	2	3	14279.76
RIGHT WIN (IRE)	4	7	1	1	0	3262.00

STALLIONS	RNRS	STARTS	WNRS	WINS	PLACES	TOTAL
RIOT HELMET	3	9	1	1	4	9344.32
RISK ME (FR)	24	94	9	14	29	131979.39
RIVER FALLS (GB)	17	36	1	1	3	6416.91
RIVER GOD (USA)	7	38	1	3	10	20644.50
RIVERHEAD (USA)	8	28	3	4	11	116367.27
RIVERMAN (USA)	8	28	2	3	13	31990.30
RIVER MIST (USA)	2	4	2	2	0	16071.34
RIVERWISE (USA)	8	41	3	7	9	312185.00
ROBELLINO (USA)	23	87	10	14	33	95981.94
ROCK CITY	14	45	1	1	11	12606.21
ROCK HOPPER	36	142	8	12	38	95877.20
ROI DANZIG (USA)	11	45	2	3	14	24746.81
ROI DE ROME (USA)	4	22	3	4	10	64210.93
ROI GUILLAUME (FR)	8	28	2	3	8	23303.78
ROLFE (USA)	6	25	2	3	8	33448.10
ROMANY RYE (GB)	3	12	1	4	1	23186.90
ROSCOE BLAKE	14	36	2	2	13	23833.50
ROSELIER (FR)	258	998	68	116	275	1253076.56
ROYAL ABJAR (USA)	16	61	2	2	17	18201.15
ROYAL ACADEMY (USA)	20	57	3	5	12	28916.35
ROYAL CHARTER (FR)	20	103	8	11	25	98191.07
ROYAL FOUNTAIN	32	79	1	1	16	16169.55
RUDIMENTARY (USA)	27	87	8	8	31	53316.73
RYMER	2	5	1	1	1	3674.50
SABREHILL (USA)	18	110	8	12	29	84954.29
SADDLERS' HALL (IRE)	21	64	7	7	21	49316.99
SADLER'S WELLS (USA)	57	255	21	30	83	320228.79
SAFAWAN	6	17	1	1	7	9010.01
SAFETY CATCH (USA)	17	49	1	1	8	10362.83
SAINT ESTEPHE (FR)	3	17	3	3	8	12396.50
SAINT PREUIL (FR)	6	24	4	6	10	62274.83
SALLUCEVA	5	12	1	1	4	14033.20
SALSE (USA)	21	69	5	7	23	58811.23
SALT DOME (USA)	2	6	1	1	0	1687.00
SASSANIAN (USA)	4	27	3	6	10	47206.13
SATCO (FR)	47	213	10	24	55	243139.98
SAUMAREZ	7	23	1	1	6	8546.00
SAXON FARM	3	7	1	1	1	4675.00
SCALLYWAG	16	65	5	6	17	49035.62
SCENIC	14	56	3	4	16	47382.23
SCOOTER BLEU (IRE)	1	4	1	2	1	26721.24
SCOTTISH REEL	7	24	3	3	10	17976.25
SEAMANSHIP	3	4	1	1	0	3809.82
SEATTLE DANCER (USA)	1	10	1	1	3	9371.16
SEATTLE SLEW (USA)	1	4	1	1	2	5077.25
SECOND SET (IRE)	6	25	1	1	9	25773.73
SECRET 'N CLASSY (CAN)	1	7	1	1	2	5560.00
SEEKING THE GOLD (USA)	3	12	2	4	5	39616.20
SELKIRK (USA)	19	60	4	4	22	37685.75
SEPTIEME CIEL (USA)	4	13	1	1	1	5254.60
SEXTON BLAKE	5	15	1	1	1	4508.00
SEYMOUR HICKS (FR)	15	61	2	3	18	81032.16
SHAAB	4	20	1	2	7	12040.25
SHAAMIT (IRE)	9	28	1	4	5	18632.65
SHADDAD (USA)	2	3	1	1	1	2521.00
SHADEED (USA)	3	16	1	2	2	8326.75
SHAFOUN (FR)	4	34	2	4	18	207117.24
SHALFORD (IRE)	22	87	4	5	18	38278.03
SHARDARI	52	190	12	20	50	198786.73
SHAREEF DANCER (USA)	19	82	6	7	14	43251.89
SHARIFABAD (IRE)	19	67	2	3	8	19476.54
SHARP CHARTER	9	28	3	3	7	14914.75
SHARP DEAL	4	23	1	2	10	38023.75
SHARP VICTOR (USA)	12	73	5	6	18	46254.15
SHERNAZAR	56	159	14	19	39	142316.14
SHINING STEEL	4	25	3	4	13	39299.76

STALLIONS	RNRS	STARTS	WNRS	WINS	PLACES	TOTAL
SHIRLEY HEIGHTS	9	34	3	9	10	45079.99
SHUAILAAN (USA)	2	18	1	1	4	5488.00
SHY GROOM (USA)	3	21	1	2	7	30602.13
SIAM (USA)	2	13	1	1	5	6869.25
SILLERY (USA)	6	33	3	7	12	68955.75
SILLY PRICES	6	24	2	3	8	19471.35
SILVER HAWK (USA)	13	62	6	9	30	101787.26
SILVER KITE (USA)	1	11	1	2	5	11063.75
SILVER OWL	3	12	1	3	4	16414.00
SILVER PISTOL (AUS)	1	9	1	3	2	16773.00
SILVER RAINBOW (GB)	7	27	4	8	6	72442.79
SIMPLY GREAT (FR)	15	69	5	7	24	43407.58
SIMPLY MAJESTIC (USA)	1	4	1	1	0	3696.00
SINGSPIEL (IRE)	3	7	1	1	2	2978.00
SIR BRINK (FR)	2	6	1	1	2	9771.00
SIR HARRY LEWIS (USA)	34	98	9	12	26	65301.30
SIRSAN (IRE)	2	12	1	1	4	5800.18
SIZZLING MELODY	4	11	1	1	3	12156.00
SKI CHIEF (USA)	2	5	1	1	1	5822.96
SKY CHASE (NZ)	1	5	1	3	2	16320.75
SKY CLASSIC (CAN)	4	30	3	7	10	33035.27
SKYLINER	4	16	1	2	4	10878.50
SLIP ANCHOR	28	116	9	14	34	120031.66
SNURGE	3	28	1	2	8	14328.00
SOLID ILLUSION (USA)	2	7	1	1	3	3772.00
THE SON (NZ)	1	8	1	1	4	6816.90
SON OF SILVER	1	5	1	1	2	6692.00
SOUTHERN MUSIC	3	12	1	3	2	15203.50
SOVEREIGN WATER (FR)	13	25	1	2	4	8558.00
SOVIET LAD (USA)	10	42	4	5	16	33144.56
SOVIET STAR (USA)	5	18	2	2	5	75048.60
SPANISH PLACE (USA)	17	81	5	8	23	82361.43
SPECTRUM (IRE)	17	58	2	4	17	121638.59
SRI PEKAN (USA)	12	40	1	1	5	16164.00
STANDIFORD (USA)	7	23	2	3	5	39616.94
STAR QUEST	7	22	1	1	7	5561.45
STAR WAY	3	18	1	2	5	11583.00
STEP TOGETHER (USA)	13	46	2	4	8	113876.59
STERNKOENIG (IRE)	1	3	1	1	0	3010.00
ST NINIAN	11	43	1	2	11	9507.25
STRONG GALE	93	388	31	47	137	624246.85
SUAVE DANCER (USA)	13	48	3	4	12	43250.85
SUBOTICA (FR)	4	17	2	3	3	14525.12
SULA BULA	21	83	4	5	24	39281.00
SUMMER SQUALL (USA)	4	20	2	2	9	20234.06
SUNNY'S HALO (CAN)	1	10	1	1	2	5630.00
SUNSHINE FOREVER (USA)	3	19	2	2	6	13979.00
SUPER ABOUND (USA)	1	19	1	4	9	23415.81
SUPREME LEADER	299	1149	78	119	298	1462062.33
SURE BLADE (USA)	12	30	1	1	2	3560.00
SYMBOLI HEIGHTS (FR)	6	30	1	1	1	3927.98
SYNEFOS (USA)	17	61	3	8	9	161270.07
SYRTOS	12	49	2	2	4	7341.00
TAGULA (IRE)	6	24	1	1	12	11158.53
TAKE RISKS (FR)	5	30	3	4	12	58448.39
TALE QUALE	7	35	3	5	8	19122.82
TAUFAN (USA)	4	31	1	1	5	4642.00
TEAMSTER	13	51	5	5	18	50406.18
TECHNOLOGY (USA)	1	6	1	1	4	13131.28
TEENOSO (USA)	43	156	10	17	49	220239.28
TEL QUEL (FR)	7	14	1	1	3	5957.00
TEMPORAL (GER)	1	4	1	1	0	4480.52
TENBY (GB)	14	57	3	4	15	45515.20
TERIMON	45	178	8	13	52	124055.16
THATCHING	11	46	3	4	9	22928.55
THEATRICAL	10	26	3	4	8	41260.22

STALLIONS	RNRS	STARTS	WNRS	WINS	PLACES	TOTAL
THEATRICAL CHARMER	5	34	2	3	8	15949.75
THEN AGAIN	12	45	2	2	7	15324.97
THOWRA (FR)	4	19	2	6	5	37060.15
TIDARO (USA)	23	112	4	4	26	57425.17
TIMELESS TIMES (USA)	11	49	2	2	12	16513.37
TINA'S PET	18	68	2	3	19	29068.95
TINOCO	1	6	1	1	2	22669.45
TIP MOSS (FR)	4	19	2	3	3	41862.50
TIRLEY GALE (GB)	1	9	1	1	2	5455.45
TIROL	18	72	2	2	23	22409.34
TOCA MADERA	10	54	2	4	11	22539.41
TOPANOORA	30	107	7	9	25	62264.48
TOP OF THE WORLD	11	33	2	3	2	16424.15
TOPSIDER (USA)	1	9	1	2	4	8524.50
TOP VILLE	5	22	3	3	4	15386.95
TORUS	54	205	8	12	65	141430.72
TOTEM (USA)	1	5	1	1	1	6794.47
TOULON (GB)	66	249	16	32	50	395129.24
TOWN AND COUNTRY	6	27	2	4	10	23511.75
TRAGIC ROLE (USA)	25	118	8	14	28	78875.60
TREASURE HUNTER	28	143	9	15	39	127885.81
TREMBLANT	22	103	8	12	24	96751.57
TREMPOLINO (USA)	10	33	6	9	12	66946.50
TRIGON	2	4	1	1	0	3598.16
TURGEON (USA)	6	41	3	7	17	60466.15
TURKOMAN (USA)	2	6	1	1	0	2933.00
TURTLE ISLAND (IRE)	32	128	10	13	33	115654.79
UNBLEST (GB)	5	19	1	1	6	46133.11
UN DESPERADO (FR)	102	373	33	54	95	726646.31
UNFUWAIN (USA)	26	87	7	9	24	65227.99
USEFUL (FR)	14	61	3	5	18	50900.00
VALANJOU (FR)	2	8	2	2	3	13617.00
VALVILLE (FR)	3	10	1	2	3	7144.50
VAN DER LINDEN (FR)	2	9	1	1	2	9311.81
VAQUILLO (USA)	1	5	1	2	1	10243.25
VARSHAN	1	12	1	1	3	6888.97
VETTORI (IRE)	6	21	1	1	3	17639.75
VIDEO ROCK (FR)	16	68	5	6	29	87275.45
VILLEZ (USA)	3	17	2	3	10	82730.50
VITAL SEASON	4	16	1	1	4	5858.30
VITERIC (FR)	1	2	1	2	0	4382.00
WAAJIB	9	25	3	5	9	45475.09
WAKASHAN (GB)	8	28	1	1	1	5929.21
WARCRAFT (USA)	41	135	5	8	18	75988.74
WARNING	11	49	3	4	21	67593.20
WARRSHAN (USA)	7	29	4	4	8	23952.40
WELD	24	64	3	7	20	54685.51
WELDNAAS (USA)	8	32	1	2	16	19479.10
WELSH CAPTAIN	3	23	1	1	11	14242.90
WELSH TERM	28	104	7	9	22	57521.64
WESAAM (USA)	2	7	1	1	2	6981.40
WESTMINSTER (NZ)	1	6	1	1	3	6686.25
WHITTINGHAM (IRE)	4	19	1	2	3	4707.30
WINGED LOVE (IRE)	2	4	1	1	1	9388.00
WITNESS BOX (USA)	19	76	6	13	16	82416.12
WOLFHOUND (USA)	7	23	1	1	9	10563.05
WONDERFUL SURPRISE	2	8	1	2	3	12895.00
WOODMAN (USA)	10	31	2	2	10	16371.68
WOODPAS (USA)	3	7	1	1	2	5269.94
WOODS OF WINDSOR (USA)	7	29	1	2	11	14403.74
YACHTSMAN (USA)	1	4	1	1	2	4271.00
YASHGAN	49	176	8	15	46	158235.09
YOUNG ERN (GB)	2	6	1	1	0	2167.20
ZABEEL (NZ)	1	8	1	1	5	8320.70
ZAFFARAN (USA)	59	214	13	21	60	168797.51
ZAFONIC (USA)	12	44	4	6	12	33952.30

STALLIONS	RNRS	STARTS	WNRS	WINS	PLACES	TOTAL
ZEDITAVE (AUS)	1	7	1	2	3	16853.50
ZIETEN (USA)	5	15	1	3	1	10274.50
ZILZAL (USA)	13	63	2	3	25	67363.15
ZINAAD (GB)	1	4	1	1	1	4096.00

BY KIND PERMISSION OF WEATHERBYS

HIGH-PRICED YEARLINGS OF 2003 AT TATTERSALLS' SALES

The following yearlings realised 110,000 guineas and over at Tattersalls' Sales in 2003:-

Name and Breeding	Vendor	Purchaser	Guineas
CH F GIANT'S CAUSEWAY (USA) - COLORSNAP	MEON VALLEY STUD.	J MAGNIER	1250000
MILLE (IRE) B F DUBAI MILLENNIUM (GB) - CLUELA (USA).	THE CASTLETON GROUP	C GORDON-WATSON BS	1200000
B C SADLER'S WELLS (USA) - DEDICATED LADY (IRE).	CAMAS PARK STUD, IRELAND	J MAGNIER	1200000
B C DIESIS - KITZA (IRE).	BRITTON HOUSE STUD	D O'BYRNE	1000000
B C KINGMAMBO (USA) - LADY CARLA (GB)	WATERSHIP DOWN STUD.	J MAGNIER	1000000
AMPELIO (IRE) CH C GRAND LODGE (USA) - BORDIGHERA (USA).	TRICKLEDOWN STUD	C GORDON-WATSON BS	800000
B C KING'S BEST (USA) - PARK EXPRESS.	LODGE PARK STUD, IRELAND	JOHN WARREN BS.	775000
B F SADLER'S WELLS (USA) - BRIGID (USA)	OAKS FARM STABLES	BBA (IRELAND)	750000
ASAWER (IRE) B F DARSHAAN - SASSY BIRD (USA)	LOUGHBROWN STUD, IRELAND	SHADWELL ESTATE	600000
KING KASYAPA (IRE) B C DARSHAAN - EZANA	CAMAS PARK STUD, IRELAND	GAINSBOROUGH STUD.	600000
B C FASLIYEV (USA) - AUNTY EILEEN.	ASHTOWN HOUSE STUD, IRELAND	D O'BYRNE	600000
MATHEMATICIAN (IRE) BR C MACHIAVELLIAN (USA) - ZIBILENE (GB)	BAROUCHE STUD (IRELAND) LTD.	JOHN FERGUSON BS	525000
CH C KINGMAMBO (USA) - IRTITA (GB)	EUROPEAN SALES MANAGEMENT	SHADWELL ESTATE.	525000
SUN BOAT (GB) B C MACHIAVELLIAN (USA) - ONE SO WONDERFUL (GB)	MEON VALLEY STUD.	JOHN FERGUSON BS.	525000
B C SADLER'S WELLS (USA) - IGREJA (ARG)	BARRONSTOWN STUD, IRELAND	JOHN WARREN BS	500000
BAHJA (USA) CH F SEEKING THE GOLD (USA) - VALENTINE WALTZ (USA)	ROUND HILL STUD, IRELAND	SHADWELL ESTATE.	500000
KAWN (GB) B F CADEAUX GENEREUX - KHURZA (GB)	USK VALLEY STUD.	SHADWELL ESTATE.	500000
HAWK'S TOR (IRE) B C DANEHILL (USA) - BORN BEAUTIFUL (USA)	LYNN LODGE STUD, IRELAND (AGENT).	C GORDON-WATSON BS	480000
B F GREEN DESERT (USA) - REPEAT WARNING (GB)	MEON VALLEY STUD	JOHN FERGUSON BS	480000
B C GREEN DESERT (USA) - LA PITIE (USA)	CAMAS PARK STUD, IRELAND	D O'BYRNE	450000
B C MONTJEU (IRE) - MOON DIAMOND (GB)	CAMAS PARK STUD, IRELAND	J MAGNIER	425000
B C MACHIAVELLIAN (USA) - TIME SAVED (GB)	MEON VALLEY STUD.	JOHN FERGUSON BS	425000
C B C SADLER'S WELLS (USA) - MISS TOOT.	LOUGHBROWN STUD, IRELAND.	VENDOR	420000
STAMFORD (GB) B/BR C DARSHAAN - SILVER LANE (USA)	WATERSHIP DOWN STUD.	D O'BYRNE	400000
GR C ALHAARTH (IRE) - CASHEW (GB)	CAMAS PARK STUD, IRELAND	C GORDON-WATSON BS	400000
GR C EL PRADO (IRE) - JUST CAUSE	HIGHCLERE STUD.	JOHN FERGUSON BS	360000
B C DANEHILL (USA) - BRUSH STROKES (GB)	GLENVALE STUD, IRELAND	SHADWELL ESTATE.	360000
B F DANEHILL (USA) - WINDMILL (GB).	FURNACE MILL STUD.	JOHN FERGUSON BS	360000
TAHRIR (IRE) GR F LINAMIX (FR) - MISS SACHA (IRE)	HUNSCOTE HOUSE FARM STUD	J DELAHOOKE	350000
KING'S KAMA (GB) B C GIANT'S CAUSEWAY (USA) - MAID FOR THE HILLS (GB)	JOHN OSBORNE, AGENT.	C GORDON-WATSON BS	350000
B C MONTJEU (IRE) - ZIVANIA (IRE)	NORMANDIE STUD	SHADWELL ESTATE.	350000
B F SADLER'S WELLS (USA) - FILIA ARDROSS	KILDARAGH STUD, IRELAND	C GORDON-WATSON BS	340000
B C GIANT'S CAUSEWAY (USA) - SHALIMAR (IRE)	IRISH NATIONAL STUD, IRELAND (AGENT).	J MAGNIER	330000
B C DIKTAT (GB) - HEART OF INDIA (IRE)	FURNACE MILL STUD.	D O'BYRNE	320000
CH F GIANT'S CAUSEWAY (USA) - NET WORTH (USA)	THE CASTLETON GROUP	MCKEEVER ST LAWRENCE BS	310000
KINGDOM OF DREAMS (IRE) B C SADLER'S WELLS (USA) - REGAL PORTRAIT (USA)	ABBEVILLE & MEADOW COURT STUDS, IRELAND	QUESNAY BS	300000
ALMANSOOR (IRE) B C SADLER'S WELLS - GROOM ORDER (USA)	BALLYGALLON STUD, IRELAND	C GORDON-WATSON BS	300000
B C SADLER'S WELLS (USA) - MINNIE HABIT	BARRONSTOWN STUD, IRELAND	SHADWELL ESTATE	300000
RING OF FIRE (IRE) B C ROYAL APPLAUSE (GB) - EMERALD CUT (GB)	YEOMANSTOWN STUD, IRELAND	PETER DOYLE BS.	300000
JALAMID (IRE) B C DANEHILL (USA) - VIGNELAURE (IRE)	BARODA STUD, IRELAND.	C GORDON-WATSON BS	300000
B C SINGSPIEL (IRE) - APACHE STAR (GB)	HASCOMBE STUD, IRELAND.	VENDOR	300000
B F GRAND LODGE (USA) - PROSKONA (USA)	ISLANMORE STUD, IRELAND.	BLANDFORD BS.	280000

BR F FASLIYEV (USA) - SIMPLICITY (GB)	BAROUCHE STUD (IRELAND) LTD.	JOHN FERGUSON BS.	280000
MURHEF (GB) B C ROYAL APPLAUSE (GB) - PETIT POINT (IRE)	KINGWOOD STUD.	SHADWELL ESTATE.	280000
B F IN THE WINGS - SHINING EYES (USA)	LAVINGTON STUD.	JOHN FERGUSON BS.	280000
MACABRE (GB) B C MACHIAVELLIAN (USA) - LADY IN WAITING (GB)	KIRTLINGTON STUD.	JOHN FERGUSON BS.	270000
B F SADLER'S WELLS (USA) - FIRE THE GROOM (USA)	FOUR STAR SALES, AGENT	BRIAN GRASSICK BS.	260000
B F DESERT PRINCE (IRE) - SEV'S CHOICE (USA)	SWORDLESTOWN STUD, IRELAND.	C GORDON-WATSON BS	260000
RAIDER OF THE EAST (IRE) B C DARSHAAN - CONVENIENCE (IRE)	CORDUFF STUD, IRELAND (AGENT).	C GORDON-WATSON BS	260000
INSINUATION (IRE) B F DANEHILL (USA) - HIDDEN MEANING (USA)	THE CASTLETON GROUP	CHEVELEY PARK STUD	260000
DANZELLINE (GB) B F DANZERO (AUS) - FLEETING RAINBOW (GB)	FURNACE MILL STUD.	CBA.	260000
B C ZAFONIC (USA) - HASTA (USA)	CRIMBOURNE STUD	JOHN WARREN BS.	250000
B C DARSHAAN - MANAKEA (USA)	THE CASTLETON GROUP	C GORDON-WATSON BS	250000
B C DANEHILL (USA) - SUN SILK (USA)	LYNN LODGE STUD, IRELAND	A O NERSES	250000
B C ROYAL APPLAUSE (GB) - AMATHEA (FR)	GLENVALE STUD, IRELAND	JOHN FERGUSON BS	250000
B C GRAND LODGE (USA) - IN FULL CRY (USA)	HASCOMBE STUD	GAINSBOROUGH STUD.	250000
B F FASLIYEV (USA) - SEA MISTRESS	YEOMANSTOWN LODGE STUD, IRELAND.	F BARRY	240000
GHARIR (IRE) GR C MACHIAVELLIAN (USA) - SUMMER SONNET (GB)	VOUTE SALES, AGENT.	SHADWELL ESTATE	240000
ZADALRAKIB (GB) CH C MACHIAVELLIAN (USA) - PARTY DOLL	GAINSBOROUGH STUD.	GAINSBOROUGH STUD.	240000
FALSAFI (GB) B C ROYAL APPLAUSE (GB) - HGH DANCER (GB)	YEOMANSTOWN STUD, IRELAND	SHADWELL ESTATE	240000
TEMPESTAD (IRE) B C GIANT'S CAUSEWAY (USA) - ARUTUA (USA)	FOUR STAR SALES	INTERNATIONAL EQUITIES	240000
B C INCHINOR (GB) - FLIRTATION (GB)	FLOORS STUD	J GOSDEN	230000
B C MONTJEU (IRE) - DANCE OF LOVE (IRE)	ASHTOWN HOUSE STUD, IRELAND.	BBA (IRELAND).	230000
B C ANABAA (USA) - STEEPLE (GB)	FLOORS STUD	JOHN WARREN BS.	230000
B C FASLIYEV (USA) - ROSE PAILE (FR)	CAMAS PARK STUD, IRELAND.	BBA (IRELAND).	230000
B C MONTJEU (IRE) - MYTHICAL CREEK (USA)	BALLYGALLON STUD, IRELAND.	SHADWELL ESTATE	220000
B C DAYLAMI (IRE) - BALLET SOCIETY (FR)	KILLEEN CASTLE STUD, IRELAND.	MCKEEVER ST LAWRENCE BS	220000
CH C CADEAUX GENEREUX - RING THE RELATIVES (GB)	MEON VALLEY STUD	JOHN FERGUSON BS.	220000
GR C MACHIAVELLIAN (USA) - CRODELLE (IRE)	BIDDESTONE STUD.	JOHN FERGUSON BS.	220000
BR F KING'S BEST (USA) - TOUJOURS IRISH (USA)	BALLYHIMIKIN STUD, IRELAND	DARLEY STUD.	220000
A THOUSAND SMILES (IRE) B F SADLER'S WELLS (USA) - BUFFING (IRE)	BARRONSTOWN STUD, IRELAND	ANTHONY STROUD BS	220000
REMARKABLE STORY (GB) B F MARK OF ESTEEM (IRE) - SPINNING THE YARN (GB)	MEON VALLEY STUD	VENDOR.	220000
GR C INDIAN RIDGE - NUIT CHAUD (USA)	NEW ENGLAND STUD, AGENT	G RICHARDSON	210000
B C GREEN DESERT (USA) - SHIMNA (GB)	VERK HOUSE STUD, IRELAND.	JOHN WARREN BS.	210000
ZAITOONA (IRE) B F SOVIET STAR (USA) - RISE AND FALL	KILDARAGH STUD, IRELAND.	SHADWELL ESTATE.	210000
WELL ESTABLISHED (IRE) B C SADLER'S WELLS (USA) - RIVERKEY (USA)	BUGLEY STUD	M A JARVIS.	210000
B F ROYAL ACADEMY (USA) - WOODLAND ORCHID (IRE)	ARLIE STUD, IRELAND	J DELAHOOKE	200000
YOSHI (USA) B C KINGMAMBO (USA) - MAJESTIC ROLE (FR)	FOUR STAR SALES	GAINSBOROUGH STUD	200000
B F DR FONG (USA) - PARK CHARGER (GB)	LODGE PARK STUD, IRELAND	MCKEEVER ST LAWRENCE BS	200000
CH C DANEHILL (USA) - MISTLE THRUSH (USA)	BUGLEY STUD, AGENT	JOHN FERGUSON BS.	200000
CH C CADEAUX GENEREUX - KATRINA (USA)	WATERSHIP DOWN STUD	C GORDON-WATSON BS	200000
CH C RAINBOW QUEST (USA) - BOMBAZINE (IRE)	VOUTE SALES, AGENT	C GORDON-WATSON BS	200000
CH C SINGSPIEL (IRE) - DASHING WATER (USA)	HIGHCLERE STUD.	O D'BYRNE	200000
CH F GRAND LODGE (USA) - NORDICA	JAMIE RAILTON, AGENT	BRIAN GRASSICK BS	200000
FOR A DANCER (IRE) B C UNFUWAIN (USA) - ANOTHER DANCER (FR)	BALLYLINCH STUD, IRELAND	C GORDON-WATSON BS	200000
MASTER OF THE RACE (GB) CH C SELKIRK (USA) - DUST DANCER (GB)	HESMONDS STUD	C GORDON-WATSON BS	200000
B C INDIAN RIDGE - TRIOMPHALE (GB)	MOUNT COOTE STUD, IRELAND	O D'BYRNE	200000
B C MONTJEU (IRE) - FALAFIL (FR)	CAMAS PARK STUD, IRELAND	SHADWELL ESTATE.	200000
B C DARSHAAN - BRIGHT HALO (FR)	USK VALLEY STUD	SHADWELL ESTATE.	200000
B C DARSHAAN - DAMASCENE (IRE)	EYREFIELD LODGE STUD, IRELAND	JOHN FERGUSON BS.	180000

Pedigree	Vendor	Buyer	Price
B C MACHIAVELLIAN (USA) - TREASURE TROVE (USA)	JOHN TROY AGENT	G RICHARDSON	180000
CH F GIANT'S CAUSEWAY (USA) - AMY HUNTER (USA)	BALLYMONEY PARK STUD, IRELAND	D O'BYRNE	180000
B C DESERT PRINCE (IRE) - CRYSTAL FLUTE (GB)	BUGLEY STUD	D WOODS	180000
HITAAF (IRE) B C MONTJEU (IRE) - HEAVEN ONLY KNOWS	FURNACE MILL STUD	SHADWELL ESTATE	180000
B F MISWAKI (USA) - HAWZAH (GB)	RATHBARRY STUD, IRELAND	ANTHONY STROUD BS	170000
B F SADLER'S WELLS (USA) - MOSAIQUE BLEUE (GB)	CROOM HOUSE STUD, IRELAND	VENDOR	170000
CH F SILVER HAWK (USA) - COPPER CACHET (USA)	ROUND HILL STUD, IRELAND	B OLSSON	170000
GR C MACHIAVELLIAN (USA) - GOOD ENOUGH (FR)	WHITSBURY MANOR STUD	R O'GORMAN BS	170000
B C GIANT'S CAUSEWAY (USA) - GLATISANT (GB)	HASCOMBE STUD	D O'BYRNE	170000
B C MONTJEU (IRE) - PACIFIC GROVE (GB)	TALLY-HO STUD, IRELAND	D O'BYRNE	170000
COUNTDOWN (GB) CH C PIVOTAL (GB) - QUIZ TIME (GB)	BARTON STUD	CHEVELEY PARK STUD	170000
CH C VAMID (GB) - SPACE TRAVEL (GB)	REDPENDER STUD, IRELAND	MRS A SKIFFINGTON	170000
LOVE ME WELL (GB) B C SADLER'S WELLS (USA) - LOVE DIVINE (GB)	HIGHCLERE STUD	C GORDON-WATSON BS	165000
GR F SADLER'S WELLS (USA) - LUNA BLUE (FR)	WATERSHIP DOWN STUD	VENDOR	165000
BLACK VELVET (GB) BR C INCHINOR (GB) - THREE OWLS (USA)	HARAS D'OUILLY, FRANCE	MCKEEVER ST LAWRENCE BS	160000
CH C GRAND LODGE (USA) - BATHE IN LIGHT (USA)	REDPENDER STUD, IRELAND	PETER DOYLE BS	160000
REQOA (GB) B C ROYAL APPLAUSE (GB) - KANGRA VALLEY (GB)	CAMAS PARK STUD, IRELAND	D O'BYRNE	160000
B C ROYAL APPLAUSE (GB) - UPEND	KIRTLINGTON STUD	SHADWELL ESTATE	160000
B C GIANT'S CAUSEWAY (USA) - WANNABE GRAND (IRE)	WHATTON MANOR STUD	R O'GORMAN BS	160000
ESPRIT DE CORPS (GB) B C HERNANDO (FR) - ENTENTE CORDIALE (USA)	CHIPPENHAM LODGE STUD LTD	B OLSSON	160000
PATRONAGE (GB) B C ROYAL APPLAUSE (GB) - PASSIONATE PURSUIT (GB)	STAFFORDSTOWN, IRELAND	SIR M PRESCOTT	160000
PINGUS (GB) B F POLISH PRECEDENT (USA) - MARAMBA (GB)	TRICKLEDOWN STUD	JOHN WARREN BS	160000
B F MONTJEU (IRE) - RED RITA (IRE)	FIVE HORSES LTD	BBA (IRELAND)	160000
B F HORSE CHESTNUT (SAF) - MUSOKA COMMAND (CAN)	VOUTE SALES, AGENT	C GORDON-WATSON BS	160000
B F SADLER'S WELLS (USA) - ANTIGUAN JANE (GB)	FOUR STAR SALES, AGENT	JOHN FERGUSON BS	160000
B F GREEN DESERT (USA) - COMME D'HABITUDE (USA)	CAMAS PARK STUD, IRELAND	PETER DOYLE BS	160000
ETLAALA (GB) CH C SELKIRK (USA) - PORTELET (GB)	EUROPEAN SALES MANAGEMENT	C GORDON-WATSON BS	160000
B F SINGSPIEL (IRE) - INDIA ATLANTA	NORELANDS STUD, IRELAND	SHADWELL ESTATE	160000
PERFECT CHOICE (IRE) GR C DAYLAMI (IRE) - FAIRY CONTESSA (USA)	STAFFORDSTOWN, IRELAND	SHADWELL ESTATE	155000
MUJAZAF (USA) B C GRAND LODGE (USA) - DECISION MAID (USA)	USK VALLEY STUD	JOHN FERGUSON BS	150000
B F MONTJEU (IRE) - RANDANCING (IRE)	MOUNT COOTE STUD, IRELAND (AGENT)	MCKEEVER ST LAWRENCE BS	150000
BARATARIA (GB) CH C BARATHEA (IRE) - AETHRA (USA)	CAR COLSTON HALL STUD	G RICHARDSON	150000
B F DANEHILL (USA) - LAKE VICTORIA (IRE)	KNOCKAINEY STUD, IRELAND	MCKEEVER ST LAWRENCE BS	150000
B C MONTJEU (IRE) - DANCE CLEAR (IRE)	ROUND HILL STUD, IRELAND	B OLSSON	150000
GALEOTA (IRE) B C MUJADIL (USA) - REFINED (IRE)	YEOMANSTOWN STUD, IRELAND	C GORDON-WATSON BS	150000
B F GREEN DESERT (USA) - WARNING BELLE (GB)	BRITTON HOUSE STUD	D O'BYRNE	150000
GR/RO C LINAMIX (FR) - SHERKIYA (IRE)	MR MAX ERVINE	PETER DOYLE BS	150000
B F MARK OF ESTEEM (IRE) - BAJLANKA (GB)	MEON VALLEY STUD	J GOSDEN	150000
B F SADLER'S WELLS (USA) - WILL BE BLUE (IRE)	MEON VALLEY STUD	MERIDIAN INT	145000
B C FASLIYEV (USA) - MOUNTAIN ASH (GB)	WATERSHIP DOWN STUD	BROADHURST AGENCY	140000
B C ROYAL APPLAUSE (GB) - TEE CEE (GB)	WATERSHIP DOWN STUD	M O'TOOLE	140000
B C MACHIAVELLIAN (USA) - TROIS GRACES (AUS)	CAMAS PARK STUD, IRELAND	G RICHARDSON	140000
HEIDI'S DASH (USA) B F GREEN DESERT (USA) - CHILD PRODIGY (IRE)	LYNN LODGE STUD, IRELAND	R O'GORMAN BS	140000
B C KING'S BEST (USA) - LIAISON (USA)	CASTLEBRIDGE CONSIGNMENT	C GORDON-WATSON BS	140000
	MARSTON STUD	DARLEY STUD	140000
	JAMIE RAILTON, AGENT	C GORDON-WATSON BS	140000
	BRINKLEY STUD	JOHN FERGUSON BS	140000

Pedigree	Consignor	Purchaser	Price
B C DANEHILL (USA) - SCRUPLE (IRE)	TULLAMAINE CASTLE STUD, IRELAND	C GORDON-WATSON BS	140000
B C DESERT PRINCE (IRE) - TYCOON'S DRAMA (IRE)	ROUND HILL STUD, IRELAND	BOZZI BS	140000
RASSEEM (IRE) B F FASLIYEV (USA) - YORBA LINDA (IRE)	VOUTE SALES, AGENT	JOHN FERGUSON BS	140000
B C ZAFONIC (USA) - GRAIL (USA)	JAMIE RAILTON, AGENT	BRIAN GRASSICK BS	135000
B C BOLD EDGE (GB) - HALLAND PARK GIRL (IRE)	PIER HOUSE STUD, IRELAND	PETER DOYLE BS	135000
B C KING'S BEST (USA) - FEMME FATALE (GB)	PER HOUSE STUD, IRELAND	JOHN FERGUSON BS	130000
B C CAPE CROSS (IRE) - DAZLYN LADY (USA)	BALLYHIMIKIN STUD, IRELAND	JOHN FERGUSON BS	130000
MAJESTIC RANIA (IRE) CH F GIANT'S CAUSEWAY (USA) - CRYSTAL RING (IRE)	DAVID TWOMEY, AGENT	G RICHARDSON	130000
B F NAMID (GB) - ALMOND FLOWER (IRE)	GOLDFORD STUD, AGENT	MRS A SKIFFINGTON	130000
FORGERY (IRE) CH C DR DEVIOUS (IRE) - MEMORY GREEN (USA)	RATHBARRY STUD, IRELAND (AGENT)	JOHN WARREN BS	130000
CH C INDIAN RIDGE - HEADY (GB)	MOUNT COOTE STUD, IRELAND	BLANDFORD BS	130000
B C ROYAL ACADEMY (USA) - THRILLING DAY (GB)	BLOOMSBURY STUD	BLANDFORD BS	130000
B/BR C MACHIAVELLIAN (USA) - DANCING SEA (USA)	VOUTE SALES, AGENT	JOHN FERGUSON BS	130000
B C ANABAA (USA) - MISTLE SONG (GB)	VOUTE SALES, AGENT	JOHN FERGUSON BS	130000
BR C PIVOTAL (GB) - PERSIAN AIR	LYNN LODGE STUD, IRELAND	BLANDFORD BS	130000
B C DANEHILL (USA) - SPRING PITCH (USA)	WATERSHIP DOWN STUD	JOHN FERGUSON BS	130000
CH C ZAMINDAR (USA) - STAFFIN (GB)	EUROPEAN SALES MANAGEMENT	JOHN FERGUSON BS	130000
B F MACHIAVELLIAN (USA) - EL OPERA (IRE)	KIRTLINGTON STUD	SHIGEYUKI OKADA	130000
CH C GIANT'S CAUSEWAY (USA) - DARYA (USA)	VOUTE SALES, AGENT	JOHN FERGUSON BS	130000
B F SINNDAR (IRE) - LILISSA (IRE)	WESTERLANDS STUD	JOHN FERGUSON BS	130000
B C THEATRICAL - PERSONAL LOVE (USA)	MOUNTARMSTRONG STUD, IRELAND	D O'BYRNE	130000
B/BR C CAPE CROSS (IRE) - ALEXANDER CONFRANC (IRE)	BALLYGALLON STUD, IRELAND	VENDOR	125000
CH C MACHIAVELLIAN (USA) - JUMILLA (USA)	CAMAS PARK STUD, IRELAND	FRANCE PUR SANG	125000
B C DANZERO (AUS) - AUSPICIOUS (GB)	CASTLEBRIDGE CONSIGNMENT	EQUINE SERVICES	125000
CRETE (IRE) B C MONTJEU (IRE) - PAESANELLA (GB)	CAMAS PARK STUD, IRELAND	JOHN FERGUSON BS	125000
B F BARATHEA (IRE) - SHOUK (GB)	LIMESTONE STUD	J GOSDEN	120000
B F DR FONG (USA) - ODETTE (GB)	YEOMANSTOWN STUD, IRELAND	JOHN WARREN BS	120000
CH C DESERT PRINCE (IRE) - SAIBHREAS (IRE)	RIDGEWAY HOUSE	MCKEEVER ST LAWRENCE BS	120000
B F DARSHAAN - BARBARA FRIETCHIE (IRE)	WHITSBURY MANOR STUD	D WOODS	120000
B F MISTER BAILEYS (GB) - POLISHED UP (GB)	STRATFORD PLACE STUD	D WOODS	120000
GOLD QUEEN (GB) B F GRAND LODGE (USA) - SILVER COLOURS (USA)	KILDARAGH STUD, IRELAND	G RICHARDSON	120000
B F EPISIO - ANOTHERANNIVERSARY (GB)	ROUND HILL STUD, IRELAND	SHADWELL ESTATE	120000
CH C NAMID (GB) - ADIFE (IRE)	HIGHCLERE STUD	BLOODHORSE INT	120000
B C CADEAUX GENEREUX - ELFIN LAUGHTER (GB)	CROOM HOUSE STUD, IRELAND	HUGO LASCELLES BS	120000
B C DANSILI (GB) - WITCH OF FIFE (USA)	CASTLETOWN STUD, IRELAND (AGENT)	JOHN WARREN BS	115000
B C FASLIYEV (USA) - GO HONEY (GB)	STRADISHALL MANOR STUD	BBA (IRELAND)	115000
B C GREEN DESERT (USA) - RUMPLIMPY (GB)	BARODA STUD, IRELAND	JOHN WARREN BS	115000
B C DANEHILL (USA) - MATILDA BAY (IRE)	KILMINFOYLE HOUSE STUD, IRELAND	BLENHEIM BS	115000
PLANET (IRE) B C SOVIET STAR (USA) - LAURENTIA (USA)	BEECHGROVE STUD	JOHN FERGUSON BS	115000
HELEN SHARP (GB) CH F PIVOTAL (GB) - SUNNY DAVIS (USA)	ASHTOWN HOUSE STUD, IRELAND	JOHN FERGUSON BS	115000
BINT IL SULTAN (IRE) B F XAAR (GB) - KNIGHT'S PLACE (IRE)	BEARSTONE STUD	JOHN FERGUSON BS	110000
B C LEND A HAND (GB) - OCEAN GROVE (IRE)	GLEBE STUD	CHEVELEY PARK STUD	110000
B C ZAFONIC (USA) - FERBER'S FOLLIES (USA)	MANOR HOUSE STUD	C GORDON-WATSON BS	110000
B C ROYAL APPLAUSE (GB) - MISS PRIMULA	GLENVALE STUD, IRELAND	RICHARD FRISBY BS	110000
ALGHARB (GB) B/BR C MUJAHID (USA) - ACTRESS	OLD MILL STUD	HUGO LASCELLES BS	110000
B C ZAFONIC (USA) - SWELLEGANT (GB)	CAMAS PARK STUD, IRELAND	SHADWELL ESTATE	110000
B C STRAVINSKY (USA) - MAY WEDDING (USA)	JOHN OSBORNE, AGENT	MRS A SKIFFINGTON	110000
KISSING LIGHTS (IRE) B F MACHIAVELLIAN (USA) - NASAIEB (IRE)	KERN/LILLINGSTON ASS	D O'BYRNE	110000

HIGH-PRICED YEARLINGS OF 2003 AT GOFFS' SALES

The following yearlings realised 60,000 Euros and over at Goffs' Sales in 2003:-

Name and Breeding	Vendor	Purchaser	Euros
B C DUBAI MILLENNIUM (GB) - SPIRIT OF TARA (IRE)	KILCARN STUD	JOHN FERGUSON BS.	1200000
WIND IN MY HEART (IRE) B F GRAND LODGE (USA) - ZOOMING (IRE)	LOUGHBROWN STUD	A. STROUD.	525000
B F SINNDAR (IRE) - ASTERITA (GB)	REDPENDER STUD	J H JOHNSON	470000
LAMA ALBARQ (USA) CH C NUREYEV (USA) - NUTS IN MAY (USA)	KILCARN STUD	SHADWELL ESTATE.	420000
B C XAAR (GB) - BELSAY (GB)	LYNN LODGE STUD.	J H JOHNSON	420000
B F SADLER'S WELLS (USA) - REX (USA)	CAMAS PARK STUD.	J H JOHNSON	400000
CH F INDIAN RIDGE - HALF-HITCH (USA)	EYREFIELD LODGE STUD.	INT. EQUITIES	380000
B C GRAND LODGE (USA) - COMMANCHE BELLE	ASHTOWN HOUSE STUD.	J FERGUSON	360000
B F DARSHAAN - STAR CRYSTAL (IRE)	GERRARDSTOWN HOUSE STUD.	J DELAHOOKE	360000
HIGHER LOVE (IRE) B F SADLER'S WELLS (USA) - DOLLAR BIRD (IRE)	AIRLIE STUD	BBA (IRELAND)	340000
CH C IN THE WINGS - CONTINUOUS (IRE)	FORENAGHTS STUD	FRANCE PUR SANG.	320000
AWAISER (USA) CH F DESS - FOREST STORM (USA)	CASTLEMARTIN STUD	SHADWELL ESTATE.	300000
B C MONTJEU (IRE) - OPARI (IRE)	ASHTOWN HOUSE STUD.	J H JOHNSON	300000
B C DESERT PRINCE (IRE) - MOY WATER (RE).	IRISH NATIONAL STUD.	J WARREN	300000
B F SADLER'S WELLS (USA) - IMITATION (GB)	JOCKEY HALL STUD (AGENT)	BBA (IRELAND).	300000
SHANGHAI LILY (IRE) B F KING'S BEST (USA) - MARLENE-D (GB)	ABBEVILE & MEADOW COURT STUDS.	CHEVELEY PARK STUD	300000
B C HALLING (USA) - EMMA PEEL (GB)	MEADOWLANDS STUD (TIPPERARY).	J H JOHNSON.	300000
CH F SINNDAR (IRE) - STYLE OF LIFE (USA)	SPRINGBANK WAY (CO. KILDARE)	R FAHEY	290000
B F FASUYEV (USA) - RAHKA ROSE (GB)	MR. JOHN COSTELLO.	D L O'BYRNE	290000
MUTAJAWEZ (IRE) B C FASUYEV (USA) - DANCE DESIRE (IRE)	MARLHILL HOUSE STUD.	SHADWELL ESTATE.	280000
CH C PIVOTAL (GB) - TRIPLE TIE (USA)	TALLY-HO STUD.	JOHN FERGUSON BS	280000
CH F GIANT'S CAUSEWAY (USA) - RUSSIAN BALLET (USA)	COLBINSTOWN LODGE STUD.	BBA (IRELAND)	260000
B C MONTJEU (IRE) - ARDMELODY	GRANGEMORE STUD.	D L O'BYRNE	260000
ALSHMAAL (IRE) B F NAMID (GB) - MISS KINABALU (GB)	YEOMANSTOWN STUD (AGENT)	SHADWELL ESTATE	260000
B C SADLER'S WELLS (USA) - PUCK'S CASTLE (GB).	CROOM HOUSE STUD.	D L O'BYRNE	260000
B C DANEHILL (USA) - ESCAPE TO VICTORY (GB).	CAMAS PARK STUD.	D L O'BYRNE	250000
B C ALHAARTH (IRE) - RING OF KERRY (USA)	THE CASTLETON GROUP	BBA (IRELAND).	240000
WINESONG (IRE) CH F GIANT'S CAUSEWAY (USA) - SUNSET CAFE (IRE)	KILCORAN HOUSE STUD.	JOHN FERGUSON BS	240000
B F IMPERIAL BALLET (RE) - LOON (FR)	YEOMANSTOWN STUD.	BBA (IRELAND)	240000
B C DANEHILL (USA) - CHAMPAKA (RE)	LODGE PARK STUD.	BBA (IRELAND).	225000
SANDYSNOWING (FR) B C SENDAWAR (IRE) - SNOW WHITE (GB)	CORDUFF STUD	J JUDD	220000
B C KING'S BEST (USA) - COLOUR DANCE (GB)	BARONSTOWN STUD.	J FERGUSON	220000
CH F GIANT'S CAUSEWAY (USA) - ASPIRATION (IRE).	GLENVALE STUD.	H JOHNSON	200000
MUTAKAAMEL (IRE) B/BR C MARJU (IRE) - WEST OF EDEN	KILCARN PARK	J FERGUSON	200000
B F SADLER'S WELLS (USA) - SAINTLY SPEECH (USA)	CROOM HOUSE STUD	F SALQUE	190000
ALEXANDER CAPETOWN (IRE) B F FASLIYEV (USA) - HAWAS (GB).	REDPENDER STUD.	SHADWELL ESTATE	190000
B C ORPEN (USA) - ANSARIYA (USA).	CAMAS PARK STUD.	PEGASUS FARMS LTD	185000
B C DANEHILL (IRE) - ALPINE LADY (IRE).	KILCARN PARK	BBA (IRELAND)	180000
B C DANEHILL DANCER (IRE) - ALPINE LADY (IRE)	ASHTOWN HOUSE STUD.	D O'BYRNE	180000
B F CAPE CROSS (IRE) - TROPICAL ZONE (GB)	CAMAS PARK STUD.	D O'BYRNE	180000
B C MONTJEU (IRE) - FLAUTIST (GB)	MR. JOHN TROY (AGENT)	JOHN FERGUSON BS.	180000
	BARONSTOWN STUD	P HARRIS.	180000
	LYNN LODGE STUD	M O'TOOLE.	175000

B F SADLER'S WELLS (USA) - PETROLEUSE	ABBEVILLE & MEADOW COURT STUDS	P HARRIS	160000
B F INTIKHAB (USA) - RIBOT'S GUEST (IRE)	VICTOR STUD	SKYMARC FARM	160000
MOZAKHRAF (USA) B C MISWAKI (USA) - ANAKID (USA)	ABBEVILLE & MEADOW COURT STUDS	SHADWELL ESTATE	160000
B C EL PRADO (IRE) - SPLENDID (IRE)	CAMAS PARK STUD	BBA (IRELAND)	160000
CH F MACHIAVELLIAN (USA) - SPRING EASY (IRE)	GERRARDSTOWN HOUSE STUD	BRIAN GRASSICK BS	160000
B F ENTREPRENEUR (GB) - TADKIYRA (IRE)	CROOM HOUSE STUD	D WACHMAN	160000
B C SADLER'S WELLS (USA) - BELLA VITESSA (IRE)	BARRONSTOWN STUD	BBA (IRELAND)	160000
B F ALMUTAWAKEL (GB) - ECHOES (FR)	RATHBARRY STUD	BBA (IRELAND)	150000
B C GIANT'S CAUSEWAY (USA) - TWICE THE EASE (GB) LYNN	LODGE STUD (AGENT)	BBA (IRELAND)	150000
LOCHRANZA (IRE) B C FASLIYEV (USA) - MYSISTRA (FR)	CAMAS PARK STUD	B OLSSON	150000
B C ROYAL ACADEMY (USA) - PREMIER PEAK (USA) PIER	HOUSE STUD	PETER DOYLE BS	150000
LUAS LINE (IRE) B F DANEHILL (USA) - STREETCAR (IRE)	MARLHILL HOUSE STUD	MRS E STOCKWELL	150000
PEEPTOE (IRE) CH F MACHIAVELLIAN (USA) - ALFAGUARA (USA)	AIRLIE STUD	G CLARKE	150000
B C DANEHILL (USA) - MOON DROP	CAMAS PARK STUD	BBA (IRELAND)	150000
CH F INDIAN RIDGE - OSKARBERG (GB)	MOUNTAIN VIEW STUD	PETER DOYLE BS	145000
B F IN THE WINGS - TROPICAL LASS (IRE)	MOUNT COOTE STUD	BBA (IRELAND)	140000
B C GRAND LODGE (USA) - MARCH HARE (GB)	RATHBARRY STUD (AGENT)	P HARRIS	140000
NATIVE AMERICAN (GB) B C INDIAN LODGE (IRE) - SUMMER SIREN (FR)	RATHBARRY STUD	M A JARVIS	140000
CH C NASHWAN (USA) - MY EMMA (GB)	STAFFORDSTOWN	D WELD	140000
PRIME NUMBER (IRE) GR C KING'S BEST (USA) - MAJINSKAYA (FR)	BALLYLINCH STUD	J BUTLER	140000
PARK APPROACH (IRE) CH F INDIAN RIDGE - ABYAT (USA)	IRISH NATIONAL STUD	S BURNS	140000
B C SADLER'S WELLS (USA) - ROSE OF TARA (IRE)	NORELANDS STUD	M O'TOOLE	140000
B F INDIAN LODGE (IRE) - TRIBAL RITE	J.K. THOROUGHBREDS	CASH	140000
COUNT KRISTO (GB) BR C DR FONG (USA) - ARYADNE (GB)	RATHMORE STUD	C COX	130000
B C MONTJEU (IRE) - CLASSIC PARK (GB)	LODGE PARK STUD	M O'TOOLE	130000
B C SPINNING WORLD (USA) - RIHAN (USA)	FORENAGHTS STUD	HEILGBRODT/NEWMARKET	130000
USHINDI (IRE) B F MONTJEU (IRE) - FERN (GB)	THE CASTLEBRIDGE CONSIGNMENT	KERN/ULLINGSTON ASS.	130000
CH F BELONG TO ME (USA) - WEST ONE (GB)	MR. JOHN OSBORNE (AGENT)	CBA	130000
RIO (IRE) CH C NAMID (GB) - RENASHAAN (FR)	MR. JOHN OSBORNE (AGENT)	CASTLEMARTIN/SKYMARC	130000
SHANEHILL (IRE) B C DANEHILL (USA) - SHUNAIRE (USA)	LOUGHBROWN STUD	RICHARD O'GORMAN BS	125000
B F MONTJEU (IRE) - STRUTTING (IRE)	SWORDLESTOWN STUD	D WACHMAN	125000
DATELINE (IRE) CH C NAMID (GB) - GRATEN (IRE)	KNOCKTORAN STUD	MR & MRS B FIRESTONE	120000
ROYAL FATIMA (IRE) B F FASLIYEV (USA) - ROYAL BOUNTY (IRE)	LANDSCAPE STUD (AGENT)	G RICHARDSON	120000
DRIVE ME WILD (IRE) B C INDIAN RIDGE - WILD BLUEBELL (IRE)	BALLYLINCH STUD	C GORDON-WATSON BS	120000
CH C INDIAN RIDGE - GAZAR (GB)	NORELANDS STUD	C GORDON-WATSON BS	120000
B C RED RANSOM (USA) - MUSICAL TREAT (IRE)	MEADOWLANDS STUD (TIPPERARY)	JOHN FERGUSON BS	120000
RUSSIAN WALTZ (IRE) B F SPECTRUM (IRE) - RUSSIAN COUNTESS (USA)	LODGE PARK STUD	MR & MRS B FIRESTONE	120000
ALEXANDER ICEQUEEN (IRE) B F SOVIET STAR (USA) - REGAL REVOLUTION (GB)	BALLYLINCH STUD (AGENT)	BBA (IRELAND)	115000
B C ROYAL ANTHEM (USA) - SEARCH COMMITTEE (USA)	FORENAGHTS STUD	HEILGBRODT/NEWMARKET	120000
B F STRAVINSKY (USA) - FESTIVE SEASON (USA)	MARLHILL HOUSE STUD	G SWIFT	120000
B C DANEHILL DANCER (IRE) - SIANA SPRINGS (IRE)	ASHTOWN HOUSE STUD	C GORDON-WATSON BS	110000
B C DESERT PRINCE (IRE) - PINTA (IRE)	BALLYLINCH STUD (AGENT)	G RICHARDSON	110000
B F ORPEN (USA) - CANTON LIGHTNING	FARRANAVARRA FARM	OLIVER COOPER BS	110000
CH C GRAND LODGE (USA) - GOLD MIST (GB)	ASHTOWN HOUSE STUD	P HARRIS	110000
B C GREEN DESERT (USA) - ROYALE (IRE)	RATHBARRY STUD	BBA (IRELAND)	110000
B C MONASHEE MOUNTAIN (USA) - GOLDENFORT QUEEN (IRE)	THE CASTLETON GROUP	JOHN FERGUSON BS	110000
B C KING'S BEST (USA) - VIJAYA (USA)	KNOCKTORAN STUD	MARK JOHNSTON RACING	110000
TOUCH OF SILK (USA) CH F NIGHT SHIFT (USA) - BLEW HER TOP (USA)	KNOCKAINEY STUD	BBA (IRELAND)	110000

Yearling	Vendor	Purchaser	Price
B C LILJAN (USA) - MILLING (IRE)	KNOCKLONG HOUSE STUD.	JOHN FERGUSON BS.	110000
B F RAINBOW QUEST (USA) - AKARITA (IRE)	BAROUCHE STUD (IRELAND) LTD.	CASH	105000
BELLE INDIENNE (IRE) CH F INDIAN RIDGE - BLOWN-OVER (GB)	RATHBARRY STUD (AGENT).	FRANCE PUR SANG.	105000
QUEEN'S LACE (IRE) B/BR F KING'S BEST (USA) - STAFF APPROVED	PIER HOUSE STUD.	CASTLEMARTIN/SKYMARC	100000
B C DIESIS - LILIAN BAYLISS (IRE)	YEOMANSTOWN STUD	MRS A SKIFFINGTON.	100000
CH C SINNDAR (IRE) - DEMURE (GB)	THE CASTLETON GROUP	B OLSSON	100000
B F TRANS ISLAND (GB) - PERSIAN POLLY	NEWLANDS HOUSE STUD	T G MILLS	100000
B F DR FONG (USA) - LAUDERDALE (GER)	ABBEVILLE & MEADOW COURT STUDS.	JOHN WARREN BS.	100000
B C IN THE WINGS - KLARIFI	REDPENDER STUD (AGENT).	CASH	100000
B C GIANT'S CAUSEWAY (USA) - MAYENNE (USA)	KILCARN STUD.	M O'TOOLE.	100000
JAZZ BABY (IRE) B F FASLIYEV (USA) - ELIAZZI	BARRONSTOWN STUD.	CASTLEMARTIN/SKYMARC	100000
CH C ZAFONIC (USA) - LOVELY LYCA (GB)	GLENVALE STUD.	MCKEEVER ST LAWRENCE BS.	100000
KHETAAB (IRE) B C ALHAARTH (IRE) - UBERI VERSI (IRE)	BALLYMONEY PARK STUD.	SHADWELL ESTATE	100000
SPECTACULAR DANCER (IRE) B C FASLIYEV (USA) - COMMITTAL (USA)	LONG POND STUD.	D WELD	100000
B F SPECTRUM (IRE) - DANSE ROYALE (IRE)	SPRINGBANK WAY (CO. KILDARE)	J OXX	100000
B C ROYAL ANTHEM (USA) - AZURE LAKE (USA)	ABBEVILLE & MEADOW COURT STUDS.	J FERGUSON	100000
B G MONTJEU (IRE) - DIAMOND FIELD (USA)	THE CASTLETON GROUP	T G MILLS	100000
NOBLESSE DE CHARME (IRE) B F FASLIYEV (USA) - SIMPLE ANNIE	ARODSTOWN STUD.	MERIDIAN INT	100000
B C DANEHILL (USA) - MUSIC AND DANCE (USA)	BARRONSTOWN STUD.	D L O'BYRNE	95000
B C FASLIYEV (USA) - DARKLING (IRE)	GRANGEMORE STUD.	D WELD.	95000
CH F KING'S BEST (USA) - IN YOUR DREAMS (IRE)	COLBINSTOWN LODGE STUD.	INT. EQUITIES.	90000
B F MONTJEU (IRE) - KARDASHINA (FR)	CAHERASS STUD	CASH	90000
LEADING ARTICLE (IRE) CH C DEFINITE ARTICLE (GB) - JAMEELA (IRE)	THE CASTLETON GROUP.	C GORDON-WATSON BS	90000
B C DANEHILL (USA) - FINAL FAREWELL (USA)	CAMAS PARK STUD.	M O'TOOLE.	90000
ETIJAHAAT (IRE) B C KING'S BEST (USA) - DANCE AHEAD (GB)	FORENAGHTS STUD.	SHADWELL ESTATE.	90000
B C KING'S BEST (USA) - BELLE ETOILE (FR)	BROGLIESTOWN STUD.	MARK JOHNSTON RACING.	90000
B F IN THE WINGS - LUMINARY (GB)	YEOMANSTOWN STUD	J JOYCE.	90000
TERMINATE (GER) CH C ACATENANGO (GER) - TAGHAREED (USA)	LYNN LODGE STUD.	SIR M PRESCOTT	90000
B C MISWAKI (USA) - QUINELLA (GB)	NEWTOWN STUD.	C COX	85000
HOH INTREPID (IRE) B F NAMID (GB) - BAZAAR PROMISE	ARLIE STUD.	KERN/ULLINGSTON ASS	85000
B F FASLIYEV (USA) - CUT THE RED TAPE (IRE)	MOUNTAIN VIEW STUD.	E LYNAM	85000
CH F DESERT PRINCE (IRE) - TRULY BEWITCHED (USA)	TARA STUD.	CASH	85000
PAGAN SWORD (GB) CH C SELKIRK (USA) - VANESSA BELL (IRE)	TALLY-HO STUD.	J DELAHOOKE.	85000
CH C INDIAN RIDGE - PLUME BLEU PALE (USA)	CORDUFF STUD.	CASH	85000
B C GIANT'S CAUSEWAY (USA) - HULA ANGEL (USA)	THE CASTLEBRIDGE CONSIGNMENT.	J STACK	85000
B/BR F GONE WEST (USA) - SEATTLE SUMMER (USA)	ABBEVILLE & MEADOW COURT STUDS.	MARK JOHNSTON RACING.	85000
B C GRAND LODGE (USA) - MISS QUEEN (USA)	ABBEVILLE & MEADOW COURT STUDS.	BRIAN GRASSICK BS	85000
B F EFISIO - ROMA (GB)	MR. JOHN OSBORNE (AGENT).	A CHOONG.	80000
B F RAINBOW QUEST (USA) - SAFAYN (USA)	KILDARGH STUD.	CASH	80000
BEST SIDE (USA) B F KING'S BEST (USA) - MOOD SWINGS (IRE)	LOUGHTOWN & CHEVINGTON STUDS	BRA (IRELAND).	80000
DICTATION (GB) B F DIKTAT (GB) - MONAYA	BALLYHIMIKIN STUD	CASTLEMARTIN/SKYMARC	80000
B C DIESIS - DANCE GALY (USA)	GENESIS GREEN STUD	CASTLEMARTIN/SKYMARC	80000
B/BR C FUSAICHI PEGASUS (USA) - LYRIC FANTASY (IRE)	LYNN LODGE STUD.	J DELAHOOKE.	80000
B F ZAFONIC (USA) - AL PERSIAN (IRE)	GLENVALE STUD (AGENT).	P DOYLE.	80000
B C DESERT PRINCE (IRE) - SOEUR TI (FR)	KNOCKTORAN STUD.	BLANDFORD BS.	80000
CH C BLUEBIRD (USA) - HIGHLY RESPECTED (IRE)	CAMAS PARK STUD.	B OLSSON	80000
B C XAAR (GB) - TANZ (IRE)	MR. JOHN OSBORNE (AGENT).	G RICHARDSON	80000

Description	Vendor	Purchaser	Price
B C SOVIET STAR (USA) - WELSH MIST (GB)	MOUNT COOTE STUD	MRS A SKIFFINGTON	77000
B C GIANT'S CAUSEWAY (USA) - ACROSS THE ICE (USA)	FORENAGHTS STUD	B O'RYAN	75000
B/BR C STRAVINSKY (USA) - DEAREST (USA)	KILCARN STUD	MAB AGENCY	75000
BR F MARJU (IRE) - A-TO-Z (IRE)	ASHTOWN HOUSE STUD	J WARREN	75000
B C NAMID (GB) - IMPERIALIST (IRE)	KILSHANNIG STUD (AGENT)	PETER DOYLE BS	75000
B F TRANS ISLAND (GB) - CIDARIS (IRE)	PORTLESTER STUD	MR & MRS B FIRESTONE	75000
GRANDE ROCHE (IRE) B C GRAND LODGE (USA) - ARABIAN LASS (SAF)	ASHTOWN HOUSE STUD	BBA (IRELAND)	75000
CROSS TIME (USA) B C CAPE CROSS (IRE) - RENE MAID (USA)	EGMONT STUD	G RICHARDSON	75000
THORNEY BRIDGE (IRE) B F DANEHILL (USA) - TOUCH OF MAGIC (IRE)	PAGET BLOODSTOCK (AGENT)	HORSE FRANCE	75000
CH F DR FONG (USA) - MY VALENTINA (GB)	KILCARN STUD	T MULLINS	75000
TAYMAN (IRE) B/BR C SINNDAR (IRE) - SWEET EMOTION (IRE)	OAKGROVE STUD	A P JARVIS	72000
B F GIANT'S CAUSEWAY (USA) - SHARP CATCH (IRE)	JOCKEY HALL STUD	REDPENDER STUD	70000
B C FASLIYEV (USA) - FOREVER (USA)	SWORDLESTOWN STUD	F BARRY	70000
CH C SINNDAR (IRE) - AMRAVATI (IRE)	CLARA VIEW STUD	M O'TOOLE	70000
QUIZZICAL QUESTION (IRE) CH F BOB BACK (USA) - QUALITY OF LIFE	ROUNDHILL STUD (IRL)	MRS A SKIFFINGTON	70000
B C INDIAN DANEHILL (IRE) - CRYSTAL BLUE (IRE)	BALLYLINCH STUD (AGENT)	CBA	70000
B C FASLIYEV (USA) - FLYLEAF (FR)	OWENSTOWN STUD	BBA (IRELAND)	70000
B F MONTJEU (IRE) - DARINA (IRE)	REDMONDSTOWN STUD	B F BARRY	70000
B F GRAND LODGE (USA) - SOME MERIT (GB)	ABBEVILLE & MEADOW COURT STUDS	P NEARY	70000
B/BR C SPINNING WORLD (USA) - MISS WOODCHUCK (USA)	BALLINLARD STUD	CASH	70000
B C ANABAA (USA) - PALACEGATE EPISODE (IRE)	KILDARAGH STUD	J GOSDEN	70000
B C INDIAN RIDGE - CHAUNCY LANE (IRE)	SWORDLESTOWN STUD	PETER DOYLE BS	70000
VANISH (IRE) B F BARATHEA (IRE) - SILVER HUT (USA)	CAMAS PARK STUD	HUGO LASCELLES BS	70000
CH C BOUNDARY (USA) - COPPER PLAY (USA)	LANDSCAPE STUD	A JARVIS	70000
B C KING'S BEST (USA) - RAGTIME RUMBLE (USA)	RATHBARRY STUD	J WARREN	70000
B/BR F DANEHILL (USA) - DELAGE (GB)	CORDUFF STUD	G BUTLER	70000
EKTISHAAF (IRE) B F MUJAHID (USA) - TAHNEE (GB)	CROOM HOUSE STUD	HIGHFORT STUD	70000
GIVEN A CHOICE (IRE) B C TRANS ISLAND (GB) - MISS AUDIMAR (USA)	LOUGHBROWN STUD	MARK JOHNSTON RACING	70000
B C WOODMAN (USA) - WHY NOT WILLIE (CAN)	RATHBARRY STUD	SHADWELL ESTATE	70000
SHIRLEY MOON (IRE) B F MONTJEU (IRE) - GREEK MOON (IRE)	RATHASKER STUD	J GIVEN	70000
—	LYNN LODGE STUD	M JOHNSTON	70000
—	ROUNDHILL STUD (IRL)	FRANCE PUR SANG	70000
CH C HIGH YELD (USA) - FARDUS (IRE)	REDMONDSTOWN STUD	DE BURGH/FARRINGTON	67000
CH F NASHWAN (USA) - GHANAI (GB)	HANLON STUD FARM	CASH	66000
B C NAMID (GB) - REMISS (IRE)	OWENSTOWN STUD	VENDOR	66000
PRINCE SAMOS (IRE) B C MILJADIL (USA) - SABANYA (FR)	RATHASKER STUD	KERR & CO	66000
B F NIGHT SHIFT (USA) - PRAY (IRE)	EYREFIELD HOUSE STUD	D WOODS	66000
B F NIGHT SHIFT (USA) - LANELLE (USA)	FORENAGHTS STUD	J MCGRATH	66000
B C IN THE WINGS - MEDWAY (IRE)	AIRLIE STUD	M O'TOOLE	66000
JEWEL IN THE SAND (IRE) B F BLUEBIRD (USA) - DANCING DROP (GB)	GERRARDSTOWN HOUSE STUD	PETER DOYLE BS	65000
SAMUEL JOHN PEPLOE (IRE) B C INTIKHAB (USA) - SADALSUD (IRE)	TALLY-HO STUD	RICHARD FRISBY BS	65000
TETRA SING (IRE) B F SINNDAR (IRE) - TETRALOGY (IRE)	GLENVALE STUD (AGENT)	S BRENCIAGLIA	65000
B C KING'S BEST (USA) - MORNING WELCOME (IRE)	MIDDLELANE FARM	MARK JOHNSTON RACING	65000
CH C NCHINOR (GB) - CHOCOLATE FOG (USA)	WOODTOWN HOUSE STUD	C GORDON-WATSON BS	65000
B C ROYAL ACADEMY (USA) - CHELSEA GREEN (USA)	GLENVALE STUD	J DELAHOOKE	64000
B C NAMID (GB) - TOURAYA	MOUNTAIN VIEW STUD	J RYAN	62000
B F ROSSINI (USA) - CHAUSSONS ROSES (USA)	GLENCARRIG STUD	M HALFORD	62000
KEY TIME (IRE) B C DARSHAAN - KASOTA (IRE)	AIRLIE STUD	SIR M PRESCOTT	60000

1000 GUINEAS STAKES (3y fillies) Newmarket-1 mile

Year	Owner	Winner and Price	Jockey	Trainer	Second	Third	Ran	Time
1964	Beatrice, Lady Granard's	POURPARLER (11/2)	G Bougoure	P J Prendergast	Gwen.	*Royal Danseuse / *Petite Gina.	18	1 38.82
1965	L Holliday's	NIGHT OFF (9/2)	W Williamson	W Wharton	Yami.		16	1 45.43
1966	Mrs J Mills's	GLAD RAGS (100/6)	P Cook	V O'Brien	Berkeley Springs.	Mabel.	21	1 40.30
1967	R Boucher's	FLEET (11/2)	G Moore	N Murless	St Pauli Girl.	Militza.	16	1 40.30
1968	Mrs N Murless's	CAERGWRLE (4/1)	A Barclay	N Murless	Photo Flash.	Lacquer.	14	1 44.76
1969	R Moller's	FULL DRESS (7/1)	R Hutchinson	P Walwyn	Hecuba.	Motionless.	13	1 40.38
1970	Jean, Lady Ashcombe's	HUMBLE DUTY (3/1)	L Piggott	P Walwyn	Gleam.	Black Satin.	12	1 44.53
1971	J Hue-Williams's	ALTESSE ROYALE (25/1)	Y Saint Martin	N Murless	Super Honey.	Catherine Wheel.	10	1 42.13
1972	Mrs R Stanley's	WATERLOO (8/1)	E Hide	J W Watts	Marisela.	Rose Dubarry.	18	1 40.90
1973	G Pope's	MYSTERIOUS (11/1)	G Lewis	N Murless	Jacinth.	Shellshock.	14	1 39.49
1974	The Queen's	HIGHCLERE (12/1)	J Mercer	R Hern	Polygamy.	Mrs Twiggywe Kie	15	1 42.12
1975	Mrs D O' Kelly's	NOCTURNAL SPREE (14/1)	J Roe	S Murless	Girl Friend.	Joking Apart.	16	1 40.32
1976	D Wildenstein's	FLYING WATER (16/1)	Y Saint Martin	A Penna	Konafa.	Kesar Queen.	25	1 41.65
1977	Mrs E Kettlewell's	MRS MCARDY (16/1)	E Hide	M W Easterby	Freeze the Secret.	Sanedtki.	18	1 40.07
1978	R Bonnycastle's	ENSTONE SPARK (35/1)	E Johnson	B Hills	Fair Salinia.	Seraphima.	16	1 41.56
1979	Helena Springfield Ltd's	ONE IN A MILLION (evens)	J Mercer	H Cecil	Abbeydale.	Yanuka.	17	1 43.06
1980	O Phipps's	QUICK AS LIGHTNING (12/1)	B Rouse	J Dunlop	Our Home.	Mrs Penny.	23	1 41.89
1981	H Joel's	FAIRY FOOTSTEPS (6/4)	L Piggott	H Cecil	Tolmi.	Go Leasing.	14	1 40.43
1982	Sir P Oppenheimer's	ON THE HOUSE (33/1)	J Reid	H Wragg	Time Charter.	Dione.	15	1 40.45
1983	M Lemos's	MA BICHE (5/2)	F Head	Mme C Head	Favoridge.	Habibti.	18	1 41.71
1984	Sheikh Mohammed's	PEBBLES (8/1)	P Robinson	C Brittain	Meis El-Reem.	Desirable.	15	1 38.18
1985	S Niarchos's	OH SO SHARP (2/1)	S Cauthen	H Cecil	Al Bahathri.	Bella Colora.	17	1 36.85
1986	S Aland's	MIDWAY LADY (10/1)	R Cochrane	B Hanbury	Maysoon.	Sonic Lady.	15	1 41.54
1987	Sheikh Mohammed's	MIESQUE (15/8)	F Head	F Boutin	Milligram.	Interval.	14	1 38.48
1988	Sheikh Mohammed's	RAVINELLA (4/5)	G W Moore	Mme C Head	Dataweyaa.	Diminuendo.	12	1 40.88
1989	Hamdan Al-Maktoum's	MUSICAL BLISS (7/2)	W R Swinburn	M Stoute	Kerrera.	Aldbourne.	7	1 42.69
1990	Hamdan Al-Maktoum's	SALSABIL (6/4)	W Carson	J Dunlop	Heart of Joy.	Negligent.	10	1 38.06
1991	Maktoum Al-Maktoum's	SHADAYID (4/6)	W Carson	J Dunlop	Kooyonga.	Crystal Gazing.	14	1 38.18
1992	Maktoum Al-Maktoum's	HATOOF (5/1)	W R Swinburn	Mme C Head	Marling.	Kenbu.	14	1 39.45
1993	Mohamed Obaida's	SAYYEDATI (4/1)	W R Swinburn	C Brittain	Niche.	Alfan.	12	1 37.34
1994	R Sangster's	LAS MENINAS (12/1)	J Reid	T Stack	Balanchine.	Coup de Genie.	15	1 36.71
1995	Hamdan Al-Maktoum's	HARAYIR (5/1)	R Hills	Major W R Hern	Aqaarid.	Moonshell.	14	1 36.72
1996	Wafic Said's	BOSRA SHAM (10/11)	Pat Eddery	H Cecil	Matiya.	Bint Shadayid.	13	1 37.75
1997	Greenbay Stables Ltd's	SLEEPYTIME (5/1)	K Fallon	H Cecil	Oh Nellie.	Dazzle.	15	1 37.66
1998	Godolphin's	CAPE VERDI (100/30)	L Dettori	S Bin Suroor	Shahtoush.	Exclusive.	16	1 37.91
1999	K Abdulla's	WINCE (4/1)	K Fallon	H Cecil	Wannabe Grand.	Valentine Waltz.	22	1 36.38
2000	Hamdan Al-Maktoum's	LAHAN (14/1)	R Hills	J Gosden	Princess Ellen.	Petrushka.	18	1 36.36
2001	Sheikh Ahmed Al Maktoum's	AMEERAT (11/1)	P Robinson	M Jarvis	Muwakleh.	Toroca.	15	1 38.36
2002	Godolphin's	KAZZIA (14/1)	L Dettori	S Bin Suroor	Snowfire.	Alasha.	17	1 37.85
2003	Cheveley Park Stud's	RUSSIAN RHYTHM (12/1)	K Fallon	Sir M Stoute	Six Perfections.	Intercontinental.	19	1 38.43

2000 GUINEAS STAKES (3y) Newmarket-1 mile

Year	Owner	Winner and Price	Jockey	Trainer	Second	Third	Ran	Time
1964	Mrs H. Jackson's	BALDRIC (20/1)	W Pyers	E Fellows	Fabergé	Balustrade	27	1 38.44
1965	W Harvey's	NIKSAR (7/1)	D Keith	W Nightingall	Silly Season	Present	22	1 43.31
1966	P Butler's	KASHMIR (100/30)	J Lindley	M Bartholomew	Great Nephew	Celtic Song	25	1 40.63
1967	H Joel's	ROYAL PALACE (100/30)	G Moore	N Murless	Taj Dewan	Missile	18	1 39.37
1968	R Guest's	SIR IVOR (11/8)	L Piggott	V O'Brien	Petingo	Jimmy Reppin	10	1 39.26
1969	J Brown's	RIGHT TACK (15/2)	G Lewis	J Sutcliffe	Tower Walk	Welsh Pageant	13	1 41.65
1970	C Engelhard's	NIJINSKY (4/7)	L Piggott	V O'Brien	Yellow God	Roi Soleil	14	1 41.54
1971	Mrs J Hislop's	BRIGADIER GERARD (11/2)	J Mercer	R Hern	Mill Reef	My Swallow	6	1 39.20
1972	Sir J Thorn's	HIGH TOP (85/40)	W Carson	B Van Cutsem	Roberto	Sun Prince	12	1 40.62
1973	Mrs B Davis's	MON FILS (50/1)	F Durr	R Hannon	Noble Decree	Sharp Edge	18	1 40.82
1974	Mme M Berger's	NONOALCO (19/2)	Y Saint Martin	F Boutin	Giacometti	Apalachee	24	1 42.97
1975	C d'Alessio's	BOLKONSKI (33/1)	G Dettori	H Cecil	Grundy	Dominion	17	1 39.53
1976	C d'Alessio's	WOLLOW (evens)	G Dettori	H Cecil	Vitiges	Thieving Demon	18	1 39.53
1977	N Schibbye's	NEBBIOLO (20/1)	G Curran	K Prendergast	Tachypous	The Minstrel	19	1 38.09
1978	A Hayter's	ROLAND GARDENS (28/1)	F Durr	D Sasse	Remainder Man	Weth Nan	19	1 38.54
1979	A Shead's	TAP ON WOOD (20/1)	S Cauthen	B Hills	Kris	Young Generation	20	1 47.33
1980	K Abdulla's	KNOWN FACT (14/1)	W Carson	J Tree	Posse	Night Alert	14	1 40.46
	(Nureyev fin first disqualified)							
1981	Mrs A Muinos's	TO-AGORI-MOU (5/2)	G Starkey	G Harwood	Mattaboy	Bel Bolide	19	1 41.43
1982	G Oldham's	ZINO (8/1)	Head	F Boutin	Wind and Wuthering	Tender King	26	1 37.13
1983	R Sangster's	LOMOND (9/1)	Pat Eddery	V O'Brien	Tolomeo	Muscatite	16	1 43.87
1984	R Sangster's	EL GRAN SENOR (15/8)	Pat Eddery	V O'Brien	Chief Singer	Lear Fan	9	1 37.41
1985	Maktoum Al Maktoum's	SHADEED (4/5)	L Piggott	M Stoute	Bairn	Supreme Leader	14	1 37.41
1986	K Abdulla's	DANCING BRAVE (15/8)	G Starkey	G Harwood	Green Desert	Huntingdale	15	1 40.00
1987	J Horgan's	DON'T FORGET ME (9/1)	W R Swinburn	R Hannon	Bellotto	Midyan	9	1 36.74
1988	H H Aga Khan's	DOYOUN (4/5)	W Carson	R Hern	Charmer	Bellefella	14	1 41.73
1989	Hamdan Al-Maktoum's	NASHWAN (3/1)	W Carson	R Hern	Exbourne	Danehill	14	1 36.44
1990	John Horgan's	TIROL (9/1)	M Kinane	R Hannon	Machiavellian	Anshan	16	1 35.84
1991	Lady Beaverbrook's	MYSTIKO (13/2)	M Roberts	C Brittain	Lycius	Ganges	14	1 37.83
1992	R Sangster's	RODRIGO DE TRIANO (6/1)	L Piggott	C Chapple-Hyam	Lucky Lindy	Pursuit of Love	23	1 38.37
1993	K Abdulla's	ZAFONIC (5/6)	Pat Eddery	A Fabre	Barathea	Bin Ajwaad	11	1 35.32
1994	G R Bailey Ltd's	MISTER BAILEYS (16/1)	J Weaver	M Johnston	Grand Lodge	Colonel Collins	13	1 35.08
1995	Sheikh Mohammed's	PENNEKAMP (9/2)	J Jarnet	A Fabre	Celtic Swing	Bahri	16	1 35.16
1996	Godolphin's	MARK OF ESTEEM (8/1)	L Dettori	S bin Suroor	Even Top	Bijou D'Inde	18	1 37.59
1997	M Tabor & Mrs J Magnier's	ENTREPRENEUR (11/2)	M Kinane	M Stoute	Revoque	Poteen	16	1 35.64
1998	M Tabor & Mrs J Magnier's	KING OF KINGS (7/2)	M Kinane	A O'Brien	Lend A Hand	Border Arrow	27	1 39.25
1999	Godolphin's	ISLAND SANDS (10/1)	L Dettori	S Bin Suroor	Enrique	Mujahid	18	1 37.14
2000	Saeed Suhail's	KINGS BEST (13/2)	K Fallon	Sir M Stoute	Giant's Causeway	Barathea Guest	22	1 37.77
2001	Lord Weinstock's	GOLAN (9/1)	K Fallon	Sir M Stoute	Tamburlaine	Frenchmans Bay	18	1 37.48
2002	Sir A Ferguson & Mrs J Magnier's	ROCK OF GIBRALTAR (9/1)	J Murtagh	A O'Brien	Hawk Wing	Redback	22	1 36.50
2003	Moyglare Stud Farm's	REFUSE TO BEND (9/2)	P J Smullen	D Weld	Zafeen	Norse Dancer	20	1 37.98

DERBY STAKES (3y) Epsom-1 mile 4 furlongs 10 yards

Year	Owner	Winner and Price	Jockey	Trainer	Second	Third	Ran	Time
1963	F Dupre's	RELKO (5/1)	Y Saint Martin	F Mathet	Merchant Venturer	Ragusa	26	2 39.40
1964	J Ismay's	SANTA CLAUS (15/8)	A Breasley	M Rogers	Indiana	Dilettante	17	2 41.98
1965	J Terrynck's	SEA-BIRD (7/4)	P Glennon	E Pollet	Meadow Court	I Say	22	2 38.41
1966	Lady Z Wernher's	CHARLOTTOWN (5/1)	A Breasley	G Smyth	Pretendre	Black Prince	25	2 37.63
1967	H Joel's	ROYAL PALACE (7/4)	G Moore	N Murless	Ribocco	Dart Board	22	2 38.36
1968	R Guest's	SIR IVOR (4/5)	L Piggott	V O'Brien	Connaught	Mount Athos	13	2 38.73
1969	H Joel's	BLAKENEY (15/2)	E Johnson	A Budgett	Shoemaker	Prince Regent	26	2 40.30
1970	C Engelhard's	NIJINSKY (11/8)	L Piggott	V O'Brien	Gyr	Stintino	11	2 34.68
1971	P Mellon's	MILL REEF (100/30)	G Lewis	I Balding	Linden Tree	Irish Ball	21	2 37.14
1972	J Galbreath's	ROBERTO (3/1)	L Piggott	V O'Brien	Rheingold	Pentland Firth	22	2 36.09
1973	A Budgett's	MORSTON (25/1)	E Hide	A Budgett	Cavo Doro	Freefoot	25	2 35.92
1974	Mrs N. Phillips's	SNOW KNIGHT (50/1)	B Taylor	P Nelson	Imperial Prince	Giacometti	18	2 35.04
1975	Dr C Vittadini's	GRUNDY (5/1)	Pat Eddery	P Walwyn	Nobiliary	Hunza Dancer	18	2 35.35
1976	N B Hunt's	EMPERY (10/1)	L Piggott	M Zilber	Relkino	Oats	23	2 35.69
1977	R Sangster's	THE MINSTREL (5/1)	L Piggott	V O'Brien	Hot Grove	Blushing Groom	22	2 36.44
1978	Lord Halifax's	SHIRLEY HEIGHTS (8/1)	G Starkey	J Dunlop	Hawaiian Sound	Remainder Man	25	2 35.30
1979	Sir M Sobell's	TROY (6/1)	W Carson	R Hern	Dickens Hill	Northern Baby	23	2 36.59
1980	Mrs A Plesch's	HENBIT (7/1)	W Carson	W Hern	Master Willie	Rankin	24	2 34.77
1981	H H Aga Khan's	SHERGAR (10/11)	W Swinburn	M Stoute	Glint of Gold	Scintillating Air	18	2 44.21
1982	R Sangster's	GOLDEN FLEECE (3/1)	Pat Eddery	V O'Brien	Touching Wood	Silver Hawk	18	2 34.27
1983	E Moller's	TEENOSO (9/2)	L Piggott	G Wragg	Carlingford Castle	Shearwalk	21	2 49.07
1984	L Miglietti's	SECRETO (14/1)	C Roche	D O'Brien	El Gran Senor	Mighty Flutter	17	2 39.12
1985	Lord H. de Walden's	SLIP ANCHOR (9/4)	S Cauthen	H Cecil	Law Society	Damister	14	2 36.23
1986	H H Aga Khan's	SHAHRASTANI (11/2)	W Swinburn	M Stoute	Dancing Brave	Mashkour	17	2 37.13
1987	L Freedman's	REFERENCE POINT (6/4)	S Cauthen	H Cecil	Most Welcome	Bellotto	19	2 33.90
1988	H H Aga Khan's	KAHYASI (11/1)	R Cochrane	L Cumani	Glacial Storm	Doyoun	14	2 33.84
1989	Hamdan Al-Maktoum's	NASHWAN (5/4)	W Carson	R Hern	Terimon	Cacoethes	12	2 34.90
1990	K Abdulla's	QUEST FOR FAME (7/1)	Pat Eddery	R Charlton	Blue Stag	Elmaamul	18	2 37.26
1991	F Salman's	GENEROUS (9/1)	A Munro	P Cole	Marju	Star of Gdansk	13	2 34.00
1992	Sidney H Craig's	DR DEVIOUS (8/1)	J Reid	P Chapple-Hyam	St Jovite	Silver Wisp	18	2 36.19
1993	K Abdulla's	COMMANDER IN CHIEF (15/2)	M Kinane	H Cecil	Blue Judge	Blues Traveller	16	2 34.51
1994	Hamdan Al-Maktoum's	ERHAAB (7/2)	W Carson	J Dunlop	King's Theatre	Colonel Collins	25	2 34.16
1995	Saeed Maktoum Al Maktoum's	LAMMTARRA (14/1)	W Swinburn	S Bin Suroor	Tamure	Presenting	15	2 32.31
1996	K Dasmal's	SHAAMIT (12/1)	M Hills	W Haggas	Dushyantor	Shantou	20	2 35.05
1997	L Knight's	BENNY THE DIP (11/1)	W Ryan	J Gosden	Silver Patriarch	Romanov	13	2 35.77
1998	Sheikh Mohammed	HIGH-RISE (20/1)	O Peslier	L Cumani	City Honours	Border Arrow	15	2 33.88
1999	Thoroughbred Corporation's	OATH (13/2)	K Fallon	H Cecil	Daliapour	Beat All	16	2 37.43
2000	H H Aga Khan's	SINNDAR (7/1)	J Murtagh	J Oxx	Sakhee	Beat Hollow	15	2 36.75
2001	M Tabor & Mrs J Magnier's	GALILEO (11/4)	M Kinane	A O'Brien	Golan	Tobougg	12	2 33.27
2002	M Tabor & Mrs J Magnier's	HIGH CHAPARRAL (7/2)	M Murtagh	A O'Brien	Hawk Wing	Moon Ballad	12	2 39.45
2003	Saeed Suhail's	KRIS KIN (6/1)	K Fallon	Sir M Stoute	The Great Gatsby	Alamshar	20	2 33.35

OAKS STAKES (3y fillies) Epsom-1 mile 4 furlongs 10 yards

Year	Owner	Winner and Price	Jockey	Trainer	Second	Third	Ran	Time
1970	Mrs S Joel's	LUPE (100/30)	A Barclay	N Murless	State Pension	Arctic Wave	16	2 41.46
1971	F Hue-Williams's	ALTESSE ROYALE (6/4)	G Lewis	N Murless	Maina	La Manille	11	2 36.95
1972	C St George's	GINEVRA (8/1)	A Murray	R Price	Regal Exception	Arkadina	17	2 39.35
1973	G Pope's	MYSTERIOUS (13/8)	G Lewis	N Murless	Where You Lead	Aureoletta	10	2 36.31
1974	L Freedman's	POLYGAMY (3/1)	Pat Eddery	P Walwyn	Furioso	Aarleletta	15	2 39.39
1975	J Morrison's	JULIETTE MARNY (12/1)	L Piggott	J Tree	Val's Girl	Matuta	12	2 39.10
1976	D Wildenstein's	PAWNEESE (6/5)	Y Saint Martin	A Penna	Roses for the Star	Moonlight Night	14	2 35.25
1977	The Queen's	DUNFERMLINE (6/1)	W Carson	R Hern	Freeze the Secret	African Dancer	13	2 36.53
1978	S Hanson's	FAIR SALINIA (8/1)	G Starkey	M Stoute	Dancing Maid	Vaguely Deb	15	2 36.82
1979	J Morrison's	SCINTILLATE (20/1)	Pat Eddery	J Tree	Bonnie Isle	Suni	14	2 43.74
1980	R Hollingsworth's	BIREME (9/2)	W Carson	R Hern	Vielle	Britannia's Rule	11	2 34.33
1981	Mrs B Firestone's	BLUE WIND (3/1)	L Piggott	D Weld	Madam Gay	The Dancer	12	2 40.93
1982	R Barnett's	TIME CHARTER (12/1)	W Newnes	H Candy	Slightly Dangerous	Leap Lively	13	2 34.21
1983	Sir M Sobell's	SUN PRINCESS (6/1)	W Carson	R Hern	Acclimatise	Last Feather	15	2 40.98
1984	Sir R McAlpine's	CIRCUS PLUME (4/1)	L Piggott	J Dunlop	Media Luna	New Coins	15	2 38.97
1985	Sheikh Mohammed's	OH SO SHARP (6/4)	S Cauthen	H Cecil	Triptych	Poquito Queen	12	2 41.37
1986	H Ranier's	MIDWAY LADY (15/8)	R Cochrane	B Hanbury	Untold	Dubian	15	2 35.60
1987	Sheikh Mohammed's	UNITE (11/1)	W R Swinburn	M Stoute	Bourbon Girl	Maysoon	11	2 38.17
1988	Sheikh Mohammed's	DIMINUENDO (7/4)	S Cauthen	H Cecil	Sudden Love	Three Tails	11	2 35.02
1989	S M Al Maktoum's	SNOW BRIDE (13/2)	S Cauthen	H Cecil	Roseate Tern	Animatrice	9	2 34.22

(Allysa finished first but was disqualified)

1990	Hamdan Al-Maktoum's	SALSABIL (2/1)	W Carson	J Dunlop	Game Plan	Mamaluna	8	2 38.70
1991	Maktoum Al-Maktoum's	JET SKI LADY (50/1)	C Roche	J Bolger	Shamshir	Knight's Baroness	9	2 37.30
1992	W J Gredley's	USER FRIENDLY (5/1)	G Duffield	C Brittain	All At Sea	Shadayid	7	2 39.77
1993	Sheikh Mohammed's	INTREPIDITY (5/1)	M Roberts	A Fabre	Royal Ballerina	Pearl Angel	14	2 34.19
1994	Godolphin's	BALANCHINE (3/1)	L Dettori	H Ibrahim	Wind In Her Hair	Oakmead	10	2 40.37
1995	Maktoum Al Maktoum/ Godolphin's	MOONSHELL (3/1)	L Dettori	S Bin Suroor	Dance A Dream	Hawajiss	10	2 35.44
1996	Wafic Said's	LADY CARLA (100/30)	Pat Eddery	H Cecil	Pricket	Pure Grain	11	2 35.55
1997	K Abdulla's	REAMS OF VERSE (5/6)	K Fallon	H Cecil	Gazelle Royale	Mezzogiorno	12	2 35.59
1998	Mrs D Nagle & Mrs J Magnier's	SHAHTOUSH (12/1)	M Kinane	A O'Brien	Bahr	Crown of Light	8	2 38.23
1999	F Salman's	RAMRUMA (3/1)	K Fallon	H Cecil	Nousitkey	Midnight Line	10	2 38.72
2000	Lordship Stud's	LOVE DIVINE (9/4)	T Quinn	H Cecil	Kalypso Katie	Zahrat Dubai	16	2 43.11
2001	Mrs D Nagle & Mrs J Magnier's	IMAGINE (3/1)	M Kinane	A O'Brien	Flight Of Fancy	Melikah	14	2 36.70
2002	Godolphin's	KAZZIA (100/30)	L Dettori	S bin Suroor	Quarter Moon	Relish The Thought	14	2 44.52
2003	W S Farish III's	CASUAL LOOK (10/1)	M Dwyer	A Balding	Yesterday	Shadow Dancing	15	2 38.07

ST LEGER STAKES (3y) Doncaster-1 mile 6 furlongs 132 yards

Year	Owner	Winner and Price	Jockey	Trainer	Second	Third	Ran	Time
1963	J Mullion's	RAGUSA (2/5)	G Bougoure	J Prendergast	Star Moss	Fighting Ship	7	3 5.40
1964	C Engelhard's	INDIANA (100/7)	J Lindley	J Watts	Pati	Soderini	15	3 5.40
1965	J Astor's	PROVOKE (28/1)	J Mercer	R Hern	Meadow Court	Solstice	11	3 18.60
1966	R Sigtia's	SODIUM (7/1)	F Durr	G Todd	Charlottown	David Jack	9	3 9.80
1967	C Engelhard's	RIBOCCO (7/2)	L Piggott	R Houghton	Hopeful Venture	Ruysdael	8	3 5.40
1968	C Engelhard's	RIBERO (100/30)	L Piggott	R Houghton	Canterbury	Cold Storage	8	3 19.80
1969	G Oldham's	INTERMEZZO (7/1)	R Hutchinson	H Wragg	Ribofilio	Prince Consort	11	3 11.80
1970	C Engelhard's	NIJINSKY (2/7)	L Piggott	V O'Brien	Meadowville	Politico	9	3 6.40
1971	Mrs J Rogerson's	ATHENS WOOD (5/2)	L Piggott	H T Jones	Homeric	Falkland	8	3 14.90
1972	O Phipps's	BOUCHER (3/1)	L Piggott	V O'Brien	Our Mirage	Ginevra	7	3 28.71
1973	W Behrens's	PELEID (28/1)	F Durr	W Elsey	Buoy	Duke of Ragusa	13	3 8.21
1974	Lady Beaverbrook's	BUSTINO (11/10)	J Mercer	R Hern	Giacometti	Riboson	10	3 9.02
1975	C St George's	BRUNI (9/1)	A Murray	R Price	King Pellinore	Libra's Rib	12	3 9.02
1976	D Wildenstein's	CROW (6/1)	Y Saint-Martin	R Penna	Secret Man	Scallywag	15	3 13.17
1977	The Queen's	DUNFERMLINE (10/1)	W Carson	R Hern	Alleged	Classic Example	13	3 5.17
1978	M Lemos's	JULIO MARINER (28/1)	E Hide	C Brittain	Le Moss	M-Lolshan	14	3 4.94
1979	A Rolland's	SON OF LOVE (20/1)	A Lequeux	R Collet	Soleil Noir	Niniski	17	3 9.02
1980	H Joel's	LIGHT CAVALRY (3/1)	J Mercer	H Cecil	Water Mill	World Leader	7	3 11.48
1981	Sir J Astor's	CUT ABOVE (28/1)	J Mercer	R Hern	Glint of Gold	Bustomi	7	3 11.60
1982	Maktoum Al Maktoum's	TOUCHING WOOD (7/1)	P Cook	H T Jones	Zilos	Diamond Shoal	15	3 3.53
1983	Sir M Sobell's	SUN PRINCESS (11/8)	W Carson	R Hern	Esprit du Nord	Carlingford Castle	10	3 16.65
1984	I Allan's	COMMANCHE RUN (7/4)	L Piggott	L Cumani	Baynoun	Alphabatim	11	3 9.93
1985	Sheikh Mohammed's	OH SO SHARP (8/11)	S Cauthen	H Cecil	Phardante	Lanfranco	6	3 7.13
1986	Duchess of Norfolk's	MOON MADNESS (9/2)	Pat Eddery	J Dunlop	Celestial Storm	Untold	8	3 5.03
1987	L Freedman's	REFERENCE POINT (4/11)	S Cauthen	H Cecil	Mountain Kingdom	Dry Dock	7	3 5.91
1988	Lady Beaverbrook's	MINSTER SON (15/2)	W Carson	N A Graham	Diminuendo	Sheriff's Star	6	3 6.80
1989	C St George's	MICHELOZZO (6/4)	S Cauthen	H Cecil	Sapience	Roseate Tern	8	3 20.72
							(Run at Ayr)	
1990	M Arbib's	SNURGE (7/2)	T Quinn	P Cole	Hellenic	River God	8	3 8.78
1991	K Abdulla's	TOULON (5/2)	Pat Eddery	A Fabre	Saddlers' Hall	Micheletti	10	3 3.12
1992	W J Gredley's	USER FRIENDLY (7/4)	G Duffield	C Brittain	Sonus	Bonny Scot	9	3 5.48
1993	Mrs G A E Smith's	BOB'S RETURN (3/1)	P Robinson	M Tompkins	Armiger	Edbaysaan	7	3 7.85
1994	Godolphin's	MOONAX (40/1)	Pat Eddery	B Hills	Broadway Flyer	Double Trigger	8	3 4.19
1995	Sheikh Mohammed's	CLASSIC CLICHE (100/30)	L Dettori	S Bin Suroor	Minds Music	Istidaad	10	3 9.74
1996	Sheikh Mohammed's	SHANTOU (8/1)	L Dettori	J Gosden	Dushyantor	Samraan	11	3 5.10
1997	P Winfield's	SILVER PATRIARCH (5/4)	Pat Eddery	J Dunlop	Vertical Speed	The Fly	9	3 6.92
1998	Godolphin's	NEDAWI (5/2)	J Reid	S Bin Suroor	High and Low	Sunshine Street	9	3 5.61
1999	Godolphin's	MUTAFAWEQ (11/2)	R Hills	S Bin Suroor	Ramruma	Adair	9	3 2.75
2000	N Jones	MILLENARY (11/4)	T Quinn	J Dunlop	Air Marshall	Chimes At Midnight	9	3 2.58
2001	M Tabor & Mrs J Magnier's	MILAN (13/8)	M Kinane	A O'Brien	Demophilos	Mr Combustible	11	3 5.16
2002	Sir Neil Westbrook's	BOLLIN ERIC (7/1)	K Darley	T Easterby	Highest	Bandari	10	2 92
2003	Mrs J Magnier's	BRIAN BORU (5/4)	J P Spencer	A O'Brien	High Accolade	Phoenix Reach	12	3 4.64

KING GEORGE VI AND QUEEN ELIZABETH STAKES Ascot-1 mile 4 furlongs

Year	Owner	Winner and Price	Jockey	Trainer	Second	Third	Ran	Time
1965	G Bell's	MEADOW COURT 3-8-7 (6/5)	L Piggott	P J Prendergast	Soderini	Oncidium	12	2 33.27
1966	J Hornung's	AUNT EDITH 4-9-4 (7/2)	L Piggott	N Murless	Sodium	Prominer	5	2 35.06
1967	S Joel's	BUSTED 4-9-7 (4/1)	G Moore	N Murless	Salvo	Ribocco	5	2 33.64
1968	J Joel's	ROYAL PALACE 4-9-7 (7/4)	A Barclay	N Murless	Felicio	Topyo	7	2 33.22
1969	Duke of Devonshire's	PARK TOP 5-9-4 (40/85)	L Piggott	B van Cutsem	Crozier	Hogarth	9	2 42.46
1970	C Englehart's	NIJINSKY 3-8-7 (40/85)	L Piggott	V O'Brien	Blakeney	Crepellana	6	2 36.16
1971	P Mellon's	MILL REEF 3-8-7 (8/13)	G Lewis	I Balding	Ortis	Acclimatization	10	2 32.56
1972	Mrs J Hislop's	BRIGADIER GERARD 4-9-7 (8/13)	J Mercer	R Hern	Parnell	Riverman	4	2 32.91
1973	N B Hunt's	DAHLIA 3-8-8 (10/1)	W Pyers	M Zilber	Rheingold	Our Mirage	12	2 30.43
1974	N B Hunt's	DAHLIA 4-9-4 (15/8)	L Piggott	M Zilber	Highclere	Dankaro	11	2 33.03
1975	Dr C Vittadini's	GRUNDY 3-8-7 (4/5)	P Eddery	P Walwyn	Bustino	Dahlia	11	2 26.98
1976	D Wildenstein's	PAWNEESE 3-8-5 (9/4)	Y Saint Martin	A Penna	Bruni	Orange Bay	10	2 29.36
1977	R Sangster's	THE MINSTREL 3-8-8 (7/4)	L Piggott	V O'Brien	Orange Bay	Exceller	11	2 30.48
1978	D McCall's	ILE DE BOURBON 3-8-8 (12/1)	J Reid	R Houghton	Hawaiian Sound	Montcontour	10	2 30.53
1979	Sir M Sobell's	TROY 3-8-8 (2/5)	W Carson	R Hern	Gay Mecene	Ela-Mana-Mou	14	2 30.48
1980	Sir M Sobell's	ELA-MANA-MOU 4-9-7 (11/4)	W Carson	R Hern	Mrs Penny	Gregorian	9	2 35.39
1981	H H Aga Khan's	SHERGAR 3-8-8 (2/5)	W Swinburn	M Stoute	Madam Gay	Fingals Cave	7	2 35.40
1982	R Barnett's	KALAGLOW 4-9-7 (13/2)	G Starkey	G Harwood	Assert	Glint of Gold	9	2 31.58
1983	E Moller's	TIME CHARTER 4-9-4 (5/1)	J Mercer	H Candy	Diamond Shoal	Sun Princess	9	2 31.50
1984	Lady Beaverbrook's	TEENOSO 4-9-7 (13/2)	L Piggott	G Wragg	Sadler's Wells	Tolomeo	13	2 27.61
1985	K Abdulla's	PETOSKI 3-8-8 (12/1)	W Carson	W Hern	Oh So Sharp	Rainbow Quest	12	2 29.49
1986	L Freedman's	DANCING BRAVE 3-8-8 (6/4)	Pat Eddery	G Harwood	Shardari	Triptych	9	2 29.49
1987	Sheikh Ahmed Al Maktoum's	REFERENCE POINT 3-8-8 (11/10)	S Cauthen	H Cecil	Celestial Storm	Triptych	9	2 34.63
1988	Hamdan Al-Maktoum's	MTOTO 5-9-7 (4/1)	M Roberts	A C Stewart	Unfuwain	Triptych	10	2 37.33
1989	Sheikh Mohammed's	NASHWAN 3-8-8 (2/9)	W Carson	R Hern	Cacoethes	Top Class	7	2 32.27
1990	Sheikh Mohammed's	BELMEZ 3-8-9 (15/2)	M Kinane	H Cecil	Old Vic	Assatis	11	2 30.76
1991	F Salman's	GENEROUS 3-8-9 (4/6)	A Munro	P Cole	Sanglamore	Rock Hopper	7	2 28.99
1992	Mrs V K Payson's	ST JOVITE 3-8-9 (4/5)	S Craine	J Bolger	Saddlers' Hall	Opera House	8	2 30.85
1993	Sheikh Mohammed's	OPERA HOUSE 5-9-7 (8/1)	M Roberts	M Stoute	White Muzzle	Commander in Chief	8	2 33.94
1994	Sheikh Mohammed's	KING'S THEATRE 3-8-9 (12/1)	M Kinane	H Cecil	White Muzzle	Wagon Master	10	2 28.92
1995	Saeed Maktoum Al Maktoum's	LAMMTARRA 3-8-9 (9/4)	L Dettori	S Bin Suroor	Pentire	Strategic Choice	7	2 31.01
1996	Mollers Racing's	PENTIRE 4-9-7 (100/30)	M Hills	G Wragg	Classic Cliche	Shaamit	8	2 28.11
1997	Godolphin's	SWAIN 5-9-7 (16/1)	J Reid	S Bin Suroor	Pilsudski	Helissio	8	2 36.45
1998	Godolphin's	SWAIN 6-9-7 (1/2)	L Dettori	S Bin Suroor	High-Rise	Royal Anthem	8	2 29.06
1999	Godolphin's	DAYLAMI 5-9-7 (3/1)	L Dettori	S Bin Suroor	Nedawi	Fruits Of Love	8	2 29.35
2000	M Tabor's	MONTJEU 4-9-7 (1/3)	M Kinane	J Hammond	Fantastic Light	Daliapour	7	2 29.98
2001	Mrs J Magnier & M Tabor's	GALILEO 3-8-9 (1/2)	M Kinane	A O'Brien	Fantastic Light	Hightori	12	2 27.71
2002	Exors of the late Lord Weinstock's	GOLAN 4-9-7 (1/2)	K Fallon	Sir M Stoute	Nayef	Zindabad	9	2 29.70
2003	H H Aga Khan	ALAMSHAR 3-8-9 (13/2)	J Murtagh	J Oxx	Sulamani	Kris Kin	12	2 33.26

PRIX DE L'ARC DE TRIOMPHE Longchamp-1 mile 4 furlongs

Year	Owner	Winner and Price	Jockey	Trainer	Second	Third	Ran	Time
1963	Baron G de Rothschild's	EXBURY 4-9-6 (36/10)	J Deforge	G Watson	Le Mesnil	Misti	15	2 34.90
1964	R Ellsworth's	PRINCE ROYAL 3-8-10 (16/1)	R Poincelet	G Bridgland	Santa Claus	La Bamba	22	2 35.50
1965	W Ternynck's	SEA-BIRD 3-8-10 (6/5)	P Glennon	E Pollet	Reliance	Diatome	20	2 35.50
1966	W Burmann's	BON MOT 3-8-10 (53/10)	F Head	W Head	Sigebert	Lionel	24	2 39.80
1967	Mme S Volterra's	TOPYO 3-8-10 (82/1)	W Pyers	M Bartholomew	Salvo	Ribocco	30	2 38.20
1968	Mrs W Franklyn's	VAGUELY NOBLE 3-8-10 (5/2)	W Williamson	E Pollet	Sir Ivor	Carmarthen	17	2 35.20
1969	S McGrath's	LEVMOSS 4-9-6 (52/1)	W Williamson	S McGrath	Park Top	Grandier	24	2 29.00
1970	A Plesch's	SASSAFRAS 3-8-10 (19/1)	Y Saint Martin	F Mathet	Nijinsky	Miss Dan	15	2 29.70
1971	P Mellon's	MILL REEF 3-8-10 (7/10)	G Lewis	I Balding	Pistol Packer	Cambrizia	18	2 28.30
1972	Countess M Batthyany's	SAN SAN 3-8-7 (37/2)	F Head	A Penna	Rescousse	Homeric	19	2 28.30
1973	H Zeisel's	RHEINGOLD 4-9-6 (77/10)	L Piggott	B Hills	Allez France	Hard to Beat	27	2 35.80
1974	W Zeitelhack's	ALLEZ FRANCE 4-9-3 (1/2)	Y Saint Martin	A Penna	Comtesse de Loir	Margouillat	20	2 36.90
1975	W Zeitelhack's	STAR APPEAL 5-9-6 (119/1)	G Starkey	T Grieper	On My Way	Comtesse de Loir	24	2 33.60
1976	R Sangster's	IVANJICA 4-9-1 (71/10)	F Head	A Head	Crow	Youth	20	2 39.40
1977	R Sangster's	ALLEGED 3-8-11 (38/10)	L Piggott	V O'Brien	Balmerino	Crystal Palace	26	2 30.60
1978	R Sangster's	ALLEGED 4-9-4 (7/5)	L Piggott	V O'Brien	Trillion	Dancing Maid	18	2 36.10
1979	Mme G Head's	THREE TROIKAS 3-8-8 (88/10)	F Head	Mme C Head	Le Marmot	Troy	22	2 28.90
1980	R Sangster's	DETROIT 3-8-8 (67/10)	Pat Eddery	O Douieb	Argument	Ela-Mana-Mou	20	2 28.00
1981	J Wertheimer's	GOLD RIVER 4-9-1 (53/1)	G W Moore	F Mathet	Bikala	April Run	24	2 35.20
1982	H H Aga Khan's	AKIYDA 3-8-8 (43/4)	Y Saint Martin	F Mathet	Ardross	Awaasif	17	2 37.00
1983	D Wildenstein's	ALL ALONG 4-9-1 (173/10)	W Swinburn	P Biancone	Sun Princess	Luth Enchantée	26	2 28.10
1984	D Wildenstein's	SAGACE 4-9-4 (29/10)	Y Saint Martin	P Biancone	Northern Trick	All Along	22	2 29.10
1985	K Abdulla's	RAINBOW QUEST 4-9-4 (71/10)	Pat Eddery	J Tree	Sagace	Kozana	15	2 29.50
1986	K Abdulla's	DANCING BRAVE 3-8-11 (11/10)	Pat Eddery	G Harwood	Bering	Triptych	15	2 27.70
1987	P de Moussac's	TREMPOLINO 3-8-11 (20/1)	Pat Eddery	A Fabre	Tony Bin	Triptych	11	2 26.30
1988	Mrs V Gaucci del Bono's	TONY BIN 5-9-4 (14/1)	J Reid	L Camici	Mtoto	Boyatino	24	2 27.30
1989	A Balzarini's	CARROLL HOUSE 4-9-4 (19/1)	M Kinane	M Jarvis	Behera	Saint Andrews	19	2 30.80
1990	B McNall's	SAUMAREZ 3-8-11 (15/1)	G Mosse	N Clement	Epervier Bleu	Snurge	21	2 30.80
1991	M Chalhoub's	SUAVE DANCER 3-8-11 (37/10)	C Asmussen	J Hammond	Magic Night	Pistolet Bleu	14	2 31.40
1992	O Lecerf's	SUBOTICA 4-9-4 (88/10)	T Jarnet	A Fabre	User Friendly	Vert Amande	18	2 37.90
1993	D Tsui's	URBAN SEA 4-9-1 (37/1)	E Saint Martin	J Lesbordes	White Muzzle	Opera House	23	2 37.90
1994	Sheikh Mohammed's	CARNEGIE 3-8-11 (3/1)	T Jarnet	A Fabre	Hernando	Apple Tree	20	2 31.10
1995	Saeed Maktoum Al Maktoum's	LAMMTARRA 3-8-11 (2/1)	L Dettori	S Bin Suroor	Freedom Cry	Swain	16	2 31.80
1996	E Sarasola's	HELISSIO 3-8-11 (18/10)	O Peslier	E Lellouche	Pilsudski	Oscar Schindler	16	2 29.90
1997	D Wildenstein's	PEINTRE CELEBRE 3-8-11 (22/10)	O Peslier	A Fabre	Pilsudski	Borgia	18	2 24.60
1998	J-L Lagardere's	SAGAMIX 3-8-11 (5/2)	O Peslier	A Fabre	Leggera	Tiger Hill	14	2 34.50
1999	M Tabor's	MONTJEU 3-8-11 (6/4)	M Kinane	J Hammond	El Condor Pasa	Croco Rouge	14	2 38.50
2000	H H Aga Khan's	SINNDAR 3-8-11 (6/4)	J Murtagh	J Oxx	Egyptband	Volvoreta	10	2 25.80
2001	Godolphin's	SAKHEE 4-9-5 (22/10)	L Dettori	S Bin Suroor	Aquarelliste	Sagacity	17	2 36.10
2002	Godolphin's	MARIENBARD 5-9-5 (158/10)	L Dettori	S Bin Suroor	Sulamani	High Chaparral	16	2 26.70
2003	H H Aga Khan's	DALAKHANI 3-8-11 (9/4)	C Soumillon	A DeRoyer-Dupre	Mubtaker	High Chaparral	13	2 32.30

GRAND NATIONAL STEEPLECHASE Aintree-4m 4f

Year	Winner and Price	Age & Weight	Jockey	Second	Third	Ran	Time
1962	KILMORE (28-1)	12 10 4	F T Winter	Wyndburgh	Mr What	32	9 50.00
1963	AYALA (66-1)	9 10 0	P Buckley	Carrickbeg	Hawa's Song	47	9 35.80
1964	TEAM SPIRIT (18-1)	12 10 3	G W Robinson	Purple Silk	Peacetown	33	9 47.00
1965	JAY TRUMP (100-8)	8 11 5	Mr C Smith, jun	Freddie	Mr Jones	47	9 52.80
1966	ANGLO (50-1)	8 10 0	T Norman	Freddie	Forest Prince	47	9 49.60
1967	FOINAVON (100-1)	9 10 0	J Buckingham	Honey End	Red Alligator	44	9 28.60
1968	RED ALLIGATOR (100-7)	9 10 0	B Fletcher	Moidore's Token	Different Class	45	9 30.80
1969	HIGHLAND WEDDING (100-9)	12 10 4	E Harty	Steel Bridge	Rondetto	30	9 30.80
1970	GAY TRIP (15-1)	8 11 5	P Taaffe	Vulture	Miss Hunter	28	9 38.00
1971	SPECIFY (28-1)	9 10 13	J Cook	Black Secret	Astbury	38	9 34.20
1972	WELL TO DO (14-1)	9 10 1	G Thorner	Gay Trip	Black Secret	42	10 08.40
1973	RED RUM (9-1)	8 10 5	B Fletcher	Crisp	L'Escargot	38	9 01.90
1974	RED RUM (11-1)	9 12 0	B Fletcher	L'Escargot	Charles Dickens	42	9 20.30
1975	L'ESCARGOT (13-2)	12 11 3	T Carberry	Red Rum	Spanish Steps	31	9 20.90
1976	RAG TRADE (14-1)	10 10 12	J Burke	Red Rum	Eyecatcher	32	9 20.90
1977	RED RUM (9-1)	12 11 8	T Stack	Churchtown Boy	Eyecatcher	42	9 30.90
1978	LUCIUS (14-1)	9 10 9	B R Davies	Sebastian V	Drumroan	37	9 33.90
1979	RUBSTIC (25-1)	10 10 0	M Barnes	Zongalero	Rough & Tumble	34	9 52.90
1980	BEN NEVIS (40-1)	12 10 12	Mr C Fenwick	Rough & Tumble	The Pilgarlic	30	10 17.40
1981	ALDANITI (10-1)	11 10 13	R Champion	Spartan Missile	Royal Mail	39	9 47.20
1982	GRITTAR (7-1)	9 11 5	E Saunders	Hard Outlook	Loving Words	39	9 12.60
1983	CORBIERE (13-1)	8 11 4	B de Haan	Greasepaint	Yer Man	41	9 47.04
1984	HALLO DANDY (13-1)	10 10 2	N Doughty	Greasepaint	Corbiere	40	9 21.70
1985	LAST SUSPECT (50-1)	11 10 5	H Davies	Mr Snugfit	Corbiere	40	9 42.70
1986	WEST TIP (15-2)	9 10 11	R Dunwoody	Young Driver	Classified	40	9 33.00
1987	MAORI VENTURE (28-1)	11 10 13	S C Knight	The Tsarevich	Lean Ar Aghaidh	40	9 19.30
1988	RHYME N'REASON (10-1)	9 11 0	B Powell	Durham Edition	Monanore	40	9 53.50
1989	LITTLE POLVEIR (28-1)	12 10 3	J Frost	West Tip	The Thinker	40	10 06.80
1990	MR FRISK (16-1)	11 10 6	Mr M Armytage	Durham Edition	Rinus	38	8 47.80
1991	SEAGRAM (12-1)	11 10 6	N Hawke	Garrison Savannah	Auntie Dot	40	9 29.90
1992	PARTY POLITICS (14-1)	8 10 7	C Llewellyn	Romany King	Laura's Beau	40	9 06.30
1993	Race Void						
1994	MINNEHOMA (16-1)	11 10 8	R Dunwoody	Just So	Moorcroft Boy	36	10 18.80
1995	ROYAL ATHLETE (40-1)	12 10 6	J Titley	Party Politics	Over The Deel	35	9 04.00
1996	ROUGH QUEST (7-1)	10 10 7	M Fitzgerald	Encore Un Peu	Superior Finish	27	9 00.80
1997	LORD GYLLENE (14-1)	10 10 0	A Dobbin	Suny Bay	Camelot Knight	36	9 05.80
1998	EARTH SUMMIT (7-1)	10 10 5	C Llewellyn	Suny Bay	Samlee	37	10 51.40
1999	BOBBYJO (10-1)	9 10 0	R Carberry	Blue Charm	Call It A Day	32	9 14.00
2000	PAPILLON (10-1)	9 10 12	R Walsh	Mely Moss	Niki Dee	40	9 09.70
2001	RED MARAUDER (33-1)	11 10 11	R Guest	Smarty	Blowing Wind	40	11 00.10
2002	BINDAREE (20-1)	8 10 4	J Culloty	What's Up Boys	Blowing Wind	40	9 09.00
2003	MONTY'S PASS (16-1)	10 10 7	B J Geraghty	Supreme Glory	Amberleigh House	40	9 21.70

WINNERS OF GREAT RACES

LINCOLN HANDICAP
Doncaster-1m

1994	**OUR RITA** 5-8-5	24
1995	**ROVING MINSTREL** 4-8-3	23
1996	**STONE RIDGE** 4-8-7	24
1997	**KUALA LIPIS** 4-8-6	24
1998	**HUNTERS OF BRORA** 8-9-0	23
1999	**RIGHT WING** 5-9-5	24
2000	**JOHN FERNELEY** 5-8-10	24
2001	**NIMELLO** 5-8-9	23
2002	**ZUCCHERO** 6-8-13	23
2003	**PABLO** 4-8-11	24

GREENHAM STAKES (3y)
Newbury-7f

1994	**TURTLE ISLAND** 9-0	8
1995	**CELTIC SWING** 9-0	9
1996	**DANEHILL DANCER** 9-0	8
1997	**YALAIETANEE** 9-0	6
1998	**VICTORY NOTE** 9-0	6
1999	**ENRIQUE** 9-0	7
*2000	**BARATHEA GUEST** 9-0	7
2001	**MUNIR** 9-0	7
2002	**REDBACK** 9-0	10
2003	**MUQBIL** 9-0	8

* Run at Newmarket

JOHN PORTER STAKES
Newbury-1m 4f 5yds

1994	**RIGHT WIN** 4-9-3	10
1995	**STRATEGIC CHOICE** 4-8-11	10
1996	**SPOUT** 4-8-8	9
1997	**WHITEWATER AFFAIR** 4-8-8	13
1998	**POSIDONAS** 6-8-12	12
1999	**SADIAN** 4-8-11	11
*2000	**YAVANA'S PACE** 8-9-1	11
2001	**LUCIDO** 5-8-12	13
2002	**ZINDABAD** 6-8-12	10
2003	**WARRSAN** 5-8-12	9

* Run at Haydock

EUROPEAN FREE HANDICAP (3y)
Newmarket-7f

1994	**BLUEGRASS PRINCE** 8-13	10
1995	**DIFFIDENT** 9-5	12
1996	**CAYMAN KAI** 9-7	8
1997	**HIDDEN MEADOW** 9-3	11
1998	**DESERT PRINCE** 9-5	9
1999	**BERTOLINI** 9-7	6
2000	**CAPE TOWN** 9-2	8
2001	**CLEARING** 9-6	6
2002	**TWILIGHT BLUES** 9-5	8
2003	**INDIAN HAVEN** 9-1	6

CRAVEN STAKES (3y)
Newmarket-1m

1994	**KING'S THEATRE** 9-0	10
1995	**PAINTER'S ROW** 8-12	5
1996	**BEAUCHAMP KING** 9-0	5
1997	**DESERT STORY** 8-12	6
1998	**XAAR** 8-12	6
1999	**COMPTON ADMIRAL** 8-9	7
2000	**UMISTIM** 8-9	6

2001	**KING'S IRONBRIDGE** 8-9	8
2002	**KING OF HAPPINESS** 8-9	6
2003	**HURRICANE ALAN** 8-9	7

VICTORIA CUP
Ascot-7f

1994	**FACE NORTH** 6-8-1	25
1995	**JAWAAL** 5-8-6	25
1996	**YEAST** 4-8-9	24
1997	**TREGARON** 6-8-13	25
1998	ABANDONED	
1999	**GREAT NEWS** 4-7-12	18
2000	**BOLD KING** 5-8-9	21
2001	**CLEARING** 9-0	10
2002	**SCOTTY'S FUTURE** 4-8-11	28
2003	**CAMP COMMANDER** 4-8-10	28

JOCKEY CLUB STAKES
Newmarket-1m 4f

1994	**SILVER WISP** 5-8-9	8
1995	**ONLY ROYALE** 6-8-11	7
1996	**RIYADIAN** 4-8-9	9
1997	**TIME ALLOWED** 4-8-6	10
1998	**ROMANOV** 4-8-9	8
1999	**SILVER PATRIARCH** 5-9-0	11
2000	**BLUEPRINT** 5-9-0	11
2001	**MILLENARY** 4-9-0	7
2002	**MARIENBARD** 5-8-9	9
2003	**WARRSAN** 5-8-9	6

CHESTER VASE (3y)
Chester-1m 4f 66yds

1994	**BROADWAY FLYER** 8-10	6
1995	**LUSO** 8-10	7
1996	**HIGH BAROQUE** 8-10	6
1997	**PANAMA CITY** 8-10	5
1998	**GULLAND** 8-10	5
1999	**PESHTIGO** 8-10	8
2000	**MILLENARY** 8-10	8
2001	**MR COMBUSTIBLE** 8-10	7
2002	**FIGHT YOUR CORNER** 8-10	8
2003	**DUTCH GOLD** 8-10	4

CHESTER CUP
Chester-2m 2f 147yds

1994	**DOYCE** 5-7-10	17
1995	**TOP CEES** 5-8-8	18
1996	**MERIT** 4-7-10	18
1997	**TOP CEES** 7-8-11	12
1998	**SILENCE IN COURT** 7-9-0	18
1999	**RAINBOW HIGH** 4-9-0	16
2000	**BANGALORE** 4-7-10	18
2001	**RAINBOW HIGH** 6-9-13	17
2002	**FANTASY HILL** 6-8-9	18
2003	**HUGS DANCER** 6-8-11	16

ORMONDE STAKES
Chester-1m 5f 89yds

1994	**SHAMBO** 7-9-2	8
1995	**ZILZAL ZAMAAN** 4-8-11	4
1996	**OSCAR SCHINDLER** 4-8-11	7
1997	**ROYAL COURT** 4-8-11	7
1998	**STRETAREZ** 5-9-2	6

1999 **SADIAN** 4-9-0 7
2000 **DALIAPOUR** 4-8-11 5
2001 **ST EXPEDIT** 4-8-11 9
2002 **ST EXPEDIT** 5-8-11 6
2003 **ASIAN HEIGHTS** 5-9-0 7

OAKS TRIAL (3y fillies)
Lingfield-1m 3f 106yds
1994 **MUNNAYA** 8-8 8
1995 **ASTERITA** 8-8 5
1996 **LADY CARLA** 8-8 4
1997 **CROWN OF LIGHT** 8-8 5
1998 **BRISTOL CHANNEL** 8-8 6
1999 **RAMRUMA** 8-8 7
2000 **FILM SCRIPT** 8-8 7
2001 **DOUBLE CROSSED** 8-8 3
2002 **BIRDIE** 8-8 7
2003 **SANTA SOPHIA** 8-8 8

DERBY TRIAL (3y)
Lingfield-1m 3f 106yds
1994 **HAWKER'S NEWS** 8-7 6
1995 **MUNWAR** 8-7 7
1996 **MYSTIC KNIGHT** 8-7 6
1997 **SILVER PATRIARCH** 8-7 5
1998 **HIGH-RISE** 8-7 6
1999 **LUCIDO** 8-7 5
2000 **SADDLER'S QUEST** 8-7 8
2001 **PERFECT SUNDAY** 8-7 8
2002 **BANDARI** 8-7 6
2003 **FRANKLINS GARDENS** 8-7 6

MUSIDORA STAKES (3y fillies)
York-1m 2f 85yds
1994 **HAWAJISS** 8-10 7
1995 **PURE GRAIN** 8-10 5
1996 **MAGNIFICIENT STYLE** 8-8 5
1997 **REAMS OF VERSE** 8-11 10
1998 **BAHR** 8-8 4
1999 **ZAHRAT DUBAI** 8-8 6
2000 **KALYPSO KATIE** 8-8 9
2001 **TIME AWAY** 8-8 11
2002 **ISLINGTON** 8-8 5
2003 **CASSIS** 8-8 8

DANTE STAKES (3y)
York-1m 2f 85yds
1994 **ERHAAB** 9-0 9
1995 **CLASSIC CLICHE** 8-11 8
1996 **GLORY OF DANCER** 8-11 7
1997 **BENNY THE DIP** 8-11 9
1998 **SARATOGA SPRINGS** 8-11 6
1999 **SALFORD EXPRESS** 8-11 8
2000 **SAKHEE** 8-11 5
2001 **DILSHAAN** 8-11 6
2002 **MOON BALLAD** 8-11 9
2003 **MAGISTRETTI** 8-11 10

YORKSHIRE CUP
York-1m 5f 194yds
1994 **KEY TO MY HEART** 4-8-9 7
1995 **MOONAX** 4-9-0 7
1996 **CLASSIC CLICHE** 4-9-0 5
1997 **CELERIC** 5-8-9 9
1998 **BUSY FLIGHT** 5-8-9 6
1999 **CHURLISH CHARM** 4-8-9 9
2000 **KAYF TARA** 6-9-0 8

2001 **MARIENBARD** 4-8-9 8
2002 **ZINDABAD** 6-8-9 7
2003 **MAMOOL** 4-8-9 8

DUKE OF YORK STAKES
York-6f
1994 **OWINGTON** 3-8-9 11
1995 **LAKE CONISTON** 4-9-4 7
1996 **VENTURE CAPITALIST** 7-9-0 12
1997 **ROYAL APPLAUSE** 4-9-0 10
1998 **BOLLIN JOANNE** 5-8-11 10
1999 **SAMPOWER STAR** 3-8-5 14
2000 **LEND A HAND** 5-9-5 10
2001 **PIPALONG** 5-9-6 14
2002 **INVINCIBLE SPIRIT** 5-9-5 12
2003 **TWILIGHT BLUES** 4-9-2 15

LOCKINGE STAKES
Newbury-1m
1994 **EMPEROR JONES** 4-9-0 11
1995 **SOVIET LINE** 5-9-0 5
1996 **SOVIET LINE** 6-9-0 7
1997 **FIRST ISLAND** 5-9-0 10
1998 **CAPE CROSS** 4-9-0 9
1999 **FLY TO THE STARS** 5-9-0 6
2000 **ALJABR** 4-9-0 7
2001 **MEDICEAN** 4-9-0 7
2002 **KELTOS** 4-9-0 10
2003 **HAWK WING** 4-9-0 6

HENRY II STAKES
Sandown-2m 78yds
1994 **MY PATRIARCH** 4-8-10 9
1995 **DOUBLE TRIGGER** 4-8-13 7
1996 **DOUBLE TRIGGER** 5-9-5 5
1997 **PERSIAN PUNCH** 4-8-10 7
1998 **PERSIAN PUNCH** 5-9-1 11
1999 **ARCTIC OWL** 5-9-3 11
2000 **PERSIAN PUNCH** 7-8-12 7
2001 **SOLO MIO** 7-9-1 11
2002 **AKBAR** 6-9-0 11
2003 **MR DINOS** 4-9-3 10

PREDOMINATE STAKES (3y)
Goodwood-1m 2f
1994 **OPERA SCORE** 8-8 5
1995 **PENTIRE** 9-0 6
1996 **DON MICHELETTO** 8-8 9
1997 **GRAPESHOT** 8-11 6
1998 **RABAH** 8-8 6
1999 **DUBAI MILLENNIUM** 8-8 6
2000 **ROSCIUS** 8-8 8
2001 **ASIAN HEIGHTS** 8-8 11
2002 **COSHOCTON** 8-8 6
2003 **HIGH ACCOLADE** 8-8 7

LUPE STAKES (3y)
Goodwood-1m 2f
1994 **BULAXIE** 9-0 6
1995 **SUBYA** 8-11 9
1996 **WHITEWATER AFFAIR** 8-8 9
1997 **MAID OF CAMELOT** 8-8 7
1998 **NAPOLEON'S SISTER** 8-8 8
1999 **CLAXON** 8-11 8
2000 **LOVE DIVINE** 8-8 6
2001 **FOODBROKER FANCY** 8-8 9

2002 **MELLOW PARK** 8-8.....................6
2003 **OCEAN SILK** 8-8.......................8

TEMPLE STAKES
Sandown-5f 6yds
1994 **LOCHSONG** 6-9-7.....................9
1995 **MIND GAMES** 3-8-8...................5
1996 **MIND GAMES** 4-9-7...................9
1997 **CROFT POOL** 6-9-3..................10
1998 **BOLSHOI** 6-9-3........................8
1999 **TIPSY CREEK** 5-9-3..................8
2000 **PERRYSTON VIEW** 8-9-3.............9
2001 **CASSANDRA GO** 5-9-0...............10
2002 **KYLLACHY** 4-9-3.......................11
2003 **AIRWAVE** 3-9-0.........................7

BRIGADIER GERARD STAKES
Sandown-1m 2f 7yds
1994 **CHATOYANT** 4-8-10..................14
1995 **ALRIFFA** 4-8-10........................7
1996 **PILSUDSKI** 4-8-10...................11
1997 **BOSRA SHAM** 4-9-0...................6
1998 **INSATIABLE** 5-8-10...................9
1999 **CHESTER HOUSE** 4-8-10.............8
2000 **SHIVA** 5-9-0............................8
2001 **BORDER ARROW** 6-8-10.............5
2002 **POTEMKIN** 4-8-10.....................4
2003 **SIGHTS ON GOLD** 4-8-10............8

DIOMED STAKES
Epsom-1m 114yds
1994 **BLUEGRASS PRINCE** 3-8-6.........11
1995 **MR MARTINI** 5-9-4....................7
1996 **BLOMBERG** 4-9-4......................8
1997 **POLAR PRINCE** 4-9-4................9
1998 **INTIKHAB** 4-9-4.......................10
1999 **LEAR SPEAR** 4-9-4....................6
2000 **TRANS ISLAND** 5-9-9................8
2001 **PULAU TIOMAN** 5-9-4................8
2002 **NAYYIR** 4-9-4..........................9
2003 **GATEMAN** 6-9-4.......................10

CORONATION CUP
Epsom-1m 4f 10yds
1994 **APPLE TREE** 5-9-0....................11
1995 **SUNSHACK** 4-9-0......................7
1996 **SWAIN** 4-9-0............................4
1997 **SINGSPIEL** 5-9-0......................5
1998 **SILVER PATRIARCH** 4-9-0...........7
1999 **DAYLAMI** 5-9-0.........................7
2000 **DALIAPOUR** 4-9-0.....................4
2001 **MUTAFAWEQ** 5-9-0....................6
2002 **BOREAL** 4-9-0..........................6
2003 **WARRSAN** 4-9-0........................9

JOHN OF GAUNT STAKES
Haydock-7f 30yds
1994 **EUROLINK THUNDER** 4-9-5..........8
1995 **MUTAKDDIM** 4-8-12...................8
1996 **INZAR** 4-9-5.............................9
1997 **DECORATED HERO** 5-9-3.............4
1998 **NIGRASINE** 4-8-12.....................7
1999 **WARNINGFORD** 5-9-5.................6
2000 **ONE WON ONE** 6-9-3.................10
2001 **MOUNT ABU** 4-9-5....................10
2002 **WARNINGFORD** 8-9-5.................7
2003 **WITH REASON** 5-8-12.................7

WILLIAM HILL TROPHY (HANDICAP) (3y)
York-6f
1994 **ENCORE M'LADY** 7-11................14
1995 **BOLD EFFORT** 8-8....................15
1996 **MALLIA** 7-10...........................18
1997 **RETURN OF AMIN** 7-7................19
1998 **FRIAR TUCK** 8-11....................22
1999 **PEPPERDINE** 8-3.....................23
2000 **COTTON HOUSE** 8-13...............23
2001 **ORIENTOR** 9-2........................20
2002 **ARTIE** 7-10............................20
2003 **DAZZLING BAY** 8-2..................19

QUEEN ANNE STAKES
Ascot-1m
1994 **BARATHEA** 4-9-8.....................10
1995 **NICOLOTTE** 4-9-2.....................7
1996 **CHARNWOOD FOREST** 4-9-2.......9
1997 **ALLIED FORCES** 4-9-5..............11
1998 **INTIKHAB** 4-9-2........................9
1999 **CAPE CROSS** 5-9-7...................8
2000 **KALANISI** 4-9-2.......................11
2001 **MEDICEAN** 4-9-7.....................10
2002 **NO EXCUSE NEEDED** 4-9-2........12
2003 **DUBAI DESTINATION** 4-9-0.........10

PRINCE OF WALES'S STAKES
Ascot-1m 2f
1994 **MUHTARRAM** 5-9-7...................11
1995 **MUHTARRAM** 6-9-8....................6
1996 **FIRST ISLAND** 4-9-3................12
1997 **BOSRA SHAM** 4-9-5...................6
1998 **FAITHFUL SON** 4-9-3.................8
1999 **LEAR SPEAR** 4-9-3...................8
2000 **DUBAI MILLENNIUM** 4-9-0..........6
2001 **FANTASTIC LIGHT** 5-9-1.............9
2002 **GRANDERA** 4-9-0.....................12
2003 **NAYEF** 5-9-0...........................10

ST JAMES'S PALACE STAKES (3y)
Ascot-1m
1994 **GRAND LODGE** 9-0....................9
1995 **BAHRI** 9-0.............................9
1996 **BIJOU D'INDE** 9-0....................9
1997 **STARBOROUGH** 9-0...................8
1998 **DR FONG** 9-0..........................8
1999 **SENDAWAR** 9-0.......................11
2000 **GIANT'S CAUSEWAY** 9-0............9
2001 **BLACK MINNALOUSHE** 9-0.........11
2002 **ROCK OF GIBRALTAR** 9-0...........9
2003 **ZAFEEN** 9-0...........................11

COVENTRY STAKES (2y)
Ascot-6f
1994 **SRI PEKAN** 8-13......................16
1995 **ROYAL APPLAUSE** 8-12.............13
1996 **VERGLAS** 8-12........................15
1997 **HARBOUR MASTER** 8-12............15
1998 **RED SEA** 8-12.........................17
1999 **FASILIYEV** 8-12.......................18
2000 **CD EUROPE** 8-12.....................12
2001 **LANDSEER** 8-12......................20
2002 **STATUE OF LIBERTY** 8-12..........16
2003 **THREE VALLEYS** 8-12...............13

KING EDWARD VII STAKES (3y)
Ascot-1m 4f

1994	**FOYER** 8-8	8
1995	**PENTIRE** 8-8	8
1996	**AMFORTAS** 8-8	7
1997	**KINGFISHER MILL** 8-8	5
1998	**ROYAL ANTHEM** 8-8	10
1999	**MUTAFAWEQ** 8-8	10
2000	**SUBTLE POWER** 8-8	7
2001	**STORMING HOME** 8-8	12
2002	**BALAKHERI** 8-10	7
2003	**HIGH ACCOLADE** 8-11	8

JERSEY STAKES (3y)
Ascot-7f

1994	**GNEISS** 8-10 DEAD HEATED WITH RIVER DEEP 8-10	21
1995	**SERGEYEV** 8-10	16
1996	**LUCAYAN PRINCE** 8-10	16
1997	**AMONG MEN** 8-13	20
1998	**DIKTAT** 8-10	16
1999	**LOTS OF MAGIC** 8-11	12
2000	**OBSERVATORY** 8-11	19
2001	**MOZART** 8-11	18
2002	**JUST JAMES** 8-11	15
2003	**MEMBERSHIP** 8-10	14

QUEEN MARY STAKES (2y fillies)
Ascot-5f

1994	**GAY GALLANTA** 8-8	16
1995	**BLUE DUSTER** 8-8	12
1996	**DANCE PARADE** 8-8	13
1997	**NADWAH** 8-8	18
1998	**BINT ALLAYL** 8-8	17
1999	**SHINING HOUR** 8-8	13
2000	**ROMANTIC MYTH** 8-8	20
2001	**QUEEN'S LOGIC** 8-8	20
2002	**ROMANTIC LIASON** 8-8	19
2003	**ATTRACTION** 8-10	14

CORONATION STAKES (3y fillies)
Ascot-1m

1994	**KISSING COUSIN** 9-0	10
1995	**RIDGEWOOD PEARL** 9-0	10
1996	**SHAKE THE YOKE** 9-0	7
1997	**REBECCA SHARP** 9-0	6
1998	**EXCLUSIVE** 9-0	9
1999	**BALISADA** 9-0	9
2000	**CRIMPLENE** 9-0	9
2001	**BANKS HILL** 9-0	13
2002	**SOPHISTICAT** 9-0	11
2003	**RUSSIAN RHYTHM** 9-0	9

ROYAL HUNT CUP
Ascot-1m

1994	**FACE NORTH** 6-8-3	32
1995	**REALITIES** 5-9-10	32
1996	**YEAST** 4-8-6	31
1997	**RED ROBBO** 4-8-6	32
1998	**REFUSE TO LOSE** 4-7-11	32
1999	**SHOWBOAT** 5-8-6	32
2000	**CARIBBEAN MONARCH** 5-8-10	32
2001	**SURPRISE ENCOUNTER** 5-8-9	30
2002	**NORTON** 5-8-9	30
2003	**MACADAMIA** 4-8-13	32

QUEENS VASE (3y)
Ascot-2m 45yds
(Since 1988 3-year-old only)

1994	**SILVER WEDGE** 8-11	12
1995	**STELVIO** 8-11	11
1996	**GORDI** 8-11	14
1997	**WINDSOR CASTLE** 8-11	11
1998	**MARIDPOUR** 8-11	8
1999	**ENDORSEMENT** 8-6	11
2000	**DALAMPOUR** 8-11	13
2001	**AND BEYOND** 8-11	16
2002	**MAMOOL** 8-11	14
2003	**SHANTY STAR** 8-11	12

CORK AND ORRERY STAKES
Ascot-6f
(Run in 2002 and 2003 as Golden Jubilee Stakes)

1994	**OWINGTON** 3-8-10	17
1995	**SO FACTUAL** 5-8-13	11
1996	**ATRAF** 3-8-6	17
1997	**ROYAL APPLAUSE** 4-9-3	23
1998	**TOMBA** 4-9-0	12
1999	**BOLD EDGE** 4-9-0	19
2000	**SUPERIOR PREMIUM** 6-9-0	16
2001	**HARMONIC WAY** 9-0	21
2002	**MALHUB** 4-9-4	12
2003	**CHOISIR** 4-9-4	17

NORFOLK STAKES (2y)
Ascot-5f

1994	**MIND GAMES** 8-13	6
1995	**LUCKY LIONEL** 8-8	9
1996	**TIPSY CREEK** 8-12	10
1997	**TIPPITT BOY** 8-12	6
1998	**ROSSELLI** 8-12	15
1999	**WARM HEART** 8-12	13
2000	**SUPERSTAR LEO** 8-7	11
2001	**JOHANNESBURG** 8-12	10
2002	**BARON'S PIT** 8-12	12
2003	**RUSSIAN VALOUR** 8-12	8

GOLD CUP
Ascot-2m 4f

1994	**ARCADIAN HEIGHTS** 6-9-2	9
1995	**DOUBLE TRIGGER** 4-9-0	7
1996	**CLASSIC CLICHE** 4-9-0	7
1997	**CELERIC** 5-9-2	13
1998	**KAYF TARA** 4-9-0	16
1999	**ENZELI** 4-9-0	17
2000	**KAYF TARA** 6-9-2	11
2001	**ROYAL REBEL** 5-9-2	12
2002	**ROYAL REBEL** 6-9-2	15
2003	**MR DINOS** 4-9-0	12

RIBBLESDALE STAKES (3y fillies)
Ascot-1m 4f

1994	**BOLAS** 8-8	9
1995	**PHANTOM GOLD** 8-8	7
1996	**TULIPA** 8-8	10
1997	**YASHMAK** 8-8	9
1998	**BAHR** 8-8	9
1999	**FAIRY QUEEN** 8-8	12
2000	**MILETRIAN** 8-8	9
2001	**SAHARA SLEW** 8-8	14
2002	**IRRESISTIBLE JEWEL** 8-8	15
2003	**SPANISH SUN** 8-11	9

HARDWICKE STAKES
Ascot-1m 4f
1994	**BOBZAO** 5-8-9	11
1995	**BEAUCHAMP HERO** 5-8-9	6
1996	**OSCAR SCHINDLER** 4-8-9	8
1997	**PREDAPPIO** 4-8-12	10
1998	**POSIDONAS** 6-8-9	7
1999	**FRUITS OF LOVE** 4-8-12	8
2000	**FRUITS OF LOVE** 5-8-12	9
2001	**SANDMASON** 4-8-9	7
2002	**ZINDABAD** 6-8-12	7
2003	**INDIAN CREEK** 5-8-9	9

WOKINGHAM STAKES
Ascot-6f
1994	**VENTURE CAPITALIST** 5-8-12	30
1995	**ASTRAC** 4-8-7	30
1996	**EMERGING MARKET** 4-8-13	29
1997	**SELHURSTPARK FLYER** 6-8-9	30
1998	**SELHURSTPARK FLYER** 7-9-7	29
1999	**DEEP SPACE** 4-8-7	30
2000	**HARMONIC WAY** 5-9-6	29
2001	**NICE ONE CLARE** 5-9-3	30
2002	**CAPRICHO** 5-8-11	28
2003	**RATIO** 5-9-3 dead heated with	
	FAYR JAG 4-9-6	29

KING'S STAND STAKES
Ascot-5f
1994	**LOCHSONG** 6-9-0	8
1995	**PICCOLO** 4-9-6	10
1996	**PIVOTAL** 3-8-10	17
1997	**DON'T WORRY ME** 5-8-13	18
1998	**BOLSHOI** 6-9-2	19
1999	**MITCHAM** 3-8-10	17
2000	**NUCLEAR DEBATE** 5-9-2	23
2001	**CASSANDRA GO** 5-8-13	22
2002	**DOMINICA** 3-8-7	15
2003	**CHOISIR** 4-9-7	20

NORTHUMBERLAND PLATE
Newcastle-2m 19yds
1994	**QUICK RANSOM** 6-8-8	20
1995	**BOLD GAIT** 4-9-10	17
1996	**CELERIC** 4-9-4	13
1997	**WINDSOR CASTLE** 3-8-10	18
1998	**CYRIAN** 4-7-13	20
1999	**FAR CRY** 4-8-10	20
2000	**BAY OF ISLANDS** 3-8-4	18
2001	**ARCHDUKE FERDINAND** 3-8-4	18
2002	**BANGALORE** 6-9-5	16
2003	**UNLEASH** 4-8-11	20

CRITERION STAKES
Newmarket-7f
1994	**HILL HOPPER** 3-8-4	6
1995	**PIPE MAJOR** 3-8-4	8
1996	**GABR** 6-9-10	9
1997	**RAMOOZ** 4-9-2	9
1998	**MUCHEA** 4-9-7	10
1999	**DIKTAT** 4-9-7	6
2000	**ARKADIAN HERO** 5-9-1	9
2001	**SHIBBOLETH** 4-9-2	6
2002	**ATAVUS** 5-9-2	6
2003	**TRADE FAIR** 3-8-7	11

ECLIPSE STAKES
Sandown-1m 2f 7yds
1994	**EZZOUD** 5-9-7	8
1995	**HALLING** 4-9-7	8
1996	**HALLING** 5-9-7	7
1997	**PILSUDSKI** 5-9-7	5
1998	**DAYLAMI** 4-9-7	7
1999	**COMPTON ADMIRAL** 3-8-10	8
2000	**GIANT'S CAUSEWAY** 3-8-10	8
2001	**MEDICEAN** 4-9-7	8
2002	**HAWK WING** 3-8-10	5
2003	**FALBRAV** 5-9-7	15

OLD NEWTON CUP
Haydock-1m 3f 200yds
1994	**GLIDE PATH** 5-8-10	11
1995	**LOMBARDIC** 4-8-12	10
1996	**KEY TO MY HEART** 6-10-0	8
1997	**ZARALASKA** 6-9-8	16
1998	**PERFECT PARADIGM** 4-9-2	8
1999	**CELESTIAL WELCOME** 4-8-10	15
2000	**RADA'S DAUGHTER** 4-8-11	14
2001	**HANNIBAL LAD** 5-8-8	14
2002	**SUN BIRD** 4-7-12	16
2003	**COLLIER HILL** 5-8-10	19

LANCASHIRE OAKS (fillies and mares)
Haydock-1m 3f 200yds
1994	**STATE CRYSTAL** 3-8-4	8
1995	**FANJICA** 3-8-4	5
1996	**SPOUT** 4-9-6	10
1997	**SQUEAK** 3-8-4	8
1998	**CATCHASCATCHCAN** 3-8-4	6
1999	**NOUSHKEY** 3-8-4	7
2000	**ELA ATHENA** 4-9-3	11
2001	**SACRED SONG** 4-9-6	8
2002	**MELLOW PARK** 3-8-5	6
2003	**PLACE ROUGE** 4-9-3	12

CHERRY HINTON STAKES (2y)
Newmarket-6f
1994	**RED CARNIVAL** 8-9	7
1995	**APPLAUD** 8-9	8
1996	**DAZZLE** 8-9	9
1997	**ASFURAH** 8-9	12
1998	**WANNABE GRAND** 8-9	10
1999	**TORGAU** 8-9	12
2000	**DORA CARRINGTON** 8-9	9
2001	**SILENT HONOR** 8-9	7
2002	**SPINOLA** 8-9	9
2003	**ATTRACTION** 8-12	8

BUNBURY CUP HANDICAP
Newmarket-7f
1994	**EN ATTENDANT** 6-9-12	20
1995	**CADEAUX TRYST** 3-9-1	19
1996	**CRUMPTON HILL** 4-8-12	16
1997	**TUMBLEWEED RIDGE** 4-9-6	20
1998	**HO LENG** 3-9-7	20
1999	**GRANGEVILLE** 4-9-3	19
2000	**TAYSEER** 5-9-9	19
2001	**ATAVUS** 4-8-9	19
2002	**MINE** 4-8-12	16
2003	**PATAVELLIAN** 5-9-1	20

PRINCESS OF WALES'S STAKES
Newmarket-1m 4f

1994	**WAGON MASTER** 4-9-0	12
1995	**BEAUCHAMP HERO** 5-9-5	9
1996	**POSIDONAS** 4-9-7	9
1997	**SHANTOU** 4-9-7	7
1998	**FRUITS OF LOVE** 3-8-3	7
1999	**CRAIGSTEEL** 4-9-2	8
2000	**LITTLE ROCK** 4-9-2	6
2001	**MUTAMAM** 6-9-2	9
2002	**MILLENARY** 5-9-2	7
2003	**MILLENARY** 6-9-2	6

JULY STAKES (2y)
Newmarket-6f

1994	**FALLOW** 8-10	6
1995	**TAGULA** 8-10	9
1996	**RICH GROUND** 8-10	8
1997	**BOLD FACT** 8-10	8
1998	**BERTOLINI** 8-10	6
1999	**CITY ON A HILL** 8-13	7
2000	**NOVERRE** 8-13	5
2001	**MESHAHEER** 8-10	9
2002	**MISTER LINKS** 8-10	10
2003	**NEVISIAN LAD** 8-10	8

FALMOUTH STAKES (fillies)
Newmarket-1m

1994	**LEMON SOUFFLE** 3-8-6	6
1995	**CARAMBA** 3-8-6	5
1996	**SENSATION** 3-8-6	9
1997	**RYAFAN** 3-8-6	7
1998	**LOVERS KNOT** 3-8-6	13
1999	**RONDA** 3-8-6	8
2000	**ALSHAKR** 3-8-6	10
2001	**PROUDWINGS** 5-9-4	11
2002	**TASHAWAK** 3-8-6	9
2003	**MACADAMIA** 4-9-1	8

JULY CUP
Newmarket-6f

1994	**OWINGTON** 3-8-13	9
1995	**LAKE CONISTON** 4-9-6	9
1996	**ANABAA** 4-9-5	10
1997	**COMPTON PLACE** 3-8-13	9
1998	**ELNADIM** 4-9-5	17
1999	**STRAVINSKY** 3-8-13	17
2000	**AGNES WORLD** 5-9-5	10
2001	**MOZART** 3-8-13	18
2002	**CONTINENT** 5-9-5	14
2003	**OASIS DREAM** 3-8-13	16

JOHN SMITH'S CUP
York-1m 2f 85yds

1994	**CEZANNE** 5-9-12	16
1995	**NAKED WELCOME** 3-8-4	16
1996	**WILCUMA** 5-9-2	17
1997	**PASTERNAK** 4-8-3	21
1998	**PORTO FORICOS** 3-8-3	20
1999	**ACHILLES** 4-8-11	15
2000	**SOBRIETY** 3-8-8	22
2001	**FOREIGN AFFAIRS** 3-8-6	19
2002	**VINTAGE PREMIUM** 5-9-9	20
2003	**FAR LANE** 4-9-4	20

PRINCESS MARGARET STAKES (2y)
Ascot-6f

1994	**TAJANNUB** 8-8	8
1995	**BLUE DUSTER** 9-0	7
1996	**SEEBE** 8-9	8
1997	**EMBASSY** 8-9	7
1998	**MYTHICAL GIRL** 8-9	6
1999	**SAINTLY SPEECH** 8-9	8
2000	**ENTHUSED** 8-9	9
2001	**LEGGY LOU** 8-9	8
2002	**RUSSIAN RHYTHM** 8-9	6
2003	**RIVER BELLE** 8-9	9

BEESWING STAKES
Newcastle-7f
(from 2000 run as a Handicap)

1994	**GABR** 4-9-0	10
1995	**SHAHID** 3-8-7	7
1996	**IKTAMAL** 4-9-0	9
1997	**WIZARD KING** 6-9-4	4
1998	**DECORATED HERO** 6-9-7	4
1999	**JOSR ALGARHOUD** 3-8-7	5
2000	**TONY TIE** 4-9-12	11
2001	**SLOANE** 5-9-11	14
2002	**MILLENNIUM FORCE** 4-9-7	14
2003	**QUITO** 6-9-6	8

STEWARDS' CUP
Goodwood-6f

1994	**FOR THE PRESENT** 4-8-3	26
1995	**SHIKARI'S SON** 8-8-13	27
1996	**COASTAL BLUFF** 4-9-5	30
1997	**DANETIME** 3-8-10	30
1998	**SUPERIOR PREMIUM** 4-8-12	29
1999	**HARMONIC WAY** 4-8-6	30
2000	**TAYSEER** 6-8-11	30
2001	**GUINEA HUNTER** 5-9-0	30
2002	**BOND BOY** 5-8-2	28
2003	**PATAVELLIAN** 5-8-11	29

GORDON STAKES (3y)
Goodwood-1m 4f

1994	**BROADWAY FLYER** 8-13	9
1995	**PRESENTING** 8-10	7
1996	**ST MAWES** 8-10	12
1997	**STOWAWAY** 8-10	10
1998	**RABAH** 8-10 dead heated with	
	NEDAWI 8-10	6
1999	**COMPTON ACE** 8-10	6
2000	**MILLENARY** 8-13	10
2001	**ALEXIUS** 8-10	11
2002	**BANDARI** 8-13	4
2003	**PHOENIX REACH** 8-10	10

OAK TREE STAKES
Goodwood-7f

1994	**BLUE SIREN** 3-8-10	10
1995	**BRIEF GLIMPSE** 3-8-7	10
1996	**THRILLING DAY** 3-8-13	14
1997	**DAZZLE** 3-8-7	8
1998	**BERAYSIM** 3-8-7	9
1999	**SELFISH** 5-9-0	6
2000	**DANCEABOUT** 3-8-7	11
2001	**MAURI MOON** 3-8-7	13
2002	**DESERT ALCHEMY** 3-8-6	7
2003	**TANTINA** 3-8-7	13

SUSSEX STAKES
Goodwood-1m
1994	**DISTANT VIEW** 3-8-13	9
1995	**SAYYEDATI** 5-9-4	6
1996	**FIRST ISLAND** 4-9-7	10
1997	**ALI-ROYAL** 4-9-7	9
1998	**AMONG MEN** 4-9-7	10
1999	**ALJABR** 3-8-13	8
2000	**GIANT'S CAUSEWAY** 3-9-0	10
2001	**NOVERRE** 3-9-0	10
2002	**ROCK OF GIBRALTAR** 3-8-13	8
2003	**REEL BUDDY** 5-9-7	9

RICHMOND STAKES (2y)
Goodwood-6f
1994	**SRI PEKAN** 8-11	6
1995	**POLARIS FLIGHT** 8-11	7
1996	**EASYCALL** 8-11	6
1997	**DAGGERS DRAWN** 8-11	4
1998	**MUQTARIB** 8-11	7
1999	**BACHIR** 8-11	7
2000	**ENDLESS SUMMER** 8-11	8
2001	**MISTER COSMI** 8-11	8
2002	***REVENUE** 8-11	9
2003	**CARRIZO CREEK** 8-11	7

* Elusive City disqualified from first place

KING GEORGE STAKES
Goodwood-5f
1994	**LOCHSONG** 6-9-7	15
1995	**HEVER GOLF ROSE** 4-9-5	11
1996	**RAMBLING BEAR** 3-8-10	14
1997	**AVERTI** 6-9-0	15
1998	**LAND OF DREAMS** 3-8-7	15
1999	**RUDI'S PET** 5-9-0	15
2000	**CASSANDRA GO** 4-8-10	13
2001	**DIETRICH** 3-8-12	15
2002	**AGNETHA** 3-8-7	14
2003	**THE TATLING** 6-9-0	9

WILLIAM HILL MILE HANDICAP
Goodwood-1m
1994	**FRAAM** 5-9-9	19
1995	**KHAYRAPOUR** 5-7-13	21
1996	**MOSCOW MIST** 5-7-10	18
1997	**FLY TO THE STARS** 3-9-6	20
1998	**FOR YOUR EYES ONLY** 4-9-6	22
1999	**LONESOME DUDE** 4-9-7	20
2000	**PERSIANO** 5-8-12	22
2001	**RIBERAC** 5-8-12	21
2002	**SMIRK** 4-9-5	21
2003	**LADY BEAR** 5-8-6	21

GOODWOOD CUP
Goodwood-2m
1994	**TIOMAN ISLAND** 4-9-5	15
1995	**DOUBLE TRIGGER** 4-9-5	9
1996	**GREY SHOT** 4-9-0	7
1997	**DOUBLE TRIGGER** 6-9-0	10
1998	**DOUBLE TRIGGER** 7-9-5	9
1999	**KAYF TARA** 5-9-7	7
2000	**ROYAL REBEL** 4-9-2	8
2001	**PERSIAN PUNCH** 8-9-5	12
2002	**JARDINES LOOKOUT** 5-9-2	9
2003	**PERSIAN PUNCH** 10-9-4	9

MOLECOMB STAKES (2y)
Goodwood-5f
1994	**HOH MAGIC** 8-10	7
1995	**ALMATY** 9-3	7
1996	**CARMINE LAKE** 8-7	7
1997	**LADY ALEXANDER** 8-12	13
1998	**INYA LAKE** 8-7	9
1999	**MISTY MISS** 8-7	10
2000	**MISTY EYED** 8-10	9
2001	**WHITBARROW** 9-1	14
2002	**WUNDERS DREAM** 8-7	13
2003	**MAJESTIC MISSILE** 8-12	9

NASSAU STAKES (fillies and mares)
Goodwood-1m 2f
1994	**HAWAJISS** 3-8-6	9
1995	**CARAMBA** 3-8-9	6
1996	**LAST SECOND** 3-8-6	8
1997	**RYAFAN** 3-8-9	7
1998	**ALBORADA** 3-8-9	9
1999	**ZAHRAT DUBAI** 3-8-6	8
2000	**CRIMPLENE** 3-8-6	7
2001	**LAILANI** 3-8-6	7
2002	**ISLINGTON** 3-8-6	10
2003	**RUSSIAN RHYTHM** 3-8-6	8

HUNGERFORD STAKES
Newbury-7f 64yds
1994	**YOUNG ERN** 4-9-3 DEAD HEATED WITH	
	POLLEN COUNT 5-9-0	12
1995	**HARAYIR** 3-8-13	9
1996	**BIN ROSIE** 4-9-0	8
1997	**DECORATED HERO** 5-9-0	10
1998	**MUHTATHIR** 3-8-8	9
1999	**LEND A HAND** 4-9-0	7
2000	**ARKADIAN HERO** 5-9-2	8
2001	**ATAVUS** 4-8-13	7
2002	**REEL BUDDY** 4-8-13	10
2003	**WITH REASON** 5-8-13	11

GEOFFREY FREER STAKES
Newbury-1m 5f 61yds
1994	**RED ROUTE** 3-8-5	6
1995	**PRESENTING** 3-8-5	6
1996	**PHANTOM GOLD** 4-9-3	7
1997	**DUSHYANTOR** 4-9-6	4
1998	**MULTICOLOURED** 5-9-3	6
1999	**SILVER PATRIARCH** 5-9-9	4
2000	**MURGHEM** 5-9-3	6
2001	**MR COMBUSTIBLE** 3-8-6	5
2002	**MUBTAKER** 5-9-3	7
2003	**MUBTAKER** 6-9-3	5

JUDDMONTE INTERNATIONAL STAKES
York-1m 2f 85yds
1994	**EZZOUD** 5-9-6	8
1995	**HALLING** 4-9-6	6
1996	**HALLING** 5-9-5	6
1997	**SINGSPIEL** 5-9-5	4
1998	**ONE SO WONDERFUL** 4-9-2	8
1999	**ROYAL ANTHEM** 4-9-5	12
2000	**GIANT'S CAUSEWAY** 3-8-11	6
2001	**SAKHEE** 4-9-5	8
2002	**NAYEF** 4-9-5	7
2003	**FALBRAV** 5-9-5	8

GREAT VOLTIGEUR STAKES (3y)
York-1m 3f 195yds

1994	**SACRAMENT** 8-9	7
1995	**PENTIRE** 8-12	4
1996	**DUSHYANTOR** 8-9	6
1997	**STOWAWAY** 8-9	5
1998	**SEA WAVE** 8-9	6
1999	**FANTASTIC LIGHT** 8-9	7
2000	**AIR MARSHALL** 8-9	5
2001	**MILAN** 8-9	9
2002	**BANDARI** 3-8-9	9
2003	**POWERSCOURT** 8-9	9

YORKSHIRE OAKS (fillies and mares)
York-1m 3f 195yds

1994	**ONLY ROYALE** 5-9-7	7
1995	**PURE GRAIN** 3-8-8	8
1996	**KEY CHANGE** 3-8-8	9
1997	**MY EMMA** 4-9-4	8
1998	**CATCHASCATCHCAN** 3-8-8	8
1999	**RAMRUMA** 3-8-8	11
2000	**PETRUSHKA** 3-8-8	6
2001	**SUPER TASSA** 5-9-4	9
2002	**ISLINGTON** 3-8-8	11
2003	**ISLINGTON** 4-9-4	8

EBOR HANDICAP
York-1m 5f 194yds

1994	**HASTEN TO ADD** 4-9-3	21
1995	**SANMARTINO** 3-7-11	21
1996	**CLERKENWELL** 3-7-11	21
1997	**FAR AHEAD** 5-8-0	21
1998	**TUNING** 3-8-7	21
1999	**VICIOUS CIRCLE** 5-8-4	21
2000	**GIVE THE SLIP** 3-8-8	22
2001	**MEDITERRANEAN** 3-8-4	22
2002	**HUGS DANCER** 5-8-5	22
2003	**SAINT ALEBE** 4-8-8	22

GIMCRACK STAKES (2y)
York-6f

1994	**CHILLY BILLY** 9-0	11
1995	**ROYAL APPLAUSE** 9-0	5
1996	**ABOU ZOUZ** 8-11	9
1997	**CARROWKEEL** 8-11	7
1998	**JOSR ALGARHOUD** 8-11	8
1999	**MULL OF KINTYRE** 8-11	10
2000	**BANNISTER** 8-11	10
2001	**ROCK OF GIBRALTER** 9-0	9
2002	**COUNTRY REEL** 8-11	11
2003	**BALMONT** 8-11	9

NUNTHORPE STAKES
York-5f

1994	**PICCOLO** 3-9-3	10
1995	**SO FACTUAL** 5-9-6	8
1996	**PIVOTAL** 3-9-7	8
1997	**YA MALAK** 6-9-9 dead heated with	
	COASTAL BLUFF 5-9-9	15
1998	**LOCHANGEL** 4-9-6	17
1999	**STRAVINSKY** 3-9-7	16
2000	**NUCLEAR DEBATE** 5-9-9	13
2001	**MOZART** 3-9-7	10
2002	**KYLLACHY** 4-9-11	17
2003	**OASIS DREAM** 3-9-9	8

ARIVA TRAINS HANDICAP
York-7f 205yds
(formerly Bradford and Bingley Handicap)

1994	**LAP OF LUXURY** 5-8-7	13
1995	**CAP JULUCA** 3-8-11	15
1996	**CONCER UN** 4-8-10	18
1997	**CONCER UN** 5-8-7	14
1998	**SUGARFOOT** 4-8-9	14
1999	**SUGARFOOT** 5-9-7	20
2000	**PEARTREE HOUSE** 6-8-2	16
2001	**TOUGH SPEED** 4-9-7	17
2002	**FUNFAIR** 3-8-1	18
2003	**TERFEL** 4-8-12	15

LOWTHER STAKES (2y fillies)
York-6f

1994	**HARAYIR** 8-11	6
1995	**DANCE SEQUENCE** 8-11	9
1996	**BIANCA NERA** 8-11	9
1997	**CAPE VERDI** 8-11	9
1998	**BINT ALLAYL** 9-0	10
1999	**JEMIMA** 8-11	9
2000	**ENTHUSED** 9-0	7
2001	**QUEEN'S LOGIC** 9-0	4
2002	**RUSSIAN RHYTHM** 9-0	5
2003	**CARRY ON KATIE** 8-11	9

PRESTIGE STAKES (2y)
Goodwood-7f
(formerly Waterford Candelabra Stakes)

1994	**PURE GRAIN** 8-9	9
1995	**BINT SHADAYID** 8-9	6
1996	**RED CAMELLIA** 8-12	5
1997	**MIDNIGHT LINE** 8-9	6
1998	**CIRCLE OF GOLD** 8-9	9
1999	**ICICLE** 8-9	6
2000	**FREEFOURRACING** 8-9	6
2001	**GOSSAMER** 8-9	6
2002	**GEMINIANI** 8-9	8
2003	**GRACEFULLY** 8-9	6

CELEBRATION MILE
Goodwood-1m
(formerly Waterford Crystal Mile)

1994	**MEHTHAAF** 3-8-11	6
1995	**HARAYIR** 3-8-12	6
1996	**MARK OF ESTEEM** 3-9-1	6
1997	***AMONG MEN** 3-8-9	4
1998	**MUHTATHIR** 3-8-9	9
1999	**CAPE CROSS** 5-9-7	5
2000	**MEDICEAN** 3-8-9	6
2001	**NO EXCUSE NEEDED** 3-8-9	7
2002	**TILLERMAN** 6-9-1	7
2003	**PRIORS LODGE** 5-9-1	6

*Cape Cross disqualified from first place

SOLARIO STAKES (2y)
Sandown-7f 16yds

1994	**LOVELY MILLIE** 8-9	7
1995	**ALHAARTH** 9-2	4
1996	**BRAVE ACT** 8-9	5
1997	**LITTLE INDIAN** 8-11	7
1998	**RAISE A GRAND** 8-11	7
1999	**BEST OF THE BESTS** 8-11	7
2000	**KING'S IRONBRIDGE** 8-11	7
2001	**REDBACK** 9-0	10

2002 **FOSS WAY** 8-11 11
2003 **BARBAJUAN** 8-11 8

SPRINT CUP
Haydock-6f
1994 **LAVINIA FONTANA** 5-8-9 8
1995 **CHEROKEE ROSE** 4-8-11 6
1996 **IKTAMAL** 4-9-0 11
1997 **ROYAL APPLAUSE** 4-9-0 9
1998 **TAMARISK** 3-8-12 13
1999 **DIKTAT** 4-9-0 16
2000 **PIPALONG** 4-8-11 13
2001 **NUCLEAR DEBATE** 6-9-0 12
2002 **INVINCIBLE SPIRIT** 5-9-0 14
2003 **SOMNUS** 3-8-12 10

SEPTEMBER STAKES
Kempton-1m
1994 **WAGON MASTER** 4-9-5 5
1995 **BUROOJ** 5-9-0 7
1996 **SACRAMENT** 5-9-5 7
*1997 **MAYLANE** 3-8-5 6
*1998 **CRIMSON TIDE** 4-9-5 5
*1999 **YAVANA'S PACE** 7-9-0 5
2000 **MUTAMAM** 5-9-0 7
2001 **MUTAMAM** 6-9-8 3
2002 **ASIAN HEIGHTS** 4-9-3 6
2003 **MUBTAKER** 6-9-8 5
* Run at Epsom

MAY HILL STAKES (2y)
Doncaster-1m
1994 **MAMLAKAH** 8-8 11
1995 **SOLAR CRYSTAL** 8-9 11
1996 **REAMS OF VERSE** 8-9 11
1997 **MIDNIGHT LINE** 9-0 9
1998 **CALANDO** 8-9 10
1999 **TEGGIANO** 8-9 12
2000 **KARASTA** 8-9 12
2001 **HALF GLANCE** 8-9 9
2002 **SUMMITVILLE** 8-9 9
2003 **KINNAIRD** 8-10 10

PORTLAND HANDICAP
Doncaster-5f 140yds
1994 **HELLO MISTER** 3-8-10 22
1995 **HELLO MISTER** 4-8-7 22
1996 **MUSICAL SEASON** 4-8-5 21
1997 **DASHING BLUE** 4-9-12 22
1998 **CADEAUX CHER** 4-8-7 21
1999 **ASTONISHED** 3-9-6 21
2000 **COMPTON BANKER** 3-8-8 22
2001 **SMOKIN BEAU** 4-9-4 22
2002 **HALMAHERA** 7-8-13 22
2003 **HALMAHERA** 8-9-4 22

PARK HILL STAKES (fillies and mares)
Doncaster-1m 6f 132yds
1994 **COIGACH** 3-8-5 8
1995 **NOBLE ROSE** 4-9-3 8
1996 **EVA LUNA** 4-9-3 6
1997 **BOOK AT BEDTIME** 3-8-5 7
1998 **DELILAH** 4-9-6 9
1999 **MISTLE SONG** 3-8-5 10
2000 **MILETRIAN** 3-8-10 11
2001 **RANIN** 3-8-5 13

2002 **ALEXANDER THREE D** 3-8-5 9
2003 **DISCREET BRIEF** 3-8-5 8

G.N.E.R. PARK STAKES
Doncaster-1m
(formerly Kiveton Park Stakes)
1994 **SOVIET LINE** 4-9-0 9
1995 **BISHOP OF CASHEL** 3-8-9 8
1996 **BISHOP OF CASHEL** 4-9-4 8
1997 **ALMUSHTARAK** 4-9-0 8
1998 **HANDSOME RIDGE** 4-9-4 6
1999 **SUGARFOOT** 5-9-0 10
2000 **DISTANT MUSIC** 3-8-9 5
2001 **TOUGH SPEED** 4-9-0 11
2002 **DUCK ROW** 7-9-0 6
2003 **POLAR BEN** 4-9-0 9

DONCASTER CUP
Doncaster-2m 2f
1994 **ARCADIAN HEIGHTS** 6-9-7 9
1995 **DOUBLE TRIGGER** 4-9-7 6
1996 **DOUBLE TRIGGER** 5-9-7 6
1997 **CANON CAN** 4-9-0 5
1998 **DOUBLE TRIGGER** 7-9-5 6
1999 **FAR CRY** 4-9-0 6
2000 **ENZELI** 5-9-7 9
2001 **ALLELUIA** 3-7-11 11
2002 **BOREAS** 7-9-1 8
2003 **PERSIAN PUNCH** 10-9-4 6

CHAMPAGNE STAKES (2y)
Doncaster-7f
1994 **SRI PEKAN** 9-0 7
1995 **ALHAARTH** 9-0 3
1996 **BAHHARE** 8-10 4
1997 **DAGGERS DRAWN** 9-0 5
1998 **AUCTION HOUSE** 8-10 8
1999 **DISTANT MUSIC** 8-10 6
2000 **NOVERRE** 9-0 8
2001 **DUBAI DESTINATION** 8-10 8
2002 **ALMUSHAHAR** 8-10 11
2003 **LUCKY STORY** 9-0 6

FLYING CHILDERS STAKES (2y)
Doncaster-5f
1994 **RAAH ALGHARB** 8-11 8
1995 **CAYMAN KAI** 8-12 8
1996 **EASYCALL** 9-3 7
1997 **LAND OF DREAMS** 8-7 7
1998 **SHEER VIKING** 8-12 13
1999 **MRS P** 8-7 14
2000 **SUPERSTAR LEO** 8-12 11
2001 **SADDAD** 8-12 13
2002 **WUNDERS DREAM** 8-12 14
2003 **HOWICK FALLS** 8-12 13

AYR GOLD CUP
Ayr-6f
1994 **DARING DESTINY** 3-8-0 29
1995 **ROYALE FIGURINE** 4-8-9 29
1996 **COASTAL BLUFF** 4-9-3 28
1997 **WILDWOOD FLOWER** 4-9-3 29
1998 **ALWAYS ALIGHT** 4-8-7 29
1999 **GRANGEVILLE** 4-9-0 28
2000 **BAHAMIAN PIRATE** 5-8-0 28
2001 **CONTINENT** 4-8-10 28

2002	**FUNFAIR WANE** 3-9-3	28
2003	**QUITO** 6-8-6	26

SELECT STAKES
Goodwood-1m 2f
(formerly Valdoe Stakes)

1994	**ALDERBROOK** 5-9-0	7
1995	**TRIARIUS** 5-9-0	6
1996	**SINGSPIEL** 4-9-3	4
1997	**FAHRIS** 3-8-7	5
1998	**MUTAMAM** 3-8-10	4
1999	**LEAR SPEAR** 4-9-5	7
2000	**EKRAAR** 3-8-10	5
2001	**NAYEF** 3-8-10	3
2002	**MOON BALLAD** 3-8-12	6
2003	**LEPORELLO** 3-8-10	5

MILL REEF STAKES (2y)
Newbury-6f 8yds

1994	**PRINCELY HUSH** 8-11	9
1995	**KAHIR ALMAYDAN** 8-12	6
1996	**INDIAN ROCKET** 8-12	10
1997	**ARKADIAN HERO** 8-12	7
1998	**GOLDEN SILCA** 8-12	5
1999	**PRIMO VALENTINO** 8-12	4
2000	**BOUNCING BOWDLER** 8-12	7
2001	**FIREBREAK** 9-1	10
2002	**ZAFEEN** 8-12	8
2003	**BYRON** 8-12	10

AUTUMN CUP (Handicap)
Newbury-1m 5f 61yds

1994	**WARM SPELL** 4-8-5	16
1995	**WHITECHAPEL** 7-9-0	23
1996	**KUTTA** 4-10-0	12
1997	**DARAPOUR** 3-8-11	13
1998	**VERONICA FRANCO** 5-8-1	20
1999	**ALBERICH** 4-9-13	13
2000	**AFTERJACKO** 4-9-13	15
2001	**MESMERIC** 3-9-5	11
2002	**WINDERMERE** 3-8-13	11
2003	**PRINS WILLEM** 4-9-2 dead heated with **STARRY LODGE** 3-8-13	11

CUMBERLAND LODGE STAKES
Ascot-1m 4f

1994	**WAGON MASTER** 4-9-5	6
1995	**RIYADIAN** 3-8-6	8
1996	**WALL STREET** 3-8-6	7
1997	**KINGFISHER MILL** 3-8-11	8
1998	**CAPRI** 3-8-7	9
1999	ABANDONED	
2000	**MUTAMAM** 5-9-3	6
2001	**NAYEF** 3-8-9	7
2002	**SYSTEMATIC** 3-8-6	5
2003	**HIGH ACCOLADE** 3-8-11	5

THE FILLIES' MILE (2y fillies)
Ascot-1m

1994	**AQAARID** 8-10	9
1995	**BOSRA SHAM** 8-10	6
1996	**REAMS OF VERSE** 8-10	8
1997	**GLOROSIA** 8-10	8
1998	**SUNSPANGLED** 8-10	8
1999	**TEGGIANO** 8-10	6
2000	**CRYSTAL MUSIC** 8-10	9
2001	**GOSSAMER** 8-10	7

2002	**SOVIET SONG** 8-10	10
2003	**RED BLOOM** 8-10	7

DIADEM STAKES
Ascot-6f

1994	**LAKE CONISTON** 3-8-11	11
1995	**COOL JAZZ** 4-9-0	15
1996	**DIFFIDENT** 4-9-0	12
1997	**ELNADIM** 3-8-12	14
1998	**BIANCONI** 3-8-12	9
1999	**BOLD EDGE** 4-9-4	11
2000	**SAMPOWER STAR** 4-9-0	11
2001	**NICE ONE CLARE** 5-8-11	15
2002	**CRYSTAL CASTLE** 4-9-0	11
2003	**ACCLAMATION** 4-9-0	14

QUEEN ELIZABETH II STAKES
Ascot-1m

1994	**MAROOF** 4-9-4	9
1995	**BAHRI** 3-8-11	6
1996	**MARK OF ESTEEM** 3-8-11	7
1997	**AIR EXPRESS** 3-8-11	9
1998	**DESERT PRINCE** 3-8-11	8
1999	**DUBAI MILLENNIUM** 3-8-11	4
2000	**OBSERVATORY** 3-8-11	12
2001	**SUMMONER** 4-9-1	8
2002	**WHERE OR WHEN** 3-8-11	5
2003	**FALBRAV** 5-9-1	8

ROYAL LODGE STAKES (2y)
Ascot-1m

1994	**ELTISH** 8-10	8
1995	**MONS** 8-11	8
1996	**BENNY THE DIP** 8-11	8
1997	**TEAPOT ROW** 8-11	8
1998	**MUTAAHAB** 8-11	6
1999	**ROYAL KINGDOM** 8-11	6
2000	**ATLANTIS PRINCE** 8-11	8
2001	**MUTINYONTHEBOUNTY** 8-11	9
2002	**AL JADEED** 8-11	9
2003	**SNOW RIDGE** 8-11	10

CHEVELEY PARK STAKES (2y fillies)
Newmarket-6f

1994	**GAY GALLANTA** 8-11	10
1995	**BLUE DUSTER** 8-11	8
1996	**PAS DE REPONSE** 8-11	8
1997	**EMBASSY** 8-11	8
1998	**WANNABE GRAND** 8-11	9
1999	**SEAZUN** 8-11	14
2000	**REGAL ROSE** 8-11	13
2001	**QUEEN'S LOGIC** 8-11	8
2002	**AIRWAVE** 8-11	6
2003	**CARRY ON KATIE** 8-11	10

MIDDLE PARK STAKES (2y)
Newmarket-6f

1994	**FARD** 9-0	10
1995	**ROYAL APPLAUSE** 8-11	5
1996	**BAHAMIAN BOUNTY** 8-11	11
1997	**HAYIL** 8-11	8
1998	**LUJAIN** 8-11	7
1999	**PRIMO VALENTINO** 8-11	6
2000	**MINARDI** 8-11	10
2001	**JOHANNESBURG** 8-11	7
2002	**OASIS DREAM** 8-11	10
2003	***BALMONT** 8-11	13

* Three Valleys disqualified from first place

SUN CHARIOT STAKES
(fillies and mares)
Newmarket-1m 2f

1994	**LA CONFEDERATION** 3-8-8	7
1995	**WARNING SHADOWS** 3-8-8	7
1996	**LAST SECOND** 3-8-11	9
1997	**ONE SO WONDERFUL** 3-8-8	8
1998	**KISSOGRAM** 3-8-8	5
1999	**LADY IN WAITING** 4-8-13	8
2000	**DANCEABOUT** 3-8-9	9
2001	**INDEPENDENCE** 3-8-10	16
2002	**DRESS TO THRILL** 3-8-10	10
2003	**ECHOES IN ETERNITY** 3-8-10	10

CAMBRIDGESHIRE
Newmarket-1m 1f

1994	**HALLING** 3-8-8	30
1995	**CAP JULUCA** 3-9-10	39
1996	**CLIFTON FOX** 4-8-2	38
1997	**PASTERNAK** 4-9-1	36
1998	**LEAR SPEAR** 3-7-13	35
*1999	**SHE'S OUR MARE** 6-7-12	33
2000	**KATY NOWAITEE** 4-8-3	35
2001	**I CRIED FOR YOU** 6-8-6	35
2002	**BEAUCHAMP PILOT** 4-9-5	30
2003	**CHIVALRY** 4-8-1	34

* Run over 1m 2f

JOCKEY CLUB CUP
Newmarket-2m

1994	**FURTHER FLIGHT** 8-9-3	5
1995	**FURTHER FLIGHT** 9-9-3	8
1996	**CELERIC** 4-9-0	8
1997	**GREY SHOT** 5-9-5	7
1998	**ARCTIC OWL** 4-9-5	7
1999	**RAINBOW HIGH** 4-9-0	3
2000	**PERSIAN PUNCH** 7-9-5	9
2001	**CAPAL GARMON** 3-8-4	7
2002	**PERSIAN PUNCH** 9-9-0	8
2003	**PERSIAN PUNCH** 10-9-5	6

SUPREME STAKES
Goodwood-7f

1994	**SOVIET LINE** 4-9-2	9
1995	**INZAR** 3-8-8	10
1996	**TAGULA** 3-8-9	9
1997	**DECORATED HERO** 5-9-2	6
1998	**DECORATED HERO** 6-9-5	8
1999	ABANDONED	
2000	**MOUNT ABU** 3-8-9	8
2001	**LATE NIGHT OUT** 6-8-12	4
2002	**FIREBREAK** 3-8-9	10
2003	**WITH REASON** 5-9-2	7

PRINCESS ROYAL STAKES
Ascot-1m 4f

1994	**DANCING BLOOM** 4-9-0	7
1995	**LABIBEH** 3-8-6	5
1996	**TIME ALLOWED** 3-8-7	11
1997	**DELILAH** 3-8-7	7
1998	**SILVER RHAPSODY** 3-8-7	7
1999	**SIGNORINA CATTIVA** 3-8-7	12
*2000	**SACRED SONG** 3-8-7	15
2001	**HEAD IN THE CLOUDS** 3-8-7	11
2002	**LOVE EVERLASTING** 4-9-0	4
2003	**ITNAB** 3-8-7	9

* Run at Newmarket

CORNWALLIS STAKES (2y)
Ascot-5f

1994	**MILLSTREAM** 8-11	7
1995	**MUBHIJ** 8-12	7
1996	**EASYCALL** 9-4	11
1997	**HALMAHERA** 8-12	13
1998	**SHOW ME THE MONEY** 8-8	12
1999	**KIER PARK** 8-12	13
*2000	**DANEHURST** 8-7	17
2001	**DOMINICA** 8-7	11
2002	**PEACE OFFERING** 8-12	11
2003	**MAJESTIC MISSILE** 9-1	11

* Run at Newbury

DEWHURST STAKES (2y)
Newmarket-7f

1994	**PENNEKAMP** 9-0	7
1995	**ALHAARTH** 9-0	4
1996	**IN COMMAND** 9-0	8
1997	**XAAR** 9-0	7
1998	**MUJAHID** 9-0	7
1999	**DISTANT MUSIC** 9-0	5
2000	**TOBOUGG** 9-0	10
2001	**ROCK OF GIBRALTAR** 9-0	8
2002	**TOUT SEUL** 9-0	16
2003	**MILK IT MICK** 9-0	12

ROCKFEL STAKES (2y)
Newmarket-7f

1994	**GERMANE** 8-8	8
1995	**BINT SALSABIL** 8-12	8
1996	**MOONLIGHT PARADISE** 8-12	6
1997	**NAME OF LOVE** 8-12	12
1998	**HULA ANGEL** 8-9	14
1999	**LAHAN** 8-9	12
2000	**SAYEDAH** 8-9	16
2001	**DISTANT VALLEY** 8-9	10
2002	**LUVAH GIRL** 8-9	11
2003	**CAIRNS** 8-9	10

CHALLENGE STAKES
Newmarket-7f

1994	**ZIETEN** 4-9-0	8
1995	**HARAYIR** 3-8-12	8
1996	**CHARNWOOD FOREST** 4-9-4	8
1997	**KAHAL** 3-8-12	12
1998	**DECORATED HERO** 6-9-4	10
1999	**SUSU** 6-8-11	10
2000	**LAST RESORT** 3-8-9	9
2001	**MUNIR** 3-8-12	14
2002	**NAYYIR** 4-9-0	17
2003	**JUST JAMES** 4-9-0	11

TWO-YEAR-OLD TROPHY (2y)
Redcar-6f

1994	**MAID FOR WALKING** 7-13	26
1995	**BLUE IRIS** 8-2	26
1996	**PROUD NATIVE** 8-7	25
1997	**GRAZIA** 8-2	26
1998	**PIPALONG** 7-13	22
1999	**KHASAYL** 8-8	26
2000	**DIM SUMS** 8-4	23
2001	**CAPTAIN RIO** 8-10	25
2002	**SOMNUS** 8-2	18
2003	**PEAK TO CREEK** 9-0	23

CHAMPION STAKES
Newmarket-1m 2f

1994	DERNIER EMPEREUR 4-9-4	8
1995	SPECTRUM 3-8-10	8
1996	BOSRA SHAM 3-8-8	6
1997	PILSUDSKI 5-9-2	7
1998	ALBORADA 3-8-8	10
1999	ALBORADA 4-8-13	13
2000	KALANISI 4-9-2	15
2001	NAYEF 3-8-11	12
2002	STORMING HOME 4-9-2	11
2003	RAKTI 4-9-2	12

CESAREWITCH
Newmarket-2m 2f

1994	CAPTAIN'S GUEST 4-9-9	32
1995	OLD RED 5-7-11	21
1996	INCHCAILLOCH 7-7-3	26
1997	TURNPOLE 6-7-10	31
1998	SPIRIT OF LOVE 3-8-8	29
1999	TOP CEES 9-8-10	32
2000	HEROS FATAL 6-8-1	32
2001	DISTANT PROSPECT 4-8-8	31
2002	MISS FARA 7-8-0	36
2003	LANDING LIGHT 8-9-4	36

HORRIS HILL STAKES (2y)
Newbury-7f 64yds

1994	PAINTER'S ROW 8-12	10
1995	TUMBLEWEED RIDGE 8-9	9
1996	DESERT STORY 8-9	8
1997	LA-FAAH 8-9	6
1998	BRANCASTER 8-9	9
1999	UMISTIM 8-9	9
2000	CLEARING 8-9	10
2001	RAPSCALLION 8-9	10
2002	MAKHLAB 8-9	9
2003	PEAK TO CREEK 8-9	9

ST SIMON STAKES
Newbury-1m 4f 5yds

1994	PERSIAN BRAVE 4-9-0	9
1995	PHANTOM GOLD 3-8-9	12
1996	SALMON LADDER 4-9-0	12
1997	KALIANA 3-8-4	10
*1998	DARK MOONDANCER 3-8-7	5
1999	SIGNORINA CATTIVA 3-8-7	10
2000	WELLBEING 3-8-7	7
*2001	HIGH PITCHED 3-8-7	5
2002	THE WHISTLING TEAL 6-9-0	13
2003	IMPERIAL DANCER 5-9-0	9

* Run at Newmarket

RACING POST TROPHY (2y)
Doncaster-1m

1994	CELTIC SWING 9-0	8
1995	BEAUCHAMP KING 9-0	4
1996	MEDAALY 9-0	9
1997	SARATOGA SPRINGS 9-0	8
1998	COMMANDER COLLINS 9-0	6
1999	ARISTOTLE 9-0	9
2000	DILSHAAN 9-0	10
2001	HIGH CHAPARRAL 9-0	9
2002	BRIAN BORU 9-0	9
2003	AMERICAN POST 9-0	4

NOVEMBER HANDICAP
Doncaster-1m 4f

1994	SAXON MAID 3-8-9	24
1995	SNOW PRINCESS 3-8-2	18
1996	CLIFTON FOX 4-8-10	22
1997	SABADILLA 3-7-8	24
1998	YAVANA'S PACE 6-9-10	23
1999	FLOSSY 3-7-7	16
2000	BATSWING 5-8-8	20
2001	ROYAL CAVALIER 4-7-10	24
2002	RED WINE 3-8-1	23
2003	TURBO 4-9-2	24

WINNERS OF PRINCIPAL RACES IN IRELAND

IRISH 2000 GUINEAS (3y)
The Curragh-1m

1994	TURTLE ISLAND 9-0	9
1995	SPECTRUM 9-0	9
1996	SPINNING WORLD 9-0	10
1997	DESERT KING 9-0	12
1998	DESERT PRINCE 9-0	7
1999	SAFFRON WALDEN 9-0	10
2000	BACHIR 9-0	8
2001	BLACK MINNALOUSHE 9-0	12
2002	ROCK OF GIBRALTAR 9-0	7
2003	INDIAN HAVEN 9-0	16

TATTERSALLS GOLD CUP
The Curragh-1m 2f 110yds

1999	SHIVA 4-8-11	6
2000	MONTJEU 4-9-0	5
2001	FANTASTIC LIGHT 5-9-0	6
2002	REBELLINE 4-8-11	8
2003	BLACK SAM BELLAMY 4-9-0	8

IRISH 1000 GUINEAS (3y fillies)
The Curragh-1m

1994	MEHTHAAF 9-0	10
1995	RIDGEWOOD PEARL 9-0	10
1996	MATIYA 9-0	12
1997	CLASSIC PARK 9-0	10

1998	**TARASCON** 9-0	13
1999	**HULA ANGEL** 9-0	17
2000	**CRIMPLENE** 9-0	13
2001	**IMAGINE** 9-0	16
2002	**GOSSAMER** 9-0	15
2003	**YESTERDAY** 9-0	8

IRISH DERBY (3y)

The Curragh-1m 4f

1994	**BALANCHINE** 8-11	9
1995	**WINGED LOVE** 9-0	13
1996	**ZAGREB** 9-0	13
1997	**DESERT KING** 9-0	10
1998	**DREAM WELL** 9-0	10
1999	**MONTJEU** 9-0	10
2000	**SINNDAR** 9-0	11
2001	**GALILEO** 9-0	12
2002	**HIGH CHAPARRAL** 9-0	9
2003	**ALAMSHAR** 9-0	9

IRISH OAKS (3y fillies)

The Curragh-1m 4f

1994	**BOLAS** 9-0	10
1995	**PURE GRAIN** 9-0	10
1996	**DANCE DESIGN** 9-0	6
1997	**EBADIYLA** 9-0	11
1998	**WINONA** 9-0	9
1999	**RAMRUMA** 9-0	7
2000	**PETRUSHKA** 9-0	10
2001	**LAILANI** 9-0	12
2002	**MARGARULA** 9-0	12
2003	**VINTAGE TIPPLE** 9-0	11

PHOENIX STAKES (2y)

Leopardstown-6f

1994	**EVA LUNA** 8-11	10
1995	**DANEHILL DANCER** 9-0	10
1996	**MANTOVANI** 9-0	9
1997	**PRINCELY HEIR** 9-0	9
1998	**LAVERY** 9-0	11
1999	**FASLIYEV** 9-0	6
2000	**MINARDI** 9-0	10
2001	**JOHANNESBURG** 9-0	11
2002	**SPARTACUS** 9-0	9
2003	**ONE COOL CAT** 9-0	7

IRISH CHAMPION STAKES

Leopardstown-1m 2f

1994	**CEZANNE** 5-9-4	8
1995	**PENTIRE** 3-8-11	8
1996	**TIMARIDA** 4-9-1	6
1997	**PILSUDSKI** 5-9-4	8
1998	**SWAIN** 6-9-4	7
1999	**DAYLAMI** 5-9-4	7
2000	**GIANT'S CAUSEWAY** 3-8-11	7
2001	**FANTASTIC LIGHT** 5-9-4	7
2002	**GRANDERA** 4-9-4	7
2003	**HIGH CHAPARRAL** 4-9-4	7

IRISH CAMBRIDGESHIRE

The Curragh-1m

1994	**SAIBOT** 5-9-0	18
1995	**THE BOWER** 6-7-8	15
1996	**RAIYOUN** 3-9-8	16
1997	**QUWS** 3-9-2	11
1998	**LADY ORANSWELL** 4-7-3	21
1999	**SEEFINN** 4-7-7	14

2000	**SILVERWARE** 4-7-11	24
2001	**OSPREY RIDGE** 8-8-13	22
2002	**MASANI** 3-9-7	21
2003	**DEFINITE BEST** 5-8-5	15

MOYGLARE STUD STAKES (2y fillies)

The Curragh-7f

1994	**BELLE GENIUS** 8-11	8
1995	**PRIORY BELLE** 8-11	13
1996	**BIANCA NERA** 8-11	10
1997	**TARASCON** 8-12	12
1998	**EDABIYA** 8-11	13
1999	**PRESELI** 8-11	12
2000	**SEQUOYAH** 8-11	10
2001	**QUARTER MOON** 8-11	17
2002	**MAIL THE DESERT** 8-11	9
2003	**NECKLACE** 8-11	11

NATIONAL STAKES (2y)

The Curragh-7f
(8f between 1997 and 1999)

1994	**DEFINITE ARTICLE** 9-0	5
1995	**DANEHILL DANCER** 9-0	7
1996	**DESERT KING** 9-0	10
1997	**KING OF KINGS** 9-0	9
1998	**MUS-IF** 9-0	9
1999	**SINNDAR** 9-0	9
2000	**BECKETT** 9-0	9
2001	**HAWK WING** 9-0	7
2002	**REFUSE TO BEND** 9-0	7
2003	**ONE COOL CAT** 9-0	8

IRISH ST LEGER

The Curragh-1m 6f

1994	**VINTAGE CROP** 7-9-8	8
1995	**STRATEGIC CHOICE** 4-9-8	7
1996	**OSCAR SCHINDLER** 4-9-8	9
1997	**OSCAR SCHINDLER** 5-9-8	7
1998	**KAYF TARA** 4-9-8	7
1999	**KAYF TARA** 5-9-8	5
2000	**ARCTIC OWL** 6-9-8	8
2001	**VINNIE ROE** 3-8-12	8
2002	**VINNIE ROE** 4-9-9	8
2003	**VINNIE ROE** 5-9-9	6

IRISH CESAREWITCH

The Curragh-2m

1994	**ELUPA** 3-7-10	22
1995	**MONTELADO** 8-8-9	14
1996	**MILTONFIELD** 7-8-6	26
1997	**WINGED HUSSAR** 4-8-9	20
1998	**SWEETNESS HERSELF** 5-9-6	15
1999	**MILTONFIELD** 10-9-0	13
2000	**TRAGIC LOVER** 4-9-7	24
2001	**RAPID DEPLOYMENT** 4-8-13	19
2002	**AMERICAN GOTHIC** 4-9-0	18

THE PIERSE HURDLE

Leopardstown-2m
(formerly The Ladbroke Hurdle)

1994	**ATONE** 7-10-8	25
1995	**ANUSHA** 5-10-2	17
1996	**DANCE BEAT** 5-9-12	22
1997	**MASTER TRIBE** 7-10-4	23
1998	**GRAPHIC EQUALISER** 6-10-0	20
1999	**ARCHIVE FOOTAGE** 7-11-8	25
2000	**MANTLES PRINCE** 6-9-12	14

2001	**GRINKOV** 6-10-7	24
2002	**ADAMANT APPROACH** 8-11-1	26
2003	**XENOPHON** 7-10-11	28

HENNESSY COGNAC GOLD CUP
Leopardstown-3m

1994	**JODAMI** 9-12-0	6
1995	**JODAMI** 10-12-0	6

1996	**IMPERIAL CALL** 7-12-0	8
1997	**DANOLI** 9-12-0	8
1998	**DORANS PRIDE** 9-12-0	8
1999	**FLORIDA PEARL** 7-12-0	7
2000	**FLORIDA PEARL** 8-12-0	7
2001	**FLORIDA PEARL** 9-12-0	7
2002	**ALEXANDER BANQUET** 9-12-0	5
2003	**BEEF OR SALMON** 7-12-0	5

WINNERS OF PRINCIPAL RACES IN FRANCE

PRIX GANAY
Longchamp-1m 2f 110yds

1995	**PELDER** 5-9-2	10
1996	**VALANOUR** 4-9-2	10
1997	**HELISSIO** 4-9-2	8
1998	**ASTARABAD** 4-9-2	5
1999	**DARK MOONDANCER** 4-9-2	4
2000	**INDIAN DANEHILL** 4-9-2	4
2001	**GOLDEN SNAKE** 5-9-2	9
2002	**AQUARELLISTE** 4-8-13	7
2003	**FAIR MIX** 5-9-2	9

POULE D'ESSAI DES POULAINS (3y)
Longchamp-1m

1994	**GREEN TUNE** 9-2	7
1995	**VETTORI** 9-2	8
1996	**ASHKALANI** 9-2	10
1997	**DAYLAMI** 9-2	6
1998	**VICTORY NOTE** 9-2	12
1999	**SENDAWAR** 9-2	15
2000	**BACHIR** 9-2	7
2001	***VAHORIMIX** 9-2	12
2002	**LANDSEER** 9-2	13
2003	**CLODOVIL** 9-2	10

* Noverre disqualified from first place

POULE D'ESSAI DES POULICHES (3y)
Longchamp-1m

1994	**EAST OF THE MOON** 9-2	8
1995	**MATIARA** 9-2	16
1996	**TA RIB** 9-0	9
1997	**ALWAYS LOYAL** 9-0	7
1998	**ZALAIYKA** 9-0	14
1999	**VALENTINE WALTZ** 9-0	14
2000	**BLUEMAMBA** 9-0	11
2001	**ROSE GYPSY** 9-0	15
2002	**ZENDA** 9-0	17
2003	**MUSICAL CHIMES** 9-0	12

PRIX LUPIN (3y)
Longchamp-1m 2f 110yds

1994	**CELTIC ARMS** 9-2	8
1995	**FLEMENSFIRTH** 9-2	6
1996	**HELISSIO** 9-2	5
1997	**CLOUDINGS** 9-2	5
1998	**CROCO ROUGE** 9-2	5
1999	**GRACIOSO** 9-2	4
2000	**CIRO** 9-2	7

2001	**CHICHICASTENANGO** 9-2	5
2002	**ACT ONE** 9-2	7
2003	**DALAKHANI** 9-2	7

PRIX SAINT-ALARY (3y fillies)
Longchamp-1m 2f

1994	**MOONLIGHT DANCE** 9-2	6
1995	**MUNCIE** 9-2	6
1996	**LUNA WELLS** 9-0	6
1997	**BRILLIANCE** 9-0	7
1998	**ZAINTA** 9-0	9
1999	**CERULEAN SKY** 9-0	10
2000	**REVE D'OSCAR** 9-0	7
2001	**NADIA** 9-0	4
2002	**MAROTTA** 9-2	12
2003	**FIDELITE** 9-0	9

PRIX JEAN PRAT (3y)
Chantilly-1m 1f

1994	**MILLKOM** 9-2	6
1995	**TORRENTIAL** 9-2	7
1996	**LE TRITON** 9-2	6
1997	**STARBOROUGH** 9-2	5
1998	**ALMUTAWAKEL** 8-11	6
1999	**GOLDEN SNAKE** 9-2	6
2000	**SUANCES** 9-2	7
2001	**OLDEN TIMES** 9-2	5
2002	**ROUVRES** 9-2	8
2003	**VESPONE** 9-2	8

PRIX D'ISPAHAN
Longchamp-1m 1f 55yds

1994	**BIGSTONE** 4-9-2	7
1995	**GREEN TUNE** 4-9-2	9
1996	**HALLING** 5-9-2	4
1997	**SASURU** 4-9-2	6
1998	**LOUP SAUVAGE** 4-9-2	6
1999	**CROCO ROUGE** 4-9-2	8
2000	**SENDAWAR** 4-9-2	5
2001	**OBSERVATORY** 4-9-2	4
2002	**BEST OF THE BESTS** 5-9-2	4
2003	**FALBRAV** 5-9-2	8

PRIX DU JOCKEY-CLUB (3y)
Chantilly-1m 4f

1994	**CELTIC ARMS** 9-2	15
1995	**CELTIC SWING** 9-2	11
1996	**RAGMAR** 9-2	15

1997 **PEINTRE CELEBRE** 9-2 14
1998 **DREAM WELL** 9-2 13
1999 **MONTJEU** 9-2 8
2000 **HOLDING COURT** 9-2 14
2001 **ANABAA BLUE** 9-2 14
2002 **SULAMANI** 9-2 15
2003 **DALAKHANI** 9-2 7

PRIX DE DIANE (3y fillies)
Chantilly-1m 2f 110yds
1994 **EAST OF THE MOON** 9-2 9
1995 **CARLING** 9-2 12
1996 **SIL SILA** 9-0 12
1997 **VEREVA** 9-2 12
1998 **ZAINTA** 9-2 11
1999 **DARYABA** 9-2 14
2000 **EGYPTBAND** 9-0 12
2001 **AQUARELLISTE** 9-0 12
2002 **BRIGHT SKY** 9-2 15
2003 **NEBRASKA TORNADO** 9-0 10

GRAND PRIX DE PARIS (3y)
Longchamp-1m 2f
(1m 7f up to 1986)
1994 **MILLKOM** 9-2 12
1995 **VALANOUR** 9-2 10
1996 **GRAPE TREE ROAD** 9-2 10
1997 **PEINTRE CELEBRE** 9-2 7
1998 **LIMPID** 9-2 9
1999 **SLICKLY** 9-2 8
2000 **BEAT HOLLOW** 9-2 9
2001 **CHICHICASTENANGO** 9-2 5
2002 **KHALKEVI** 9-2 6
2003 **VESPONE** 9-2 11

GRAND PRIX DE SAINT-CLOUD
Saint-Cloud-1m 4f
1994 **APPLE TREE** 5-9-8 8
1995 **CARNEGIE** 4-9-8 8
1996 **HELISSIO** 3-8-8 9
1997 **HELISSIO** 4-9-9 4
1998 **FRAGRANT MIX** 4-9-8 9
1999 **EL CONDOR PASA** 4-9-8 10
2000 **MONTJEU** 4-9-8 4
2001 **MIRIO** 4-9-9 9
2002 **ANGE GABRIEL** 4-9-8 6
2003 **ANGE GABRIEL** 5-9-9 10

PRIX MAURICE DE GHEEST
Deauville-6f 110yds
1995 **CHEROKEE ROSE** 4-8-13 10
1996 **ANABAA** 4-9-2 9
1997 **OCCUPANDISTE** 4-8-13 8
1998 **SEEKING THE PEARL** 4-8-13 12
1999 **DIKTAT** 4-9-2 10
2000 **BOLD EDGE** 5-9-2 11
2001 **KING CHARLEMAGNE** 3-8-12 9
2002 **MAY BALL** 5-8-13 9
2003 **PORLEZZA** 4-8-12 12

PRIX JACQUES LE MAROIS
Deauville-1m
1994 **EAST OF THE MOON** 3-8-8 9
1995 **MISS SATAMIXA** 3-8-8 9
1996 **SPINNING WORLD** 3-8-11 9
1997 **SPINNING WORLD** 4-9-4 6
1998 **TAIKI SHUTTLE** 4-9-4 8

1999 **DUBAI MILLENNIUM** 3-8-11 5
2000 **MUHTATHIR** 5-9-4 11
2001 ***VAHORIMIX** 3-8-13 9
2002 **BANKS HILL** 4-9-1 8
2003 **SIX PERFECTIONS** 3-8-9 12
*Proudwings disqualified from first place

PRIX MORNY (2y)
Deauville-6f
1994 **HOH MAGIC** 8-10 6
1995 **TAGULA** 9-0 8
1996 **BAHAMIAN BOUNTY** 9-0 5
1997 **CHARGE D'AFFAIRES** 8-13 7
1998 **ORPEN** 9-0 13
1999 **FASLIYEV** 9-0 7
2000 **BAD AS I WANNA BE** 9-0 6
2001 **JOHANNESBURG** 9-0 11
2002 **ELUSIVE CITY** 9-0 6
2003 **WHIPPER** 9-0 8

PRIX DU MOULIN DE LONGCHAMP
Longchamp-1m
1994 **SKI PARADISE** 4-8-13 7
1995 **RIDGEWOOD PEARL** 3-8-8 8
1996 **ASHKALANI** 3-8-11 9
1997 **SPINNING WORLD** 4-9-2 9
1998 **DESERT PRINCE** 3-8-11 7
1999 **SENDAWAR** 3-8-11 9
2000 **INDIAN LODGE** 4-9-2 8
2001 **SLICKLY** 5-9-2 8
2002 **ROCK OF GIBRALTAR** 3-8-11 7
2003 **NEBRASKA TORNADO** 3-8-8 14

CRITERIUM INTERNATIONAL (2y)
Saint-Cloud-1m
(Prix de la Salamandre, run over
7f at Longchamp prior to 2001)
1994 **PENNEKAMP** 8-11 8
1995 **LORD OF MEN** 8-11 7
1996 **REVOQUE** 9-0 5
1997 **XAAR** 9-0 8
1998 **ALJABR** 9-0 6
1999 **GIANT'S CAUSEWAY** 9-0 5
2000 **TOBOUGG** 9-0 4
2001 **ACT ONE** 9-0 6
2002 **DALAKHANI** 9-0 5
2003 **BAGO** 9-0 7

PRIX VERMEILLE (3y fillies)
Longchamp-1m 4f
1994 **SIERRA MADRE** 9-2 9
1995 **CARLING** 9-2 10
1996 **MY EMMA** 9-0 9
1997 **QUEEN MAUD** 9-0 9
1998 **LEGGERA** 9-0 11
1999 **DARYABA** 9-0 11
2000 **VOLVORETA** 9-0 11
2001 **AQUARELLISTE** 9-0 12
2002 **PEARLY SHELLS** 9-0 11
2003 **MEZZO SOPRANO** 9-0 11

PRIX DU CADRAN
Longchamp-2m 4f
1994 **MOLESNES** 4-8-13 8
1995 **ALWAYS EARNEST** 7-9-2 6
1996 **NONONITO** 5-9-2 10
1997 **CHIEF CONTENDER** 4-9-2 7

1998	**INVERMARK** 4-9-2	9
1999	**TAJOUN** 5-9-2	8
2000	**SAN SEBASTIAN** 6-9-2	9
2001	**GERMINIS** 7-9-2	9
2002	**GIVE NOTICE** 5-9-2	16
2003	**WESTERNER** 4-9-2	10

PRIX DE L'ABBAYE DE LONGCHAMP
Longchamp-5f

1994	**LOCHSONG** 6-9-7	10
1995	**HEVER GOLF ROSE** 4-9-7	12
1996	**KISTENA** 3-9-8	10
1997	**CARMINE LAKE** 3-9-8	12
1998	**MY BEST VALENTINE** 8-9-10	14
1999	**AGNES WORLD** 4-9-10	14
2000	**NAMID** 4-9-11	9
2001	**IMPERIAL BEAUTY** 5-9-8	19
2002	**CONTINENT** 5-9-11	20
2003	**PATAVELLIAN** 5-9-11	19

PRIX MARCEL BOUSSAC (2y fillies)
Longchamp-1m

1994	**MACOUMBA** 8-11	6
1995	**MISS TAHITI** 8-11	11
1996	**RYAFAN** 8-11	13
1997	**LOVING CLAIM** 8-12	11
1998	**JUVENIA** 8-11	11
1999	**LADY OF CHAD** 8-11	11
2000	**AMONITA** 8-11	10
2001	**SULK** 8-11	9
2002	**SIX PERFECTIONS** 8-11	10
2003	**DENEBOLA** 8-11	16

GRAND CRITERIUM (2y)
Longchamp-1m

1994	**GOLDMARK** 8-11	4
1995	**LOUP SOLITAIRE** 8-11	7
1996	**REVOQUE** 9-0	9
1997	**SECOND EMPIRE** 9-0	5
1998	**WAY OF LIGHT** 9-0	7
1999	**CIRO** 9-0	3
2000	**OKAWANGO** 9-0	7

2001	**ROCK OF GIBRALTAR** 9-0	5
2002	**HOLD THAT TIGER** 9-0	14
2003	**AMERICAN POST** 9-0	6

PRIX DE LA FORET
Longchamp-7f

1994	**BIGSTONE** 4-9-11	12
1995	**POPLAR BLUFF** 3-9-0	10
1996	**A MAGICMAN** 4-9-2	11
1997	**OCCUPANDISTE** 4-8-13	10
1998	**TOMBA** 4-9-2	9
1999	**FIELD OF HOPE** 4-8-12	11
2000	**INDIAN LODGE** 4-9-2	11
2001	**MOUNT ABU** 4-9-2	11
2002	**DEDICATION** 3-8-11	10
2003	**ETOILE MONTANTE** 3-8-11	10

PRIX ROYAL-OAK
Longchamp-1m 7f 110yds

1994	**MOONAX** 3-8-11	7
1995	**SUNSHACK** 4-9-4	7
1996	**RED ROSES STORY** 4-9-1	5
1997	**EBADIYLA** 3-8-7	11
1998	**TIRAAZ** 4-9-4	7
1999	**AMILYNX** 3-8-9	7
2000	**AMILYNX** 4-9-4	11
2001	**VINNIE ROE** 3-8-9	13
2002	**MR DINOS** 3-8-9	7
2003	**WESTERNER** 4-9-4	14

CRITERIUM DE SAINT-CLOUD (2y)
Saint-Cloud-1m 2f

1994	**POLIGLOTE** 9-0	9
1995	**POLARIS FLIGHT** 9-0	5
1996	**SHAKA** 9-0	10
1997	**SPECIAL QUEST** 9-0	7
1998	**SPADOUN** 9-0	6
1999	**GOLDAMIX** 8-10	7
2000	**SAGACITY** 9-0	8
2001	**BALLINGARRY** 9-0	10
2002	**ALBERTO GIACOMETTI** 9-0	10
2003	**VOIX DU NORD** 9-0	10

WINNERS OF OTHER OVERSEAS RACES

DUBAI WORLD CUP
Nad Al Sheba-1m 2f dirt

1996	**CIGAR** 6-8-13	11
1997	**SINGSPIEL** 5-9-0	12
1998	**SILVER CHARM** 4-9-0	9
1999	**ALMUTAWAKEL** 4-9-0	8
2000	**DUBAI MILLENNIUM** 4-9-0	13
2001	**CAPTAIN STEVE** 4-9-0	12
2002	**STREET CRY** 4-9-0	11
2003	**MOON BALLAD** 4-9-0	11

KENTUCKY DERBY
Churchill Downs-1m 2f dirt

1994	**GO FOR GIN** 9-0	14
1995	**THUNDER GULCH** 9-0	19
1996	**GRINDSTONE** 9-0	19
1997	**SILVER CHARM** 9-0	13
1998	**REAL QUIET** 9-0	15
1999	**CHARISMATIC** 9-0	19
2000	**FUSAICHI PEGASUS** 9-0	19
2001	**MONARCHOS** 9-0	17
2002	**WAR EMBLEM** 9-0	18
2003	**FUNNY CIDE** 9-0	16

BREEDERS' CUP TURF
Various-courses-1m 4f

Year	Winner		
1994	**TIKKANEN** 3-8-10		14
1995	**NORTHERN SPUR 5** 4-9-0		14
1996	**PILSUDSKI** 4-9-0		13
1997	**CHIEF BEARHEART** 4-9-0		11
1998	**BUCK'S BOY** 5-9-0		13
1999	**DAYLAMI** 5-9-0		13
2000	**KALANISI** 4-9-0		13
2001	**FANTASTIC LIGHT** 5-9-0		11
2002	**HIGH CHAPARRAL** 3-8-9		8
2003	**JOHAR** 4-9-0 dead heated with		
	HIGH CHAPARRAL 4-9-0		9

BREEDERS' CUP CLASSIC
Various courses-1m 2f dirt

1994	**CONCERN** 3-8-10		14
1995	**CIGAR** 5-9-0		11
1996	**ALPHABET SOUP** 5-9-0		13
1997	**SKIP AWAY** 4-9-0		10
1998	**AWESOME AGAIN** 4-9-0		10
1999	**CAT THIEF** 3-8-10		13
2000	**TIZNOW** 3-8-10		13
2001	**TIZNOW** 4-9-0		13
2002	**VOLPONI** 4-9-0		12
2003	**PLEASANTLY PERFECT** 5-9-0		10

MELBOURNE CUP
Flemington-2m

1994	**JEUNE** 5-8-13		24
1995	**DORIMUS** 5-8-8		21
1996	**SAINTLY** 4-8-9		22
1997	**MIGHT AND POWER** 4-8-11		22
1998	**JEZABEEL** 6-8-0		24
1999	**ROGAN JOSH** 7-7-12		24
2000	**BREW** 6-7-10		22
2001	**ETHEREAL** 3-8-2		22
2002	**MEDIA PUZZLE** 5-8-4		23
2003	**MAKYBE DIVA** 4-8-0		23

JAPAN CUP
Tokyo-1m 4f

1994	**MARVELLOUS CROWN** 4-9-0		14
1995	**LANDO** 5-9-0		14
1996	**SINGSPIEL** 4-9-0		15
1997	**PILSUDSKI** 4-9-0		14
1998	**EL CONDOR PASA** 3-8-5		15
1999	**SPECIAL WEEK** 4-9-0		14
2000	**T.M. OPERA** 4-9-0		16
2001	**JUNGLE POCKET** 3-8-10		15
2002	**FALBRAV** 4-9-0		16
2003	**FALBRAV** 4-9-0		16
2004	**FALBRAV** 5-9-0		14

WINNERS OF PRINCIPAL NATIONAL HUNT RACES

THOMAS PINK GOLD CUP H'CAP CHASE
Cheltenham-2m 4f 110yds
(formerly Mackeson Gold Cup and Murphy's Gold Cup)

1994	**BRADBURY STAR** 9-11-11		14
1995	**DUBLIN FLYER** 9-11-8		12
1996	**CHALLENGER DU LUC** 6-10-2		12
1997	**SENOR EL BETRUTTI** 8-10-0		9
1998	**CYFOR MALTA** 5-11-3		12
1999	**THE OUTBACK WAY** 9-10-0		14
2000	**LADY CRICKET** 6-10-13		15
2001	**SHOOTING LIGHT** 8-11-3		14
2002	**CYFOR MALTA** 9-11-9		15
2003	**FONDMORT** 7-10-13		9

HENNESSY COGNAC GOLD CUP H'CAP CHASE
Newbury-3m 2f 110yds

1994	**ONE MAN** 6-10-0		16
1995	**COULDN'T BE BETTER** 8-10-8		11
1996	**COOME HILL** 7-10-0		11
1997	**SUNY BAY** 8-11-8		14
1998	**TEETON MILL** 9-10-5		16
1999	**EVER BLESSED** 7-10-0		13
2000	**KING'S ROAD** 7-10-7		17
2001	**WHAT'S UP BOYS** 7-10-12		14
2002	**BE MY ROYAL** 10-10-0		25
2003	**STRONG FLOW** 6-11-0		21

TRIPLEPRINT GOLD CUP H'CAP CHASE
Cheltenham-2m 4f

1994	**DUBLIN FLYER** 8-10-2		11
1995	ABANDONED		
1996	**ADDINGTON BOY** 8-11-10		10
1997	**SENOR EL BETRUTTI** 8-11-3		9
1998	**NORTHERN STARLIGHT** 7-10-1		13
1999	**LEGAL RIGHT** 6-10-13		9
2000	**GO ROGER GO** 8-11-0		12
2001	ABANDONED		
2002	**FONDMORT** 6-10-5		9
2003	**IRIS ROYAL** 7-10-13		17

PERTEMPS CHRISTMAS HURDLE
Kempton-2m

1994	**ABSALOM'S LADY** 6-11-2		6
1995	ABANDONED		
1996	ABANDONED		
1997	**KERAWI** 4-11-7		5
1998	**FRENCH HOLLY** 7-11-7		5
1999	**DATO STAR** 8-11-7		4
2000	**GEOS** 5-11-7		7
2001	**LANDING LIGHT** 6-11-7		5
2002	**INTERSKY FALCON** 5-11-7		6
2003	**INTERSKY FALCON** 6-11-7		6

PERTEMPS KING GEORGE VI CHASE
Kempton-3m

1994	**ALGAN** 6-11-10		9
1995	**ONE MAN** 8-11-10 (RUN AT SANDOWN)		11

1996 **ONE MAN** 8-11-10.............................5
1997 **SEE MORE BUSINESS** 7-11-10...........9
1998 **TEETON MILL** 9-11-10.....................8
1999 **SEE MORE BUSINESS** 9-11-10...........9
2000 **FIRST GOLD** 7-11-10.......................9
2001 **FLORIDA PEARL** 9-11-10..................8
2002 **BEST MATE** 7-11-10......................10
2003 **EDREDON BLEU** 11-11-10................12

CORAL WELSH NATIONAL H'CAP CHASE

Chepstow-3m 6f
1994 **MASTER OATS** 8-11-6 (RUN AT NEWBURY)..8
1995 ABANDONED
1996 ABANDONED
1997 **EARTH SUMMIT** 9-10-13...................14
1998 **KENDAL CAVALIER** 8-10-0................14
1999 **EDMOND** 7-10-0............................16
2000 **JOCKS CROSS** 9-10-4......................19
2001 **SUPREME GLORY** 9-10-4..................13
2002 **MINI SENSATION** 9-10-4..................16
2003 **BINDAREE** 9-10-9...........................14

VICTOR CHANDLER H'CAP CHASE

Ascot-2m
1994 **VIKING FLAGSHIP** 7-10-10 (RUN AT WARWICK)..4
1995 **MARTHA'S SON** 8-10-9......................8
1996 **BIG MATT** 9-10-4...........................11
1997 **ASK TOM** 8-10-10 (RUN AT KEMPTON).....8
1998 **JEFFELL** 8-10-11............................9
1999 **CALL EQUINAME** 9-11-3 (RUN AT KEMPTON)..7
2000 **NORDANCE PRINCE** 9-10-0.................10
2001 **FUNCTION DREAM** 9-10-11.................10
2002 **TURGEONOV** 7-10-4..........................8
2003 ABANDONED

TOTE GOLD TROPHY H'CAP HURDLE

Newbury-2m 110yds
1994 **LARGE ACTION** 6-10-8.....................11
1995 **MYSILV** 5-10-8...............................8
1996 **SQUIRE SILK** 7-10-12......................18
1997 **MAKE A STAND** 6-11-7.....................18
1998 **SHARPICAL** 6-11-1..........................14
1999 **DECOUPAGE** 7-11-10.......................18
2000 **GEOS** 5-11-3................................17
2001 **LANDING LIGHT** 6-10-2....................20
2002 **COPELAND** 7-11-7...........................16
2003 **SPIRIT LEADER** 7-10-0.....................27

RACING POST H'CAP CHASE

Kempton-3m
1994 **ANTONIN** 6-10-4............................16
1995 **VAL D'ALENE** 8-11-2........................9
1996 **ROUGH QUEST** 10-10-8......................9
1997 **MUDAHIM** 11-10-2...........................9
1998 **SUPER TACTICS** 10-10-10...................7
1999 **DR LEUNT** 8-11-5............................9
2000 **GLORIA VICTIS** 6-10-0.....................13
2001 **YOUNG SPARTACUS** 8-11-3.................15
2002 **GUNTHER MCBRIDE** 7-10-3................14
2003 **LA LANDIERE** 8-11-7.......................12

IRISH INDEPENDANT ARKLE CHALLENGE TROPHY (NOVICES' CHASE)

Cheltenham-2m
1994 **NAKIR** 6-11-8...............................11
1995 **KLAIRON DAVIS** 6-11-8....................11
1996 **VENTANA CANYON** 7-11-8.................16
1997 **OR ROYAL** 6-11-8............................9
1998 **CHAMPLEVE** 5-11-0........................16
1999 **FLAGSHIP UBERALLES** 5-11-0.............14
2000 **TIUTCHEV** 7-11-8...........................12
2001 ABANDONED
2002 **MOSCOW FLYER** 8-11-8.....................12
2003 **TRAVADO** 7-11-8.............................8

SMURFIT CHAMPION HURDLE

Cheltenham-2m 110yds
1994 **FLAKEY DOVE** 8-11-9.......................15
1995 **ALDERBROOK** 6-12-0.......................14
1996 **COLLIER BAY** 6-12-0........................16
1997 **MAKE A STAND** 6-12-0.....................17
1998 **ISTABRAQ** 6-12-0...........................18
1999 **ISTABRAQ** 7-12-0...........................14
2000 **ISTABRAQ** 8-12-0...........................12
2001 ABANDONED
2002 **HORS LA LOI III** 7-12-0....................15
2003 **ROOSTER BOOSTER** 9-12-0.................17

QUEEN MOTHER CHAMPION CHASE

Cheltenham-2m
1994 **VIKING FLAGSHIP** 7-12-0....................8
1995 **VIKING FLAGSHIP** 8-12-0..................10
1996 **KLAIRON DAVIS** 7-12-0......................7
1997 **MARTHA'S SON** 10-12-0.....................6
1998 **ONE MAN** 10-12-0............................8
1999 **CALL EQUINAME** 9-12-0.....................9
2000 **EDREDON BLEU** 8-12-0.......................9
2001 ABANDONED
2002 **FLAGSHIP UBERALLES** 8-12-0..............12
2003 **MOSCOW FLYER** 9-12-0......................11

ROYAL & SUNALLIANCE NOVICES' CHASE

Cheltenham-3m
1994 **MONSIEUR LE CURE** 8-11-4.................18
1995 **BRIEF GALE** 8-10-13........................13
1996 **NAHTHEN LAD** 7-11-4.......................12
1997 **HANAKHAM** 8-11-4..........................14
1998 **FLORIDA PEARL** 6-11-4.....................10
1999 **LOOKS LIKE TROUBLE** 7-11-4.............14
2000 **LORD NOELIE** 7-11-4..........................9
2001 ABANDONED
2002 **HUSSARD COLLONGES** 7-11-4..............19
2003 **ONE KNIGHT** 7-11-4..........................9

JCB TRIUMPH HURDLE (4Y)

Cheltenham-2m 1f
1994 **MYSILV** 10-9................................28
1995 **KISSAIR** 11-0...............................26
1996 **PADDY'S RETURN** 11-0.....................29
1997 **COMMANCHE COURT** 11-0..................28
1998 **UPGRADE** 11-0..............................25
1999 **KATARINO** 11-0.............................23
2000 **SNOW DROP** 10-9...........................28
2001 ABANDONED

2002 **SCOLARDY** 11-0 28
2003 **SPECTROSCOPE** 11-0 27

TOTE CHELTENHAM GOLD CUP
Cheltenham-3m 2f 110yds
1994 **THE FELLOW** 9-12-0 15
1995 **MASTER OATS** 9-12-0 15
1996 **IMPERIAL CALL** 7-12-0 10
1997 **MR MULLIGAN** 9-12-0 14
1998 **COOL DAWN** 10-12-0 17
1999 **SEE MORE BUSINESS** 9-12-0 12
2000 **LOOKS LIKE TROUBLE** 8-12-0 12
2001 ABANDONED
2002 **BEST MATE** 7-12-0 18
2003 **BEST MATE** 8-12-0 15

MARTELL CUP CHASE
Aintree-3m 1f
1994 **DOCKLANDS EXPRESS** 12-11-5 4
1995 **MERRY GALE** 7-11-9 6
1996 **SCOTTON BANKS** 7-11-5 6
1997 **BARTON BANK** 11-11-5 5
1998 **ESCARTEFIGUE** 6-11-13 8
1999 **MACGEORGE** 9-11-5 5
2000 **SEE MORE BUSINESS** 10-12-0 4
2001 **FIRST GOLD** 8-12-0 7
2002 **FLORIDA PEARL** 10-11-12 6
2003 **FIRST GOLD** 10-11-12 7

MARTELL AINTREE HURDLE
Aintree-2m 4f
1994 **DANOLI** 6-11-7 9
1995 **DANOLI** 7-11-7 6
1996 **URUBANDE** 6-11-7 8
1997 **BIMSEY** 7-11-7 7
1998 **PRIDWELL** 8-11-7 6
1999 **ISTABRAQ** 7-11-7 7
2000 **MISTER MOROSE** 10-11-7 10
2001 **BARTON** 8-11-7 8
2002 **ILNAMAR** 6-11-7 14
2003 **SACUNDAI 6-11-7 ....11**

GALA GROUP SCOTTISH GRAND NATIONAL (H'CAP CHASE)
Ayr-4m 1f
1994 **EARTH SUMMIT** 6-10-0 22
1995 **WILSFORD** 12-10-12 22
1996 **MOORCROFT BOY** 11-10-2 20
1997 **BELMONT KING** 9-11-10 17
1998 **BARONET** 8-10-0 18
1999 **YOUNG KENNY** 8-11-10 15
2000 **PARIS PIKE** 8-11-0 18
2001 **GINGEMBRE** 7-11-2 30
2002 **TAKE CONTROL** 8-10-6 18
2003 **RYALLUX** 10-10-5 19

attheraces GOLD CUP (H'CAP CHASE)
(formerly Whitbread Gold Cup)
Sandown-3m 5f 110yds
1994 **USHERS ISLAND** 8-10-0 12
1995 **CACHE FLEUR** 9-10-1 14
1996 **LIFE OF A LORD** 10-11-10 17
1997 **HARWELL LAD** 8-10-0 9
1998 **CALL IT A DAY** 8-10-10 19
1999 **EULOGY** 9-10-0 19
2000 **BEAU** 7-10-9 20
2001 **AD HOC** 7-10-4 25
2002 **BOUNCE BACK** 6-10-9 20
2004 **AD HOC** 9-10-10 16

MEREWOOD HOMES SWINTON H'CAP HURDLE
Haydock-2m
1994 **DREAMS END** 6-11-4 18
1995 **CHIEF MINISTER** 6-11-6 13
1996 **TRAGIC HERO** 4-10-9 19
1997 **DREAMS END** 9-11-11 19
1998 **RAINBOW FRONTIER** 4-10-0 16
1999 **SHE'S OUR MARE** 6-10-0 22
2000 **MIRJAN** 4-10-6 23
2001 **MILLIGAN** 6-11-4 23
2002 **INTERSKY FALCON** 5-11-10 11
2003 **ALTAY** 6-10-0 14

Foaling dates are shown for two-year-olds where these are provided, and the purchase price (in guineas) as a yearling.

DATES OF PRINCIPAL RACES

(SUBJECT TO ALTERATION)

JANUARY

Cantor Sport "Dipper" Novices' Chase (Newcastle) 3rd
Gerrard Wealth Management Tolworth Novices' Hurdle (Sandown Park) 3rd
Slaney Novices' Hurdle (Naas) 4th
Juvenile Hurdle (Punchestown) 7th
Victor Chandler Chase (Handicap) (Ascot) 10th
Victor Chandler Lightning Novices' Chase (Ascot) 10th
Tote Scoop6 Warwickshire Gold Cup Handicap Chase (Warwick) 10th
Leamington Novices' Hurdle (Warwick) 10th
Pierse Hurdle (Leopardstown) 11th
Leopardstown Handicap Chase (Leopardstown) 11th
Paddy Fitzpatrick Memorial Novices' Chase (Leopardstown) 11th
Tote Scoop6 Lanzarote Handicap Hurdle (Kempton Park) 17th
Normans Grove Chase (Fairyhouse) 18th
Galmoy Hurdle (Gowran Park) 22nd
Thyestes Handicap Chase (Gowran Park) 22nd
Byrne Bros Cleeve Hurdle (Cheltenham) 24th
Pillar Property Chase (Cheltenham) 24th
Ladbroke Trophy Chase (Handicap) (Cheltenham) 24th
Wragge & Co Finesse Juvenile Novices' Hurdle (Cheltenham) 24th
Bet Direct Peter Marsh Chase (Limited Handicap) (Haydock Park) 24th
Red Square Reloaded Champion Hurdle Trial (Haydock Park) 24th
Premier Hurdle (Haydock Park) 24th
Woodlands Park Naas Novices' Chase (Naas) 24th
Arkle Novices' Chase (Leopardstown) 25th
Golden Cygnet Novices' Hurdle (Leopardstown) 25th
AIG Champion Hurdle (Leopardstown) 25th
Kinloch Brae Chase (Thurles) 29th
Anaglogs Daughter Mares Novices' Chase (Thurles) 29th
Great Yorkshire Handicap Chase (Doncaster) 31st
River Don Novices' Hurdle (Doncaster) 31st
Singer & Friedlander National Trial Chase (Handicap) (Uttoxeter) 31st
Classic Novices' Hurdle (Uttoxeter) 31st

FEBRUARY

Tied Cottage Chase (Punchestown) 1st
Novice Hurdle Series (Punchestown) 1st
National Trial Handicap Chase (Punchestown) 1st
Tote Scoop6 Sandown Hurdle (Handicap) (Sandown Park) 7th
Scilly Isles Novices' Chase (Sandown Park) 7th
Agfa Diamond Chase (Handicap) (Sandown Park) 7th
Gerrard Wealth Management Rossington Main Novices' Hurdle (Wetherby) 7th
Towton Novices' Chase (Wetherby) 7th
Dr P. J. Moriarty Novices' Chase (Leopardstown) 8th
Deloitte & Touche Novices' Hurdle (Leopardstown) 8th
Hennessy Gold Cup Chase (Leopardstown) 8th
Spring 4yo Hurdle (Leopardstown) 8th
Tote Gold Trophy Hurdle (Handicap) (Newbury) 14th
Sodexho Prestige Game Spirit Chase (Newbury) 14th
AON Chase (Newbury) 14th
AON Standard Open Bumper (Newbury) 14th
Red Mills Trial Hurdle (Gowran Park) 14th
Danoli Chase (Gowran Park) 14th
Flyingbolt Novices' Chase (Navan) 15th
Ten Up Novices' Chase (Navan) 15th
Boyne Hurdle (Navan) 15th
Ritz Club Ascot Chase (Ascot) 21st
Amlin Reynoldstown Novices' Chase (Ascot) 21st
Tote Northern National Chase (Handicap) (Newcastle) 21st

Axminster Kingwell Hurdle (Wincanton) 21st
Country Gentleman's Association Chase (Wincanton) 21st
Winning Fair Juvenile Hurdle (Fairyhouse) 21st
INHSO Series Final (Novices' Handicap Hurdle) (Fairyhouse) 21st
Bobbyjo Chase (Fairyhouse) 21st
Collins Stewart National Spirit Hurdle (Fontwell Park) 22nd
Nas Na Riogh Novices' Chase (Naas) 22nd
Newlands Chase (Naas) 22nd
Johnstown Novices' Hurdle (Naas) 22nd
Michael Page International Kingmaker Novices' Chase (Warwick) 22nd
Michael Page International Standard Open Bumper (Warwick) 27th
Rendlesham Hurdle (Kempton Park) 27th
Gerrard Wealth Management Dovecote Novices' Hurdle (Kempton Park) 27th
Racing Post Chase (Handicap) (Kempton Park) 27th
Pendil Novices' Chase (Kempton Park) 28th
Adonis Juvenile Novices' Hurdle (Kempton Park) 28th
Bet Direct from Littlewoods Winter Derby Trial Stakes (Lingfield Park) 28th
Haydock Park Gold Cup Chase (Handicap) (Haydock Park) 28th
De Vere Prestige Novices' Hurdle (Haydock Park) 28th

MARCH

Tote Exacta Premier Kelso Novices' Hurdle (Kelso) 6th
EBF Novices' Handicap Chase Final (Navan) 6th
Sunderlands Imperial Cup Hurdle (Handicap) (Sandown Park) 13th
European Breeders Fund 'National Hunt' Novices' Hurdle Final (Handicap) (Sandown Park) 13th
Littlewoods Bet Direct Lincoln Trial Stakes (Handicap) (Wolverhampton) 13th
Smurfit Champion Hurdle Challenge Trophy (Cheltenham) 16th
Irish Independent Arkle Challenge Trophy Novices' Chase (Cheltenham) 16th
Gerrard Wealth Management Supreme Novices' Hurdle (Cheltenham) 16th
Fulke Walwyn Kim Muir Challenge Cup Chase (Handicap) (Cheltenham) 16th
Pertemps Hurdle Final (Handicap) (Cheltenham) 16th
William Hill NH Chase (Handicap) (Cheltenham) 16th
Queen Mother Champion Chase (Cheltenham) 17th
Royal & SunAlliance Novices' Chase (Cheltenham) 17th
Royal & SunAlliance Novices' Hurdle (Cheltenham) 17th
Coral Eurobet Cup (Handicap Hurdle) (Cheltenham) 17th
Weatherbys Champion Bumper (Cheltenham) 17th
NH Challenge Cup Chase (Cheltenham) 17th
Mildmay of Fleet Challenge Cup Chase (Handicap) (Cheltenham) 17th
Dawn Run Mares Novices' Chase (Limerick) 17th
Tote Cheltenham Gold Cup Chase (Cheltenham) 18th
Bonusprint Stayers' Hurdle (Cheltenham) 18th
JCB Triumph Novices' Hurdle (Cheltenham) 18th
Vincent O'Brien County Hurdle (Handicap) (Cheltenham) 18th
Cathcart Challenge Cup Chase (Cheltenham) 18th
Cheltenham Grand Annual Challenge Cup Chase (Handicap) (Cheltenham) 18th
Christie's Foxhunter Challenge Cup Chase (Cheltenham) 18th
Littlewoods Bet Direct Winter Derby Stakes (Lingfield Park) 18th
John Smith's Midlands Grand National Chase (Handicap) (Uttoxeter) 20th
EBF Tattersalls (Ireland) Mares Final Novices' Chase (Handicap) (Uttoxeter) 20th
Weatherbys Long Distance Hurdle (Ascot) 20th
Doncaster Mile (Doncaster) 25th
Freephone Stanley Spring Mile (Handicap) (Doncaster) 26th
Freephone Stanley Lincoln (Handicap) (Doncaster) 27th
Cammidge Trophy (Doncaster) 27th
EBF Crandon Park Stud Mares 'NH' Novices' Hurdle Final (Handicap) (Newbury) 27th
An Uaimh Chase (Navan) 27th
Ashleybank Investments Scottish Borders National Chase (Handicap) (Kelso) 28th
Gordon Lamb Further Flight Stakes (Nottingham) 31st

APRIL

Martell Cup Chase (Aintree) 1st
Martell XO Anniversary 4yo Novices' Hurdle (Aintree) 1st
Martell Red Rum Handicap Chase (Aintree) 1st
Martell Handicap Hurdle (Aintree) 1st
Martell Mersey Novices' Hurdle (Aintree) 1st

Champion 4yo Hurdle (Punchestown) 29th
John Smith's Durham National (Handicap Chase) (Sedgefield) 29th
Tickell Novice Hurdle (Punchestown) 30th
Fighting Blindness Handicap Chase (Punchestown) 30th
Punchestown Champion Hurdle (Punchestown) 30th

MAY

Merewood Homes Swinton Hurdle (Handicap) (Haydock Park) 1st
Merewood Homes Spring Trophy (Haydock Park) 1st
Jockey Club Stakes (Newmarket) 1st
Newmarket Stakes (colts) (Newmarket) 1st
2000 Guineas Stakes (colts & fillies) (Newmarket) 1st
Victor Chandler Palace House Stakes (Newmarket) 1st
1000 Guineas Stakes (fillies) (Newmarket) 2nd
R.L. Davison Pretty Polly Stakes (fillies) (Newmarket) 2nd
Dahlia Stakes (fillies) (Newmarket) 2nd
Jubilee Handicap Stakes (Kempton Park) 3rd
Victor Chandler Chester Vase (Chester) 5th
Tote Chester Cup (Handicap) (Chester) 6th
UPM-Kyemmene Cheshire Oaks (fillies) (Chester) 6th
Betfair.com Ormonde Stakes (Chester) 7th
Philip Leverhulme Dee Stakes (Chester) 7th
Breitling Watches & Waltons of Chester Huxley Stakes (Chester) 7th
attheraces Derby Trial Stakes (colts & geldings) (Lingfield Park) 8th
Tote Scoop6 Sprint Handicap Stakes (Lingfield Park) 8th
attheraces Racing Oaks Trial Stakes (fillies) (Lingfield Park) 8th
Chartwell Stakes (fillies) (Lingfield Park) 8th
Derrinstown Derby Trial (Leopardstown) 8th
Derrinstown 1000 Guineas Trial (Leopardstown) 9th
Murphys Hurdle (Killarney) 9th
Royal Windsor Stakes (Windsor) 9th
Tattersalls Musidora Stakes (fillies) (York) 10th
Duke of York Stakes (York) 11th
Tote Dante Stakes (York) 11th
Bank of Scotland Business Banking Hambleton Rated Stakes (Handicap) (York) 12th
Tote.co.uk Middleton Stakes (fillies) (York) 12th
Yorkshire Cup (York) 12th
Michael Seely Memorial Glasgow Stakes (York) 13th
(Braveheart Rated Stakes (Hamilton Park) 13th
Swettenham Stud Fillies' Trial Stakes (Newbury) 14th
Juddmonte Lockinge Stakes (Newbury) 14th
Aston Park Stakes (Newbury) 15th
Carnarvon Stakes (Newbury) 15th
Kilvington Stakes (fillies) (Nottingham) 15th
Letheby & Christopher Predominate Stakes (colts & geldings) (Goodwood) 18th
Victor Chandler Lupe Stakes (fillies) (Goodwood) 19th
Festival Stakes (Goodwood) 19th
European Breeders Fund Conqueror Stakes (fillies) (Goodwood) 20th
EBF Pinnacle Stakes (fillies and mares) (Haydock Park) 20th
Tote Credit Club Silver Bowl (Handicap) (Haydock Park) 22nd
Dunwoody Sports Marketing Sandy Lane Rated Stakes (Haydock Park) 22nd
Coral Sprint Stakes (Handicap) (Newmarket) 22nd
King Charles II Stakes (Newmarket) 22nd
Haven and British Holidays Fairway Stakes (Newmarket) 22nd
Intrum Justitia Cup Champion Hunter Chase (Stratford-on-Avon) 22nd
Irish 2000 Guineas (Curragh) 22nd
Greenlands Stakes (Curragh) 22nd
Gallinule Stakes (Curragh) 22nd
Tattersalls Gold Cup (Curragh) 22nd
Irish 1000 Guineas (Curragh) 23rd
Heron Stakes (Kempton Park) 23rd
Achilles Stakes (Kempton Park) 29th
Freephone Stanley Zetland Gold Cup (Handicap) (Redcar) 29th
Tripleprint Temple Stakes (Sandown Park) 31st
Bonusprint Henry II Stakes (Sandown Park) 31st

JUNE

Brigadier Gerard Stakes (Sandown Park)	1st
National Stakes (Sandown Park)	1st
Hilary Needler Trophy (fillies) (Beverley)	2nd
Vodafone Oaks (fillies) (Epsom Downs)	4th
Vodafone Coronation Cup (Epsom Downs)	4th
Princess Elizabeth Vodafone Stakes (fillies) (Epsom Downs)	4th
Vodafone Surrey Stakes (Epsom Downs)	4th
Vodafone Derby (colts & fillies) (Epsom Downs)	5th
Vodafone Diomed Stakes (Epsom Downs)	5th
Vodafone 'Dash' Rated Stakes (Epsom Downs)	5th
Vodafone Woodcote Stakes (Epsom Downs)	5th
Betfair.com John of Gaunt Stakes (Haydock Park)	5th
Stanley Racing Cecil Frail Stakes (fillies) (Haydock Park)	5th
City of Perth Gold Cup Chase (Handicap) (Perth)	6th
Pipalong Stakes (fillies and mares) (Pontefract)	7th
Ballycorus Stakes (Leopardstown)	9th
Ballymacoll Stud Stakes (Newbury)	10th
William Hill Trophy (York)	12th
Leicester Mercury Stakes (Leicester)	12th
Axminster Carpets Cathedral Stakes (Salisbury)	13th
Ballyogan Stakes (Cork)	13th
St James's Palace Stakes (colts) (Royal Ascot)	15th
King's Stand Stakes (Royal Ascot)	15th
Queen Anne Stakes (Royal Ascot)	15th
Coventry Stakes (Royal Ascot)	15th
Duke of Edinburgh Stakes (Handicap) (Royal Ascot)	15th
Balmoral Stakes (Handicap) (Royal Ascot)	15th
Ascot Stakes (Handicap) (Royal Ascot)	16th
Prince of Wales's Stakes (Royal Ascot)	16th
Royal Hunt Cup (Handicap) (Royal Ascot)	16th
Jersey Stakes (Royal Ascot)	16th
Chesham Stakes (Royal Ascot)	16th
Queen Mary (fillies) (Royal Ascot)	16th
Gold Cup (Royal Ascot)	17th
Ribblesdale Stakes (fillies) (Royal Ascot)	17th
King George V Stakes (Handicap) (Royal Ascot)	17th
Hampton Court Stakes (Royal Ascot)	17th
Britannia Handicap Stakes (colts & geldings) (Royal Ascot)	17th
Norfolk Stakes (Royal Ascot)	17th
Coronation Stakes (fillies) (Royal Ascot)	18th
King Edward VII Stakes (colts & geldings) (Royal Ascot)	18th
Queen's Vase (Royal Ascot)	18th
Albany Stakes (Royal Ascot)	18th
Buckingham Palace Handicap Stakes (Royal Ascot)	18th
Wolferton Rated Stakes (Royal Ascot)	18th
Sandringham Rated Stakes (Handicap) (Royal Ascot)	19th
Golden Jubilee Stakes (Royal Ascot)	19th
Hardwicke Stakes (Royal Ascot)	19th
Wokingham Stakes (Handicap) (Royal Ascot)	19th
Queen Alexandra Stakes (Royal Ascot)	19th
Windsor Castle Stakes (Royal Ascot)	19th
Eternal Stakes (fillies) (Warwick)	19th
Crowther Homes Carlisle Bell Stakes (Handicap) (Carlisle)	23rd
Tote Credit Club Cumberland Plate (Handicap) (Carlisle)	24th
On The House Stakes (Goodwood)	25th
Foster's Lager Northumberland Plate (Handicap) (Newcastle)	26th
EBF Hoppings Stakes (fillies) (Newcastle)	26th
Kronenbourg 1664 Chipchase Stakes (Newcastle)	26th
Criterion Stakes (Newmarket)	26th
Fred Archer Stakes (Newmarket)	26th
Empress Stakes (fillies) (Newmarket)	26th
Gala Bingo Berkshire Stakes (Windsor)	26th
Tote Scoop6 Leisure Stakes (Windsor)	26th
Pretty Polly Stakes (Curragh)	26th
Curragh Cup (Curragh)	26th
Britannia Building Society English Summer National Chase (Handicap) (Uttoxeter)	27th

Railway Stakes (Curragh) 27th
Irish Derby (Curragh) 27th

JULY

Gala Stakes (Sandown Park) 2nd
Dragon Stakes (Sandown Park) 2nd
Old Newton Cup (Handicap) (Haydock Park) 3rd
Lancashire Oaks Stakes (fillies) (Haydock Park) 3rd
Coral Eurobet Eclipse Stakes (Sandown Park) 3rd
Distaff Stakes (fillies) (Sandown Park) 3rd
Esher Stakes (Sandown Park) 3rd
Tote Scoop6 Handicap Stakes (Sandown Park) 3rd
Porcelanosa Sprint Stakes (Sandown Park) 3rd
Brownstown Stakes (Leopardstown) 3rd
Princess of Wales's UAE Equestrian & Racing Federation Stakes (Newmarket) 6th
Cherry Hinton Stakes (fillies) (Newmarket) 6th
Falmouth Stakes (fillies) (Newmarket) 7th
Juy (TNT July Stakes (colts & geldings) (Newmarket) 7th
Bahrain Trophy (Newmarket) 7th
Darley July Cup (Newmarket) 8th
Ladbrokes Bunbury Cup (Handicap) (Newmarket) 8th
Weatherbys Superlative Stakes (Newmarket) 8th
Cuisine de France Summer Stakes (fillies) (York) 9th
Michael Page International Silver Trophy (Ascot) 10th
City Wall Stakes (Chester) 10th
John Smith's Cup (Handicap) (York) 10th
Webster's Silver Cup Rated (Handicap) (York) 10th
Manchester Evening News July Trophy (colts & geldings) (Haydock Park) 11th
Shadwell Stud Rose Bowl Stakes (Newbury) 16th
Weatherbys Super Sprint (Newbury) 17th
Steventon Stakes (Newbury) 17th
David Wilson Homes Hackwood Stakes (Newbury) 17th
Food Brokers Aphrodite Stakes (fillies) (Newmarket) 17th
Tote Scoop6 Summer Plate Handicap Chase (Market Rasen) 17th
Tote Exacta Summer Hurdle (Market Rasen) 17th
International Stakes (Curragh) 17th
Irish Oaks (Curragh) 18th
Minstrel Stakes (Curragh) 18th
Anglesey Stakes (Curragh) 18th
Daily Record Scottish Derby (Ayr) 19th
Star Stakes (fillies) (Sandown Park) 22nd
Oakgrove Stud Golden Daffodil Stakes (fillies) (Chepstow) 23rd
October Club EBF Valiant Stakes (fillies) (Ascot) 23rd
King George VI and Queen Elizabeth Diamond Stakes (Ascot) 24th
Tote International Stakes (Handicap) (Ascot) 24th
Princess Margaret Stakes (fillies) (Ascot) 24th
Meld Stakes (Leopardstown) 24th
Hong Kong Jockey Club Sprint Stakes (Handicap) (Ascot) 24th
Richmond Stakes (colts & geldings) (Goodwood) 25th
Theo Fennell Lennox Stakes (Goodwood) 27th
Peugeot Gordon Stakes (Goodwood) 27th
Sussex Stakes (Goodwood) 27th
Tote Gold Trophy Stakes (Handicap) (Goodwood) 28th
Veuve Cliquot Vintage Stakes (Goodwood) 28th
Galway Plate (Handicap Chase) (Galway) 28th
Lady O Goodwood Cup (Goodwood) 28th
King George Stakes (Goodwood) 29th
Betfair Molecomb Stakes (Goodwood) 29th
Galway Hurdle (Handicap) (Galway) 29th
Oak Tree Stakes (fillies) (Goodwood) 29th
William Hill Mile (Handicap) (Goodwood) 30th
Glorious Rated Stakes (Goodwood) 30th
Stewards' Sprint Handicap Stakes (Goodwood) 30th
Vodafone Stewards' Cup (Handicap) (Goodwood) 31st
Vodafone EBF Gladness Stakes (fillies and mares) (Goodwood) 31st
Vodafone Nassau Stakes (fillies) (Goodwood) 31st
Vodafone Thoroughbred Stakes (Goodwood) 31st

AUGUST

Queensferry Stakes (Chester)	1st
EBF Chalice Stakes (fillies) (Newbury)	1st
Blue Square Shergar Cup Day (Ascot)	7th
Petros Rose of Lancaster Stakes (Haydock Park)	7th
Sweet Solera Stakes (fillies) (Newmarket)	7th
Phoenix Sprint (Leopardstown)	8th
Phoenix Stakes (Leopardstown)	8th
Stonehenge Stakes (Salisbury)	11th
European Breeders Fund Upavon Stakes (fillies) (Salisbury)	11th
Sovereign Stakes (colts & geldings) (Salisbury)	12th
Newbury Racecourse Washington Singer Stakes (Newbury)	13th
Stan James St Hugh's Stakes (fillies) (Newbury)	14th
Stan James Geoffrey Freer Stakes (Newbury)	14th
Stan James Hungerford Stakes (Newbury)	14th
William Hill Great St Wilfrid Stakes (Handicap) (Ripon)	14th
EBF Dick Hern Stakes (Bath)	15th
Slatch Farm Stud Flying Fillies' Stakes (Pontefract)	15th
Desmond Stakes (Curragh)	15th
Debutante Stakes (Curragh)	15th
Royal Whip Stakes (Curragh)	15th
Juddmonte International Stakes (York)	17th
Great Voltigeur Stakes (colts & geldings) (York)	17th
Weatherbys Insurance Lonsdale Stakes (York)	17th
Acomb Stakes (York)	17th
Aston Upthorpe Yorkshire Oaks (fillies) (York)	18th
Scottish Equitable Gimcrack Stakes (colts & geldings) (York)	18th
Tote Ebor (Handicap) (York)	18th
Costcutter Roses Stakes (colts & geldings) (York)	18th
Peugeot Lowther Stakes (fillies) (York)	19th
Victor Chandler Nunthorpe Stakes (York)	19th
European Breeders Fund Galtres Stakes (fillies) (York)	19th
City of York Stakes (York)	19th
Bet Direct Chester Rated Stakes (Chester)	21st
Iveco Daily Solario Stakes (Sandown Park)	21st
Sunley Atalanta Stakes (fillies) (Sandown Park)	21st
Futurity Stakes (Curragh)	21st
Flower of Scotland Stakes (fillies and mares) (Hamilton Park)	23rd
Winter Hill Stakes (Windsor)	23rd
Tote Exacta Virginia Rated Stakes (fillies) (Brighton)	25th
Denny Handicap Chase (Tralee)	26th
Celebration Mile (Goodwood)	28th
San Miguel March Stakes (Goodwood)	28th
Hopeful Stakes (Newmarket)	28th
Touchdown in Malaysia Prestige Stakes (fillies) (Goodwood)	29th
Betfair.com Ripon Champion Two Years Old Trophy (Ripon)	30th

SEPTEMBER

Strensall Stakes (York)	1st
EBF Dick Poole Stakes (fillies) (Salisbury)	2nd
Stanley Leisure Sprint Cup (Haydock Park)	4th
Stanleybet.co.uk Old Borough Cup (Haydock Park)	4th
Superior Mile Stakes (Haydock Park)	4th
Milcars September Stakes (Kempton Park)	4th
Sirenia Stakes (Kempton Park)	4th
Flying Five Stakes (Curragh)	5th
Moyglare Stud Stakes (Curragh)	5th
£200,000 St Leger Yearling Stakes (Doncaster)	8th
Park Hill Stakes (fillies) (Doncaster)	8th
Tote Trifecta Portland Stakes (Handicap) (Doncaster)	8th
GNER Doncaster Cup (Doncaster)	9th
GNER Park Stakes (Doncaster)	9th
May Hill Stakes (fillies) (Doncaster)	9th
JRA London Office's Kyoto Sceptre Stakes (fillies) (Doncaster)	9th
Scarbrough Stakes (Doncaster)	9th
Fortune Stakes (Epsom Downs)	

Champagne Stakes (colts & geldings) (Doncaster)..10th
DBS St Leger Yearling Stakes (Doncaster)...10th
Amco Corporation Troy Stakes (Doncaster)...10th
Henry Gee Stakes (fillies and mares) (Chester)...11th
Stardom Stakes (Goodwood)...11th
St Leger (colts & fillies) (Doncaster)..11th
Polypipe Flying Childers Stakes (Doncaster)..11th
Irish Champion Stakes (Leopardstown)..11th
Matron Stakes (Leopardstown)...11th
Select Stakes (Goodwood)...11th
Starlit Stakes (Goodwood)...12th
John Musker Stakes (fillies) (Yarmouth)..12th
Harry Rosebery Stakes (Ayr)...15th
Dubai Duty Free Mill Reef Stakes (Newbury)...16th
Dubai Duty Free Cup (Newbury)..17th
Tote Ayr Gold Cup (Handicap) (Ayr)..17th
Doonside Cup (Ayr)...18th
Faucets First for Faucets Firth of Clyde Stakes (fillies) (Ayr)..18th
Courage Best Handicap Stakes (Newbury)...18th
Dubai Duty Free Arc Trial (Newbury)..18th
Dubai International Airport World Trophy (Newbury)...18th
Irish St Leger (Curragh)..18th
MacDonagh Boland Stakes (Curragh)..18th
National Stakes (Curragh)..19th
Blandford Stakes (Curragh)..19th
Lartigue Handicap Hurdle (Listowel)...21st
Kerry National (Handicap Chase) (Listowel)...22nd
Watership Down Stud Sales Stakes (fillies) (Ascot)...24th
EBF Harvest Stakes (fillies) (Ascot)..24th
Queen Elizabeth II Stakes (Ascot)...25th
Meon Valley Stud Fillies' Mile (Ascot)...25th
Hackney Empire Royal Lodge Stakes (colts & geldings) (Ascot)...25th
Diadem Stakes (Ascot)...25th
Rosemary Rated Stakes (fillies) (Ascot)...25th
Young Vic Theatre Cumberland Lodge Stakes (Ascot)..26th
Windsor Forest Stakes (Ascot)..26th
Mail On Sunday Mile Final (Handicap) (Ascot)..26th
Hamilton Park 2yo Series Final (Hamilton Park)..27th
Foundation Stakes (Goodwood)...30th
Charlton Hunt Supreme Stakes (Goodwood)...30th
UAE Equestrian & Racing Federation Rous Stakes (Newmarket)...30th
Cheveley Park Stakes (fillies) (Newmarket)..30th
Somerville Tattersall Stakes (colts & geldings) (Newmarket)...30th
Unicoin Homes Noel Murless Stakes (Newmarket)...30th

OCTOBER

Shadwell Stud Middle Park Stakes (colts) (Newmarket)..1st
Fishpools Godolphin Stakes (Newmarket)...1st
Shadwell Stud Joel Stakes (Newmarket)...1st
Tote Cambridgeshire Stakes (Handicap) (Newmarket)..2nd
Peugeot Sun Chariot Stakes (fillies) (Newmarket)...2nd
Oh So Sharp Stakes (fillies) (Newmarket)..2nd
Betabet Two-Year-Old Trophy (Redcar)..2nd
Guisborough Stakes (Redcar)..2nd
Park Stakes (Curragh)..2nd
Concorde Stakes (Tipperary)...3rd
Joe Mac Novices' Hurdle (Tipperary)...3rd
Grimes Novices' Chase (Tipperary)..3rd
McManus Hurdle (Tipperary)...3rd
National Lottery Chase (Gowran Park)...7th
Princess Royal Willmott Dixon Stakes (fillies) (Ascot)...9th
Willmott Dixon Cornwallis Stakes (Ascot)..9th
Miles & Morrison October Stakes (fillies) (Ascot)...9th
Tom McGee Autumn Stakes (Ascot)...9th
Coral Eurobet Sprint Trophy (Handicap) (York)..9th
Newton Fund Managers Rockingham Stakes (York)...9th
Beresford Stakes (Curragh)...10th

Munster National (Handicap Chase) (Limerick) 10th
EBF Boadicea Stakes (fillies and mares) (Newmarket) 14th
Lanwades Stud Severals Stakes (fillies) (Newmarket) 14th
£100,000 Tattersalls Autumn Auction Stakes (Newmarket) 15th
Bentinck Stakes (Newmarket) 15th
Darley Stakes (Newmarket) 16th
Emirates Airline Champion Stakes (Newmarket) 16th
Darley Dewhurst Stakes (colts & fillies) (Newmarket) 16th
Tote Cesarewitch (Handicap) (Newmarket) 16th
Victor Chandler Challenge Stakes (Newmarket) 16th
Owen Brown Rockfel Stakes (fillies) (Newmarket) 16th
Jockey Club Cup (Newmarket) 16th
Tote Bookmakers Silver Tankard Stakes (Pontefract) 18th
DBS October Yearling Stakes (Doncaster) 22nd
Vodafone Horris Hill Stakes (colts & geldings) (Newbury) 22nd
Racing Post Trophy (colts & fillies) (Doncaster) 23rd
Doncaster Stakes (Doncaster) 23rd
Charisma Gold Cup Chase (Handicap) (Kempton Park) 23rd
St Simon Stakes (Newbury) 23rd
Swettenham Stud Radley Stakes (fillies) (Newbury) 24th
Fieldspring Desert Orchid Chase (Limited Handicap) (Wincanton) 24th
Ballybrit Novices' Chase (Galway) 25th
Killavullan Stakes (Leopardstown) 27th
Lady Godiva Stakes (fillies and mares) (Yarmouth) 29th
James Seymour Stakes (Newmarket) 29th
EBF Bosra Sham Stakes (fillies) (Newmarket) 30th
United House Handicap Chase (Ascot) 30th
Tote Rising Stars Novices' Chase (Chepstow) 30th
Persian War Novices' Hurdle (Chepstow) 30th
Ben Marshall Stakes (Newmarket) 30th
Zetland Stakes ((Newmarket) 30th
European Breeders Fund Montrose Stakes (fillies) (Newmarket) 30th
Peterhouse Group Charlie Hall Chase (Wetherby) 30th
John Smith's West Yorkshire Hurdle (Wetherby) 30th
Stanley Racing Wensleydale Juvenile Novices' Hurdle (Wetherby) 30th
Brown Lad Handicap Hurdle (Naas) 30th
EBF Fleur de Lys Stakes (Lingfield Park) 31st

NOVEMBER

Williamhill.co.uk Haldon Gold Cup Chase (Limited Handicap) (Exeter) 2nd
Willie Park Trophy (Musselburgh) 3rd
EBF Gillies Stakes (fillies and mares) (Doncaster) 6th
Tote Scoop6 November Handicap (Doncaster) 6th
CIU Serlby Stakes (Doncaster) 6th
Charles Sidney Mercedes Benz Wentworth Stakes (Doncaster) 6th
Badger Brewery Handicap Chase (Wincanton) 6th
K J Pike & Sons Elite Hurdle (Limited Handicap) (Wincanton) 6th
Nicholson Chase (Down Royal) 6th
WFA Chase (Down Royal) 6th
Cork National (Cork) 7th
Fortria Chase (Navan) 7th
Lismullen Hurdle (Navan) 7th
For Auction Novices' Hurdle (Navan) 7th
Gerrard Wealth Management Sharp Novices' Hurdle (Cheltenham) 12th
Paddy Power Gold Cup Chase (Handicap) (Cheltenham) 13th
Tote Bookmakers Handicap Hurdle (Cheltenham) 13th
Intervet Trophy Chase (Handicap) (Cheltenham) 13th
Morgiana Hurdle (Punchestown) 13th
Craddockstown Novices' Chase (Punchestown) 13th
Edward Hanmer Memorial Chase (Limited Handicap) (Haydock Park) 14th
Rehabilitation of Racehorses Hurdle (Handicap) (Cheltenham) 14th
Independent November Novices' Chase (Cheltenham) 14th
Betfair Open Bumper (Cheltenham) 14th
Irish Field Novices' Chase (Punchestown) 14th
Clonmel Chase (Clonmel) 18th
PricewaterhouseCoopers Ascot Hurdle (Ascot) 19th
First National Gold Cup Chase (Limited Intermediate Handicap) (Ascot) 20th

BBA Peterborough Chase (Huntingdon)..20th
Littlewoods Bet Direct Churchill Stakes (Lingfield Park)..20th
Poplar Square Chase (Naas)..20th
Tote Becher Chase (Handicap) (Aintree)..21st
Sussex National Chase (Handicap) (Plumpton)..21st
Monksfield Novices' Hurdle (Navan)..21st
Troytown Handicap Chase (Navan)..21st
RBI Promotions Newbury Novices' Chase (Newbury)...27th
Hennessy Cognac Gold Cup Chase (Handicap) (Newbury)...27th
Stan James Gerry Feilden Hurdle (Limited Intermediate Handicap) (Newbury)....................27th
RBI Promotions Long Distance Hurdle (Newbury)..27th
Systems by Design Fulke Walwyn Novices' Chase (Newbury)..27th
Pertemps 'Fighting Fifth' Hurdle (Newcastle)...27th
Porterstown Handicap Chase (Fairyhouse)...27th
Juvenile Hurdle (Fairyhouse)...27th
New Stand Handicap Hurdle (Fairyhouse)...27th
Royal Bond Novices' Hurdle (Fairyhouse)...27th
Drinmore Novices' Chase (Fairyhouse)..28th
Hattons Grace Hurdle (Fairyhouse)..28th

DECEMBER

Winter Novices' Hurdle (Sandown Park)..3rd
John Hughes Rehearsal Chase (Limited Handicap) (Chepstow)...4th
Mitsubishi Shogun Tingle Creek Trophy Chase (Sandown Park)..4th
William Hill Hurdle (Handicap) (Sandown Park)..4th
Sun "King of the Punters" Mildmay Cazalet Memorial Handicap Chase (Sandown Park)........4th
Extraman Trophy Henry VIII Novices' Chase (Sandown Park)..4th
John Durkan Memorial Chase (Punchestown)...4th
Tripleprint Gold Cup Chase (Handicap) (Cheltenham) 5th
Victor Chandler Bula Hurdle (Cheltenham)..11th
Tripleprint Bristol Novices' Hurdle (Cheltenham)...11th
Arena Racing December Novices' Chase (Lingfield Park)..11th
Summit Novices' Hurdle (Lingfield Park)..11th
Hilly Way Chase (Cork)..11th
Cork Stayers Novices' Hurdle (Cork)..12th
Barry & Sandra Kelly Memorial Novices' Hurdle (Navan)...12th
Tara Hurdle (Navan)...12th
Cantor Sport Long Walk Hurdle (Ascot)...17th
Gerrard Novices' Hurdle (Ascot)..17th
Silver Cup Chase (Handicap) (Ascot)...18th
Cantor Sport Noel Novices' Chase (Ascot)...18th
Ladbroke Handicap Hurdle (Ascot)...18th
Tommy Whittle Chase (Haydock Park)..18th
Pertemps King George VI Chase (Kempton Park)..26th
Pertemps Christmas Hurdle (Kempton Park) 26th
Pertemps Feltham Novices' Chase (Kempton Park)..26th
Castleford Chase (Wetherby)...26th
Denny Juvenile Hurdle (Leopardstown)..26th
Denny Gold Medal Novices' Chase (Leopardstown)..26th
Greenmount Park Novices' Chase (Limerick)...26th
Rowland Meyrick Chase (Handicap) (Wetherby)...26th
Future Champion Novices' Hurdle (Leopardstown)..27th
Dial A Bet Chase (Leopardstown)...27th
Paddy Power Handicap Chase (Leopardstown)...27th
Coral Eurobet Welsh National Chase (Handicap) (Chepstow)...27th
Finale Juvenile Hurdle (Chepstow)..28th
"Championship" Standard Open Bumper (Chepstow)...28th
Neville Novices' Chase (Leopardstown)..28th
Ericsson Chase (Leopardstown)...28th
Christmas Hurdle (Leopardstown)..28th
Dorans Pride Novices' Hurdle (Limerick)..28th
TFM Cyntergy Challow Hurdle (Newbury)..29th
December Hurdle (Leopardstown) 29th

The information contained within the Principal Races section is supplied by the BHB and is provisional. In all cases the dates and names of sponsors are correct at the time of going to press but subject to possible alteration.

LEADING TRAINERS ON THE FLAT: 1896-2003

1896 A Hayhoe
1897 R Marsh
1898 R Marsh
1899 J Porter
1900 R Marsh
1901 J Huggins
1902 R S Sievier
1903 G Blackwell
1904 P P Gilpin
1905 W T Robinson
1906 Hon G Lambton
1907 A Taylor
1908 C Morton
1909 A Taylor
1910 A Taylor
1911 Hon G Lambton
1912 Hon G Lambton
1913 R Wootton
1914 A Taylor
1915 P P Gilpin
1916 R C Dawson
1917 A Taylor
1918 A Taylor
1919 A Taylor
1920 A Taylor
1921 A Taylor
1922 A Taylor
1923 A Taylor
1924 R C Dawson
1925 A Taylor
1926 F Darling
1927 Frank Butters
1928 Frank Butters
1929 R C Dawson
1930 H S Persse
1931 J Lawson

1932 Frank Butters
1933 F Darling
1934 Frank Butters
1935 Frank Butters
1936 J Lawson
1937 C Boyd-Rochfort
1938 C Boyd-Rochfort
1939 J L Jarvis
1940 F Darling
1941 F Darling
1942 F Darling
1943 W Nightingall
1944 Frank Butters
1945 W Earl
1946 Frank Butters
1947 F Darling
1948 C F N Murless
1949 Frank Butters
1950 C H Semblat
1951 J L Jarvis
1952 M Marsh
1953 J L Jarvis
1954 C Boyd-Rochfort
1955 C Boyd-Rochfort
1956 C F Elsey
1957 C F N Murless
1958 C Boyd-Rochfort
1959 C F N Murless
1960 C F N Murless
1961 C F N Murless
1962 W Hern
1963 P Prendergast
1964 P Prendergast
1965 P Prendergast
1966 M V O'Brien
1967 C F N Murless

1968 C F N Murless
1969 A M Budgett
1970 C F N Murless
1971 I Balding
1972 W Hern
1973 C F N Murless
1974 P Walwyn
1975 P Walwyn
1976 H Cecil
1977 M V O'Brien
1978 H Cecil
1979 H Cecil
1980 W Hern
1981 M Stoute
1982 H Cecil
1983 W Hern
1984 H Cecil
1985 H Cecil
1986 M Stoute
1987 H Cecil
1988 H Cecil
1989 M Stoute
1990 H Cecil
1991 P Cole
1992 R Hannon
1993 H Cecil
1994 M Stoute
1995 J Dunlop
1996 Saeed bin Suroor
1997 M Stoute
1998 Saeed bin Suroor
1999 Saeed bin Suroor
2000 Sir M Stoute
2001 A O'Brien
2002 A O'Brien
2003 Sir M Stoute

CHAMPION JOCKEYS ON THE FLAT: 1894-2003

1894 M Cannon 167
1895 M Cannon 184
1896 M Cannon 164
1897 M Cannon 145
1898 O Madden 161
1899 S Loates 160
1900 L Reiff 143
1901 O Madden 130
1902 W Lane 170
1903 O Madden 154
1904 O Madden 161
1905 E Wheatley 124
1906 W Higgs 149
1907 W Higgs 146
1908 W Maher 139
1909 F Wootton 165
1910 F Wootton 137
1911 F Wootton 187
1912 F Wootton 118
1913 D Maher 115
1914 S Donoghue 129
1915 S Donoghue 62
1916 S Donoghue 43

1917 S Donoghue 42
1918 S Donoghue 66
1919 S Donoghue 129
1920 S Donoghue 143
1921 S Donoghue 141
1922 S Donoghue 102
1923 S Donoghue 89
1923 C Elliott 89
1924 C Elliott 106
1925 G Richards 118
1926 T Weston 95
1927 G Richards 164
1928 G Richards 148
1929 G Richards 135
1930 F Fox 129
1931 G Richards 145
1932 G Richards 190
1933 G Richards 259
1934 G Richards 212
1935 G Richards 217
1936 G Richards 174
1937 G Richards 216
1938 G Richards 206

1939 G Richards 155
1940 G Richards 68
1941 H Wragg 71
1942 G Richards 67
1943 G Richards 65
1944 G Richards 88
1945 G Richards 104
1946 G Richards 212
1947 G Richards 269
1948 G Richards 224
1949 G Richards 261
1950 G Richards 201
1951 G Richards 227
1952 G Richards 231
1953 G Richards 191
1954 D Smith 129
1955 D Smith 168
1956 D Smith 155
1957 A Breasley 173
1958 D Smith 165
1959 D Smith 157
1960 L Piggott 170
1961 A Breasley 171

1962 A Breasley 179	1976 Pat Eddery 162	1990 Pat Eddery 209
1963 A Breasley 176	1977 Pat Eddery 176	1991 Pat Eddery 165
1964 L Piggott 140	1978 W Carson 182	1992 M Roberts 206
1965 L Piggott 160	1979 J Mercer 164	1993 Pat Eddery 169
1966 L Piggott 191	1980 W Carson 166	1994 L Dettori 233
1967 L Piggott 117	1981 L Piggott 179	1995 L Dettori 211
1968 L Piggott 139	1982 L Piggott 188	1996 Pat Eddery 186
1969 L Piggott 163	1983 W Carson 159	1997 K Fallon 202
1970 L Piggott 162	1984 S Cauthen 130	1998 K Fallon 204
1971 L Piggott 162	1985 S Cauthen 195	1999 K Fallon 201
1972 W Carson 132	1986 Pat Eddery 176	2000 K Darley 152
1973 W Carson 164	1987 S Cauthen 197	2001 K Fallon 167
1974 Pat Eddery 148	1988 Pat Eddery 183	2002 K Fallon 151
1975 Pat Eddery 164	1989 Pat Eddery 171	2003 K Fallon 221

LEADING OWNERS ON THE FLAT: 1894-2003

1894 Mr H. McCalmont	1930 H.H. Aga Khan	1967 Mr H J Joel
1895 Ld de Rothschild	1931 Mr J A Dewar	1968 Mr Raymond R Guest
1896 Ld de Rothschild	1932 H.H. Aga Khan	1969 Mr D Robinson
1987 Mr J Gubbins	1933 Ld Derby	1970 Mr C Engelhard
1898 Ld de Rothschild	1934 H.H. Aga Khan	1971 Mr P Mellon
1899 Duke of Westminster	1935 H.H. Aga Khan	1972 Mrs J Hislop
1900 H.R.H. The Prince	1936 Ld Astor	1973 Mr N B Hunt
of Wales	1937 H.H. Aga Khan	1974 Mr N B Hunt
1901 Sir G Blundell Maple	1938 Ld Derby	1975 Dr C Vittadini
1902 Mr R S Sievier	1939 Ld Rosebery	1976 Mr D Wildenstein
1903 Sir James Miller	1940 Lord Rothermere	1977 Mr R Sangster
1904 Sir James Miller	1941 Ld Glanely	1978 Mr R Sangster
1905 Col W Hall Walker	1942 His Majesty	1979 Sir M Sobell
1906 Ld Derby (late)	1943 Miss D Paget	1980 S Weinstock
1907 Col W Hall Walker	1944 Ld Derby	1981 H.H. Aga Khan
1908 Mr J B Joel	1945 Ld Derby	1982 Mr R Sangster
1909 Mr "Fairie"	1946 H.H. Aga Khan	1983 Mr R Sangster
1910 Mr "Fairie"	1947 H.H. Aga Khan	1984 Mr R Sangster
1911 Ld Derby	1948 H.H. Aga Khan	1985 Sheikh Mohammed
1912 Mr T Pilkington	1949 H.H. Aga Khan	1986 Sheikh Mohammed
1913 Mr J B Joel	1950 M M Boussac	1987 Sheikh Mohammed
1914 Mr J B Joel	1951 M M Boussac	1988 Sheikh Mohammed
1915 Mr L Neumann	1952 H. H. Aga Khan	1989 Sheikh Mohammed
1916 Mr E Hulton	1953 Sir Victor Sassoon	1990 Mr Hamdan Al-Maktoum
1917 Mr "Fairie"	1954 Her Majesty	1991 Sheikh Mohammed
1918 Lady James Douglas	1955 Lady Zia Wernner	1992 Sheikh Mohammed
1919 Ld Glanely	1956 Maj L B Holliday	1993 Sheikh Mohammed
1920 Sir Robert Jardine	1957 Her Majesty	1994 Mr Hamdan Al-Maktoum
1921 Mr S B Joel	1958 Mr J McShain	1995 Mr Hamdan Al-Maktoum
1922 Ld Woolavington	1959 Prince Aly Khan	1996 Godolphin
1923 Ld Derby	1960 Sir Victor Sassoon	1997 Sheikh Mohammed
1924 H.H. Aga Khan	1961 Maj L B Holliday	1998 Godolphin
1925 Ld Astor	1962 Maj L B Holliday	1999 Godolphin
1926 Ld Woolavington	1963 Mr J R Mullion	2000 H.H. Aga Khan
1927 Ld Derby	1964 Mrs H E Jackson	2001 Godolphin
1928 Ld Derby	1965 M J Ternynck	2002 Mr Hamdan Al-Maktoum
1929 H.H. Aga Khan	1966 Lady Zia Wernher	2003 K Abdullah

LEADING SIRES ON THE FLAT: 1894-2003

1894 St Simon	1902 Persimmon	1910 Cyllene
1895 St Simon	1903 St Frusquin	1911 Sundridge
1896 St Simon	1904 Gallinule	1912 Persimmon
1897 Kendal	1905 Gallinule	1913 Desmond
1898 Galopin	1906 Persimmon	1914 Polymelus
1899 Orme	1907 St Frusquin	1915 Polymelus
1900 St Simon	1908 Persimmon	1916 Polymelus
1901 St Simon	1909 Cyllene	1917 Bayardo

1918 Bayardo
1919 The Tetrarch
1920 Polymelus
1921 Polymelus
1922 Lemberg
1923 Swynford
1924 Son-in-Law
1925 Phalaris
1926 Hurry On
1927 Buchan
1928 Phalaris
1929 Tetratema
1930 Son-in-Law
1931 Pharos
1932 Gainsborough
1933 Gainsborough
1934 Blandford
1935 Blandford
1936 Fairway
1937 Solario
1938 Blandford
1939 Fairway
1940 Hyperion
1941 Hyperion
1942 Hyperion
1943 Fairway
1944 Fairway
1945 Hyperion
1946 Hyperion

1947 Nearco
1948 Big Game
1949 Nearco
1950 Fair Trial
1951 Nasrullah
1952 Tehran
1953 Chanteur II
1954 Hyperion
1955 Alycidon
1956 Court Martial
1957 Court Martial
1958 Mossborough
1959 Petition
1960 Aureole
1961 Aureole
1962 Never Say Die
1963 Ribot
1964 Chamossaire
1965 Court Harwell
1966 Charlottesville
1967 Ribot
1968 Ribot
1969 Crepello
1970 Northern Dancer
1971 Never Bend
1972 Queen's Hussar
1973 Vaguely Noble
1974 Vaguely Noble
1975 Great Nephew

1976 Wolver Hollow
1977 Northern Dancer
1978 Mill Reef (USA)
1979 Petingo
1980 Pitcairn
1981 Great Nephew
1982 Be My Guest (USA)
1983 Northern Dancer
1984 Northern Dancer
1985 Kris
1986 Nijinsky (CAN)
1987 Mill Reef (USA)
1988 Caerleon (USA)
1989 Blushing Groom (FR)
1990 Sadler's Wells (USA)
1991 Caerleon (USA)
1992 Sadler's Wells (USA)
1993 Sadler's Wells (USA)
1994 Sadler's Wells (USA)
1995 Sadler's Wells (USA)
1996 Sadler's Wells (USA)
1997 Sadler's Wells (USA)
1998 Sadler's Wells (USA)
1999 Sadler's Wells (USA)
2000 Sadler's Wells (USA)
2001 Sadler's Wells (USA)
2002 Sadler's Wells (USA)
2003 Sadler's Wells (USA)

LEADING BREEDERS ON THE FLAT: 1909-2003

1909 Mr "Fairie"
1910 Mr "Fairie"
1911 Ld Derby (late)
1912 Col. W Hall Walker
1913 Mr J B Joel
1914 Mr J B Joel
1915 Mr L Neumann
1916 Mr E Hulton
1917 Mr "Fairie"
1918 Lady James Douglas
1919 Ld Derby
1920 Ld Derby
1921 Mr S B Joel
1922 Ld Derby
1923 Ld Derby
1924 Lady Sykes
1925 Ld Astor
1926 Ld Woolavington
1927 Ld Derby
1928 Ld Derby
1929 Ld Derby
1930 Ld Derby
1931 Ld Dewar
1932 H.H. Aga Khan
1933 Sir Alec Black
1934 H.H. Aga Khan
1935 H.H. Aga Khan
1936 Ld Astor
1937 H.H. Aga Khan
1938 Ld Derby
1939 Ld Rosebery
1940 Mr H E Morriss
1941 Ld Glanely

1942 National Stud
1943 Miss D Paget
1944 Ld Rosebery
1945 Ld Derby
1946 Lt- Col H Boyd-Rochfort
1947 H.H. Aga Khan
1948 H.H. Aga Khan
1949 H.H. Aga Khan
1950 M M Boussac
1951 M M Boussac
1952 H. H. Aga Khan
1953 Mr F Darling
1954 Maj L B Holliday
1955 Someries Stud
1956 Maj L B Holliday
1957 Eve Stud
1958 Mr R Ball
1959 Prince Aly Khan and the late
     H.H. Aga Khan
1960 Eve Stud Ltd
1961 Eve Stud Ltd
1962 Maj L B Holliday
1963 Mr H F Guggenheim
1964 Bull Run Stud
1965 Mr J Ternynck
1966 Someries Stud
1967 Mr H J Joel
1968 Mill Ridge Farm
1969 Lord Rosebery
1970 Mr E P Taylor
1971 Mr P Mellon
1972 Mr J Hislop
1973 Claiborne Farm

1974 Mr N B Hunt
1975 Overbury Stud
1976 Dayton Ltd
1977 Mr E P Taylor
1978 Cragwood Estates Inc
1979 Ballymacoll Stud
1980 P Clarke
1981 H.H. Aga Khan
1982 Someries Stud
1983 White Lodge Stud
1984 Mr E P Taylor
1985 Dalham Stud Farms
1986 H.H. Aga Khan
1987 Cliveden Stud
1988 H. H. Aga Khan
1989 Mr Hamdan Al- Maktoum
1990 Capt. Macdonald- Buchanan
1991 Barronstown Stud
1992 Swettenham Stud
1993 Juddmonte Farms
1994 Shadwell Farm & Estate Ltd
1995 Shadwell Farm & Estate Ltd
1996 Sheikh Mohammed
1997 Sheikh Mohammed
1998 Sheikh Mohammed
1999 H. H. The Aga Khan's Studs
2000 H. H. The Aga Khan's Studs
2001 Shadwell Farm & Estate Ltd
2002 Gainsborough Stud
     Management Ltd
2003 Juddmonte

LEADING TRAINERS OVER JUMPS: 1945-2003

1945-46 T Rayson	1966-67 H R Price	1987-88 D R C Elsworth
1946-47 F T T Walwyn	1967-68 Denys Smith	1988-89 M C Pipe
1947-48 F T T Walwyn	1968-69 T F Rimell	1989-90 M C Pipe
1948-49 F T T Walwyn	1969-70 T F Rimell	1990-91 M C Pipe
1949-50 P V F Cazalet	1970-71 F T Winter	1991-92 M C Pipe
1950-51 T F Rimell	1971-72 F T Winter	1992-93 M C Pipe
1951-52 N Crump	1972-73 F T Winter	1993-94 D Nicholson
1952-53 M V O'Brien	1973-74 F T Winter	1994-95 D Nicholson
1953-54 M V O'Brien	1974-75 F T Winter	1995-96 M C Pipe
1954-55 H R Price	1975-76 T F Rimell	1996-97 M C Pipe
1955-56 W Hall	1976-77 F T Winter	1997-98 M C Pipe
1956-57 N Crump	1977-78 F T Winter	1998-99 M C Pipe
1957-58 F T T Walwyn	1978-79 M H Easterby	1999-00 M C Pipe
1958-59 H R Price	1979-80 M H Easterby	2000-01 M C Pipe
1959-60 P V F Cazalet	1980-81 M H Easterby	2001-02 M C Pipe
1960-61 T F Rimell	1981-82 M W Dickinson	2002-03 M C Pipe
1961-62 H R Price	1982-83 M W Dickinson	
1962-63 K Piggott	1983-84 M W Dickinson	
1963-64 F T T Walwyn	1984-85 J T Winter	
1964-65 P V F Cazalet	1985-86 N J Henderson	
1965-66 H R Price	1986-87 N J Henderson	

CHAMPION JOCKEYS OVER JUMPS: 1900-2003
Prior to the 1925-26 season the figure relates to racing between January and December

1900	Mr H S Sidney	53	1935-36 G Wilson	57	1969-70 B R Davies ... 91
1901	F Mason	58	1936-37 G Wilson	45	1970-71 G Thorner ... 74
1902	F Mason	67	1937-38 G Wilson	59	1971-72 B R Davies ... 89
1903	P Woodland	54	1938-39 T F Rimell	61	1972-73 R Barry ... 125
1904	F Mason	59	1939-40 T F Rimell	24	1973-74 R Barry ... 94
1905	F Mason	73	1940-41 G Wilson	22	1974-75 T Stack ... 82
1906	F Mason	58	1941-42 R Smyth	12	1975-76 J Francome ... 96
1907	F Mason	59	1942-43 No racing		1976-77 T Stack ... 97
1908	P Cowley	65	1943-44 No racing		1977-78 J J O'Neill ... 149
1909	R Gordon	45	1944-45 H Nicholson	15	1978-79 J Francome ... 95
1910	E Piggott	67	T F Rimell	15	1979-80 J J O'Neill ... 117
1911	W Payne	76	1945-46 T F Rimell	54	1980-81 J Francome ... 105
1912	I Anthony	78	1946-47 J Dowdeswell	58	1981-82 J Francome ... 120
1913	E Piggott	60	1947-48 B Marshall	66	P Scudamore ... 120
1914	Mr J R Anthony	60	1948-49 T Moloney	60	1982-83 J Francome ... 106
1915	E Piggott	44	1949-50 T Moloney	95	1983-84 J Francome ... 131
1916	C Hawkins	17	1950-51 T Moloney	83	1984-85 J Francome ... 101
1917	W Smith	15	1951-52 T Moloney	99	1985-86 P Scudamore ... 91
1918	G Duller	17	1952-53 F Winter	121	1986-87 P Scudamore ... 123
1919	Mr H Brown	48	1953-54 R Francis	76	1987-88 P Scudamore ... 132
1920	F B Rees	64	1954-55 T Moloney	67	1988-89 P Scudamore ... 221
1921	F B Rees	65	1955-56 F Winter	74	1989-90 P Scudamore ... 170
1922	J Anthony	78	1956-57 F Winter	80	1990-91 P Scudamore ... 141
1923	F B Rees	64	1957-58 F Winter	82	1991-92 P Scudamore ... 175
1924	F B Rees	108	1958-59 T Brookshaw	83	1992-93 R Dunwoody ... 173
1925	E Foster	76	1959-60 S Mellor	68	1993-94 R Dunwoody ... 197
1925-26	T Leader	61	1960-61 S Mellor	118	1994-95 R Dunwoody ... 160
1926-27	F B Rees	59	1961-62 S Mellor	80	1995-96 A P McCoy ... 175
1927-28	W Stott	88	1962-63 J Gifford	70	1996-97 A P McCoy ... 190
1928-29	W Stott	65	1963-64 J Gifford	94	1997-98 A P McCoy ... 253
1929-30	W Stott	77	1964-65 T Biddlecombe	114	1998-99 A P McCoy ... 186
1930-31	W Stott	81	1965-66 T Biddlecombe	102	1999-00 A P McCoy ... 245
1931-32	W Stott	77	1966-67 J Gifford	122	2000-01 A P McCoy ... 191
1932-33	G Wilson	61	1967-68 J Gifford	82	2001-02 A P McCoy ... 289
1933-34	G Wilson	56	1968-69 B R Davies	77	2002-03 A P McCoy ... 256
1934-35	G Wilson	73	T Biddlecombe	77	

LEADING OWNERS OVER JUMPS: 1945-2003
(Please note that prior to the 1994-95 season the leading owner was determined by win prizemoney only)

1945-46 Mr J Morant	1965-66 Duchess of Westminster	1985-86 Sheikh Ali Abu Khamsin
1946-47 Mr J J McDowell	1966-67 Mr C P T Watkins	1986-87 Mr H J Joel
1947-48 Mr J Proctor	1967-68 Mr H S Alper	1987-88 Miss Juliet E Reed
1948-49 Mr W F Williamson	1968-69 Mr B P Jenks	1988-89 Mr R Burridge
1949-50 Mrs L Brotherton	1969-70 Mr E R Courage	1989-90 Mrs Harry J Duffey
1950-51 Mr J Royle	1970-71 Mr F Pontin	1990-91 Mr P Piller
1951-52 Miss D Paget	1971-72 Capt T A Forster	1991-92 Whitcombe Manor
1952-53 Mr J H Griffin	1972-73 Mr N H Le Mare	Racing Stables Ltd
1953-54 Mr J H Griffin	1973-74 Mr N H Le Mare	1992-93 Mrs J Mould
1954-55 Mrs W H E Welman	1974-75 Mr R Guest	1993-94 Pell-Mell Partners
1955-56 Mrs L Carver	1975-76 Mr P B Raymond	1994-95 Roach Foods Limited
1956-57 Mrs Geoffrey Kohn	1976-77 Mr N H Le Mare	1995-96 Mr A T A Wates
1957-58 Mr D J Coughlan	1977-78 Mrs O Jackson	1996-97 Mr R Ogden
1958-59 Mr J E Bigg	1978-79 Snailwell Stud Co Ltd	1997-98 Mr D A Johnson
1959-60 Miss W H Wallace	1979-80 Mr H J Joel	1998-99 Mr J P McManus
1960-61 Mr C Vaughan	1980-81 Mr R J Wilson	1999-00 Mr R Ogden
1961-62 Mr N Cohen	1981-82 Sheikh Ali Abu Khamsin	2000-01 Sir R Ogden
1962-63 Mr P B Raymond	1982-83 Sheikh Ali Abu Khamsin	2001-02 Mr D A Johnson
1963-64 Mr J K Goodman	1983-84 Sheikh Ali Abu Khamsin	2002-03 Mr D A Johnson
1964-65 Mrs M Stephenson	1984-85 T Kilroe and Son Ltd	

LEADING AMATEUR RIDERS OVER JUMPS: 1945-2003

1945-46 Mr A B Mildmay 11	1964-65 Mr M Gifford 15	1983-84 Mr S Sherwood 28
1946-47 Ld Mildmay 32	1965-66 Mr C Collins 24	1984-85 Mr S Sherwood 30
1947-48 Ld Mildmay 22	1966-67 Mr C Collins 33	1985-86 Mr T Thomson Jones ... 25
1948-49 Ld Mildmay 30	1967-68 Mr R Tate 30	1986-87 Mr T Thomson Jones ... 19
1949-50 Ld Mildmay 38	1968-69 Mr R Tate 17	1987-88 Mr T Thomson Jones ... 15
1950-51 Mr P Chisman 13	1969-70 Mr M Dickinson 23	1988-89 Mr P Fenton 18
1951-52 Mr C Straker 19	1970-71 Mr J Lawrence 17	1989-90 Mr P McMahon 15
1952-53 Mr A H Moralee 22	1971-72 Mr W Foulkes 26	1990-91 Mr K Johnson 24
1953-54 Mr A H Moralee 22	1972-73 Mr R Smith 56	1991-92 Mr M P Hourigan 24
1954-55 Mr A H Moralee 16	1973-74 Mr A Webber 21	1992-93 Mr A Thornton 26
1955-56 Mr R McCreery 13	1974-75 Mr R Lamb 22	1993-94 Mr J Greenall 21
Mr A H Moralee 13	1975-76 Mr P Greenall 25	1994-95 Mr D Parker 16
1956-57 Mr R McCreery 23	Mr G Jones 25	1995-96 Mr J Culloty 40
1957-58 Mr J Lawrence 18	1976-77 Mr P Greenall 27	1996-97 Mr R Thornton 30
1958-59 Mr J Sutcliffe 18	1977-78 Mr G Sloan 23	1997-98 Mrs S Durack 41
1959-60 Mr G Kindersley 22	1978-79 Mr T G Dun 26	1998-99 Mr A Dempsey 47
1960-61 Sir W Pigott-Brown 28	1979-80 Mr O Sherwood 29	1999-00 Mr P Flynn 41
1961-62 Mr A Biddlecombe 30	1980-81 Mr P Webber 32	2000-01 Mr T Scudamore 24
1962-63 Sir W Pigott-Brown 20	1981-82 Mr D Browne 28	2001-02 Mr D Crosse 19
1963-64 Mr S Davenport 32	1982-83 Mr D Browne 33	2002-03 Mr C Williams 23

LEADING SIRES OVER JUMPS: 1985-2003

1985 Deep Run	1991-92 Deep Run	1998-99 Strong Gale
1986 Deep Run	1992-93 Deep Run	1999-00 Strong Gale
1987 Deep Run	1993-94 Strong Gale	2000-01 Be My Native (USA)
1988 Deep Run	1994-95 Strong Gale	2001-02 Be My Native (USA)
1989 Deep Run	1995-96 Strong Gale	2002-03 Be My Native (USA)
1989-90 Deep Run	1996-97 Strong Gale	
1990-91 Deep Run	1997-98 Strong Gale	

JOCKEY AGENTS

Jockeys Agents and their Contact Details

Agent	Telephone	Mobile	Fax
N M ADAMS	01488 72004/72964	07778 032906	
W ADAMS	01656 734416 welshwizard@wadams.fsbusiness.co.uk	07767 847025	01656 731915
D M BOOTH	01977 557167	07932 151933	
KEITH BRADLEY	01638 666350 keith.bradley2@ntlworld.com	07754 690050	
C D BROAD	01452 760482/447 c.j.broad@talk21.com	07836 622858	01452 760394
MRS RUTH BURCHELL	01495 352464	07816 450026	01495 302551
EDDIE BYRNE	00353 87205 1461	00353 87 2051461	
MATT CHAPMAN	01638 661576	07939 325286	01638 660293
MRS G S CHARNOCK	01653 695004/690097	07951 576912	
RAY COCHRANE	01223 812008	07798 651247	
R T DODDS	023 80222985	07952 226092	
S T DODDS	01273 487092	07974 924735	

Agent	Telephone	Mobile	Fax
SHIPPY ELLIS	01638 668484 shippy.jockeys@virgin.net	07860 864864	01638 660946
MISS F J ENEFER	01842 828049	07810 123446	
JOHN W FORD	01954 261122	07860 390904	01954 261565
SARAH GANDOLFO	01235 770552	07885 101540	
MARK GILCHRIST	01903 883356	07810 821787	
W P GRUNDY	01845 597850/597532 (2nd pref)	07973 817634	01845 597945
RICHARD A HALE	01768 886990/887320	07909 520542	
JOHN HAMNER	01235 762450	07715 565488	
ALAN HARRISON	01969 625006/623788	07740 530298	01969 625006
R T HARRISON	01325 732186/182		
MIKE HAWKETT	01844 202120	07836 206127	
TONY HIND	01923 264771	07779 208430	01638 723157
GAVIN HORNE	01823 661371	07833 697987	
RICHARD HUNTER	01262 670008	07801 248644	

Agent	Telephone	Mobile	Fax
L R JAMES	01653 699466	07947 414001	01653 691455
G D JEWELL	01672 861231 guy.jewel@talk21.com	07765 248859	01672 861231
J LEES	01306 888318	07711 972643	
G MACDONALD	01628 770766	07770 262686	
TERRY J NORMAN	01279 304844	07900 525033	01279 306304
G R OWEN	01638 669968 gareth.owen@ntlworld.com	0795 8335206	
DAVID A POLLINGTON	01751 477142	07850 015711	
DAVE ROBERTS	01737 761369	07860 234342	
B J ROBERTSON	01284 850805/850807	07860 235151	01284 850807
J B SIMPSON	01765 688535	07734 112941	
R W STUBBS	01653 698731	07747 613962/ 07801 167707 (car)	
S C TURNER	01782 327697 scott@jockeyagent.co.uk	07803 619968	
I P WARDLE	01761 453555	07831 865974	
JENNIFER WALSH	00353 87252 8025		

Agent	Telephone	Mobile	Fax
I P WARDLE	01761 453555	07831 865974	
A WATERWORTH	0113 2174396 trueprofessional2002@yahoo.co.uk	07968 911848	
L H WAY	01704 834488	07775 777494	
BOB WILLIAMS	01638 750032	07774 662278	

FLAT JOCKEYS

Riding weights and their contact details.
An Index of Agents appears on page 703

An Index of Agents appears on page 703

Name	Weight	Agent
AHERN, E	8-1	J Lees
ASHLEY, T	8-2	(01372) 386465
BADGER, MISS J	7-12	Richard Hunter
BAKER, G	8-9	Richard Hunter
BASTIMAN, H	9-7	D M Booth/(01423) 359397
BATCHELOR, M	9-0	Dave Roberts
BRAMHILL, J	7-12	Richard Hunter
BRISLAND, R	7-12	D M Booth
CALLAN, N	8-5	S T Dodds
CARROLL, J	8-4	Mrs L H Way
CARSON, S	8-2	Keith Bradley
CARTER, G	8-1	Shippy Ellis
CATLIN, C	7-12	N M Adams
CHIN, S	8-2	c/o (01969) 622237
CLARK, A	8-4	I P Wardle
COGAN, C	7-12	Richard Hunter
CULHANE, A	8-6	W P Gundry
DALGLEISH, K	8-4	Richard Hunter
DALY, A	8-0	G D Jewell
DARLEY, K	8-4	Terry Norman
DAVIES, S	8-0	c/o (01638) 663801
DAY, N	8-2	(0771) 911346
DETTORI, L	8-6	R Cochrane
DOBBS, P	8-4	Tony Hind
DOE, P	8-0	Mark Gilchrist
DOYLE, B	8-5	G D Jewell
DROWNE, S	8-4	I P Wardle
DUFFIELD, G	8-2	Keith Bradley/(01677) 450303
DURCAN, T	8-4	Mrs L H Way
DWYER, M	8-0	G R Owen
EDDERY, PAUL	8-2	(01488) 71632
EDMUNDS, J	8-2	Bob Williams/(01302) 719734
EDWARDS, J	9-5	(01534) 482666
EGAN, J	8-1	I P Wardle
FALLON, K	8-7	David A Pollington
FANNING, J	8-1	W P Gundry
FAULKNER, G	8-3	Alan Harrison/(01638) 663984
FENTON, M	8-5	Keith Bradley
FESSEY, P	7-12	Richard Hale
FFRENCH, R	8-0	Richard Hale
FITZPATRICK, R	8-2	Alan Harrison
FITZSIMONS, P	8-0	G D Jewell
FORTUNE, J	8-6	Tony Hind
FOWLE, J	7-12	I P Wardle
GADSBY, J P	8-5	c/o (01638) 663193
GIBBONS, G	8-0	Mrs L H Way
GIBSON, D	7-12	W P Gundry/(07970) 149415
GOODE, P	8-2	(01884) 839363
GREAVES, MISS A	8-12	(01845) 501470
HALLIDAY, V	8-4	L R James
HANAGAN, P	7-13	Richard Hale
HANNON, G	8-5	R T Dodds
HARKER, MRS J	7-12	c/o (01969) 624507
HARTLEY, MISS A	7-12	c/o 01772 812780
HAVLIN, R	8-4	I P Wardle
HENRY, M	7-12	G D Jewell
HILLS, M	8-4	B J Robertson
HILLS, R	8-4	B J Robertson
HIND, G	8-2	(01638) 561096
HOLLAND, D	8-5	Matt Chapman

APPRENTICES

Their employers and contact details.
An Index of Agents appears on page 703

O'NEILL, B (M Channon).. 8-0
O'REILLY, J (J O'Reilly)... 7-13
ORMONDROYD, B (Dean Ivory).................................. 7-3
PARSONS, MISS A (A M Balding)................................ 7-5
PARSONS, S (M P Tregoning).................................... 8-0
PEIPPO, MISS K (B G Powell)..................................... 7-7
PIERREPONT, K (R Guest)... 8-0
PIKE, MISS L (W J Musson)..................................... 7-12
PLANK, C (J R Poulton).. 7-6
POLLI, N (M G Quinlan).. 7-6
POOLE, C (Michael Bell)... 7-12
POSTE, C (R A Fahey).. 8-0
POULTON, H (G L Moore).. 8-4
QUINN, A (G L Moore)... 8-2
REID, MISS S (L A Perratt).................................... 7-11
REILLY, A (K R Burke)... 7-13
REILLY, B (S Williams)... 7-13
REYNOLDS, MISS L (J S Moore).............................. 7-7
ROBERTS, A (G L Moore)... 8-3
ROCHE, MISS C (D Nicholls)................................... 7-3
RUTTER, A (W J Musson)... 8-0
SAUNDERS, M (B R Millman).................................... 8-5
SAVAGE, M (N E Berry).. 8-2
SAYER, MISS S (R Hollinshead)............................ 7-10
SCALLAN, P (B J Curley)... 8-4
SEWELL, C (S Kirk).. 8-6
SMITH, MISS H (N Littmoden)................................. 7-5
STAINTON, M (B Smart)... 7-8
STAMP, D (K R Burke).. 8-0
STEVENSON, J (R F Marvin)..................................... 8-3
STRETTON, MISS C (Mrs Nerys Dutfield)................. 8-3
STUBBS, MISS K (G Margarson)............................... 7-7
SWARBRICK, B (M Brisbourne)................................ 7-5
SWIFT, D (R Fahey)... 8-0
SWIFT, L (J S Wainwright).................................... 7-13
THOMAS, P (Mrs A L M King).................................... 8-0
THOMAS, R (G B Balding)... 7-7
TREADWELL, L (D Nicholls)..................................... 8-0
TUCKER, J (William R Muir)..................................... 8-0
TUDHOPE, D (D Carroll)... 8-0
TURNER, MISS H (Michael Bell)............................... 7-7
VARLEY, P (J Balding)... 7-5
WAITE, M (J Toller)... 8-0
WAKENSHAW, D (P C Haslam)................................. 8-3
WATSON, B (I Semple).. 8-0
WATSON, MISS D (D Shaw)..................................... 7-12
WEBB, A (M C Chapman).. 7-7
WEBSTER, MISS J (Don Enrico Incisa)................... 7-11
WILEMAN, MISS S (C N Kellett)............................... 8-4
WILLIAMS, C (P F I Cole)...................................... 7-12
WILLIAMS, D (G C H Chung)..................................... 7-5
WISHART, B (A P Jarvis).. 7-5
WORRELL, M (Sir Mark Prescott)............................. 8-2
YOURSTON, S (P Blockley)...................................... 7-5

Mark Gilchrist
c/o (01226) 711123
c/o (01923) 855337
(01635) 298210
c/o (01488) 73300
c/o (01488) 638433
Bob Williams
(01638) 663371
c/o (01273) 300127
c/o (01638) 603530
c/o (01638) 666567
Richard Hale
R T Dodds
c/o (01273) 620106
c/o (01292) 266232
Alan Harrison
G D Jewell/(01296) 625716
(01488) 648822
c/o (01273) 620405
(01845) 501470
(01638) 663371
c/o (01749) 841011
Mark Gilchrist
c/o (01543) 490298
c/o (01638) 668755
c/o (01488) 73215
c/o (01638) 663375
(01845) 597481
Alan Harrison
c/o (01636) 814481
R T Harrison
R W Studds
Richard Hunter
Richard Hale
c/o (01653) 658537
c/o (01793) 815009
I P Wardle
Mark Gilchrist/(01845) 501470
(01488) 73098
Alan Harrison
Richard Hunter
Bob Williams
c/o (01638) 668918
c/o (01969) 624351
c/o (01555) 773335
c/o (01444) 456566
(01673) 843663
c/o (01969) 640653
c/o (01283) 226046
c/o (01488) 638433
Mark Gilchrist/(01638) 664348
(01235) 851341
(07780) 664503/(01638) 662117
c/o (01636) 819082

JUMPS JOCKEYS

Riding weights and their contact details
An Index of Agents appears on page 703

Jockey	Weight	Contact
AIZPURU, X.	10-0	L R James
ASPELL, L.	10-0	N M Adams/(01903) 893323/(0797) 1675127
BASTIMAN, H	10-0	D M Booth/(01423) 359397
BATCHELOR, M	10-0	Dave Roberts
BRADBURNE, M	10-0	L R James/(01337) 810325 (07773) 327377
COOPER, L	10-0	c/o (01386) 584209
COYLE, A	10-0	L R James
CROWLEY, B J	10-0	Dave Roberts
CROWLEY, J	10-0	Richard Hale/(01274) 564930
CULLOTY, J	10-0	C D Broad
CURRAN, S	10-0	W Adams
DEMPSEY, A	10-0	Richard Hale/(01969) 622750
DENNIS, D	10-0	C D Broad
DOBBIN, A	10-0	Richard Hale
DOWLING, W	10-0	Richard Hale
DOYLE, T	10-0	Dave Roberts
DUFFIELD, G	10-0	Keith Bradley/(01677) 450303
DURACK, S	10-0	Dave Roberts
EARLE, S	11-0	(01672) 861157
EDWARDS, M	10-0	(01534) 482666
FEHILY, N	10-0	C D Broad
FENTON, B	10-0	Dave Roberts
FITZGERALD, M A	10-5	Dave Roberts/(01235) 751695/(07771) 768368
FLYNN, P	10-0	Dave Roberts/(01782) 327697/(07803) 619968
FOLEY, M	10-0	Dave Roberts/(07884) 054921
FOX, S	10-4	L R James/(07887) 943041 (0468) 737575
GARRITTY, R	10-7	G MacDonald
BRUCE GIBSON, B	10-0	Richard Hale
GICQUEL, B	10-0	G Macaire 0033 6088 31272
GOLDSTEIN, J	10-0	L R James
GREENE, R	10-0	L R James/(01323) 509086
HARDING, B	10-0	Richard Hale
HIDE, P	10-0	L R James/(01903) 877323/(07768) 233324
HITCHCOTT, B	10-0	Dave Roberts/(07881) 633099
HOLLEY, P	10-3	(01297) 553560
HOURIGAN, P	10-4	(045) 530080
HUSBAND, E	10-0	(01453) 490298/(0831) 330265
JARDINE, I	10-3	Alan Harrison
JOHNSON, K	10-0	Richard Hunter/(01388) 721813/(01926) 74464
JOHNSON, R	10-0	Dave Roberts
LEE, G	10-0	Richard Hale/(01642) 763500/(07885) 888020
LLEWELLYN, C	10-0	C D Broad/(07236) 783223
MAGUIRE, J M	10-2	Dave Roberts
MARSTON, W	10-0	C D Broad/(01451) 821553/(07831) 664745
MCCARTHY, J	10-0	L R James/(07860) 905017
MCCORMACK, C	10-0	Richard Hale/(07710) 195536
MCCOY, A P	10-0	Dave Roberts
MCGRATH, R.	10-0	Richard Hale/(07775) 680895
MCNAMARA, J P	10-2	Dave Roberts
MCPHAIL, O	10-0	L R James
MITCHELL, MISS S	10-0	(01672) 540863
MOGFORD, J	10-0	Dave Roberts/(01451) 810165/(07808) 799959
MOLONEY, P	10-0	C D Broad
MURPHY, T J	10-0	C D Broad/(07866) 681565
NAUGHTON, M	10-0	L R James/(01653) 699466
O'CONNOR, T	10-0	R T Harrison
OLIVER, H	10-0	Richard Hale
O'MEARA, D	10-0	Richard Hale
PROCTER, A	10-0	(07919) 521773
RAFTER, C	10-0	L R James/07919 008041

RENWICK, K	10-0	Richard Hale
RICOU, J	10-0	0033 6804 19253
ROSS, A	10-0	Richard Hale
RUSSELL, D	10-5	Richard Hale
SCHOLES, A	10-0	G MacDonald
SCUDAMORE, T	10-0	Dave Roberts/(07809) 131121
SIDDALL, T	10-0	Dave Roberts
SLATTERY, V	10-0	(01242) 820907/(07831) 545789
STRONGE, S	10-0	L R James/(07775) 727 778
THORNTON, A	10-2	Dave Roberts/(07831) 102065
THORNTON, R	10-0	Dave Roberts
TIZZARD, J	10-0	Dave Roberts
VERCO, D	10-4	Miss L V Davis/(01785) 284371
WALSH, R	10-4	Jennifer Walsh
YOUNG, R	10-0	L R James

Are your contact details missing or incorrect?
If so please update us by email: simon.turner@mgn.co.uk
or leave a message on 0500 007071

CONDITIONALS

Their employers and contact details.
An Index of Agents appears on page 703

ASPELL, P (Mrs M. Reveley)	9-7	Richard Hale
BAILEY, T (J R Jenkins)	9-12	c/o (01673) 241141
BALFOUR, T (M C Pipe)	10-0	c/o (01884) 840715
BARBER, L (J A Supple)	9-12	W Adams
BERRIDGE, G (L. Lungo)	9-7	Richard Hale/(01387) 840361/(07970) 041568
BERRIDGE, L (L. Lungo)	9-7	c/o (01387) 840361
BEST, T (G B Balding)	10-7	Dave Roberts/(01264) 772278
BIDDLECOMBE, R (N. A. Twiston-Davies)	10-7	C D Broad
BOLGER, C (Miss A. Newton-Smith)	10-0	N M Adams/(01273) 300127
BRENNAN, P (P J Hobbs)	9-7	C D Broad
BRIMBLE, A (A Crook)	9-7	(01969) 640303
BUCHANAN, P (H Johnson)	9-7	Richard Hale
BUNSELL, J (M Bradstock)	9-10	(01235) 760780
BURKE, K M F (C. Tizzard)	9-7	c/o (01963) 250598
BURTON-PYE, T (P Haslam)	9-7	(01969) 624351
BYRNE, J (H Daly)	9-10	Dave Roberts/(07974) 262246
CARENZA, G (M W Easterby)	10-0	Richard Hale/(01228) 675376
CARTER, N (I Williams)	9-7	Dave Roberts
CLARE, J (P Beaumont)	9-10	c/o (01347) 888208
COOPER, E (Jonjo O'Neill)	9-7	c/o (01386) 277202
COSGRAVE, D (B. De Haan)	9-7	(01488) 72163
COSTELLO, D (Mrs M. Reveley)	9-2	Richard Hale
CRAINE, S (C Mann)	9-7	C D Broad
CROSSE, D (C Mann)	9-7	Dave Roberts/(07775) 920489
CRAWFORD S J (J Osborne)	9-7	(01488) 73139
DAVIES, J (B G Powell)	9-7	L R James
DAY, A (G. L. Moore)	10-0	c/o (01273) 620106
DEADY, M (N Chance)	9-7	A Waterworth/(07814) 325607/(01488) 73436
EDDERY, C (A Swinbank)	9-12	L R James
ELLIOTT, J (M C Pipe)	9-9	c/o (01884) 840715
ELLIOTT, S (G. B. Balding)	9-7	Richard Hunter/(01264) 772278
ELSWORTH, D (Mrs S. Smith)	9-11	Richard Hale
EVANS, A (N. A. Twiston-Davies)	9-7	C D Broad/(07789) 936986
FLAVIN, J (K C. Bailey)	9-13	L R James/(01327 361733)
FLAVIN, R (B De Haan)	9-11	L R James
GRAY, T (J. R. Best)	9-7	(01622) 880276
GREENWAY, T (Mrs H Dalton)	9-7	c/o (01952) 730322
GRIFFITHS, P (Miss K George)	10-0	Gavin Horne
HANNITY, N (G A Harker)	10-0	Richard Hale
HAROLD, D (K A Morgan)	9-5	c/o (01664) 464711
HARRIS, D (J R Jenkins)	9-7	c/o (01673) 241141
HOBSON, R (Mrs J Candish)	9-12	L R James
HOGAN, K (Jonjo O'Neill)	9-7	c/o (01386) 584209
HONEYBALL, A (P F Nicholls)	9-12	Dave Roberts/(07815) 898569
HONOUR, C (J D Frost)	9-10	L R James/(01653) 699466/(0777) 1861219
HOPKINS, A (M D Hammond)	9-7	(01969) 625223
HOUSTON, F (Mrs S Smith)	9-7	A Waterworth
HUTCHINSON, W (A King)	9-11	C D Broad/(01793) 815009
JONES, W (Jonjo O'Neill)	9-7	c/o (01386) 584209
KARNICNIK, S (S Gollings)	9-7	c/o (01507) 343204
KAVANAGH, N (M C Pipe)	9-7	Gavin Horne
KEANE, V (B Ellison)	10-7	Richard Hale
KENNEDY, W (N Chance)	9-7	c/o (01488) 73436
KING, F (Mrs M. Reveley)	10-0	Richard Hale
KOZAK, O (O. Sherwood)	9-7	G D Jewell/(07766) 735536
LAVERTY, D (N J G Gifford)	9-7	L R James/(01905) 697061
LUCEY-BUTLER, R (P. Butler)	9-7	(01273) 880124
MACKENZIE, R (I Williams)	9-7	Chris Board
MADDEN, P (Mrs S Smith)	9-7	c/o (01274) 564930

MCGANN, D (D W Thompson)	9-7	(07834) 005415
MCNALLY, R (P F Nicholls)	10-0	L R James/(07958) 475171
MELLO, M (J R Upson)	9-10	C D Broad/(01327) 860043
MOORE, J (M C Pipe)	9-7	Dave Roberts
MULHOLLAND, N (F Murphy)	9-9	c/o (01969) 622289
MURPHY B (B J Curley)	10-0	W Adams
MURRAY, C (J F Panvert)	9-9	L R James
NICOLLS, M (M. Harris)	9-7	L R James
NOLAN, D (P Blockley)	9-7	c/o (01636) 819082
O'KEEFFE, A (Miss V M Williams)	9-7	Dave Roberts
O'NEILL, P (T R George)	9-10	c/o (01452) 814267
ORDE-POWLETT, B (G. M. Moore)	9-7	Alan Harrison
OWEN, MISS Z (T R George)	9-7	(07866) 460939
PHELAN, T (Jonjo O'Neill)	9-7	Dave Roberts
POGSON, A (J R Cornwall)	9-7	L R James/(07977) 734139
POULTON, H (G L Moore)	9-7	c/o (01273) 620405
PRENDERGAST, K (M Scudamore)	10-0	c/o (01989) 750844
PRITCHARD, J (R Dickin)	9-7	S C Turner/(01789) 450052
QUINTIN, J (P G Murphy)	10-0	c/o (01488) 648473
RICHARDS, G (J. G. M. O'Shea)	9-9	L R James
ROBSON, P (N G. Richards)	10-0	Richard Hale/(01450) 376886/(07789) 403404
RYAN, J (Mrs S Smith)	9-7	c/o (01274) 564930
SHARKEY, C (F Murphy)	9-7	Richard Hale
SMITH, M (G Prodroumou)	9-9	(01953) 717224
SPATE, R (R Guest)	9-10	Richard Hale
STEPHENS, L (D. R. Gandolfo)	9-12	c/o (01235) 763242
STRETTON, MISS C (W G M Turner)	9-7	c/o (01963) 220523
SUPPLE, G (M. C. Pipe)	10-0	L R James
THOMAS, G (N G Richards)	9-7	(07775) 93362/(01768) 88699
THOMAS, S (Miss V Williams)	9-7	Dave Roberts
WINKLER A (N J Henderson)	9-7	Dave Roberts/(07812) 134077
TLEY, R (F Murphy)	9-7	Richard Hale
VICKERS, L (J. S. Wainwright)	9-11	L R James
WALFORD, R (R. Alner)	9-9	Dave Roberts/(07900) 935781/(01258) 818117
WALSH, B (Mrs M. Reveley)	9-7	c/o (01287) 650456
WHELAN, P (R. A. Fahey)	9-11	Richard Hale
WILEMAN, MISS S (C. N. Kellett)	9-7	c/o (01283) 226046
WILLIAMS, C R (P F Nicholls)	9-11	Dave Roberts/(07815) 774306
WORTHINGTON, W (Ian Williams)	9-12	C D Broad

Foaling dates are shown for two-year-olds
where these are provided, and the purchase
price (in guineas) as a yearling.

AMATEUR RIDERS

Riding weights and contact details.
An Index of Agents appears on page 703

ADAMS, A R 9-0 ....
AITCHISON, S R 10-2 ....
ALERS-HANKEY, D 11-9 ....(07811) 335979
ALEXANDER, A A 9-7 ....
ALEXANDER, J F 11-0 ....(0131) 3328850
ALLAN, MISS LOUISE 9-0
ALLISON, MISS J 10-0 ....(01488) 73656
ANGELL, D 10-0 ....
ARMITAGE, MISS A 9-0 ....
ARMSON, R 10-7 ....(01332) 865293
ARNOLD, MISS S N 8-10 ....
ARTHUR, F 9-10 ....(07815) 057729
BAGGALEY, MISS C 8-6..
BAINES, G 9-7 ....
BALDOCK, M 10-0 ....(07796) 260429
BANDEY, R J 11-0 ....
BANKS, JAMES BYRON 8-10 ....
BARBER, M 10-2 ....D M Booth/
...............................(01437) 763772/(07977) 778172
BARFOOT-SAUNT, G 10-7 ....
BARLOW, A M E 11-0 ....
BARLOW, J R 11-0 ....
BARNES, J 10-0 ....(07763) 384169
BARNETT, MISS A L 8-7..
BARR, MISS V G 10-7 ....
BARRETT, RAY 9-7 ....
BARRETT, RICHARD 10-7 ....
BARTLEY, G J 9-0..
BASHTON, MISS D M 8-3 ....
BASTIMAN, MISS R 9-7 ....(01423) 359397
BATES, LEE 10-5 ....(01429) 837087
BEDDOES, MISS S 9-0 ....c/o (01273) 620106
BELL, MRS D 7-7..
BENSTEAD, N R 10-12 ....
BERRY, A J 10-0...
BERRY, MRS M L 9-12 ....
BEST, JAMES 9-7 ....
BEST, MRS L A 10-0 ....
BEST, T G 9-7 ....
BEVAN, MISS A 8-7 ....(01531) 634846
BEVIS, R N 10-5 ....(01948) 770427
BISSESSUR, S 9-0...
BLOOM, N M 11-4 ....
BOSLEY, MRS S J 9-0 ....(01367) 820115/
....(07778) 938040
BOYD, MISS H L 7-10 ....
BOYNTON, J E 10-5 ....
BRADBURNE, MISS L 9-4 ....(01337) 810325
BRAITHWAITE, A J 10-0..
BRAMLEY, MISS F H 8-7 ....
BREWER, G C 10-12 ....(01653) 648166
BREWER, MISS L J 8-10..........................(07974) 765506
BRIDGES, MISS L H DOVETON 8-8....(01747) 852825
BRINT, M 9-10 ....(01534) 481461
BRITTON, MISS M 8-12 ....
BROOKE, A D 10-3 ....
BROOKE, MISS L R 9-0...
BROTHERTON, MISS S 9-0 ....c/o (01653) 618620
BROWN, A C 9-7 ....(01544) 267322
BROWN, MISS F C 9-0.............................(01638) 577470

BRYAN, MISS H G 8-12 ....
BUCK, MISS J M 10-0 ....
BULL, MISS M J 9-0 ....(01636) 816717
BULL, MR P ....(01634) 235253
BURROWS, M 9-13 ....(07773) 317775
BURROWS, T J 9-7 ....
BURTON, R P L 10-10 ....(01743) 709697
BUXTON, JOHN 11-0 ....
COLLINSON, R E 9-7 ....
CALLAGHAN, P G 9-7 ....
CALLAGHAN, S A 10-0 ....(01638) 664040
CAMPBELL, M T P 9-5...
CARRY, P M 10-0 ....
CARTER, M R 10-0 ....
CASSIDY, MISS S C 9-0 ....(07985) 296945
CAVE, MISS T C 9-0 ....
CHARLES-JONES, MR A 10-0 ....(01993) 823265
CHAPMAN, N A B 10-0 ....
CHILTON, MISS K N 9-12 ....(01743) 741536
CLARE, J E 9-10...
CLARK, R S 11-5 ....(01347) 810700/
....(07989) 805873
....(01327) 860043
CLEARY, A 9-7 ....
CLEMENTS, MISS H A 9-3 ....
CLUBB, MRS H 8-12 ....
COE, A R 10-6 ....
COLE, O N I 10-6 ....
COLLIER, TJADE 8-2...
COLLINGTON, P 8-12 ....(07946) 516070
COLLINS, C M P 9-0..
COLLINSON, R E 10-2 ....
COLTHERD, W S 11-0 ....
COOGAN, V L 10-0 ....(01488) 73065/
....(07977) 236699

COOK, D R 9-7 ....
COOK, J R F 10-0 ....(01281) 690864
CORNFORTH, P J 11-7 ....
COTTRILL, MISS V L 9-0 ....(01829) 760095
COUMBE, M A 8-3 ....
COURIER, MISS L A 9-0...
COURNANE, J K 10-2..
COWARD, MISS J M 9-3...
COWLEY, P E 10-4 ....(07775) 943346
CRAGGS, T G 9-0...................................(01740) 620239
CROSS, S P B 9-12...
CROW, A H 11-10 ....
CULLIGAN, K T 9-7 ....(01403) 700911
CULLY, C J 9-12 ....
CUMANI, MISS F 9-11 ....c/o (01638) 665432
CUMANI, MISS S D 9-6............................c/o (01638) 665432
CUMMINGS, R 9-7 ....
CUTHBERT, MISS H E 9-0 ....(01228) 560822
D'ARCY, MISS RACHEL EMMA 8-0.......................
DA SILVA, D B B 10-0 ....(01887) 830354
DAINTON, MISS DOMINIQUE 8-10..........................
DAVIDSON, J T 10-4 ....
DAVIDSON, MISS R P 9-0 ....(01488) 648077
DAVIES, C J 8-10 ....
DAVIES, C W 9-1 ....

HARDISTY, G W 10-9.....................................

HARLER, MISS S E 8-13...................................

HARRIS, MRS A 10-2..

HARRIS, G P 9-0...

HARRIS, M C M 10-10......................................

HARRIS, NEIL J 10-7..

HARRISON, MISS K C 8-4...................Alan Harrison

HARRISON, S 9-0...

HARRISON, MISS T S 9-4...................................

HARVEY, M J 9-0 .... (01638) 66457/(01638) 662117

HARWOOD, MISS L J 8-7...................(01798) 873011

HASLAM, B M R 10-10....................c/o (01969) 624351

HATFIELD, MISS F J 9-7....................................

HAYNES, M Y 9-7...........................(01372) 722664

HAYNES, M F 9-5............................(01793) 762437

HEARN, MISS P M 8-0......................(01269) 850805/
(07747) 056917

HENNESSY, MR R 10-0......................(045) 521490

HICKS, L W 11-4.............................(07961) 1557720

HICKS-LITTLE, MISS E M 8-7..............................

HILL, MRS J M 9-0...

HILL, MISS V J 8-11...

HILLS, MRS K M 9-0...

HISLOP, MISS L 9-7...

HODGES, R J 10-3..

HODGSON, MISS G 8-10....................................

HOLLANDS, MISS J M 10-7.................................

HOLLEY, MRS D 8-0..

HOLMES, MISS J F 9-10.....................................

HOPE, MISS A K 9-7..

HORN, MISS RUTH ALISON 10-0..........................

HORNER, MISS L V 9-3......................(01235) 835888/
(01488) 638636

HORSFALL, MISS L J 7-12..................................

HOWELL, MRS R 10-10......................................

HUGHES, MISS J A 9-7......................................

HUGHES, S M 10-0...........................(01829) 760095

HUMPHREY, A R 10-10.......................................

HURLEY, MISS C R 9-7......................................

HUTCHINSON, MISS A L 9-2-2............(01638) 577288

HUTCHINSON, MR D 9-2.....................(01372) 721490

HUTSBY, F A 11-0.............................(01789) 740241

ILLMAN, MR R 9-0.............................(01428) 722528

IRVING, MISS H M O 10-0...................................

IRVING, S A 9-10..

JACOB, D A 9-10..

JACKSON, MISS T 9-7.......................................

JACKSON, MRS V S 10-0....................(01830) 530218

JARVIS, P J 10-0..

JEFFORD, L D B 10-0.........................(01884) 35839/
(01884) 266320

JENKINS, J A 10-2..

JENKINS, M C 11-4............................Dave Roberts

JESSOP, MISS C 7-12........................(01638) 667870

JEWELL, MISS K C 8-10......................(01622) 842788

JEWETT, D J 11-0..............................(01768) 484649

JOHNSON, S M 9-7...

JOHNSON, P 10-9.............................(091) 2674464

JOHNSON HOUGHTON, MISS E A 9-7...(01235) 850500/
(07721) 622700

JOHNSON HOUGHTON, G F 10-7..........................

JONES, ADAM M E 9-9.......................................

JONES, D 11-0................................(07831) 641434

JONES, MISS E J 9-3.........................Mrs Ruth Burchell

KEDDY, MRS H E 8-2.........................(07710) 450982

KEITH, MISS L D 8-0..........................(01372) 721490

KELLEWAY, MISS S G 7-12..................(01638) 664292

KEMP, D J 11-0..

KENDALL, MISS B 9-5..

KENDALL, MISS L 10-0.......................................

KENT, J N 10-4..

KERR, G R 11-1..

KINCHIN, H J 10-0..

KING, B A 9-10.......................L R James/(01865) 361260

KING, F F 10-0.................................(01768) 982291/
(07909) 520542

KING, J A 9-9..................................(01974) 640532

KING, J J 9-12.................................(01403) 700911

KING, N B 10-2..

KING, MRS M J 9-0...

KINGTON, J R 9-0...

KINSELLA, P D 9-10..........................(07970) 673351

KIRKBRIDE, P 8-0...

KNAPP, MISS L A 9-0...

KNOTT, A C W 10-7..

KWIATKOWSKI, J W 11-8....................................

LEAHY, MISS S. J. 8-8.......................(063) 90676

LAMB, MISS S K 9-7..........................(01665) 720251

LANGLEY, R G 10-4...........................(07866) 532722

LE BROCQ, J 9-13.............................(01534) 481461

LEON PENATE, E 9-6...

LEWIS, D W 9-10..

LEWIS-PRICE, MISS D A 9-0................(01488) 72324

LIDDIARD, MRS S A 8-10....................(07887) 991292

LILLY, MISS Z E 8-12...

LINDSAY, T M 10-9...

LITTMODEN, MISS E P 9-2..................(01638) 663375

LLEWELLYN, J L 10-5........................(0685) 841259/
(0685) 843467

LOUGHRAN, MR R 10-0......................(045) 521490

LOWE, D J 9-7...

LUFF, D 11-0..................................(01934) 733341

LURCOCK, M J 10-9..

LUND, B V 10-0...

MACKLEY, M R 10-4..

MACLEAN, MISS S L 8-10...................................

MACTAGGART, J 11-07......................(01450) 860314

MALONE, T J 9-5..............................Dave Roberts

MANN, P R 10-4...

MANN, MRS S M 9-3 .....c/o (01488) 73118/71717

MANSELL, D 10-4...

MARCH, J 9-7..

MARSHALL, MISS J E 8-12..................................

MARTIN, L 8-12...

MASKILL, A P 9-6...

MASON, P W 10-12...

MASTORAS, C 9-10...

MAXSE, J J I 9-12..

MACTAGGART, MR J 11-07.................(01450) 860314

MCALISTER, M J 10-2........................Richard Hale/
(01387) 840361/(0774) 5954000

MCCARTHY, MISS M A 9-4...................................

MCCARTHY, R I 10-4...

MCCAVANA, C 10-0..........................(01488) 71411

MCCOURT, T M 9-6...........................(01235) 867453/
(01451) 850182

MCCUBBIN, D R 10-0(01748) 825272/(07970) 982338

MCGEORGE, S D 9-5.........................(01638) 663375

MCGLINCHEY, B J 10-0......................................

MCGRATH, L R 9-7............................Richard Hale

MCHUGH, S S 11-0...........................(07904) 089322

MCINTOSH, MISS L S 8-7....................................

MCKEE, N B 10-2...

MCKIM, B L 10-2...

MCKIM, MISS N A 9-7..

MCLAUGHLIN, MR W 10-0...................(01515) 200299

MCSHANE, J A 9-4 ....
MEAD, J H 10-8 ....
MEAKINS, MISS A M 10-0 ....
MERCER, K J 9-7 ....Richard Hale
MERRIAM, A G L 11-7 ....
MESSENGER, T H 9-7 ....(07977) 279026
METCALFE, MISS C 10-0 ....(0191) 3736277
MICHAEL, CAPT A H L 10-10 ....
MIDDLETON, A 11-0 ....
MILLMAN, J R 8-10 ....(01884) 266620
MILNE, MISS C P 9-0 ....(01403) 700911
MINTON, MISS R P 9-7 ....
MITCHELL, N R 11-4 ....(01258) 880633
MOLLHALL, MRS S 9-7 ....(01638) 668503
MOONEY, MISS C H 9-0 ....
MOORE, J E 9-3 ....c/o (01884) 840715
MOORE, MRS NICOLA JANE 9-0 ....
MOORE, MRS S J 8-0 ....(01488) 648822
MOORE, N P 10-7 ....
MOREAN, MR J 10-0 ....
MORGAN, J J 9-7 ....(01403) 700911
MORGAN, L 9-7 ....(07813) 944107
MORGAN-EVANS, R D E 9-12 ....
MORGAN-MURPHY, MISS Z M 9-8 ....
MORRIS, MRS M A 8-10 ....(01400) 273930/
                                                      (07702) 719902
MORRIS, R C 9-0 ....
MORRIS, S W 10-7 ....(07771) 922808
MOULSON, L M F 9-3 ....(07789) 681512
MUIR, J F W 12-0 ....
MULHALL, MRS C A 10-9 ....
MULHALL, MRS S M 9-0 ....(01904) 691510
MULLINEAUX, MISS M J L 8-7 ....(01829) 261440
MURPHY, B 10-0 ....
MURPHY, M 11-9 ....
MUSGRAVE, C B 10-2 ....
NASH, J 10-7 ....(086) 8259787
NEALE, MR B 10-0 ....(01905) 381077
NEEDHAM, MRS F E 9-7 ....(01638) 750546
NELMES, O J 9-4 ....L R James
NEWBOLD, J D 10-0 ....(01327) 361733
NEWMAN, E 9-0 ....
NEWNES, L A 9-3 ....R T Harrison/(07879) 630324
NOSWORTHY, MISS C C 8-5 ....(07971) 106044
O'BRIEN, MISS D J E 9-5 ....
O'DONOGHUE, D E 9-0 ....(07900) 477863
O'KEEFFE, A CH 9-5 ....(01969) 622289/
                                             625006/(0776) 1106485
OLIVER, NICHOLAS HENRY 10-12 ....
OWEN, J P 10-4 ....
OWEN, MRS S J 8-9 ....
PAGE, A 10-12 ....(01638) 664669
PAGE, D J 10-0 ....
PAINTER, D W 10-0 ....
PATTINSON, M I 8-12 ....(01372) 748800
PAYTER, L R 9-7 ....(01327) 860043
PEARCE, S 7-10 ....(01638) 664669
PEARCE, N A 9-4 ....D M Booth
PEARSON, K D 10-0 ....
PEARSON, M J 9-7 ....
PEBODY, D M 9-7 ......(01295) 750807/(07909) 834113
PEMBERTON, J 9-7 ....(01273) 479183
PEOPLES, B O 9-10 ....
PERRY, MISS S J 9-0 ....
PETERS, J F 9-0 ....
PETTITT, N J 10-0 ....
PEWTER, G R 10-2 ....
PHILLIPS, N J 10-10 ....

PHIZACKLEA, MISS S J 9-0 ....
PICKARD, MISS F I 8-0 ....
PIDCOCK, MISS D M 7-8 ....
PITMAN, MISS T 8-0 ....
PLEDGE, MISS J A 8-8 ....(01638) 663371
POLLOCK, B N 10-7 ....
POOLES, R L 10-0 ...(01488) 73032/(07977) 099953
POULTON, H 9-7 ....(01273) 300127
POWELL, MRS R A 9-0 ....
PRENDERGAST, K M 9-10 ....
PRICE, A S O 9-5 ....(07771) 608475
PRICE, MRS C J 9-4 ....
PRICE, MISS V J 9-7 ....
PRITCHARD-GORDON, P A 10-5 ....
PRITCHARD, J D 8-10 ....(01789) 450052
PRITCHARD, J M 11-0 ....
PRITCHARD, DR P L J 9-9 ....(01453) 811881/
                                                      (01453) 811989
PRITCHARD, MISS S 9-0 ....
PROCTER, MISS S 8-7 ....
PURDY, MISS A. J. 9-0 ....(01823) 350311/
                                                      (07970) 803706
QUAYLE, MISS K G 8-0 ....(01235) 835888
QUINTIN, J S 9-7 ....
QUIRK, S P 10-7 ....
RAMSAY, W B 11-10 ....
RAMSDEN, MISS E L 8-7 ....c/o (01845) 587226
REES, J 9-12 ....(01635) 281678
REES, MISS J M 9-0 ....(01488) 639100/
                                                      (07881) 821500
REES, S P 8-10 ....(01638) 577470
RENWICK, MISS S L 8-0 ....
RICH, W D 9-11 ....
RICHARDSON, J A 10-4 ....(0498) 584711
RIDING, MISS J E 9-0 ....
RIMELL, M G 10-7 ....(01451) 820819/(07778) 648303
ROCKEY, MISS K C 9-8 ....(01743) 741536
ROBERTS, MRS M S 9-7 ....(01305) 761745/
                                                      (07803) 752831
ROBINSON, STUART COLGATE 12-0 ....
ROBINSON, MISS S E 9-7 ....
ROBINSON, S J 11-0 ....
ROBSON, MISS P 9-3 ....(01830) 530241,
                                   (01484) 608000/(07721) 887489
RODDA, M G 10-0 ....
RODDICK, MISS C 9-7 ....(773) 4543439
ROE, M I 9-7 ....
ROSS, R B 10-7 ....
ROSS, S I 10-5 ....
ROTHERY, MISS A C 7-5 ....
ROWSELL, MRS L A 10-0 ....(07814) 148932
RUSSELL, MISS K 10-0 ....
RUTTY, MISS L A 8-0 ....(01969) 640330
SAINT, M C 8-4 ....
SALAMAN, M B 10-0 ....(01672) 541048/
                                                      (01488) 72324
SAMWORTH, MISS S L 9-0 ....(01235) 751507
SANDERCOCK, MISS M-A 8-2 ....
SANSOME, A D 11-2 ....
SANTANA, K 10-0 ....
SAVILLE, N S 10-7 ....
SCALES, M N 9-7 ....
SCHERER, MISS M J 9-0 ....(07740) 255588/
                                   (01302) 539090/(01638) 661999
SCOTT, MISS E L 9-0 ....
SCRASE, MRS A M 8-10 ....
SEARBY, MISS K E 9-7 ....
SESTON, M 9-12 ....Richard Hale

SHARKEY, C D 9-7 ....(01984) 640419,
..................................(01884) 860225/(07980) 913121
SHARRATT, MISS S 10-4 ....(07966) 467879
SHAW, B T 10-10 ....
SHEEN, MISS L J 9-0 ....(07788) 122942
SHENKIN, MISS S I 10-0 ....(01398) 332077
SHERWOOD, MISS N E 8-4 ....
SIMMS, D A 9-10 ....
SKIDMORE, MISS N E 8-4 ....
SMART, MRS V R 9-0 ....(01845) 597481/
....(07780) 673520
SMITH, MISS A J 9-7 ....
SMITH, MISS K L 8-7 ....
SMITH, N M 9-7 ....
SNOWDEN, J E 10-8 ....
SOARES, N M 8-10 ....
SOUTHCOMBE, MISS W L 8-5 ....(0797) 1225621
SOWERBY, MISS M N 8-10 ....(01635) 298210
SPATE, R C 9-7 ....
SPEARING, MISS T S 9-7 ....(01789) 772639
STEARN, R R P 10-6 ....
STEDMAN, MISS A C 9-0 ....
STEPHENS, L A 9-11 ....
STEPHENS, R D 9-7 .... Dave Roberts
STEPHENS, MISS V A 10-0 ....
STIRLING, MISS N C 10-0 ....
STONE, MISS T N 10-0 ....
STOREY, C 10-0 ....(01573) 420615/
....(07976) 587315
STRATTON, MISS J A 7-5 ....
STUDD, C M 9-3 ....
STURGIS, MISS V C 9-0 ....
SWAN, D 9-3 ....
SWAN, MISS G T 8-13 ....
SWEETLAND, M S 10-5 ....
SWINSWOOD, A 9-7 ....
TATE, R T A 10-7 ....(01937) 835774
TATE, MR J J S 10-8 ....(01937) 836036
TATE, DR M P 10-5 ....
THOMAS, G R 9-12 ....(07775) 933621
THOMAS, T N 8-4 ....(01638) 664348
THOMPSON, MRS C A 9-0 ....(01483) 200135/
....(0836) 205579
THOMPSON, C D 9-7 ....(01539) 624314
THOMPSON, M 10-6 ....(01665) 76272
THOROGOOD, MISS G M 9-0 ....
TINKLER, N J 9-7 ....(01653) 695981/(0786) 6761618
TIZZARD, MISS C A 9-7 ....(01258) 817271
TORY, MISS E C 10-5 ....
TRICE-ROLPH, J C 11-2 ....
TROTTER, R J 10-0 ....(07802) 427351
TUCK, MISS E J 8-10 ....
TUCKER, MISS E A 9-7 ....
TUDOR, J E 10-0 ....
TUMELTY, G A 9-7 ....(01793) 815009
TUNNICLIFFE, MISS V C 9-3 ....
TURBUTT, MISS K L 9-0 ....
TURNER, MISS A L 9-0 ....(07939) 585526/
....(01664) 464351
TURNER, D I 9-5 ....(01722) 337399/(07768) 094908
TURNER, MISS F K 9-0 ....(07788) 541106
TUTTY, N D 10-11 ....(01609) 883624
VAUGHAN, T E 10-12 ....
VOLLARO, M L 8-7 ....
WADLOW, A G 10-10 ....
WAKEHAM, R T H 10-0 ....(0771) 697452
WALLACE, MISS A 8-4 ....(07734) 489685

WALEY-COHEN, S B 10-5 ....(07887) 848425/
....(0131) 440 2309
WALFORD, MARK T 10-7 ....((01653) 648166
....(07734) 265687
WALKER, N M 9-7 ....(01638) 663375
WALKER, S A 9-7 ....
WALL, M J 9-10 ....
WALLACE, MISS A L 8-5 ....(07721) 785503
WALLING, MISS K-J 9-3 ....
WALSH, J P 9-4 ....
WALSH, S P 9-7 ....C D Broad/(07765) 382613
WATERS, T 9-7 ....(01634) 668088
WALTON, A E 9-7 ....(01400) 50531
WARING, MISS J L 8-9 ....(01969) 640330
WARREN, S M 9-0 ....
WATSON, MAJOR M R 11-2 ....
WEBB, MISS D F 9-0 ....
WEBB-BOWEN, COL R I 11-7 ....
WEBSTER, MISS H J 9-5 ....(01638) 668115
WEEKES, D T 9-0 ....(07977) 599596
WELLS, MISS L C 8-6 ....
WEST, MISS S 10-0 ....
WHARFE, B W 9-7 ....(01451) 850278/
....(07900) 812334
WHARFE, MRS P 9-7 ....(01565) 777275
WHEELER, G F 11-7 ....
WHILLANS, E A 9-9 ....(01450) 376642
WHITE, J A 9-8 ....
WICKENS, MISS J H 9-2 ....
WIGLEY, G J 10-7 ......(01903) 872226/(07790) 614037
WILESMITH, MR M. C. 10-9 ....(01531) 890410/
....(07768) 431894
WILKINSON, MRS D S 7-7 ....
WILLEY, J P 9-0 ....
WILLIAMS, MRS C A 8-12 .... Alan Harrison
WILLIAMS, C R P 9-7 ....(07815) 774306
WILLIAMS, D F 9-7 ....
WILLIAMS, MISS J C 8-10 ....
WILLIAMS, N 9-7 .... Dave Roberts
WILLIAMS, S T 11-0 ....
WILLOUGHBY, GUY N J 10-4 ....
WILMOT-SMITH, MISS J B 9-2 ....
WILSON, MISS D Y 8-6 ....(01242) 519008
WILSON, MISS F 9-0 ....(01642) 784587
WILSON, MRS N C 8-13 ....(01759) 368249
WILSON, N 11-0 ....(01759) 368249
WINTLE, A A 11-0 ....(07767) 351144
WISE, MISS F C R 9-10 ....(01296) 655255
WITHEFORD, C W 9-11 ....
WOODHOUSE, B R 11-7 ....
WOODMAN, MISS R E 8-7 ....(01903) 871421
WOOLLACOTT, R M 10-0 ....
WORMALL, MISS J 9-7 ....
WORTHINGTON, W A 9-9 ....
YOUNG, A 10-0 ....
YORK, P 10-4 ....(01372) 457102/(07774) 962168
YOUNG, R D 10-0 ......(01258) 817271/(07970) 356510
YOUNG, MISS S E M 10-0 ....

NOTES

NOTES

NOTES

NOTES